RUGBY SCHOOL
WHO'S WHO

RUGBY SCHOOL WHO'S WHO

Edited by

A. G. BLUNT

Published by
THE OLD RUGBEIAN SOCIETY
RUGBY
1975

RUGBY SCHOOL REGISTERS

Vol. I:	1675–1842	Published 1901
Vol. II:	1842–1874	Published 1903
	1850–1874	Published 1886
Vol. III:	1874–1887	Published 1891
	1874–1904	Published 1904

These Registers were revised as follows:

Vol. I:	1675–1857	Published 1933
	1858–1891	Published 1952
Vol. IV:	1892–1921	Published 1929
	1911–1946	Published 1957

Since the revision of the earlier Registers and consequent overlapping caused confusion in the numbering of volumes, no volume number was allotted to the 1858–1891 revision, or that of 1911–1946.

©

ISBN 0 9503697 0 5

PRINTED AND BOUND IN ENGLAND BY
HAZELL WATSON AND VINEY LTD
AYLESBURY, BUCKS

FOREWORD

It is more than twenty-five years since the last volume of the Rugby School Register was compiled, edited by Colonel A. H. Maude (Stanley, 99–04) covering the years 1911–1946. Rather than publish a new Register in the old form it was decided that a Rugby School "Who's Who", listing all Old Rugbeians, would be of greater interest. Arthur Blunt (Cotton, 23–28) kindly agreed to be Honarary Editor and we are most grateful to him for undertaking such a formidable task and for completing the work so successfully.

We regret any omissions or errors, but Rugbeians tend to be somewhat shy about their achievements and do not always answer letters. However, the Editor has compiled a volume which we hope will be of great interest to Rugbeians.

DAVID PHYSICK,
President, Old Rugbeian Society, 1970–1971

GEDDES,
President, Old Rugbeian Society, 1972–1973

FRANK ROBERTS,
President, Old Rugbeian Society, 1974–1975

October 1974

NOTES BY THE EDITOR

The compilation of a new volume of the Rugby School Register to follow the 1911–1946 edition was initiated by the Old Rugbeian Society in 1972 during the Presidency of F. D. Physick and I was appointed Hon. Editor. A school register by its very nature can have only a limited circulation and readership, as, in the past, it has only included details of entries to the School over a limited period. It was felt, therefore, that to attract a wider circulation, the form which the Register has taken since 1675 should be retained as only one part of the volume and details of all living Rugbeians should be given as another part. The period of the Register was, therefore, determined as from January 1947 to the end of the Christmas term 1966, and is herein included as Part II. The order is, as heretofore, in date of entry, by houses and each entry is numbered and indexed as such. Part I, which is new to the Register, is an alphabetical list of all known living Rugbeians who entered the School before January 1947 and, as is customary, the Governing Body, Headmasters and Masters together on this occasion with the Presidents of the Old Rugbeian Society have been included in Part III. Due to the volume's comprehensive nature, it has been decided to call it "Rugby School Who's Who".

A considerable effort has been made to ensure that each entry relating to a living Old Rugbeian has been checked by the subject of the entry, but where a communication has not been returned for one reason or another, I have given only the House and dates with an asterisk in Part I and as much information as has been gleaned from the records of Allen Tatham, former Old Rugbeian Society Honorary Secretary and Registrar, about the entries in Part II. There may be many errors and omissions in the text and for the former I accept responsibility, while in the latter cases, more often than not the item omitted could not be deciphered.

For reasons of space, free use of abbreviations has been necessary. Most of these are in common use and explanations may be found in "Who's Who" and other reference books. Again, for economy of space, the presence in the sixth form of an entry and successes in Honours Schools at Universities or other places of higher education have been omitted. Active service in the first world war has been denoted by the symbol ✗ and in the second world war and later campaigns by ✕. National service is indicated by N/S. Some cross-references have been included where known. Details of marriages are omitted, as since the form sent out did not seek such information, it was felt it would be wrong to include this where in a few cases it has been provided gratuitously.

My thanks are due to the Governing Body and the Committee of the Old Rugbeian Society for agreeing to underwrite this publication, to Laurence Viney for arranging the printing and publication, and Hubert Snowden, the present Honorary Secretary of the Old Rugbeian Society, for keeping me informed of the latest news of anyone included in this volume. Lastly, without the card-index records, which Allen Tatham has been maintaining since 1947, my job would have been immensely more difficult.

I only hope that what is produced here will make good bedside reading and a suitable addition to the owner's library.

A. G. BLUNT

October 1974

CONTENTS

CONTENTS

PART I
Pre-1947

A

ABBOTT, Alan St. George. B, 44^2–48^2.*

ABBOTT, John Richard, b. 3 Apr. 31, eldest s. of T. D. Abbott. Sh, 44^3–50^1; Levée; S. VIII, 48–49. St. John's, Oxford, M.A. Company Secretary. Son, David John, Sh, 71^3–.

ABBOTT, Peter Harry, M.D., M.R.C.P., b. 19 Jan. 17, eldest s. of late H. J. E. Abbott. Sh, 30^3–35^2; XV, 35. Trinity, Cambridge, M.A., M.D. St. Thomas's Hospital, M.R.C.P., D.T.M. & H., M.R.C.G.P. Sudan Med. Service, 42–55. Med. Inspector, 42–50. Med. Specialist, 50–55. Med. Officer, Shell in Sarawak and Singapore, 55–60. Consultant Phys., Nat. Iranian Oil Co., 60–64. Since 64 General Practitioner, Haslemere. Royal Society of Tropical Medicine.

ABBOTT, Richard St. George. B, 41^2–44^3.*

ABBOTT, Stuart Evelyn, O.B.E., b. 21 Aug. 10, elder s. of late E. R. Abbott, C.I.E., I.C.S. SH, 24^3–29^2; Scholar; Levée; Head of House; Major and Jex-Blake Leaving Exhibitions. Balliol, Oxford, B.A. Indian Civil Service, Punjab (1st in open Exam), 34–47. Retired, 49. Ottoman Bank, 48—Director (London Committee) from 49. Basildon Development Corp., 53–54. Henry Simon Holding Co., Stockport, 54–59. Trinity Hall, Camb., Fellow and Bursar since 59. Junior Proctor, Camb., 63–64. O.B.E., 44. M.A. (Cantab.), 59. Sons, 654, 945 & 2004.

ABEL, Keith Paterson, F.R.C.S. B, 40^1–44^2.*

ACHESON, Vincent William, b. 10 Mar. 18, s. of F. D. Acheson. Sh, 32^1–36^2. Trinity College, Dublin, B.A., LL.B. ✕ Army Field Regt., R.A. N. Africa & Italy (56 Div.). Major. Wounded in head. Dispatches, 40–46. Man. Dir., Dundalk Linen Co. Ltd. & D. Acheson Ltd. Farmer at Grange Park, Dungannon, N. Ireland. *Ulster Club, Belfast.*

ACLAND, John Ben Dyke. Tu, 30^3–34^3.*

ACLAND, Sir Richard Thomas Dyke, T.D., Bt., b. 26 Nov. 06, eldest s. of late Sir Francis Acland, Bt. (OR W 88). W, 20^2–24^2; R. VIII, 24; Head of House. Balliol, Oxford, B.A. Bar, Inner Temple, 31. Liberal M.P., North Devon, 35–45. Labour M.P., Gravesend, 47–55. Teacher at Wandsworth Comprehensive School, 55–59. Lecturer at St. Luke's College, Exeter, 60–72. Now part-time lecturer, semi-retired. Succeeded as 15th Bt. in 39.

ACTON, Thomas Stackhouse, J.P., b. 1 Jan. 25, elder s. of late R. C. Acton, J.P. SF, 38^3–43^2. Oriel, Oxford, M.A. Commission of Peace, County of Salop, 61. Served as Temporary Officer with Royal Navy, 44–46 & 51–55. Farmer and Country Estate Owner. Organist at St. Margaret's Church, Acton Scott.

ADAM, Alexander Chivas Gilbert. C, 32^3–37^2.*

ADAM, Denys Peter, b. 4 Feb. 33, s. of L. M. Adam. SF, 46^2–51^2; R. VIII, 50–51; Holder of Bigside Bags, 51. N/S. R.A., 51–53, 2nd Lt. Sidney Sussex, Cambridge, B.A. Lay Reader (C. of E.). Fruit Grower.

ADAM, Malcolm Cyrus, b. 30 Jan. 20, s. of late C. C. Adam. Sh, 34^1–37^2. Commercial Studies (Paris, 1 year). ✕ R. West Kent Regt. (T.A.), 39. Wounded at Dunkirk and P.O.W. till 46. Cpl. Director and General Manager, West Midlands Press Ltd. (Weekly Newspaper Group). Sons, 2319 & Nicholas John, Sh, 70^2–72^2.

ADAM, Thomas, J.P., b. 20 May 14, elder s. of late T. L. Adam (OR C 94). C, 28^2–32^3. Cadet Scholar, R.M.C., Sandhurst. Army (the Gordon Highlanders for 13 years). ✕ 39–45. Major. Company Director, Denmore Farms Ltd. (Managing), Adam Brothers Contingency Ltd., Underwriting Member of Lloyd's. *Royal Northern Club, Aberdeen.* J.P., County of Aberdeen. Son, 1073.

ADAMS, William Anthony, J.P. B, 23^3–28^2.*

ADAMSON, William Owen Campbell, b. 26 June 22, s. of late J. Adamson. Sh, 36¹-40². Corpus Christi, Cambridge, M.A. Unity Fellow, Nuffield College, Oxford. Management Trainee in Baldwins Ltd., 20 years in various positions in the Steel Industry. Dir. & Gen. Manager of R.T.B. Spencer Works near Newport, 60. Industrial Adviser and subsequently Co-Ordinator of Industrial Advisers, Dept. of Economic Affairs, 67. At present Director-General of Confederation of British Industry. Sons, 2073 & 3009.

ADCOCK, Robert Wadsworth. C, 46³-50³.*

ADDIS, Sir John Mansfield, K.C.M.G., b. 11 June 14, fifth s. of Sir C. Addis, K.C.M.G., LL.D. SH, 27³-32²; Scholar; Head of House. Scholar, Christ Church, Oxford, B.A. H.M. Diplomatic Service from 38, served in N. Africa, Italy, France and China. A Private Secretary to the Prime Minister, 45-47. Ambassador to Laos, 60; Philippines, 63; China, 72. C.M.G., 58, K.C.M.G., 73. Brother, Sir William Addis, K.B.E., C.M.G.

ADDIS, Richard Thomas, b. 7 Sept. 31, eldest s. of Sir W. Addis, K.B.E., C.M.G. (OR SH 16). SH, 45³-49³; R. VIII, 49; S. VIII, 49; Fencing III. Corpus Christi, Oxford, M.A. M.I.P.M. 2nd Lt., Coldstream Guards, 50-51. H.M.O.C.S. (Malaya and Gambia), 55-64. Personnel Manager, Courtaulds Ltd., since 64. *Gridiron*. Son, Richard James, SH, 69³-. Brothers, 152, 1367 & 1663.

ADDIS, Sir William, K.B.E., C.M.G. SH, 16¹-20².*

AGNEW, George Colin, b. 28 Oct. 82, younger s. of late Sir G. Agnew, Bt., M.P. (OR B 65). M, 96³-00³; Cap, 00. Kings, Cambridge.✕Intelligence Corps att. G.H.Q. Lt. Dispatches. Partner in Thos. Agnew & Sons. Fine Art Publishers. Art Dealer, retired. *Carlton, Travellers' & Royal Automobile Clubs.*

AGNEW, George Keith, T.D., J.P., b. 25 Nov. 18, 2nd s. of late Sir J. S. Agnew, Bt., T.D., J.P., D.L. (OR M 93). M, 32²-36². Trinity, Cambridge, B.A. Territorial Army (Suffolk Yeomanry), 37-56. ✕ 55th (Suffolk Yeomanry) Anti-Tank Regt., R.A. Major, 39-46. Landowner and Farmer. Country Landowners' Assoc., President, Suffolk. National Farmers' Union, Chairman, Suffolk. T.D., J.P. (Suffolk). *Cavalry Club.* Brother, S. W. Agnew.

AGNEW, Lt.-Col. John Nevin, b. 10 May 22, 2nd s. of late Col. H. C. Agnew. SH, 35³-40²; Cap. Anglo-American scholarship to Taft College, Connecticut (not taken up because of war). Christ Church, Oxford, M.A. Gazetted to Coldstream Guards, 41. ✕ N. Africa, 42-43. N.W. Europe, 44-45. Wounded. Major. p.s.c. j.s.c. Joint Services Staff College. Instructor, Staff College, Camberley, 63-65. Lt.-Col. (retired, Coldstream Guards). *Royal Over-Seas League.* Brother, P. W. Agnew.

AGNEW, Patrick William, b. 6 Mar. 27, youngest s. of late Col. H. C. Agnew. SH, 40³-44²; Scholar. Exhibitioner. Scholar of Trinity, Cambridge, B.A.; Univ. Ice Hockey Team. Civil Engineer. At present lecturer in Mechanical Engineering at Glasgow University. Brother, J. N. Agnew.

AGNEW, Lt.-Col. Richard Leslie, b. 4 Mar. 00, younger s. of late W. Agnew (OR B 75). M, 13³-16³. Boxing Lightweight, 15. R.M.C., Sandhurst. ✕ Gazetted to 15th The Kings Hussars, 18. Lt., 20. Retired from Regular Army, 36. Joined Northants Yeomanry, 38. Major, 39. ✕ 15/19 Hussars, 40. Commanded E. Riding Yeomanry, 41. Lt.-Col., 146 Regt., R.A.C. (Duke of Wellington's), 43. Served in Arakan, 44-45. Dispatches. Retired.

AGNEW, Stephen William, b. 31 July 21, 3rd s. of late Sir J. S. Agnew, Bt., T.D., D.L., J.P. (OR M 93). M, 34³-39². Trinity, Cambridge, course interrupted by war service.✕7th Q.O. Hussars, 42-45. Lt. Wounded in Italy, 44. Local Director for Norfolk Sun Alliance, London Insurance Corp., from 64. General Commissioner of Income Tax from 65. Marriage Guidance Counsellor from 66. Director, Agnew Farming Co. Ltd. & Rogate Farms Ltd. *Norfolk Club, Cavalry Club.* Brother, G. K. Agnew.

AINSCOW, Donald Mason Chalmers, b. 3 Jan. 23, s. of Dr. A. E. Ainscow. Sh, 37¹-41¹. Gonville and Caius, Cambridge, M.A., M.B., B.Chir. St. Thomas' Hospital, London, M.R.C.S., L.R.C.P. N/S. R.A.M.C., 47-49. Major. Medical Practitioner.

AITCHISON, David Lachlan, b. 25 Nov. 28, 3rd s. of late Sir W. de L. Aitchison, Bt. M, 42³-47²; XI, 47. Chairman and Managing Director, Walter Willson Ltd. (Multiple Grocers).

AKENHEAD, David, O.B.E., b. 23 Mar. 94, younger s. of late Rev. E. Akenhead (OR SH 64). SF, 07^3-12^2. New College, Oxford, M.A. Wye College, Kent. B.Sc. (Agric.) London. ✕ 6 Bn. Lincolnshire Regt. Capt. Gallipoli and France. Wounded twice. Invalided, 19. Lecturer and Warden, Royal Agricultural College, Cirencester, 22–23. I/C of the Commonwealth Bureau of Horticulture, East Malling, 29–59. Retired since 59. O.B.E. *United Oxford & Cambridge Club.*

AKENHEAD, Edmund, T.D., b. 5 Sept. 13, 2nd s. of late F. Akenhead (OR SF 95). SF 27^3-32^2. Solicitor, 36. Solicitor in private practice, 36–39. ✕ Searchlights then Glider Pilot Regt., 39–45. Major T.D. and clasp. Colonial Legal Service, Tanganyika, 46–62 (when retired as Commissioner for Lands). Private Solicitor's practice, 62–70. "The Times" Crossword Editor since 65. The Magic Circle. *High Post Golf Club*, Great Durnford, Salisbury, Wilts. Son, 2470. Brothers, John & Michael Akenhead.

AKENHEAD, Major John, b. 26 Dec. 11, eldest s. of late F. Akenhead (OR SF 95). S.F., 25^3-30^2. University College of South Wales and Mons, B.Sc. Indian Army German Interpreter, 2nd class, 39. Indian Army (4th Bn., 6th Rajputana Rifles), 35–48. Retired as Major. Tea Planting Assam Frontier Tea Co., 48–51. Prep. School Master (Orwell Park, Nr. Ipswich) 52–69 (maths & music). Jan. 70, retired. *Royal Commonwealth Society.* Brothers, Edmund & Michael Akenhead.

AKENHEAD, Michael, b. 5 Sept. 13' 3rd s. of late F. Akenhead (OR SF 95). SF, 27^3-31^2.WyeCollege, Univ. of London, B.Sc. (Agric.) Dip. (Agric.). Corpus Christi, Cambridge. Imperial College of TropicalAgriculture,Trinidad, A.I.C.T.A. Colonial Agriculture Service, 37–53. Scientific Assistant, Commonwealth Agricultural Bureau, 53–54. Director of Agriculture, Western Samoa, 54–55. Teacher and Lecturer at Chester College of Further Education, Chester, 56–72. F.R.G.S. Brothers, John & Edmund Akenhead.

ALCOCK, Reginald John. Sh, 31^2-35^2.*

ALDERSON, Sidney Roy Chapman, b. 19 Sept. 15, s. of late A. R. Alderson. St, 29^3-33^2. ✕ R. A. Lt. Designer & Painter.

ALEXANDER, Col. John Osmond Macdonald, D.S.O., M.C., T.D., b. 29 Mar. 16, s. of late J. M. Alexander. SF, 29^3-33^3. Clare, Cambridge, B.A. ✕ R.E. T.A., 39–46. Lt.-Col., D.S.O., M.C., T.D. Retired as Col., 60. Hon. Col., 72. Engr. Regt., T.A.V.R. since 67. Procter & Gamble Ltd., from 37, Director from 57. Chairman of Council, Newcastle upon Tyne Univ., from 66. D.L. *Army & Navy, Northern Counties, Newcastle.*

ALFORD, Charles Ronald Warrington, b. 17 Aug. 08, s. of C. E. Alford. Tu, 22^2-26^1. Commercial Career in the Far East with B.A.T. Co., now retired. ✕ Served with Army in Far East. *Travellers' Club.*

ALLAN, Richard. M, 12^3-16^3.*

ALLEN, David Elliston, b. 17 Jan. 32, s. of late G. E. Allen, T.D. (OR SF 10). SF, 45^3-50^2; Levée; Head of House. Clare, Cambridge, M.A. Graduate School, London School of Economics, 61–63. Market research executive, 56–65. Administrative staff, Social Science Research Council from 67. Botanical Society of the British Isles (past Hon. General Secretary).

ALLEN, George Cameron, C.B.E., b. 26 Nov. 08, elder s. of G. H. Allen. C, 22^3-27^2; Scholar; Head of House; Levée. King's Medal. Scholar of Trinity, Oxford, M.A. English Lektor, Univ. of Hamburg. Commonwealth Fellow in Literature, Western Reserve and Harvard Univs. Cultural Relations Adviser to U.K. High Commissioner, Germany, 51–54. H.M.I. Staff Inspector for English. Professor of Education, Univ. of Sussex from 66. C.B.E., 55. *United Oxford & Cambridge.* Son, 2036.

ALLEN, The Rt. Rev. Geoffrey Francis, D.D., b. 25 Aug. 02, 2nd s. of late J. E. T. Allen (OR C 78). W, 15^3-20^3; Scholar; History Scholarship to University College, Oxford, B.A. (P.P.E.), 24. Ripon Hall, Oxford, Theol., 26. Ordained Deacon, 27. Priest, 28. Archdeacon, Birmingham, 44–47. Consecrated as Bishop in Egypt, 47–52. Principal of Ripon Hall, Oxford, 52–59. Bishop of Derby, 59–69. D.D. Retired, 69. *Athenæum, English Speaking Union.*

ALLEN, The Rev. John Edward, b. 9 June 32, eldest s. of Rev. Canon R. E. T. Allen (OR W 11). W, 46^2-51^1; Head of House; Levée; Cadet Officer; Dewar Travelling Scholarship; Mynors Exhibitioner. Exhibitioner of University College,

Oxford, M.A. N/S. 2nd Lt. 1st Bn., K.S.L.I., 54–56. 1st Devonshire Course, Public Administration, University College, Oxford, 56–57. Overseas Civil Service, District Office, Kenya, 57–63. Marketing Manager, Kimberley-Clark Ltd., 63–66. Fitzwilliam, Cambridge, 2nd class Hons., Theol., Pt. III, 66–68. Ordained Deacon by Archbishop of Canterbury, 68, Priest, 69. Curate of Deal, Kent, 68–71. Senior Chaplain to Bristol Univ. Vicar of St. Paul's, Clifton, from 71. Contributed to "The Trial of Jesus", ed. E. Bammel, published by S.C.M., 69. Brothers, 2262 & 2724.

ALLEN, Lt.-Col. John George, M.B.E., b. 13 Sept. 14, s. of late Lt.-Col. J. F. Allen. W, 28²–32³; XV, 32. R.M.C., Sandhurst. Cadet Scholarship, Pentathlon, 34. Commissioned Dorsetshire Regt., 34, wounded in Palestine, 36. Transferred R.A.P.C. Major, Area Paymaster, South Caribbean, 45–48. Lt.-Col., Assistant Command Paymaster, H.Q. Western Command, Chester 48–49. Assistant Command Paymaster at H.Q., E. Africa Command, Nairobi, 50–51. Retired, 52. M.B.E.

ALLEN, The Rev. Canon Ronald Edward Taylor, b. 21 Apr. 97, eldest s. of late J. E. T. Allen (or C 78). W, 11²–15³. ✕ R.F.A. Lt. M.C. Dispatches. Reserve of Officers. University College, Oxford, M.A. London School of Economics. Ripon Hall, Oxford. Ordained, 27. Hon. Canon of Birmingham, 50–65. Hon. Chaplain, Univ. of Birmingham, 58–65. R.D. of Edgbaston, 60–65. Perm. to Offic. Dio., Hereford, 65–68. L. to Offic. from 68. Priest-in-charge, Ashford Bowdler, Hereford Diocese. Sons, The Rev. J. E. Allen & 2262 & 2724.

ALLEN, Richard Paul, b. 4 Dec. 27, 2nd s. of late J. G. Allen, J.P. SF, 41³–45¹. LL.B. Senior partner at Perks & Wakerley, Manufacturing Jewellers.

ALLEN, Robert John Lea. M, 21³–25².*

ALLEN-JONES, Air Vice Marshal John Ernest, C.B.E. SH, 23²–28².*

ALLISON, Joseph William Sloan, D.S.C., b. 26 Aug. 19, s. of J. Allison, J.P. C, 33²–38². ✕ R.N.V.R. Lt. D.S.C. Chartered Accountant, 52. *Western Club, R.N.V.R. Club (Scotland), Royal Northern Yacht Club.* Son, 1606.

ALLISON, Brig. William Ingram, C.B.E. SF, 09³–12³.*

ALLPORT, George Joseph Bokenham. T, 18³–23¹.*

ALSOP, Frederick Humphrey, LL.B., b. 24 Apr. 21, s. of F. J. Alsop. B, 35¹–39¹. Trinity Hall, Cambridge, M.A., LL.B. ✕ R.A. (City of London Yeomanry), 40–46. Admitted Solicitor, 50. A.D.C. to Governor of Bermuda, 52. Under Sheriff of Wiltshire. Practising Solicitor. *Royal Lymington Yacht Club.*

ALSTON, Lt.-Col. George Robert Goodwille, O.B.E., M.C., b. 7 Apr. 93, elder s. of late G. R. Alston. SH, 07³–11². St. John's, Oxford, Royal Military Academy, Woolwich. ✕ 1st Bn., H.A.C. 112th Bde., R.F.A. Captain. Wounded. M.C. Dispatches. Lt. Col., retired. (Served in Royal Field Artillery and in Trinidad Artillery Volunteers.) Lived from 20–71 in Trinidad, West Indies. Director of family business, Alstons Ltd., in Trinidad. O.B.E. (for public services in Trinidad), 54. *Naval & Military Club, Royal Overseas League.* Son, R. A. C. Alston.

ALSTON, Raymond Anthony Croll, b. 25 Oct. 22, 2nd s. of Lt.-Col. G. R. G. Alston (or SH 07). Sh, 36²–40²; S. VIII, 39. ✕ R.A.F. F/Lt., 40–46. Company Director. *Royal Over-Seas League, Royal Commonwealth Society.*

ALSTON, Wilfred Louis, b. 10 Jan. 00, eldest s. of L. G. Alston. SH, 14¹–17³. ✕ R.A.F. Lt., 18–19. Director of Alstons Ltd., Port of Spain, Trinidad. Now retired. *R.A.F. Club, London.* West India Committee, London. Son, 1.

ALTHAUS, Frederick Rudolph, C.B.E., b. 9 Sep. 95, s. of late T. F. Althaus. C, 09³–14²; Minor Exhibitioner. ✕ 7th Bn., Suffolk Regt. Capt. Wounded. Dispatches. Balliol, Oxford. Senior Partner in Pember & Boyle, Stockbrokers, from 50. Member, Council of the Stock Exchange, 49–73. Deputy Chairman, 59–63. Chairman or Vice-Chairman of various committees, notably Quotations and Public Relations. London delegate to Conference of European Stock Exchanges (now enlarged as Federation Internationale des Bourses de Valeurs—F.I.B.V.) since 57. Vice-President (Acting President), 68–69. President, 70–71. Member, Jenkins Committee on Company Law, 59. A Commissioner, Public Works Loan Board, 65–69. A General Commissioner of Income Tax for South Bucks, 64–70. C.B.E., 70. *Oriental, City, University.*

AMBROSE, John Anthony. SF, 39^2–43^2.*

ANDERSON, Anthony Laurence, b. 23 Dec. 32, 3rd s. of late L. R. D. Anderson. SF, 46^3–51^2. N/S. R.A., 51–53. 2nd Lt. St. John's, Cambridge, 53–56, Law Tripos Part I. Student member, Institute of Cost & Management Accountants, 4 parts passed out of 5. Work study Engineer. F. B. Trethewey & Partners, Management Consultants of Manchester, 56–61. Industrial Engineer & Production Planner, 61–72. Cost Accountant, Nicholas Products Ltd, Slough, Bucks, from 72. *East Berkshire Squash Club.* Brothers, C. W. & J. D. Anderson.

ANDERSON, Colin William. SF, 43^2–48^2.*

ANDERSON, Derek Pitcairn. SH, 45^1–49^2.*

ANDERSON, Frank Cordue Kennedy, b. 8 Sept 02, 5th s. of late J. D. Anderson, M.A., Litt D. (OR St 67). St, 16^2–19^3. Faraday House Electrical Engineering College. Diploma. Member, Institution of Electrical Engineers. Ass. Transmission Engineer, United River Plate Telephone Co., 25–29. Transmission Engineer, Chile Telephone Co., 29–31. Engineer, Barbados Telephone Co., 32–36. B.B.C., 36–62 (outside broadcasts manager, 40–62). *R.A.C.*

ANDERSON, Frederick Hume. B, 41^3–45^2.*

ANDERSON, Frederick Le Hunte, J.P., b. 8 Mar. 98, s. of late F. Anderson. M, 11^3–15^2. R.M.C., Sandhurst. ✗ Royal Scots Greys (2nd Dragoons). Lt. New College, Oxford. ✗ Royal Scots Greys, 39–45. Attached C.M.P., S.O. III Civil Affairs in Germany, Capt. J.P. for Berkshire. Retired farmer & landowner. *Cavalry Club.*

ANDERSON, Godfrey Alard. Tu, 22^2–26^2.*

ANDERSON, James Gordon, b. 22 June 03, elder s. of late Lt.-Col. G. H. Anderson. St, 17^3–19^2. Trinity Hall, Cambridge, B.A. Joined Colonial Service, Sarawak, 25. District Officer, 35. Resident from 40. Chrmn., Commission on Native Officers' Terms of Service, 41. Retired. Companion of the Star of Sarawak (C.S.S.).

ANDERSON, John Dacre, b. 12 Feb. 28, eldest s. of late L. R. D. Anderson, M.C., M.A. (OR SF oo). SF, 41^3–46^3; Cap. St. John's, Cambridge, B.A. Joined Unilever, 51. Plant Manager. T. Wall & Sons (Meat & Handy Foods) Ltd. Brothers, C. W. & A. L. Anderson.

ANDERSON, The Rev. John Edward, b. 5 May 03, eldest s. of late J. C. Anderson (OR B 67). Tu, 17^3–21^2; Scholar; Levée; Major & Minor Exhibitioner. Scholar of the University College, Oxford. Cadet Pair Bisley, 18. School Rep. Rugby Fives, 20. Head of House. Queen Victoria History Gold Medal. Univ. College, Oxford, B.A. Univ., golf 2nd team. Teaching cert., in French and German. Westcott House Theol. College, Camb., 35–36. Ordained, 36. Ass. Master, 25–45 (Joint Chaplain), 36–45. Rector of Lamport, Northants, 45–53. Ass. Master & Chaplain, Aldenham School, 55–59. Free-lance Teaching and Chaplain to the Beehive School, Bexhill, 59–63. Translation of books from French and German into English for the Press (theol., biography, etc.). Selected by National Translation Centre, U.S.A., to translate "Les Propos d'Alain", 63–70. Now Chaplain of St. John's Anglican Church, Menton, France. Authors' Society. Brothers, W. F. & G. A. Anderson.

ANDERSON, The Rev. Kenneth Mackenzie, b. 10 Sept. 23, younger s. of J. B. M. Anderson, M.D. M, 37^1–42^1; Levée. ✗ R.N.V.R., Sub-Lt. Scholar of Brasenose, Oxford, M.A., B.D. (St. Andrews, 54). American Dept., Foreign Office, 50–51. Missionary of Church of Scotland in W. Pakistan, 55–70. Minister of Hillington Park Church, Glasgow from 71. *R.N.V.R., Glasgow Academical Club.*

ANDERSON, Lawrence Robert Dacre, M.C. SF, 00^3–05^2.*

ANDERSON, Malcolm Webster, b. 20 Nov. 16, s. of late H. W. Anderson, C.E. W, 30^3–34^2. Pembroke, Cambridge, M.A. Learnt to fly with C.U.A.S. (R.A.F. certificate of proficiency, 37). Pupillage with W. H. Allen & Co. Ltd., Mechanical & Electrical Engineers, Bedford. R.A.F. School of Aeronautical Engineering, Henlow. C.Eng., F.R.Ae.S.; M.S.A.E.; M.I.C.E.; A.F.A.I.A.A. Commissioned service in R.A.F.V.R., 38–57. Private Pilot's Licence granted 37. Canadian Commercial Air Pilot's Certificate granted 49. ✗ R.A.F., 39–47. Pilot and Engineering duties. In Canada, 41–43. Pilot and Chief Technical Officer at Empire Central

Flying School, Hullavington, 43–45. Wing Cdr., Bomber Command, 45–46. B.O.A.C. from 47. Project and Development Engineer, and General Manager Engineering in Montreal and at Bristol Aeroplane Co. Ltd. Freeman, Guild of Air Pilots & Air Navigators. *Wentworth Golf Club, C.U. Engineers, Royal Horticultural.*

ANDERSON, Michael Brandon. M, 44³–49².*

ANDERSON, Peter George, b. 21 Jan. 19, eldest s. of late F. G. Anderson. B, 32³–36³; H. XI, 36. Queen's, Oxford, B.A. ✕ The Black Watch. Lt.-Col. Plastic Manufacturer. Brother, F. H. Anderson.

ANDERSON, Brig. Robert Charles Beckett, D.S.O., M.C. C, 09¹–13².*

ANDERSON, The Rev. Stuart Knox. SF, 98³–02².*

ANDERSON, Theodore Farnworth, C.M.G., O.B.E., M.D., b. 22 Oct. 01, eldest s. of late The Rev. J. F. Anderson. SF, 15³–19². Trinity Hall, Cambridge, Univ. College Hospital, London. M.A., B.Ch. (Cantab.), M.R.C.S., L.R.C.P., D.T.M. & H. General Practice, Nairobi, Kenya, 25–27. Colonial Medical Service, 28–57. ✕ Seconded to Army, 39–45. A.D.H. (Lt.-Col.), E.A. Command, 40–44. O.C., No. 6 General Hospital, Mombasa, 45. D.M.S., Somaliland, 45–49. D.M.S., Kenya, 50–57. Retired, 57. C.M.G., O.B.E. (Military), Dispatches, North Persian Forces Memorial Medal. *East India & Sports Club, Royal Commonwealth Society, Muthaiga & Limuru Clubs, Nairobi.*

ANDERSON, Brig. William Faithfull, C.B.E., M.C., b. 17 June 05, 2nd s. of late J. C. Anderson (OR B 67). Tu, 19³–23²; Scholar; XXII, 23. R.M.A., Woolwich. Gazetted to Royal Engineers. Emmanuel, Cambridge. M.A. Exhibitioner, 26. M.I.C.E., C.Eng. Royal Engineers, 25–59. Brigadier on retirement. Practised as Civil Engineer, 59–70. Consultant, Highways Planning, from 71. Institute of Civil Engineers. C.B.E., M.C. and Bar, Dispatches. Sons, 912 & 1922.

ANDREWS, Archie Moulton, b. 29 July 19, s. of late A. M. Andrews. B, 37³–38²; Sw. VI, 38. Princeton Univ., U.S.A. B.A. ✕ State Dept., Washington & U.S. Embassy in London. Dictograph Products Inc., Danbury, Conn., U.S.A. (President), 46–64. Dep. Dir., Bureau of International Commerce, U.S. Dept. of Commerce, Washington, D.C., 64–70. Counsellor for Commercial Affairs, U.S. Embassy, London from 70. *The American Club, London.*

ANSON, Everard Anchitel. W, 09¹–12².*

ANSTED, Leslie Baillie. T, 10³–12².*

ANSTIS, John Neville, b. 13 Aug. 31, eldest s. of W. C. Anstis. SH, 45³–50². Scholar; Cap; Fencing III, 48 (Capt., 49 & 50). N/S. 5th Dragoon Guards, 50–52, Capt. Magdalene, Cambridge. Director, Meat Trade Suppliers Ltd.

ANTILL, David Patrick Leith. K, 42²–46².*

ANTILL, Michael William Oliver, b. 9 Sept. 26, eldest s. of W. S. Antill. K, 40³–44²; XI, 43 & 44; H. XI. Holder of Bigside Bags. Leeds College of Commerce. N/S. R.N., 46–47, A.B. Financial Director, Rabone Chesterman Ltd., Sheffield 11. *Royal Lymington Yacht Club.* Brothers, D. P. L. & S. P. Antill.

ANTILL, Simon Philip, b. 8 May 30, 3rd s. of W. S. Antill. K, 44²–48²; H. XI, 48; XXII. R.M.A., Sandhurst. Royal Tank Regt., 50–57. ✕ Korea, 52–53. From 57 with Arthur Lee & Sons, Sheffield, currently doing Stainless Steel Market Development. (Developing new application outlets for S/S.) Brothers, M. W. O. & D. P. L. Antill.

ANTON, Charles Graeme Fraser, J.P., b. 20 Aug. 31, 3rd s. of Col. C. S. Anton, M.C., J.P., D.L. Sh, 45¹–49³; XXII, 48–49; H. XI, 48; Capt. of Rackets. N/S. Scots Guards & Worcestershire Regt. 2nd Lt. Gonville & Caius, Cambridge, M.A. Carpet Manufacturer. J.P. Brothers, G. S. F. & J. H. H. Anton.

ANTON, George Stewart Fraser, b. 15 Aug. 24, eldest s. of Col. C. S. Anton, M.C., J.P., D.L. Sh, 38²–42². ✕ Royal Signals, 45–48. 2nd Lt. Leeds Univ. Company Director. Brothers, J. H. H. & C. G. F. Anton.

ANTON, John Hamish Hugh, b. 19 Sept. 26, 2nd s. of Col. C. S. Anton, M.C., J.P., D.L. Sh, 40²–44²; XI, 43–44 (Capt.); Cap 44. H. XI, 43–44; Rackets Pair, 43–44 (Capt.) ✕ R.N.V.R., 44–47. Gonville & Caius, Cambridge, Hockey Blue, 48–49. Crusader Cap, 48. M.A. Managing Director, Victoria Carpet Co. Ltd., Victoria, Australia. *Hawks Club; Naval & Military Club, Melbourne.* Brothers, G. S. F. & C. G. F. Anton.

APPLEBY, Ernest Saxton. M, 29²–33³.*

APPLEBY, Ian Bertram, b. 28 May 17, 2nd s. of late E. B. Appleby. M, 31³–35²; XI, 34. Cap, 34–35. Durham Univ., M.B., B.S. ⋈ R.A.M.C. Capt. Brother, E. S. Appleby. Son, 1594A.

APPLETON, Ronald John Walter, b. 23 Apr. 10, elder s. of late L. Appleton. C, 24¹–25². M.B.I.M., L.I.Fire E. Man. Dir., Firemaster Extinguisher Ltd., *et al. R.A.C.* Ex-racing-driver, drove for Aston Martin pre-war, raced own car.

APPLEYARD, Raymond Kenelm, Ph.D. B, 36³–41².*

ARMES, Philip Arthur Harcourt, b. 28 Nov. 22, s. of A. H. H. Armes. Sh, 36³–41³. One year at Trinity, Oxford. ⋈ The Life Guards, 43–47. Capt. Chrmn. and Man. Dir. of Private Wine Company in the City. Son, Simon Philip Harcourt, Sh, 70³–.

ARMES, Richard John, b. 12 Aug. 28, s. of Col. R. J. Armes, C.M.G. SH, 42³–46²; XV, 45; XXII, 45. Scholar of Queen's, Oxford.

ARMISTEAD, Michael Burnie Beetham, b. 6 Feb. 28, s. of late R. B. Armistead. B, 41³–45³. Peterhouse & Fitzwilliam, Cambridge, M.A. ⋈ R.E., Lt., R.A. (T.A.) Armour Hess Chemicals Ltd., Harrogate, Yorks. *Farmers' Club.*

ARMITAGE, Philip Michael, b. 3 June 06, 2nd s. of late Rev. P. Armitage, M.A. M, 20¹–24²; XXII, 24; H. XI, 24. Trinity, Cambridge, B.A. Solicitor, 31. Former partner in Norton, Rose Greenwell Ltd., of London. Retired. *Bath, Oxford & Cambridge Golf Society, Swimley Forest Golf Club.* Brother, R. S. Armitage. Son, 415.

ARMITAGE, Lt.-Col. Reginald Maclaren, b. 7 June 98, eldest s. of late A. K. Armitage. B, 12¹–16¹. Royal Military College, Sandhurst. Lt. Served in both World Wars. Regular Army Lt.-Col. (Retired). *Army & Navy Club.*

ARMITAGE, Robert Selby, G. C., G.M., b. 28 Mar. 05, eldest s. of late Rev. P. Armitage, M.A. M, 18³–23¹; H. XI, 20–

23. Trinity, Cambridge, B.A. Bar. Inner Temple, 39. ⋈ R.N.V.R., 39–46. Retired as Commander. George Cross, George Medal. Member of London Stock Exchange from 46. At present associated with W. Greenwell & Co., Stockbrokers. *Brooks's, Royal Cruising Club, Royal Lymington Yacht Club.* Brother, P. M. Armitage.

ARMSTRONG, Hilary John Bradley, T.D., b. 7 Oct. 10, 2nd s. of F. Armstrong. Tu, 24³–28³; XV, 28; Levée. Admitted Solicitor, 37. Territorial Army, 33–45 (Sherwood Foresters). ⋈ 39–45. Major. Dispatches, T.D. Assistant Solicitor with Acton Simpson Hanson, Nottingham, 45–52. Partner from 52. Brother, P. B. Armstrong.

ARMSTRONG, Philip Bryan, b. 5 Nov. 08, eldest s. of F. Armstrong. Tu, 22³–27². Solicitor, 31. ⋈ Sherwood Foresters & Pioneer Corps, 39–45. Major. Alderman. Non-County Borough of Mansfield, Notts. Brother, H. J. B. Armstrong.

ARNING, Charles Wilfred, O.B.E., b. 24 Aug. 99, eldest s. of A. W. Arning. St, 13³–17²; R. VIII, 17; Sw. VI, 16–17 (Capt.) ⋈ R.F.C./R.A.F. 2nd Lt., 17–19. Queen's, Oxford, B.A. Rowing VIII, Capt. of Boats, 20. Foreign Service, 41–65. O.B.E.

ARNOLD, Thomas Sorell, b. 13 Mar. 30, s. of F. T. Arnold. SH, 43³–47³. M.Sc. (Lon.), M.Inst.Biol.

ARTHUR, Allan James Vincent, M.B.E., b. 16 Sept. 15, elder s. of late Col. Sir C. Arthur, M.C., V.D. K, 29²–34²; Levée; Cap; Sw. VI, 32–34 (Capt., 34); Cadet Officer, 34. Magdalene, Cambridge, M.A. Half Blue Sw., 35–38 (Capt., 37) and Water Polo, 37–38, and Univs. of England and Wales in Paris, 37. 2nd Lt. I/C Cavalry Squadron, C.U.O.T.C. Indian Civil Service, 38–47 (Deputy Commissioner in the Punjab). Sudan Political Service, 49–54 (District Commissioner and Deputy Governor). Woodhouse, Drake & Carey Ltd., Commodity Brokers, 54 (Director, 56; Chairman, 72). High Sheriff of Essex, 71–72. Governor, London Hospital Medical College. Governor, Chigwell School. Governor, Brentwood School. M.B.E., 48. *Hawks Club, Oriental Club.* Sons, 2599 & 2983.

ARTHUR, Anthony John Nevill, b. 26 Dec. 31, eldest s. of F. S. Arthur. C, 45³–50¹; Sw. VIII, 48–49. N/S. Royal Signals, 50–51. 2nd Lt. Lincoln, Oxford,

M.A. Employed F. S. Arthur & Co. (Woolbrokers), 54–63. Director, 63–67. Manager, New Zealand Wool Commission, London Branch, 68–72. New Zealand Society, London. *New Zealand Cricket Club.*

ARTHUR, James Bryant George, M.B., B.S. b. 12 Aug. 33, eldest s. of J. C. Arthur, M.B., B.S. B, 46³–51²; Cap. Entered Medical School, Newcastle-on-Tyne, 51. Qualified, 56. M.B., B.S. (Dunelm), 56. M.R.C.S. (Eng.), L.R.C.P. (London), 57. House Surgeon, R.V.I., Newcastle, 57. House Physician, Newcastle General Hospital, 57. N/S.R.A.M.C., 58–60. In general practice in Low Fell, Gateshead, from 61. *Gateshead Fell Rugby Club.* Medical Institute, Newcastle. Brothers, 1261 & 1262.

ASCROFT, Robert William, M.B.E. W, 04²–06².*

ASHCROFT, David, T.D. SH, 33³–38¹.*

ASHCROFT, Edward Worsley. W, 18²–22².*

ASHTON, John Anthony, b. Aug. 15, s. of late J. Ashton. T, 29³–33³. Birmingham Univ.

ASHTON, The Rev. Thomas Eyre Maunsell, b. 2 Aug. 13, s. of late T. W. Ashton (OR M 89). C, 27³–31³. St. Edmund's Hall, Oxford, M.A. Wycliffe Hall, Oxford. Ordained, Winchester, 38. Curate, St. James, Shirley, Southampton, 38–41. ✗ Chaplain, R.A.F.V.R., 41–46. Dispatches. Perpetual Curate, The Ascension, Derringham Bank, Hull, 46–48. Vicar of St. Martin, Hull, 48–54. Vicar of Crewkerne, Somerset, 54–66. Rector of Lee, London, from 66.

ASHTON-DAVIES, Major Ivor, M.B.E., T.D., B.Sc., b. 4 Aug. 02, eldest s. of C. E. Davies. T, 16²–20². Univ. of Birmingham, B.Sc. Zürich Federal Univ., Dr.Sc. Tech. Joined Imperial Chemical Industries, Billingham, 28, as Industrial Chemist. Remained with them until retirement, May 63 (ill health). Gazetted Lt., R.A.O.C. (later R.E.M.E.), 37. T.A. Embodied, Aug. 39. Returned to T.A., 45. Retired from T.A. with rank of Lt.-Col., R.E.M.E. 57. M.B.E. (services in Italy). T.D. with bar. Brother, M. E. Ashton-Davies.

ASHTON-DAVIES, Montague Edward. T, 19²–23¹.*

ASKE, The Rev Sir Conan, Bt., M.A., b. 22 Apr. 12, elder s. of late Sir R. W. Aske, Bt., Q.C., LL.D., T.D. C, 25³–30². Balliol, Oxford, M.A. ✗ 39–51. East Yorkshire Regt., Sudan Defence Force, Somaliland Scouts, etc. Major. Civil Affairs Officer, reserved area of Ethiopia and the Ogaden, 49–51. (Territorial Efficiency Medal.) Schoolmaster, Hill Stone, Malvern, 52–69. Wycliff Hall, Oxford, 69–70. Ordained. Assistant Curate, St. John-in-Bedwordine, Worcester, 72.

ASPINALL, John Victor. C. & W, 39³–43³.*

ASTBURY, John Schönberg, B.M., B.Ch., b. 30 Aug. 13, s. of A. R. Astbury, C.S.I., C.I.E. Tu, 27²–32¹. Christ Church, Oxford, B.M., B.Ch. Guy's Hospital, D.R.C.O.G. General Practitioner. *Parkstone Yacht Club.* Son, 2416.

ASTON, James Minter. (Name changed to Peter James Minter Aston in 49). b. 27 Aug. 22, s. of late A. L. Aston. Tu, 36³–40³; Scholar. ✗ R.N.V.R., 42–46. Lt. Selwyn, Cambridge, B.A., A.R.I.C.S. Fellow of Institute of Work Study Practitioners. Fellow of Institute of Materials Handling. I.C.I., Estate Dept., Alkali Division, 49–56. Head of Rural Dept., College of Estate Management, 56–58. Private Practice as Agricultural Management & Investment Consultant, 58–72.

ATKEY, Richard James, b. 6 June 09, s. of late J. F. H. Atkey. SH 22³–27². New College, Oxford, B.A. Solicitor, 34. ✗ R.A. Major. Family Solicitor (Atkey & Son to 57, Atkey, Sandelson & Co., 57–65) and from 65 partner with Nabarro Nathanson & Co. *Phyllis Court (Henley) Club, Oxford & Cambridge United University Club.*

ATKIN, Charles Philip, b. 27 Apr. 24, eldest s. of late Dr. C. S. Atkin. St & W, 38¹–42¹; R. VIII, 41–42. Gonville & Caius, Cambridge, M.B., B.Chir. Late House Surgeon, Middlesex Hospital, London, & Royal Infirmary, Sheffield. Late Surgeon, P & O Steam Nav. Co. Medical Practitioner. Son, Matthew Philip. St, 71³–.

ATKINS, Geoffrey Willoughby Thomas, b. 20 Jan. 27, younger (twin) s. of late Lt.-Col. G. W. Atkins, M.C. T, 40³–45²; Cap, 44; XI, 45; H. XI, 45; Sw. VIII (Diving); Rackets Pair, 45; Public Schools Squash Rackets Champion, 45. Queens', Cambridge, B.A. Squash,

Rackets & Tennis Half Blues, 50. Combined Services Rackets, 48–49. Played Squash for England, 51. British Amateur Rackets (singles), 52–53, doubles (with P. Kershaw O.R.), 53. American & Canadian Rackets Singles Champion & Open N. American Champion, 45. Winner of U.S.A. & Canadian doubles (with W. Wood-Prince), 54. Three times Amateur (Real) Tennis Champion. World Rackets Champion, 54–72. In U.S.A. working for Prince Trusts (Chicago & New York), 53–60. Conch Methane Services Ltd., London. Far East Manager, 60–67. Senior Economic Adviser, Armour & Co., Chicago, 67–72. Presently, Commercial Manager, Burmah Oil Co. of Australia Ltd., Perth, W. Australia. *Hurlington Club; Tennis & Rackets Assoc.; London Racquet Club of Chicago; Montreal Racket Club; M.C.C.* Brother, R. E. W. Atkins.

ATKINS, Prof. Sir Hedley John Barnard, K.B.E., M.D., M.Ch., F.R.C.S., b. 30 Dec. 05, s. of late Sir J. Atkins, K.C.M.G., K.C.V.O. SH, 19^3–25^1; XV, 24; G. VIII, 21–22 (Capt.) 23; Physics Prize. Trinity, Oxford, Hon. Fellow. Guy's Hospital. D.M., M.Ch., F.R.C.S., F.R.C.P. Hon. Fellow, Am. Coll. Surg.; Royal Aus. Coll. Surg.; Royal Coll. Surg., Can.; Coll. Surg., S.A.; Royal Coll. Surg., Glasgow; Hon. D.Sc., E. Anglia & Kent Univs.; Prof. Surg., Guy's Hospital, Univ. London (Emeritus); Past President, Royal Coll. Surg. of England. President, Royal Society Med.; President, Med. Society, London. Past President, Surg. Research Society. Past Member of Med. Res. Council & G.M.C. Chrmn. Queen Elizabeth Coll. Lon. Univ. & Hon. Fellow, Retired. Various Publications. K.B.E., 67. K. St. J. Played for Harlequins, Guy's Hospital, Middlesex County at Rugby Football. *Garrick, Athenæum, Vincent's.*

ATKINS, Michael, b. 24 Nov. 26, s. of G. R. Atkins. SF, 40^3–44^2. Pembroke, Cambridge, M.A. N/S. R.A.E.C., 47–49. Capt. Teaching. Senior Mathematician, Pangbourne College.

ATKINS, Robert Everett William, M.C., b. 20 Jan. 27, elder (twin) s. of late Lt.-Col. G. W. Atkins, M.C. T, 40^3–45^1. Regular Army, 45–59. 8th & 6th Gurkha Rifles. Partner of Thomas & Atkins, London, Property Development Consultants. M.C., 53, Malaya. Brother, G. W. T. Atkins.

ATTENBOROUGH, Anthony Ralph, b. 13 Jan. 13, 3rd s. of late R. E. Attenbor-

ough. K, 26^3–31^2; H. XI, 30–31. Trinity, Oxford, M.A. Solicitor, 38. ✕ West Somerset Yeomanry, 40–42 & 3rd R.T.R., 42–43. Wounded. Staff Officer Civil Affairs (Legal), 43–45. Major. *Vincent's Club, Oxford; The Club, Beckenham.* Brother, R. J. Attenborough. Sons, 1978 & 2296.

ATTENBOROUGH, Bernard, b. 19 Jul. 96, 4th s. of late S. J. Attenborough. SH, 10^3–14^2. ✕ 2nd Bn., London Regt., R.F.C. Capt. Wounded. Croix de Guerre. Company Director. Retired, 69. Brothers, James & Stanley Attenborough.

ATTENBOROUGH, Col. James, C.M.G., b. 7 Aug. 84, eldest s. of late S. J. Attenborough. K, 98^3–01^2. Solicitor, 05, of Stanley Attenborough, London. Retired, 64. ✕ 2nd Bn., London Regt., Comdt School of Technical Training, R.F.C., Halton. Lt.-Col. C.M.G. Dispatches 3 times. Col. retired. T.D. Past Hon. Treasurer & President, O.R.S. *Devonshire Club; Royal St. George's Golf Club.* Brothers, Bernard & Stanley Attenborough.

ATTENBOROUGH, Kenneth Cyril, b. 17 May 18, 3rd s. of late C. P. Attenborough (OR K 96). K, 32^1–35^2. Grenoble University. ✕ R.A., 39–46. Capt. Wounded. Dispatches. Underwriting Member of Lloyd's. *M.C.C.* Son, Nicholas Brian, K, 67^1–.

ATTENBOROUGH, Ralph John, C.B.E., b. 30 Dec. 08, eldest s. of late R. E. Attenborough. K, 22^3–27^2. Trinity, Oxford, M.A. ✕ R.A. (H.A.C.). Major. Dispatches 3 times. M.B.E. President, Publishers' Association, 65–67. Leader of Book Development Council Missions in India & Ceylon, 69, & Pakistan & Bangladesh, 71. Joint Chief Executive & Deputy Chairman, Matthew Hodder Ltd., Book Publishers. C.B.E. (Civil). *Athenæum, Society of Bookmen, Royal St. George's Golf Club.* Brother, A. R. Attenborough. Sons, 411 & 926.

ATTENBOROUGH, Brig. Stanley, b. 10 June 98, 5th & youngest s. of late S. J. Attenborough. SH, 12^1–15^2. R.M.A., Woolwich. Gazetted R.F.A., 16. ✕ 22nd Bde., R.F.A., 16–19. Lt. ✕ R.A. N. Africa, 40–41. B.L.A., 44–45. Lt.-Col. Dispatches. A.-Brigadier, 47. Retired, 47. Kent Arch. Soc. National Trust. Field Survey Soc. Brothers, James & Bernard Attenborough.

ATTOCK, Martin Oldacres, b. 25 Mar. 09, younger s. of late G. H. Attock. T,

23^2–25^1. Rugby Technical College. Chartered Engineer, F.I.Mech.E. Formerly Chief Technical Service Engineer, Traction Dept., The English Electric Co. Ltd. Now retired. *Vintage Sports Car Club.*

ATTWELL, John Anthony Finnis. T, 30^2–32^2.*

AVAKUMOVIC, Prof. Ivan. K, 42^3–44^2.*

AWDRY, Simon John Douglas, b. 11 Nov. 32, s. of late J. A. H. E. Awdry. Sh, 46^3–50^3. Cap. N/S. Royal Corps of Signals, 51–52. 2nd Lt. Exhibitioner of Corpus Christi, Cambridge, M.A. Solicitor. Partner of Osborne, Chance & Co., Bristol, since 59.

AYKROYD, Frederick Howard, b. 10 Oct. 07, 2nd s. of late Sir F. Aykroyd, Bt.

M, 21^3–25^1. Jesus, Cambridge, B.A. Retired.

AYKROYD, Col. Harold Hammond O.B.E., M.C., b. 7 Apr. 96, 2nd s. of late Sir W. Aykroyd, Bt. C, 10^1–14^2; XI, 14. ✕ 4th Bn. Duke of Wellington's (West Riding) Regt. (T.F.). Captain, M.C. Major, 25. Col., O.B.E., M.C. Carpet Manufacturer retired. *East India, Sports & Public Schools Club.*

AYLWARD, Richard Scott, b. 19 Apr. 20, s. of Major R. N. Aylward, D.S.O., M.C. SH, 33^3–38^2. ✕ R.E., 40–46. Attached 14 Field Coy., Q.V.O., Madras Sappers & Miners. In Italy with 10th Indian Div. Wounded. Sidney Sussex, Camb., B.A. M.I.C.E. Resident Engineer, Charles, Weiss & Partners, Consulting Structural Engineers, London.

B

BABBEDGE, Harman Paul, b. 23 Jan. 26, youngest s. of late J. R. Babbedge. T, 39^3–44^2. Major Foundationer. Organ Scholarship to Queens', Cambridge, M.A. Served in Intelligence Corps and Royal Army Education Corps at Sandhurst, 45–48. Bognor College of Education. Trinity College of Music, London. Licentiate, Trinity College of Music, A.R.C.O. Teacher's Cert., Southampton University, Registration Exam of Library Association. Music Master in Warwickshire, 54–56. Assistant Director of Music, Tonbridge School, 57–60. Music Master at Gravesend Grammar School, 60–62. Assistant Director at Cheltenham College Junior School, 62–63. Director of Music, Dean Close Junior School, 63–70. Lecturer in Music, St. Mary's College of Education, Cheltenham, 70–72. At present Director of Music, Charlton Park Convent School from 72. Member of Council of Incorporated Society of Musicians.

BABST, Squadron Leader Edgar Francis. K, 37^3–41^3.*

BACH, Quintin Vaughan Simpson. T, 41^3–45^2.*

BACKHOUSE, The Rev. Canon. Thomas Porter. C, 11^3–13^2.*

BACKHOUSE, Major Wilfred Jasper, M.B.E., b. 28 July 13, 3rd s. of late M. R. C. Backhouse, D.S.O. Tu, 27^2–31^2. R. Signals. Major. M.B.E. Dispatches. Farmer. *Farmers' Club.*

BACON, Allon Roger Sewell. SF, 36^3–40^2.*

BACON, Colin Hugh Christopher, b. 8 July 30, s. of G. P. Bacon, T.D. (OR SF 20). SF, 44^2–49^1. N/S. 43rd Light Infantray. 2nd Lt. Cyprus, 49–50. Corpus Christi, Oxford, M.A. Dip.M., M.I.M., M.I.M.C. Oil Industry, 54–61. (U.K. & E. Africa) Export Agent, 62–63. College of Marketing, 64–66. P-E Consulting Group, 66–71. Senior Consultant, Business Development Analysis Ltd., Epsom, Director of Terminal Systems Assoc. Ltd. from 72. Fauna Preservation Society, East Africa Wildlife Society.

BACON, Gordon Patrick, T.D., b. 17 Mar. 06, younger s. of late S. Bacon. SF, 20^2–24^1; H. XI, 24. ✕ R.A., 39–45. Capt., T.D. (Served in Burma.) Member of Incorporated Practitioners in Advertising. Writer, Advertising Agent (Chairman & Director of London Ad. Agency) now retired, but still advertising consultant and Director of Finance Co. President of Richard III Society. *R.A.C.*

BADDELEY, Arnold Gerald, b. 28 Aug. 28, s. of late Sir F. Baddeley, K.B.E., C.M.G. SH, 42^2–46^2; H. XI, 46. N/S. R. Ulster Rifles, 48. Lt. Parachute Bn. T.A. Magdalene, Cambridge, B.A. Colonial Devonshire Course, Oxford, 51. Colonial Administrative Service, Nigeria, 51–54. Shell-Mex & B.P. Ltd., 54–71. Smith Builders Merchants (Old Stratford) Ltd., from 71, Chrmn. & Man. Dir. *Royal Commonwealth Society*. Sons, Patrick Charles Morrish, S.H., 67³–71³ & Timothy William Gerald, SH., 69³–.

BADENOCH, John, D.M., F.R.C.P., b. 8 Mar. 20, s. of Dr. W. M. Badenoch. Sh, 33³–38². Oriel, Oxford. Cornell Medical College, New York Hospital. M.A., D.M., F.R.C.P. Consultant Physician, United Oxford Hospital. Fellow of Merton College. Sons, 1800 & 2935.

BAER, Alan Frank. W, 34³–38³.*

BAGGS, Peter John Bennett. W, 40³–43³.*

BAGNALL, Charles Frederick Rex, C.B.E. C, 18¹–19³. Son, 284.*

BAGSHAWE, Nicholas Thomas, b. 11 Mar. 27, youngest s. of T. W. Bagshawe (OR St 15). St & W, 40³–44². Gonville & Caius, Cambridge, M.A. N/S. R.A.F.V.R., 46–48. F.C.A. Director of Hobourn-Eaton Mfg. Co. Ltd., Oil Pump Manufacturer, Rochester, from 56. Master of Curriers' Company, 72. Brother, R. W. Bagshawe. Sons, William Nicholas St, 70³– & James Richard St, 72²–.

BAGSHAWE, Richard Wyatt, b. 22 Aug. 24, eldest s. of T. W. Bagshawe (OR St 15) St & W, 38³–42². Gonville & Caius, Cambridge, M.A. ✠ R.A.F.V.R., 43–46. F/Officer. Qualified Pilot. C.Eng., M.I.Mech.E. Lucas Aerospace Ltd., Hemel Hempstead, Herts., Mechanical Designer Aircraft Equipment. Liveryman, Curriers' Company. Brother, N. T. Bagshawe.

BAGSHAWE, Thomas Wyatt, b. 18 Apr. 01, 2nd s. of A. Bagshawe. St, 15¹–18². Gonville & Caius, Cambridge, Geologist. Expedition to Graham Land (Antarctica), 20–22. F.S.A., F.R.Hist.S. Director Bagshawe & Co. Ltd., Dunstable, 25–47. Hon. Curator, Later Director, Luton Museum, 28–47. Past Master Curriers' Company. ✠ R.A.F.V.R. & Combined Operations, 40–45. S/Ldr. High Sheriff, Beds., 49. Trustee, Cecil Higgins Museum, Bedford, 51–56. Vice-Pres., Royal Anthropological Institute, 52–55. Name given to Bagshawe Glacier, Antarctica, 58. Sundry Publications. *Antarctica Club*. Sons, R. W. & N. T. Bagshawe.

BAILEY, Cecil Henry, b. 31 Aug. 88, elder s. of late T. H. Bailey. B, 03²–06¹. Birmingham Univ., B.Sc. A.M.Inst.C.E., F.R.I.C.S. ✠ S. Midland Div. Train., A.S.C. R.E. Lt. Member of S. & J. Bailey, Mining Engineers & Surveyors, Birmingham. Divisional Estates Manager, N.W. Div., Coal Commission, and National Coal Board. Lands Tribunal, 50–58. Son, J. C. L. B. Bailey.

BAILEY, James Cecil Lees Bodington, b. 19 July 18, s. of C. H. Bailey, F.R.I.C.S., M.I.C.E. (OR B 03). S.F., 32¹–35²; Paddison Art Prize (twice). Architectural Assoc., 35–37. Liverpool University, 39 & 46–50. Bachelor of Architecture, Liverpool, 50. A.R.I.B.A., 50. Partner in Blackwell, Storey & Scott, Architects, London and Kettering.

BAILEY, John Desmond Warren. SH, 41²–45². Brother, 19.*

BAILIE, Charles William Hugh, D.L., b. 5 Apr. 95, 2nd s. of late Major-General T. M. Bailie. B, 09¹–12². R.M.C., Sandhurst. ✠ 2nd Bn. Oxford & Bucks Light Infantry. Wounded. Dispatches. Capt. Major, 32. Retired, 33. Re-employed, 39–45. Member, R. Company of Archers (Queen's Body Guards for Scotland). M.F.H., Berwickshire Fox Hounds, 39–40 & 51–57. D.L., 37. J.P., 52, Berwickshire. J.P., 32, Berks. *New Club (Edinburgh)*.

BAKER, Derek Collingwood. W, 15³–19³.*

BAKER, The Rev. Eric Paul, b. 14 Sept. 06, eldest s. of late R. M. Baker (OR SF 91). SF, 20³–24³. New College, Oxford, M.A. Westcott House, Cambridge. Ordained, 33. Clerk in Holy Order. Vicar of Great Milton, Oxford. F.S.A.

BAKER, Giles Herman, b. 24 Oct. 32, eldest s. of late Air Chief Marshal Sir J. W. Baker, K.C.B. St, 46³–50². R.A.F. College, Cranwell. Left R.A.F., 61. Started boatyard, 63. Now co-owner of most successful and largest yard of hire fleet on the canals.

BAKER, John Edward Alan, b. 21 June 14, younger s. of late G. F. Baker. C, 28³–33²; Scholar, XI, 32–33, H. XI, 32–33. Corpus Christi, Oxford, B.A. ✠ 11th Nigerian Regt., R.W.A.F.F. Capt., 40–43. Recalled Nigerian Administration, 43. Colonial Administrative Service, 38–62. 1st Permanent Secretary, Ministry of Health, N. Nigeria. In charge of Province. Administrator, Botany Dept., Oxford University from 62. Elected Councillor, Oxford City Council, 72. *Vincent's Club*.

BAKER, John Raymond, b. 21 Mar. 32, s. of late J. J. Baker. K, 46¹–49³. Chartered Accountant. Partner, Baker, Sutton & Co., Chartered Accountants.

BAKER, Martin Henry Percival, b. 29 Apr. 25, younger s. of late R. P. Baker, M.C. (OR B oo). B, 38³–43². Diploma in Vocational Guidance. ✕ Royal Signals. Lt., 44–47. Worked in family textile printing business of G.P. & J. Baker Ltd., Director, 48–61. Now a Deputy Senior Careers Officer in Inner London Education Authority. F.R.G.S.

BAKER-COURTENAY, John Charles Cutforth. Tu, 44¹–48¹.*

BAKEWELL, Brian. K, 04²–08².*

BALDOCK, John Markham, V.R.D., b. 19 Nov. 15, s. of late Capt. W. P. Baldock. SF, 29³–33². Balliol, Oxford, B.A. ✕ R.N.V.R., 39–45. Lt.-Cdr. V.R.D. M.P. (C) Harborough, 50–59. Farmer. Chairman, Lenscrete Ltd. Director, Ciba-Geigy. *Farmers' Club.*

BALDWIN, Major Christopher Lacy, M.C., b. 24 June 97, 2nd s. of late J. H. L. Baldwin. W, 11³–14². R.M.A., Woolwich. ✕ 58th Bde., R.F.A. Wounded twice. M.C. Capt., 26. Major, R.A., 35. Retired, 38. J.P., Yorkshire (W.R.), 41. *Naval & Military Club.* Sons, 730 & 1522.

BALDWIN, Lt. Col. Ian Hugh Trevor, R.A. B, 22³–27².*

BALDWIN, Air Marshal Sir John Eustace Arthur, K.B.E., C.B., D.S.O., D.L., J.P., b. 13 Apr. 92, eldest s. of late J. H. L. Baldwin. W, 06³–10². R.M.C., Sandhurst. Gazetted to 8th Hussars 11. Capt. Transferred to R.A.F., 19, having been seconded to R.F.C. in 14. Air Marshal, R.A.F. (retired). Commanded Cranwell, 36–39. A.O.C., 3 Group, 39–42. Dep. A.O.C.-in-C., India, 42–43. C. in C., Burma, 43–45. Retired, R.A.F., 45. Farmer. *Cavalry, R.A.F.* Past President of the O.R. Society. K.B.E., 43. C.B., D.S.O. D.L., Lincs. J.P., Rutland. Officer Crown & Croix de Guerre, Belgium. White Lion & Czech War Cross. American Air Medal. *Cavalry, R.A.F.* Brother, C. L. Baldwin.

BALDWIN, Walter Sydney, C.M.G. St, 34³–35³.*

BALFOUR, David Ross. Tu, 12³–14³.*

BALFOUR, Gilbert Graham, b. 23 Feb. 99, elder s. of late Sir T. G. Balfour. SH, 13²–17²; S. VIII, 15–17 (Capt.). Trinity, Oxford, B.A. ✕ R.F.A. Brit. Salonica & Trans. Caucasian Forces, S. Russia. Lt. F.R.I.C.S., F.L.A.S. Rural land utilisation officer appointed by Minister of Agriculture—Kent, Surrey & Sussex. Partner in Smith, Woolley & Co., Chartered Surveyors. Retired. *Farmers' Club.* Brother, M. L. G. Balfour.

BALFOUR, Michael Leonard Graham, C.B.E., b. 22 Nov. 08, 2nd s. of Sir T. G. Balfour. SH, 22²–27²; S. VIII, 26–27; Minor Leaving Exhibition; Exhibitioner of Balliol, Oxford, M.A. Senior Demy Magdalen, Oxford, 31–32. Lecturer, Magdalen, Oxford, 32–36. Research Secretary, Royal Inst. of International Affairs, 36–39. Principal, Ministry of Information, 39–42. Political Warfare Executive, 42–45. Control Commission for Germany, 45–47. Chief Information Officer, Board of Trade, 47–64. University of East Anglia from 66 (Prof. of European History, 69). Publications: "States and Mind", "Four-power control in Germany", "The Kaiser and his times", "West Germany", "Helmuth von Moltke". C.B.E., 63. Brother, G. G. Balfour.

BALFOUR, Michael Selby, b. 8 July 32, s. of D. R. Balfour (OR Tu 12). Tu, 45³–50². Chartered Accountant. Senior Partner of Cooper Brothers & Co., in France. Cercle Interallié, Paris.

BALFOUR-BROWNE, John William Alexander Francis, b. 15 May 07, s. of late W. A. F. Balfour-Browne. SH, 21³–24³. Magdalen, Oxford. Caius, Cambridge, M.A. Entomologist, Junta Geral, Madeira, 32–34. Principal Scientific Officer, British Museum (Nat. Hist.), 34–67. Retired from Civil Service, Nov. 67. Zoological Society of London. Royal Entomological Society of London.

BALL, Norman John. W, 43¹–46².*

BALL-ACTON, Charles. SH, 28³–33².*

BALLANTYNE, Alexander Hanson, C.V.O., C.B.E., b. 27 Feb. 11, eldest s. of late Dr. H. S. Ballantyne. K, 24³–29². Exhibitioner of Christ's, Cambridge, B.A. Taught at Heidelberg University, 33–34. Oct. 34 entered Consular Service, which was later merged with the Diplomatic Service. Vice-Consul Bangkok, Valencia, Tokyo, Antananarivo. 1st Secretary, Istanbul, later Acting Consul General. Consul General, Copenhagen. Chargé d'Affaires, later Counsellor, Ankara. Consul General,

Frankfurt-am-Main. Retired from Diplomatic Service, 70. Consultant to O.E.C.D., Paris, since 71. C.V.O., 57 and Commander of the Danebrog, 57, C.B.E., 63. Son, 2667.

BALLARD, Brig. James Archibald William, C.B.E., D.S.O., b. 31 July 05, younger s. of late Admiral G. A. Ballard. SF, 19¹–21². R.M.C., Sandhurst. 1st Bn. Northants Regt., 25. Lt., 27. Staff College, 39. ✕ Gen. Staff, 2nd Corps, B.E.F., 39–40. Military Mission to S. Africa, 41–42. Lt.-Col. commanding 2nd Bn., Sicily, Italy & Germany. D.S.O., M.B.E. Chief of Staff, S.H.A.E.F. Mission to Denmark, 45. B.G.S., Egypt, 46–50. Trieste, 50–51. Brig. (retired). C.B.E. *Naval & Military*.

BALLINGALL, Horace Campbell. Sh, 30²–32².*

BANCHONG, Phya Srishtikar. T, 07¹–08².*

BANKS, Richard Alford, C.B.E., J.P., b. 11 July 02, s. of late W. H. Banks (OR SF 81). K, 16²–20²; Cap, 18. Trinity, Cambridge, B.A. C.B.E., 65. J.P. for Herefordshire, 63–73. Joined Brunner, Mond & Co., 24, later to become Imperial Chemical Industries Director from 52–64. Chairman of Industrial Training Council, 63–64. Member of Water Resources Board from 64. R.H.S. Royal Forestry Society. Son, 747.

BANTING, John Lindsay, b. 1 Oct. 21, s. of late P. E. Banting. Sh, 35²–40¹. H. XI, 38–39. Emmanuel, Cambridge, M.A. ✕ R.E. Capt. Commercial Engineer, Electrical Industry. Now self-employed, Picture Framer & Rural Crafts. Life member, Wanderers Hockey Club. Vice-President, Warks. County Hockey Assoc. Sons, 2398 & 2845.

BARBER-FLEMING, Charles Elphinstone. St & K, 38²–42³.*

BARBER-STARKEY, John Richard Anthony. W, 44¹–47³.*

BARBOR, Ronald Charles Blair, b. 1 May 10, s. of late C. Barbor. W, 23³–28²; XXII; H. XI, 26–28 (Capt.). St. John's, Cambridge, B.A., M.B., B.Chir. St. Thomas's Hospital Medical School; M.R.C.S., L.R.C.P. ✕ R.A.M.C. Capt. Late Chairman, British Association of Manipulative Medicine. General Practitioner, 35–55. Consultant Orthopaedic Physician since 55. Fellow of the Royal Society of Medicine.

BARBOUR, Alec Walter, b. 15 Jan. 25, 2nd s. of G. F. Barbour, D.Phil. (Edin.), M.A. B, 38³–42². Edinburgh University, B.Sc. Vans Dunlop Scholarship. F.R.I.C.S. Land Agent. Partner, Renton, Finlayson & Co., Chartered Surveyors & Land Agents. Brother, R. A. S. Barbour.

BARBOUR, James. B, 22³–26².*

BARBOUR, The Rev. Robert Alexander Stewart, b. 11 May 21, eldest s. of G. F. Barbour, D.Phil. (Edin.), M.A. B, 35¹–39²; Scholar. Levée. Head of House, Exhibitioner. Scholar of Balliol, Oxford, St. Mary's College, St. Andrews, Yale University. ✕ Scottish Horse. Capt., M.C., M.A., B.D., S.T.M. Secretary, Studiorum Novi Testamenti Societas. Ordained. Chaplain to Overseas Students, Edinburgh, 53–55. Lecturer, University of Edinburgh, 55–71. Prof. of New Testament Exegesis, University of Aberdeen, from 71. *New Club, Edinburgh*. Brother, A. W. Barbour.

BARBOUR, Walter Terence. C, 01¹–03¹.*

BARCLAY, Lt.-Col. Alexander Hubert, D.S.O., M.C. St, 14¹–17².*

BARCLAY, John Innes Monkhouse. B, 18²–21². Son, 311.*

BARCLAY, Paul Stuart, M.C., M.R.C.S., L.R.C.P., b. 3 Oct. 15, s. of late J. M. Barclay. SH, 29¹–33³; Cap. Trinity, Cambridge, B.A. St. Bart's Hospital, M.R.C.S., L.R.C.P., D.A. ✕ R.A.M.C., 41–46. M.C. Capt., T.D. General Practitioner, Anaesthetist.

BARCLAY, Peter Harold Lovat. Tu, 32³–34².*

BARFORD, Edward James, M.C. M, 12¹–15².*

BARING-GOULD, Edward Darragh, b. 13 June 06, 2nd s. of late Major E. S. Baring-Gould. St, 20³–22¹; G. VIII. Trinity, Cambridge, B.A. ✕ 45 Group, R.A.F. Transport Command, 42–45. Flying Officer. E. D. Baring-Gould Co., Investments. E. W. Axe & Co. Inc., Investment Council. President, A-B-G, Instrument & Engineering Inc. Brother, S. L. Baring-Gould.

BARING-GOULD, Sabine Linton. St, 15²–20². Brother, E. D. Baring-Gould.*

BARKER, Brig. Charles Norman, M.B.E., M.C., b. 19 Nov. 19, 2nd s. of G. G. Barker. St, 33^3–35^2. R.M.C., Sandhurst. Commissioned to Gordon Highlanders. p.s.c. j.s.s.c. Instructor, R.M.A.S., Sandhurst. War service in France, 39–40. Western Desert, Tunisia, Sicily & N.W. Europe. Post-War Service in India, Germany, West Africa & Malaya. Commanded Infantry Junior Leaders Bn. A/Secretary, Chiefs of Staff Committee. Col. i/c. Admin., Scotland. Asst. Secretary to P.U.S., Ministry of Defence. Deputy Commander, West Midland District. M.B.E., M.C. Dispatches. Brigadier.

BARKER, Christopher Shelley, b. 13 Nov. 32, s. of E. A. Barker, C.B.E., LL.D. (OR W 19). W, 46^2–50^2. New College, Oxford, B.A. Solicitor (Private Practice). Treasurer, University of Sheffield. Partner in Heals & Shelley Barkers, Solicitors, Sheffield. *The Club, Sheffield; R. & A. Golf Club.*

BARKER, Major Eric Clement, M.B.E. W, 97^3–02^2.*

BARKER, Ernest Anthony, C.B.E., LL.D., b. 29 Jan. 06, 2nd s. of late H. S. Barker (OR W 83). W, 19^3–23^2. New College, Oxford, M.A. Chairman, United Sheffield Hospital. Solicitor. Senior partner, Heals & Shelley Barkers. C.B.E., LL.D. *O. & C. Golfing Society; R. & A.*

BARKER BENNETT, Assheton Charles, b. 7 Apr. 06, eldest s. of late S. Barker Bennett (OR K 87). K, 20^3–23^2. ✕ H.A.C., H.A.A. Regt., 39–40. Commissioned, R.A.S.C., 40–45. Major. Motor Trader. Son, 318.

BARLOW, Anthony Norman. SH, 11^2–14^2. Son, 512.*

BARLOW, Michael Roderick. W, 44^2–47^3.*

BARLOW, Peter Douglas, D.S.C. W, 32^3–37^2.*

BARLOW, Peter Norman. SH, 44^2–48^2.*

BARLOW, William, b. 4 Nov. 29, s. of late W. Barlow. W, 43^3–48^3. N/S. R.A.S.C., 49. 2nd Lt. Managing Director, George Barlow & Sons Ltd. (Family Co. – Shopfitting). Also Director of other Ltd. Cos. *Sheffield Club.*

BARNETT, Leslie Winterton. SH, 98^2–01^2.*

BARNWELL, Col. Ralph Ernest, C.B.E., b. 20 Jan. 95, s. of late E. F. Barnwell. T, 10^3–14^1. ✕ Joined H.A.C., 14. 2nd Lt. Royal Warwickshire Regt., 16. Served in France and Flanders, 14–18. Dispatches. Staff College, 28–29. Lt.-Col., 39. Col., 41. Served in France and Flanders, 39–40, and as A.A.G., War Office, 40–45. Retired, 45. Commandant, Duke of York's Royal Military School, Dover, 45–53. C.B.E., 43. *Army & Navy Club.*

BARR, Charles John Hall, b. 19 July 08, s. of late T. H. Barr. SF, 22^2–25^3. Magdalene, Cambridge, B.A., C.A. ✕ 86th Regt., H.A.A. & R.A.O.C. Capt., 39–45. Chartered Accountant, retired. H.A.C. Son, 1293.

BARRACLOUGH, Maurice William Read, b. 25 July 13, s. of late A. Barraclough, M.A., F.R.G.S. K, 27^3–32^2; Scholar, Head of House. Exhibitioner of Sidney Sussex, Cambridge, M.A. ✕ R.A. (Field & A.A.) 40–46. Senior Maths Master, Ardingly College, Sussex, since 35.

BARRAN, Hugh Rowland Murray. SH, 43^1–46^3. Son, Patrick Robin, S.H., 72^3–.*

BARRETT, Thurston, b. 20 Aug. 14, elder s. of late P. T. Barrett. M, 28^2–32^2. XXII, 32.

BARRON, John Jeremy Michael, b. 29 Jan. 33, elder s. of late Col. J. Barron, M.C., R.A. (OR Tu 12). SH, 46^3–51^2; Head of House. Levée. XI, 50–51 (vice-captain, 51). Cadet officer. State Scholar, 2nd Pair Rackets, 50–51. Pembroke, Cambridge, B.A. Captain, C.U. Rackets Club, 52. A.M.B.I.M. Shell-Mex & B.P. Ltd., since 54. *Jesters, M.C.C.* Brother, 201.

BARROW, Derek Bazil W. B, 22^3–26^3. Brother, J. Barrow.*

BARROW, John, O.B.E., b. 30 Dec. 03, elder s. of late Maj.-Gen. H. P. W. Barrow, C.B., C.M.G., D.S.O., O.B.E. B, 17^3–22^1; R. VIII, 22. Gonville & Caius, Cambridge, M.A. Univ. Coll., London. Univ. of Hong Kong, passed all four Cantonese language exams, three with credit. Hong Kong Civil Service, 26–53. Private Secretary to Governor. Asst. Sec. for Chinese Affairs. Asst. Superintendent of Imports & Exports. District Officer (North). P.O.W. (Lt.), 41–45. District Commissioner, New Territories. Member of Committee on Chinese Law & Custom.

Vice-Chairman of Board of Examiners in Chinese, 53–69. Schoolmaster, teaching French and some German. Life member of *Hong Kong Club*. O.B.E., 46. Member of Yeovil R.D.C. Brother, D. B. W. Barrow.

BARSON, Charles Anthony, b. 2 Apr. 33, 2nd s. of A. C. Barson. T, 46^3–51^2. Foundationer. Birmingham University, B.Sc., Ph.D. Senior chemistry master, Bromsgrove School, 57–61. Senior research Fellow, Univ. of Birmingham, 61–64. Lecturer in Chemistry, Univ. of Birmingham, since 64. Chemical Soc., London.

BARSTOW, Lt.-Col. John Anthony Tristram, D.S.O., T.D., D.L., b. 26 Aug. 06, eldest s. of Sir G. L. Barstow, K.C.B. SH, 20^2–25^2; XV, 24. Trinity, Oxford, B.A. O.U. Greyhounds, 26–28. O.U.R.F.C. Irish Tour, 28. Solicitor – Partner Messrs. Trower, Still & Keeling of Lincoln's Inn. Solicitor to Bridewell Royal Hospital, Bethlem Royal Hospital & The Maudsley Hospital, 36–71. Director of Companies including The Prudential Assurance Co. Ltd. Honourable Artillery Company, 29. ✕ Lt.-Col. comdg., 12 (H.A.C.) Regt., R.H.A., 42–45. 1st Regt., Honourable Artillery Company, R.H.A., 48–51. Deputy Colonel Commandant, 51–55. Bt.-Col., 51. D.S.O., 43. Dispatches. T.D. D.L., Radnorshire. High Sheriff of Radnorshire, 71. *Garrick Club, M.C.C.*

BARTLETT, Major Anthony, b. 13 Sep. 00, s. of late F. Bartlett. (OR St 85). K, 14^3–18^3. R.M.C., Sandhurst. Gazetted to Duke of Cornwall's Light Infantry, 20. Served in Ireland. N.W. Frontier, India. ✕ 39–45. Major. Retired, 47. Control Commission for Germany, 47–50.

BARTON, Richard Juxon. B, 42^2–46^2.*

BARTRAM, George Christopher, b. 23 Aug. 27, elder s. of R. A. Bartram, M.C., T.D., J.P. Sh, 41^2–45^2. Emergency Commission, Durham Light Infantry, 46. St. Catharine's Cambridge, M.A. T.D.

BARWISE, Dr. William Arthur David, b. 11 May 20, eldest s. of late H. B. Barwise. K, 34^1–38^2. St. Thomas's Hospital Medical School. University College, London. M.R.C.S., L.R.C.P. N/S. Capt., R.A.M.C., 46–48. Anaesthetics Registrar, Bristol Royal Infirmary, General Medical Practice. Member, Dolmetsch Foundation.

BASDEN, Harold Edward Lenox. W, 14^1–18^1.*

BATCHELOR, Peter George, b. 26 Oct. 26, s. of G. W. Batchelor. T, 40^3–44^2. Keble, Oxford, M.A. Consultant, Rural Development Consultancy for Christian Churches in Africa. Agricultural Missionary.

BATES, David Vincent, M.D., M.R.C.P., b. 20 May 22, younger s. of late Dr. J. V. Bates. Sh, 35^3–39^2. Pembroke, Cambridge, B.A., M.D. St. Bartholomew's Hospital, London. R.A.M.C. Capt. ✕ F.R.C.P. (C)., F.R.C.P. (London), F.R.S. (Canada). Dean, Faculty of Medicine. Prof. of Medicine and Physiology, University of British Columbia, Vancouver 8, B.C. *Royal Vancouver Yacht Club.* Robert Cooke Medal, American Academy of Allergy. Brother, J. A. V. Bates.

BATES, Lt.-Col. Eric George, M.B.E., T.D., LL.B., b. 20 Apr. 08, s. of G. B. Bates. B, 22^1–26^2. Jesus, Cambridge, LL.B., M.A. Solicitor, 33. Partner, Wedlake, Haines & Bates, 33–39. ✕ Commanded 40 L.A.A. Regt., R.A. 51st Highland Div. Lt.-Col. M.B.E. Dispatches. T.D. Alamein, Sicily, Normandy. Resident Magistrate, Northern Rhodesia, 47–53. With Linklaters & Paines, Solicitors, from 55. *City Livery and Constitutional Clubs.* Magistrates' Association. W. M. Wheelwrights' Company.

BATES, Eric Percy Richard, b. 6 Nov. 15, s. of E. M. Bates. T, 29^1–34^2. Levée. Major Leaving Exhibition. Cadet Officer. Minor Scholarship to Gonville & Caius, Cambridge. ✕ Inns of Court Regt., R.A.C. Major. Corn Merchant to 62. Now retired. *Hawks.*

BATES, John Alexander Vincent, M.B., B.Chir. Sh, 32^3–37^2. Brother, D. V. Bates. Sons, 2237 & 2486.*

BATES, Peter Nelson. St, 44^3–45^1.*

BATESON, Alec John, b. 23 Jan. 25, s. of Rear-Admiral S. L. Bateson, C.B., C.B.E., R.N. (OR C 12). C & Tu, 38^3–43^2; Scholar. Levée; Cadet Officer, 42. XV, 42. Scholar of Trinity, Oxford. ✕ The Rifle Brigade, 6th Airborne Div. Capt. Solicitor, 50. Partner in Trower, Still & Keeling of Lincoln's Inn. *United Service Club.* Sons, David Stuart, Tu, 68^3–. Hugh Comrie, Tu, 70^3–.

BATESON, Cecil William. SH, 99^2–03^2.*

BATESON, James William, b. 7 Oct. 27, elder s. of late W. L. Bateson. (OR C 08). M, 41³-45²; Sw. VIII, 44-45 (Capt.), XXII, 45. Solicitor. President, Liverpool Law Society, 71-72 (4th generation to hold this office). Chairman, Liverpool Trustee Savings Bank, 70-72. Deputy Treasurer, Liverpool University since 72. Partner, Alsop, Stevens, Batesons & Co., Liverpool & London. Brother, M. J. Bateson.

BATESON, Michael John, b. 8 Sept. 29, younger s. of late W. L. Bateson. (OR C 08). M, 43³-47². Director of Edward Bates Securities Ltd. Investment Management Subsidiary of Edward Bates & Sons Ltd, Merchant Bankers, London, Liverpool & Edinburgh. Brother, J. W. Bateson.

BATESON, Rear-Admiral Stuart Latham, C.B., C.B.E., D.L., b. 7 July 98. 2nd (twin) s. of late Sir A. D. Bateson, K.C. (OR C 81). C, 12³-16². R.N. College, Keyham, Devonport, 16-17. Short course at Cambridge and Portsmouth, 20. Long course as Torpedo Specialist, 21-23, Greenwich & Vernon. Torpedo Specialist. M.I.E.E. Commander, 34, Captain, 40, Rear-Admiral (L), 49, Retired (Invalided), 51. Commanded H.M.S. *Latona*, 41, sunk off Tobruk; H.M.S. *Ajax*, 41-42; H.M.S. *London*, 44-46; Admiralty, 34-36, 40-41, 42-44, 46-50. C.B.E., 48, C.B., 50 County Commissioner for Boy Scouts, 53-66. Since 54, Chairman, Rutland Historic Churches Preservation Trust. High Sheriff, Rutland, 58. Vice-Lt., 57-72. D.L., 56. *United Service Club*. Son, A. J. Bateson. Grandsons, David Stuart, Tu, 68³-. & Hugh Comrie, Tu, 70³-.

BATHGATE, Douglas Arthur. W, 15¹-19³.*

BATLEY, The Rev. Paul Manwaring Graveley (Brother Christopher). B, 10³-14².*

BATT, Charles Dorrington, b. 18 Sept. 91, 3rd s. of late C. D. Batt, M.B. W, 06¹-09¹. Solicitor. ✕ 19th P.S. Bn., Royal Fusiliers, 4th Bn. Beds. Regt. Lt. Wounded. With Grover, Humphreys & Boyes, Solicitors.

BATT, Peter Aubrey, b. 5 Mar. 20, s. of late E. G. Batt. T, 33³-38¹; R. VIII, 38. ✕ Royal Warwickshire Regt. & Staff, 40-46. Wounded. Capt. Partner, Howkins & Harrison, Auctioneers & Estate Agents, Rugby. O. St. J. Mayor of Rugby, 59-60. Alderman since 62. Son, 2184.

BATTEN, James Macdonald, b. 6 Jan. 29, s. of G. J. Batten, M.B.E. M & St, 42³-47²; Head of House. Levée; Holder of Bigside Bags; Cap, 46; R. VIII, 46-47 (Capt.); Junior Athletics Cup. Short Service Commission, Grenadier Guards, 48, Lt. R.A.R.O. Trinity Hall, Cambridge, Cert. Ed., Athletics Half Blue. Bar, Lincoln's Inn. Assistant Master, Radley College, 54-69 (Housemaster, 64-69). Headmaster, King's College, Taunton, from 69. *Hawks Club*.

BATTY, Timothy John, b. 2 Jan. 32, elder s. of W. H. Batty. M, 45³-50²; XI, 49-50; H. XI, 50; Cap, 49.

BATTY-SHAW, Anthony, b. 19 June 22, s. of Dr. H. Batty-Shaw, F.R.C.P. Sh, 36¹-40²; XV, 39; H. XI, 39-40. Balliol, Oxford, M.A., D.M. University Exhibitioner to Guy's Hospital, F.R.C.P. ✕ R.A.M.C., 46-48. Dispatches (Palestine). Temp. Major. Consultant Physician, Norfolk & Norwich Hospital, Norwich. *Vincent's Club, Oxford; Norfolk Club*.

BAYLEY, Arthur Desmond Charles. W, 26³-31¹.*

BAYLEY, Commander John Maurice, D.S.C., b. 8 Jan 05, 2nd s. of late K. C. Bayley (OR SF 86). SF, 20¹-23². Royal Navy, 23-54. Retired as Commander. ✕ D.S.C., 41. Member of Church Assembly, 65-70. *United Service Club*. Son, 495.

BAYLISS, Richard Ian Samuel, M.D., F.R.C.P., b. 2 Jan. 17, s. of late F. W. Bayliss. K, 30²-34³. Clare, Cambridge. Columbia Univ., New York. St. Thomas's Hospital, London. Royal Postgraduate Medical School, London. M.A., M.B., B.Chir. (Cantab), F.R.C.P. (Lon.) Physician, H.M. The Queen since 70. Head of the Royal Medical Household since 73. Consultant Physician, Westminster Hospital since 54, and King Edward VII Hospital for Officers since 64. Medical Director of Swiss Re-Insurance Co. Member, Assoc. of Physicians, British Cardiac Society, Royal Society of Medicine, Endocrine Society, London Thyroid Club. Various Medical Publications. Son, 1821.

BAYLISS, Vincent Scott, b. 5 Mar. 98, s. of late V. G. Bayliss. T, 11¹-14¹. ✕ 1st Bn. Royal Warwickshire Regt. Dispatches. Capt., 23. Universities of London, B.A. & Giessen (Germany). Retired Schoolmaster.

BAYLY, Edward Hugh, b. 3 Mar. 13, 3rd s. of late R. Bayly. SF, 26³-31². Exhibitioner, Levée, XXII. Leaving Exhibition. New College, Oxford, M.A. Schoolmaster, Shawnigan Lake College, B.C., 35–37. Ampleforth College, 37–38. Eton College, 41–46. Dover College from 46. *Royal Cinque Ports Yacht Club.* Sons, 2684 & Jeremy John, SF, 68³–.

BAYNES, Humphrey. K, 96³–99³.*

BEAK, George Orsi, B, 31³–36².*

BEAL, John Malcolm, SH, 41³–44³.*

BEALE, Charles, b. 7 July 13, 2nd s. of late E. P. Beale (OR C 86). C, 27²–31²; S. VIII, 28–31 (Capt.). Exhibitioner of Trinity, Cambridge, M.A. Solicitor. Life Governor and member of Council, Birmingham University, Governor of Edgbaston High School for Girls and Dr. Williams's School for Girls, Dolgellau. Admitted, 38; Senior partner, Beale & Co., Solicitors, Birmingham. Commissioned, R.A.S.C. (T.A.), 34, resigned 68 as Hon. Lt.-Col. Dispatches twice. T.D. & Bar. *Union Club, Birmingham.*

BEAMAN, Michael Ardern Christopher, M.C., b. 6 Aug. 21, elder s. of late Lt.-Col. A. A. H. Beaman, D.S.O. (OR B 00). S.H., 34³–39²; XI, 38–39. Trinity, Cambridge. ✕ K.R.R.C., 40–45. Lt. M.C. Wounded. Magistrate. Farmer. *Gloucester & Green Jackets.* Son, 2903.

BEAN, George Reginald. B. 95³–97².*

BEARDSLEY, Robert Charles Bent, b. 27 Jan. 21, 2nd s. of W. F. B. Beardsley. B, 34³–39²; Paddison Art Prize, 39. ✕ Lance-Corporal, Quorn Home Guard, 40–41. F/Lt., R.A.F. (South East Asia Command), 41–46. Solicitor & Commissioner for Oaths. Assistant Solicitor with Trower, Still & Keeling, London, 49–52. Partner in Woolley, Beardsleys & Bosworth, Loughborough, Leics., 52 to date. Member of Trout & Salmon Association. Gold Badge of Royal British Legion, 72, awarded as Hon. Treasurer of Quorn Branch, 57 to date. Brother, W. J. B. Beardsley.

BEARDSLEY, William John Bent, b. 3 Mar. 16, eldest s. of W. F. B. Beardsley. B, 29²–34². Solicitor, 39. ✕ R.A.P.C. Staff Paymaster. Local Dir., Sun Alliance Group, Leicester Board. Partner in Woolley, Beardsleys & Bosworth, Solicitors, Loughborough, Leics. Chairman, Quorn Branch, Royal British Legion. Brother, R. C. B. Beardsley.

BEATTIE, Major Alexander Richard. W, 28³–32³.*

BEATTIE, Geoffrey Bartlett, M.C. W, 26³–29².*

BEATTIE, Brig. Joseph Hamilton, C.B.E., D.S.O., b. 29 Sept. 03, 4th s. of M. H. Beattie. B, 17³–21³. R.M.A., Woolwich. Commissioned in Royal Regt. of Artillery, 24. A.D.C. to Viceroy of India, 33–34. C.O., 79th (Scottish Horse) Med. Regt., 43–44. C.R.A., 19th Ind. (Dagger) Div., 45. C.R.A., 51st H. Div., 48–51. B.R.A., N.A.G., 52–53. Insp. Coast Arty. (Home) & Comdt. Coast Arty. School, 54–56. Retired as Brigadier, 56. C.B.E., D.S.O. p.s.c.

BEATTIE, Capt. Stephen Halden, R.N., V.C., b. 29 Mar. 08, eldest s. of late Rev. E. H. Beattie (OR SH 91). SH, 22¹–25². Royal Navy, 26. ✕ Coastal & Atlantic Convoys. P.O.W. from 42 after attack on St. Nazaire. V.C. Dispatches twice. Capt. (retired). *Army & Navy Club.* Sons, 176 & 2005.

BEAUCHAMP, Robert Stoney (formerly Archer). K, 22²–26².*

BEAUMONT, Alex Boyce, b. 5 Nov. 13, 2nd s. of R. H. Beaumont. K, 27³–32². Clare, Cambridge, M.A. Publicity Officer, London Transport. ✕ Royal Signals, 40–46. Major. Arts Club (Dover Street). Son, 1582.

BEAUSIRE, Henry James, b. 30 Nov. 01, 2nd s. of late H. M. Beausire. M, 15³–18³; XXII, 18. Now sole owner of Joseph Beausire & Co. Export/Import Merchant, Peru. Insurance & Lloyd's Agents since 96. *"Old Hall & Palatine", Liverpool; M.C.C.; Gentlemen of Cheshire.*

BEAVAN, Geoffrey, b. 31 Dec. 13, s. of late J. Beavan (OR SF 98). SF, 27³–31². ✕ R.A. (T.A.), T.D. A.C.I.I. Insurance Manager with Royal Insurance Co. Ltd. Now retired. *Old Hall, Exchange & Palatine, Liverpool.*

BEAZLEY, Jasper Morland. St & K, 40¹–44¹.*

BEAZLEY, John Allan. K, 45¹–48².*

BECK, Anthony Michael Ian, b. 10 Sept. 31, elder s. of R. G. Beck. SF, 45³–51¹. University College, Oxford. N/S. Parachute Regt. I.C.I. Fibres from 54. Now Marketing Manager. *Vincent's Club, Oxford.* Brother, 270.

BECKER, Denis Robert Sydney. W, 20³–23².*

BEDDINGTON, Julian Roy, b. 16 June 10, 2nd s. of late R. Beddington, C.B.E. (OR W 91). W, 23³–27². Corpus Christi, Oxford, M.A. Slade School of Art. Professional Artist. F.R.S.A. Author & Journalist. *Arts Club.* Brother, K. L. Beddington.

BEDDINGTON, Col. Keith Lionel, C.B.E., J.P., b. 23 May 02, eldest s. of late R. Beddington, C.B.E. (OR W 91). W, 15³–20³. Represented School at Boxing in Public Schools Competition in London. R.M.A., Woolwich. Staff College, Camberley. p.s.c. Gazetted to R.A., 23. Now Col. (retired). J.P. for Surrey (Dep. Chrmn. of Bench) President, N.W. Surrey Conservative Association. On Hospital Committee. Chrmn., R.A. Association, E. Region. *Army & Navy Club.* Magistrates' Assn. O.B.E. (Military), 48. C.B.E. (Civil), 64. Brother, J. R. Beddington. Son, 888.

BEDDOWS, Major Ian Alexander, T.D., b. 20 Oct. 20, s. of late Col. W. J. Beddows, M.C., T.D., D.L., J.P. B, 34³–39². Exeter, Oxford. ⚔ R.A., 40–46. Capt. Company Dir. (now redundant). Underwriting Member of Lloyd's. Major, R.A. (T.A.), T.D. *Army & Navy Club.*

BEDFORD, Peter Francis. SF, 27¹–31².*

BEEBEE, Benjamin Royston, b. 5 Dec. 23, s. of H. Beebee. B, 37¹–41². Cadet Pair. National Certificate Engineering, Wolverhampton Tech. Member of Lloyd's. Industrial Power Units Ltd., Dir., Wolverhampton. James Tabb & Son Ltd., Newcastle-upon-Tyne. Pilot member, B.L.A.C. Son, Robert Talbot, B, 72¹–.

BEHRENS, Derick Jacob, b. 9 Feb. 17, s. of late H. J. Behrens (OR B 94). B, 30³–34³; Scholar. Scholar of King's, Cambridge, B.A. Manchester Univ., B.Sc. Atomic Energy Research Establishment, 46–54. School Teacher since 56 (mainly Physics & Maths), Roedean School, Brighton, 59–70. Royal Naval School, Haslemere, since 70. Fellow of the Royal Numismatic Society. Son, 2597.

BEHRENS, Edgar Charles, C.B.E., b. 13 May 85, 3rd s. of late G. Behrens, J.P. B, 99³–03². Dir. of family Textile firm, Sir Jacob Behrens & Sons, Shipping Merchants, Bradford & Manchester. Also Dir. of several other Textile Companies. ⚔ A.S.C., Staff Capt., War Office. Capt.

O.B.E. (Mil.). Dispatches twice. Chrmn. of Convalescent Home for Children, Morecambe, 27–67. President of Bradford Chamber of Commerce, 38–40. President of several musical societies in Yorkshire. J.P., West Riding. C.B.E. (Civil), 51. Brother, Sir L. F. Behrens. Son, J. S. Behrens.

BEHRENS, Edward Lionel, b. 22 Oct. 99, eldest s. of late H. L. Behrens (OR W 88). W, 13³–17². R.M.C., Sandhurst. Queen's Royal Regt., 19–25. ⚔ Manchester Regt., 39–45. Major. Textiles Exporter, The United Africa Co. Ltd. Now retired. *St. James's Club, Manchester.* Brother, G. H. Behrens.

BEHRENS, Geoffrey Harold, b. 29 Jan. 06, 3rd s. of late H. L. Behrens (OR W 88). W, 20¹–24². Trinity, Cambridge, M.A. ⚔ 41st S.L. Regt., R.A. (5th North Staffs), 41–45. Lt. With Bentley, Smith & Co. Ltd, Merchants, Manchester. Cotton Trade Executive, now retired. *St. James's Club, Manchester.* Brother, E. L. Behrens.

BEHRENS, John Stephen, b. 9 July 27, s. of E. C. Behrens, C.B.E., J.P. (OR B 99). B, 41²–45¹. J.P. Chrmn., Craig Convalescent Home for Children and Bradford Tradesmen's Homes. President, Country Wool Merchants' Assoc. Dir., Sir Jacob Behrens & Sons Ltd. & Associated Cos. Chrmn. Francis Willey (British Wools 1935) Ltd. & Associated Cos. *E.S.U.*

BEHRENS, Sir Leonard Frederick, C.B.E., J.P., b. 15 Oct. 90, 5th s. of late G. Behrens, J.P. B, 04³–08³. Manchester University, M.Com. President, Liberal Party, 55–57. Manchester Chamber of Commerce, Dir. Emeritus. Royal Manchester College of Music, Dep. Chrmn., Hon. Pres. World Federation, United Nations Assoc. Retired. C.B.E., J.P. Knight Bachelor. Yugoslavia, Order of St. Sava. China, Brilliant Star with Ribbon. *Manchester Club, E.S.U.* Brother, E. C. Behrens.

BEHRENS, William Edward Boaz, b. 14 Oct. 08, 2nd s. of late C. Behrens. W, 21³–26²; Scholar. Christ Church, Oxford, B.A. Bar. Inner Temple. J.P. (N.R. Yorkshire). ⚔ Queen's Bays. Col. Barrister, 31–39 & 46–53. Farmer since 53.

BEILBY, Julius Harald, M.B., B.Ch., M.R.C.S., L.R.C.P., b. 11 Oct. 04, elder s. of late Dr. J. H. Beilby. St, 18³–23². King's, Cambridge, M.B., B.Ch. St. Thomas's Hospital, London, M.R.C.S.,

L.R.C.P. House Surgeon, St. Thomas's Hospital. House Physician, Nottingham General Hospital. Hon. Surgeon, Rutson Hospital, Northallerton. Retired. General Medical Practitioner. *Hawks, United Sports Club.*

BELL, Neville Gavin Hamilton. M, 29^2–33^2.*

BELL, Robert Anthony Randall, b. 29 Sept. 27, s. of late R. S. Bell. K, 41^2–45^3; XV, 44–45 (Capt.); XI, 44–55; H. XI, 43–44; Rackets Pair (Capt.), 45; Sw. VIII. Trinity, Oxford, Univ. Royal Tennis V, 50. In Steel Industry. Company Dir. Capt. T.D.

BELLAMY, Cecil, b. 21 Feb. 02, s. of late W. H. Bellamy. SH, 15^3–20^2. Trinity, Oxford, M.A. Assistant Master, House Master, Bradfield College, 25–53. Producer of the Greek & English plays during those years. Later, free-lance Broadcaster, Lecturer & Producer. Now retired. Son, C. G. Bellamy.

BELLAMY, Christopher Grey, b. 6 Aug. 27, s. of C. Bellamy (OR SH. 15). SH, 41^2–45^2. XV, 43–44; XI, 44–45; H. XI, 43–45 (Capt.). Royal Marines, 45. Invalided as Capt., 66. Group Training Adviser for East Kent (Construction) Training Group. *Free Foresters, Harlequins R.F.C.*

BELLRINGER-HOWARTH, Hubert Ernest. W, 95^3–99^2.*

BENFIELD, Adalbert Edwin, Ph.D., F.R.A.S., b. 30 Nov. 11, s. of late A. M. Benfield. K, 25^3–30^1. Massachusetts Institute of Technology, B.Sc. Trinity, Cambridge, Ph.D. Fellow, Royal Astronomical Society & American Physical Society. Senior member, Institute of Electrical & Electronics Engineers. Member, American Geophysical Union Society of the Sigma XI. Instructor, 39–44, later Ass. Prof. of Physics, 45–46, Williams College, Massachusetts, U.S.A. Staff Member, 44–45, Radiation Laboratory, Massachusetts Institute of Technology. Ass. Prof. & Lecturer, 46–60, Harvard University. Present employment, Chrmn. Conservation Committee, Carlisle, Mass., U.S.A. Treas. Carlisle Conservation Foundation, Inc. Numerous scientific publications.

BENN, Allan Cosmo, b. 2 June 29, 3rd s. of R. T. Benn. T, 42^3–47^2; Major Foundationer, Senior Scholar, 45; XV, 46; Classical Leaving Exhibition. Open Classical Scholar of St. John's, Oxford, M.A. Job Study Engineer, Procter & Gamble Ltd. Consultant, P.A. Management Consultants Ltd. Yale & Towne Ltd. Sterling Winthrop Ltd. Production Dir., Trebor Sharps Ltd. *Blackheath R.F.C.*

BENN, Sir Patrick Ian Hamilton, Bt., b. 26 Feb. 22, s. of late Col. I. B. H. Benn (OR W 01). W, 35^3–40^2. ⚔ Duke of Cornwall's Light Infantry, N. Africa, Italy & Greece. Capt. Dispatches. Korea, 51–52. Retired, 55. Company Dir. *Norfolk Club.* Succeeded Grandfather as 2nd Baronet, 61.

BENNETT, Abraham Francis, A.R.I.B.A., b. 6 Dec. 24, s. of late A. F. Bennett. M, 38^3–42^2. Trinity Hall, Cambridge, M.A. ⚔ U.S.A.A.F., 43–46. A.R.I.B.A. Architect.

BENNETT, Alfred Edwin Peto, b. 7 Aug. 05, elder s. of late C. P. Bennett. W, 19^3–23^2; G. VIII, 22. Retired. F.R.G.S. *City of London Club, Norwegian Club.* Brother, C. P. Bennett.

BENNETT, Charles Peter, O.B.E., b. 8 Dec. 06, younger s. of the late C. P. Bennett. W, 20^3–23^2. ⚔ R.A.F.V.R., 40–46. Sqn. Ldr. Past Master, Worshipful Co. of Woolmen. Liveryman, Fishmongers Company. Retired, but at present Dir. of Kleinwort Benson (C.I.) Ltd. F.R.G.S. *Bath Club, Royal Corinthian Yacht Club* (ex-Commodore). Freedom Cross (Norway). O.B.E. Brother, A. E. P. Bennett.

BENNETT, Wing-Cdr. David Edmund, b. 5 Feb. 17, s. of late Cdr. H. T. Bennett, D.S.O., F.R.G.S., R.N. B, 30^3–34^3. R.A.F. College, Cranwell (entered after competitive Civil Service exam); Blue for Athletics and Cross-country Running (Capt.). Commissioned in R.A.F., 36, as pilot. Invalided out, 57, as Wing Cdr. Served in Bomber, Middle East, Coastal & Transport Commands. Commanded 47th, 167th & 238th Squadrons. 4,000 hrs. flying (110 different types). Aviation Journalist & Consultant. P.R.O. to 424th (A.T.C.) Sqdn. (Free-lance). Hon. Member, Southampton Univ. Air Squadron. Wildfowl Trust. Royal Aeronautical Society. Dispatches, 41. Queen's Commendation for valuable services in the air, 54.

BENNETT, Hubert Thomas. T, 25^1–28^3.*

BENNETT, Leon William Edward. K, 22^1–25^3.*

BENNETT, Peter Walter Dryden. B, 42^2–45^3.*

BENNETT, Rodney Hewson, b. 24 May 20, s. of G. W. H. Bennett. St, 34¹–39¹. R. VIII, 39. Merton, Oxford, M.A. ✕ Duke of Wellington's Regt., 40–42. Indian Army, 42–46. H.M. Colonial Service, 46–61. Administration Officer, Gold Coast and Ghana. Dir. of Herefordshire Community Council, 61–72. Organiser, Worcs. Rural Community Council from 72. Member, West Midlands Economic Planning Council, 65–69. Chrmn., West Midlands Arts Association, 71–72. Society for the Promotion of Nature Reserves.

BENNETT, William Woodhouse Swain. K, 24³–27².*

BENNETTS, Lt.-Col. Arthur, b. 21 Mar. 00, 2nd s. of late C. B. Bennetts. SH, 14²–18¹; Cap, 17. R.M.A., Woolwich. S.M.E., Chatham. Commissioned R.E., 19. ✕ R.E., 39–45. Lt.-Col., retired, 49. P.W.D., Kenya, 49–52.

BENSON, Kenneth Ian Giles. W, 39¹–40³.*

BENSON, Michael Stewart, b. 23 July 29, s. of Air Commodore S. S. Benson, A.F.C. (OR W 11). W, 43²–47²; XV, 46. N/S, 47–49. 2nd Lt., Royal Artillery. British-American Tobacco Co. Ltd., East & North Africa, 49–62. Givaudan & Co. Ltd., England, Sales/Marketing Dir. from 62. *Lansdowne Club.* Son, Peter James Michael, W, 69³–.

BENSON, Air Commodore Seymour Stewart, A.F.C., b. 4 Dec. 96, eldest s. of late R. S. Benson. W, 11¹–13². Sidney Sussex, Cambridge, B.A. Joined R.N.A.S., 15. R.A.F., 18. Retired, 45, with rank of Air Commodore. Air Force Cross. Son, M. S. Benson. Grandson, Peter James Michael, W, 69³–.

BENTLEY, Robert Isaac Lloyd, b. 30 June 06, s. of late Col. F. I. Bentley, T.D., D.L. M, 20²–24². King's, Cambridge, M.A. President, National Lubricating Oil & Grease Federation, 55–56. Chrmn. & Man. Dir. of Isaac Bentley & Co. Ltd., Oil Refiners, of Manchester, 38–72. *Manchester Tennis & Racquets Club; East India, Sports & Public Schools Club.*

BERENT, Herbert Siegmund, b. 3 July 00, s. of late S. Berent. C, 14³–18³. S. VIII, 18. Wye Agricultural College. Nestlé's Milk, Far Eastern & Overseas Staff, 25–37. Advertising Manager, London, 39–46. Now retired.

BERGEL, Hugh Charles, O.B.E., b. 19 Nov. 05, younger s. of late C. Bergel. K, 19³–23². Engineer with various Engineering firms & Advertising Agencies, 27–40. ✕ Air Transport Auxiliary, 40–45, as Pilot and Officer commanding No. 9 Ferry Port. O.B.E. (Civil). Mostly in advertising as a Copywriter, retiring at 60. *Bugatti Owners Club; Vintage Sports Car Club.*

BERKELEY, Aubrey William Grandidier, b. 13 May 20, youngest s. of late W. T. B. Berkeley. M, 34¹–38². ✕ R.A. & H.L.I. Lt., 39–46. A.C.I.I. Fellow of the Corporation of Insurance Brokers. Member of Lloyd's. Dir., Bray, Gibb, Wrightson (U.K.) Ltd., Insurance Brokers. Sons, 1673 & 2150.

BERLAGE, Thomas Nicholas. W, 14¹–17³.*

BERTHOUD, Martin Seymour, b. 20 Aug. 31, elder s. of Sir E. A. Berthoud, K.C.M.G., D.L. Sh, 44³–49³; Capt. of Fives, 48; Tennis VI, 49 (Capt.). N/S. Army. Magdalen, Oxford. Half Blue Rugby Fives. H.M. Diplomatic Service. Brother, 114.

BESLY, Donald Maurice. W, 29³–34². Sons, 2725 & Bernard Maurice, W, 68³–.*

BEST, Stuart. W, 96¹–99¹.*

BESWICK, Joseph Hubert, M.B., Ch.B., b. 2 July 25, s. of J. W. Beswick. T, 38³–43². Birmingham University, M.B., Ch.B. London University, Diploma in Theology. Clerk in Holy Orders. (Ordained, 60.) Licensed Preacher, Diocese of Southwell. Medical Adviser (Industrial Physician), Plessey. Telecommunications Ltd., Beeston. Local Civil Service Medical Adviser, Beeston, Notts. Certificate of Honour & Hon. Life Member of the British Red Cross Society.

BETTINGTON, Major John James Brindley, K.S.L.I., b. 27 Jan. 25, s. of Brig. J. B. Bettington, D.S.O., M.C. M, 38³–43¹. Durham University. Army Course, 43. Served in Italy during 2nd World War, in Korean War and in the Malaya and Kenya emergencies. Adj. of Hereford L.I. (T.A.). Training Officer, 4 K.S.L.I. Staff of Allied Forces, Central Europe. Regular Army Officer in the King's Shropshire L.I. since 44. To be Station Staff Officer, Antwerp, 73–76. *United Hunts Club.*

BEVINGTON, Robert James, b. 11 July 91, 2nd s. of the late A. Bevington. St, 05³–09². Further Education in Germany. ✕ 1st Bn., H.A.C., R.F.A., att. R.F.C. Lt. Wounded twice. Prisoner, 17. Engineer. R.D.S., M.I.M.I. Garage Proprietor.

BIART, David, LL.B. T, 40³–46².*

BIART, Douglas, b. 14 Sept. 25, elder s. of D. E. Biart. T, 38³–43². Oriel, Oxford, 43–44. ✕ Royal Signals, 44–47. Signalman. Birmingham Univ., LL.B. Solicitor, 51. Partner, Neve, Son & Co., Solicitors, Luton. Secretary, Harpenden & District Building Society. Brother, David Biart.

BIBBY, Major Sir Arthur Harold, Bt., D.S.O., D.L., LL.D., b. 18 Feb. 89, s. of late A. W. Bibby (OR T 58). M, 03³–07². ✕ 14th Lancashire Battery, R.F.A. (T.F.). Major. Wounded. D.S.O. Dispatches twice. Senior Partner, Bibby Bros. & Co. Chrmn., Bibby Line Ltd., Martins Bank Ltd., Liverpool Steamship Owners' Assoc., & Dir. of other Assocs. & Cos. connected with the sea. Governor of Rugby School, 32–67. High Sheriff of Cheshire. D.L. Hon. LL.D., Liverpool. Hon. Freeman of City of Liverpool. Knight Bachelor, 56. Created Baronet, 59. *Bath Club; Palatine Club, Liverpool.* Sons, D. J. & J. C. Bibby.

BIBBY, Derek James, M.C., b. 29 June 22, 2nd s. of Major Sir A. H. Bibby, Bt., D.S.O., D.L., LL.D. (OR M 03). M, 36²–40³. ✕ R.A., Capt. M.C. Wounded. Trinity, Oxford, M.A. Chrmn., Bibby Line Ltd. Brother, J. C. Bibby.

BIBBY, John Christopher. M, 46²–50³.*

BICKERSTETH, The Rev. Canon Edward Monier, O.B.E., b. 20 Nov. 82, eldest s. of late Rev. Dr. S. Bickersteth, D.D. St, 96³–00². Christ Church, Oxford, M.A. Wells Theological College, 06. Ordained, 07. Rector, Castle Bromwich, 11–15. Gen. Sec. of Jerusalem & the East Mission, 15–35. Rector, Chiddingstone, 35–50. Hon. Canon, Rochester, 46–50. Rector of the Orchestons, Salisbury, 50–59. Commissary to Archbishop in Jerusalem & to Bishop in Egypt & the Sudan from 20. Hon. Canon of St. George's, Jerusalem from 53. Retired since 59. Chrmn. of Missions to Seamen during their Centenary. O.B.E., 62. Brother, R. M. Bickersteth. Son, J. M. Bickersteth. Grandsons, 2238 & 2696.

BICKERSTETH, The Rt. Rev. John Monier (Bishop of Warrington), b. 6 Sept. 21, 2nd s. of The Rev. Canon E. M. Bickersteth (OR St 96). Sh, 35³–40². Scholar. Levée. Cadet Officer. Stovin Exhibition. ✕ Capt., Royal Artillery, 41–46. Christ Church, Oxford, B.A. Wells Theological College, 48–50. Deacon, 50, to serve as Curate, St. Matthew's, Bristol, 54. Vicar of Hurst Green, Oxted, 54–62. St. Stephen's, Chatham, 62–70. Hon. Canon of Rochester Cathedral, 68–70. Suffragan Bishop of Warrington from 70. *Travellers'*.

BICKERSTETH, Peter Maurice Grafton, b. 29 Mar. 24, s. of R. M. Bickersteth (OR St 08). Sh, 38³–42²; XXII, 42. Cadet Officer. ✕ Rifle Brigade, 42–47. Regular Commission, 43. N.W. Europe. Wounded thrice & invalided out. Insurance Broker since 47. F.C.I.B. A. W. Bain & Sons Ltd., Man. Dir., 46–49. Matthews Comfort & Co. Ltd., Man. Dir. from 70. Acting Lt. Col., London Rifle Brigade. Substantive Major. *M.C.C.; Cavalry.* Sons, 2585A & 3010.

BICKERSTETH, Ralph Monier, b. 28 Oct. 94, 6th s. of late Rev. Canon Dr. S. Bickersteth, D.D. St, 08³–13²; XV, 12; XI, 12–13. Cadet Officer. Christ Church, Oxford, M.A. ✕ 7th Bn., West Yorkshire Regt. Capt. Lloyd's Broker, 20–60. Underwriting Member, 21–37. President, Corporation of Insurance Brokers, 51–53. Retired, 60. Brother, E. M. Bickersteth. Son, P. M. G. Bickersteth. Grandsons 2585A and 3010.

BIERNACKI, Roderick Herbert Korneli. M, 16¹–19².*

BILBE-ROBINSON, Allan. K, 23³–27².*

BILES, John Harvard. M, 28³–32².*

BINNEY, Anthony Lockhart, C.S.I., C.I.E. St, 04³–09¹.*

BINNEY, Humphrey Lockhart. St, 34³–38³.*

BIRD, Frederic Vincent Godfrey. K, 22³–27¹.*

BIRD, John Robin Denys. Sh, 44³–49².*

BIRLEY, Sir Robert, K.C.M.G., LL.D., b. 14 July 03, s. of late L. Birley, C.S.I., C.I.E. K, 17³–22¹. Balliol, Oxford, M.A. (Brackenbury Scholar, 22). Gladstone Memorial Prize, 25. Assistant Master, Eton College, 26–35. Headmaster of Charterhouse, 35–47. Educational Adviser,

Control Commission, Germany, 47–49. Headmaster of Eton College, 49–63. Visiting Prof. Univ. of the Witwatersrand, Johannesburg, 64–66. Prof. and Head of Dept. of Social Science & Humanities, City Univ., London, 67–71. Gresham Prof. in Rhetoric, City of London, from 67. Fellow of Royal Society of Antiquaries. C.M.G., 50. K.C.M.G., 67. Hon. Doc. Ing., Technical Univ., Berlin; Hon. LL.D., Edinburgh, Leeds, Liverpool, Witwatersrand; Hon. D.Phil., Frankfurt; Hon. D.C.L., Oxford; Hon. Doc. Engineering, Aston. *Travellers' Club.*

BIRKETT, Richard Alan Maule, b. 1 Nov. 19, s. of late Brig. R. M. Birkett, D.S.O. (OR C 98). SF, 33^3–38^2; XV, 36–37; XXII, H. XI, 38. St. Andrews Univ., Rugger Blue. ✗ R.A.F., 40. Army & Military Administration, Somalia, 44–48. Colonial Administrative Service, Kenya. Now, Administrative Officer, Food & Agricultural Organisation of United Nations. Royal Overseas League.

BIRTLES, Anthony Frederic, F.R.I.C.S., b. 4 Aug. 31, eldest s. of R. A. Birtles. Sh, 45^3–48^3. F.R.I.C.S. Governor, Lawnside School, Gt. Malvern and Ardenhurst Prep. School, Henley-in-Arden. Partner, Chesshire, Gibson & Co., Chartered Surveyors, Birmingham.

BISCHOFF, Bernard Crompton, b. 10 Jan. 10, s. of late H. C. Bischoff (OR K 91). K, 23^3–28^2. Trinity, Oxford, M.A. ✗ City of London Rifles, R.A. T.A. & General Staff, A.A. Command, 39–45. Major. T.D. Solicitor, Bischoff & Co., London. Travelled much in Middle East, 49–68, as legal adviser to Iraq Petroleum Co. Ltd. and associated Cos. *United Oxford & Cambridge Univs. Club.* Member, Royal Central Asian Society.

BISCHOFF, Edward Colby, b. 22 June 11, s. of late C. E. Bischoff (OR K 86). K, 25^3–30^2. Trinity, Oxford, M.A. Solicitor, 37. ✗ R.A. (A.A.), 40–46. Capt. Solicitor, Bischoff & Co., London. *The Justinians.*

BISHOP, Leslie Gurney, b. 14 July 08, s. of late D. F. W. Bishop (OR SH 91). SH, 22^1–27^2. Open Scholar of St. John's, Oxford, M.A. Military Reporter, "Winnipeg Free Press", 39–45. London Correspondent, 47–49. Founded Osterley Tutors College, Isleworth, 64, retired from there, 69. Now a Publisher. Life member, *National Liberal Club.* Author of three books, "Essays Blackwell", 29, "Paper Kingdom", 36, "Bereavement", 71.

BISSELL, Peter Robin, B, 40^2–44^2.*

BLABER, Col. Hugh Kenneth, C.B.E., b. 22 Aug. 99, elder s. of late P. L. Blaber, M.R.C.S., L.R.C.P. (OR M 86). K, 13^2–15^1. Gazetted to Indian Army, 18. ✗ 70th Burma Rifles. Capt., 23. C.B.E., 48. Col., retired, 49. Brother, M. P. W. Blaber.

BLABER, Michael Percy William. M, 20^2–24^2. Son, 2829B.*

BLACK, Prof. John Nicholson, Ph.D., b. 28 June 22, eldest s. of Dr. H. Black. Sh, 35^3–40^2. ✗ R.A.F. Sqn. Ldr. Exeter, Oxford, M.A., D.Phil., D.Sc. (Adelaide). F.R.S.E., F.I.Biol. Lecturer, Senior Lecturer, Reader in Agronomy, Univ. of Adelaide, Australia, 52–63. Prof. of Forestry & Natural Resources, Univ. of Edinburgh, 64–71. Principal, Bedford College, London Univ. from 71. Various Publications. Brother, N. C. Black.

BLACK, Neil Cathcart, b. 28 May 32, 3rd s. of Dr. H. Black. Sh, 45^3–50^2. Exeter, Oxford, B.A. Hon. R.A.M. Professional Musician. Incorporated Society of Musicians. Brother, Prof. J. N. Black.

BLACKBURN, Albert Raymond. SH, 27^3–32^3.*

BLACKBURN, Guy, M.B.E., M.Chir., F.R.C.S., b. 20 Nov. 11, eldest s. of Dr. A. E. Blackburn. St, 24^3–29^2; Scholar; Nat. Sc. & Baines Exhibitioner, 29, Exhibitioner of Clare, Cambridge, M.A., M.Chir. St. Bartholomew's Hospital, London, F.R.C.S. ✗ R.A.M.C. T/Lt.-Col. M.B.E. Later Hunterian Prof., Royal College of Surgeons. Surgeon, Guy's Hospital & Putney Hospital. Hon. Sec., Assoc. of Surgeons, Gt. Britain & Ireland. Consulting Surgeon, British Army in Europe. *Garrick, R.A.C.* Brother, A. R. Blackburn.

BLACKLOCK, Douglas Stewart. Tu, 22^3–27^1.*

BLACKMAN, Peter Francis. M, 32^2–37^2.*

BLACKWOOD, Henry Conor Turnour. SH, 95^3–00^2.*

BLAIR, James David, b. 6 June 15, 2nd s. of the late D. Blair, C.B.E. (OR C 91). C, 29^2–33^2. Technician with Blundell Spence & Co. Ltd., Hull, 33–35. Viña del Mar, Chili, 35–42. Presidente, Minera e Industrial Argentina Auca-Mahuida, S.A.,

Buenos Aires, from 43. F.R.S.A. *Valparaiso Sporting Club, San Isidro Golf Club.*

BLAIR-WHITE, Arthur, M.B.E., b. 3 July 91, 2nd s. of late R. Blair-White. Tu, 06¹–10¹. Rackets pair, 10; and XXII, 09. Trinity College, Dublin, B.A. Senior Moderatorship in History (Gold Medal). Trinity College Cricket XI, 11–13, H. XI, 13. ✕ R.F.A. Lt. Croix de Guerre avec Palme. Dispatches. M.B.E. Market Gardener, retired. Brother, C. W. Blair-White.

BLAIR-WHITE, Cyril Walter. Tu, 15³–19¹. Brother, A. Blair-White.*

BLAKE, Martin William, b. 8 Apr. 03, elder s. of late Major-Gen. G. F. Blake, R.M.L.I. Tu, 16³–21¹; Scholar. Scholar of Magdalene, Cambridge, M.A. Schoolmaster, 24–39 (Westminster School from 31). Bar, Gray's Inn, 38. Entered British Council Service, 39; retired, 63. Representative in Czechoslovakia, Jamaica, Portugal & Denmark. *Savile Club,* 42–72. *Chatham House,* 41–72.

BLAKEWAY, John Denys, b. 27 May 18, 2nd s. of late Lt.-Col. Sir D. B. Blakeway, C.I.E. M, 31³–36¹; Scholar. Levée, Head of House. Magdalen, Oxford (Doncaster Scholar), M.A. ✕ 1st Punjab Regt. Capt. Wounded, 39–46. Joined Foreign Service, 46; served at Sofia, Lyons, Tripoli, Bologna, Rome, Athens, Ibadan & The Hague. Counsellor at British Embassy, The Hague, from July 73. Brother, R. A. Blakeway. Son, Denys Brickdale, SH, 69¹–.

BLAKEWAY, Brig. Richard Allestree, O.B.E., b. 30 May 16, eldest s. of Sir D. B. Blakeway, C.I.E. M, 29³–34². R.M.A., Woolwich, Cadet Scholarship & Maths. Prizeman. Gazetted to R.E., 36. Trinity, Cambridge, B.A. ✕ R.E. T/Lt.-Col. O.B.E. Retired, Brigadier, 71. A.D.C. to H.M. The Queen, 70–71. Brother, J. D. Blakeway.

BLANDY, John Reeder, O.B.E., b. 20 Nov. 09, younger s. of J. E. Blandy. SH 23¹–27²; S. VIII, 25–27 (Capt.). St. John's, Oxford. Univ. S. VIII, 28–30 (Capt.). Hon. British Consul, Funchal, Madeira. ✕ General List. 40–45, Major. Chrmn., Blandy Brothers & Co. Ltd., Funchal, Madeira. O.B.E. *City of London Club.*

BLANDY, Peter Maret, M.B.E., b. 12 July 14, 3rd s. of late C. M. Blandy (OR Tu 94). Tu, 28¹–32¹. Solicitor, 37. ✕

R.A., 39–45. Major. M.B.E. Under Sheriff of Berkshire. Registrar of the Archdeaconry of Berkshire. Partner of Blandy & Blandy of Reading. Piscatorial Society. Son, 2328.

BLEASBY, Major Henry, M.C., b. 23 June 17, elder s. of late H. Bleasby, J.P. SH, 30³–33². Regular Officer, Royal Artillery, p.s.c. Retired Officer, Grade II. Mod (A). M.C. Major, retired. *Army & Navy Club, M.C.C.*

BLISS, Sir Arthur Edward Drummond, K.C.V.O., C.H. b. 2 Aug. 91, eldest s. of late F. E. Bliss. C, 05³–10²; Scholar. Exhibitioner of Pembroke, Cambridge, B.A., Mus.Bac., Hon. Fellow, 53. Hon. A.R.C.M., 28. ✕ 13th Bn. Royal Fusiliers. Grenadier Guards. Lt. Wounded twice. Dispatches. Master of The Queen's Musick since 53. Hon. Mus.D., Edinburgh, London, Cambridge, Bristol & Lancaster. Hon. LL.D., Glasgow. Hon. Freeman, Worshipful Co. of Musicians, 54. Gold Medallist, Royal Philharmonic Society. K.C.V.O., 69. C.H., 71. *Athenæum, Garrick Clubs.* Brother, J. H. Bliss.

BLISS, James Howard, b. 21 June 94, 3rd s. of late F. E. Bliss. C, 07³–08². Trinity, Cambridge. Musician (Cellist). Brother, Sir A. E. D. Bliss.

BLOMFIELD, Christopher. K, 13³–16². Brother, V. Blomfield.*

BLOMFIELD, Maj.-Gen. Valentine, C.B., D.S.O., b. 29 Mar. 98, elder s. of late F. C. Blomfield. K, 11³–15². R.M.C., Sandhurst. Staff College, Camberley. Commissioned to Border Regt, 16. Served in France, 16–18. Dispatches. N.W. Frontier, India, 22–23. Served in France, 39–40. Dispatches, D.S.O., 44. Dir. of P.O.W.s, War Office, 45–47. Dir., Personal Services, War Office, 47–50. Commander, N.W. District, 42nd Div., 50–53. Retired, Major-General, 54. Col., The Border Regt., 52–59. Col., The Kings Own Royal Border Regt., 59–61. C.B., 47. *Naval & Military Club.* Brother, C. Blomfield.

BLOXHAM, Owen Astley. Tu, 00³–03³.*

BLUMER, William Frederick Croft, B.M., B.Ch., b. 8 Feb. 29, elder s. of late Dr. C. E. M. Blumer. B, 42³–47²; Leaving Exhibition. Christ Church, Oxford, M.A., B.M., B.Ch. King's College Hospital, London. Senior Lecturer in Anatomy, Univ. of Western Australia. Nedlands, Western Australia, 6009.

BLUNT, Anthony John Gaire, b. 8 Aug. 28, s. of Major B. G. Blunt, I.C.S. (retd.). SH, 42³–45³. Chrmn., Elsenham Quality Foods Ltd. Dir., Bradstock, Blunt & Thompson. Lloyd's Brokers.

BLUNT, Arthur Graham, V.R.D., b. 7 May 10, s. of late G. Blunt (OR C 80). C, 23³–28²; XI, 27. Trinity Hall, Cambridge, M.A. Solicitor, 34. ⚔ R.N.V.R. Lt.-Cdr. (S.) V.R.D. Senior Partner, Knapp, Fishers, Westminster. Retired. *M.C.C.* Master Grocers Company, 62. Sons, 242, 1123 & 1374.

BLUNT, James Charles. W, 13¹–15³.*

BLYTH, Alan Geoffrey Frederic Cecil, b. 27 July 29, younger s. of H. C. Blyth (OR M 11). K, 43³–48¹. Scholar of Pembroke, Oxford, M.A. Assistant Editor, "Opera" Magazine. Free-lance music critic working for "The Times", "The Gramophone", "Opera" & other musical publications. Critic's Circle.

BLYTH, Alexander Liston. K, 97³–00¹.*

BLYTH, Gordon James. M, 08¹–12².*

BLYTH, Herbert Cecil. M, 11¹–13³.*

BLYTHE, William Hetherington. B, 22²–26³.*

BOASE, Thomas Sherrer Ross, M.C., b. 31 Aug. 98, s. of late C. M. Boase. Tu, 12³–17¹; Head of House; King's Medal, 16. Exhibitioner of Magdalen, Oxford, M.A. ⚔ 4th Bn. Oxford & Bucks L.I., 17–19. 2nd Lt. M.C. Hon. D.C.L. (Oxford); Hon. LL.D. (St Andrew's & Melbourne); Hon. D.Litt. (Durham & Reading); F.B.A. Fellow and Tutor in History at Hertford College, Oxford, 22–37. Prof. of History of Art, London and Dir. of Courtauld Institute, 37–47. Pres., Magdalen College, Oxford, 47–68. Governor of Rugby School, 51–65. *United Oxford & Cambridge Universities.*

BODDINGTON, Charles Geoffrey, b. 2 Mar. 97, 4th s. of late R. S. Boddington. W, 11³–15³; XV, 15; XI, 15. ⚔ 11th Hussars, 15–19, Lt. Brewer, becoming Chrmn. in 52 of Boddington's Breweries Ltd. of Manchester, retired, 70. Chrmn. of Manchester N.S.P.C.C. Central Executive Committee in London of N.S.P.C.C. *St. James's Club, Manchester; R.A.C.* Brother, R. A. Boddington.

BODDINGTON, Myles Alan, b. 30 Nov. 24, s. of R. A. Boddington (OR W 06). SH, 38³–43²; Cap, 42; XI, 41–43 (Capt.); H. XI, 42. ⚔ R.A.F. Farmer.

BODDINGTON, Philip John McLean, b. 28 Sept. 21, elder s. of late P. Boddington (OR W 08). W, 35³–40². ⚔ R.A., 40–46, N. Africa & Italy. Capt. Joined Boddington's Breweries Ltd. in 46, Man. Dir. Served in Cheshire Yeomanry, 47–58. Brevet Major, T.D. *St. James's Club, Manchester.* Brother, R. S. Boddington.

BODDINGTON, Richard Stewart, b. 1 Feb. 30, younger s. of late P. Boddington (OR W 08). W, 43³–48². Trinity, Oxford, M.A. N/S., 51–53. Commissioned in 14th/20th King's Hussars. A.C.A., 57. Since 61, Partner in Messrs. Spicer & Pegler, Chartered Accountants, Manchester. *St. James's, Manchester.* Brother, P. J. M. Boddington.

BODDINGTON, Robert Alan, b. 30 June 92, 2nd s. of late R. S. Boddington. W, 06³–11²; XI, 10–11. Trinity, Oxford, B.A. University Racquets Pair, 13–14. ⚔ Duke of Lancaster's Own Yeomanry, 14–19, Capt. A.D.C. Retired Stockbroker. *M.C.C.* Brother, C. G. Boddington. Son, M. A. Boddington.

BOIS, Claude Herbert. M, 20²–24². Son, 2384.*

BOIS, Reginald Cosmo. M, 25²–29².*

BOLCKOW, John Dorman. W, 20³–23².*

BOLTON, Frederic Bernard, M.C., b. 9 Mar. 21, s. of late L. H. Bolton (OR SH 97). SH, 34³–39³; XV, 38–39; Sw. VIII, 39 (Capt.); Cadet Officer. ⚔ 40–46, Major, Welsh Guards, N. Africa & Italy. M.C. Pres., Chamber of Shipping of U.K., 66–67. Pres., Institute of Marine Engineers, 68–70. Pres., British Shipping Federation, 72. Member, Board of Port of London Authority, 64–71. Member, National Ports Council since 67. Chrmn., Bolton Steam Shipping Co. Ltd. since 53. Chrmn., Atlantic Steam Nav. Co. Ltd., 60–71. Dir., B.P. Tanker Co. since 67. *City of London, Club.*

BOLTON, Major Hugh Collingridge. M, 31³–35³.*

BOLTON, Patrick John. M, 28³–33². Sons, 2059 & 2385.*

BOLTON, Robert Henry, b. 7 Sept. 07, 3rd s. of late A. T. Bolton, F.R.I.B.A., F.S.A. Tu, 21^3–26^2; Minor Exhibitioner. Scholar of Trinity, Oxford, B.A., B.M., B.Ch. Guy's Hospital. A.M.O., Peckham Health Centre. Asst. Surgeon, Emergency Service, 40–45. Birmingham University Medical Officer, 45–70.

BOLTON-CARTER, John Felix, M.Chir., F.R.C.S., J.P., b. 27 Feb. 19, s. of late F. Bolton-Carter, M.D., M.S., F.R.C.S. St, 32^3–37^1. Trinity, Cambridge, M.A., M.B., B.Chir. University College Hospital, London, M.R.C.P., F.R.C.S. ✕ R.N.V.R., 43–46. Surg. Lt. Hon. Consultant, U.C.H., 57–58 as 1st Asst. Surgical Unit. Consultant Surgeon, Leicester Royal Infirmary, 58. *Lansdowne Club.* Royal Society of Medicine. Publication, "Crohn's Disease". J.P. for City of Leicester.

BOND, John Derek, b. 12 Mar. 14, s. of late A. D. Bond (OR T 98). Tu, 27^3–32^2; Kitchener Scholar. Peterhouse, Cambridge, B.A. Solicitor, 39. ✕ R.A. (Field), 39–46. Capt. Solicitor, Partner in Tyas & Sons of Barnsley.

BOOKER, Charles Anthony. M, 41^3–45^2.*

BOOTH, Allen Layland. K, 02^3–06^2.*

BOOTH, George Kendall, b. 24 July 15, s. of late G. Booth. K, 29^1–32^2. ✕ R.A. Staff Capt. 8th & 9th Armies, 42–44. Attd. Canadian Army, 44–45. Capt. F.C.I.B. Incorporated Insurance Broker in Bain Dawes Group. Dir. of A. W. Bain & Sons (Northern) Ltd. Dir. of Bain Stutter & Partners Ltd. *Union Club in Bradford.* Northern Sec. of O.R. Golfing Society since 58. Son, 2144.

BOOTH, Philip Alfred, b. 29 Dec. 11, s. of late A. Booth. SH, 26^1–30^3. University College, Oxford, B.A. Cloth Manufacturer. ✕ R.A.F., 43–45. Chrmn., Henry Booth & Sons Ltd., Morley, Leeds. *Moortown & Ganton Golf Clubs.*

BOOTHEWAY, Kenneth Charles Hartley, F.I.C.E., b. 15 Feb. 14, 2nd s. of G. Bootheway; W. 28^1–32^2. Capt. St. John's, Cambridge, M.A. Civil Engineer. F.I.C.E. Sudan Irrigation Dept., 36, (Dir., 53). ✕ R.A.F., 40–44. F/Lt.

BOOTHROYD, Francis. T, 26^3–32^2.*

BORRIE, Peter Forbes, M.B., F.R.C.P., b. 26 Mar. 18, s. of late Dr. D. F. Borrie.

SF, 31^3–36^2. Clare, Cambridge, B.A., M.B., B.Chir. St. Bartholomew's Hospital. F.R.C.P. ✕ R.A.M.C., 42–47. Physician in charge, Skin Dept. of St. Bartholomew's Hospital. Royal Society of Medicine.

BOSMAN, Charles Bryan Forbes. W & T, 37^2–42^2.*

BOSMAN, Patrick Alexis Forbes. T, 43^2–49^2.*

BOSTOCK, Michael Ingram, B.M., F.R.A.C.P., b. 2 Aug. 22, younger s. of late Col. J. S. Bostock, C.B.E. Sh, 36^3–40^2. New College, Oxford, B.M., B.Ch., M.A. The London Hospital, M.R.C.P., F.R.A.C.P. Senior Visiting Physician at Hastings Memorial Hospital, New Zealand. Consultant Physician.

BOSTON, Antony Harley, b. 15 Aug. 23, eldest s. of E. L. Boston. Sh, 37^3–42^2; Cap. XXII; H. XI, 42; Athletics Cup, 42; Racquets Pair, 40–41; Racquets Cup, 42. Cadet Officer, 41. Lees Knowles Exhibition. Trinity, Cambridge, M.A. University H. XI, 43–44. ✕ H.M. Torpedo Experimental Establishment, 44–47. Lt. R.N.V.R. With Garston Tanning Co. Ltd., Liverpool, since 47. Director. *R.A.C.; Hurlingham; Liverpool Racquet Club.* Brother, M. E. Boston.

BOSTON, Malcolm Edward. Sh, 38^3–43^2.*

BOURDILLON, Henry Townsend, C.M.G. SF, 27^3–31^2.*

BOURNE, Christopher Ralph, b. 2 May 28, s. of H. R. Bourne. Sh, 42^2–46^2. R.M.A., Sandhurst. Gazetted to R.A., 48. Regular Commission. Army Pilot. Instructor at School of Army Aviation. Various yacht clubs including *Royal Artillery, Parkstone & Keyhaven.*

BOURNE, Sir Frederick Chalmers, K.C.S.I., C.M.G., C.I.E., b. 12 Aug. 91, eldest s. of the late Sir F. S. A. Bourne, C.M.G. K, 05^3–10^2; Scholar; XV, 09; R. VIII, 09–10; Cadet Officer; Boxing Heavyweight, 08, & won, 09–10, at Aldershot. Scholar of Christ Church, Oxford, B.A. Half Blue Boxing, 11–14. ✕ 4th Bn. Royal West Kent Regt. Capt. Indian Civil Service, 20. Governor of Assam, Central Province, East Bengal. Retired. K.C.S.I., C.I.E. *Junior Army & Navy Club.*

BOURNE, General Lord (Geoffrey Kemp), G.C.B., K.B.E., C.M.G., b. 5

Oct. 02, eldest s. of late Col. W. K. Bourne. C, 16^3-20^3; XV, 19–20; R. VIII, 20; XI, 20. R.M.A., Woolwich. Cadet Scholarship; XV, 21–22; XI, 22. Gazetted to R.F.A., 23. p.s.c., i.d.c. Major-General, Head of British Services Mission, Burma, 48. G.O.C., British Sector, Berlin, 49–51. G.O.C., 16th Airborne Div. (T.A.), 51–52. G.O.C.-in-C., Eastern Command, 53. Dir. of Operations, Malaya, 54–56. C.-in-C., Middle East Land Forces, 57. Commandant, Imperial DefenceCollege, 58–59. Retired, 60. A.D.C. General to H.M. The Queen, 59–60. G.C.B., 60. K.B.E., 54. C.M.G., 52. Order of Merit (U.S.). Life Peer, 64, of Atherstone. *Army & Navy Club.* Chrmn., Officers Pension Society. Brother, P. K. Bourne.

BOURNE, Henry Roland, b. 23 Nov. 05, elder s. of late H. Bourne. C, 19^2-22^2. Pembroke, Cambridge, M.A. Member of the Stock Exchange, London. Dir. of Public Companies. ✕ R.A.F. (A.&S.D, Intelligence), 40–45. Sqn. Ldr. *The East India, Sports and Public Schools Club.* Sons, 243 & 1877.

BOURNE, James Gerald, b. 6 Mar. 06, 4th s. of late W. W. Bourne. M, 20^1-23^1. Corpus Christi, Cambridge, M.A. Exhibitioner, 25. Also 33–34 (as postgrad. Med. Student). MD., B.Chir., F.F.A.R.C.S., D.A. Qualified in Medicine, in 37. ✕ R.A.M.C., 39–45. Major. Senior Consultant Anaesthetist, St. Thomas's Hospital, 46, and Salisbury Hospital Group, 50. Retired, 71. Brothers, S. & J. Bourne.

BOURNE, John, b. 9 Oct. 04, 2nd s. of late W. W. Bourne. M, 18^2-22^2; S. VIII, 22; G. VIII, 20–22. Corpus Christi, Cambridge, M.A. Governing Dir. of Bourne & Hollingsworth, London. Cotswold Farmer. F.R.G.S. Served Met. "Spec". Asst. Commander of B.H. 2 Div. Constabulary. Long Service Medal & Home Defence. Brothers, S. & J. G. Bourne. Sons, 255 & 1447.

BOURNE, Peter Kemp, b. 6 Mar. 08, 3rd s. of late Col. W. K. Bourne. C, 22^1-26^2. Worcester, Oxford, M.A. Public Schoolmaster, St. Peter's, York; King's School, Bruton; Stowe; Bedford School. At Bedford, Housemaster 15 years, C.O. of C.C.F. 10 years, Head of French Dept. Now teaching at Hordle House prep. school. Brother, Gen. Lord Bourne.

BOURNE, Stafford, b. 20 Feb. 00, eldest s. of late W. W. Bourne. M, 14^1-18^2; S. VIII, 18. ✕ 1st Cavalry Cadet School. Reserve of Officers. Corpus Christi, Cambridge, M.A. Vacational Course, C.A.E.N. University. ✕ Member of the Admiralty Ferry Crews, 39–45. Entire career with Bourne & Hollingsworth Ltd. (Chrmn. since 38). Relinquished directorial responsibilities and became President for life, 72. *United Oxford & Cambridge University, Royal Thames Yacht, Royal Cruising Clubs.* Brothers, J. & J. G. Bourne. Son, 2145.

BOWATER, Sir Noel Vansittart, Bt., G.B.E., M.C., b. 25 Dec. 92, s. of late Sir F. H. Bowater. 1st Bt. Tu, 06^3-10^2. Commanded Territorial Force, R.A., 13. ✕ Served in France, 15–19. Sheriff of London, 48. Lord Mayor of London, 53–54. Master of Vintners Company, 54–55. K. St. J. *City Livery, United Wards, St. James's, Guildhall Clubs.* Succeeded father, 47. G.B.E., 54. M.C.

BOWDEN, Sir Frank Houston, Bt., b. 10 Aug. 09, s. of the late Sir H. Bowden, Bt., G.B.E. W, 23^1-28^2. Merton, Oxford, M.A. R.N.V.R., 31–36. ✕ R.N.V.R., 39–44. Lt. (S). President, University Hall, Buckland, 69–72. Industrialist and Landowner. President, British Kendo Assoc., 69. Vice-Chrmn., Japan Society of London, 70. Hobbies, collecting Japanese swords and armour. *White's, Royal Thames Yacht, Bath Clubs.*

BOWDEN-SMITH, Ralph Philip, b. 10 June 99, s. of the late F. H. Bowden-Smith. St, 13^2-17^2. ✕ 129th Heavy Battery, R.G.A. Gunner. University College, Reading. Market Farmer. Son, 1021.

BOWDEN-SMITH, William Harold, b. 8 Mar. 11, s. of the late Rev. H. Bowden-Smith (OR St 82). St, 25^3-30^2; R. VIII, 28–30 (Capt.); Crick winner, 29; Holder of Bigside Bags, 30; Cadet Officer; Stovin Exhibition & Open Classical Scholar of Brasenose, Oxford, B.A. ✕ Indian Army, 4/3 Q.A.O. Gurkha Rifles, 41–45. Capt. G.S.O.3, Intell., Karachi, 44–45. With The Burmah Oil Co. Ltd. and Shell International Petroleum Co. Ltd., 34–68. At present a whisky investment specialist in Jersey. *The Victoria Club, St. Helier.*

BOWDLER, The Rev. Richard Edward Hope, b. 11 Feb. 22, s. of R. H. Bowdler, B.C.L. M, 35^3-40^3; XV, 39–40; H. XI, 39–40; XXII, 40. Trinity, Oxford, B.A. Ridley Hall, Cambridge. Master, Rugby School, 45–46; Dragon School, Oxford, 46; Rugby School, 48–49. Ordained, 49. Curate, Morden Parish Church, 49–54. Curate, All Soul's, Langham Place, 54–58.

Secretary, Youth Work Church Society since 58. (C.Y.F.A., Pathfinders, Explorers & Climbers.)

BOWEN, Humphry John Moule, D.Phil., b. 22 June 29, s. of Dr. E. J. Bowen. SF, 42^3-47^2; Scholar; Head of House; Levée; Demyship of Magdalen, Oxford, M.A., D.Phil. Lecturer in Chemistry, Reading University.

BOWER, Capt. Graham John, R.M. W, 30^2-34^2.*

BOWER, Norman Adolf Henry. K, 21^3-24^2.*

BOWES, Richard Norton, b. 6 Aug. 32, s. of D. Y. Bowes. C, 45^3-50^3; Head of House; Levée; XV, 48–49, (Capt.) 50. Exhibitioner of Brasenose, Oxford, B.A. Master of Wine. N/S. 2nd Lt. Bedfordshire & Hertfordshire Regt. Invalided, 52. Wine & Spirit Trade. Currently Production and Distribution Dir. International Distiller & Vintners (U.K.) Ltd.

BOWLEY, William Richard Lyon, b. 18 Feb. 13, eldest s. of late F. B. L. Bowley. B, 26^3-30^3. Chartered Accountant, 35. ✕ R.N.V.R. Pay Lt. P.O.W., Hong Kong, 41–45. Now retired.

BOWRING, Charles Miles Thurston, T.D., b. 6 Sept. 15, 2nd s. of late C. Bowring (OR SH 92). SH, 29^2-34^1; XV, 31–32, Capt., 33. Trinity, Oxford, M.A. Schoolmaster, Mill Hill School, 38–62 (Housemaster, 55–62). ✕ Middlesex Regt., 40. Attd. R.I.A.S.C., 42–45. Major. T.D. Living in Bahamas since 66. Brothers, G. E. & R. G. Bowring.

BOWRING, George Edward. SH, 24^3-28^2. Son, 602.*

BOWRING, Peter Ralph, b. 17 May 13, eldest s. of late H. Bowring (OR SH 99). SH, 26^3-30^2; XV, 29–30; S. VIII, 29–30. Trinity, Cambridge, B.A. Rugby Football Blue. ✕ R.A., 39–45. Underwriter at Lloyd's. *R.A.C.* Son, 796.

BOWRING, Robert Greer. SH, 32^2-36^3.*

BOYD, Austin Gordon, b. 21 Feb. 05, 2nd s. of late H. de H. Boyd, Ph.D. SH, 18^3-23^2; Minor Exhibitioner; XV, 22. University College, Oxford, B.A. ✕ The Royal Scots. Major. Local Dir., Barclay's Bank Ltd. Retired in Feb. 73. *United Oxford & Cambridge Universities Club.* Brother, K. C. Boyd. Son, 946.

BOYD, Francis Robert Bethune. SH, 26^3-30^2.*

BOYD, Col. Kenneth Crawford, M.B.E., T.D., b. 17 Jan. 13, youngest s. of the late H. de H. Boyd. Ph.D. SH, 26^3-31^2; Cap., 28–30; R. VIII, 29–31, Capt. Trinity, Oxford, M.A. Barclay's Bank Ltd, 35–37. 51st London H.A.A. Regt. R.A.T.A., 37. Stock Exchange, 37–39. ✕ Norway, Egypt, H.Q. 10th Corps, H.Q. 13th Corps, 39–45. Dep. Mil. Gov. Styria, 45–47. Since 47, Whitbread & Co. Ltd. (Dir.). M.B.E., 43. T.D., 45. *Bath Club.* Brother, A. G. Boyd. Son, 946.

BOYD, Samuel Michael Anthony, b. 17 Apr. 25, s. of late Lt.-Col. S. R. Boyd (OR Tu 15). Tu, 39^1-39^2. Trinity College, Dublin, B.A., B.A.I., M.I.C.E. Civil Engineering Contractor. Institution of Civil Engineers. Son, Richard Samuel John, Tu. 68^3–.

BOYDELL, Brian Patrick, Mus.D., b. 17 Mar. 17, s. of J. F. Boydell. SF, 30^3-35^1; Peppin Cup for Pianoforte playing, 34. Choral Exhibitioner of Clare, Cambridge, B.A. Royal College of Music. Royal Irish Academy of Music, L.R.I.A.M. Mus.B., Dublin, 42. Mus.D., Dublin, 59. Prof. of Music at University of Dublin, 62. Conductor, now President, Dublin Orchestral Players, 42–68. Fellow of Trinity College, Dublin, 72. Member of Irish Arts Council since 60. Prof. of Singing, R.I. Academy of Music, 44–52. Guest conductor of orchestras in Ireland, London & Canada. Composer and Musicologist. Adjudicator at Music Festivals. At present engaged on "Music and Society up to 1850", for the *New History of Ireland*, and a number of articles for the *Grove's Dictionary of Music & Musicians.* Founder, Council Member, Music Assoc. of Ireland. Vice-Pres., Assoc. for the Promotion of Music in Education. F.T.C.D., 72.

BOYES, Eric Simeon, b. 13 Feb. 16, eldest s. of the late A. S. Boyes. St, 29^3-34^2; XI, 33–34, Cap; H. XI, 33–34. Corpus Christi, Cambridge, M.A. ✕ R.E., 39–45. Capt. Ministry of Defence (Army Dept.). Royal Military College of Science, Shrivenham, Wilts. Brother, J. A. Boyes. Sons, 1766, 2408 & 2855.

BOYES, James Ashley, b. 27 Aug. 24, 2nd s. of the late A. S. Boyes. St & K, 37^1-42^3; Head of House; Levée; XV, 40–42 (Capt.); XI, 40–42 (Capt., 41 & 42); H. XI, 41–42; Racquets Pair, 41–42

(Capt.). Scholar of Clare, Cambridge, M.A. Mellon Fellowship at Yale University, 48–50, M.A. ✕ R.N.V.R., 43–46. S/Lt. Asst. Master, Rugby School, 50–54. Headmaster, Kendal Grammar School, 54–60. Dir. of Studies, Royal Air Force College, Cranwell, 60–65. Headmaster, City of London School from 65. *Hawks, Cambridge; R.A.C.; Hurlingham.* Brother, E. S. Boyes.

BOYLE, Lt.-Col. Hugh MacCormac, O.B.E., M.C. SH, 11^1–14^2.✱

BOZMAN, John Michael. M, 44^3–49^2.✱

BRACEWELL, Graham Acton. M.B., B.Chir. M, 36^3–41^2.✱

BRADBY, Edward Lawrence, b. 15 Mar. 07, 4th s. of late H. C. Bradby. SH, 20^3–25^2; R. VIII, 24–25; winner of Crick; Hon. Exhibitioner of New College, Oxford, M.A. Study in Austria and Germany, 29–30. Asst. Master, Merchant Taylors School, London, 30–34. International Student Service, 34–39. Principal, Royal College, Colombo, Ceylon, 39–46. Principal, Eastbourne Emergency Training College, 47–49. Principal, St. Paul's College, Cheltenham, 49–72. Hon. M.Ed., Bristol, 72. *Royal Commonwealth Society.* Brother, R. C. Bradby. Sons, 1236, 1846 & 2625.

BRADBY, Robert Christopher, b. 18 Jan. 05, 3rd s. of late H. C. Bradby. SH, 18^3–23^1. Language & Lit. courses, France. Oxford University Press. Church Information Board. Head, Oxford House, Bethnal Green. ✕ R.A.S.C. A/Major, 39–45. *Savile Club.* Brother, E. L. Bradby.

BRADDELL, Thomas Lyndhurst. SH, 22^1–24^3.✱

BRADFORD, David Cordley, M.B., B.Ch., b. 4 Sept. 22, 2nd s. of late Dr. E. C. Bradford (OR SH 04). SH, 36^2–40^3. Pembroke, Cambridge, B.A., M.B., B.Ch. St. Bartholomew's Hospital, London, M.R.C.S., L.R.C.P. General Medical Practitioner. ✕ With the Red Cross at Belsen Camp. *South Cerney Sailing Club; Wotton Tennis Club, Gloucester.* Brother, T. C. Bradford.

BRADFORD, Brigadier Frank William Percy, M.B.E., b. 23 May 07, eldest s. of late P. R. Bradford (OR St 90). St, 21^2–25^2; Junior Athletics Cup, 23; R. VIII, 25. R.M.A., Woolwich; XV, 26. Gazetted to Royal Corps of Signals, 27. N.W. Frontier,

India, 30–31. ✕ Adjt., 39–40. Major, 44. Staff College Graduate. Retired in the rank of Brigadier, 59. M.B.E. *Army & Navy Club.*

BRADFORD, Peter James, D.S.O., M.C. M, 24^3–28^2.✱

BRADFORD, Lt.-Col. Robert Danby, b. 21 Oct. 05, eldest s. of A. D. Bradford. M, 19^3–23^2; Cap, 22. New College, Oxford, M.A. ✕ Coldstream Guards, Lt.-Col., 40–45. Insurance Broker retired. Member of Council, Salmon & Trout Assoc.; Member of Exec. Committee, Scottish Salmon Anglers Federation. *New Club, Edinburgh.* Brother, P. J. Bradford.

BRADFORD, Timothy Cordley, M.B., B.Ch., b. 28 Aug. 29, 3rd s. of late Dr. E. C. Bradford (OR SH 04). SH, 42^3–47^2. Pembroke, Cambridge, B.A., M.B., B.Chir. St. Bartholomew's Hospital, London. General Medical Practitioner, Staunton, Gloucester. Brother, D. C. Bradford.

BRADLEY, Dennis Richard. Tu, 45^3–49^3.✱

BRADLEY-MOORE, Ralph, b. 26 Oct. 99, youngest s. of the late H. F. Bradley-Moore. SF, 13^3–14^2. London Matric. (Hons.), 17. Manchester University, B.Sc. Played Rugger for University. C.M.E., A.M.I.Cert.E. ✕ Cadet, R.F.C., Infantry, 20th Londons, Wiltshire Yeomanry, 6th Wilts in England, Ireland, France & Belgium, 17–19. Manchester University, 19–22. Industry in Lancashire, 22–26. Farming in Rhodesia, 27. Engineer in South Africa including design, two machines patented, 28–44. Visits to England and Scotland. Retired in England, 44. Son, 559.

BRADSHAW, Averell Stuart, b. 28 Feb. 08, s. of late H. S. Bradshaw. SH, 21^3–26^2; Levée; XI, 24–25; Capt., 26; Cap, 25; H. XI, 26. Brasenose, Oxford, B.A. Golf Blue, 27–29 (Capt.). N.S.W. President Australian Society of Breeders of British Sheep, 64–66. Federal Council, A.S.B.B.S., 64–70. ✕ Staff Officer Intelligence (Air) General Douglas MacArthur. South West Pacific Area, 42–43. Owned grazing properties N.S.W., Australia, Mona Vale, Ladysmith & Barragan, Cudal. Studmaster, Mona Vale, Hereford Cattle & Dorset Horn Sheep Studs. *Union Club, Sydney; Vincent's; R. & A.; Royal Sydney Golf Club.* Royal Agricultural Society of N.S.W. (Represented England Amateur International Golf against Scotland, Ireland & Wales, 32. N.S.W. Inter-State Matches, 47.)

BRADSHAW, Haydon Dorman, b. 6 Dec. 09, s. of the late R. G. Bradshaw. W, 23^3-28^2; XV, 26–27; XI, 28; H. XI, 28. ✕ H.A.C. & R.A.S.C., 39–45. Major. T.D. Tea Broker retired. *M.C.C.; Gresham Club.* Sons, 115, 499 & 1197.

BRADSHAW, James Sutcliffe. T, 02^3-03^3.＊

BRADSHAW, John Rylance, b. 6 May 15, s. of J. Bradshaw. W, 28^3-34^1. Levée. R. VIII, 34. Merton, Oxford, M.A. Asst. Master, Sedbergh School, 38–39, and Trinity College, Glenalmond, 39–40. ✕ R. Signals, 40–46. Major. Despatches twice. Administrative Asst., Bootle, 47–48. Asst. Sec. for Education, Shropshire, 48–53. Deputy County Education Officer, Dorset, 53–59; Education Officer, 59–74. Society of Education Officers. Member, Bishop of Durham's Commission on Religious Education, 67–70.

BRAGG, David William, b. 1 Mar. 26, younger s. of the late Sir L. Bragg, F.R.S., D.Sc., C.H. SH, 40^1-44^1. Coal mining during war. Art Student. Agricultural Botanist, Cambridge. Brother, S. L. Bragg.

BRAGG, Stephen Lawrence, b. 17 Nov. 23, elder s. of the late Prof. Sir L. Bragg, F.R.S., D.Sc., C.H. SH, 37^3-41^3. Trinity, Cambridge, M.A. Commonwealth Fund Fellow at Mass. Inst. of Tech., 48–49. S.M., F.I.Mech.E., F.R.Ae.S. Member, A.R.C., 70–73. Member, U.G.C., 66–71, C.S.P., 71–72. Rolls Royce Ltd. (Aero Engine Div.), 44–48, 51–71. Vice-Chancellor, Brunel University since 71. *Athenæum.* Brother, D. W. Bragg. Sons, 2904 & Andrew Christopher, SH, 71^2-.

BRAIDWOOD, Walter Standish, M.B., F.R.C.S., b. 21 Aug. 04, s. of the late H. L. Braidwood, M.A., C.S.I. W, 18^3-23^2; R. VIII, 23; S. VIII, 21–23. Corpus Christi, Cambridge, B.A. Queen's University, Belfast, M.B., B.Ch., B.A.O., F.R.C.S. (Edin.). Consultant Surgeon, Belfast and North Down Hospital Groups. Surgeon, now retired. ✕ R.A.M.C., 39–45. Major. B.M.A. Ulster Medical Society. *Royal Ulster Yacht Club.*

BRAITHWAITE, Lt.-Col. Douglas Elliott. K, 24^1-28^2.＊

BRAITHWAITE, Lt.-Col. Thomas Colin, O.B.E., T.D., b. 10 Apr. 13, 2nd s. of C. W. Braithwaite. K, 26^3-31^2; XI, 31. Trinity, Cambridge. Stockbroker, 38. ✕

G.S.O.1, H.Q., 2nd Army. Lt.-Col. Wounded twice. O.B.E., T.D. Dispatches. General Commissioner (Income Tax). *Northern Counties Club, Newcastle-upon-Tyne.* Brother, D. E. Braithwaite. Son, 2280.

BRAMMAR, John Adams, L.D.S., R.C.S., b. 19 June 24, s. of T. A. Brammar. T, 38^2-42^2; R. VIII, 41–42. Birmingham University, B.D.S., L.D.S., R.C.S. Dental Surgeon. Surg.-Lt. (D) R.N., 47–52. Son, Hugh Timothy, SH, 73^1-.

BRAMWELL, Brian Courtenay Francis, b. 17 Oct. 23, s. of the late F. H. Bramwell. SH, 37^3-41^3; XV, 41; Sw. VIII, 39–41. Trinity, Cambridge, M.A. Squash Blue. I.C.I., Northwich, Cheshire, Research Chemist, 44–49; Plant Management, 49–50; Techno-Commercial, 59–70; Marketing from 70. J.P. Chrmn., Cheshire Squash Rackets Assoc. Chrmn., Lancashire & Cheshire Squash League, 62–72. Played Squash and Rugger for Cheshire. *Hawks, Pitt, Mid-Cheshire Clubs.*

BRAMWELL, Christopher Addison, b. 8 May 27, s. of late N. A. Bramwell (OR St 12). St & W, 41^2-45^1; Head of House; Levée. King's, Cambridge. Army short course. N/S., 45–47. Regular Officer in Royal Engineers, 47–67, p.s.c. Retired as Major. Sales Engineer with Acrow Engineers from 67. *Army Ski Club, Royal Engineer Yacht Club.* Wolfe Society.

BRANDER, Capt. Michael Spieker. Sh, 33^3-38^2.＊

BRANDT, Henry Augustus, b. 3 Feb. 02, 2nd s. of late H. B. Brandt. SF, 15^3-20^1; Rackets Pair, 19–20 (Capt.). New College, Oxford. Merchant Banker. ✕ Intelligence Corps, 40–43. Capt. Worked for 50 years in family Merchant Bank, W. M. Brandts, Sons & Co. Ltd., London. *Bath Club.* Brother, W. E. Brandt. Sons, 643 & 1054.

BRANDT, John Mowbray, b. 8 July 28, younger s. of Capt. W. E. Brandt, M.C. (OR SF 10). SF, 42^2-46^2. W. M. Brandts, Sons & Co. Ltd., London. *Bath Club.* Brother, W. R. Brandt.

BRANDT, William Edward, M.C., b. 28 Apr. 97, eldest s. of late H. B. Brandt. SF, 10^3-15^2. ✕ 10th Bn. Sherwood Foresters, 15–18. Capt. Wounded twice. M.C. In 20 joined family Merchant Banking firm of W. M. Brandts, Sons & Co. Ltd.,

London. Became Partner in 26, and retired from business in 68. *City of London Club, Bath Club.* Brother, H. A. Brandt. Sons, W. R. & J. M. Brandt.

BRANDT, William Rupert, b. 6 Jan. 26, eldest s. of Capt. W. E. Brandt, M.C. (OR SF 10). SF, 40^1–44^1. Farmer. Brother, J. M. Brandt.

BRANSON, James Frederick Harold. SH, 30^3–35^1. Son, 2427.*

BRASHER, Christopher William, b. 21 Aug. 28, 2nd s. of late W. K. Brasher. SH, 42^3–46^2; R. VIII, 45–46. St. John's, Cambridge, B.A., 51. Cross Country Half Blue, 47; Athletics Blue, 49. Capt., C.U. Hare & Hounds, 49–50. Winner, Steeplechase, Melbourne Olympics, 56. Journalist, Television Reporter, Author. *Alpine Club.*

BRAZIER-CREAGH, George Edward Brian. SH, 22^1–25^1.*

BRAZIER-CREAGH, Major-General Sir Kilner Rupert, K.B.E., D.S.O. SH, 23^2–27^3.*

BRAZIER-CREAGH, The Rev. Neville Henry Sherlock. SH, 24^2–28^1.*

BREAKWELL, Ernest Raven Watmough, b. 27 Feb. 10, eldest s. of the late E. R. Breakwell. B, 24^3–28^2; Scholar. Brasenose, Oxford, B.A. ✕ Army General List. 2nd Lt. Retired after being Man. Dir., Dunlop, Switzerland. *Bath Club.*

BRETHERTON, The Rev. Humphrey, b. 24 Aug. 89, eldest s. of late Rev. H. W. Bretherton (OR SH 71). SH, 03^3–08^2. Trinity, Cambridge, B.A. Ely Theological College. Ordained, 12. Curate, St. Augustine's, Pendlebury, Manchester, 12–18. ✕ Artists Rifles. Pte., 19. Rector of Eccleston, 19–58. Retired. Brothers, R. D. Bretherton & J. T. Bretherton-Hawkeshead-Talbot.

BRETHERTON, The Rev. Richard Dolben, b. 4 Feb. 11, 5th s. of late Rev. H. W. Bretherton (OR SH 71). SH, 24^3–29^2. Exhibitioner of Trinity, Cambridge, B.A. Historical Exhibition. Ely Theological College, 32–34. Rector of Eccleston, Chorley, Lancs. Secretary for the Additional Curates Society, Diocese of Blackburn. Brothers, H. Bretherton & J. T. Bretherton-Hawkeshead-Talbot.

BRETHERTON - HAWKESHEAD - TALBOT, Lt.-Col. John Talbot, M.C. (formerly Bretherton, John Talbot), b. 19 May 94, 3rd s. of late Rev. H. W. Bretherton (OR SH 71). SH, 08^2–12^2; XV, 11; XI, 11–12; R. VIII, 12. R.M.C., Sandhurst. Gazetted Royal Warwickshire Regt., 13. ✕ 1st Bn. Royal Warwickshire Regt. Attd. 10th Bn. Royal West Surrey Regt. 4th Bn. Wiltshire Regt. Capt. Wounded thrice. M.C. ✕ The Malay Regt. P.O.W., Changi, 42–45. Lt.-Col. Brothers, H. & R. D. Bretherton.

BRETT, Charles Edward Bainbridge, b. 30 Oct. 28, elder s. of C. A. Brett. Tu, 42^3–46^2; History Scholarship to New College, Oxford, M.A. Solicitor. Past Chrmn. to Northern Ireland Labour Party. Sons, Charles Christopher Carter, Tu, 67^3–71^3 & Adam Thomas Garrett, Tu, 70^3–.

BRETT, Michael Jeffrey, b. 24 Oct. 28, s. of late A. J. Brett. T, 42^3–46^1. F.C.A. Self-employed Chartered Accountant.

BRETT-SMITH, John Ralph Brett. SF, 31^3–36^1.*

BRETT-SMITH, Richard Nigel Brett, b. 1 Jan. 23, 2nd s. of H. F. B. Brett-Smith. SF, 36^3–41^1; Scholar; Levée; Head of House; H. XI, 41; Editor, "The New Rugbeian", 40–41. Christ Church, Oxford, M.A. ✕ 11th Hussars (P.A.O.), 43–47. Capt. Dispatches. "Oxford Mail", 47–48. Foreign and Defence Correspondent for the "Daily Telegraph", 50–65. Free-lance Writer and Journalist. Author of "Berlin '45" and "The 11th Hussars". *Cavalry Club, Vincent's.* Member of Institute of Journalists. Brother, J. R. B. Brett-Smith.

BREW, Richard Maddock. K, 44^3–49^2.*

BREWERTON, Richard Stanley Elmore, b. 6 Aug. 18, elder s. of late E. W. Brewerton, F.R.C.S. B, 32^1–36^2. St. Bartholomew's Hospital. M.R.C.S., L.R.C.P. ✕ R.A.M.C., 42–47. D.O.M.S. Ophthalmic Consultant, Watford General Hospital. Fellow, Royal Society of Medicine.

BREWIN, Arthur Herbert, b. 25 June 12, eldest s. of the late J. A. Brewin (OR SH 89). SH, 26^2–30^2. Magdalen, Oxford, M.A. Prime Warden of the Dyers Company, 55–56. Member of the Stock Exchange since 38. Partner in Brewin, Edwards & Scrutton. Brother, T. B. Brewin.

BREWIN, Thurston Berkeley, M.R.C.P., F.F.R., b. 20 Dec. 21, 3rd s. of late J. A. Brewin (OR SH 89). SF, 35^3–40^1. ✕ 11th Hussars, 40–43, Libya & Italy. Wounded & P.O.W., 42, Invalided, 43. Guy's Hospital Medical School, 43–49. M.B., B.S., M.R.C.P., F.R.C.P. (Glasgow). F.F.R. Consultant, Glasgow Institute of Radiotherapeutics. Fellow, Royal Society of Medicine. Brother, A. H. Brewin.

BREWIS, Peter Errington. B, 37^3–41^2.*

BRIDGER, The Rev. John Richard. Sh, 34^1–39^1.*

BRIERLEY, Norman Crofton Beswicke, b. 12 Feb. 07, s. of the late N. H. Brierley. K, 20^3–25^2. King's College, London, B.Sc. (Eng.). Fellow, Institution of Civil Engineers. Retired, acting as Civil Engineering Consultant.

BRIGHAM, Commander John Graham, R.N., b. 26 Aug. 30, s. of late R. W. G. Brigham. T, 44^2–47^3. Special entry to R.N. College, Dartmouth. Naval Officer, Commander, Royal Navy (Pilot).

BRIGHT, John Leatham. W, 98^1–01^3.*

BRISCOE, Ralph Cay Benjamin. C. 00^3–04^2.*

BROADBENT, William Benedict, b. 10 Jan. 24, 2nd s. of W. K. B. Broadbent. W, 38^1–41^3. Manchester College of Technology (Mech. Engineering). Associate, Institute of Mechanical Engineers. Associate Fellow, Institute of Petroleum. Mechanical Engineering, Petroleum & Chemical Engineering, Transport. Dir. & Gen. Man., Southern Co., South East Lancs., North East Cheshire Passenger Transport Executive. E.R.D. *Sheffield Club*.

BRODIGAN, Francis Brian. B, 30^3–34^3.*

BROMAGE, James Richard Vincent Arthur, C.B.E., b. 12 June 14, eldest s. of J. V. B. R. Bromage. St, 27^3–33^2. New College, Oxford, M.A. Administrative Service, Nigeria, 38–61. ✕ Capt. Royal West Africa Frontier Force, 39–43. Government Service (Overseas Development) since 61. First Secretary, British High Commission, Accra, 64–69. C.B.E. *Royal Commonwealth Society*.

BROMLEY, Frederick Keith, b. 2 Feb. 12, eldest s. of late F. R. Bromley. SF, 25^3–29^2. ✕ R.N.V.R. Lt. Member of

Lloyd's. Farmer. *Puffin's*, Brother, M. C. Bromley. Son, 1902.

BROMLEY, Michael Cornish, b. 16 May 14, 2nd s. of late F. R. Bromley. SF, 28^2–32^2. ✕ 133 Field Regt., R.A., 43–45. Lt. Chrmn. & Man. Dir. of Russell & Bromley Ltd. Brother, F. K. Bromley.

BROMLEY, Sir Thomas Eardley, K.C.M.G., b. 14 Dec. 11, s. of late T. E. Bromley, I.C.S. C, 25^3–30^2; Exhibitioner of Magdalen, Oxford, B.A. H.M. Consular Service, 35. H.M. Foreign Service on amalgamation. Consular Service, Japan, 36–40. F.O., 40–46. Asst. Private Secretary & Private Secretary to Permanent Under-Secretary, 43–46. Washington. Baghdad. Head of African Dept., F.O., 54–56. Imperial Defence College, 56. Cabinet Office, 57–60. Ambassador to Somalia, Syria, Algeria, Ethiopia, 60–69. Retired, 69. Secretary, Churches Main Committee, 70–72. Anglo-Ethiopian Society. K.C.M.G., 64.

BROOK-LAWSON, Donald Michael (formerly D. M. B. Lawson), b. 31 May 29, s. of Dr. W. A. D. Lawson. M, 42^3–46^2. Loughborough College of Technology. B.Sc., D.L.C., C.Eng. Appointed to Court & Council of Loughborough University of Technology, 66. Consulting Engineer. *East India, Sports & Public Schools Club*. British Light Aviation Centre. Son, Andrew Michael, SH, 70^1–.

BROOKS, George, T.D., J.P., b. 16 Aug. 03, 3rd and youngest s. of the late S. Brooks. C, 17^3–21^2. ✕ R.A., 39–45, Major, T.D. J.P., 52. Farmer & Industrial Banker. *Army & Navy Club*. Brother, S. R. Brooks. Son, 536.

BROOKS, John Henry James, B, 15^3–18^3.*

BROOKS, Major Samuel Roy, b. 14 Nov. 99, 2nd s. of late S. Brooks. C, 13^3–17^3; XXII, 17. ✕ Coldstream Guards, 18–20. ✕ and 39–45, Major. W. Sussex County Councillor for 21 years, Alderman for 6 years. Vice-Chrmn. of Education. Chrmn. of W. Sussex School of Agriculture. Governor of Steyning G.S. & The Weald Comprehensive. Industrial Banker, now retired. Farming in West Sussex since 46. Pedigree Prize Herd of Jersey Cattle. *Guards Club, Pratt's Club*. Brother, G. Brooks.

BROOME, Richard Neville, O.B.E., M.C., b. 25 May 09, 2nd s. of late H. H.

Broome, C.I.E., I.M.S. Tu, 23^2–27^2. St. John's, Cambridge, B.A. Malayan Civil Service, 32–57. ✕ Seconded to Special Forces, 42–45. In Malayan jungle with Guerilla Forces, 43–45, Colonel. Research Asst., Foreign Office, with service in S.E.A.T.O., Bangkok, 58–62. Retired as Sec. for Defence & Internal Security, Singapore. M.C., 44. O.B.E., 51. Sons, 1319 & 2091.

BROUNLIE, Lt.-Col. Charles Anthony de Bels, M.C., b. 2 May 08, s. of late G. de B. Brounlie (OR W 91). W, 22^1–26^2. R.M.C., Sandhurst. Gazetted to Q.O. Royal West Kent Regt., 28. Lt.-Col. retired, 55. Farming (Dorset). M.C.

BROWN, Anthony Penton, b. 8 Mar. 06, s. of H. W. Brown. SH, 20^1–24^2; R. VIII, 22–24 (Capt.); Holder of Bigside Bags, 24; XV, 23. Trinity, Oxford, M.A. Painter & Sculptor.

BROWN, Col. Eric Carmichael. T, 99^1–03^2.*

BROWN, George Eustace Grant. B, 25^2–28^2.*

BROWN, James Cyril, b. 25 May 87, younger s. of late T. W. Brown. B, 01^3–02^3. Manchester Municipal Schoo lof Technology, Diploma. Three years in workshop of Hans Renold, chair makers, to obtain practical training. Drawing office of National Gas Engine Co. Ltd., 10. Design of large vertical gas engines. National Gas Engine Co., Ltd., Estimating Dept., Contracts Dept., in charge. Retired, 54.

BROWN, John Michael, M.C., T.D., M.B., b. 16 May 17, s. of the late C. S. Brown, B.D.S., R.C.S. (OR T 96). St, 31^1–36^2; Levée; Head of House; XV, 35; Cadet Officer, 35. Gonville & Caius, Cambridge, M.B., B.Chir. London Hospital. L.R.C.P., M.R.C.S., D.Obst.R.C.O.G., ✕ R.A., 39–46, M.C. Dispatches. Major. T.D. & Clasp. General Practitioner. Son, 2553.

BROWN, Kenneth John Noel. Sh, 41^3–45^2.*

BROWN, Maurice Ashley. C, 19^2–23^2.*

BROWN, Michael George Harold. K, 21^2–24^3.*

BROWN, Peter, b. 12 May 32, s. of late O. C. Brown (OR SF 06). SH, 45^3–51^1; Levée; Head of House; Classics Scholarship to Oriel, Oxford, B.A. Commenced as Student Psychiatric Nurse, training at Claybury Hospital, Woodford Bridge, Essex, in Oct. 72. After $4\frac{1}{2}$ years work (unqualified) in the same field at St. Clement's Hospital, London.

BROWN, Peter Beale Harold, b. 3 Dec. 02, eldest s. of H. G. Brown. K, 16^3–21^2. Trinity, Cambridge, B.A. C.Eng., F.M.I.Mech.E., M.Inst.R. President, Scottish Engineering Employers Assco., 57–58. President, Glasgow Chamber of Commerce, 64–65. Dean of Guild, Glasgow, 69–70. Apprentice Engineer, L. Sterne & Co. Ltd., Gen. Man., 27; Man. Dir., 32; Chrmn., 59–69. Chrmn., Worthington, Simpson Ltd., 59–70. Now retired. *Western Club, Glasgow; Junior Carlton Club.* Sons, 249 & 640.

BROWN, Thomas William Henry, b. 17 May 25, s. of late A. H. Brown. Tu, 39^3–42^3. College of Aeronautical & Automobile Engineering (Chelsea). C.Eng., A.F.R.Ae.S. Rolls Royce (1971) Ltd. Small Engine Division. *Vintage Sports Car Club.*

BRUCE, Major Erracht Pryce Cameron, M.C. W, 19^2–23^2.*

BRUCE, Robert Hunter Wingate, C.B.E. (formerly Wingate, R. B.), b. 11 Oct. 07, s. of J. B. Wingate. SH, 21^3–26^2; XV, 25; XI, 26. Balliol, Oxford, B.A. L.M.S. Railway, 30–46. Man., Northern Counties Railways, Belfast, 43–46. Chief Rep., Rio Tinto Co., Southern Africa, 52–57. Member, Crofters Commission, from 60. Landowner in Shetland. Lord Lieut. of Shetland. C.B.E. *United Oxford & Cambridge University Club; New Club, Edinburgh; Highland Club, Inverness.*

BRUCE, Robert Richard Fernie, D.F.C., B.Mus., b. 17 Aug. 15, 2nd s. of L. Bruce. B, 29^3–31^2; Scholar. Edinburgh University, Mus.Bac. ✕ R.A.F. F/Lt. D.F.C. & Bar. Lecturer, University College, Cardiff, since 47. Sons, 1342 & 2275.

BRUCE JONES, Thomas Dunlop, M.C., b. 2 May 20, s. of late J. C. Bruce Jones. Tu, 34^2–37^3. St. John's, Cambridge, M.A. ✕ R.A., 40–46. Capt. M.C. F.C.I.S. Man. Dir., Jones & Campbell Ltd., Iron Founders. Dir. of Timber Merchants & Jones Buckie Shipyard Ltd.

BRUCE-LOCKHART, John McGregor, C.B., C.M.G., O.B.E., b. 9 May 14, eldest s. of late J. H. Bruce-Lockhart (A). SH, 28²–32³; XV, 31–32, Capt.; XXII, 32. Senior Scholar to St. Andrew's University, M.A. Blues for Rugger, Cricket & Tennis. Asst. Master, Rugby School, 37–39. T.A. Commission, Seaforth Highlanders. ⚔ 39–45, U.K. Paiforce, Middle East & Italy, Lt.-Col. Asst. Military Attaché, Paris, 45–47. H.M. Foreign Service, 47–65. Head of Courtaulds' Personnel Dept., 66–71. Living in semi-retirement near Rugby. C.B., C.M.G., O.B.E. *Boodle's, Reform, Rye Golf Club.*

BRUMWELL, John Robert Marcus, b. 20 Apr. 01, s. of late M. Brumwell. Tu 14³–19³; Scholar; Levée; S. VIII, 19. Retired Advertising Agent, Industrial Designer & Scientific Editor. Royal Society of Arts. Centenary Gold Medal "For Services to Industrial Art". *Reform Club.*

BRUNYATE, William Michael Waddingham, M.C., b. 6 Mar. 98, eldest s. of late Sir J. B. Brunyate, K.C.S.I., K.C.I.E. SH, 12³–15³; Scholar. ⚔ 150th Field Co., R.E., 15–19, Lt. Wounded. M.C. Dispatches twice. Senior Scholar Trinity, Cambridge, M.A., A.M.Inst.C.E. Mechanical Engineering, Ruston & Hornsby Ltd., Lincoln. Harland & Wolff Ltd., Belfast. Chief Labour Supply Inspector, N.I., 42–48. Now retired. Son, 1094.

BRUUN, Henrik Sven Otto. St, 45³–47².*

BRYAN, John Lindsay, M.C., T.D., b. 26 May 96, eldest s. of Lt.-Col. L. E. G. Bryan. Tu, 11¹–14²; Cap, 13; XI, 12–14 (Capt.); Rackets & Fives pair, 14. ⚔ 1st Bn., H.A.C., 5th Bn. Manchester Regt. 42nd Bn. Machine Gun Corps. Major. M.C. St. John's, Cambridge, M.A. Cricket Blue, 21. Partner, St. Andrew's School, Eastbourne. Dispatches, 40. T.D. Schoolmaster now retired. *M.C.C.* (Australian Tour 24–25). *Kent County C.C.* Son, P. J. Bryan.

BRYAN, Patrick John, b. 25 June 29, s. of J. L. Bryan (OR Tu 11). Sh, 43³–47³; Scholar. Major Classics Scholarship to St. John's, Cambridge, M.A. Postgraduate certificate in Education (London). Education Officer, N. Rhodesia, 52–61. Asst. Master, Royal Hospital School, Holbrook, 61–69. Asst. Master, Dean Close Junior School, Cheltenham, from 67.

BRYANS, Peter de Wyckoff. W, 33¹–37².*

BRYANT, Richard Charles, C.B., b. 20 Aug. 08, eldest s. of C. J. Bryant. K, 22³–27¹. History Scholar of Oriel, Oxford. Administrative Class of Home Civil Service. Board of Trade (Under-Secretary) now retired. C.B. *Travellers'.*

BRYCE-SMITH, David Ingram, b. 25 Dec. 29, s. of H. Bryce-Smith (OR Tu 11). Tu, 43³–47². R.M.A., Sandhurst. Commissioned, 49, The Royal Scots (The Royal Regt.). Retired, 55 (having served with the 1st Bn.). Hunt, Leuchars & Hepburn Ltd., 55–60. Victoria Wine-Tylers Ltd., Marketing Man., from 60. Member of the Free Painters & Sculptors (M.F.P.S.).

BRYCE-SMITH, Herbert, b. 17 Feb. 97, eldest s. of the late N. J. Bryce-Smith (OR St 79). Tu, 11¹–13³. ⚔ 3rd P.S. Bn. Royal Fusiliers. 4th Bn. Royal North Lancs. Regt. attd. R.F.C. Capt. Wounded twice. Son, D. I. Bryce-Smith.

BRYMER, John Anthony, b. 25 Jan. 13, 3rd s. of C. J. Brymer. Tu, 27¹–30³. Cap. ⚔ 33rd Field Regt., R.A., Adj., 41. N.W. Europe. Dispatches. Capt. Printer.

BUCHANAN, Edward Handasyde. SF, 20¹–24².*

BUCHANAN, Major George, T.D., b. 4 Sept. 14, 3rd s. of E. Buchanan. SF, 27³–31³. University College, London. ⚔ R.A., 39–45. Major. Wounded. Dispatches twice. T.D. Dir., Buchanan & Curwen Ltd., Electrical Installation Contractors, London. *H.A.C.*

BUCHANAN, John Hair Scouler, M.B., B.Chir., b. 21 May 22, s. of J. S. Buchanan, M.B., Ch.B., F.R.F.P.S. Sh, 36²–40²; XV, 39. Gonville & Caius, Cambridge, B.A. University Rugby XV, 42–43. St. Bartholomew's Hospital, London. M.B., B.Chir. (Cantab.), M.R.C.S., L.R.C.P. ⚔ R.N.V.R. Surg. Lt. Medical Practitioner. *Hawks Club.* Sons, 2769 & Charles Robert Scouler, Sh. 71²–.

BUCHANAN, Robert Hamilton. B, 10³–11².*

BUCK, Stephen Crosbie, b. 3 Aug. 12, s. of F. S. Buck, M.B.E. St, 26²–30². King's, Cambridge, & London Hospital. M.A., M.B., B.Chir., M.R.C.S., L.R.C.P. ⚔ R.A.M.C., 39–45. Major. Lately, Senior Pathologist, Uganda.

BUCKLAND, Gerald Frederick Waldie, b. 11 June 26, s. of late Brigadier G. C. B. Buckland, C.B., D.S.O., M.C. (OR SF 97). SF, 39³–44². Corpus Christi, Cambridge, B.A.

BUCKLEY, Arthur Donald. SF, 16³–21¹.*

BUCKNILL, John Birch, b. 1 Oct. 96, 3rd s. of late G. E. Bucknill. SH, 10³–14². ✕ 9th Bn. Middlesex Regt. Lt. Wounded. Invalided, 20. Solicitor, 26–49. Son, J. D. Bucknill.

BUCKNILL, John David. W, 44³–49¹.*

BUER, Arthur Knill. W, 95¹–99¹.*

BULGER, His Honour Judge Anthony Clare, b. 5 Oct. 12, s. of late D. D. Bulger. C, 26³–31²; XV, 30; Sw. VIII. Oriel, Oxford, B.A. B.Ch. Bar, Inner Temple, 36. ✕ R.A.C., 27th Lancers, 39–45. Lt.-Col. Wounded. Dispatches twice. Bar, 46–63. Deputy Chrmn., Gloucestershire Quarter Sessions, 58–70. Chrmn., 70–72. Recorder of Abingdon, 60–63. H.M. Circuit Judge from 63.

BULL, Alan John Gilbert. SF, 44²–49¹.*

BULL, Oliver Richard Silvester, b. 30 June 30, s. of W. H. Bull, B.A. M, 44³–49²; Scholar; Levée; Head of House; Head of School; XI, 47–49; H. XI, 49; Scholarship in Classics to Brasenose, Oxford, M.A. Half Blue for Golf. Housemaster, Eton College.

BULL, Randolph Cecil. K, 35³–39².*

BULLARD, Julian Leonard, b. 8 Mar. 28, 3rd s. of Sir R. W. Bullard, K.C.B., K.C.M.G., C.I.E. SF, 41³–46²; Scholar; Levée; Head of School; XV, 44–45 (Capt.); XI, 46; Cadet Officer, 45. Demy of Magdalen, Oxford. Gaisford Greek Verse Prize, 47. Craven Scholar, 48. B.A. Fellow of All Soul's College, Oxford, 50–57. N/S. Army, 50–52. H.M. Diplomatic Service from 53. Served in Vienna, Amman, Bonn, Moscow & Dubai. Head of Eastern European & Soviet Dept., F. & C.O., since 71.

BULLIVANT, Roger Francis Taylor, B.Mus., D.Phil. T, 34³–40².*

BULLOCK, Edward Anthony Watson, b. 27 Aug. 26, younger s. of late Sir C. Bullock, K.C.B., C.B.E. (OR T 04). SH, 40¹–44²; Scholar; Levée; R. VIII; Head of House; Leaving Exhibition. N/S, 44–47. Lt. The Life Guards. Exhibitioner of

Trinity, Cambridge, B.A. Diplomatic Service from 50. Counsellor, 69. Service in Bucharest, Brussels, La Paz & Harvard. In U.K. at F. & C.O., Ministry of Overseas Development & H.M. Treasury. *United Oxford & Cambridge University Club.* Brother, R. H. W. Bullock.

BULLOCK, The Rev. Canon Frederick William Bagshawe, Ph.D., D.D., b. 20 July 03, s. of Rev. W. C. Bullock, M.A. W, 17³–21². Emmanuel, Cambridge, M.A., M.Litt., Ph.D., B.D., D.D. Manchester, B.D. Ordained Deacon, 27. Priest, 28. Curate of St. Peter's, St. Albans, 27–29; of Holy Trinity, Cambridge, 29–30; and of Great St. Mary's Cambridge, 30–36. Chaplain, 30–31 & Vice Principal of Ridley Hall, Cambridge, 31–36. Examining Chaplain to Bishop of Worcester, 35–41. Chaplain to the Forces, 40–43. Rector of Hollington, Sussex, 43–46. Residentiary Canon and Treasurer of Truro Cathedral, 46–48. Canon Emeritus of Truro from 48. Author of eleven volumes. Member of the Sussex Archaeological Society and of the Burton's St. Leonards Society. Select Preacher, University of Cambridge, 37.

BULLOCK, Richard Henry Watson, C.B., b. 12 Nov. 20, elder s. of late Sir C. Bullock, K.C.B., C.B.E. (OR T 04). SH, 34³–39²; Scholar; Levée; Head of House; Cap, 38; H. XI, 38–39. Lees Knowles Leaving Exhibition. Scholar of Trinity, Cambridge (course not completed due to Military Service). ✕ Westminster Dragoons & Indian Armoured Corps. Officers' Training School, 40–46. Major. Served in England, N.W. Europe (D-Day), Italy & India. Entered Ministry of Supply, 47. Served in Ministry of Aviation, War Office, Ministry of Technology & Dept. of Trade & Industry. Deputy Secretary, D.T.I., since 70. C.B., 71. *M.C.C., Hurlingham.* Pres., Dulwich Hockey Club, Hon. Life Member, Dulwich Sports Club. Vice-Pres., Berkshire & Westminster Dragoon's Old Comrades Assoc. Member, Executive Committee O.R. Society. Brother, E. A. W. Bullock. Son, 2627.

BULMAN, John Forster Harrison, F.R.C.S., b. 5 Mar. 11, eldest s. of late H. F. Bulman (OR SH, 70). M, 24³–29¹. Trinity, Cambridge, M.A. Senior Research Scholar in Physiology, 34. St. Thomas's Hospital Medical School, M.B., B.Ch., F.R.C.S.Eng. Senior Hospital Medical Officer. Consultant Surgeon. Medical House Surgeon Post, 37–39. ✕ Emergency Commission, R.A.M.C., mostly in Middle East, 39–45. Capt. Consultant General

Surgeon, S.W. Metropolitan Regional Hospital Board. Fellow, Royal Society of Medicine. Life Member, British Ornithologists' Union.

BULMER, Michael George. Tu, 44³–48³.*

BUNBURY, Brigadier Francis Ramsay St. Pierre, C.B.E., D.S.O., b. 16 June 10, s. of late Lt.-Col. G. B. St. P. Bunbury. Tu, 24²–28²; XXII; S. VIII, 27–28. R.M.C., Sandhurst. Gazetted to the Duke of Wellington's Regt., 40. ⚔ 39–45. Italy. D.S.O. Dispatches. Lt.-Col. Korea, Commanding 1st Bn. D.W.R. Bar to D.S.O., 53. Brigadier (Staff College) retired. Won Army 100 Cup at Bisley, 50. C.B.E. Son, 1168.

BUNTING, Guy William Walker, LL.B., b. 24 Nov. 08, elder s. of W. H. Bunting, M.D., F.R.C.S. W, 22³–27²; H. XI, 27. King's, Cambridge, B.A., LL.B. Solicitor, 33. ⚔ 40–45. The King's Regt. (Liverpool). Major. D.A.A.G., Tripolitania. Sons, 2484 & 2899.

BURBRIDGE, Sir John Richard Woodman, Bt. B, 44³–48³.*

BURCHARDT, Ernest Martin St. George. SF, 23¹–25³.*

BURCHARDT, Godfrey, b. 1 Aug. 11, younger s. of late E. A. Burchardt (OR SF 67). SF, 25²–30¹. Balliol, Oxford (Nettleship Scholar), M.A. Asst. Master, Housemaster & Dir. of Studies, Gordonstoun School, Elgin, 36–72 (except for War Service in Intelligence Corps, N. Africa & Italy). Brother, E. M. St. G. Burchardt.

BURCHARDT-ASHTON, John Frederick. SH, 00¹–03³.*

BURCHELL, Tufnell Charles, T.D., b. 20 Oct. 98, s. of T. Burchell. B, 12³–16³. ⚔ R.A.S.C., 17–19. 2nd Lt. Solicitor, 22. ⚔ R.A. (T.A.)., 39–42. Lt. Col. R.A.F., 42–45. Wing Commander. T.D. D.L. British Legion.

BURDETT, Edward Priestley, b. 14 Mar. 96, younger s. of late H. P. Burdett (OR SF 82). SH, 10¹–13³. ⚔ 3rd & 7th Bns., South Lancashire Regt., att. R.F.C. 2nd Lt. Wounded. Peterhouse, Cambridge M.A. C.Eng., F.I.E.E.

BURGOYNE-JOHNSON, John Charles. SH, 27²–31³.*

BURLINGHAM, David Henry, b. 20 Jan. 30, 2nd s. of R. H. Burlingham, J.P. Tu, 43³–47². M.I.Ag.E. Dir., H. Burlingham & Co. Ltd., Unispec Ltd. Pres., 65–66, Agricultural Machinery & Tractor Dealers' Assoc. Chrmn., The Lower Avon Navigation Trust Ltd.

BURLTON, Col. Henry Lionel Granville, M.C. C, 10²–13³.*

BURMAN, Sir John Charles, D.L., J.P. B, 22²–25³.*

BURN, Harold John David, b. 26 Mar. 06, elder s. of the late J. H. Burn (OR SH 78). SH, 19³–24²; XV, 24; S. VIII, 24. University College, Oxford. Man. Dir. Brother, R. S. Burn.

BURN, Lt.-Col. Richard Stanley, b. 26 Apr. 08, younger s. of late J. H. Burn, (OR SH 78). SH, 21²–26². University College, Oxford, M.A. Heidelberg University (extra-mural). Paris & Vienna (private). Former J.P. Chrmn., Newcastle Diocesan Board of Finance Ltd. Chrmn., Bellingham Rural District Council. Member, General Synod Church of England & Central Board of Finance. Private family business-colliery owners, refractory manufacturers, estates, 32–39. ⚔ Ministry of Supply, Raw Materials Dept., 39–42. H.M. Forces, Supreme H.Q. Control Commn., Berlin, Lt.-Col., 42–46. National Coal Board (Northumberland) 47–55. Since 55, farming. *Northern Counties Club, Newcastle-upon-Tyne; Oxford & Cambridge University Club.* Brother, H. J. D. Burn. Son, 2137.

BURNESS, John Walter Alexander. Tu, 18²–22².*

BURNETT, Lt.-Col. Maurice John Brownless, D.S.O., D.L., b. 24 Sept. 04, s. of E. J. Burnett, M.B.E., J.P., M.B., B.S., M.R.C.P., O.St.J. C, 18³–22². R.M.A., Woolwich. Army First Class Interpreter (Italian), 32. Commissioned Royal Artillery, 24. p.s.c., 37. ⚔ Lt.-Col., 42. West Africa, 39–41. Home Defence, 41–44. N.W. Europe, 44–45. S.E. Asia, 45–47. D.S.O., 44. Retired, 48. Secretary, North Riding Territorial & Auxiliary Forces Assoc., 50–68. County Councillor, North Riding, 62. Committee Chrmn., 64 & 69. Councillor, Richmond (Yorks.) Rural District Council, 58. Chrmn., 67–69. County Commissioner, N. Riding Scouts, 61–71. Chrmn., N. Riding Youth Assoc. Pres., 71. Deputy Lieut., N. Riding, 58. J.P., N. Riding, 57. Church Assembly,

55–70. General Synod, 70. Ripon Diocesan Board of Finance, 53, Vice-Chrmn. from 56.

BURNEY, Sir Anthony George Bernard, O.B.E., s. of T. B. Burney. W, 23²–27³; Scholar. Exhibitioner of Corpus Christi, Cambridge. F.C.A. Chartered Accountant. Partner in Binder, Hamlyn & Co. Various Directorships. Dir. of Reorganisation, Cotton Board, 59–60. Member, Shipbuilding Inquiry Committee, 65. Now Chrmn., Debenham's Ltd. Knight Bachelor. O.B.E. *Brooks's, Buck's, Garrick.* Australia Society.

BURNEY, Cecil Stanley. K, 98³–99³.*

BURNEY, Charles Douglas Ernest. St, 36³–40².*

BURNLEY, The Rt. Rev. The Bishop of (see Watson, R. C. C.).

BURNYEAT, Lt.-Col. Peter James Anthony, M.B.E., R.A., b. 3 Mar. 16, elder s. of late M. F. Burnyeat (OR Tu 93). W, 29³–32³; S. VIII, 32. Faraday House, A.M.I.E.E. ✕ R.A., 39–46. Lt.-Col. M.B.E. Chrmn., Burnyeat Ltd. Chrmn., United Mersey Supply Co. Ltd. Chrmn., National Federation of Shop Stores Merchants. Pres., International Shop Suppliers Assoc. *Den Norsk Klub.*

BURNYEAT, Major William Harrison Ponsonby, M.B.E., T.D., b. 13 Sept. 11. s. of late Lt.-Col. H. P. Burnyeat, R.A. SH, 25²–29². R.M.A., Woolwich. Gazetted to Royal Artillery, 32. ✕ R.A. & R. Bucks Yeomanry. Major. M.B.E., T.D. Member of Lloyd's. Co. Dir. *Royal St. George's & Woking Golf Clubs.*

BURRELL, Denis James, b. 25 May 30, s. of late E. C. M. Burrell. Sh, 43³–48³. Clare, Cambridge, M.A. Asst. Man. Dir., Martin Baker Aircraft Co. Ltd.

BURRELL, Robert John, Q.C., b. 28 Nov. 23, s. of late R. E. Burrell, Q.C. SH, 37³–41³; Music Scholar; Holder of Bigside Bags. Trinity Hall, Cambridge, M.A. ✕ R.N., 42–44. Lt. R.N.V.R. Bar, Inner Temple, 48. Patent Bar. Q.C., 73. *Royal Welsh Yacht Club.*

BURROWS, John Nicholas, b. 25 Apr. 29, s. of M. K. Burrows. M, 43¹–47¹. N/S. K.O.Y.L.I., Malaya, 48–49. 2nd Lt. University of London. College of Estate Management. F.R.I.C.S. W. H. Robinson & Co., Manchester. *Alpine Club, British Balloon & Airship Club.*

BURT, Norman Frank, b. 27 Sept. 99, 4th s. of late W. O. Burt. B, 13²–17³; Cap, 17; Boxing Welterweight, 17. R.M.A., Woolwich. Won R.M.A. Boxing Welterweight. Jesus, Cambridge, B.A. Blue Athletics. Half Blue Boxing. Govt. Staff Surveyor, Tanganika, 22–25. Colonial Administration, Tanganika, 25–46. Clerk, District Valuation Board, Ministry of Fuel & Power, 48–52. Bursar, Dover College, 53–64.

BURTON, Morris Markham. T, 40³–44².*

BURTON, Terence Peter, b. 11 June 32, s. of late K. E. Burton. W, 45³–49². Solicitor, 54. Asst. to Secretary, Dunlop Rubber Co. Ltd., 54–57. Asst. Solicitor, Imperial Tobacco Co. Ltd., 57–60. Solicitor, Marley Ltd. from 60. Current Appointment, Group Secretary & Solicitor, Marley Ltd., Kent.

BURTT, Basil John. Sh, 41³–46¹.*

BUSBY, Horace David Coysh, T.D., J.P., b. 2 June 14, eldest s. of W. D. L. Busby. T, 28²–32². St. Peter's College, Birmingham. ✕ Royal Warwickshire Regt. & Combined Operations Command, U.K. & India, 39–45. Major. T.D. & Clasp. Headmaster, South Oxford School, 50–55. Headmaster, Plymstock School, Devon, 55–74. J.P. *Royal Western Yacht Club of England.* Son, 1467.

BUTCHER, Ralph Douglas Denne, b. 24 May 13, s. of late A. D. D. Butcher (OR C 98). C, 27³–31³; S. VIII, 30–31; Member of Public Schools Canadian "Athelings" Team, 32. Christ's, Cambridge, B.A. Double Half Blue for Shooting. ✕ Royal Engineers, 40–46. Major. Dispatches thrice. Business career in Sudan, Egypt, Aden & Ethiopia. Presently, Gen. Man., Massey Ferguson in Ethiopia. Cambridge University Rifle Assoc. Commonwealth Parliamentary Assoc.

BUTLER, Clarence Francis. C, 34³–39¹.*

BUTLER, David Ernest. T, 43³–48².*

BUTLER, Lt.-Col. Henry Arthur Cavendish, b. 11 May 09, eldest s. of Major H. C. Butler, M.B.E. SH, 23¹–27². R.M.A., Woolwich. Pembroke, Cambridge, B.A. ✕ Burma, 39–45. 434th Indian Field Coy. Major, 42. Lt.-Col., Comdg. 9th Indian Engineer Bn. Dispatches. Commissioned Royal Engineers, 29–54. Farming, Angus, Scotland, 54–66. Retired, 66. Now resident in N. Ireland. Royal Highland Society.

BUTLER, John Fawcett, b. 21 May 31, younger s. of R. F. Butler (OR St 13). K, 44³–47¹. Real Estate Agent. *St. Moritz Tobagganing Club.* Brother, P. F. Butler.

BUTLER, Kenneth Frederick, M.C., b. 29 Oct. 23, s. of late F. W. Butler. Sh, 37²–41². ✕ 15/19th King's Royal Hussars. M.C. Dispatches.

BUTLER, Peter Fawcett, b. 30 Mar. 27, elder s. of R. F. Butler (OR St 13). St & K, 41¹–44³. *Various Racing Clubs.* Brother, J. F. Butler.

BUTLER, Rodney Fawcett, b. 9 Nov. 99, s. of late B. Butler. St, 13³–18¹. ✕ O.C. Bn. Cadet, 18. Ironmaster. Chrmn. & Man. Dir., Kirkstall Forge Engineering Leeds. Retired, 70. Sons, J. F. & P. F. Butler.

BUTLER-COLE, Robert Falcon Clarke, b. 20 July 04, eldest s. of T. C. Butler-Cole. SH, 18²–20¹. Edinburgh University, B.Sc. Pembroke, Oxford. Colonial Forest Service (retired).

BUTT, Sir (Alfred) Kenneth (Dudley), Bt., b. 7 July 08, s. of late Sir A. Butt, Bt. B, 22²–26³; XV, 26; H. XI, 26; Capt. of Fives; 2nd Pair Rackets (won Junior Trophy). Brasenose, Oxford. Chrmn., Thoroughbred Breeders' Assoc., 73. Pres., Aberdeen Angus Cattle Society, 68–69. Lloyds Underwriter, 29–73. ✕ Major, R.A., 39–45. Chrmn., Parker Wakeling Co., 47–52. Farming. Bloodstock breeding since 48. *Junior Carlton Club. Farmers' Club.*

BUTTERWORTH, Harrison. Sh, 36³–37².*

BUTTERWORTH, Richard Mayall, b. 11 Mar. 26, s. of late Major H. E. Butterworth. W, 40¹–44². Trinity Hall, Cambridge, B.A. Sole Proprietor of American Book Service, London. *M.C.C.; United Oxford & Cambridge University Club.* Son, Richard Wheldon, W, 69³–72².

BUTTERY, David John, M.B., B.Chir., b. 11 Oct. 28, s. of late J. W. D. Buttery, F.R.C.S., M.R.C.O.G. K, 42²–47²; Levée; Head of House. Clare, Cambridge, B.A. St. Bartholomew's Hospital. M.B., B.Chir., M.R.C.G.P. General Medical Practitioner, Ashford, Kent. Folkestone Med. Soc. Ashford Med. Soc. Kent Postgraduate Med. Soc. *Travellers' Hockey Club.* Late Surgeon Lt., R.N. Son, Jonathan Robert, K, 72²–.

BUXTON, Paul William Jex, b. 20 Sept. 25, s. of late D. A. J. Buxton, D.L., J.P. (OR SH 08). SH, 39³–43³; Scholar; Levée. ✕ Coldstream Guards, 44–47. With 6th Guards Tank Bde. N.W. Europe, 45. Wounded. Intelligence Officer, 5th Guards Bde., 46. A.D.C. to Regional Commissioner, Nordheim/Westfallen, 47. Capt. (R.A.R.O.). Scholar of Balliol, Oxford, B.A. Diplomatic Service, 50–71. Investment Banking. *Brooks's Club.*

BYFORD, Charles Barrie, b. 14 Mar. 31, younger s. of D. Byford. M, 44³–49². Leicester Technical College. Associate of Textile Institute (A.T.I.). Dir., D. Byford & Co. Ltd., Leicester. Brother, D. C. K. Byford.

BYFORD, Donald Cady Key. M, 39²–42².*

C

CADE, Peter John. W, 41³–45².*

CAIRNES, Major Francis Herbert, M.C. M, 07³–10¹.*

CAIRNES, William David Elliot. M, 39²–43².*

CALDER, John William. W, 18²–23².*

CALVERLEY, Joseph Alan, b. 17 Nov. 03, eldest s. of late J. E. G. Calverley, C.M.G., M.D. K, 17³–21¹. Brasenose, Oxford, B.A., A.C.A. ✕ R.A.P.C., 39–44. Lt.-Col. Chartered Accountant.

CAMERON, David Charles, O.B.E., b. 22 Oct. 12, elder s. of late Capt. C. P. G. Cameron, M.C., R.A. B, 26³–29³. Colonial Service. Asst. Commissioner of Prisons, Kenya, 47. Commissioner of Prisons, Northern Rhodesia, 50. Dir. of Prisons, Federation of Rhodesia & Nyasaland, 54–63. Dir. of National Assoc. of Property Owners, London. *Salisbury Club, Rhodesia; Naval & Military; M.C.C.* O.B.E., 64.

CAMERON, Ewen Murdoch. B, 22²–25³.*

CAMPBELL, Col. Colin Seymour Roy, O.B.E., M.C., b. 7 Sept. 03, 2nd s. of late H. R. Campbell. (OR St 90). M, 17^3-22^2; XV, 20–21; G. VIII, 21. R.M.C., Sandhurst. XV, 22. Gazetted to Gloucestershire Regt., 24. Adjt., 31–34. Capt., 35. ✕ 39–45. M.C., 40. Major, 41. T/Lt.-Col., 47. p.s.c. Malaya, 50–51. O.B.E. Dispatches. Retired, 55. *Army & Navy Club.*

CAMPBELL, Donald MacGregor. St, 98^3-03^2.*

CAMPBELL, Lt.-Col. Duncan Lorne, M.B.E., M.C., b. 7 Oct. 13, s. of late T. L. Campbell (OR SF 98). SF, 27^3-30^3. R.M.C., Sandhurst. Entrance Scholarship & Senior Term Scholarship. Under Officer. Gazetted to Argyll & Sutherland Highlanders, 34. ✕ Served with Sudan Defence Force in Force 133 & No. 1 Special Force of S.O.E. M.B.E., M.C. & Bar. Dispatches. Lt.-Col. Commanded The Camel Corps, Sudan, 45–49. Farmer. *Royal Over-Seas League.*

CAMPBELL, John Lorne, Hon. LL.D. SF, 20^3-25^2.*

CAMPBELL, Major-General Victor David Graham, C.B., D.S.O., O.B.E., D.L., b. 9 Mar. 05, s. of late Gen. Sir D. G. M. Campbell, G.C.B. SH 19^1-22^1. R.M.C., Sandhurst. Prize Cadet. Passed out 1st, The King's Gold Medal. Anson Memorial Sword. Gazetted to Queen's Own Cameron Highlanders, 24. Adjt., 2nd Bn., 33–35. Instructor, R.M.C., Sandhurst, 35–37. p.s.c., 38. G.S.O.3, G.H.Q., B.E.F., 39. Bde. Major, 152 Bde., 40. A.Q.M.G. & D.A. & Q.M.G., H.Q. A.F.N.E.I., 45–46. Comdg. 1st Bn. Q. O. Cameron Highlanders, 47. Lt.-Col. Comdg. 1st Bn. Gordon Highlanders, 48–50. Comdg. Lorried Infantry Brigade, B.A.O.R., 51–52. Imperial Defence College, 53. B.G.S., Western Command, 54. Major-General & Chief of Staff, H.Q. Scottish Command, 54–57. J.P. (Devon), 62. Chrmn., Totnes Petty Sessional Div. since 72. D.L. (Devon), 62. Chrmn., Totnes R.D.C., 71–72. C.B., D.S.O., O.B.E. Founded The Sandhurst Beagles.

CAMPBELL-BLAIR, Niall. St, 45^1-48^3.*

CARD, Frederick William Farmer, M.C. C, 05^1-05^2.*

CARDWELL, John, b. 11 Apr. 30, s. of H. Cardwell. M, 43^3-48^2. M.Inst.M. Reed International.

CAREY, Charles John, b. 11 Nov. 33, 2nd s. of R. M. Carey (A). SF, 46^3-51^2; Leaving Exhibitioner. Scholar of Balliol, Oxford. Joined H.M. Treasury, 57. Now an Asst. Secretary in the Treasury. Brother, W. G. Carey.

CAREY, William Geoffrey, b. 23 Sept. 26, eldest s. of R. M. Carey (A). T, 40^1-44^2; Minor Scholarship in Classics to Gonville & Caius, Cambridge, B.A. N/S. Intelligence Corps, 45–47. 2nd Lt. Foreign Office, Research Dept., 55–58. Asst. Prof. in Russian, University of Alberta, 62–66. Lecturer in Russian, Ealing Technical College since 68. Brother, C. J. Carey.

CARNEGIE, David Michael, b. 3 Oct. 17, eldest s. of late Sir F. Carnegie, C.B.E. B, 31^3-36^2. Guy's Hospital Medical School, M.B., B.S. (Lond.); F.F.A.R.C.S.; D.A.; L.M.S.S.A. ✕ R.A.M.C. Capt., 43–47. Consultant Anaesthetist, Guy's Hospital, Chelsea Hospital for Women & Evelina Hospital. Fellow, Royal Society of Medicine. Fellow, Assoc. of Anaesthetists of Great Britain & Ireland. *Royal Lymington Yacht Club.* Brother, R. M. Carnegie. Son, 2140.

CARNEGIE, Brigadier Robin MacDonald, O.B.E., b. 22 June 26, youngest s. of late Major-General Sir F. Carnegie, C.B.E. B, 40^3-44^2; Cadet Officer. Commissioned to 7th Queen's Own Hussars, 46. Commanded The Queen's Own Hussars, 67–69. Commanded 11th Armoured Brigade, 71–72. M.B.E., 59. O.B.E., 68. Dispatches, 67–68. *Cavalry Club.* Brother, D. M. Carnegie. Son, Rupert Alexander, B, 72^3-.

CARNELLEY, Stephen Henry, b. 23 Sept. 80, elder s. of late Prof. T. Carnelley, D.Sc. SH, 95^1-97^2; R. VIII, 97. Exeter, Oxford. Double Blue for Athletics. Member of Olympic Team, Athens, 06. Solicitor. Practised as Ad. & Solicitor in Malaya (Producer & Editor of "Onlooker of Malaya"). Travelled in China, joined Colonial Service, posted to Gold Coast (Ghana) as D.C. for 4 years. Transferred to Kenya as D.C. and then seconded to Army, 14. Returned to Colonial Service, 19, and retired in 32 as Senior Resident Magistrate, Kenya. Royal Geographical Society. *Royal Aero Club; Muthaiga Country Club, Kenya.*

CARNES, The Rev. Gerald Lambton, b. 23 Sept. 12, 4th s. of late C. S. Carnes. W, 26^3-30^2. Disc jockey, Radio Luxembourg, 31. Radio Lyons, 34. ✕ K.O.S.B., 40–46. Lt.-Col. Dispatches. Member of

U.N.E.S.C.O. Liaison Mission to the U.N., 46–58. Theological College of the Episcopal Church in Haiti, W. Indies, 58–61. Ordained Priest in the Episcopal Church of the U.S.A., 61. Vicar-General of the Episcopal Church in Haiti, 64–68. Vicar of Hampton Wick, Middlesex, since 69.

CARR, Andrew Quintin, M.B.E., b. 8 Oct. 05, 3rd s. of Rev. E. S. Carr. M, 19^2–23^2. Chartered Accountancy in the City of London. Missionary in India, 29–40. ✕ Lt.-Col. in 9th Gurkha Rifles, I.A., 40–46. Lt.-Col. M.B.E. Dep. Gen. Sec. of The Scripture Union, 47–70 Now retired. Sons, 845 & 1219.

CARR, Charles Raymond, b. 18 June 31, s. of Prof. C. T. Carr. St, 44^3–49^2. Travel Exhibition. Exhibitioner of St. John's, Cambridge, M.A. Joined Shell in 52. Worked in Uganda, Kenya, Tanganyika, Sudan, Malaya, Ghana & Curaçao. At present, Sales Manager, Shell & B.P. Tanzania Ltd. *R. & A.G.C.*

CARR, Ian Cufaude, b. 12 Aug. 28, s. of late L. Carr. M, 43^3–47^2; Rackets, 2nd Pair, 46–47. N/S., 47–49. Commissioned R.A., served in Hong Kong, 48–49. T.A. 251st (W. & C. Yeo.) Fd. Regt., R.A. Major. Bty. Cdr. Chrmn., Penrith & Border Conservative Assoc. since 70. Dir. Carr & Co. Ltd., Biscuit Manufacturers, 50–62. Carr's Milling Industries Ltd., Stanwix, Carlisle, since 62, Chrmn. & Dir. since 64. *R. & A.; United Services Club, London.*

CARR, John Griffith, b. 11 Dec. 08, s. of J. W. Carr, C.B.E., M.D. W, 22^2–26^3. Wadham, Oxford, M.A. ✕ R.E., 41–46. Capt. Retired Shipowner. Lloyd's Underwriter. *Railway Club.* Haberdashers Company.

CARR, Rupert Ellis, b. 16 Feb. 10, eldest s. of late P. Carr. C, 23^3–28^1; Cap. Harvard University. Business School, Boston, Mass., U.S.A. Past Chrmn., Associated Biscuit Mfrs. Ltd. Retired. *Royal Thames Yacht Club.*

CARRITT, Hugh David Graham, b. 15 Apr. 27, s. of R. G. Carritt (OR M o6). M, 40^3–45^2; Exhibitioner. Scholar of Christ Church, Oxford, B.A. Formerly a Dir. of Christies, Auctioneers. Art Dealer. Dir. of several Cos. Liveryman of Grocers Company. *Travellers' Club.*

CARRITT, Hugh Denis, b. 28 Apr. 18 eldest s. of late H. B. Carritt (OR M, 99).

M, 31^3–36^1. Peterhouse, Cambridge, B.A. ✕ R.A., 39–46. Capt. Man. Dir., Gow Wilson Ltd., Produce Brokers. *Royal Thames Yacht Club.* Liveryman of Grocers Company. Brother, R. L. B. Carritt.

CARRITT, Reginald Graham, b. 25 Aug. 92, 4th s. of late T. Carritt. M, 06^1–11^2; XV, 10; R. VIII, 10–11; Athletics Cup, 11. ✕ Inns of Court. O.T.C. 1st Bn. London Regt. (T.F.). 17th O.C. Bn. Capt. (retired). New College, Oxford, M.A. Royal College of Music, A.R.C.M. Lecturer in History & Theory of Music at City Lit. & University of London. Asst. Music Master at Westminster School. Examiner for the Assoc. Board of the Royal Schools of Music since 44. Lectured on music in New Zealand, Denmark, Norway, Singapore, India, Ceylon & Malta. Liveryman of Grocers Company. Son, H. D. G. Carritt. Nephews, H. D. & R. L. B. Carritt.

CARRITT, Rodney Lorraine Blasson, b. 26 Mar. 27, 2nd s. of late H. B. Carritt. (OR M 99). M, 40^3–45^2. ✕ R.N., 45–48. Dir. of Thos. Nelson (Insurance) Ltd., Insurance Brokers. *Royal Yacht Squadron.* Liveryman of Grocers Company. Brother, H. D. Carritt.

CARSLAKE, John, b. 27 Aug. 07, s. of late H. B. Carslake (OR St 89). Tu, 21^2–25^2; S. VIII, 24–25 (Capt.); Cadet Officer. University College, Oxford, B.A. S. VIII, 27–28. Solicitor, 31. Partner with Ryland, Martineau & Co., Birmingham, 31. ✕ R.A. Major. Wounded. *Union Club, Birmingham.* Sons, 1169, 1997 & Richard Charles, Tu, 69^2–.

CARSON, Alan Macleod, M.B.E., b. 18 Sept. 17, 2nd s. of J. F. Carson, O.B.E., V.D. C, 30^3–36^2; Scholar; XV, 34; Head of School; Cadet Officer; Major & Minor Exhibitions. Demy of Magdalen, Oxford, M.A. ✕ 12th Royal Lancers. Major. Royal Wiltshire Yeomanry, 51–63. M.B.E. With Imperial Tobacco Group since 47. *Cavalry Club.*

CARTER, Prof. Charles Frederick, b. 15 Aug. 19, 3rd s. of late F. W. Carter, Sc.D., F.R.S. T, 33^3–38^2; Minor Entrance Scholarship. Maths Exhibition, St. John's Cambridge, M.A. Bayliss Scholar (St. John's), 38. Fellow of the British Academy. Sec. Gen., Royal Economic Soc. Hon. Fellow, Emmanuel College, Cambridge. Hon. Fellow, Royal Irish Academy. Hon. D.Econ.Sc. National University of Ireland. Lecturer in Statistics,

Cambridge, 45–51. Prof. of Applied Economics, Belfast, 52–59. Prof. of Political Economy, Manchester, 59–63. Vice-Chancellor, University of Lancaster since 63. *Athenæum*. Brothers, G. W. & J. R. Carter.

CARTER, Prof. Geoffrey William, b. 21 May 09, eldest s. of late F. W. Carter, Sc.D., F.R.S. T, 23^1–28^2; Major Foundationer. Levée; Head of House; Major & Minor Leaving Exhibitions. Scholar of St. John's, Cambridge, M.A. Mayhew Prize. Rex Moir Prize (Bracketed). Fellow of the Institution of Electrical Engineers. Fellow of the Institute of Electrical and Electronic Engineers. British Thomson-Houston Co. Ltd., Rugby, 32–45. University Demonstrator, Oxford, 46. Prof. of Electrical Engineering & Head of Dept., University of Leeds, since 46. Brothers, J. R. & C. F. Carter.

CARTER, Hugh Gordon, b. 27 Aug. 09, elder s. of the late J. G. Carter, O.B.E. (OR W 88). W, 23^2–26^3. ✕ Union Defence Forces, 40–46, in Madagascar & Middle East. Capt. Chartered Accountant (S.A.). Joined Union Corporation. Now retired.

CARTER, James Roger, b. 11 Oct. 11, 2nd s. of late F. W. Carter, Sc.D., F.R.S. T, 25^1–30^2; Levée; Head of House. St. John's, Cambridge, M.A. Various posts in Adult Education, 33–44. Official in U.N.R.R.A., 44–47. Official in Home Civil Service, 47–60; established Civil Servant, 49; including Ministry of Education, 47–49, 52–60, and 1st Sec., British Embassy, Washington, 49–52. Education Service, Government of Kenya, 60–67. Educational Planning Adviser to Government of Tanzania, under the Ford Foundation, 67–71. University Planning Officer, University of Dar es Salaam, Tanzania, under the Ford Foundation since 71. Sec. of Kenya Education Commission, 63–65. Brothers, G. W. & C. F. Carter.

CARTER, John Gordon Howard. W, 18^3–22^1.*

CARTER, Peter George. M, 26^3–31^2.*

CARTER, Stanley Cyril, M.C. Tu, 04^1–06^1.*

CARTWRIGHT, James Arthur D'Arcy, T.D., b. 1 Oct. 07, s. of J. S. Cartwright. B, 21^3–25^3. Christ Church, Oxford. Half Blue Fencing (Epée). Bar, Gray's Inn. Regent Polytechnic (Diploma Technology). Film Director. University Lecturer

and Training Consultant. Dir. of Grafton Consultants Ltd. Shell Film Unit (Dir.-Producer). ✕ General Staff Officer. Directorate of Military Training (War Office). Dir. of Studies, Training Div., Shell International Petroleum Ltd. Author (Books about Educational Technology). National Institute of Industrial Psychology. Institute of Scientific & Technical Communicators Ltd. T.D. Freiherr Edle Von Fallut-Gemeiner.

CARTWRIGHT, Percy Blake, b. 28 Oct. 06, 3rd s. of late F. S. Cartwright (OR St 87). St, 20^3–24^2. In Advertising with Kodak Ltd. till 39. ✕ R.A., 40–43. Lt. Invalided. Acting till 60.

CARTWRIGHT, Reginald William Broadbent. Tu, 06^3–08^2.*

CARTWRIGHT, Thomas James Nelson, b. 3 Nov. 31, s. of T. N. Cartwright (OR Tu 19). Tu, 45^3–49^3; Head of House; Levée; XV, 47–49; XI, 49; H, XI, 48. Queens', Cambridge, M.A. Nottingham School of Architecture. F.R.I.B.A. Employment with Architectural Practices in London & New York, 59–63. Partner in Cartwright, Woollatt & Ptnrs., Chartered Architects, Nottingham, since 63. Royal Naval Sailing Assn. *United Services Club, Nottingham.*

CARTWRIGHT, Thomas Nelson, D.S.C., J.P. Tu, 19^1–23^2.* Son, T. J. N. Cartwright.

CARTWRIGHT, William Frederick, T.D., D.L., J.P., b. 13 Nov. 06, 3rd s. of Rev. W. D. Cartwright. Tu, 20^3–24^3; XV, 24. Pupil G.W.R. Mech. Eng., M.I.Mech.E., LL.D., University of Wales. Companion of Inst. Elec. Eng. D.L., Glamorgan. Deputy Chrmn., British Steel Corp. Chrmn. & Man. Dir., Steel Co. of Wales. *Royal Ocean Racing Club, Royal Yacht Squadron.* Sons, 1030 & 1362.

CARUS, Louis Revell (formerly Carus-Wilson, L.R.), b. 22 Oct. 27, eldest s. of late Col. M. McD. Carus-Wilson. K, 41^3–46^2; Music Scholar; Head of School Music; Tom Hughes Prize; R. VIII. Brussels Conservatoire. Peabody Conservatory, Baltimore, U.S.A. L.R.A.M. (Violin Performer). Warden, Solo Performers Committee of the Incorporated Society of Musicians, 73–74. Former member of Scottish National Orchestra. Head of Dept. (Strings), Royal Scottish Academy of Music. Member of Scottish Trio, Scottish Piano Quartet & Clarina Ensemble. Incorporated Society of Musicians. Brother, A. Carus-Wilson.

CARUS-WILSON, Alan, b. 22 June 29, 2nd s. of late Col. M. McD. Carus-Wilson. SH, 43³–45¹; Music Scholar. N/S. R.A.O.C., 47–48. L/Cpl. Associated Board Scholar, Royal College of Music. Cellist. B.B.C. Midland Light Orchestra. Brother, L. R. Carus.

CARUS-WILSON, Charles Denny, b. 2 Sept. 86, eldest s. of late Rev. F. N. Carus-Wilson, M.A. C, 00²–04²; S. VIII, 03–04. Architect, A.R.I.B.A. Gazetted to the Middlesex Yeomanry, 12. ✕ 1st London Yeomanry. Capt. Wounded. M.C. Lecturer in Architecture at Sheffield University. Designed City of Sheffield's War Memorial. Brother, E. Carus-Wilson.

CARUS-WILSON, Eric, M.C., b. 2 Sept. 90, 3rd s. of late Rev. F. N. Carus-Wilson, M.A. C, 04³–08². Trinity, Cambridge, B.A. McGill University, Montreal, B.Sc. A.M.I.C.E. ✕ Active Service in Belgium & France, 15–18. Royal Engineers, Signals Service. M.C. Dispatches twice. Capt. With the English Electric Co., London, 19–21. Man. Dir. of nine bacon factories in Denmark, 27–34. British Vice-Consul, Aalborg, Denmark, 27–34. Farming in Gloucestershire since 34. Retired, 46. Brother, C. D. Carus-Wilson.

CARUS-WILSON, Louis Revell (see Carus, L. R.).

CARVER, Francis Kenelm MacKenzie, b. 9 June 07, 4th s. of late F. Carver. K, 21²–25³. Scholar of Hertford, Oxford, B.A. Cameraman & Dir. of Photography, Elstree, Denham & Pinewood, 29–39. ✕ 39–45. T.A./R.A. Army Film Unit, S.O.E. Rank Orgn., Pinewood, 45–51. Foreign Office, 51–67. Retired. Making photographic records for the local National Trust, Wiltshire Archaeological Society, etc., as a voluntary retirement project. Cross of St. Olav (Norway). Brothers, M. F. & H. S. M. Carver.

CARVER, Humphrey Stephen Mumford, b. 29 Nov. 02, 3rd s. of late F. Carver. K, 17¹–21²; XXII, 19–21. Corpus Christi, Oxford, Dip. in Economics & Political Science. The Architectural Association School, London, A.R.I.B.A. Fellow & past Pres. of the Town Planning Institute of Canada. Hon. Member, Canadian Society of Landscape Architects. Moved to Canada, 30. Career in Housing & Town Planning, 48–67, with Federal Government Housing Agency. Chrmn. of Advisory Group (Policy & Research). Author of "Cities in the Suburbs" and many other writings. Retired, 67. Subsequently Consultant in urban affairs, etc. Life Member, *Arts & Letters Club, Toronto.* Brothers, M. F. & F. K. M. Carver.

CARVER, Maurice Fraser, b. 30 Mar. 99, 2nd s. of late F. Carver. K, 13¹–17²; Head of House. ✕ 16th Bn., K.R.R.C. 2nd Lt. Wounded. Exhibitioner of Corpus Christi, Oxford, M.A. 2nd Master and late Headmaster of Ruzawi School, Rhodesia. ✕ W. Rhodesian Forces, E. Africa Pioneer Corps & Force 133 in Greece. Capt. Bursar, Malosa Secondary School, Malawi. Brothers, H. S. M. & F. K. M. Carver.

CARVER, Sydney Drinkwater, b. 7 Oct. 08, eldest s. of late S. R. P. Carver. C, 22³–26². Christ Church, Oxford. Pres. of College Boat Club. Half Blue Skiing. Cotton & Cottonseed in Egypt, 30–56. ✕ 40–45. Royal Artillery. Light A.A. Lt. P.O.W. (Tobruk), 42–45. Cotton, Cottonseed & Coffee in Peru, 57–61. Schoolmaster since 62.

CASSELS, Ambrose Kennedy, b. 3 May 06, 2nd s. of late J. K. Cassels (OR K 79). K, 20²–23². Estancia Los Ceibos, Charlone, F.N.G.S.M., Argentina. Sons, 31, 347, 773 & 1527.

CASSELS, Field-Marshal Sir Archibald James Halkett, G.C.B., K.B.E., D.S.O., b. 28 Feb. 07, s. of late Gen. Sir R. Cassels, G.C.B., G.C.S.I., D.S.O. Tu, 20³–24³; XI, 21–24; XV, 22–24; Fives Pair, 23–24. R.M.C., Sandhurst. Cadet Scholar. XV, 25; XI, 25–26; Rackets Pair, 25–26; Army Scholarship, 26. Gazetted to the Seaforth Highlanders, 26. A.D.C. to C. in C., India, 39. ✕ Depot, Seaforth Highlanders, 39. In France with 157 (H.L.I.) Bde., 40. Various Staff Appointments in U.K., 40–43. Chief of Staff, 12 Corps, 44. G.O.C., 51st Highland Div., N.W. Europe, 45. Major-General. G.O.C., 6 Airborne Div., Palestine, 46. Imperial Defence College, 47. Dir., Land/Air Warfare, War Office, 50–51. Head of Liaison Staff, Australia. G.O.C., 1st Commonwealth Div., Korea, 51–52. Gen. Comdg., 1 Corps, 52. K.B.E., 53. Lt.-Gen., 54. Dir.-Gen. of Military Training, W.O., 54–57. Dir. of Emergency Operations, Fed. of Malaya, 57–59. G.O.C., Eastern Command, 59. C.-in-C., British Army of the Rhine & Comdr., N.A.T.O. Northern Army Group, 60–63. Adjt.-Gen. to the Forces, 63–64. C.I.G.S., 65–68. Field-Marshal, 68. A.D.C. Gen. to The Queen, 60–63. Col., Seaforth Highlanders, 61–66. Pres., Co. of

Veteran Motorists since 70. *United Services, Royal Aero Clubs.*

CASSELS, John Hugh Houston. K, 98³-01¹.*

CASSELS, Kenneth Alexander Home, b. 24 Aug. 19, s. of late Lt.-Col. K. S. Cassels (OR B 82). B, 32³-37². Magdalene, Cambridge, M.A. Member of the Royal Institution of Chartered Surveyors. ✕ Pioneer Corps. Lt. Land Agent, Forestry Commission (Scotland). Wildfowl Trust. Pheasant Trust.

CASSIDI, Francis Paul, b. 12 June 25, s. of late F. L. Cassidi (OR SH 04). SH, 39¹-43². St. Thomas's Hospital Medical School, M.B., B.S. House Surgeon, St Thomas's Hospital, 48-50. N/S. Capt. R.A.M.C., 50-52. General Practitioner, Canterbury, since 52. M.O., H.M. Prison, Canterbury. M.O., St. Edmund's School, Canterbury. T.D. *East India, Sports & Public Schools Club.*

CATON, Robert Dennis, b. 13 Oct. 10, s. of late J. W. Caton, M.D. W, 24³-29². Pembroke, Cambridge, M.A., M.B., B.Chir. King's College Hospital,D.M.R.E. ✕ E.M.S., 39-46. Consultant Radiologist, University Hospitals, Southampton.

CATTERALL, John. B, 44³-49².*

CATTERALL, Robert Adam, M.B., B.Chir., b. 7 Oct. 29, eldest s. of J. Catterall. B, 43³-48²; Sw. VIII, 46-48. Peterhouse, Cambridge, M.A. Half Blue for Athletics, 51. St. Mary's Hospital, M.B., B.Chir. Pilot in Cambridge University Air Squadron. Judo Black Belt. Double Purple, London University. Medical Practitioner in Kuala Lumpur. *Achilles; Royal Selangor Golf Club, Kuala Lumpur.* Son, Stephen Adam, B, 72³-.

CATTERALL, Robert Christopher Fielden, b. 5 Apr. 10, s. of late Rev. R. Catterall, M.A. C, 23³-28². Trinity, Cambridge, M.B., M.Chir. University College Hospital, F.R.C.S. ✕ R.A.M.C. Lt.-Col. Senior Consultant Orthopaedic Surgeon, King's College Hospital, London, from 51. Vice-Dean of the Medical School, 60. Vice-Pres., British Orthopaedic Assoc. for 73. (Hon. Treas., 66-71.) Fellow (Past Pres. of Orthopaedic Section), Royal Society of Medicine. Chrmn., Orthopaedic Advisory Committee, S.E. Met. Regional Hospital Board.

CATTLEY, Major Gilbert Acheson, b. 24 Dec. 92, 2nd s. of late J. E. Cattley. B, 07¹-11². Trinity, Oxford. ✕ 14/18 War. Special Reserve Commission. 4th Dragoon Guards. Lt. 6th Dragoon Guards, 20. Capt., 28. Major.

CAVE, Adam Gotch Darlington. M, 46³-51¹.*

CAVE, Alan Darlington, b. 19 Dec. 04, younger s. of late H. W. Cave (OR SH 76). SH, 18³-23²; XI, 22-23; H. XI, 23. Trinity, Oxford. ✕ R.A., T.A. 35-45. Major. Stockbroker & Schoolmaster, retired. Capt., *Oxford University Golf Club,* 26. Capt., *R. & A.G.C.,* 71-72. Brother, J. D. Cave. Son, A. G. D. Cave.

CAVE, John Darlington, b. 1 Feb. 98, elder s. of late H. W. Cave (OR SH 76). SH, 12²-17²; XI, 16-17; Rackets Pair, 17; Fives Pair, 16-17. ✕ French Red Cross, Driver. Balliol, Oxford, M.A. Asst. Master, Clifton College, 21-63. Retired. *Vincent's Club, Oxford; R. & A.G.C.; Oxford & Cambridge Golfing Society.* Brother, A. D. Cave.

CHADWICK, Arthur John Mackenzie, b. 4 Oct. 15, eldest s. of R. M. Chadwick (OR C 99). C, 29³-34²; XI, 34. Trinity, Oxford, M.A. ✕ R.A.F., 39-45. Sqn. Ldr. Pres., Trinity International Co. Ltd. *Vincent's, Oxford. R.A.F.*

CHADWICK, Sir John Edward, K.C.M.G., b. 17 Dec. 11, eldest s. of J. Chadwick. W, 25³-30²; Scholar; Levée; S. VIII. Scholar of Corpus Christi, Cambridge, M.A. Dept. of Overseas Trade, 34. In Nov. 38 went to Calcutta as Asst. to the Senior Trade Commissioner in India, Burma & Ceylon. Eastern Group Supply Council, Simla, 41. 1st Secretary (Commercial) at Washington, 46-48. Tel Aviv, 50-53. Counsellor (Commercial), Tokyo, 53-56. Minister (Economic), Buenos Aires, 60-62. (Commercial), Washington, 63-67. Ambassador to Rumania, 67-68. U.K. Delegate to the Organisation for Economic Cooperation & Development (O.E.C.D.) at Paris, 69-71. Retired on pension. Now Special Adviser to the President of the Asian Development Bank, the H.Q. of which is at Manila. C.M.G., 57. K.C.M.G., 67. *Travellers' Club, London; The Travellers', Paris; The Brook, New York.*

CHADWICK, Leonard Arthur, M.C. B, 07³-11¹.*

CHALK, Laurence, D.Phil., F.L.S., b. 7 Apr. 96, younger s. of late A. Chalk. K, 10^1–14^2. University College, Oxford, M.A., D.Phil., F.L.S. ✕ 2nd P.S. Bn. Royal Fusiliers, 3rd Bn. Royal Berkshire Regt. Lt. Wounded. Forest Officer, Uganda, 21–23. Oxford Dept. of Forestry, Empire Forestry Institute & Commonwealth Forestry Institute. At first as University Demonstrator and later as University Reader, 24–63. Retired. Fellow of Linneau Society, London.

CHALK, Peter John, b. 20 Jan. 25, s. of Dr. L. Chalk. K, 38^3–40^1. University College, Oxford, M.A. Solicitor & Notary Public. Partner in Messrs. Michelmores of Exeter. ✕ Royal Navy, 42–46. Son, Christopher Martin, K, 71^3–.

CHALLEN, Henry Denis, b. 21 Feb. 11, 2nd s. of W. B. Challen. Tu, 24^3–28^3; Scholar. Trinity, Cambridge, B.A., F.I.Mech.E. Now retired. Brother, J. B. Challen. Son, 1538.

CHALLEN, John Bernard, O.B.E., b. 3 Aug. 06, elder s. of W. B. Challen. Tu, 20^2–24^2. Trinity, Cambridge, B.A. ✕ Royal Signals, 39–45. Lt.-Col. O.B.E., T.D. Grazier, Poll Hereford Stud Breeder. *Lansdowne Club, London; Union Club, Sydney.* Brother, H. D. Challen.

CHALLIS, Gerald George. T, 32^2–35^3.＊

CHAMBERLAIN, Paul. St, 28^1–32^1.＊

CHAMBERS, William Stuart, b. 8 Feb. 13, s. of late S. W. Chambers. B, 26^3–30^3; Cadet Officer. ✕ East Yorks. Regt. Capt. Dispatches. Company Director. Retired.

CHAMPNESS, Major Philip Harvey, b. 30 Aug. 19, 3rd s. of C. M. Champness. K, 33^3–38^2; Leaving Exhibition. Exhibitioner of King's, Cambridge, M.A. ✕ D.C.L.I., 40. Attd. 6th Rajputana Rifles, I.A., 41–45. Major. A.C.A., 50. Chartered Accountant in Public Practice, City of London. *Guildhall Club.* Member of Court of Commons Council, Corporation of London since 66.

CHANDLER, Geoffrey Pretor, M.D., M.R.C.P., b. 30 Sept. 02, s. of P. W. Chandler. SH, 16–20^2. Trinity, Cambridge, M.A., M.D. St. Thomas's Hospital, M.R.C.P. Physician, King Edward VII Hospital, Windsor. Physician, Broadmoor Institution. ✕ R.A.M.C., 44–46. Major. Medical Practitioner, retired. Fellow, Medical Society of London.

CHAPLIN, Stephen, b. 30 Mar. 07, s. of late Rev. A. Chaplin, M.A. St, 20^3–24^1. Faraday House Electrical Engineering College, London. Fellow of the Institution of Electrical Engineers. Enfield Cables Ltd., 29–72. Leading through mergers and takeovers to The Delta Metal Co. Ltd., making 43 years with what is essentially the same Company. Retired Apr. 72, now working as a Consultant. Pres. of the Electrical Industries Club, London, 72–73. *Athenæum.* F.R.G.S., F.R.S.A.

CHARLES, Sir Noel Hughes Havelock, Bt., K.C.M.G., M.C., b. 20 Nov. 91, younger s. of late Sir R. H. Charles, 1st Bt., G.C.V.O., K.C.S.I. K, 05^3–08^2; XI, 08. Christ Church, Oxford, M.A. ✕ 14–18. France, 15–18. M.C. Dispatches twice. Entered Diplomatic Service, 19. 1st Secretary, British Embassy, Tokyo, 26. Foreign Office, 29. Stockholm, 31. Moscow, 33. Counsellor, Brussels, 36–37. Rome, 37–39. Minister there, 39–40. Minister at Lisbon, 40–41. Ambassador to Brazil, 41–44. High Commissioner in Italy with rank of Ambassador, 44–47. Ambassador to Turkey, 49–51. Retired, 51. K. St. J., 3rd Cl. Rising Sun. K.C.M.G., 41. 3rd Baronet, succeeded Brother, 36. *White's, R.A.C.*

CHARLESWORTH, Arthur Heywood. St & K, 39^2–43^3.＊

CHARLESWORTH, George Stansfeld, b. 20 Aug. 00, s. of C. P. Charlesworth. B, 14^3–18^3; XV, 18. Pembroke, Cambridge, M.A. Solicitor, 26. ✕ R.A.F. (A.T.S.D.—Intelligence), 39–45. Asst. Registrar, County Courts, 47. Registrar, County Courts and District Registrar, High Court of Justice, Huddersfield Group of 5 Courts, Feb. 49. Retired Aug. 70.

CHARLTON, Foster Ferrier Harvey, D.F.C., b. 26 Mar. 23, 2nd s. of F. F. Charlton. St, 36^3–41^2; Levée; Head of House; Cap; Evers Exhibition. Wadham, Oxford, M.A. ✕ R.A.F.V.R., 42–45. F/Lt. D.F.C. Solicitor, 50. Partner in Linklaters & Paines since 53. Alpine Garden Society.

CHARLTON, Col. Frederick Noel, C.B., C.B.E., b. 4 Dec. 06, 2nd s. of late F. W. Charlton (OR Tu 94). Tu, 21^1–25^2. Hertford, Oxford, M.A. Solicitor, 32. Private Practice, 32–39. ✕ Army. General List. Deputy Director, Claims Commission, 44. Colonel, C.B.E. U.S. Bronze Star. Principal Asst. Solicitor, Treasury Solicitor, 46–71. (Head of Litigation Dept.)

Lord Chancellor's Dept., Secretary of Defamation Committee since 71. C.B. (Civil). Hon. Alderman, London Borough of Croydon. *Junior Carlton Club*. Brother, T. A. G. Charlton.

CHARLTON, Maurice Henry, b. 3 May 26, s. of H. J. Charlton. T, 39^3-44^2; Benn Scholarship; Jex-Blake Exhibition. New College, Oxford, M.A. Craven & Ireland Scholar. Gaisford Prizeman, Prose & Verse. O.U. Medical School & Columbia University College of Physicians & Surgeons. M.D. Fellow & Tutor, Hertford, Oxford, and Tutor, Lincoln, Oxford, 50–52. N/S, 44–46. R.N.V.R. S/Lt. Asst. Prof. of Neurology, Columbia Univ., 68–72. Assoc. Prof. of Neurology & Pediatrics, University of Rochester since 72. Fellow, American Academy of Neurology. New York Academy of Medicine. Many Medical Publications.

CHARLTON, Thomas Alfred Graham, C.B., b. 29 Aug. 13, 3rd s. of late F. W. Charlton (OR Tu 94). Tu, 27^1-31^3; Levée. Exhibitioner of Corpus Christi, Cambridge, B.A. Qualified for Home Civil Service (Administrative Grades), 36. Asst. Private Secretary to Secretary of State for War, 37–39. Principal, 39. Employed in Ministry of Defence apart from 2 years secondment to Cabinet Office, 47–49, and 2 years secondment to N.A.T.O., 50–52. Currently Asst. Under Secretary of State, Ministry of Defence. C.B., 70. *Anglo-Belgium Club, Beaconsfield Golf Club*. Brother, F. N. Charlton.

CHAUNDY, Maurice, b. 1 Mar. 20, s. of L. F. Chaundy. St, 34^1-38^2. English Speaking Union Exchange Scholarship to The Choate School, Wallingford, Connecticut, 38–39. ✕ R. Pioneer Corps, 40–47. Major. Staff Officer (grade II) to the High Commission Territories at the British Military Mission, Pretoria, 46–47. Systems Analyst, Shell. Emigrated to S. Africa, 47. *E.S.U., Western Province Cricket Club*. African Wildfowl Enquiry.

CHAWORTH-MUSTERS, Major Anthony, b. 3 Apr. 92, 3rd s. of late J. P. Chaworth-Musters. K, 06^2-10^2; S. VIII, 09; Winner of Ashburton Shield. R.M.A., Woolwich. Gazetted to R.F.A., II. ✕ 71st Battery, R.F.A. Capt. Wounded. Instructor, R.M.A. Retired, 21.

CHEAPE, David Ogilvy, b. 9 Nov. 06, younger s. of late J. Cheape. Tu, 20^2-23^3. Landowner & Rice Planter. Retired. *Royal Yacht Club, Jersey; Malta Union Club*.

CHENEY, Robert Gardner, b. 4 Dec. 32, s. of W. G. Cheney. SF, 46^3-50^2; Scholar. Diploma in Printing at London College of Printing, 53. At Cheney & Sons Ltd., Printers, Banbury, 55–72. (Dir., 58, Company Sec., 61.)

CHESSHYRE, Col. Hubert Layard, b. 29 May 06, elder s. of late Major General H. Isacke, C.B., C.S.I., C.M.G., SH, 20^1-24^2; S. VIII, 24. R.M.A., Woolwich. Cadet Scholar. Gazetted to R.E., 26. Lt., 29. Trinity, Cambridge, M.A. p.s.c. Retired as Colonel, 54. Dispatches, 44. Re-employed as Technical Author, 59–71. *Army & Navy Club*. Brother, N. H. L. Chesshyre.

CHESSHYRE, Brigadier Neville Henry Layard, C.B.E., b. 5 Mar. 10, younger s. of late Major-General H. Isacke, C.B., C.S.I., C.M.G. SH, 23^3-28^2; Levée; Head of House. R.M.A., Woolwich. Cadet Scholar. Gazetted to R.E. Christ's, Cambridge, M.A. School of Military Engineering, Chatham. p.s.c. Staff College, Quetta, 43. N.A.T.O. Defence College, Paris, 54. Interpreter in French, 54. Retired from Army as Brigadier in 62. C.B.E., 63. Principal (Admin. Class) in Civil Service, Ministry of Transport & Overseas Development. Retired, 70, owing to ill health. *Army & Navy Club*. Institute of Royal Engineers. Brother, H. L. Chesshyre. Son, 1237.

CHESTERTON, Sir Oliver Sidney, M.C., b. 28 Jan. 13, s. of late F. S. Chesterton. SH, 26^3-30^3; Cap. S. VIII. Architect & Chartered Surveyor. A.R.I.C.S., 35. Registered Architect, 38. ✕ Irish Guards, N. Africa. Wounded thrice, M.C. Major. Fellow and Past President, Royal Institution of Chartered Surveyors. Knight Bachelor. Vice-Chrmn., Woolwich Equitable Building Society. Crown Commissioner. Governor, Rugby School. Various Directorships. President of Commonwealth Assoc. for Surveying & Land Economy. *White's Club, Senior Golfing Society*. Son, 1814.

CHILD, Geoffrey Edmund, b. 4 Sept. 14, s. of E. H. Child. Tu, 28^2-32^2. Berlin University. ✕ Intelligence Corps, 39–46. Capt. B.B.C. Austrian Service from 48.

CHITTICK, Hubert Neville, b. 18 Sept. 23, s. of late H. S. Chittick (OR St 99). Sh, 37^3-42^2. Peterhouse, Cambridge, M.A. Diploma in Archaeology. ✕ Intelligence Corps, 44–48. Lt. Bar, Lincoln's Inn, 50. Curator, Sudan Museums, 52–55. Conservator of Antiquities, Tanganyika, 57–61. Dir., British Institute in Eastern Africa from 61. Fellow, Society of Antiquaries. Royal Anthropological Institute. Royal Geographical Society.

CHRISTIE, John Arthur Kingsley, b. 8 Feb. 15, eldest s. of late H. D. Christie (or Tu 84). Tu, 28^3–32^2; Scholar; Minor Exhibitioner. Exhibitioner of Magdalen, Oxford, B.A. Principal, Ministry of Agriculture & Fisheries. ✕ R.N.V.R., 42–45. Uncle, L. R. Christie.

CHRISTIE, Major Lionel Ronald, O.B.E., b. 15 Aug. 87, 4th s. of late J. A. Christie. Tu, 01^3–03^3. With Great Central Railway Co. from 08. ✕ Railway Transport Officer. D.A.D.G. of Transport. Major. O.B.E. Dispatches thrice. G.S.O. 2. British Armistice Commission, 18–19. Gen. Man., Dean & Dawson Ltd., 23–39, subsequent to being Asst. Man., 20–23. ✕ Port Master, Grimsby & Immingham Docks, and in charge of Humber Ferries, 39–47. Dir., Polytechnic Touring Assoc., 48–62. *Reform Club.* Nephew, J. A. K. Christie.

CHRISTY, Hector Gerald, T.D., b. 29 Dec. 09, s. of G. Christy. Tu, 23^3–27^3. With Christy & Co. Ltd., London & Stockport. H.A.C. (Inf. Bn.) T.A., 32–39. Commissioned, Essex Regt. (T.A.), 39. Capt. ✕ Essex Regt. & Staff, 39–45. Major retired, T.D. H.A.C. *Royal Commonwealth Society.*

CHUBB, John Oliver, b. 21 Apr. 20, s. of C. Chubb. Tu, 33^3–38^2; Levée; R. VIII, 37. Scholar of Pembroke, Oxford, M.A. ✕ Scots Guards, 40–46, Capt. H.M. Diplomatic Service from 46. *R.A.C., Berkshire Golf Club.* Son, William John Jeremy, Tu, 68^2–.

CHURCHILL, George Stanislas, M.C. SF, 25^3–30^1.*

CHURCHILL, John Adrian. SF, 21^2–25^2.*

CLARE, Denis Raymond. SH, 23^3–28^1.*

CLARE, Terence Cecil, b. 26 Mar. 07, eldest s. of late Lt.-Col. O. C. Clare, D.S.O., M.C. C, 20^3–24^2. Magdalene, Cambridge, B.A. With Triplex Safety Glass Co. Ltd., London. Landowner. Retired. Brother, D. R. Clare.

CLARENCE SMITH, John Ashton, b. 8 Mar. 17, eldest s. of late A. E. Clarence Smith. K, 30^3–35^2; Scholar; Levée; Exhibitioner of Christ's, Cambridge, M.A. University Diving Champion, 37–39. Indian Civil Service, 39–49. Bar, Middle Temple, 50. Eritrea (Ethiopia): Judge, 53–56. Attorney General, 56–62. West Cameroon, Supreme Court Judge, 62–66. Prof. of Law, University of Manitoba, 66–70 and University of Ottawa since 70. (Dir., Canadian & Foreign Law Research Centre.) Brother, K. Clarence Smith. Nephews, 2922, Peter Kenneth, K, 68^1–71^3 & Christopher Ralph, K, 69^3–.

CLARENCE SMITH, Kenneth. K, 35^2–40^1.*

CLARK, Antony Urling. K, 27^2–31^2.*

CLARK, Major David Graham, M.C., b. 27 Jan. 19, 3rd s. of late H. C. Clark. M, 32^3–37^2; XI, 35–37. Farmer. Brothers, L. W. and J. R. Clark. Son, 2831.

CLARK, Francis Allen. Tu, 98^2–01^3.*

CLARK, George Geoffrey. B, 07^1–09^3.*

CLARK, John Allen, b. 26 Sept. 26, s. of late H. Clark. SH, 40^1–44^2. ✕ R.N. Timber Merchant.

CLARK, John Rorie, b. 1 Apr. 29, 4th s. of late H. C. Clark. M, 42^3–47^1. N/S. R.N., 47–49. Lincoln, Oxford, B.A., Dip. Ed. Slade School of Art. Dragon School, Oxford, 55–68. Lower Canada College, Montreal, 64–65. Winchester College from 69. *Vincent's, Oxford.* Royal Central Asian Society. Brothers, L. W. and D. G. Clark.

CLARK, Laurence Walter, b. 16 May 14, 2nd s. of late H. C. Clark. M, 28^3–32^2. Exhibitioner of Peterhouse, Cambridge, M.A. ✕ R. Fusiliers, East Kent Regt. Lt. Dogra Regt. & Special Forces, S.E. Asia. Capt. Dispatches. Author and Publisher, Society of Authors. Brothers, D. G. and J. R. Clark.

CLARK, Malcolm Gale. W, 39^3–40^2.*

CLARK, Richmond Castleman Rowland, b. 29 Apr. 09, s. of C. R. R. Clark. SF, 22^3–26^1. Macmillan & Co. Ltd., Publishers, from 27–70. Dir. for the last twelve years. ✕ Army, 39–45. Major. Now free-lance publishing consultant, concerned mainly with educational publishing of audio & visual media. Veteran member of H.A.C. Member of the Council of the

Publishers' Assoc. (6 years) and of two Government working parties: The Educational Mission to Kenya, 71, and the Dept. of Education & Science working party on Central Arrangements for Promoting Educational Technology, 71–72. *Garrick Club, Frilford Heath Golf Club.* Son, 1598.

CLARK, Robert Bruce, b. 20 Oct. 05, younger s. of late R. Clark. Tu, 19^3-23^2. ✂ S. African Pay Corps, Union Defence Force. Staff. Sgt. King's Commendation. Company Secretary/Accountant. Retired. Hon. Chrmn. of The Shareholders' Assoc. of South Africa. *Western Province Sports Club.* Newlands, C.P., South Africa.

CLARK, William Harold. Tu, 97^3-99^3.*

CLARKE, Barry Michael. Sh, 44^1-48^3.*

CLARKE, Major Charles Nicholas Swift. St, 20^2-23^2.*

CLARKE, Edward Granville Woodchurch, b. 7 Apr. 14, s. of late F. G. Clarke. W, 27^3-33; R. VIII. Oriel, Oxford, M.A. St. Thomas's Hospital, London, B.M., B.Ch. ✂ R.A.M.C. Major. M.C. General Practitioner.

CLARKE, Ernest Joseph. B, 93^2-96^3.*

CLARKE, George Barry, b. 5 Feb. 25, eldest s. of The Rev. H. G. M. Clarke. SH, 38^3-43^2; Cadet Officer, 43; Exhibitioner; Tom Hughes Prize. Scholar of Clare, Cambridge, B.A. ✂ R.N.V.R., 44–47. S/Lt. Schoolmaster. Asst. Master, Stowe School since 50. (Housemaster of Grenville House, 62.) Son, Adrian Michael George, SH, 68^3-.

CLARKE, John Walrond Edward. B, 26^3-30^1.*

CLARKE, Peter Geoffrey Woodchurch. SH, 27^2-31^2.*

CLARKE, Ralph Christopher Gooding, b. 18 July 07, 2nd s. of late S. H. Clarke. St, 21^2-25^2. Trinity, Oxford, B.A. Solicitor, 31. ✂ 5th Bn. Suffolk Regt., 40–45. Lt. P.O.W. Malaya & Thailand, 42–45. Retired, 71. *United Oxford & Cambridge University Club.* Son, 2807.

CLARKE, Major Richard Basil Were, T.D., b. 16 May 04, eldest s. of late G. F. Clarke. SH, 18^1-21^2; R. VIII, 21. Tea Merchant, 27–39 & 45–51. ✂ Essex Yeomanry, R.H.A., 39–45. Major. T.D. Landowner & Farmer from 51. Son, 1186.

CLAYTON, David Francis, b. 27 Apr. 29, eldest s. of late Lieut-Commander W. H. Clayton, R.N. (OR SH 11). SH, 42^3-47^2; Paddison Art Prize (twice); Minter Open Entrance Scholarship and Architects' Registration Council Maintenance Scholarship; both to the Architectural Assoc. School of Architecture. National College for the Training of Youth Leaders, 62. R.I.B.A. Intermediate Examinations, 51. Architectural Asst. and Youth and Social Worker (in voluntary and professional capacities). The Architectural Assoc. Community and Youth Service Assoc.

CLAYTON, Frank, M.D., F.R.C.P., b. 3 Apr. 82, s. of late C. H. Clayton. C, 97^1-00^2. Trinity, Cambridge, M.A., M.D. University College Hospital, London, F.R.C.P. Physician, retired, 50. ✂ 20th Gen. Hospital, R.A.M.C. Major. Dispatches. B.M.A. *Hawks, Cambridge,* President.

CLAYTON, Jonathan Maurice. SH, 99^3-02^2.*

CLAYTON, Michael Denzil Grierson, b. 27 May 31, s. of J. D. G. Clayton. St, 45^2-49^2. N/S. R.A.C., 49–51. Liverpool Cotton Market, 52–59. Christies, London, 59–67. Christies, Geneva (Dir.), 67–72. Christies, Scotland (Dir.) from 72. *Travellers'.* Publication: "A Dictionary of the Silver and Gold of Great Britain and North America", 71.

CLEAVER, Edward Eric, b. 6 May 12, 2nd s. of late H. Cleaver, O.B.E., J.P. St, 26^2-29^3; XV, 28. 1st Class Certificate of Competency for Mine Management, issued by Ministry of Mines. Mining, Engineer, N.C.B. Deputy Dir. (Mining) South Durham area. Past Pres. of North of England Institute of Mining Engineers. Member of General Synod of C. of E. Chrmn. of House of Laity, Durham Diocesan Synod. Commissioner of Inland Revenue. Member of Local Parole Board. Brothers, L. H. & R. G. Cleaver. Son, 2409.

CLEAVER, Leonard Harry, b. 27 Oct. 09, eldest s. of late H. Cleaver, O.B.E., J.P. St, 23^2-28^1. F.C.A. Played Rugger for Warwickshire, 33–34. Sec. & Chief Accountant, Chance Brothers, Ltd., 35–51. Partner, Heathcote & Coleman, 51–59. M.P. (Con.) Yardley, Birmingham, 59–64. P.P.S. to Parliamentary Secretary to Minister of Housing. Birmingham City Council, 66–70. City Magistrate from 54. Birmingham Probation Committee from 55.

Chrmn., A. W. Phillips Ltd. Central Council Probation & After Care Committee for England & Wales from 66. Governor, Yardley Educational Foundation from 68. *Carlton Club*. Brothers, E. E. & R. G. Cleaver.

CLEAVER, Ronald Guy, b. 27 Sept. 17, 3rd s. of late H. Cleaver, O.B.E., J.P. St, 31^1–36^1; Cap. Trinity, Cambridge, M.A. ✂ 1st Indian L.A.A. Regt., R.A., 39–45. Major. Solicitor, 49. *Oriental Club*. Brothers, L. H. & E. E. Cleaver.

CLEEVE, Patrick Charles Aylmer. Sh, 30^2–33^2.*

CLEGG, John Charles. SH, 42^1–46^2.*

CLEGHORN, Lt.-Col. John Rutherford, D.S.O., b. 2 Apr. 14, eldest s. of W. R. Cleghorn. K, 27^3–32^3; Cap; Cadet Officer. R.M.C., Sandhurst. Winner of The Saddle, 34. Commissioned 2/Lt., 34, Royal Fusiliers. p.s.c. C.O., 9th Bn. Royal Fusiliers, 43–45. College Chief Instructor, R.M.A., Sandhurst, 49–51. C.O., 16/5 The Queen's Royal Lancers, 51–54. Lt.-Col. D.S.O. Dispatches twice. Farmer from 54. *Cavalry Club*. Brother, M. F. Cleghorn.

CLEGHORN, Michael Fortune, b. 7 Nov. 18, 2nd s. of W. R. Cleghorn. K, 32^3–36^2. Articled to Cooper Bros., Chartered Accountants. ✂ Royal Fusiliers, 40–42. G.H.Q. Liaison Regt. (Phantom), 42–46. Capt. American Bronze Star. Man. Dir., Cleghorn & Harris Ltd., Cape Town, S. Africa. *Bath Club; City Club, Cape Town; Jockey Club of S. Africa*. Brother, J. R. Cleghorn.

CLEMENT JONES, Martin Clement Trevor, b. 20 June 15, eldest s. of late Sir C. W. Jones, C.B. SH, 28^3–32^3; Cap, 32. Trinity, Cambridge. With Willis, Faber & Dumas Ltd., Insurance Brokers at Lloyd's, 35–49. ✂ R.N.V.R., 40–46. N.I.D., Admiralty. Staff of C.-in-C. Eastern Fleet. Lt.-Cdr. Control Commission for Germany, 46–47. Since 61, Dir. of Alexander Howden & Swann Ltd., London, Lloyd's Brokers and other Group Companies in the U.K. and Bermuda. Member of Insurance Advisory Council of the University of Texas in Austin, Texas, U.S.A. Insurance Mentor to the University of Alabama at Tuscaloosa, Alabama, U.S.A. Brother, M. L. Clement Jones.

CLEMENT JONES, Maurice Llewelyn, b. 12 Oct. 17, 2nd s. of late Sir C. W. Jones, C.B., Sh., 31^3–35^2. Lees Knowles

Exhibition. Trinity, Cambridge, M.A. ✂ Intelligence Corps. Major, 40–46. Member of Institute of Personnel Management. Member of British Institute of Management. Member of Industrial Tribunal for England & Wales. Asst. Labour Officer, Steel Co. of Wales, 46–50. Personnel, Newton Chambers & Co., 50–55. Group Personnel Manager, Albright & Wilson Ltd., from 56. *Athenæum*. Brother, M. C. T. Clement Jones. Son, 1759.

CLEMINSON, James Arnold Stacey, M.C., b. 31 Aug. 21, s. of late A. R. Cleminson. K, 35^1–40^2; XV, 39; R. VIII, 39–40; Cadet Officer. ✂ Army, 40–46. Commissioned & posted to Parachute Regt. Wounded. Capt. M.C. Joined Reckitt & Colman Ltd., 46. Dir. (Vice-Chrmn.). *Lansdowne Club*.

CLEMINSON, John Arnold Scott. K, 28^1–32^1.*

CLEVERLY, Geoffrey Charles, b. 25 May 95, younger s. of late C. F. M. Cleverly. B, 10^2–14^2. ✂ 5th Bn., Royal West Surrey Regt. Lt. Dispatches. Capt., Reserve of Officers. Magdalen, Oxford, B.A. Solicitor, 23. Partner in Wigan & Co., London. Son, 70.

CLEVERLY, William Geoffrey, b. 9 Sept. 26, 2nd s. of late Sir O. Cleverly, C.B., C.V.O. (OR B 05) B, 40^2–44^2; Cap, 43; XXII, 44; Cadet Officer. Middlesex Hospital, M.B., B.S. General Practitioner. *M.C.C.* Sons, 2966 & William Bernard B, 69^3–.

CLIFF, Antony Dewhurst, b. 15 Aug. 13, s. of late H. T. Cliff. M, 27^2–31^3. Trinity, Cambridge, B.A. Farmer & Landowner. N. Riding C.C., 53. Alderman, 68. *Farmers' Club*. Son, 1511.

CLIFFORD-TURNER, Howard Norman. M, 27^3–31^2.*

CLIFFORD-TURNER, Raymond (formerly Turner, R. C.). M, 20^1–23^3.*

CLOSE, John Frederick, b. 29 Feb. 12, eldest s. of late F. Close. M, 25^3–29^1. McGill University, Montreal, B.Comm. London University, B.Sc. Chartered Accountant. Senior Vice-Pres., The Royal Trust Co. (Montreal). *University Club (Montreal)*.

CLOTWORTHY, John Michael. M, 43^3–48^2.*

CLOUGH, Francis Hugh Butler, b. 20 Nov. 16, elder s. of late H. T. B. Clough (OR K 04). K, 30^3–35^2. University College, Oxford, M.A. ✕ R.A., 39–46. Wounded. Hon. Major. Solicitor, 48. Courts Administrator, Crown Court, Middlesex Guildhall, Westminster. *St. Stephen's Club, Roehampton Club.* Hon. Treasurer, Magistrates' Golfing Society. Sons, 1584 & 2119.

CLOUGH, Harold Percy. C, 19^2–23^2.*

CLUNIES-ROSS, Wilfred George Francis, M.R.C.S., L.R.C.P. M, 27^2–31^2.*

CLUTTON-BROCK, Arthur Guy, b. 5 Apr. 06, 2nd s. of late H. A. Clutton-Brock. SF, 20^2–24^1; XV, 23. Magdalene, Cambridge, B.A. Social Worker. Cambridge House, 27. Rugby House, 29. Borstal Service, 33. Head of Oxford House, 40–45. Agriculturist in St. Faith's Mission, 49. Field Worker of African Development Trust, 59–65. Retired. Brother, H. A. Clutton-Brock.

CLUTTON-BROCK, Hugh Alan, b. 7 June 04, eldest s. of late H. A. Clutton-Brock. SF, 18^2–22^2. Magdalene, Cambridge, M.A. Housemaster, Christ's Hospital Prep. School, 26–33. Headmaster, Westwood Prep. School to Kingswood School, Bath, 33–43. Headmaster, Colet Court, St. Paul's Junior School, 43–46. Headmaster, Cheltenham College Junior School, 46–64. Retired, 64. Brother, A. G. Clutton-Brock. Son, 1986.

COAKER, Edward Carey, b. 17 July 04, younger s. of late F. W. J. Coaker. SH, 18^2–22^2. Queen's, Oxford, M.A., B.M., B.Ch. St. Mary's Hospital, London, M.R.C.S., L.R.C.P. ✕ R.N.V.R., 40–45. Surg. Lt.-Cdr. Retired. *Lansdowne Club, London.* Member, British Medical Assoc. Member, Somerset County Council.

COATES, Hamish Hustler Howard, O.B.E., b. 8 Dec. 90, s. of late Rev. W. H. Coates. B, 04^3–09^1. Trinity, Cambridge. Officer, Supreme Court of Judicature, 14–56. (Acting Registrar, Principal Probate Registry, 39–46. District Probate Registrar, York & Wakefield, 46–56, Wakefield only from 50.) Co-Editor of "Mortimer on Probate Law and Practice" (2nd edition). Co-Editor of "Rayden and Mortimer on Divorce" (3rd edition). Retired, 56. O.B.E., 56.

COATES, Philip Greenhalgh. SF, 41^3–45^2.*

COATES, Ralph Evelyn Thomas. K, 45^3–50^2.*

COATMAN, John Sidney Berrill. M, 33^3–37^3.*

COBB, Francis David Cecil, b. 23 Oct. 18, elder s. of late F. C. Cobb (OR K 89). K, 32^2–36^2. R.A. (T.A.), 38. ✕ R.A., 39–46. Lt.-Col. T.D. (3 Bars). Fellow, British Bottlers Institute (F.B.B.I.). Member of the Institute of Brewing. Member of the Incorporated Brewers Guild. Brewer, Dir., Whitbread Fremlins Ltd., Maidstone, having been Chrmn. of Cobb & Co. (Brewers) Ltd., Margate, acquired by Whitbread & Co. Ltd. in 68. *M.C.C., Royal St. George's Golf Club.* R.I. of D. (Danish).

COBB, Francis Reginald Juxon. K, 40^2–44^2.*

COBB, Reginald Morphett, O.B.E., b. 9 Sept. 02, eldest s. of late W. M. Cobb. W, 16^3–21^2; R. VIII, 20–21 (Capt.); Cadet Officer; G. VIII, 20–21. In Cockburn Smithes & Co. Ltd. (Port Wine Shippers), Vila Nova de Gaia, Portugal, from 23. Man. Dir., 28–67. Retired, 68. *Bath Club; British Club, Oporto, Portugal.* O.B.E. Brother, W. J. F. Cobb.

COBB, William John Frederick. W, 34^2–38^2.*

COBURN, Alan Henry, b. 7 June 16, elder s. of late C. I. Coburn. SH, 29^3–34^2. Merton, Oxford, M.A. ✕ R.A.F., 40–46. F/O. Dispatches. Member, Institute of Personnel Management. Management Consultant, Ashley Associates, Manchester. *M.C.C., E.S.U.* Councillor, Wilmslow U.D.C. Brother, C. O. L. Coburn.

COBURN, Charles Oliver Louis, b. 16 Dec. 17, 2nd s. of late C. I. Coburn. SH, 31^3–36^2. Scholar of Wadham, Oxford, M.A. ✕ Friends Ambulance Unit, 40–46. Egypt, N. Africa, Italy & France. Author of "Youth Hostel Story" and "Flavius Josephus". Translator of French and German books. Research worker for biography of Lord Attlee (being written by Mr. Kenneth Harris). Free-lance journalism for National Playing Fields Assoc. Hon. Sec., Berkhamsted Amateur Operatic & Dramatic Society. *Berkhamsted Golf & Tennis Clubs; New Arts Theatre Club, London.* Brother, A. H. Coburn.

COCHRAN, Major James Gordon, b. 28 Jan. 28, s. of late Col. G. W. Cochran, D.S.O. (OR Tu 96). Tu, 41³–46¹; XV, 43–45. R.M.A., Sandhurst. Royal Military College of Science, Degree course, 53–54. Technical Staff course, 59–60. B.Sc., F.I.E.R.E. Major, R.A. Retired, 61. Product Man., Plessey Radar. Various appointments in design and management of A.T.C. Systems. *St. George's Hill Golf Club.*

COCKBURN, Colin, b. 17 Aug. 02, 2nd s. of E. C. Cockburn. SH, 16²–20². R.M.C., Sandhurst. Gazetted to 1st Bn., Sherwood Foresters, 23. Attd. to Sudan Defence Force, 34. ⚔ 39–45. Major. Dispatches. Retired. *Bembridge Sailing Club, Seaview Yacht Club.* Brother, J. C. Cockburn.

COCKBURN, Cmdr. John Clayton, D.S.C., R.N., b. 21 Jan. 07, 4th & youngest s. of E. C. Cockburn. SH, 20³–25². R.N., 26. Lt.-Cdr., 39. ⚔ R.N., 39–45. D.S.C. Cmdr., 47. Capt., 50. Retired. *White's, Royal Yacht Squadron.* Brother, C. Cockburn.

COCKERTON, Richard William Penn, F.S.A., b. 14 Oct. 04, eldest s. of V. R. Cockerton. Tu, 18³–21³. LL.B. (London) External, 27. Solicitor, 27. Principal Partner in Goodwin, Cockerton & Colhoun, Bakewell, Derbyshire. Pres., Derby Law Society, 72. Fellow of the Society of Antiquaries. Son, 2165.

COGGIN, Henry Anthony, b. 20 Mar. 20, s. of late H. F. F. Coggin. SH, 33³–39². Trinity, Cambridge, M.A. ⚔ R.N., 41–46. Lt. (E). Gas Turbine Engineer. A.M.I.Mech.E. Oil Operations Div., Iraq Petroleum Co., of London.

COGHLAN, Granville Boyle, b. 6 Jan. 07, elder s. of late H. G. Coghlan. Tu, 21¹–25²; Levée; XV, 23–24 (Capt.); XXII, 25; Athletics Cup, 25. Exhibitioner of Clare, Cambridge, M.A. Rugger Blue, 26–28. Retired Headmaster, Seafield Prep. School, Bexhill. *United Oxford & Cambridge, Hawks.* Ex-Alderman, ex-Mayor, Bexhill Borough Council, 53–54. Son, 172. Grandson, Terence Granville, Tu, 71²–.

COGHLAN, Kenneth Lake, b. 11 May 11, 2nd s. of late H. L. Coghlan. Tu, 25¹–29²; XXII; Sw. VIII. Pembroke, Cambridge. Bar, Inner Temple, 33. ⚔ R.A.F., 40–45. Sqn./Ldr. Chancery Bar from 33–56. Currently, Dir. of Companies. Brother, P. B. L. Coghlan. Sons, 583 & 880.

COGHLAN, Patrick Boyle Lake, b. 15 Aug. 07, eldest s. of late H. L. Coghlan. Tu, 21³–25²; Cap, 23; XI, 24–25; Fives Pair. Pembroke, Cambridge, M.A. East India Merchant, 28. F.C.I.S., 36. Dir. & Chrmn., Rubber Producing Companies. Chrmn., Rubber Growers Assoc., 53. ⚔ R.A.F., 40–44. (Invalided.) Sqn. Ldr. Dir. of Public Companies. J.P., W. Sussex. *Gresham Club, M.C.C.* Brother, K. L. Coghlan. Son, 881.

COHEN, Christopher David Arthur, b. 23 June 28, eldest s. of Judge N. A. J. Cohen (OR W 12). W, 41³–46²; Levée; Head of House. Solicitor. Partner, Holman Fenwick & Willan, Solicitors. *M.C.C.* Brother, J. S. Cohen.

COHEN, Jeremy Sandford, b. 14 June 30, 2nd s. of Judge N. A. J. Cohen (OR W 12). W, 43³–48³; Lees Knowles Exhibition. N/S. R.A., 49–50. Lt. Trinity, Cambridge, B.A. Dir., Willis, Faber & Dumas Ltd., 68. (now Life Dir.). *United Oxford & Cambridge University Club.* Brother, C. D. A. Cohen.

COHEN, His Honour Judge Nathaniel Arthur Jim, b. 19 Jan. 98, 2nd s. of late Sir B. A. Cohen, K.C. (OR W 76). W, 12²–15³. ⚔ R.N. H.M.S. *Tirade*. S/Lt. Corpus Christi, Oxford, B.A. Bar, Inner Temple, 24. ⚔ R.N., 39–45. Cmdr. Senior Legal Adviser to European H.Q. of U.N.R.R.A., 46–48. Deputy Chrmn., Foreign Compensation Commission, 50–55. County Court Judge, 55–70. Now retired. *United Oxford & Cambridge Club, Oxford & Cambridge Golfing Society.* Sons, C. D. A. & J. S. Cohen.

COHEN, Lt.-Col. Sir Rex Arthur Louis, K.B.E., b. 27 Nov. 06, s. of R. D. Cohen. W, 20³–24³. Trinity, Cambridge, B.A. ⚔ King's Shropshire L.I., 39–45. Lt.-Col. O.B.E. Officer of Order of Orange Nassau. Deputy Chrmn., Lewis's Investment Trust, Lewis's Ltd. & Associated Companies. Joint Man. Dir., Selfridge's Ltd. Chrmn., N.A.A.F.I., 62–64. Meat & Live Stock Commission, 67–71. Member, Committee for Consumer Protection, 59–62, British Travel Assoc. and Television Advisory Committee. Retired Company Chairman. K.B.E., 64. *Garrick, White's, Jockey Club.*

COLBECK, Eric Winearls, b. 5 Sept. 99, s. of late E. H. Colbeck, M.D., F.R.C.P., O.B.E. W, 14³–18¹. ⚔ No. 1 Special Co., R.E., 2nd Lt. Gonville & Caius, Cambridge, M.A. Founder Fellow

Institute of Metallurgists. Vice-Pres., Iron & Steel Institute (now Hon. Vice-President). Junior Sc. Officer, Metallurgy Div., National Physical Lab., 22–24. Personal Asst. to Gen. Man., Armstrong Whitworth M/C, 24–28. Metallurgist, I.C.I. (Alkali Div.), 28–47. Metallurgical Dir., Hadfield Ltd., Sheffield, 47–63 (Deputy Chrmn., 63). Now retired. Pres., Institute of Metallurgists, 50–51. Also Pres. of Manchester and Sheffield Met. Soc., 52. Member of *Athenæum* and *Savile Clubs*, prior to retirement in 64. Member of Cutlers Company in Hallamshire. ⚔ 39–45. On loan part-time to Atomic Energy Authority as Metallurgical Consultant to Sir John Cockcroft & Lord Hinton.

COLBY, Richard. B, 23^1–27^2.* Son, 2438.

COLCHESTER, Christopher Dering, b. 24 Feb. 12, 3rd s. of late M. H. Colchester. SF, 25^3–30^2; Scholar; Levée. Peterhouse, Cambridge, B.A. Joined Marconi's, 33. Chief Scientist, Marconi Radar Systems Ltd., 70.

COLDSTREAM, Sir George Phillips, K.C.B., K.C.V.O., Q.C., b. 20 Dec. 07, 2nd s. of late F. M. Coldstream. SH, 21^3–26^2; XV, 25. Oriel, Oxford, M.A. Bar, Lincoln's Inn, 30; Bencher, 54. Clerk of the Crown in Chancery & Permanent Secretary to the Lord Chancellor, 54–68. Chrmn., Council of Legal Education since 70. Special Consultant to the Institute of Judicial Administration, New York University since 68. K.C.B., 55. K.C.V.O., 68. Q.C., 60. Hon. LL.D. (Columbia University), 66. *Athenæum, Royal Cruising.* Brother, G. R. Coldstream.

COLDSTREAM, Gerald Rawson. SH, 35^2–37^2.*

COLE, Brian Spearing. St, 09^3–12^2.*

COLE, Charles Livesey, b. 2 Oct. 89, s. of late H. L. Cole. Tu, 04^1–07^2; XI, 05–07. Gazetted to 4th Bn. Royal Warwickshire Regt., 09 (resigned, 11, due to serious illness). Lever Bros. Ltd. (afterwards Unilever Ltd.), 13–54, retired. *Banstead Tennis & Bowls Club.*

COLE, Derwent Davey, b. 25 Jan. 04, eldest s. of late E. L. D. Cole, M.A. (A). St, 17^3–22^2. Balliol, Oxford, M.A., F.C.A. Retired, 64. For many years executive Dir. of Mitchells & Butlers, Cape Hill Brewery, Birmingham. Brother, K. D. Cole.

COLE, John Vernon, b. 8 Dec. 32, elder s. of K. D. Cole (OR St 19). St, 46^3–51^2; R. VIII, 50–51. N/S. R.A.S.C., 51–53. 2nd Lt. Balliol, Oxford, B.A. Solicitor. Notary Public. Articled, Linklaters & Paines, London. Asst. Solicitor with them, 60–65. Asst. Solicitor, Mellersh & Lovelace, Godalming, Surrey, 65–66. Partner in that firm from 66–70. Partner, Barlows, Godalming, 70–72, now Dir. of Property Companies. *County Club, Guildford.* Brother, 323.

COLE, Kenneth Davey, b. 12 Apr. 06, 2nd s. of late E. L. D. Cole, M.A. (A). St, 19^3–24^2; XV, 22; XXII, 23. Balliol, Oxford. Winter Williams Law Scholar, 27, B.A. Solicitor, 31. Dir., Clerical, Medical & General Life Assurance Society. Partner in Linklater & Paines. Retired. Brother, D. D. Cole. Son, J. V. Cole & 323.

COLEMAN, Stephen Charles, F.C.A., b. 31 Jan. 26, 2nd s. of late Rev. L. W. Coleman. T, 38^3–44^2; Levée; Head of House; State Scholarship; Leaving Exhibition. Queens', Cambridge, B.A. Chartered Accountant. Group Administrative Controller, Moorgate Mercantile Holdings Ltd.

COLENSO-JONES, Lt.-Col. Gilmore Mervyn Boyce, b. 4 Sept. 30, s. of Dr. G. L. C. Colenso-Jones. St, 44^3–49^2. N/S. Welsh Guards, Officer Cadet. Served in Royal Welch Fusiliers, 50–72. Retired as Major. Attended Join Services Staff College, Latimer (j.s.s.c.), 68–69. Present employment: Regimental Secretary, The Royal Welch Fusiliers, The Barracks, Caernarvon, North Wales. Officer in the Order of St. John. *United Service & Royal Aero Club.*

COLERIDGE, Arthur Nicholas, b. 19 Nov. 15, 2nd s. of J. D. Coleridge, F.R.I.B.A. SH, 29^1–34^2. King's Medal. Queen Victoria Memorial Prize. Scholar, New College, Oxford, M.A. Harmsworth Scholar, Middle Temple, 38. Bar, Middle Temple, 39. Western Circuit. ⚔ Army (Capt., Irish Guards), 39–43. Asst. Secretary, War Cabinet Office, 43–45. Man. Dir., Simpkin Marshall Ltd., 45–53. Man., Book Dept., The Reader's Digest Assoc. Ltd., since 53. *Garrick Club, M.C.C.* Society of Bookmen.

COLEY, Howard William Maitland, b. 14 July 10, elder s. of late W. H. Coley. St, 24^1–29^2. Christ's, Cambridge, B.A., LL.B. Bar, Middle Temple, 34. ⚔ R.A.F., 40–45. Sqn. Ldr. Recorder of Wenlock, 46.

Recorder of Burton upon Trent, 56–61. Deputy Chrmn., Staffordshire Quarter Sessions, 59–71. Stipendiary Magistrate for South Staffordshire since 61. *Union Club, Birmingham.*

COLLIN, Paul Ries, b. 5 June, 30, s. of D. A. Collin. W, 44³–48³; Scholar; Wells Bible Scholar of Oriel, Oxford, M.A. Solicitor, 59. Solicitor with Peacock & Goddard since 65. *National Liberal Club.*

COLLINS, Sir Geoffrey Abdy, LL.B., b. 5 June 88, 3rd s. of late P. G. Collins. M, 02³–07². Christ's, Cambridge, B.A., LL.B. ✕ 11th Bn., Rifle Brigade. Capt., 14–18. Solicitor, 13. Late senior partner, Peake & Co., London. Now retired. Law Society Council, 31–56. Pres., 51–52. Royal United Kingdom Beneficent Assoc. Committee, 26–54. Chrmn., 50–54. Hon. Sec. & Hon. Treasurer of Hockey Assoc. for second year and a Vice-Pres. since 26. Knight. Son, 2217.

COLLINS, Geoffrey Havelock, b. 21 Nov. 00, elder s. of H. J. Collins. SH, 14³–18². Trinity, Cambridge. Royal Agricultural College, Cirencester. F.R.I.C.S. ✕ Hirings & Claims Officer (T/Capt., Gen. List), 40–42. Chartered Surveyor & Estate Agent. Self-employed. *United Oxford & Cambridge University Club.*

COLLIS, John Stewart, b. 16 Feb. 00, 2nd (twin) s. of W. S. Collis. B, 14¹–18¹; Cap, 18. Inns of Court O.T.C. ✕ Irish Guards. 2nd Lt. Balliol, Oxford, B.A., F.R.S.L. Author. Heinemann Award for Literature, 47. Civil List Pension since 68. Brother, W. R. F. Collis.

COLLIS, William Robert Fitzgerald, M.D., b. 16 Feb. 00, 3rd (twin) s. of W. S. Collis. B, 14¹–18¹; XV, 15–17. ✕ Guards Cadet Bn. Trinity, Cambridge, M.A. Rugger Blue, 19–20. Scholar of Yale University. Burney-Yeo Scholar, King's College Hospital, M.D., F.R.C.S., F.R.C.P.I., M.B., B.Ch., D.Ph. Physician, National Children's Hospital, Dublin, 32–57. Consultant in Dublin, 32–57. Helped to establish three Medical Schools in Nigeria, 57–70. Prof. of Paediatrics, Lagos University, 60. *University Club, Dublin.* Publications: "Silver Fleece", "Doctor's Nigeria", "Nigeria in Conflict". Plays: "Marrowbone Love" and "The Barrel Organ". Brother, J. S. Collis.

COLVILLE, Duncan Hobson, b. 18 Nov. 29, s. of late G. T. Colville. K, 43³–48². Trinity Hall, Cambridge, B.A. Man. Dir., Shell Norden, Stockholm.

COLVILLE, John Mark Alexander, Viscount Colville of Culross, b. 19 July 33, eldest s. of late Commander The Viscount Colville of Culross, Royal Navy. Sh, 46³–51¹; Scholar. Scholar of New College, Oxford, M.A. Bar, Lincoln's Inn, 60. Member, Royal Company of Archers. Practised at Bar, 60–72. Minister of State, Home Office, from April 72. Succeeded father, 45. Brothers, 280 & 863. Son, Charles Mark Townsend, Sh, 72³–.

COMBE, Andrew Nicholson, b. 7 July 11, 2nd s. of late R. G. N. Combe. W, 25³–29²; S. VIII, 28–29. R.A.F. College. J. A. Chance Memorial Prize. Sword of Honour. Commissioned in R.A.F., 32. Co-holder of World's Long Distance Flying Record, 38–45. ✕ A.F.C. American Bronze Star. Wing-Cdr. Management Consultant. Conservation & Fish Husbandry Contractor. Brother, R. G. N. Combe.

COMBE, Robert George Nicholson, O.B.E., M.C., b. 12 Oct. 07, eldest s. of late R. G. N. Combe. W, 21³–26¹; Levée; S. VIII, 24 (Won Ashburton Shield). Clare, Cambridge, B.A. Bar, Lincoln's Inn, 29. Administrative Officer with British North Borneo (Chartered) Co. ✕ R.A. Gunner to Major, 39–43. Special Forces, 43–45. M.C. Parachuted into N. Borneo, 45. British Military Admin., 45–46. Colonial Admin. service from 46. O.B.E. Brother, A. N. Combe.

COMPTON, Sir Edmund Gerald, G.C.B., K.B.E., b. 30 July 06, eldest s. of late E. S. Compton, M.C., C, 20³–25²; Scholar; Leaving Exhibitioner; Jex Blake. Scholar of New College, Oxford, M.A. Hon. Fellow, 72. Entered Administrative Grade, Home Civil Service, 29. Colonial Office, 30–31. H.M. Treasury, 31–58. Comptroller & Auditor General, 59–66. Parliamentary Commissioner (Ombudsman in N. Ireland, 69–71), 67–71. Chrmn., Governing Body of Rugby School, 70–72. Chrmn., Local Government Boundaries Commission for England from 72. Chrmn., Central Board of Finance of the Church of England from 65. Bach Choir. Hon. F.R.A.M., 68. G.C.B., 71. K.B.E., 55. *Athenæum, Boodle's.* Son, 1212.

CONACHER, John Roy Hamilton, b. 15 Sept. 24, s. of H. Conacher, C.B.E. C & Tu, 38³–42³. London, Midland & Scottish Railway, 43–47. Ulster Transport Authority, 48–60. Bible Churchmen's Missionary Society, Ethiopia, from 60. Publication: "An Initial Readership Survey of Ethiopia".

CONESFORD, The Rt. Hon. Lord, Q.C. (Strauss, H. G.), b. 24 June 92, s. of late A. H. Strauss. SF, 06³–11²; Scholar; Head of House. Open Scholarship to Christ Church, Oxford, B.A. Bar, Inner Temple, 19. Q.C., 46. Hon. Bencher, 69. M.P. (Con.), Norwich, 35–45; Combined English Universities, 46–50; Norwich South, 50–55. Parl. Private Sec. to Attorney-General, 36–42; Joint Parl. Sec., Ministry of Works & Planning, 42–43; Parl. Sec., Ministry of Town & Country Planning, 43–45; and Board of Trade, 51–55. Life Peer, 55. *Carlton, Beefsteak & Pratt's Clubs.* Past Pres., *Architecture Club,* Design & Industries Assoc. London Society. Hon. F.R.I.B.A. Author of "Trade Unions & The Law" and various publications.

CONNELL, Arthur Blackall, M.B., b. 20 Mar. 02, 2nd s. of late T. B. Connell. Tu, 15³–19²; R. VIII, 19. Gonville & Caius, Cambridge, M.A., M.B., B.Ch. St. Thomas's Hospital, M.R.C.S., L.R.C.P. General Practitioner. Brother, J. C. Connell. Nephew, 827.

CONNELL, Dennis. SF, 14³–17¹.*

CONNELL, John Clifford, b. 2 Jan. 01, eldest s. of late T. B. Connell. C, 14³–19³; XV, 18–19; R. VIII, 18–19; Winner of Crick, 19. One-time member of London Stock Exchange, retired, 65. Also Dir. of John Connell, Dickins & Co., Australian Merchants, etc. Brother, A. B. Connell. Nephew, 827.

CONYBEARE, Anthony Macaulay. M, 26³–31².*

COOK, Frank Patrick. K, 33³–38¹. Sons, 1966 & Frank Edward, SH, 67²–71³.*

COOK, Michael Christopher Bult, b. 9 Jan. 32, elder s. of late Brigadier E. F. B. Cook. K, 45³–49². Three years Chartered Accountancy. Joined Pakhuismeesteren (Rotterdam, Holland), 52. Presently Pres. of Paktank & Member Executive Committee Pakhoed Holdings & other outside Directorships. *Royal Rowing & Sailing Club, De Maas, Rotterdam.*

COOK, Raymond James Foxwell, T.D., b. 24 Jan. 10, s. of late J. Cook, O.B.E. W, 23²–28². New College, Oxford, M.A. ✕ Intelligence Corps, 40–46. Capt. T.D. Asst. Master, Ampleforth College, 34–35. Asst. Master, Marlborough College, 35–40 & 46–67 (retired). *R.A.C.*

COOKSEY, Richard William Greville, b. 20 Mar. 23, s. of late M. W. Cooksey. St, 36³–40³. ✕ Royal Marines, 41–50. F.R.I.C.S. Presently Partner in Hampton & Sons, Chartered Surveyors, London.

COOPER, Brian William Tyas, b. 23 Apr. 23, s. of late A. T. Cooper. SH, 36³–41²; XV, 40; Tom Hughes Prize, 41. ✕ Royal Navy, 42–46. Lt. Oriel, Oxford, M.A. F.C.A. Chartered Accountant (in practice). J.P. (Bolton Borough) from 61. *The Manchester Club.* Sons, Colin Tyas, SH, 69²– & David Charles Tyas, SH, 71³–.

COOPER, George. K, 24²–27³.*

COOPER, George Grant. Sh, 41²–45³.*

COOPER, Leslie Charles Seymour, b. 28 Feb. 26, s. of Col. C. H. S. Cooper. K, 39³–44¹. Dir., Hull Brewery Co. Ltd. Sons, 2881 & Barnaby William Andrew, K, 68¹–.

COOPER, Patrick Priestley. K, 17³–23¹.*

COOPER, Peter Reinagle, B.M., B.Ch., b. 7 Feb. 14, 3rd s. of Dr. H. Cooper. Tu, 27³–32². Oriel, Oxford, M.A., B.M., B.Ch. Guy's Hospital, M.R.C.S., L.R.C.P., D.P.H., D.T.M. (Liverpool). Colonial Medical Service, 41–58, Gold Coast & Nigeria. Last appointment, Deputy Dir. Medical Services, Western Nigeria. Principal Airport Medical Officer Health Control, Heathrow Airport, London from 58. *Bath Club.*

COOPER, Reginald Culmer. Sh, 42³–47².*

COOPER, Sidney Neville. T, 10²–12³.*

COOPMAN, George Emile, b. 4 Jan. 10, s. of late E. H. Coopman. K, 23³–26¹. Solicitor, 31. ✕ R.N.V.R. S/Lt. Partner in firm of Solicitors. Son, 1528.

COOTE, Sir Colin Reith, D.S.O., b. 19 Oct. 93, elder s. of late H. Coote. SF, 07²–11²; XV, 10; XXII, 11. Balliol, Oxford, B.A. ✕ Huntingdonshire Cyclist Bn., 4th Bn. Gloucestershire Regt. Capt. Wounded thrice. D.S.O. Dispatches. Legion of Honour. Italian War Medal. French Medalle de la Reconnaisance. M.P. for Isle of Ely, 17–22. "Times" Rome Correspondent, 22–25. Parl. "Sketch", 25–30. Leader writer, 30–40. War Office Civil Asst. to D.P.R., 39–45. "Daily Telegraph" Deputy Editor, 42–51. Managing Editor,

51–64. Trilingual, French & Italian. Knight Bachelor, 61. Author of "Italian Town & Country Life", "In and About Rome", "Through Five Generations", and others. *The Other Club, All England Lawn Tennis & Croquet Club*. Son, 460. Grandson, Colin Howard, SH, 72^1–.

COPE, Bryan Ivan. Sh, 44^3–49^1.*

COPELAND, William Brian. C, 04^2–09^1.*

CORNER, Prof. Edred John Henry, C.B.E., F.R.S., F.L.S., b. 12 Jan. 06, s. of late E. M. Corner, F.R.C.S. M, 19^3–23^2; XV, 22. Scholar of Sidney Sussex, Cambridge, B.A. Research Scholar, 27. Asst. Dir., Gardens Dept., Straits Settlements, 29–46. Principal Field Scientific Officer, U.N.E.S.C.O., Latin America, 47–48. Lecturer in Botany, Cambridge, from 49. Prof. of Tropical Botany of Cambridge from 66. Governor of Rugby School. Fellow, Sidney Sussex, Cambridge. F.R.S. 55. F.L.S.

CORRY, John Swaine, b. 1 June 12, eldest s. of late H. W. Corry (OR St 93). St, 26^2–29^3. In Shipping Trade. ✕ R.A. Anti-Tank Regt., 39–45. Capt. Dir., Port Line. Retired. *Wildernesse Golf Club*. N.Z. Society. Brother, W. H. Corry. Son, 2477.

CORRY, William Heath, b. 5 Aug. 13, 2nd s. of late H. W. Corry (OR St 93). St, 27^2–31. ✕ 3rd King's Own Hussars, 39–45. Agricultural Engineer. Brother, J. S. Corry.

COTT, Hugh Bamford, D.Sc., b. 6 July 00, 3rd & youngest s. of Rev. A. M. Cott. SF, 14^3–18^2. R.M.C., Sandhurst. Selwyn, Cambridge, B.A. Lecturer in Zoology, Glasgow University, 32–38. Lecturer in University of Cambridge, 38–67. Lecturer, 45–67 and Dean, 66–67, of Selwyn, Cambridge. D.Sc. (Glasgow), Sc.D. (Cambridge). Lt. 1st Leicestershire Regt., 19–22. ✕ Chief Instructor, Middle East Camouflage School. G.S.O.2, Mountain Warfare Training Centre, Western District. Major, R.E. (dispatches). Publications: "Adaptive Coloration in Animals", "Zoological Photography in Practice", "Uganda in Black & White". Self-employed writer & artist. Life Fellow, Royal Photographic Society. Founder Member, Society of Wildlife Artists. Fellow, Selwyn, Cambridge.

COTTON, Henry Egerton, b. 21 July 29, 3rd s. of late Col. V. E. Cotton, C.B.E.

M, 43^2–47^2. Magdalene, Cambridge, B.A. Vice-Chrmn., Liverpool Repertory Theatre Ltd. Vice-Chrmn., Liverpool Diocesan Board of Finance. Governor, Liverpool Blue Coat School. Retail Trade from 52. Dir. & Gen. Man., Owen Owen Ltd., Liverpool.

COUBROUGH, Charles Ronald Lacy. SH, 35^2–40^2.*

COUBROUGH, Ian Frank Ellis, b. 5 May 24, 2nd s. of late C. E. M. Coubrough. SH, 37^3–42^2. ✕ 13th (H.A.C.) Regt., R.H.A., 42–47. Wounded. In Plastics Industry, 47. Company Dir. Brother, C. R. L. Coubrough. Nephew, David Charles, St, 68^3–.

COULSON, Sir John Eltringham, K.C.M.G., b. 13 Sept. 09, elder s. of late H. J. Coulson. W, 23^3–28^2; Scholar; Head of House; Major & Jex Blake Leaving Exhibitions. Scholar of Corpus Christi, Cambridge, B.A. H.M. Diplomatic Service, 32–65. Secretary-General of European Free Trade Assoc. (E.F.T.A.), 65–72. Served, *inter alia*, as H.M. Minister, British Embassy, Washington, 55–57. H.M. Ambassador, Stockholm, 60–63. Deputy Under-Secretary of State, F.O., 63–65. Chief of Administration of H.M. Diplomatic Service, 65. K.C.M.G., 57. *St. James' Club*. Son, 1928.

COURAGE, Kenneth Gordon. SF, 11^3–13^3.*

COURT, Richard Ambrey. SF, 23^3–27^2.*

COUSINS, Richard Morris George. T, 24^2–26^2.*

COWAN, Ian William Wilson. St, 36^3–38^3.*

COWAN, Brigadier James Alan Comrie, M.B.E., b. 20 Sept. 23, s. of late A. C. Cowan. Tu, 37^3–41^3; Cap; Cadet Officer. Gazetted to the Rifle Brigade (Prince Consort's Own), 42. ✕ From Jan. 42. Service in Egypt, Italy, Germany, Kenya, Malaya, Aden, Malta and Northern Ireland. Served also in the Royal Leicestershire Regt. and the Royal Anglian Regt. Many Appointments in Command and on Staff. Current rank, Brigadier. A.M.B.I.M. M.B.E., 56. Dispatches, Italy, 45; Malaya, 56. *M.C.C., Army & Navy Club*. Son, Adrian Malcolm Comrie, Tu, 68^3.

COWAN, John Lewis, b. 28 June 09, s. of H. D. Cowan. SH, 22^3–27^2. Trinity, Cambridge, B.A. Bar, Lincoln's Inn, 32. ✕ 49th Bn. Royal Tank Regt., 40–46. Pianist Retired.

COWELL, Commander Louis Francis, R.N. C, 22^2–26^2.*

COWEN, Major Denis Joseph, O.B.E., J.P., D.L., b. 27 Mar. 08, 3rd s. of J. E. Cowen. Tu, 22^1–26^1. Magdalene, Cambridge, M.A. ✕ Northumberland Hussars, 30–44. Dispatches. Wounded. F.R.I.C.S. Prize winner in examinations & Member of Council, 53–63. Member & Vice-Chrmn., Leicestershire Agric. Executive Committee, 45–72. Member of Wise Committee on Small Holdings since 63. Partner (since 44, Senior Partner) in Fisher & Co., Chartered Land Agents & Surveyors. J.P., Leicestershire, 58. High Sheriff, Leicestershire, 61–66. D.L., Leicestershire, 62. O.B.E., 68. Brothers, J. D. & G. A. Cowen.

COWEN, George Anthony, b. 11 Nov. 06, 2nd s. of J. E. Cowen. Tu, 20^3–25^2. Trinity, Cambridge, B.A. Retired, Master of Derwent Foxhounds, 45–68. Vice-Chrmn., Regional Committee of National Trust. *Northern Counties Club, Newcastle-upon-Tyne.* Brothers, J. D. & D. J. Cowen. Sons, 1202 & 1487.

COWEN, John David, M.C., T.D., D.C.L., F.S.A., b. 16 Nov. 04, eldest s. of J. E. Cowen. Tu, 18^3–23^2; Scholar; Cap, 22; Cadet Officer. Scholar of Hertford, Oxford, M.A. Final Law Society Exams and joined Barclays Bank Ltd. at Newcastle-upon-Tyne, 31. ✕ Northumberland Hussars Yeomanry, 39–45. Major. Gen. Man., Barclays Bank, 47–65. Dir. from 65. Soc. Antiquaries of London, Treasurer, 64–71; Vice-Pres. from 71. Pres., Newcastle Soc. Ant., 66–67. Pres., The Prehistoric Soc., 66–69. M.C., T.D. Hon. D.C.L., Durham. *Athenæum.* Brothers, G.A. & D. J. Cowen.

COWGILL, Timothy John, b. 4 Jan. 33, elder s. of J. H. C. Cowgill. C, 46^3–51^2; XI, 49; H. XI, 50–51. Technical College, Bristol, 51–52. N/S. R.N.V.R., 52–54. S/ Lt. London Div., R.N.R. from 56. Lt.-Cdr., R.N.R. Joined G. N. Haden & Sons Ltd., 54. J. Roger Preston & Partners, Consulting Engineers, 62; Hong Kong, 65. Clinkscales, Maughan-Brown & Partners, Port Elizabeth, S.A., 68. Associate Partner, 71. Brother, 344.

COWLEY, Geoffrey Willis. T, 31^2–35^2.*

COWPER, Michael Roy, b. 22 Oct. 16, 2nd s. of late A. E. Cowper. Tu, 30^3–34^2. St. John's, Cambridge, LL.B., M.A. Solicitor, 41. ✕ R.A.P.C., 40–46. Capt. Practising Solicitor, Partner in Godden, Holme & Co., London. Son, 2714.

COX, Arthur Vincent Maidstone, b. 3 May 09, s. of late L. M. R. Cox (OR T 94). T, 22^2–25^1. Tea Planter. ✕ R.N.V.R., 40–45. Lt.-Cdr. Retired Coy. Dir. Life Member, *Ceylon Motor Sports Club* and *Ceylon Amateur Dramatic Club.*

COX, Brian Robert Escott, Q.C., b. 30 Sept. 32, younger s. of G. R. E. Cox. Tu, 45^3–50^2. Oriel, Oxford, M.A. Bar, Lincoln's Inn, 54. Recorder of the Crown Court. Practising Barrister and Head of Chambers at 3 Fountain Court, Birmingham 4. Q.C., 74. Brother, J. V. E. Cox. Son, James Nelson Escott, Tu, 72^2–.

COX, David Edmund. M, 40^2–44^2.*

COX, Euan Hillhouse Methven. SH, 07^3–11^1.*

COX, Geoffrey Arthur. Tu, 39^3–44^2.*

COX, Graham Fortnam. W, 36^2–40^3.*

COX, Joseph Edgar. T, 42^3–47^2.*

COX, John Vickery Escott, b. 23 Mar. 30, elder s. of G. R. E. Cox. Tu, 43^3–48^2. Birmingham University, LL.B. Solicitor, 54. *Cirencester Water-Ski Club.* Brother, B. R. E. Cox.

COX, Philip Joseph, D.S.C., Q.C., b. 28 Sept. 22, eldest s. of J. P. Cox. T, 36^3–41^2. Queens', Cambridge, B.A. ✕ R.N.V.R., 42–46. Lt. D.S.C. Bar, Gray's Inn, 49, Midland Circuit. Queen's Counsel, 67. Practised in London. Recorder of Crown Court, 72. Bencher, Gray's Inn, 72. *Naval Union (Birmingham), Royal Cruising Club, Bar Yacht Club.*

COZENS-HARDY, Basil, b. 4 Feb. 85, elder s. of late S. Cozens-Hardy. C, 00^1–03^2; XV, 01–02; XI, 01–03. Trinity, Oxford, B.A. Rugby XV, 04–06; Capt., 06. Solicitor, 11. ✕ 4th Bn. Norfolk Regt. Wounded, leg amputated, 18. Capt. Consultant Solicitor. Hon. Treasurer, Norfolk and Norwich Archaeological Society. D.L. for Norfolk. F.S.A. Sheriff of Norwich, 35. Brother, S. N. Cozens-Hardy Sons, J. N. & J. R. Cozens-Hardy.

COZENS-HARDY, John Nathaniel, B.M., B.Ch., F.R.C.S., b. 19 Feb. 22, eldest s. of B. Cozens-Hardy (OR C 00). C, 35³–40¹; H. XI, 40. New College, Oxford, B.A., B.M., B.Ch. St. Bartholomew's Hospital Medical School, London. Surg.-Lt., R.N., 47–53. F.R.C.S. Consultant Surgeon (Orthopaedics), Good Hope General Hospital, Sutton Coldfield. Fellow of the Royal Society of Medicine. Brother, J. R. Cozens-Hardy.

COZENS-HARDY, Jeremy Raven, b. 24 Aug. 29, 3rd s. of B. Cozens-Hardy (OR C 00). M, 43²–47². Trinity, Oxford, M.A. Royal Agricultural College. Landowner & Farmer. Brother, J. N. Cozens-Hardy.

COZENS-HARDY, Sydney Noel, b. 18 Dec. 94, younger s. of late S. Cozens-Hardy. C, 09²–13²; XV, 12; XI, 13. ✕ 8th & 7th Bns. Norfolk Regt. Wounded twice. Lecturer to Cadet Units. Capt. Paper Maker. Gen. Man., Alex Pirie & Sons, 34–44. Dir., Wiggins Teape Ltd., 44–59. Retired, 59. Brother, B. Cozens-Hardy.

CRABB, Robert James Lawson, D.F.C., b. 9 Apr. 18, 2nd s. of late Dr. R. L. Crabb. W, 32¹–34³. Edinburgh University, B.Sc. ✕ R.E., 40–41. R.A.F., 41–46. D.F.C. Captain B.O.A.C. from end of the war until 54. The Decca Record Co. Ltd. *R.A.F. Club.*

CRABBIE, Donald, D.S.C., b. 22 Mar. 20, 3rd s. of late G. E. Crabbie. Tu, 34¹–37³; XV, 37. Special Entry to Royal Navy, 38. ✕ R.N., 39–44. D.S.C. Wounded. Invalided as Lieut., R.N., 44. Now Company Director. Brother, I. A. Crabbie.

CRABBIE, Ian Anthony, O.B.E., b. 17 Feb. 13, eldest s. of late G. E. Crabbie. Tu, 26³–31²; Levée; Head of House; XV, 30–31; XXII, 30–31; Capt. of Fives. Trinity, Cambridge, B.A. Chartered Accountant. Man. Dir., Singer & Friedlander, Merchant Bankers, London. ✕ R.A. (T.A.). Lt.-Col. O.B.E. Croix de Guerre. T.D. Dispatches. *Hawks Club, Cambridge.* Brother, D. Crabbie.

CRACE, Herbert Stanley. W, 99³–04².*

CRAIG, James. St, 17²–20².*

CRAIG, Peter Robert. K, 44³–48².*

CRAIG, Wilson James, C.B.E., b. 15 Jan. 10, s. of late C. Craig (OR M 89). M, 23³–29². Scholar of Corpus Christi, Cambridge, M.A. Schoolmaster & Lecturer,

32–38. Librarian, British School of Rome, 38–39. Wartime Civil Servant (Ministry of Aircraft Production), 40–45. British Council Officer, 45–71. Retired. C.B.E., 71.

CRANFIELD, Michael Claude. St, 37³–41².*

CRANSTON, Robert Stanley K, 29²–34¹. Sons, 1979 & 2377.*

CRAVEN, Harold Evelyn Andrew. SH, 99³–03¹.*

CRAW, Major John Patrick, R.A., b. 6 Oct. 20, s. of late Sir H. H. Craw, K.B.E., C.I.E. Sh, 34³–38³. R.M.A., Woolwich. Gazetted to R.A., 39. Lt.-Col., retired, 66.

CRAWFORD, Brigadier Henry Nevay, M.B.E., D.L., J.P., b. 23 May 07, elder s. of late C. J. Crawford. SH, 21¹–25²; Cap, 24; Cadet Officer. R.M.A., Woolwich. Gazetted to Royal Corps of Signals, 27. C.Eng.M.I.E.E. ✕ Egypt & Western Desert, 39–42. H.Q., 30 Corps. Brigadier, 44. British Army Staff, Washington, D.C., 45–46. M.B.E. Dispatches thrice. Retired as Brigadier, 49. Now Factor & Farm Man. Company Director. D.L. for Fife, 60. J.P., 65. *United Service Club.*

CRAWFURD, Kenneth, b. 14 June 04, 3rd s. of late Sir R. H. P. Crawfurd. K, 17³–21². London School of Economics. Retired Deputy Chief, Gen. Man., National and Grindlays Bank. *Oriental Club.*

CRAWLEY, William Desmond Chetwode. C, 20²–25¹.*

CREASY, Anthony Robert. Tu, 40³–45².*

CREASY, Sir Gerald Hallen, K.C.M.G. K.C.V.O., O.B.E., b. 1 Nov. 97, 3rd s. of L. Creasy. Tu, 11³–16²; Scholar; Major & Minor Leaving Exhibitions; XV, 15; XXII, 16. Scholar Elect of King's, Cambridge. ✕ Royal Artillery. Lt. Wounded. Home Civil Service (Colonial Office), 20–45. Chief Secretary, West African Council, 45–47. Governor, Gold Coast, 47–49. Governor, Malta, 49–54. Retired, 54. K.C.M.G., 46. K.C.V.O., 54. O.B.E. Hon. LL.D. (Malta). Bailiff Grand Cross. Order of St. John.

CRESWELL, Sir Michael Justin, K.C.M.G., b. 21 Sept. 09, 3rd s. of Col. E. W. Creswell, R.E. K, 23³–28²; Levée; Scholar; Head of House. New College, Oxford, B.A. Laming Fellowship, The

Queen's College, Oxford. H.M. Diplomatic Service, 33–69. Ambassador to Finland, 54–58; Yugoslavia, 60–64; Argentine, 64–69. Retired, 69. Anglo-Finnish Society. K.C.M.G., 60. *Brooks's, Shikar Club*. Son, 1438.

CRITTENDEN, Frederick Kenneth, M.R.C.S., L.R.C.P., b. 2 Oct. 18, s. of H. Crittenden. T, 32^2–37^2. Guy's Hospital Medical School, M.R.C.S., L.R.C.P. ✕ R.A.M.C., 42–46. Capt. Wounded twice. 1st Irish Guards & 5th Grenadier Guards, Africa & Italy. House Surgeon, Guy's Hospital. Royal Victoria & West Hants. Hospitals, Bournemouth. General Practitioner, Yoxall, Burton-on-Trent. Medical Officer, Meynell Ingram Cottage Hospital. Police Surgeon. British Medical Assoc. Guards Assoc.

CROCKATT, John Henry. C, 38^1–41^2.*

CROCKATT, Major Richard Meredith, b. 27 Nov. 21, eldest s. of late Brigadier N. R. Crockatt, C.B.E., D.S.O., M.C. (OR C 07). C, 35^2–39^3. Regular Army Officer. ✕ The Royal Scots. G.S.O.3, XIVth Army, 45. Capt. Dispatches. G.S.O.3, War Office, 46–48. p.s.c. Major, 52. Served in India, Burma, Malaya, Korea, Egypt, Cyprus. Retired, 56. Member of the London Stock Exchange, 56. *St. James' Club, City of London Club, Swinley Forest Golf Club*. Brother, J. H. Crockatt.

CROCKETT, John Robert. SF, 29^3–33^3. Son, 1384.

CROCKFORD, David Allen, M.B., F.R.C.S., b. 21 Aug. 30, s. of Brigadier A. L. Crockford, C.B.E., D.S.O., M.C., T.D., M.A., M.B., B.Chir. Sh, 44^1–49^2; S. VIII, 46–49 (Capt.); scored highest possible total score in the Ashburton Shield—the first time that this had ever been done, 47. N/S. Coldstream Guards. 2nd Lt. King's, Cambridge, M.A. St. Thomas's Hospital Medical School, M.B., B.Chir., F.R.C.S. Plastic Surgeon. Senior Registrar in Plastic Surgery, Newcastle University Hospital Group. *Royal Ocean Racing Club*. British Schools Exploring Society. Yacht Racing Assoc.

CROFTS, Frank Norman, b. 23 July 06, eldest (twin) s. of late T. R. N. Crofts (OR SH & T 87). SH, 20^3–25^2; Levée; XV, 24; H. XI, 25; Major & Minor Exhibitions. Scholar of Gonville & Caius, Cambridge. John Stewart of Rannoch Scholar, 27. B.A. Indian Civil Service, 28–47. In United Provinces (Magistrate,

29–34; District & Sessions Judge, 35–48). Examiner, British Board of Film Censors, 48–71. *M.C.C.* Brothers, J. R. & G. T. Crofts. Son, 761.

CROFTS, Geoffrey Thomas, b. 20 Aug. 09, 3rd s. of late T. R. N. Crofts (OR SH & T 87). SH, 23^2–27^2. ✕ R.A.S.C., 43–46. B.L.A. & M.E.L.F. Dispatches. Capt. Engineer. Retired. Brothers, F. N. & J. R. Crofts.

CROFTS, John Raymond, b. 23 July 06, 2nd (twin) s. of late T. R. N. Crofts (OR SH & T 87). SH, 20^3–25^2; Cap, 24; XI, 25. Sizar of St. John's, Cambridge, B.A. Asst. Master, Uppingham School, 29–60. Retired. Brothers, F. N. & G. T. Crofts.

CROOK, Peter Timothy, b. 29 Sept. 27, s. of late P. C. Crook (OR SF 15). SF, 41^2–45^2; XV, 44; XXII, 45. Company Director. Son, Peter Bruce Lee, SF, 67^3–71^2.

CROSS, Christopher Turner, b. 16 Sept. 20, s. of late H. T. Cross. B, 34^3–39^2; Levée; Head of House; S. VIII, 38–39; Cadet Officer, 38–39; Leaving Exhibition. Clare, Cambridge, M.A. Administrative Staff College, Henley, 52. ✕ Oxfordshire & Buckinghamshire L.I. (in 6th Airborne Div.). Capt. C.-in-C.'s Certificate of Gallantry. In Advertising. M.I.P.A. Market Research & Advertising. Present, Dir. of J. Walter Thompson Co. Ltd., London. *United Oxford & Cambridge Club*.

CROSSE, Ian Sydney Benn, b. 7 Mar. 20, s. of late C. S. Crosse. B, 33^3–38^2; XXII, 38. Queen's, Oxford, B.A. ✕ R.N.V.R. Lt. Underwriting Member of Lloyd's. Marine Insurance Broker. *M.C.C., Ferndown Golf Club*. Member, Court of Assistants. The Haberdashers' Company.

CROSSE, Victor Martin, b. 11 Nov. 97, 2nd s. of E. M. Crosse. St, 11^2–11^3. Eastbourne College, 12–16. ✕ Lt. in 5th Royal Sussex Regt., 16–19. ✕ Staff-Capt. "Q" in A.A. Command, 39–45. Dir. and later P.R.O. to family business, Crosse & Blackwell Ltd. Retired in 62. *Bath Club*.

CROSTHWAITE, Sir Ponsonby Moore, K.C.M.G., b. 13 Aug. 07, s. of late P. M. Crosthwaite, M.I.C.E. M, 21^3–25^1; Scholar. Corpus Christi, Oxford (Hon. Scholarship, 27). Laming Travelling Fellowship, 31. H.M. Diplomatic Service, 32–66. Served in Foreign Office and at Baghdad, Moscow, Madrid and others.

Deputy U.K. Representative at U.N., 52–58. Ambassador, Beirut, 58–63; Stockholm, 63–66. Retired, 66. K.C.M.G., 60. *Athenæum.*

CROW, Geoffrey Beves, O.B.E., b. 27 Apr. 03, eldest s. of late A. H. Crow. SH, 17¹–21²; XV, 19–20. Pembroke, Cambridge. Chrmn. and Man. Dir., Beves & Co. Ltd.,Timber Importers, Shoreham-by-Sea, 24–70. Now retired. Part-time Consultant, 39–46, in Timber Control, latterly an Asst. Controller. Fellow of Institute of Wood Science. Past Chrmn., Timber Development Assoc. Past Pres., British Woodwork Manufacturers' Assoc. and European Joinery Federation. O.B.E. *R.A.C.*

CROWE, David Wilton. Tu, 38¹–41².*

CROZIER, John Edwin Digby, M.D., B.Ch., b. 4 Jan. 00, s. of late E. Crozier. Tu, 13³–17¹. ✕ Guards Cadet Bn. Cadet. Gonville & Caius, Cambridge, M.A., M.D., B.Ch. St. Thomas's Hospital, London, M.R.C.S., L.R.C.P. ✕ Australian Army Medical Corps., A.I.F. Capt. Grazier. Melbourne, Adelaide.

CRUICKSHANK, Col. Alexander John, D.S.O., O.B.E., b. 11 Mar. 91, 3rd s. of late A. W. Cruickshank, C.S.I. SF, 05³–09²; Scholar; R. VIII, 09. R.M.A., Woolwich. Commissioned in Royal Engineers, 10. ✕ 2nd Sappers & Miners. G.S.O.3, Gen. Staff. Capt. D.S.O. Dispatches thrice. Major, 26. Col., 37. Retired, 38. ✕ Re-employed, 39–44. Secretary, Sussex Territorial & Auxiliary Forces Assoc., 38–51. O.B.E., 52.

CRUMP, Kenneth Leslie. C, 24²–28².*

CUBITT, Lt.-Col. Alan Blakiston, b. 24 Feb. 03, younger s. of late Sir B. B. Cubitt, K.C.B. (OR C 75). C, 17¹–20¹. R.M.C., Sandhurst. Gazetted to R. Norfolk Regt., 23. Served in W. Indies, Egypt, Shanghai, India, Gibraltar, N.W. Campaign, 37. ✕ Malaya Campaign. Commanded 6th Bn. R. Norfolk Regt., 42–45. P.O.W. Commanded 1st Bn., 46–47. H.Q. B.A.O.R., Oberhausen, 48–53. Retired, 53. Lt.-Col.

CULLEN, Charles Douglas, b. 15 Dec. 17, eldest s. of late Capt. W. D. Cullen, R.F.C. M, 31³–35³. Farmer in Kenya Colony. Master of the "Copston Hounds", Kenya, 39–66. Riding Instructor at Kaptogat since 66. Dairy Farmer at Equator, Kenya.

Racehorse Trainer and Owner in Kenya. Member of the British Field Sports Club since its foundation in 30. ✕ Kenya Defence Force & Kenya Police Reserve prior to Independence.

CULLEN, Peter, D.S.C., b. 22 Aug. 20, 2nd s. of late W. D. Cullen. M, 34²–38²; R. VIII, 38. Oriel, Oxford, for 1 year. ✕ R.N., 40–49. Lt. D.S.C., 44. Transferred from R.N.V.R. to R.N., 47. Invalided after service in Palestine, 49. Company Director & Secretary. Sons, 2151 & 2446.

CUMBERLEGE, Francis Charles Ray. St, 06³–09³.*

CUMMING, Norman Ronald Clifford. C, 05³–09¹.*

CUMMING, William Angus. Tu, 09³–12³.*

CUNLIFFE, Prof. Anthony Clegg, b. 23 Aug. 12, eldest s. of late Dr. E. N. Cunliffe. C, 26²–31¹. Trinity Hall, Cambridge, M.A., M.B., B.Ch. St. George's Hospital Medical School, M.R.C.S., L.R.C.P., M.D., F.R.C.Path. Prof. of Medical Microbiology, University of London. Consultant Microbiologist, King's College Hospital. Royal Society of Medicine. Pathological Society of Great Britain & Ireland. Asst. Registrar, 66–69, Vice-Pres., 69–72, Royal College of Pathologists. *Medical Research Club.* Brothers, C. J. & P. N. Cunliffe.

CUNLIFFE, His Honour Judge Christopher Joseph. C, 29³–34².*

CUNLIFFE, James (formerly Pugh, C. J. C.), b. 23 May 25, s. of late E. C. Pugh. C & Tu, 38³–43². Queens', Cambridge, M.A. ✕ R. Signals T.A., 44–47. Lt. T.D. Bar, Lincoln's Inn, 51. Joined Civil Service (H.M. Land Registry), having become disabled by Multiple Sclerosis, in Dec. 67. H.M. Land Registry. Disablement Income Group (now Chrmn. of Croydon & District Branch). Multiple Sclerosis Society. Disabled Drivers' Assoc.

CUNLIFFE, Peter Nicholson, M.B., B.Ch., b. 20 Feb. 19, 3rd s. of late Dr. E. N. Cunliffe, C, 32²–37¹. Trinity Hall, Cambridge, B.A., M.B., B.Chir. Manchester Royal Infirmary, M.R.C.S., L.R.C.P., D.(Obst.)R.C.O.G., D.A. (England). ✕ R.N.V.R. Surg. Lt. Anaesthetist, Watford General Hospital, Herts. Brothers, A. C. & C. J. Cunliffe.

CUNNINGHAM, The Rev. John, b. 18 Mar. 23, s. of T. E. Cunningham (OR SH 01). SH, 36³–40². Phillips Academy, Andover, Mass. McGill University, Montreal, B.A. Queen's College, Birmingham. ✕ R. Canadian Air Force. Sgt. Ordained, 48. Vicar of Pirbright, Surrey. Son, 2629.

CUNNINGHAM, John Wellington. M, 33³–37².*

CUNNINGHAM, Rupert Vincent, b. 14 June 95, 5th & youngest s. of late D. Cunningham. SH, 08³–13¹; XV, 12. ✕ 25th Bn. Liverpool Regt. Lt. Retired. Brother, T. E. Cunningham.

CUNNINGHAM, Tom Eric. SH, 01³–05². Son, J. Cunningham. Grandson, 2629.*

CURGENVEN, John Parr, b. 12 Mar. 07, eldest s. of late Sir A. J. Curgenven, I.C.S. M, 21¹–25². Hertford, Oxford, M.A. University of Paris. Lecturer in English, Queen's University of Belfast, 29–38. Served with British Council in Bulgaria, Turkey, Egypt, 39–44. Lecturer in English, University of Durham, 45–54. Prof. of English, University of Istanbul, 54–59. Lecturer in English, Bedford College, University of London, 62–69. Retired, 69. A.R.C.O., 36.

CURRAN, Charles Hugh Desmond, b. 31 Jan. 29, s. of L. C. Curran, M.P. St, 42³–47¹; Scholar; Levée; Head of House; XV, 45–46; H. XI, 47; Capt. of Fives, 47. Classical Scholar of Trinity, Oxford, M.A. Member of the Stock Exchange, London. *M.C.C.*

CURRAN, Edward John. B, 42²–46².*

CURRIE, Andrew John. St, 42³–46².*

CURRIE, Hamish Alexander David. SF, 12¹–16³.*

CURRIE, John Alexander, M.B., B.S. M, 13³–17³. Son, A. J. Currie.*

CURRIE, Piers William Edward, M.C., b. 26 Feb. 13, s. of late P. A. Currie, O.B.E. C, 26³–32²; Scholar; Levée; Head of House; Head of School; Jex Blake & Major Classical Exhibitions, 32. Scholar of Brasenose, Oxford, M.A. Solicitor, 39. ✕ 4th Regt., R.H.A. Capt. M.C. National Coal Board, 47–67. Sec. and Legal Adviser, West Midlands Div., 55–62. Deputy Sec., National Coal Board, 62–67. Legal Adviser, Land Commission, 67–71. Deputy Master, Court of Protection from 71. *Athenæum.*

CURWEN, David Niel. SF, 43³–47³.*

CUTFORTH, David Ecroyd, Mus.B., b. 31 May 23, 2nd s. of Sir A. E. Cutforth, C.B.E., F.C.A. SH, 37²–41². Corpus Christi, Cambridge, B.A. Royal Academy of Music, Mus.B., A.R.A.M. Dir. of Music, Strathallan School, Perthshire, 51–54, and Maidstone Grammar School, 54–68. Lecturer, North-East Essex Technical College & School of Art. *Fell and Rock Climbing Club, Swiss Alpine Club.* Incorporated Society of Musicians.

CUTHBERT, William Alexander, b. 25 May 02, s. of W. M. Cuthbert. W, 15³–20³; Scholar; Levée; Head of School; Head of House; XV, 19–20; Cadet Officer. Scholar of Brasenose, Oxford, B.A. Motor & Machine Tool Engineer (now retired). B.R.D.C., B.A.R.C. Brooklands Society. *Sea View Sailing Club.*

D

DAGLISH, John Richard Ainslie, b. 17 Dec. 32, s. of F. J. H. Daglish. Sh, 46³–50². N/S. R.A., 52. 2nd Lt. Asst. Secretary, Liverpool Cotton Assoc.

DAGNALL, Hubert John Armand, b. 2 Oct. 16, 2nd s. of late H. C. R. Dagnall. C, 30³–35²; XI, 35; Rackets Pair, 34–35, Capt. College of Aeronautical Engineering. Sales Dept., Airspeed (1934) Ltd., Portsmouth, 38–40. ✕ R.N.V.R. (F.A.A.), 40–43. Lt.-Cdr. Bullers Ltd., 46–49; Dept. Man., 49; Sales Man., 51. Yardley of London (Africa) (Pty) Ltd. (Cape Town),

Man. Dir. *M.C.C.; Western Province Sports Club, Cape Town.* Brother, P. M. Dagnall. Son, 1366.

DAGNALL, Peter Murcott. C, 35³–40².*

DAINTON, Arthur Harold. T, 01¹–05².*

DALBY, Col. Charles, C.B.E., b. 22 May 03, 2nd s. of late Major J. Dalby (OR C 85). C, 16³–21¹; Exhibitioner; XV, 19–20; S. VIII, 20; R. VIII, 21. Balliol, Oxford, B.A. Shooting Half Blue, 22–23; Rugger

Blue, 23. Gazetted to General List, T.A., 23. Lieut., 25. ✕ K.R.R.C., 26. p.s.c. Served in G.B., India, Burma, Germany. Retired Officer, 55–68; when finally retired, rank of Colonel. C.B.E., 55. *Army & Navy Club, Derby County Club.* Son, 2307.

DALDY, Alfred Frederick, b. 13 Nov. 05, s. of late Col. A. W. Daldy. K, 19³–22². F.I.C.E. Engineering Overseas, 25–58. Mainly Public Works Depts. Building Research Station, 58–71. Self-employed consultant since 71. British Philatelic Assoc.

DALGLIESH, Stanley Spencer Woodbridge, b. 16 Apr. 08, s. of R. S. Dalgliesh. B, 21³–26². Jesus, Cambridge, B.A. ✕ 2nd Lt., R.A., T.A. Dunkirk, May 40. Asst. Dir., Ship Management Div., Ministry of Shipping, later Ministry of War Transport, 40–42. Ministry of War Transport Representative, North Russia, 42–43; Cherbourg, 44; Germany, 45. Chrmn., North of England Shipowners' Assoc., 49–50. Member of Council of Chamber of Shipping, 48. Member of the Council of the British Shipping Federation, 50–68. Member of National Maritime Board, 52–68. Vice-Chrmn., British Shipping Federation, 65–68. Member of the Tyne Improvement Commission, 52–65. Chrmn. of the Trustees Savings Bank, Newcastle, 51–58. Member of Committee for Exports to Canada, 65–68. Pres. of the Tyne & Wear Chamber of Commerce, 69–71. *Royal Thames Yacht Club, Union Club, Newcastle.* Son, 668.

DALRYMPLE, Ian Murray, b. 26 Aug. 03, 3rd s. of late Lt.-Col. Sir W. Dalrymple, K.B.E. C, 17³–22²; Levée; Head of House. Trinity, Cambridge, B.A. Edited "The Granta", 24–25. Producer, Crown Film Unit, Ministry of Information, 40–43. Chrmn., British Film Academy, 57–58. Since 27, entirely in Film Production, as Film Editor, then Scenarist and Screen-play Writer, and finally as Producer of both fictional and factual films. Now retired. F.R.S.A. Brother, W. E. Dalrymple. Sons, I. S. W. Dalrymple, 828 & 1375.

DALRYMPLE, Ian Sebastian William. C, 45³–49².*

DALRYMPLE, William Edmonstone, b. 13 Aug. 98, eldest s. of late Lt.-Col. Sir W. Dalrymple, K.B.E. C, 12³–16³. ✕ 3rd Bn. Black Watch. Lt. Wounded. Trinity, Cambridge, B.A. In business in

S. Africa. Member of the Johannesburg Stock Exchange from 33. Hon. Commandant, 2nd Bn. Transvaal Scottish Regt. ✕ Transvaal Scottish Regt., 39–42. S.A. Staff Corps, 42–45. Lt.-Col. E. D. Director of Companies. *United Oxford & Cambridge University Club; Rand Club, Johannesburg* (Hon. Life Member); *Johannesburg Country Club*, Brother, I. M. Dalrymple.

d'AMBRUMENIL, David Philip, b. 1 Aug. 30, s. of Sir P. d'Ambrumenil (OR B 00). M, 44²–48¹. Scholar of New College, Oxford. N/S. Intelligence Corps. Chrmn., Seascope Ltd. Member of Lloyd's. *Turf Club, Corviglia, Buck's.*

d'AMBRUMENIL, Sir Philip, b. 28 Dec. 86, 4th s. of B. H. d'Ambrumenil. B, 00³–03³. ✕ R.N.V.R. 3rd Mounted Bde., R.G.A. 2nd Lt. Deputy Chrmn., War Risks Insurance Office (Ministry of Transport), 39–44. Deputy Chrmn., Lloyd's, 45–46. Chrmn., Lloyd's, 47. Deputy Chrmn., Lloyd's Register of Shipping, 48–49. Chrmn., Gardner, Mountain, D'Ambrumenil & Rennie Ltd., 36–62. Retired. Officer Order of the Crown, Officer Order of Orange Nassau, Knight 1st degree Order St. Olav, Commander Order of George I (Greece). Knight Bachelor, 45. Gold Medal of Corporation of Lloyd's, 43. Son, D. P. d'Ambrumenil.

d'AMBRUMENIL, Robert Paul, b. 28 May 19, 2nd s. of late L. d'Ambrumenil. SH, 33¹–36³. ✕ R.A., 39–46. Gibraltar, N. Europe, Germany. Major. Wounded. Dispatches. Member of Lloyd's. Group Man. Dir. of The Frizzell Group Ltd. *Boodle's, Berkshire Golf Club.*

DAMEN, Edward Albert Louis Jean. B, 15¹–16¹.*

DANGAR, Dudley Frederick Oliphant, b. 19 Sept. 02, 2nd s. of D. R. Dangar. St, 16³–21³. Jesus, Cambridge. ✕ Capt., General List, 41–45. Retired. *Alpine Club; Osterreichischer Alpen Club, Vienna.*

DANIEL, Henry James Abbot. SF, 23³–27².*

DANIELS, Charles Graham, b. 7 Apr. 33, elder (twin) s. of late C. B. Daniels (OR SH 16). SH, 46³–51²; Rackets Pair, 50–51; Squash V; Capt. of Lawn Tennis, 51. N/S. R.A., 52–53. Worcester, Oxford, M.A. Investment Consultant. *All England Lawn Tennis Club.* Brother, D. B. Daniels.

DANIELS, Denis Brian. SH, 46³–51².*

DANIELS, John Nicholson, b. 13 Sept. 12, 2nd s. of late C. N. Daniels. SH, 26²–30¹. Pembroke, Oxford, M.A. R.A.F.V.R., 40–46. Leather Trade, 33–40 & 46–72 in U.K. & U.S.A. Now retired.

DANKS, Francis Stephen, b. 1 Aug. 06, s. of E. Danks. SH, 20¹–25¹. Queen's, Oxford, B.A. Schoolmaster, now retired.

DANVERS, John. T, 44³–49³.*

DAUNT, Patrick Eldon, b. 19 Feb. 25, youngest s. of Dr. F. E. Daunt. SH, 38³–43²; Scholar; Levée; Head of House; XXII, 43. ✕ R.N.V.R., 43–46. S/Lt. Scholar of Wadham, Oxford, M.A. Goldsmiths Travelling Scholar, 49–50. Member, Nat. Advisory Council Education for Industry & Commerce, 70. Chrmn., Campaign for Comprehensive Education, 71. Tutor (St. Paul's College) & Lecturer (Greek Dept.), University of Sydney, 49–50. Asst. Master, Christ's Hospital, 53. Senior Housemaster, 59. Senior Classical Master, 64. Headmaster, Thomas Bennett Comprehensive School from 65. F.R.S.A., I.A.H.M., N.A.N.T. (Member).

DAVENPORT, Basil Hope. SF, 17¹–20². Son, 305.*

DAVENPORT, Wing-Cdr. John Roderick, b. 10 Sept. 11, eldest s. of late Major J. A. Davenport (OR SH 92). C, 25²–29³. Gazetted to R.A., 31. Seconded to R.A.F., 38. Transferred to R.A.F., 46. R.A.F. Staff College. Joint Services Staff College. Flying Instructor, R.A.F. Retired, 58. Brother, O. C. Davenport. Son, 1269.

DAVENPORT, Ormus Colin, b. 8 Apr. 20, 3rd s. of late Major J. A. Davenport (OR SH, 92). C, 34²–38². ✕ R. Signals. Major. Man. Dir. of H. C. D. Research Ltd., Burgess Hill, Sussex. Brother, J. R. Davenport.

DAVENPORT, Thomas Rodney Hope, b. 5 Jan. 26, elder s. of T. Davenport. B, 39³–41². St. John's College, Johannesburg. Rhodes University, Grahamstown. Queen's, Oxford. M.A. (Univ. of S. Africa & Oxford). Ph.D. (Cape Town). Lecturer/Senior Lecturer in History, University of Cape Town, 53–65. Reader/Associate Prof. of History, Rhodes University, 65–72.

DAVEY, Major Horace Balfour, M.C. B, 07³–11².*

DAVID, John Brooke, F.R.C.S., D.L.O., b. 12 July 12, eldest s. of late Rt. Rev. A. A. David, D.D. SH, 25³–30². Liverpool University, M.B., Ch.B. Fellow in Anatomy, 37. F.R.C.S., L.R.C.P., D.L.O. ✕ Indian Medical Service, 5 years. Major. Specialist (E.N.T.) to Government of Ghana, West Africa. Royal Society of Medicine. Royal Society of Tropical Medicine. Brother, W. M. David.

DAVID, William Miles, b. 5 Dec. 15, 2nd s. of late Rt. Rev. A. A. David, D.D. SH, 29²–33². Maltster. High Sheriff, Hallamshire, 68–69. *Boodle's, Royal Fowey Yacht Club.* Brother, J. B. David. Sons, 2176 & 2435.

DAVIDSON, Lt.-Col. Angus Graeme. B, 13³–17³.*

DAVIDSON, Colin Mackenzie, F.R.C.S., M.Ch. B, 41³–45³.*

DAVIES, Arthur Christopher. SF, 30²–34².*

DAVIES, Carlton Griffith, C.M.G., M.C., b. 2 Aug. 95, 2nd s. of late W. Davies, M.B.E., J.P. Tu, 09³–14²; Head of House; XV, 12–13 (Capt.); XXII, 12; Cadet Officer. ✕ 24th Bn. London Regt., Machine Gun Corps. Major. M.C. Wounded. Dispatches twice. Exeter, Oxford. Sudan Government Political Service from 20–45. ✕ Sudan Defence Force, 39–40. Dispatches. Sudan Government Agent in London, 47–55. Retired. C.M.G. Order of the Nile. Order of King Leopold. *Vincent's Club, Oxford; Royal Overseas Club, London.* Sons, W. & N. C. Davies. Grandsons, Malcolm David Carlton, Tu, 70³– & Philip Graham Carlton, Tu, 72³–.

DAVIES, Forbes Evelyn Oliveira, b. 27 Oct. 10, eldest s. of late D. O. Davies (OR SH, 88). Tu, 24²–28². Chartered Accountant, 34. Senior Partner, Davies, Behr & Co., Chartered Accountants, Salisbury, Rhodesia.

DAVIES, Sir Martin, C.B.E., b. 22 Mar. 08, 2nd s. of late E. W. Davies, C.B.E. C, 21³–26²; Scholar. Major & Minor Exhibitions. King's, Cambridge, B.A. At the National Gallery since 32, now Director. F.B.A., 66; F.S.A., F.M.A. Knighted, 72. C.B.E., 65. Hon. D.Litt.(Oxon.), 68. *Reform Club.* Brother, O. Davies.

DAVIES, Nevin Carlton, b. 21 July 30, 2nd s. of Major C. G. Davies, C.M.G., M.C. (OR T 09). Tu, 44²–48². Exeter,

Oxford, B.A. R.A. (T.A.). Lt. Farming. Self-employed. Brother, W. Davies.

DAVIES, Oliver, b. 7 May 05, eldest s. of late E. W. Davies, C.B.E. C, 18³–23²; Scholar; King's Medal, 22; Major and Jex-Blake Exhibitions. Scholar of Exeter, Oxford, B.A. Craven Fellow, British School at Athens, 27–29. D.Litt., Dublin, 46. Lecturer and then Reader, Archaeology and Ancient History, Queen's University, Belfast, 30–47. Prof. of Classics, University of Natal, 48–51. Reader and then Prof. of Archaeology, University of Ghana, 52–66. Retired. Hon. Keeper of Antiquities, Natal Museum. Chrmn. of Eurafrican Shorelines Sub-commission. International Quaternary Assoc. *Victoria Club, Pietermaritzburg.* Royal Anthropological Institute, London. Brother, M. Davies.

DAVIES, Oliver John Hunter, b. 9 Apr. 19, s. of late A. H. Davies (OR St 91). St, 32³–38²; Levée. Trinity, Cambridge. Associate, Chartered Insurance Institute, 50. ✕ R.N.V.R., 40–46. Lieut-Cmdr. (A). Insurance and Reinsurance. *City University Club, M.C.C.* Son, 2936A.

DAVIES, Trevor, b. 3 Jan. 32, s. of I. I. Davies. T, 46¹–50²; Scholar; Levée; Sw. VIII, 49–50. Exhibitioner of Jesus, Oxford, M.A. Liverpool College of Commerce (Diploma in Russian, 66). Advertising, Wickman Ltd. Teaching, various posts in secondary schools. Investment/Insurance Consultant. *Bowdon Hockey Club, Bala Sailing Club.*

DAVIES, Walter, b. 31 Aug. 28, elder s. of Major C. G. Davies, C.M.G., M.C. (OR Tu 09). Tu, 42³–47²; Scholar; Levée; Head of House; Cadet Officer; Cap, 45; Capt. of Chess. Leaving Exhibition to Pembroke, Cambridge, M.A. M.B.I.M. Joined Imperial Tobacco Co., 52. Technical Asst., Engineer Dept., John Player & Sons, 54. Manager, Research Dept., 64. Secretary to Board, 66. Dir. & Sec., 69. Production Dir., 70. Personnel Dir. from 1 Jan. 74. *Outlaws Golfing Society; Notts. Golf Club, Hollinswell.* Greenlands Assoc. (Admin. Staff Col., Henley). Brother, N. C. Davies. Sons, Malcolm David Carlton, Tu, 70³– & Philip Graham Carlton, Tu, 72³–.

DAVIS, Michael Justin, b. 9 Feb. 25, s. of D. L. Davis. St & K, 38³–42³. ✕ R.N.V.R., 43–46. S/Lt. Pembroke, Cambridge, M.A. Schoolmaster at Marlborough College, Wilts.

DAVIS, Peter Julian Geoffrey, M.C. M, 35²–40².*

DAVY, Charles Bertram, b. 25 June 97, s. of late Col. C. W. Davy, R.E. St, 11³–16²; Scholar; Head of House. ✕ French Red Cross, Driver. Croix de Guerre. Exhibitioner of Corpus Christi, Oxford. King's College, London. Dip. in Journalism with distinction. Journalist. Asst. Editor, "The Observer", London. Soil Assoc. Anthroposophical Society of Great Britain.

DAW, Anthony Fabyan, b. 15 July 15, elder s. of late W. F. B. Daw (OR M 03). M, 28³–30¹. Magdalene, Cambridge, M.A. Gazetted to Royal Berkshire Regt. ✕ R. Berkshire Regt. p.s.c. Major, 49. Brother, J. W. à B. Daw.

DAW, James William à Beckett, b. 7 Jan. 22, 2nd s. of late W. F. B. Daw (OR M 03). M, 35³–39³; Cap. ✕ R.A., 40–46. Capt. Chartered Surveyor, 51. F.R.I.C.S. Senior Partner, Messrs. McDaniel & Daw, Chartered Surveyors, London. Brother, A. F. Daw.

DAWKINS, The Rev. Cuthbert Howard. B, 24³–29¹.*

DAWKINS, Edwin Herbert Haswell, b. 22 May 08, eldest s. of E. H. Dawkins. B, 21³–26². Corpus Christi, Cambridge, B.A. F.C.A., M.I.Q. (Member of Institute of Quarrying). Chartered Accountant, still in practice. Brother, The Rev. C. H. Dawkins.

DAWSON, Harry. SF, 02³–07².*

DAWSON, Horace Cortlandt. C, 15³–19².*

DAWSON, Robert Clarkson Crosbie, M.C., b. 21 Jan. 16, s. of late G. C. Dawson. W, 29³–32³; Cap. Royal Agricultural College, Cirencester. Land Agent and Surveyor. ✕ The Queen's Bays, 39–45. Major. M.C. Dispatches. Dir. of Farming Company.

DAWSON, Lt.-Col. William Charles Palliser, M.B.E., b. 20 Oct. 96, younger s. of late P. Dawson. St, 11²–14¹. Regular Army. Royal Artillery and Royal Tank Regt. Adviser & Instructor, Chinese Army, 36–42. Invalided, 45. Fruit Growing & Farming, 44–59. Handed over to son (286), and finally retired. M.B.E., 24, for services in Constantinople. Class A, No. 1 Medal of Land, Sea & Air Forces, Republic of China.

DAWSON-GROVE, Glascott Eyre, b. 9 Sept. 24, 2nd s. of late H. Dawson-Grove. M, 38³–39³. Royal School of Mines, Imperial College, University of London. M.Sc. in Structural Geology, A.R.S.M. Emmanuel, Cambridge. Half Blue, Judo. Registered Professional Geologist and Registered Professional Engineer (Prov. of Alberta). Past President, Canadian Petrophysical (Well Logging) Society. Former Dir. of (American) Society of Professional Well Log Analysts. Petrophysical Engineer, Shell Oil Co., U.S.A. (8 years). Now (Chief) Petrophysicist, Home Oil Co., Canada. Fellow, Geol. Soc. of London. Member of Canadian & American Petrophysical (Well Logging) Societies & Economics Soc. of Alberta. Exec. Vice-President, Alberta Rowing Assoc.

DAWSON-HALL, Eric Edward (formerly Hall, E.E.D.). St, 19¹–23².*

DAY, Reginald Crewdson. St, 12³–15².*

DEACON, David Stuart. SH, 25¹–29².*

DEACON, Malcolm Martin. T, 44³–47³.*

DEAKIN, Patrick William Ireland, b. 19 Oct. 03, elder s. of late W. R. Deakin (OR M 82). M, 17³–20². Farmer. Retired. Son, 2884.

DEAN, Lt.-Col. Geoffrey John, M.C., b. 12 Nov. 09, s. of late C. G. Dean (OR SH, 91). SH, 23³–28²; XV, 26–27. Pembroke, Cambridge, M.A. Commissioned into Royal Tank Regt., 31, as 2nd Lt. with ante-date to 30. Adjt., 2nd R. Tank Regt., 36–39. Squadron Leader, 6th R. Tank Regt., 40–41. P.O.W., 41–42. Repatriated and went to R.A.C., O.C.T.U., Sandhurst, as Squadron Leader. Then Chief Instructor, O.C., R.A.C., Pre-O.C.T.U. O.C., 52nd Training Regt., R.A.C. Chief Instructor, R.A.C. Depot., Staff College, Camberley. Bde. Major, 9th Armoured Bde., T.A. Retired as Hon. Lt.-Col., 49. Farmed in Dorset, 50–65. Retired. *Harlequin R.F.C.* Played Rugger for England v. Ireland, 31. Combined Services v. Springboks, 31. Combined Services v. All Blacks, 35. Army, 33–38. Capt., 36–38. M.C., 41. Leg amputated, 41, when P.O.W.

DEAN, Sir Patrick Henry, G.C.M.G., b. 16 Mar. 09, s. of late Prof. H. R. Dean. SH, 22³–28²; Levée; Head of House; Cap, 26–27; XXII, 27–28; Sw. VI, 25–28; Capt., Leaving Exhibition; Scholar of Gonville & Caius, Cambridge, B.A. Fellow

of Clare, Cambridge, 32–35 & Lecturer in Law, 32–39. Bar, Lincoln's Inn, 34. Governor, Rugby School, 39. H.M. Diplomatic Service, 39–69. U.K. Permanent Representative at U.N., 60–64. H.M. Ambassador, Washington, 65–69. Dir. Taylor Woodrow Ltd. Chrmn., Crowell, Collier & Macmillan Ltd. International Adviser, American Express. Chrmn., Rugby School Governing Body, 71. G.C.M.G. Hon. Fellow, Gonville & Caius College, Cambridge, Hon. Bencher, Lincoln's Inn. *Brooks's; Beefsteak; The Brook (New York).* Sons, 2337 & 2630.

DEAN, Theodore Francis Marcham, b. 10 Apr. 13, s. of H. J. Dean. SH, 27¹–32¹. University College, London, B.A. Schoolmaster & Educational Administrator, 37–42. Journalist in B.B.C. External Services, 43–72. Chrmn., Radio & Television Journalists' Council, 67–68.

de BOURSAC, Vladimir, b. 20 Aug. 14, eldest s. of S. de Boursac. W, 28²–31². Lycée de Nice. ✕ 40–45. R.A.F. Sqn. Ldr. Secretary, Paris Office International Air Transport Assoc., 45–68. Presently, Asst. Dir. General, I.A.T.A. Sons, 1867, 2361 & 2914.

de BRETT, The Rev. Rodney John Harry, b. 3 July 13, 2nd s. of late E. A. de Brett. Tu, 27¹–28³. École de Commerce, Lausanne, 29–31. R.M.C., Sandhurst, 32–34. E. Yorks. Regt., 34–49. ✕ 40–46. G.S.O.2, 50th Div. G.S.O.2 (Ops.) H.Q. 21st Army Group. 2nd in Command, 4th Bn. R. Welch Fusiliers. Wounded. Dispatches. R.A.F. Regt., 49–63. Wing-Cdr. Wells Theological College, 63–64. Curate, St. Cuthbert's, Wells, 64–66. Vicar, Stoke St. Gregory from 66.

de FONBLANQUE, Major-Gen. Edward Barrington, C.B., C.B.E., D.S.O., b. 29 May 95, younger s. of late L. R. de Fonblanque. SF, 09²–12². R.M.A., Woolwich, 12–14. 2nd Lt., R.A., 14. ✕ 14–18. Instructor, School of Equitation, Weedon, 21–25. Staff College, Camberley, 31–32. Instructor, Staff College, Quetta, 34–38. Major, 33. Bt. Lt.-Col., 37. ✕ Served, 39–45. Dispatches. Col., 40. Brig., 40. Major-General, 44. Col. Commandant, R.A., 59–60. A.D.C. to the King, 47. C.B., 48, C.B.E., 45, D.S.O., 45. Legion of Merit (U.S.A.). *Army & Navy Club.*

DELAFIELD, Michael Wyndham. SF, 34³–39².*

de la HEY, Anthony. W, 33¹–36².*

DELAMAIN, Lt.-Col. Walter Thomas. St, 16^2–19^2.*

DELAP, Hugh Alexander, b. 21 Oct. 06, s. of A. D. Delap. M, 20^3–24^3. Trinity College, Dublin, B.A. B.A.I. With Local Authority, $2\frac{1}{2}$ years. With Consultants, 6 years. In Government Service, 34 years— Office of Public Works, Ireland (Chief Engineer, 66–71). Since 72 in private practice. Fellow, Institution of Civil Engineers. Fellow, Institution of Engineers of Ireland (Pres., 73–74). Pres. Institute of Professional Civil Servants, Ireland (67–69). Royal Dublin Society. *Engineers' Club, Dublin.*

de LASZLO, Paul Leonardo, O.B.E., b. 6 Jan. 06, 3rd s. of P. A. de Laszlo, M.V.O. St, 20^1–24^2; Levée. Balliol, Oxford, B.A. Bar., Inner Temple, 29–39. $\times$ 40–45. R.N.V.R., Lt.-Cdr., O.B.E. Joined English Electric Co., 45–69. Originally as P.A. to Chairman, later as Dir. of Corporate Affairs and member of Board of Directors of English Electric Co., & Marconi Co. etc. *White's,* Royal Photographic Society, Royal Society of Art. Nephew, Stephen Ernest, St, 71^2–.

DELL, David Michael, b. 30 Apr. 31, s. of M. R. Dell. St, 44^3–49^2; Scholar; Levée; Jex-Blake Exhibitioner. Scholar of Balliol, Oxford, M.A. N/S. Royal Signals, 53–55. 2nd Lt. Civil Service from 55.

DEL STROTHER, Ralph Ormesby, b. 6 May 21, 3rd s. of W. L. A. Del Strother. M, 35^2–39^2. $\times$ Royal Signals. Sgt. Queens', Cambridge, M.A. Schoolmaster, Ardingly College, Haywards Heath, Sussex.

DEMUTH, William Henry Horner, M.C. SF, 12^3–17^1.*

DENNES, John Mathieson, b. 19 May 26, s. of late N. Dennes, B.Sc., M.I.C.E. Sh, 40^1–44^2. Classical Scholarship to Christ's, Cambridge, M.A. Solicitor, 52. In private practice. Partner in firm of Waltons & Co., London, since 57.

DENNY, William. Tu, 22^2–26^2.*

de PAULA, Frederic Clive, C.B.E., T.D., b. 17 Nov. 16, 2nd s. of late F. R. M. de Paula, C.B.E., F.C.A. B, 30^3–34^1; Levée; Head of House. $\times$ Liaison duties with Free French, 40–41. Intelligence duties in Africa, Madagascar, India & Burma, 41–45. Finance Div. Control Commission for Germany, 45–46. Major. T.D.

& Clasp. Joined Robson Morrow & Co., Management Consultants, 46. Partner, 51 (Senior Partner, 70). Dept. of Economic Affairs, then Ministry of Technology as Industrial Adviser, 67. Coordinator of Industrial Advisers to the Government, 69. Man. Dir., Agricultural Mortgage Corporation Ltd., 71. F.C.A., J.Dip.M.A., M.B.C.S., F.B.I.M. C.B.E. (70). *City of London Club, Bath Club, Farmers' Club, Sheffield Club.* Brother, H. F. M. de Paula.

de PAULA, Hugh Francis Mackley, T.D., b. 9 Dec. 13, elder s. of late F. R. M. de Paula, C.B.E., F.C.A. B, 27^3–32^3. $\times$ R.A., Capt., T.D. Member of London Stock Exchange, 39–69. Firm, W. Mortimer & Son, Chancery Brokers. *Gresham Club.* Brother, F. C. de Paula. Son, 1787.

de PEYER, Everard Esmé Vivian, b. 2 Nov. 99, eldest s. of late E. C. de Peyer. K, 13^2–18^1. Exhibition offered by Magdalen, Oxford. $\times$ R.E., 2nd Lt.

DE QUINCEY, Robert Gerald, b. 9 Feb. 15, 3rd s. of late B. De Q. Quincey. M, 28^3–33^2; H. XI. Trinity, Oxford, M.A. Golf Blue, 34–36. Solicitor, 39. $\times$ Suffolk Regt. Capt. Dispatches. P.O.W., Japanese, 42–45. Farming. *Rye Golf Club, Oxford & Cambridge Golfing Society, Junior Carlton Club.*

DERBY, John Kirkpatrick Walker, b. 15 June 27, elder s. of late Major J. Derby. K, 41^2–44^3. King's, Cambridge, M.A. Legal Dept., Royal Automobile Club.

DERIAZ, Marcel George, B.Sc., Ph.D., b. 31 July 26, 2nd s. of P. E. Deriaz. T, 39^3–44^2. Birmingham University, B.Sc. Chidlaw Post-Graduate Research Scholarship (2 years). University A. E. Hill's Research Scholarship (1 Year), Ph.D. Technical Officer (Chemist) in I.C.I. Ltd., Mond Div. from 50. Senior Research Scientist from 70. Brother, R. E. Deriaz.

DERIAZ, Roger Edmond, B.Sc., Ph.D. T, 37^3–42^2.*

DERRY, Duncan Ramsay, Ph.D., b. 27 June 06, eldest s. of late Dr. D. Derry. C, 20^2–24^2. Corpus Christi, Cambridge, B.A. University of Toronto, M.A. Ph.D. Fellow of Royal Society of Canada. Pres. of Geological Assoc. of Canada, 51, and 71–72. Lecturer in Geology, University of Toronto, 31–35. Geologist, Ventures Ltd., 35–40. $\times$ R.C.A.F., 40–45. Sqn. Ldr. Chief Geologist, Ventures Ltd., 45–54.

Vice-Pres., Exploration, Rio Tinto Mining Co. of Canada, 54–60. Consulting Geologist from 60. *University Club of Toronto, Toronto Golf Club.* Royal Society of Canada.

DERRY, John Edward, b. 8 Mar. 28, s. of late F. W. Derry. B, 41^3–46^1. N/S. Rifle Brigade & R.A., 46–48. Lt. London University, LL.B. Solicitor, 52. Sons, Andrew Charles, B. 69^3– & Nicholas John, B. 71^3–.

de St. CROIX, Arthur Michael John, b. 9 Aug. 29, s. of late B. J. de St. Croix. W, 43^2–46^3. Architectural Assoc., A.R.I.B.A. Architect to the Peabody Trust, London.

de SALIS, Rodolph Patrick Fane, b. 18 Mar. 30, eldest s. of J. P. F. de Salis. W, 43^3–47^3. St. John's, Oxford, M.A. Rolls-(71) Ltd., Bristol Engine Div. Lay Reader (Hon. Secretary, Bristol Diocesan Board of Readers). Brother, 299.

de SELINCOURT, Geoffrey Martin. M, 14^3–17^1.*

DETERDING, George William, b. 7 Apr. 33, 2nd s. of late R. F. Deterding (OR M 14). M, 46^3–51^2; R. VIII, 51. N/S. (P. of W.) Dragoon Guards, R.A.C., 51–53. 2nd Lt. Gonville & Caius, Cambridge, B.A. A.R.I.C.S. Company Dir. & Farmer. Pres., Norfolk County Golf Union, 73–74. Local Chrmn., Conservatives.

DETERDING, Henry, b. 28 Aug. 97, elder s. of late Sir. H. Deterding, K.B.E. M, 11^3–15^2. Trinity, Cambridge. ✕ Montgomeryshire Yeomanry, 16–19. Lt. ✕ R.N.V.R., 39–45. Lt. (A), P.O.W., Germany, 40–45. Farming at Newnham Grounds, Daventry, from 22. Sons, J. H. & R. Deterding.

DETERDING, John Henry, b. 2 Mar. 23, elder s. of H. Deterding (OR M 11). M, 36^3–41^2; Levée; S. VIII, 39–40 (Capt.); 41 (Capt.); Exhibitioner. Scholar of Trinity, Cambridge, M.A. ✕ 43–46. R.N.V.R. Lt. (SP). Seismologist with Bataafsche Petroleum Maatschappij, 48–50. Research Scientist with Shell Research Ltd., from 50. Brother, R. Deterding.

DETERDING, Richard, b. 6 June 30, younger s. of H. Deterding (OR M 11). M, 44^2–48^2. Trinity, Cambridge, 50. Brother, J. H. Deterding.

DETERDING, Ronald James, b. 17 Dec. 30, elder s. of late R. F. Deterding.

M, 44^3–49^2; S. VIII, 48–49. Gonville & Caius, Cambridge, B.A. Farmer & Company Director.

DEWAR, William Quentin. SH, 36^2–40^2.*

DEWEY, The Rev. Meredith Ballard, b. 10 Mar. 07, 5th and youngest s. of late Rev. Sir S. D. Dewey, Bt. SH, 20^2–25^2. Pembroke, Cambridge, Exhibitioner, M.A. Ely Theological College. Curate of Wigan, 31–35. Fellow & Dean of Pembroke, Cambridge, 36–73, retired. Governor of Rugby School, 60–74. ✕ R.N.V.R. Chaplain, *Effingham, Revenge,* R.N.C., Dartmouth. Brother, T. S. Dewey.

DEWEY, Richard Stanley. B, 29^2–34^2.*

DEWEY, Theodore Stanley, M.B., B.Ch., b. 7 Feb. 02, 4th s. of late The Rev. Sir S. D. Dewey, Bt. SH, 15^3–20^2; S. VIII, 19–20. Scholar of Pembroke, Cambridge, M.A., M.B., B.Ch. St. Thomas's Hospital, M.R.C.S., L.R.C.P. Medical Officer of Tonbridge School. Retired. Brother, The Rev. M. B. Dewey.

DHANI, Mom Chao (H.H. The Prince Dhani), b. 7 Nov. 85, eldest s. of Krom Mune Bidyalabh of Bangkok, Thailand. T, 02^1–04^2. Merton, Oxford. Entered Siamese Civil Service, 09. Private Secretary to H.M. The King (18), Secretary of the Cabinet Council (18), Minister of Public Instruction (26), retired as result of the '32 Revolution. App. Member of the Council of Regency (48), Regent (51). Membership of the Privy Council upon the King's resumption of duty. President of the Privy Council. Siam Society (Hon. Pres.). Knight of the Royal House of Chakri, Grand Cordon of the Japanese Order of the Rising Sun. Publications including: "The Old Siamese Conception of the Monarchy", "The Reconstruction of Rama I of the Chakri Dynasty", "A History of Buddhism in Siam".

DIACRE, Kenneth William Deacon (formerly Deacon, K. W.). Tu 37^1–41^1.*

DIAMOND, Anthony Edward John, b. 4 Sept. 29, s. of A. S. Diamond. B, 43^1–47^3. Exhibitioner of Corpus Christi, Cambridge, M.A. N/S. R.A., 48–49. 2nd Lt. Barrister (Gray's Inn).

DICK, Derek Robert Robertson, b. 19 Nov. 12, 2nd s. of the late N. A. Dick. Tu, 26^2–30^2. University College, London, B.Sc. Diploma in Civil & Municipal Engineering.   C.Eng.,   F.I.C.E.,

F.I.Struct.E., Consulting Engineer, then Ministry of Works, then U.K. Atomic Energy Authority. Senior Director, W. S. Atkins & Partners, Consulting Engineers, since 55. Institute of Directors. Son, Anthony Robert, Tu 71³-.

DICKIE, Alexander Hugh Hamon Massy, M.B.E., b. 9 May 07, s. of A. A. Dickie, K.C. Tu, 21³–26²; Scholar; Major & Minor Exhibitioner. Scholar of Corpus Christi, Oxford, M.A. Solicitor, 33. (John Mackenzie Prize & 1st Class Hons.) Solicitor with Messrs. Freshfields, 33–40. ⚔ 40–45. R.A.F. Wing-Cdr. M.B.E. Since 47 Partner in Messrs. Freshfields.

DICKINSON, Alan Edgar Frederic, b. 9 July 99, younger s. of late F. W. Dickinson. St, 13³–17³; Scholar; Minor Exhibitioner. ⚔ R.G.A. 2nd Lt. Balliol, Oxford, M.A., B.Mus. Royal College of Music, London, Hon. A.R.C.M. Asst. Music Master, Malvern College, 23. 2nd Music Master, Uppingham School, 26–29. Dir. of Music, Campbell College, Belfast, 29–36. Lecturer in Music, Durham University, 46–64. Free-lance Writer on Music. *Penn Club.* Berlioz Society. Author of "Introduction of R. Vaughan Williams", "Beethoven", "The Art of J. S. Bach", "The Music of Berlioz".

DICKINSON, Alan Michael, M.R.C.S., L.R.C.P. St, 35³–39³.*

DICKINSON, John Anthony, b. 31 May 29, 3rd s. of late G. F. Dickinson, M.A., LL.D. (OR St 04). K, 43²–47². A.R.I.C.S. Chartered Surveyor. *Royal Ocean Racing Club, Royal Harwich Yacht Club.* Brothers, R. F. & A. M. Dickinson. Son, Peter Fryer, K. 68³-.

DICKINSON, John Watson, b. 17 July 06, 2nd s. of late W. W. Dickinson. SH, 20²–25²; R. VIII, 25. Trinity, Cambridge, B.A. ⚔ 39–45, Royal Artillery & R.E.M.E. Major. Joseph Lucas Ltd., 45–64. Retired.

DICKINSON, Ronald Fryer, D.L., J.P., b. 25 Sept. 16, eldest s. of late G. F. Dickinson, M.A., LL.D. (OR St 04). St, 30³–35¹. Pembroke, Cambridge, B.A. Dip. Agric., Dip. Arbor, R.F.S. ⚔ 40–46. Lt., R.N.V.R. (Coastal Forces). Nurseryman, Garden Designer and Arboriculturist, 46–66. Since 66, Portrait Artist. D.L., J.P. C. Alderman. Vice-Chrmn., Cumberland County Council. Lt.-Cdr., R.N.R. R.D. *Naval Club.* Royal Forestry Society. Society of Foresters. Brothers, A. M. & J. A. Dickinson. Son, 2410.

DICK-READ, Robert Nevill, b. 24 July 30, 2nd s. of late G. Dick-Read. SH, 44²–48²; XI, 47–48; H. XI, 48. Post-Graduate Course, London University, Social Anthropology.

DICKSON, Alexander Graeme, C.B.E., b. 23 May 14, 3rd s. of late N. B. Dickson, O.B.E. Tu, 27³–32². New College, Oxford, M.A. Editorial Staff, "Yorkshire Post", 36–37. Foreign Correspondent, "Daily Telegraph", 37–39, in London & Berlin: ran Scout troop in Leeds, became Prison Visitor at Wandsworth. ⚔ War-time service in East Africa with 1st King's African Rifles in Ethiopia: founded E.A. Army Mobile Propaganda Unit. After war, introduced mass education movement in Gold Coast, 47–49: founded Man o' War Bay training scheme in Nigeria/Cameroons, 50–54, to involve young West Africans in community development. In Iraq served as Chief of Unesco Technical Assistance Mission, 55–56. Founded Voluntary Service Overseas, 58, & Community Volunteers, 62 (Hon. Dir.). Consulted by U.S. Peace Corps, U.N., Governments of India, Hong Kong, Nigeria, Nepal etc. on participation of their youth in service & relating studies to social action. C.B.E., 57; Hon. LL.D., Leeds University, 70. Brothers, S. G. & M. G. Dickson.

DICKSON, Arthur Watson. St, 10³–13².*

DICKSON, Hugh Harper, M.B., B.S. M, 29¹–33².*

DICKSON, James Farquhar Gordon, b. 30 June 28, 2nd s. of Dr. R. A. McK. Dickson. B, 41³–45². Magdalen, Oxford. With Andrew Reid & Co. Ltd., Printers, Newcastle-upon-Tyne, 50–51. With Balding & Mansell Ltd., Printers, London & Wisbech, 52. Property Developer. Brother, J. T. McK. Dickson.

DICKSON, John Heron Dunbar, b. 1 July 24, s. of I. D. Dickson, M.D., M.C. SF, 38²–42². Trinity Hall, Cambridge. ⚔ Rifle Brigade, 43–46. Wounded. Capt. Norfolk County Council, Countryside Committee. Colonial Administrative Service, Gold Coast, 46–57. Farmer, dairy & arable.

DICKSON, John Todd McKinnel, b. 1 May 25, elder s. of Dr. R. A. McK. Dickson. B, 38³–43²; Cap. Queen's, Oxford, M.A. ⚔ R.A. Lt. Sudan Political Service (Magistrate), 51–54. Colonial Administrative Service, Northern Nigeria, 55–59. Manager, Arthur Guinness, from 60.

Vincent's, M.C.C. Brother, J. F. G. Dickson.

DICKSON, Malcolm Douglas Hamilton, b. 23 Nov. 25, s. of Dr. J. D. H. Dickson. SF, 39^3–43^2; R. VIII, 42–43. Trinity, Cambridge, M.A. Ran for University Cross Country (O.U.H. & H.). Awarded Representative Colours, 44–45. ✕ R.A.F.V.R., 45–48. M.I.C.E. Member, Eng. Inst. of Canada. Professional Eng., Ontario, Yukon, Alberta & Nova Scotia. Vice-Pres., Albery, Pullerits Dickson & Associates Ltd., Toronto, Consulting Engineers. *Craigleith Ski Club* (Pres., 72–73).

DICKSON, Murray Graeme, C.M.G., b. 19 July 11, 2nd s. of late N.B. Dickson, O.B.E. Tu, 25^2–29^2; Levée; Head of House. New College, Oxford, M.A. Dip. Ed., London. Dir. of Education, Sarawak, 55–66. Unesco Adviser on Educational planning to Government of Lesotho, 67–68. Retired. C.M.G. Brothers, S. G. & A. G. Dickson.

DICKSON, Col. Seton Graeme, D.L., J.P., b. 11 Nov. 09, eldest s. of late N. B. Dickson, O.B.E. Tu, 23^3–28^2; Boxing Winner, Lightweight, 28. R.M.C., Sandhurst, Prize Cadet. Commissioned, 30, The Royal Scots (The Royal Regt.). ✕ Flanders, Iceland, Haifa, 39–45. Lt.-Col., G.S.O.1, British Troops in Austria. Staff College, Camberley, 41. Retired, 56. Ayr County Councillor. Hon. Colonel, Ayrshire Bn., A.C.F. Member, Queen's Bodyguard for Scotland (Royal Company of Archers). M.St.J., D.L., J.P. *United Service Club, Pall Mall; New Club, Edinburgh.* Brothers, M. G. & A. G. Dickson. Son, 2536.

DINELEY, Mark. C, 15^3–19^3.*

DIX, Peter Carlton, b. 7 June 17, s. of late E. C. Dix. B, 31^1–35^2. University College, Oxford, B.A. Two Fencing Half Blues, University Foil, Epée & Sabre Champion. Entered Lloyd's, 39. ✕ R. Tank Regt. Capt. Wounded twice. P.O.W. Model Millinery, Dir., 46. British Epée Champion, 47 and 49. British Fencing International Reserve, Olympic Epée Team, 48. Irish Open Epée Champion, 47. Winner, British International Epée (Miller-Hallett Cup), 49. Retired. Sons, 2439, 2803B, William Tage Edward Carlton, B, 68^3– & Robert George Carlton, B, 70^3–.

DIXON, Christopher John Arnold, b. 17 Aug. 28, s. of late H. J. Dixon, M.C. K,

42^3–47^2. R.A. (Short Service Commission), 47–50. Trinity Hall, Cambridge. Solicitor, Partner in Norton, Rose, Botterell & Roche. T.D. Son, Anthony John, K, 71^3–.

DIXON, Francis James Bassett. SH, 07^3–10^2.*

DIXON, John Wolryche, b. 22 May 91, eldest s. of late C. W. Dixon. W, 05^3–10^2; R. VIII, 10. Corpus Christi, Oxford, B.A. ✕ H.A.C., 6th Bn. Middlesex Regt. Machine Gun Corps. Capt. A.C.A. Chartered Accountant. Retired. *Leander.* Sons, M. W. & R. S. Dixon.

DIXON, Michael Wolryche, b. 14 Oct. 19, eldest s. of J. W. Dixon. W, 33^2–38^1. Corpus Christi, Oxford. ✕ R.A., 40–46. Solicitor, 49. With Thomson Snell & Passmore, Solicitors, of Crowborough, Sussex. Notary Public. Brother, R. S. Dixon.

DIXON, Richard Stansfeld. W, 39^3–45^1.*

DOBIE, John Jardine, b. 26 Sept. 17, 2nd s. of late Capt. J. J. Dobie, D.S.O., M.C. (OR St 92). St, 31^2–35^3; XV, 35. Corpus Christi, Cambridge, M.A. ✕ Malayan Police Force, 39–45. Asst. Superintendent, interned in Malaya, 41–45. F.R.I.C.S. Chartered Surveyor & Land Agent until 60. Farming on own account from 60. *New Club, Edinburgh.*

DOD, Henry Arthur Cecil, b. 18 Dec. 21, s. of T. F. Dod. M, 35^3–39^2. Brasenose, Oxford, M.A. ✕ 132 (Welch) Field Regt., R.A. & 2nd Regt., R.H.A., Lt., 42–45. Solicitor, 49. Legal Associate Member, Royal Town Planning Institute. Fellow, Institute of Arbitrators. Partner, Baileys, Shaw & Gillett, Solicitors, London. Member, British Museum Society.

DODDS, George Christopher Buchanan. W, 30^2–35^1.*

DODGSON, Hubert Cecil. K, 08^3–11^2.*

DODS, Marcus, D.F.C., b. 19 Apr. 18, s. of late Sheriff M. Dods. St, 32^2–36^2; Music Scholar; XV, 35–36. Choral Scholar of King's, Cambridge XV, 38. M.A., Mus.B. Royal Academy of Music, F.R.A.M. ✕ R.A.F., 40–46. Sqn. Ldr. Pilot, D.F.C. Music Dir., J. Arthur Rank Organisation, 47–51. Conductor & Chorus Master, Sadlers Wells Opera Co., 52–58. Freelance Conductor, 58–66. Principal

Conductor, B.B.C. Concert Orch., 66–69. Free-lance Conductor from 69. Incorporated Society of Musicians. *Savile Club.*

DODSON, Eric Horsfall, b. 18 Jan. 24, s. of J. H. Dodson. W, 38^3–41^2. Exhibitioner of Trinity Hall, Cambridge, M.A., LL.B. ✕ Inns of Court Regt., R.A.C., 44–45. Capt. Civil Affairs E. Africa, 45–47. Solicitor, 51. Partner in Addleshaw, Sons & Latham, Solicitors, Manchester, from 53. *St. James', Manchester; National Liberal.*

DODSWORTH, Bryan Leonard Charles, M.C., Tu, 34^1–38^2. Sons, 2590 & 2939.*

DOHERTY, Hugh Carrington, b. 16 Feb. 18, s. of late A. H. C. Doherty. Tu, 31^3–35^3. Jesus, Cambridge, M.A. Secretary to Public Rubber Cos., operating in Malaya, Java & Sumatra. Retired. Son, 2419.

DOHERTY, Hugh David, b. 31 Aug. 27, eldest s. of late W. D. Doherty, M.Ch., F.R.C.S. M, 41^3–45^2; XV, 44. Pembroke, Cambridge, M.A. Rugby Football Blue, 50. Bar, Middle Temple, 54. Military Service, 45–48. Lt. Royal Inniskilling Fusiliers. Since 52, with The British United Shoe Machinery Co. Ltd., Leicester, & its Associates, & now Legal Director & Law Counsel for the Group. *Hawks Club, British Sportsman's Club.*

DONNER, Richard Elliot, D.F.C. (formerly Elliot, R.). M, 35^1–38^2.*

DONOVAN, Christopher Ferrier. SF, 43^2–48^2.*

DONOVAN, Richard Alexander, SF, 41^1–45^2.*

DOREY, Norman John, b. 9 July 03, 3rd s. of J. J. Dorey. SF, 17^3–20^1. Dir., Joseph Dorey & Co. Ltd., Brentford. Dir., Goldhawk Building Society, London. National Trust.

DORMAN, Lt.-Col. Sir Charles Geoffrey, Bt., M.C., b. 18 Sept. 20, s. of late Sir B. Dorman, Bt., C.B.E. (OR M 93). M, 34^2–38^2. Brasenose, Oxford, M.A. Army: p.s.c. p.t.s.c. Gazetted to 3rd The King's Own Hussars, 41. 13th/18th Royal Hussars (Q.M.O.), 47–70. Last appointment, Lt.-Col. G.S.O.1(W.), I.F.V.M.E. Farmer, Company Director. Member, R.A.S.E. F.R.H.S. M.C.

DORMAN, Richard, b. 25 May 18, s. of late A. J. Dorman, M.A., J.P. (OR M 95). M, 31^3–36^2. ✕ 39–46, The Green Howards. Capt. & Adj. P.O.W., 43. Peat, Marwick, Mitchell, 37–39 & 46–50. Acton Bolt Ltd., G.K.N. Bolts & Nuts Ltd., 50–71. Retired. *M.C.C.*

DOUGLAS, John Philip. M, 43^1–47^2.*

DOUGLAS, Philip Sholto. M, 46^3–50^2.*

DOUIE, Kenneth McCrone Gaskell, b. 8 Feb. 32, 2nd s. of late Col. F. M. Douie, D.S.O., M.C. (OR C oo). Tu, 45^3–50^2. N/S. 1st Wiltshire Regt., 50–52. B.A., Dip. Ed., Oxford. Headmaster of the Lower School, St. Dunstan's College, Catford, London. *Oxford & Cambridge.*

DOVE, William George, b. 5 Mar. 11, elder s. of W. Dove. SF, 24^3–29^2; XV, 27–28; XI, 29. Wine Shipper, 29–48. Farmer, 48–54. Wine Shipper, 54–71. Retired to Spain, 71. *Senior Golfers Society.*

DOW, Hugh Peter. B, 33^3–38^1.*

DOWELL, Richard Gough, b. 5 Jan. 15, eldest s. of R. S. Dowell. St, 28^3–33^2. Magdalene, Cambridge, M.A. Chrmn., John Dowell & Sons Ltd., & Associated Companies (Private). ✕ R.A.F., 40–45. Pilot, 570 Squadron. F/Lt. J.P., Surrey, 64. General Commissioner of Income Tax, 68. *Junior Carlton Club, M.C.C.*

DOWNES, Martin John Mulgrave. SH, 07^2–11^2.*

DOWSON, Peter Malcolm, M.C., b. 30 Mar. 15, s. of M. Dowson. SH, 28^3–33^2; XI, 30–33; XV, 32; H. XI, 32–33. Burma Shell, India, 37–53. ✕ R.A. (Mounted Artillery), 39–44. Major. M.C. Dispatches. Shell, South Africa, 53–60. Shell International Pet. Co., London, 60–71. *Junior Carlton Club, M.C.C.* Son, Charles Malcolm Eastment, SH, 68^1–72^3.

DOXFORD, Theodore Bertram, J.P. W, 20^3–24^2. Son, 2173.*

D'OYLY, Michael John, b. 13 Oct. 31, s. of late J. R. D'Oyly. M, 45^3–48^2. Cert. of Competency as 2nd Mate of a Foreign-Going Steamship (9.6.54). Farming, 48–49. Merchant Navy, 49–57. Crammers, 57–59. Bristol University, B.Sc., M.I. Biol. Cert. Ed., 59–63. Field Studies Council, 63–66. Assistant Warden, 66; Assistant Regional Officer, The Nature Conservancy. B.S.B.I., B.T.O., F.S.C. Br. Lichen Soc.

DRAPER, Alick Darby, b. 24 Feb. 84, younger s. of late H. M. Draper (OR W 58). W, 99²–01². Engineering apprentice, McLarens of Leeds. Leeds University, B.Sc. Engineer. ⚔ A.S.C., 2nd Army Anti-Aircraft Workshop. Capt. Hon. Member, Institute of Mechanical Engineers. Retired.

DREW, James. Tu, 20²–25².*

DRIVER, Christopher Prout, b. 1 Dec. 32, s. of A. H. Driver. M, 46²–51²; Scholar; Levée; Head of School; Leaving Exhibition. Scholar of Christ Church, Oxford, M.A. "The Guardian", 60–68 (Reporter & latterly Features Editor). Free-lance writer, and Editor of the "Good Food Guide" since 68. Author of "A Future for the Free Churches", "The Disarmers: a study in protest", "The Exploding University".

DRIVER, Norman. B, 20²–22¹.*

DRUMMOND, Major Patrick Hamilton, b. 27 Dec. 26, s. of late Sir W. J. Drummond. B, 40²–44². Regular Officer, The Life Guards, 44–58; Major, 55. Executive, Balfour Williamson & Co., Dir. of Balfour Williamson (Export Service) Ltd., 58–64. Group Premises Controller, Bank of London & South America, 65–73. Gen. Man., Hume Property Investments Ltd., since 73. *Cavalry Club.*

DRURY, The Rev. Michael Dru, b. 20 Nov. 31, eldest s. of N. D. Drury (OR M 14). M, 45³–50²; XV, 48–49; XI, 50. N/S. R.A., 50–52, in B.A.O.R. Trinity, Oxford, M.A. Wycliffe Hall, Oxford, 56–58, Diploma of Theology, 57. Ordained, 58. Curate, St. Mary's, West Kensington, 58–62. Curate, St. John's, Blackheath, 62–64. Asst. Chaplain, Canford School, 64–71; Chaplain from 72. *Butterflies C.C.*

DRURY, Norman Dru, b. 4 June 00, elder s. of late W. E. Drury. M, 14²–18³. London Stock Exchange, 18–21. Forbes & Walker Ltd., Colombo, 22–55. Senior Dir., Tea, Rubber, Freight Exchange, Share Brokers. Retired. ⚔ Ceylon Garrison Artillery, 42–45. Major. Brother, W. N. D. Drury. Son, M. D. Drury.

DRURY, Walter Neville Dru, b. 30 June 08, 2nd s. of late W. E. Drury. M, 22²–25²; XXII, 25; Sw. VI (Capt.), 25. ⚔ R.A. (A.A.)., 39–45. Major. T.D. Insurance Broker & Underwriting Member of Lloyd's since 27. Retired, 73. *Bath Club, Senior Golfers.* Brother, N. D. Drury. Sons, 694 & 1348.

DRYSDALE, Alasdair Morrison, LL.B., T.D., b. 20 July 15, s. of late J. W. W. Drysdale. Tu, 29²–33². Clare, Cambridge, B.A. Glasgow University, LL.B. ⚔ Highland Light Infantry, 39–45. Major. Dispatches. T.D. With J. P. Coats Ltd., 46–70. Company Secretary and thereafter Group Personnel Dir. Presently Chrmn. (part-time) of Wm. Low & Co. Ltd., Dundee. *Western Club, Glasgow; Hon. Company of Edinburgh Golfers, Muirfield; & Elie Golf House Club.* Sons, 1658 & 2420.

DU BUISSON, Major Thomas Gerard, M.B.E., M.C., b. 8 Jan. 92, younger s. of late T. Du Buisson. SH, 05³–10². R.M.A., Woolwich. Gazetted to R.F.A. 11 R.H.A. ⚔ R.F.A., 12–18. Major. Wounded twice. M.C. Dispatches twice. Instructor, R.M.A., Woolwich, 18–22. Remount Officer to 39. ⚔ Re-employed, 40–44. M.B.E. *Cavalry Club.*

DUCKHAM, Henry Richard Godwin, b. 22 July 20, 2nd s. of T. H. Duckham. K, 34¹–38²; XI, 38; Cap, 37–38; R. VIII, 38. Clare, Cambridge, until 39. ⚔ The Cameronians (Scottish Rifles), France. Dispatches. Seconded R.W.A.F.F., 41–42. Transferred R.E. Major. Demobilised, 46. Insurance Broker. Underwriting Member of Lloyd's. Chrmn., Lionel Sage & Co. Ltd., Lionel Sage (Underwriting Agencies) Ltd., Lionel Sage (Life & Pensions Consultants) Ltd. and Lionel Sage (South Africa) Pty. Ltd. Liveryman, Worshipful Company of Curriers.

du CROS, Edouard Pierre, b. 22 Mar. 19, younger s. of H. du Cros. Tu, 32³–37². Gonville & Caius, Cambridge. ⚔ R.A. & Royal Horse Guards, 39–43. 2nd Lt. Refugee Camps, Germany, Quaker Relief, 46–47. In film industry, underwater films, 54–60. Racing Driver, 61–67. N.S.W. State Government Service Course in Law, Psychology & Social Work. Probation Officer, Sydney, N.S.W., from 68. Permanent Officer, Public Service, N.S.W., Australia.

DUDGEON, Patrick Orpen, b. 26 Sept. 14, elder s. of L. S. Dudgeon, C.B.E., M.D., F.R.C.P. C, 28²–32². Gonville & Caius, Cambridge, M.A. Fellow, Institute Escuela, Valencia, Spain, 35–36. Prof. Eng. Lang. & Lit., Asociacion Argentina de Caltura Inglesa, Buenos Aires. Prof. Eng. Lang., Institute Nacional Superior del Profesorade en Lenguas Vivas, Buenos Aires, 57–68. Prof. Eng. Lit., University of Buenos Aires, 70–71. Dir., Instituto Santo

Tomas Moro, Buenos Aires. *P.E.N.,*
Argentina; Anglo-Argentine. Walter Owen
Society.

DUFF, David Skene, b. 9 July 12, eldest
s. of Dr. C. H. Duff, F.R.C.S. M, 26[1]–
28[3]. Author of "Edward of Kent", "The
Life of H.R.H. Princess Louise", "The
Shy Princess", "Mother of The Queen",
"Hessian Tapestry", "Victoria Travels",
"Victoria in the Highlands", "Albert and
Victoria", "Elizabeth of Glamis". Society
of Authors. ✕ R.A., 39–47. Major.

DUFFY, John Rutherford, b. 16 Aug. 32,
elder s. of T. L. Duffy. T, 45[3]–50[1];
H. XI, 50; Junior Athletics Cup, 48.
Solicitor. Governor, Lawrence Sheriff
School, Rugby. Partner, Bretherton, Turpin & Pell, Solicitors, Rugby. Joined firm
on leaving school.

DUFTY, Arthur Richard, A.R.I.B.A.,
C.B.E., b. 23 June 11, s. of T. E. Dufty. C,
25[2]–29[2]. Liverpool School of Architecture.
A.R.I.B.A., F.S.A. ✕ R.N.V.R., 42–46.
Lt. Secretary, Royal Commission on
Historical Monuments (England). Master
of the Armouries in Her Majesty's Royal
Palace & Fortress of the Tower of London.
C.B.E. *Athenæum, Arts, Naval Clubs.*

**DUGDALE, Christopher David (now
Fenwick, C. D.),** K, 26[2]–29[2].*

DUGDALE, John Frederick, M.C. K,
27[3]–31[2].*

DUKES, Arthur Kerr. T, 36[1]–41[2].*

DUKES, John Marcus Cuthbert, b. 21
June 22, s. of Dr. C. Dukes, O.B.E., M.D.,
M.Sc., D.P.H. K, 36[1]–40[2]; R. VIII, 40.
Trinity, Cambridge, M.A. Imperial Col-
lege of Science & Technology, 49–50.
D.I.C. Chartered Electrical Engineer.
M.I.E.E. ✕ Friends Ambulance Unit in
Africa, France & Germany with 2nd
French Armd. Div. Médaille d'Argent de
la Croix Rouge Française. Standard Tele-
phones & Cables, 47–59. The Plessey Co.
Ltd., 59–65. Cossor Electronics Ltd. (Man.
Dir.), 65–68. Raytheon Europe Inter-
national Co. (Technical Dir.), from 68.
Maison de la Deuxieme Division Blindée.
Various Technical Publications, including
"Printed Circuits—Their Design &
Application". *Norwegian Club.*

DULLEY, John Edgar, b. 31 Oct. 15, 2nd
s. of late E. H. Dulley. K, 29[2]–33[1]. Learnt
French in France & German in Germany
under Hitler. Worked since 34 in the

manufacturing chemist business, largely in
perfumery & toiletries. At present, Sales
Dir. of Scott & Bowne Ltd. ✕ Northamptonshire Regt. Major. Dispatches twice.

DUMBELL, John Frederick, b. 26 June
29, eldest s. of A. F. Dumbell. K, 43[3]–
48[2]. Clare, Cambridge, M.A. Esso Europe
Inc. M.C.S. Dept.

DUMMETT, George Anthony, b. 13
Oct. 07, elder s. of late G. H. Dummett.
W, 21[3]–25[2]; Levée; Head of House; R.
VIII, 25. Scholar of Birmingham Univer-
sity; Pembroke, Cambridge, M.A. Stoker
Research Fellowship, 30–31. M.I.Chem.E.,
F.I.Chem.E. Pres., Institution of Chemi-
cal Engineers, 68–69. Chrmn., Research
Committee, 58–65. Thorncliffe Coal Dis-
tillation, 32. A.P.V. Co. Ltd.: Research
Asst., 35, and then to Research Dir., 56.
Deputy Man. Dir., 65–72. A.P.V. (Hold-
ings) Ltd., Dir. 62–72. Now consultant.
Diamond Power Specialty Ltd., Dir. from
61. A.C.E. (Machinery) Holdings Ltd.,
Dir. from 72. *Alpine Club, Climbers' Club.*
Institute of Brewing. Brother, R. B.
Dummett. Son, 1063.

DUMMETT, Robert Bryan, C.B.E., b.
15 July 12, younger s. of late G. H. Dummett. W, 26[1]–30[2]. Gottingen University.
Trinity, Cambridge. Joined the then
Anglo-Iranian Oil Co. Ltd. in 36. Retired
from British Petroleum Co. Ltd. in 72
as Deputy Chrmn. London Board, Commercial Bank of Australia. C.B.E. Knight
Grand Cross of Order of Merit, Republic
of Italy. *Australia Club, Melbourne.*
Brother, G. A. Dummett.

DUNCAN, Col. Anthony Arthur,
O.B.E., b. 10 Dec. 14, 2nd s. of late J.
Duncan (OR B 94). B, 28[3]–33[2]; XI, 33.
Balliol, Oxford. Golf Blue, 34–36 (Capt.).
Gazetted to Welsh Guards. ✕ Welsh
Guards. Major. Belgium Croix de Guerre.
Order of Leopold. Army Golf Champion,
37–38 & 48. Welsh Amateur Champion,
38 & 48. Runner-up, British Amateur
Championship, 39. Retired from Army as
Col., 70. Re-employed with Army as a
Retired Officer at the Staff College, Cam-
berley, from 70. O.B.E. *R. & A. Golf
Club of St. Andrews, Oxford & Cambridge
Golfing Society, M.C.C.* Sons, 2653 &
2967.

DUNCAN, Sir Arthur Bryce, b. 27 Aug.
09, 2nd s. of J. B. Duncan. C, 23[3]–26[3]. St.
John's, Cambridge, B.A. Chrmn., Nature
Conservancy, 53–61. Chrmn., Dumfriesshire County Council, 55–61. Convener,

61–69. Lord Lieutenant, Dumfriesshire, 67–69. Chrmn., Crichton Royal Institution, 58–71. Served on innumerable Government Committees. Landowner, Farmer, Company Director. Knight Bachelor, 61. *British Ornithologists, Zoological, Scottish Ornithologists, Farmers', New (Edinburgh).* Brother, W. Duncan.

DUNCAN, Derek Cecil, b. 10 June 32, 2nd s. of late J. H. Duncan (OR B 01). B, 45^3–50^2. Gonville & Caius, Cambridge, M.A. Solicitor. Asst. Secretary, The Law Society, formerly Asst. Secretary, The Stock Exchange, London. Grocers Company. *Oxford & Cambridge Golf Society.* Brother, H. R. Duncan.

DUNCAN, Prof. Douglas James McKerrow, Ph.D. SH, 44^3–49^2.*

DUNCAN, George Travis. B, 43^2–47^3.*

DUNCAN, Hugh Ross, b. 19 Dec. 29, eldest s. of late J. H. Duncan (OR B 01). B, 43^2–47^3; Cap, 47. 75th H.A.A. Regt., R.A., 48. Man. Dir. (Manufacturing Chemists). Brother, D. C. Duncan.

DUNCAN, Kenneth MacKenzie, M.R.C.S., L.R.C.P., b. 11 Apr. 19, s. of late K. M. Duncan, Sh, 32^3–36^3. King's, Cambridge, M.A. The London Hospital, M.R.C.S., L.R.C.P., M.R.C.G.P. ✕ 43–46, R.A.F.V.R. F/Lt. General Practitioner (until illness in 71) from 47. At present, Medical Officer, National Blood Transfusion Service.

DUNCAN, Peter Colin, M.C., Q.C., b. 3 Oct. 95, s. of late P. T. Duncan. Tu, 09^3–14^2. Trinity, Oxford. ✕ 4th Bn. Royal West Surrey Regt., Capt. Wounded. M.C. Dispatches. Barrister-at-Law, 28. Master of the Bench, Inner Temple, 60. Q.C., 63. Recorder, Bury St. Edmunds. Recorder, Norwich. Deputy Chrmn., Surrey Q.S. J.P. Practising Barrister.

DUNCAN, Peter David Grahame. S.F., 43^3–47^2.*

DUNCAN, Walter, b. 19 Aug. 06, eldest s. of J. B. Duncan. C, 20^2–24^1. Oriel, Oxford, M.A. Berlin University. J.P. F.E.I.S. Landowner, Farmer & Forester. ✕ 40–45, R.A.F.V.R. Sq. Ldr. Dispatches. Member, Dumfries County Council, 32–64. Chrmn., Education & Probation Committees. Zoological & Agricultural Societies of London. Society Antiquaries of Scotland. Knight of The Order of St. Olav of Norway (1st class). *Himalayan Club.* Brother, Sir A. B. Duncan.

DUNHILL, The Rev. Robin Arnold, b. 5 Jan. 15, elder s. of T. F. Dunhill. SH, 28^3–33^2; Scholar; Stovin Exhibition. Scholar of Brasenose, Oxford, M.A. Cuddesdon College, Oxford, 41 & 46. ✕ R.A.M.C., 41–45. Pte. Ordained Deacon, 46; Priest, 47. Vicar, All Saints, Wellingborough, 53–63. Vicar, St. Jude-on-the-Hill, Hampstead Garden Suburb, London, from 63. Son, Stephen Robin, SH, 67^3–71^3.

DUNKERLEY, Arthur Henry, M.R.C.S., L.R.C.P., b. 14 Oct. 06, 2nd s. of late W. C. Dunkerley (OR C 85). M, 20^3–24^2. Gonville & Caius, Cambridge, B.A. Manchester Royal Infirmary, L.R.C.P., M.R.C.S., M.B., B.Chir. General Medical Practitioner to Sept., 72. Now retired.

DUNKERLEY, Charles Robertson. M, 19^3–21^3.*

DUNKLEY, George Samuel, b. 7 Dec. 01, eldest s. of late W. E. Dunkley. T, 15^2–18^3; Scholar; Levée; Head of House. Barclays Bank, Rugby, 19–23. Hong Kong & Shanghai Banking Corporation, 23–52. Retired as Man., Tientsin Office.

DUNLOP, George Teacher, b. 27 May 23, eldest s. of late R. J. Dunlop. Tu, 37^2–41^3; Cap, 41; Sw. VIII, 39–41 (Capt.). ✕ 42–46. Capt. Fife & Forfar Yeomanry, T.A. Major. Joined William Teacher & Sons Ltd., Scottish Whisky Distillers, 51. Dir. & Company Secretary until 64, also of Teacher (Distillers) Ltd. (Parent Co.). Joint Man. Dir., 66. Man. Dir., 68. Dir. of Chamber of Commerce, Glasgow. *Western Club, Glasgow; Royal Northern Yacht Club,* Vice-Commodore. Son, Nicholas George Teacher, Tu, 69^3–.

DUNLOP, Major Henry Craufurd, M.B.E., b. 30 June 14, eldest s. of late C. T. Dunlop. Tu, 27^3–31^1. Clare, Cambridge. ✕ Royal Northumberland Fusiliers, 39–47. Lt.-Col. M.B.E. Dir. of Companies & Merchant Bank Dir. *Oriental Club.* Son, 405.

DUNN, George, b. 4 July 90, s. of late P. H. Dunn, M.D. C, 04^3–09^2; Scholar; Exhibitioner. Scholar of Corpus Christi, Oxford, B.A. Gaisford Prize for Greek Verse, 13. Civil Servant, Admiralty, 14–50.

DUNNETT, William Herbert Derek, b. 9 Feb. 21, s. of W. H. Dunnett. Tu, 34^3–39^2; XV, 38; XI, 36, 38, 39; Rackets

Pair, 39; H. XI, 38–39. ✕ R.A.F. Formerly Man. Dir., Carters Tested Seeds Ltd. Now Chrmn. & Man. Dir., Raynes Park Securities Ltd. *Royal London Yacht Club; Queen's; East India, Sports & Public Schools.*

du PARCQ, The Hon. John Renouf, b. 9 June 17, s. of the late Lord du Parcq of Grouville. SH, 30³–35². Exeter, Oxford. M.I.E.E. Engineering & Production Management. Dir. of Manufacturing, The Sperry Gyroscope Div. of Sperry Rand.

DUPEN, Arthur Vivian. SF, 19¹–21².*

DURNO, Leslie George, b. 27 July 92, elder s. of late Rev. G. Durno, M.A. T & W, 05³–11¹. University College, Oxford, B.A. ✕ 3rd Bn. Seaforth Highlanders. Lieut. Wounded in France. I.C.S. (Bengal), 21–40. District Magistrate, Dacca, 30–31. Divisional Commissioner, Chittagong, 38. Retired, 40. ✕ Company Commander, Home Guard, Suffolk.

DUVEEN, Denis Ian. SH, 24¹–28¹.*

E

EADEN, Harold David Buckland, D.S.C. W, 28³–32.*

EADIE, George Patrick, b. 4 Dec. 12, s. of G. Eadie. W, 26³–28². Royal Technical College, Glasgow. Glasgow University, B.Sc., A.M.I.Mech.E. Member of Society of Glass Technology, U.K. Chrmn. & Man. Dir. of Laidlaw Drew & Co. Ltd. (Combustion Engineers), Edinburgh.

EARLE, William Herbert, C.B.E., b. 25 July 13, eldest s. of late Lt.-Col. F. W. Earle, D.S.O., J.P. B, 26³–31³. Christ Church, Oxford, M.A. Ski-ing v. Cambridge, 33–36; Lawn Tennis v. Cambridge, 36–37. British Council Officer, 42–70. Representative, Syria, 52–56. Deputy Controller, Commonwealth Div., 57–60. Representative, Pakistan, 60–62. Controller, Finance Div., 62–64. Representative, India, 64–69. Retired, 70. C.B.E., 66. *Athenæum, All England Lawn Tennis Club.*

EASTHAM, Ernest John Desmond. Tu, 28²–32².*

EASTHAM, Robert David. Tu, 29²–34².*

EASTON, John Lawrence Howland, M.D., F.R.C.P., b. 22 Sept. 03, eldest s. of Dr. F. Easton. M, 17³–22¹. Pembroke, Cambridge, M.A., M.D. Burney Yeo Exhibitioner to King's College Hospital, London, F.R.C.P. Hon. Physician, Kent & Sussex Hospital, Tunbridge Wells, 38–48. Senior Physician, Bedford General Hospital, 48–66. ✕ Medical Specialist, Lt.-Col., R.A.M.C., 40–45. Dispatches. Retired, 66. Royal Society of Medicine.

EATON, Anthony Denzil Musgrave. M, 14³–18¹.*

ECCLES, Col. Hubert Anthony, M.B.E., b. 14 Oct. 16, elder s. of late J. L. Eccles (OR W 02). W, 30³–34². Ecole de Commerce, Neuchâtel, Switzerland. ✕ R.A.S.C., 39–45. Col. M.B.E. Dispatches twice. Shell, from 37. *Oriental Club.* Son, Nigel Anthony Benedict, W. 68³–.

ECCLES, Ralph Alexander Oscar Alan. W, 39³–44².*

ECCLES, Roger Joe. SF, 09³–12³.*

EDDISON, Arthur Geoffrey, M.B., B.Chir., b. 14 May 02, younger s. of late J. A. Eddison. M, 16¹–19³. Pembroke, Cambridge, M.A., M.B., B.Chir. University College Hospital, London, M.R.C.S., L.R.C.P. General Medical Practice. Now retired. *East India, Sports & Public Schools.* Son, 258.

EDDISON, James Andrew, b. 9 May 21, 2nd s. of J. H. Eddison, M.C. B, 34³–39²; Cap; Athletics Cup, 39. Trinity, Cambridge, M.A. War-time Blue for Athletics, 40. ✕ R.E. Capt. Dispatches. F.I.C.E., F.I.Struct.E. Senior Partner in Blyth & Blyth, Consulting Engineers, Edinburgh. *Caledonian Club, Hawks.* Fellow of the Royal Society of Edinburgh. Brother, J. S. B. Eddison. Son, 2509.

EDDISON, John Stephen Briscoe, b. 19 Sept. 19, eldest s. of J. H. Eddison, M.C. B, 33¹–37³; Levée; Head of House; XV, 36–37. ✕ R.A. Capt. P.O.W. Hong Kong, 41–45. Dir., Smith (Allerton) Ltd. and Robert Clough (Keighley) Ltd., both now merged to form British Mohair Spinners Ltd. Dir., Worsted Spinners Federation Ltd. *Bradford Union Club.* Brother, J. A. Eddison. Sons, William John, B, 68²– & Stephen Nicholas, B, 70¹–.

EDDOWES, Alfred Bowman, M.B., B.Ch., b. 3 Aug. 01, s. of late A. Eddowes. C, 14^3–19^1; Minor Exhibitioner. Scholar of St. John's, Cambridge, B.A., M.B., B.Ch. St. George's Hospital, M.R.C.S., L.R.C.P. Retired General Medical Practitioner. *Local Golf Club & Sailing Club.* Son, 406.

EDE, William Oswald Moore, M.B., B.Chir., b. 12 June 07, eldest s. of late Dr. W. E. M. Ede. St, 21^3–26^1. King's, Cambridge, M.A., M.B., B.Chir. The London Hospital, D.A.Eng., L.M.C.C. (Canada). Active Consultant in Anaesthesia, York Central Hospital, Richmond Hill, Ontario.

EDEN, Conrad William, T.D., B.Mus., b. 4 May 05, s. of W. E. Eden. T, 20^2–23^2; Music Scholar. Royal College of Music. St. John's, Oxford. Organ Exhibition, College Organist. Mus.B., Hon. F.R.C.O. Organist, Wells Cathedral, 33–36. Organist, Durham Cathedral from 36. ✕ R.A., 39–45. Capt. T.D.

EDEN, Robert John Pulleine, b. 16 Feb. 20, eldest s. of late Brig. H. C. H. Eden, M.C., C.B.E. SF, 33^3–36^3. Solicitor's Articled Clerk. ✕ London Welch (T.A.), 39–46. Service in M.E., Yugoslavia, etc. Capt. T.A.R.O. 21 S.A.S. (Artists) Regt., T.A. Commerce, Finance & Manufacturing. Dir. various companies. Alderman, Essex County Council. Now farming in Devon.

EDEN, The Hon. Roger Quentin Eden, b. 18 June 22, younger s. of late Lord Henley. Sh, 36^1–39^2. College of Aeronautical & Automobile Engineering, Chelsea. A.F.R.Ae.S., C.Eng. ✕ Royal Air Force (Engineer Officer), 43–47. D. Napier & Son (Research Engineer), 47–50. Shell International Petroleum Co. Ltd., from 50 (Marketing Executive). Son, 2474.

EDGAR, William John. SF, 44^2–48^2.*

EDGSON, Gerald Stanley, b. 20 Nov. 28, 2nd s. of late W. S. Edgson. W, 43^2–44^2. N/S. R.N., 47–49, A.B. Chrmn., Forum Properties Ltd. Brother, P. S. Edgson.

EDGSON, Peter Silvester, b. 12 Nov. 18, elder s. of late W. S. Edgson. W, 32^2–36^2. Trinity Hall, Cambridge, M.A. ✕ R.A., 39–46. Capt. F.R.I.C.S. Hillier, Parker, May & Rowden (Surveyors, Valuers & Estate Agents) from 39. Partner, 51. Senior Partner, 61. *Bath Club.* Brother, G. S. Edgson.

EDMEADES, Col. Ashton William, M.B.E., b. 11 Oct. 09, s. of late Lt.-Col. W. A. Edmeades, D.S.O. SH, 23^2–27^3. R.M.A., Woolwich. Staff College, Camberley. Gazetted to R.A., 29. Lt., 32. ✕ M.B.E. Dispatches twice. p.s.c. Commander, Solent Garrison. H.Q., Rhine Army. A/Colonel. *M.C.C., Army & Navy Club.* Sons, 2782, Michael David, SH, 67^2– & Evelyn Hugh, SH, 69^3–.

EDWARDS, Arthur Middleton, b. 11 Feb. 18, s. of A. C. Edwards. SF, 31^3–35^3. Corpus Christi, Cambridge, B.A., A.R.I.B.A., 44. M.R.T.P.I. Principal Lecturer in Dept. of Social & Environmental Planning at Polytechnic of Central London.

EDWARDS, Lionel Yeo. B, 17^1–20^2.*

EDWARDS, Richard Lionel, Q.C., b. 1 Aug. 07, eldest s. of L. T. Edwards. C, 21^3–25^1. Oriel, Oxford. Bar, 30. Queen's Counsel, 52. Bencher, Lincoln's Inn, 57. *E.S.U.*

EDWARDS, William Philip Neville, C.B.E., b. 5 Aug. 04, s. of N. P. Edwards. St, 18^2–22^3. Corpus Christi, Cambridge, M.A. Princeton University, U.S.A. (Davison Scholar). Joined Underground Electric Rlys. Co. of London Ltd., 27. Sec. of Standing Joint Committee of Main Line Rlys. & L.P.T.B., 33. Ministry of Supply, 41–42. Head of Industrial Information Div., Ministry of Production, 43–45. Dir. of Information Div., Board of Trade, 45–46. Head of British Information Services in U.S.A., 46–49. C.B.E., 49. Deputy Overseas Dir. of F.B.I. from 49. Man. Dir., British Overseas Fairs Ltd., 59–66. Chrmn., 66–68. Retired, 68. *Carlton Club, Walton Heath Golf Club.*

EDWARDS JONES, Ian, Q.C., b. 17 Apr. 23, s. of H. V. Edwards Jones, M.C., D.L. Tu, 36^3–40^2. Trinity, Cambridge, B.A. ✕ R.A., 42–47. Capt. Bar, Middle Temple & Lincoln's Inn, 48. Q.C., 67. *Oxford & Cambridge University, Bar Yacht Clubs.* Sons, Mark, Tu. 68^3– & Michael Christopher, Tu. 70^3–.

EGERTON, Arthur Edward, M.C., b. 7 Aug. 93, 2nd s. of late H. E. Egerton (OR SH 68). SH, 07^3–11^2; Scholar. Balliol, Oxford, M.A. ✕ 11th Hussars. 3rd Bn. West Yorkshire Regt. 69th Trench Mortar Bty. Gen. Staff, Intelligence. Capt. Wounded. M.C. ✕ Intelligence Corps, Middle East, 41–42. N. Africa, Italy etc., 43–45. Control Commission in Germany,

Education Branch, 46–50. *Royal Commonwealth Society*. R. Central Asian Society.

EGGLESTON, Albert Leslie Hunter. B, 10³–13¹.

EILOART, Ian Robert, b. 3 June 30, 2nd s. of late A. C. Eiloart (OR Tu 07). Tu, 44²–48²; XI, 48. Chartered Accountant. Group Accountant, Lindustries Ltd. Brother, N. C. Eiloart.

EILOART, Nigel Colin, b. 28 Apr. 27, elder s. of late A. C. Eiloart (OR Tu 07). Tu, 41¹–45²; XI, 44–45. Trinity Hall, Cambridge, M.A. Professional Engineer, Province of Ontario. Executive Vice-Pres., J. Brockhouse & Co. (Canada) Ltd., Toronto. *M.C.C.* R.H.S. Brother, I. R. Eiloart.

ELLICE, Charles. St, 18³–23².*

ELLINGER, Alexander Geoffrey, b. 27 Oct. 04, elder s. of late M. Ellinger. St, 18³–23²; Head of House; Leaving Exhibition. Scholar of Oriel, Oxford, B.A. Textiles, Ellinger & Co. Ltd., Manchester, 27–30. Office work with Stockbrokers in London, 30–40. ✕ 40–45. R.A.S.C. Capt. Founded Investment Research, Cambridge, 45, now Senior Partner. *National Liberal, Hellenic, Travellers', Cambridge U.L.T. & Croquet Club.* Author of "The Art of Investment" and others.

ELLIOT, Ian Frederick Lettsom, b. 25 Oct. 93, 2nd s. of late Col. W. H. W. Elliot, D.S.O., I.M.S. M, 07³–12²; Scholar; Head of House; XV, 10–11; XI, 10–12 (Capt.). Scholar of Christ Church, Oxford, M.A. ✕ 14–18. Capt. 4th Bn. Suffolk Regt. & M.G.C. Wounded. Guest, Keen & Nettlefolds Ltd., 19–36. Commercial Dir., British Iron & Steel, 36–42. British Purchasing Mission, New York Federation (Steel & Raw Materials), Washington, 40–42. Chrmn., Eastern Group Supply Council, 43–44. Ministry of Supply, Special Duties, 44–45. U.S. Steel Corporation, 45–64 (Personal Rep. of Chrmn., European Liaison). Retired. Chevalier Legion d'Honneur. *Bath Club.* Sons, 560, 1296 & 1297.

ELLIOTT, Alistair Walter Guy, M.B., B.Ch., b. 14 Aug. 17, eldest s. of late Rev. W. A. H. Elliott. T, 31²–36²; Cap. Edinburgh University, M.B., Ch.B. ✕ R.A.M.C., 42–46. Capt. Surgical Specialist. Medical Practitioner. *Royal Yachting Assoc., Little Ship Club.* Brother, B. C. G. Elliott.

ELLIOTT, Brian Clair Guy, LL.B. T, 35¹–38².

ELLIOTT, John Basil Churchill. SH, 15¹–19².*

ELLIOTT, John Gordon, M.B., B.Chir., b. 26 Oct. 25, youngest s. of F. Elliott. SF, 39³–43². Clare, Cambridge, M.A. Middlesex Hospital, M.B., B.Chir. M.R.C.S., L.R.C.P. Medical Practitioner.

ELLIS, Anthony Norman, b. 2 Feb. 33, 2nd s. of N. D. Ellis, O.B.E. M, 46³–51². N/S. 4th Queen's Own Hussars, 51–53. 2nd Lt. Christ's, Cambridge, M.A. Rural Estate Management, Cert. of Proficiency in Estate Management. Associate of Inst. of Corn & Agricultural Merchants. M.B.I.M., M.I.B.M., M.I.M. Joined Ellis & Everard Ltd., 56. Now Group Property Dir. & Man. Dir., Building Supplies Div. *The Rottweiler Club.* The Game Conservancy.

ELLIS, Errington, M.B., B.Chir. Sh, 35³–40².*

ELLIS, Major Henry Campbell, b. 30 Mar. 91, s. of late O. A. Ellis. St, 05³–08³. Operating Dept., North Eastern Rly., 09. ✕ 17th Bn. Northumberland Fusiliers, Invalided. Pers. Staff Officer to Dir. of Railways & Roads, War Office, 16–19. Major. Sec. to Agent, M. & S. M. Railway, Madras, India, 20–24. Asst. Gen. Man., Rhodesia Railways, Bulawayo, 25–46, now retired.

ELLIS, Henry Ratcliffe, b. 8 Apr. 85, 3rd s. of late Sir T. R. Ellis. C, 99³–03²; XXII, 03. Solicitor, 09. ✕ 5th Bn. Manchester Regt. Capt. Solicitor, now retired. Pres. (former Capt.), *Wigan Cricket Club.* Son, T. R. Ellis.

ELLIS, James Douglas, M.B., B.Ch., F.R.C.S., M.R.C.O.G., b. 26 July 30, eldest s. of N. D. Ellis, J.P., M.A. M, 44²–48²; S. VIII, 46–48. Christ's, Cambridge, M.A. Guy's Hospital, M.B., B.Ch., F.R.C.S. (Eng.), M.R.C.O.G. Obst. & Gynaec., United Oxford Hospitals. M.A. (Oxon.).

ELLIS, Michell George, B.M., B.Ch., b. 6 Mar. 19, s. of W. E. Ellis. B, 32³–37³; Baines Leaving Exhibition. Queen's, Oxford, B.A., B.M., B.Ch., D.M. Radcliffe Infirmary, Oxford. Casualty Officer, Radcliffe Infirmary. ✕ R.A.M.C., 43–44. Lt. Invalided. Med. Off., Kelling Sanatorium, Holt, Norfolk, 44; and Mundesley

Sanatorium, Norfolk, 49. Senior Registrar, Cheshire Joint Sanatorium & City General Hospital, Stoke-on-Trent. Medical Officer, Precomoconiosis Medical Panel, Dept. of Health and Social Security.

ELLIS, Thomas Ratcliffe, b. 26 Dec. 15, s. of H. R. Ellis (OR C 99). C, 29^3–34^2; XV, 32–33. Trinity, Oxford, M.A. ✕ 5th Bn. The Manchester Regt. (T.A.), 39–46. Major. Solicitor, 46. *Vincent's Club, Oxford.*

ELLIS-JONES, Dennis George, b. 10 Sept. 11, s. of late Rev. G. Ellis-Jones. SH, 25^3–29^2; St. Peter's Hall, Oxford, B.A. ✕ R.A. Capt. Major, T.A. Gen. List. Schoolmaster at St. John's School, Leatherhead from Sept. 35. Housemaster, 47–65. Second Master from 69. R.S.P.B. Son, 1239.

ELLISON, Bartholomew Guy. SH, 28^3–31^3.*

ELLISON, Richard Moreton, M.D., D.P.M., b. 28 Dec. 14, elder s. of late G. M. Ellison (OR SH 98). SH, 28^3–31^3. Edinburgh University, M.D., D.P.M., M.R.C.Psych., F.A.N-Z.C.P. ✕ R.A.M.C., 41–45. Medical Supt., Heathcote Hospital, Perth, W.A. Consultant Psychiatrist, Australian Army H.Q. Colonel, R.A.A.M.C. Brother, B. G. Ellison.

ELLISON, Thomas Herbert, Ph.D., b. 1 Aug. 27, s. of late Rev. Canon. C. H. Ellison. SH, 41^3–45^2. Clare, Cambridge, M.A., Ph.D.

ELMES, Prof. Peter Cardwell, B.M., F.R.C.P., b. 12 Oct. 21, 2nd s. of Capt. F. R. Elmes, J.P. SH, 35^2–39^3. Christ Church, Oxford, B.Sc., M.A., B.M., B.Ch., F.R.C.P., M.D. Western Reserve University, Cleveland. Whitla Prof. of Therapeutics & Pharmacology, Queen's University, Belfast. Assoc. of Physicians.

ELMHIRST, Richard. Tu, 14^2–18^2.*

ELPHICK, George Denis, F.R.C.S. B, 25^1–28^2.*

ELSEE, Peter Henry John. K, 35^1–39^3.*

ELSTUB, Sir St. John de Holt, C.B.E., b. 16 June 15, s. of late E. Elstub. SH, 29^1–33^2. Manchester University, B.Sc. Governor, Administrative Staff College, Henley. ✕ R.A.F., Bomber Pilot & Armament Officer, 39–45. Sqn. Ldr. Hon. D.Sc. (Aston), B.Sc., C.Eng., F.I.Mech.E.,

F.Inst.P., F.R.S.A., F.B.I.M. Plowden Committee on Aircraft Industry, 64–65. Midlands Electricity Board from 66. Review Board for Government Contracts from 69. Chrmn., Joint Government & Industry Committee on Aircraft Industry, 67–69. Chrmn. & Man. Dir., Imperial Metal Industries Ltd.; Dir., Rolls Royce (1971) Ltd., Royal Insurance Ltd. Life Governor, Univ. of Birmingham. Inst. of Mech. Eng. (Vice-Pres.). Inst. of Physics. Knight, 70. C.B.E., 54. *United Services.*

ELY, Richard Ganly. C, 46^2–50^2.*

EMERSON, Gerald Herbert, O.B.E., b. 3 Dec. 07, eldest s. of late Sir H. Emerson, G.C.I.E., K.C.S.I., C.B.E. SH, 21^2–26^2; G. VIII, 23; Minor Exhibitioner. Magdalene, Cambridge, B.A. I.C.S., 30–47. O.B.E. Bar, Inner Temple, 43. National Council of Social Service, 47–72. *Travellers' Club; Island Sailing Club, Cowes; Ski Club of Great Britain.* Brother, J. A. Emerson.

EMERSON, John Anthony, b. 25 Nov. 15, 3rd s. of late Sir H. Emerson, G.C.I.E., K.C.S.I., C.B.E. SH, 29^3–34^2; Scholar; Levée; H. XI, 31–34 (Capt.); Exhibitioner. Classical Scholarship to Trinity, Cambridge, B.A. A.C.I.S., A.T.I.I. ✕ Army, 39–45. Major, R.A. Dispatches. M. Samuel & Co. Ltd., 38–67 (Dir., 56). Chief Executive, E. D. Sassoon Banking Co. Ltd., 67–72. Executive Dir., Tozer Kemsley & Millbourn (Holdings) Ltd., 72. *White's, Rye Golf Club.* Brother, G. H. Emerson.

EMRYS-JONES, Mansel Franklin. Tu, 97^2–99^2.*

ENOCH, Cdr. Cyril Emile Delgado, R.D., F.C.A., b. 9 Feb. 07, s. of Major C. D. Enoch. K, 20^3–22^2. In Paris, Piano Pupil to late Tobias Matthay. Chartered Accountant, F.C.A., C.A. (S.A.). Commissioned in R.N.R., 32. ✕ R.N.R., 39–45. R.D. Commander (S) Retired, 46. Pensioned from Silverton Engineering Ltd. (A.E. Group), 71. Re-employed as Statistician from date of retirement. Fellow, Royal Philatelic Society, London. Chrmn., Philatelic Federation of S. Africa Expert Committee, 51–60 & 66 to date.

ENSOR, Peter John, b. 11 Apr. 30, eldest s. of A. H. Ensor. M, 43^3–48^3. Pembroke, Oxford. National Cash Register Co. Ltd., 53–60. McAnally, Montgomery & Co., Stockbrokers, London, from 60. Partner, 63. *Boodle's, R.A.C.*

Hon. Treasurer, Royal National Mission to Deep Sea Fishermen. Metropolitan Housing Trust & other Housing Assocs.

ENTWISLE, Arthur. B, 02^1–05^3.*

ENTWISLE, Peter Kevan, b. 13 July 17, s. of Lt.-Col. T. Entwisle (OR B 00). B, 31^1–35^2. Exeter, Oxford. ✕ Lancashire Fusiliers, 39–46. Lt. Wounded. P.O.W. A.C.I.S. Son, 2510.

ENTWISLE, Lt.-Col. Thomas, M.C., b. 21 Feb. 87, elder s. of late A. J. Entwisle. B, 00^3–06^2; Cap, 05; XXII, 06. Trinity, Oxford, B.A. ✕ Gazetted to 5th Bn. Loyal North Lancashire Regt. (T.F.), 10. Capt. M.C. Wounded. Dispatches. Reserve of Officers (T.A.). Lt.-Col., retired. *Barbarian R.U.F.C., R. Lytham St. Annes Golf Club.* Brother, A. Entwisle. Son, P. K. Entwisle. Grandson, 2510.

ERRINGTON, Lt.-Col. Sir Geoffrey Frederick, Bt., b. 15 Feb. 26, eldest s. of late Sir E. Errington, Bt., J.P. B, 40^1–44^1; Cadet Officer. Gazetted to The King's Regt., Emergency Commission, 45. Regular Commission, 49. p.s.c. A.M.B.I.M. G.S.O.3, (Int.,) H.Q. 11 Armd. Div., 50–52. G.S.O.3, M.I.3 (b) War Office, 55–57. B.M., 146 Inf. Bde., 59–61. Coy. Comdr. R.M.A., Sandhurst, 63–65. M.A. to Adjt.-Gen., 65–67. C.O., 1 Kings, 67–69. G.S.O.1, 1 Corps, 69–71. Col. G.S., N.W. Dist., from 71. Succeeded to Baronetcy, 73. *Army & Navy.* Brother, S. G. Errington.

ERRINGTON, Stuart Grant, b. 23 June 29, 2nd s. of late Sir E. Errington, Bt. B, 43^2–47^3; Levée; Head of House; Cadet Officer. Trinity, Oxford, M.A. Executive Dir., Mercantile Credit Co. Ltd. Man. Dir., Mercantile Leasing Co. Ltd. *Army & Navy, Palatine, Liverpool, and St. James', Manchester.* J.P. Brother, Sir G. F. Errington, Bt. Son, David Grant, B, 70^3–.

ERSKINE, John Francis, M.B., B.Ch., D.P.H., b. 20 Mar. 15, eldest s. of R. M. Erskine. Tu, 28^3–33^2. Christ's, Cambridge, B.A., M.B., B.Ch. Prizeman & Exhibitioner, Charing Cross Hospital. ✕ R.A.M.C., 44–46. Capt. London School of Hygiene & Tropical Medicine, D.P.H., 47. Resident Med. Off., Charing Cross Hospital. Occupational Med. Off., Unilever, National Coal Board. At present, Regional Med. Adviser, Central Electricity Generating Board. Society of Occupational Medicine. Community Health Panel of National Assoc. for Mental Health. Son, 2421.

ETCHES, Col. William Whitson, O.B.E., M.C., b. 15 May 21, 5th s. of late Major C. E. Etches, C.B., O.B.E. B, 35^1–39^2; S. VIII, 37–39 (Capt.); Cadet Officer. R.M.C., Sandhurst. Gazetted to 6th Regt., 39. ✕ 3rd Commando, 40–42. Dispatches. P.O.W., 42–45. Capt., 45; Major, 51. p.s.c., 52, j.s.s.c., 58. C.O., 3rd Bn. Queen's Own Nigeria Regt., 61–63. Brigade Col., The Fusiliers Bde., 65–68. Regimental Colonel, R.R.F., 69. Lt.-Col., 61; Col., 65. Retired, 71. Now Regimental Secretary, The Royal Regt. of Fusiliers, H.M. Tower of London. A.R.A. N.R.A. M.C., 45. O.B.E., 63. *Army & Navy Club.* Sons, 2195 & John Philip, B, 69^2–.

EVANS, Alan Lile Llewellyn. K, 20^1–24^2. Sons, 1378 & 1793.*

EVANS, Antony Grindrod. SH, 37^3–42^2.*

EVANS, Major Arthur Percivale, D.S.O. SH, 96^3–00^2.*

EVANS, Charles Frederick Holt, b. 17 Nov. 03, elder s. of Lt.-Col. B. Evans. SF, 17^3–22^2. Trinity, Oxford, M.A. Librarian to Charterhouse, Godalming, Surrey. Retired. F.S.A.

EVANS, David Lawrence, F.R.C.S., b. 21 Sept. 19, s. of A. Evans, M.S., F.R.C.S. Tu, 33^3–37^2; H. XI, 36–37; Fives VI. Gonville & Caius, Cambridge, M.A. Westminster Medical School, M.R.C.S., L.R.C.P. ✕ R.N.V.R. Surg.-Lt. F.R.C.S., 49. Consultant Orthopaedic Surgeon, Westminster Hospital, London.

EVANS, Frederick Vaughan, b. 30 June 12, elder s. of late F. W. Evans. B, 26^1–30^2; XV, 29. ✕ Ceylon Planters Rifle Corps. Major. M.B.E. Resident, and worked in Ceylon with Gordon Frazer & Co. Ltd., managing Tea and Rubber plantations from 34–69. Retired as senior Dir. of that firm. *M.C.C.*

EVANS, John Marten Llewellyn, C.B.E., T.D., b. 9 June 09, 3rd s. of late M. Ll. Evans (OR B 79). K, 23^2–27^2. Trinity, Oxford, M.A. Solicitor, 34. Official Solicitor to the Supreme Court, 50–70. ✕ R.A., 39–45. Major. M.B.E. T.D. Vice-Chrmn., Austin Reed Group Ltd. J.P., City of London. C.B.E., 56. *Garrick, M.C.C.* Brother, A. L. L. Evans.

EVANS, Robert Holland. W, 17^2–21^2.*

EVANS, Walter Francis Adrian. B, 41^1–44^3.*

EVANS-PROSSER, Caryl Donough Geraint, B.M., B.Ch., b. 4 May 32, s. of Rev. R. A. Evans-Prosser, M.A. K, 45^3–50^2; Cap; Sw. VIII, 50. Corpus Christi, Oxford, M.A., B.M., B.Ch. Westminster Hospital, F.F.A.R.C.S., D.A., D.(Obsts.)., R.C.O.G. Consultant Anaesthetist, Basingstoke District General Hospital.

EVELEGH, Lt.-Col. John Robin Garnet Nial, b. 23 Nov. 32, 2nd s. of late Col. E. N. Evelegh, D.S.O., M.C. (OR W 05). SH, 46^2–50^3; S. VIII, 47–49 (Capt.); Cadet Officer. Magdalen, Oxford, M.A. Lt.-Col., Regular Army. C.O., 3rd Bn. The Royal Green Jackets. *Army & Navy Club*.

EVELEIGH, Michael, M.C. B, 27^3–32^1. Son, 1938.*

EVELYN, Francis Heron Lyndon, M.C. C, 03^3–08^2.*

EVELYN-JONES, Lorence, M.B.E., b. 3 Dec. 07, s. of late F. Evelyn-Jones. B, 21^3–25^1. St. John's, Cambridge, B.A. ✕ R.A. Major. M.B.E. Dispatches. Chrmn. & Man. Dir., Tex Abrasives Ltd., Tex Abrasives (Allied Products) Ltd., Tex Abrasives (Ireland) Ltd. Chrmn., Integrated Machinery & Accessories Ltd., Sennerskov (London) Ltd., Freud (England) Ltd. *Royal Thames Yacht Club, Bath Club, Hawks Club, Oxford & Cambridge Golfing Society*. Son, 2654.

EVEREST, Arthur Bernard, Ph.D., B.Sc., b. 10 Sept. 01, 2nd s. of late A. R. Everest, M.I.E.E. T, 15^2–19^2. Birmingham University, B.Sc., Ph.D. Fellow, Institution of Metallurgists. P.P., Fellow & Hon. Life Member, Institute of British Foundrymen. Life Service Member, American Foundrymen's Assoc. P.P., International Committee of Foundry Technical Assocs. International Nickel Ltd., 26–66, Research and Development Dept. Man., Nickel Technical Office, 62. Retired. Gold Medallist of Institute of British Foundrymen & Assoc. Technique de Fonderie Français. Award of Scientific Merit of American Foundry Society. Brothers, R. L. & F. J. Everest.

EVEREST, Francis John. T, 20^3–25^2.*

EVEREST, Robert Lawrence, b. 4 June 05, 3rd s. of late A. R. Everest. T, 19^2–22^2. F.R.I.C.S., P.A.S.I. Consultant Chartered Quantity Surveyor to Davis Belfield

& Everest, London. Mayor, City of Westminster, 60–61. Knight of Sovereign, Military Order of Malta. *Compton Croquet Club*. Brothers, A. B. & F. J. Everest.

EVERS, Bryan Grosvenor, M.C. C, 25^3–30^2.*

EVERS, Claude Ronald, b. 17 Jan. 08, elder s. of late C. P. Evers (OR C 90). SF, 21^3–27^2; Scholar; Head of School; Head of House. Scholar of Trinity, Oxford, M.A. Asst. Master, Wellington College, 31–35, and Rugby School, 36–40. ✕ R. Warwick Regt. Staff College (War Course), War Office, 40–45. Headmaster, Berkhamsted School, 46–53. Headmaster, Sutton Valence School, 53–67. Warden, Pendley Residential Centre of Adult Education, 67–73. Retired, 73. Chrmn., Pendley Shakespeare Festival. Chrmn., Society of Schoolmasters. *Arts Theatre Club*. Sons, 697, 837, 1599 & 2226.

EVERS, Frank Antony, b. 5 May 09, eldest s. of late F. P. Evers (OR C 83). C, 23^2–27^3. Birmingham University, B.Comm. Dir. of a small soap co., 34–53. ✕ 39–46, National Fire Service. Caravan Site Operator, 53–70. Retired. Brother, R. H. K. Evers. Son, 676.

EVERS, Ralph Herbert Keith, b. 9 Apr. 16, 3rd s. of late F. P. Evers (OR C 83). C, 30^1–34^2. With Carpet Manufacturers, Kidderminster, 34–39. ✕ Worcestershire Regt., 39–45. Capt. Owner, Holiday Camp. Brother, F. A. Evers. Sons, 1941 & 2114.

EVES, Douglas Kenneth Heath, b. 26 May 22, 2nd s. of late Pay. Capt. W. H. Eves, R.N. SF, 36^2–40^2. Corpus Christi, Cambridge, M.A. ✕ 15/19 Hussars, 42–45. Wounded, 44. Lt. Dispatches. Croix de Guerre. Bar, Middle Temple, 52. Dir., Ibstock Brick & Tile Co. Ltd., near Leicester, 53. *Bath Club*.

EWART, John Burnell, b. 17 July 24, s. of late C. B. Ewart. SH, 38^2–42^3; XV, 42; R. VIII, 42. University College, London, B.Sc. ✕ R.A.F. (2½ yr.) & K.R.R.C. (1 yr.) A.I.S. Associate Dir., J. Walter Thompson Co. Ltd. (Advertising Agency), 50–72. *Chipstead Sailing Club, Island Cruising Club*.

EWENS, Bernard Creasy. SH, 02^3–06^2.*

EWING, James Turner, b. 17 June 21, s. of W. T. Ewing. Tu, 35^3–39^2; Scholar;

Levée. Peterhouse, Cambridge, John Cosyn Scholar, B.A. ✕ R. Signals, 41–46. Asst. Man., Harrisons & Crosfield, Calcutta, 47–56. Vegetating in Scotland, 57–65. Vegetating in England from 66.

EYDEN, Maurice Victor. T, 11^1–15^2.*

F

FABIAN WARE, Arthur Henry. SH, 17^3–19^3.*

FABRICIUS, Leslie, b. 12 Nov. 87, 2nd s. of the late H. D. Fabricius. Tu, 01^3–05^2. Queens', Cambridge, B.A. Engineer. A.M.Inst.C.E. Retired.

FACER, Roger Lawrence Lowe, b. 28 June 33, elder s. of J. E. Facer. SH, 46^3–51^2; Scholar; Leaving Exhibition. Scholar of St. John's, Oxford, M.A. Administrative Civil Service, War Office, 57–64. Ministry of Defence, 64–66 & 68–72. Cabinet Office, 66–68. At present seconded to the International Institute for Strategic Studies. *United Oxford & Cambridge Club.*

FAGAN, Richard Feltrim, M.B., B.S., D.P.H., b. 5 Feb. 91, 2nd s. of late Col. C. G. F. Fagan. St, 05^3–06^2. University College Hospital, London, M.B., B.S., M.R.C.S., L.R.C.P., D.P.H. ✕ R.A.M.C., 14–19. Capt. Demonstrator, Bacteriology & Pathology, University College Hospital, London, and House Surgeon, General & H.S. Eye Dept. Hon. Anaesthetist, King Edward VII Hospital, Windsor. Hon. Medical Officer, Chalfonts & Gerrards Cross Hospital. Senior Medical Officer, Chalfont Epileptic Colony, Chalfont St. Peter, Bucks. General Practitioner, Gerrards Cross, Bucks. Retired, 61. British Medical Society. National Society for Epileptics. Church Warden & Member of P.C.C., Fulmer, Bucks.

FAIRBANK, Thomas John, F.R.C.S., b. 26 June 12, s. of late Sir H. A. T. Fairbank. M, 26^2–31^1; Levée; Head of House; H. XI, 31. Scholar of Trinity, Cambridge, M.A., M.B., B.Chir. Scholar of St. Thomas's Hospital, F.R.C.S., L.R.C.P. Bristow Medallist, Chiselden Medallist & Beaney Scholar. ✕ R.A.M.C. Major & Surgical Specialist. Orthopaedic Surgeon, United Cambridge Hospitals & East Anglian Regional Hospital Board. *R.A.C.* Many Medical Societies. Pres. Elect, British Orthopaedic Assoc. Son, 2218.

EYRE, John Washbourn, b. 30 Sept. 03, s. of late Professor J. W. H. Eyre, M.D., F.R.S.E. SH, 17^3–20^3. University College, Oxford. Shell-Mex & B.P. Ltd., 30–67. Latterly as Senior Training Officer, now retired. ✕ R.A.S.C., 41–45. Capt. Nephew, 855.

FAIRCLOUGH, Col. John, O.B.E. B, 29^3–34^2. Sons, 1868, 2110 & Clive Anthony, B, 68^1–72^1.*

FAIRCLOUGH, Thomas Anthony, b. 20 Jan. 08, 2nd s. of late J. Fairclough. B, 21^3–26^2; Cadet Officer; S. VIII, 25, Capt., 26. Gonville & Caius, Cambridge, B.A. Joined, Tootal Broadhurst Lee & Co. Ltd., 29. Dir., 39. Chrmn., Tootal Ltd., 57–63. Brother, W. D. Fairclough.

FAIRCLOUGH, William Donald, b. 26 July 06, eldest s. of late J. Fairclough. B, 20^1–24^2. Steel Brothers & Co. Ltd., 25–47, London, Rangoon & branches. This period includes 44–46, served with the Government of Assam, India. Presently farming in Scotland. *R & A Golf Club, The Oriental Club.* Brother, T. A. Fairclough. Son, 972.

FAIRE, Joseph Nevill, M.C. SF, 11^3–15^2.*

FAIRE, Stuart Wellington, b. 9 Apr. 00, younger s. of L. C. Faire. SF, 14^3–18^2. Accountant, retired. *Reform Club.* Brother, J. N. Faire.

FALK, Lt.-Col. Cecil Joseph, M.C., T.D., b. 3 Dec. 97, eldest s. of late M. Falk. M, 11^3–15^3. ✕ 7th Bn. Wiltshire Regt., 8th Bn. Worcestershire Regt. Capt. M.C. Lt.-Col. 5th Bn. Manchester Regt. (T.A.), 34–38. T.D. Bt. Col., 38. ✕ Comd., 2/7th The Queen's Royal Regt., 39–40. Late Chrmn., Falk Ltd., & Falks (N.Z.) Ltd. Retired. Sons, J. G. Falk & 1381.

FALK, John Gerald, b. 20 Oct. 29, eldest s. of Lt.-Col. C. J. Falk, M.C., T.D. (OR M 11). M, 43^2–48^2; Head of School Music, 47^1–48^2. Organ Scholar of Trinity Hall, Cambridge, M.A. Dir. of Music, Abbot's Hill School. Brother, 1381.

FANSHAWE, Col. John Guy Dalrymple, b. 19 Aug. 18, 3rd s. of late Capt. G. D. Fanshawe, R.N. St, 32^2–36^3. R.M.C., Sandhurst. Staff College, Camberley. p.s.c. A.M.B.I.M. ✕ Argyll & Sutherland Highlanders from 38. Wounded. O.C. Depot, 52. Colonel. *Army & Navy.*

FARGUS, Col. Brian Alfred, O.B.E., b. 3 Jan. 18, s. of late Col. N. H. S. Fargus (OR SF 96) SF, 31^3–36^2; Scholar; H. XI, 36; Cadet Officer. R.M.C., Sandhurst (Passed in First). Leaving Scholar. Gazetted to the Royal Scots, 38. ✕ The Royal Scots, 39–45. 2nd Bn., Hong Kong. Adj., 8th Bn., N.W. Europe. Dispatches. Major. Served also in Nigeria, Egypt, Malaya, Aden & Germany. p.s.c., 48. Military Attaché, Pretoria, 71–73. O.B.E., 64. *Army & Navy.* Son, 2127.

FARNCOMBE, The Rev. Edgar Basil Tuberville, b. 7 Oct. 01, s. of Dr. W. T. Farncombe. K, 15^3–20^2. St. John's, Oxford, M.A. Ripon Hall, Oxford, 26–27. Ordained Deacon, 27; Priest, 28. Curate, St. Peter's Parish Church, Harborne, Birmingham, 27–34. Vicar, St. George's Edgbaston, 34–50. During this time Chaplain to various Hospitals & Schools in the Midlands, & from 40–46 Officiating Chaplain to the Forces (W. Command). Rector, Birmingham, Pershore, 52–59. Vicar of Hanley Castle, Worcestershire, 59–64. Retired in 64 due to ill health, but licensed to officiate in Dioceses of Worcester & Hereford. St. John's College Society.

FARQUHARSON, Colin Andrew, D.L., J.P., b. 9 Aug. 23, eldest s. of late N. D. Farquharson (formerly Robertson) (OR C 90). C & Tu, 37^3–41^3. ✕ Grenadier Guards, 42–48. Capt. A.D.C. to Field-Marshal Earl Alexander of Tunis & Lt.-Gen. William Morgan, Supreme Commander, Central Mediterranean, 45. Chartered Land Agent. Fellow, Chartered Land Agents Society & of Auctioneers & Estate Agents Institute until amalgamation with Royal Institution of Chartered Surveyors —Fellow. Estate Factor in General Practice. D.L., 66 and J.P., 69. Aberdeenshire. *M.C.C.; Royal Northern Club, Aberdeen.* Brother, N. S. Farquharson.

FARQUHARSON, Norman Stewart, b. 16 May 25, 2nd s. of late N. D. Farquharson (formerly Robertson) (OR C 90). C & Tu, 39^2–43^2. Edinburgh University, B.Sc. ✕ Grenadier Guards. Lt. Wounded, N.W. Europe, 45. Shell Chemicals Ltd., 52. At present, Regional Man. with Shell Star Ltd., a wholly owned subsidiary of Shell Chemicals. Brother, C. A. Farquharson. Son, Donald Henry, C, 67^2–72^2.

FARRANT, Major-Gen. Ralph Henry, C.B., b. 2 Feb. 09, eldest s. of late H. Farrant (OR M 92). M, 22^3–27^2. R.M.A., Woolwich. Gazetted to Royal Artillery, 29. ✕ Lt.-Col. R.A. Technical Staff Officer. Major-General, 61. Pres. of the Ordnance Board, M. of D., 63–64. Retired, 64. C.B. Chrmn., R.Y.A. Olympic Committee, 64–72. Dep. Chrmn., R.N.L.I. from 72. *Army & Navy Club. Royal Yacht Squadron.*

FARRAR, Charles Brooke. SH, 12^3–16^1.*

FARRER, Bryan David, b. 30 June 06, 3rd s. of late B. Farrer. C, 20^2–25^2; Levée; Head of House. Scholar of Balliol, Oxford, B.A. Bar, Lincoln's Inn, 30. Private Sec. to Lord Beaverbrook, 40–46. Literary Dir., Martin Secker & Warburg since 60. *Garrick Club.* Brother, Sir W. L. Farrer, K.C.V.O.

FARRER, Sir Walter Leslie, K.C.V.O., b. 30 Jan. 00, 2nd s. of late B. Farrer. C, 13^2–18^1. Williams Exhibition in History to Balliol, Oxford, B.A. Solicitor, 26. Partner in Farrer & Co., 27–64. Member of the Council of the Law Society, 45–52. Disciplinary Committee, 53–63. Private Solicitor to H.M. King George VI & Queen Elizabeth II, 37–64. K.C.V.O., 64. Pres., London Life Association to 73. Prime Warden of the Fishmongers Co., 68–69. *Travellers' Club.* Brother, B. D. Farrer.

FARRINGTON, Robin Neville, M.C., b. 1 July 28, s. of late Group-Capt. W. B. Farrington, D.S.O., R.A.F. Sh, 42^2–46^2; Cadet Officer. Awarded Belt of Honour at 164 Infantry O.C.T.U., Chester, 47. N/S. Rifle Brigade. 2nd Lt. Awarded M.C. in Palestine with 2 K.R.R.C., 47–48. Magdalene, Cambridge, B.A. Dir., Whitbread & Co. Ltd. Chrmn., Whitbread London Ltd. and Whitbreads Ltd. Dir., Whitbread Fremlins Ltd.

FAULKNER, Irvine John, b. 15 Sept. 01, eldest s. of late T. Faulkner. T, 15^2–20^3; Minor Exhibitioner. Birmingham University, B.Sc. Emmanuel, Cambridge, Ph.D. Technical Chemist with I.C.I. Ltd. F.R.I.C., 47. Retired. Chrmn., Pollution Prevention Committee, Northumbrian River Authority. Diocesan Reader, Diocese of Ripon. Salmon & Trout Assoc. *Rotary Club of Knaresborough, Yorks.* Brother, T. Faulkner. Son, 890.

FAULKNER, Thomas, F.R.C.S., b. 27 May 13, 2nd s. of late T. Faulkner. T, 27^2–32^2. Emmanuel, Cambridge, M.A. St. Bartholomew's Hospital, London, M.R.C.S., L.R.C.P., F.R.C.S. ✕ R.A.M.C., 40–45. Capt. Registrar in Plastic Surgery, Queen Victoria Hospital, East Grinstead, 48–58. Consultant Plastic Surgeon to N.W. Metropolitan Regional Hospital Board; S.E. Metropolitan Regional Hospital Board; H.M. Prison Commission. Hon. Consultant Plastic Surgeon to St. Mary's Hospital, Paddington; Royal Academy of Dramatic Art. Worshipful Society of Apothecaries of London. Exhibitor, Summer Exhibition, Royal Academy of Arts, 71 & 72. Brother, I. J. Faulkner. Son, 2568.

FAURE, Eric Simon Noel, b. 25 Dec. 13, 3rd s. of H. M. F. Faure. SF, 27^3–31^3. École de Commerce, Neuchâtel. University College, Oxford, B.A. Hon. Treasurer, Federation of Oils, Seeds & Fats Assoc. Chrmn., F.O.S.F.A. Contract Committee. Dir., Faure Fairclough Ltd., United Oils & Fats Ltd. and United Associations Ltd. *Rye Golf Club; Thorpeness Golf Club; Baltic Exchange;* Pres., *Baltic Exchange Golfing Society;* Capt., *Old Rugbeian Golfing Society,* 63–64. Skinner. Brother, H. F. Faure. Nephew, 1082.

FAURE, Henry Frederick. SF, 24^3–28^3.*

FAWCETT, Charles Leonard. SH, 23^3–28^2.*

FAWCETT, James Edmund Sandford, D.S.C., b. 16 Apr. 13, younger s. of Rev. J. Fawcett, M.A. SH, 26^3–31^2; Scholar; Levée; Exhibitioner. Scholar of New College, Oxford, M.A. Eldon Law Scholar, 35. Bar, Inner Temple, 37. Practised, 37–39 & 50–55. Fellow of All Souls College, Oxford, 38 & 60–69. ✕ R.N.V.R., 39–45. Lt.-Cdr. D.S.C. Asst. Legal Adviser, Foreign Office, 45–50. General Counsel, International Monetary Fund, 55–60. Member of European Commission of Human Rights from 62, Vice-Pres., 69; Pres., 72. Dir. of Studies, Royal Institute of International Affairs from 69.

FAWCETT, Robert, M.B.E., T.D., b. 16 June 17, 4th s. of late P. C. Fawcett. SH, 30^3–35^1. Trinity, Oxford, B.A. ✕ Royal Artillery, 39–46. Lt.-Col. Dispatches. M.B.E., T.D. F.C.A. *M.C.C., City of London Club.* Brother, C. L. Fawcett.

FAWCETT, Robert John, F.C.A., b. 25 Apr. 07, s. of late J. Fawcett, M.D.,

F.R.C.P. SH, 20^3–26^2; Cap, 25; R. VIII, 25–26 (Capt.); Crick Winner, 26. King's, Cambridge, B.A. Exhibitioner. F.C.A. Price Waterhouse & Co., 30–44. Company Sec., C.I.B.A. (ARL) Ltd., 44–70. Retired, 70. Sons, 177 & 515.

FAWCETT, Richard Peter, b. 19 Feb. 23, s. of R. A. Fawcett. B, 36^3–40^2. ✕ R.N.V.R. Lt. (A). In Wool Trade. J.P.

FAWCETT, John Boyce, M.R.C.S., L.R.C.P., b. 25 Sept. 14, elder s. of R. Fawcett. K, 28^2–30^2. Edinburgh University. The London Hospital, M.R.C.S., L.R.C.P., D.M.R.(D). ✕ R.A.F. Medical Service. Sqn. Ldr., 42–47. Consultant Radiologist in Charge, N.E. Manchester Hospitals. Royal Society of Medicine. *The Manchester Club.*

FAWCUS, Charles Russell, b. 26 May 14, younger s. of late R. E. Fawcus. W, 28^1–32^2; won Schoolboys Lawn Tennis Championships at Queen's Club. Peterhouse, Cambridge, B.A. Lawn Tennis Blue, 34–35 (Capt.). Fellow of the Corporation of Insurance Brokers. Dir., Hartley Cooper & Co. Ltd., Lloyd's Insurance Brokers. Underwriting Member of Lloyd's. *Hawks Club, International Lawn Tennis Club, All England Lawn Tennis Club.*

FAWCUS, Nigel Derwent Frank, b. 12 Aug. 13, eldest s. of late D. D. J. Fawcus. C, 27^3–31^2; Cap, 30. Tea & Coffee Planter. ✕ King's African Rifles. Major. *Kiambu Golf Club.* E.A. Wild Life Society.

FAWKNER-CORBETT, Roger Picton, b. 7 Feb. 29, 3rd s. of Lt.-Col. W. V. Fawkner-Corbett, R.A.M.C. T, 42^3–47^2; Minor Foundationer. N/S. R.A., 47–49. Fellow, Institute of Freight Forwarders. Member, Institute of Export. S.H. Lock & Co. Ltd., 49–69 (Dir., 54–69). Man. Dir., Geo. Thompson & Co. Ltd. (Parent Company—Shaw Savill Line, Member of the Furness Withy Group) from 69. Hon. Treasurer, The Dockland Settlements. Member of the Port of London Authority, 64–68.

FEATHERSTONE, Lt.-Col. William Patrick Davies, M.C., T.D., D.L., b. 17 Sept. 19, s. of late Dr. H. W. Featherstone, O.B.E., M.D., LL.D., J.P. SH, 33^2–38^2. Trinity, Cambridge, B.A. ✕ R.A., 39–46. Wounded, M.C., T.D. Staffordshire Yeomanry, 48–62 (Lt.-Col.). Farmer. D.L., J.P. High Sheriff of Staffordshire, 69. Hon. Col. Staffordshire Yeomanry from 72.

FEHR, Basil Henry Frank, b. 11 July 12, eldest s. of late F. E. Fehr, C.B.E. K, 26^2–30^2; XI, 29–30; H. XI, 30. Dir., Baltic Mercantile & Shipping Exchange Ltd., London; Dir., Frank Fehr & Co. Ltd., London; Dir., Frank Fehr (S.A.) (Pty.) Ltd., Durban; Dir., Frank Fehr & Co. (Hong Kong) Ltd.; Dir., Fehrstock Investments Ltd., London; Dir., Oilseed Trade Benevolent Assoc., London; Dir., London Commodity Exchange Co. Ltd. Pres., Frank Fehr & Co. (Canada) Ltd., Vancouver. Chrmn., Fehr Bros. Inc., N.Y. Chrmn., Fehr Bros. (Industries) Inc., N.Y. Chrmn., Fehr Bros. (Commodities) Inc., N.Y. Joined Frank Fehr & Co., 33; Partner, 37; Man. Dir. since 48. ✕ R.A., 39–45. Major. *M.C.C., City Livery, H.A.C., Littlestone Golf Club.* Sons, 1278 & 1671.

FELL, The Rev. Bryan Greg. Tu, 19^2–21^1.*

FELL, Col. Michael Edwin, C.B.E., M.C. K, 03^2–08^1.*

FENLEY, David Douglas. T, 32^3–36^3.*

FENLEY, William Laurence John, b. 3 May 31, s. of L. Fenley. T, 44^3–50^1; Benn Scholar; Levée; Head of House; Cap; Boxing Capt., 49–50. Gonville & Caius, Cambridge, M.A. F.C.A. Cdr., R.N.R. V.R.D. Chrmn. & Man. Dir., William Goode Ltd. (Rugby, family business), previously Sec., Doulton & Co. Ltd. (now part of Pearson Group), preceded by various finance posts in industry. *Hurlingham, Royal Naval Sailing Assoc.* (Hon. Treas.).

FENWICK, Christopher David (formerly C. D. Dugdale). K, 26^2–29^2.*

FENWICK, John James. C, 45^3–50^1.*

FERGUSSON, Ewen Alastair John, b. 28 Oct. 32, elder s. of Sir. E. Fergusson. SH, 45^3–51^1; Scholar; XV, 49–50 (Capt.); H. XI, 50–51 (Capt.); Sw. VIII, 47; XXII, 49–50; Athletics Cup, 50. Scholar of Oriel, Oxford, M.A. Rugby Football Blue. Entered H.M. Diplomatic Service, 56. Foreign Office, 56–57. Asst. Private Sec. to Minister of Defence, 57–59; 2nd Sec., British Embassy, Addis Ababa, Ethiopia, 60–63; Foreign Office & Diplomatic Service, 63–67; British Trade Development Office, N.Y., 67–71; Counsellor & Head of Chancery, Office of U.K. Permanent Representative to the European Communities from 72. Brother, 949.

FERNAU, Francis John, T.D. SF, 16^3–20^3.*

FERNYHOUGH, Brig. Alan Henry, C.B.E., M.C., b. 15 Apr. 04, elder s. of late Col. H. C. Fernyhough, C.B., C.M.G., D.S.O. Tu, 18^3–22^2. R.M.A., Woolwich. Gazetted to Royal Artillery, 24. Ordnance Course, 36. Staff College, 41. Regimental Service, U.K. & India, till 40. France, 40. Canada (Staff Appointment), 41–42. French North Africa & Italy (Staff & Service), 42–44. Middle East (Service Appointment), 44–45. U.K. & B.A.O.R. (Service Appointment), 45–59. Retired. C.B.E., 57; M.C., 40. Wrote "History of the Royal Army Ordnance Corps—1920 to 1945". *Army & Navy Club.*

FERRAR, John Russell, b. 11 Nov. 20 2nd s. of late Lt.-Col. M. L. Ferrar (OR C 90). C, 34^3–39^1. Clare, Cambridge, M.A. Solicitor, 50. Partner in Monro Pennefather & Co., London. The Bach Choir. *Blackwater Sailing Club.* Brother, M. E. Ferrar.

FERRAR, Michael Evelyn, b. 27 Sept. 06, eldest s. of late Lt.-Col. M. L. Ferrar (OR C 90). C, 20^3–24^2. ✕ R. Wilts Yeomanry, 39–40. Lt. Green Howards, 40–42. R.I.A.S.C. (Animal Transport), 42–46. Major. Varied—Farming, Commerce & later farming in Rhodesia, 50–65. Since then in administrative work in schools. Now Bursar of Eagle Prep. School, Umtali. South African & Rhodesian Ornithological Society. *Umtali Polo Crosse Club.* Brother, J. R. Ferrar.

FERRAR, Michael Leslie, b 6 Sept 27, s. of Dr. W. L. Ferrar, D.Sc., M.A. B, 41^3–45^2. Army short course, The Queen's Oxford, 45–46 (commissioned 2nd Lt., R.A., 47). Returned to The Queen's Oxford, 48–51. M.A. Trainee—Buying Office—Personnel—Containers Buyer, The Boots Company Ltd., Nottingham. Greenlands Assoc. (The Administrative Staff College, Henley.)

FERRIS, Ian Samuel Spencer, F.C.A., b. 2 June 26, s. of late Cdr. J. S. Ferris, R.N. Sh, 40^2–44^2; Head of School; Cap; XXII, 44 (Capt.); H. XI, 44; Stovin Exhibition. Exhibitioner of King's, Cambridge, M.A. F.C.A. Man. Dir., The Iveagh Trustees Ltd. *United Oxford & Cambridge, Hawks (Cambridge).*

FERRY, Robert Bird, A.F.C. B, 26^3–31^2.*

FESTER, Norman Detmar. B, 22¹–24².*

FFORDE, Sir Arthur Frederic Brownlow, G.B.E., b. 23 Aug. oo, s. of late A. B. fforde, I.C.S. SH, 14³–19¹; Scholar; Head of School; Cadet Officer; XV, 17–18. For Career, see Part III, "Headmasters". *Athenæum Club, City Law Club.* City of London Solicitors Coy. Married, 26, Allison MacLehose, sister of Rev. A. MacLehose (2s. 1d.) see A. J. B. fforde; d. married Michael McCrum (see Part III under "Masters"). Grandson, Arthur William Brownlow, SH, 70¹–.

FFORDE, Arthur John Brownlow, b. 18 Apr. 27, elder s. of Sir A. F. B. fforde, G.B.E. (OR SH 14). SH, 40³–45²; Levée; Head of House; XV, 43–44; H. XI, 45; S. VIII, 45 (Capt.); Cadet Officer. Trinity, Oxford. Solicitor. Linklater & Paines. Son, Arthur William Brownlow, SH, 70¹–.

FIDDIAN, William Evelyn Harold, b. 22 Oct. 23, s. of C. M. Fiddian. SH, 37³–41². King's, Cambridge, M.A. National Institute of Agricultural Botany, Cambridge.

FIELD, John. St, 99³–02².*

FIELD, Group-Capt. Roger Martin, C.B.E. SH, 04³–07².*

FIELD, Wilfred John Sutcliffe, b. 6 Nov. 09, s. of J. Field (OR St 99). St, 23³–27³. Gonville & Caius, Cambridge, B.A. Passed final exam of Land Agents' Society, 34, while an Associate Member of that Society, but withdrew from membership on becoming a Forestry Consultant, & ceasing to be employed in general estate management. Forestry Consultant, as West Norfolk representative of "Woodland Management Assoc. Ltd.", Oxford. Member of E. Anglian Div. of Royal Forestry Society of England, Wales & Northern Ireland.

FINCH, John Harold, b. 19 July 30, elder s. of R. H. Finch (OR Tu 15). Tu, 44²–49². O.N.C. in Mechanical Engineering, 55. Design Engineering in Bell Canada (formerly Bell Telephone Co. of Canada).

FINCH, Brig. John Richard Gerard, O.B.E., b. 26 Feb. 11, s. of late W. G. Finch (OR M 91). M, 25¹–29². R.M.A., Woolwich. Gonville & Caius, Cambridge, B.A. Chartered Engineer. M.I.C.E. Commissioned 2nd Lt. in Royal Engineers, 31. Retired from Army with substantive rank

of Brigadier, 64. Dispatches twice. First Sec. to be appointed by Council of Engineering Institutions, 65. Retired, 68. O.B.E. *Alpine Club, United Services Club.*

FINCH, Ralph Herbert, b. 24 Sept. 01, 3rd s. of H. K. Finch. Tu, 15³–20²; Head of House; Cap, 19; S. VIII, 18–19 (Capt.), 20; Cadet Officer. Scholar of Gonville & Caius, Cambridge, B.A. Bar, Lincoln's Inn, 25. Practised as Advocate & Solicitor in Penang & Malaya, 26–33. Admitted Solicitor in England, 35. Practised in Leamington, 36–48. ✕ R.A.F.V.R., 40–45. Dispatches.

FINN, William Colthup, b. 25 Oct. 31, eldest s. of T. P. Finn. SH, 45²–49². Jesus, Oxford, B.A. Farmer, 54–58. A. C. Nielson & Co., 58–63. Member of the London Stock Exchange from 63. *M.C.C.*

FIRTH, Basil Guthrie, b. 10 June 13, s. of T. H. Firth. Tu, 27²–31³. Solicitor, 38. ✕ K.O.Y.L.I., 40. D.A.A.G., 20th Indian Division, Burma, 45. Dispatches. Practising Solicitor. Son, 2562.

FIRTH, Frederick Cecil Whiteley. B, 13¹–16².*

FIRTH, George Samuel, b. 14 Apr. 29, s. of F. Firth. W, 42³–47¹; Cap, XXII. Leeds University. Woollen Manufacturer.

FISHER, John Ronald, b. 22 July 16, s. of late Brigadier Sir G. T. Fisher. K.B.E., C.S.I., C.I.E. C, 30³–34². Lincoln, Oxford, M.A. Articled to Chartered Accountants, 37. ✕ R.A., 39–46. Major. At present Sales Dir. of Manbré Sugars Ltd., London, & other companies. *Army & Navy Club.* Son, William Thomas, C, 69³–.

FISKE, Roger Elwyn. M, 24³–29².*

FITT, Stanley Warton. W, 21²–26².*

FITZGERALD, Hans Nikolas (formerly Sauer, H. N.). Tu, 13²–16³.*

FLEMING, Alan Bulmer, b. 12 Apr. 18, s. of N. L. Fleming. W, 32³–36¹. Leeds University, LL.B. ✕ R.A., 40–46. Capt. Attd. to Intelligence Corps, 45–46. Solicitor, 46. Asst. Solicitor to Leeds Corp., 47; to Bradford Corp., 48. At present, Senior Asst. Solicitor to West Riding County Council.

FLEMING, John, b. 12 June 19, s. of late J. Fleming. Tu, 33²–37². Trinity, Cambridge, B.A. Solicitor, 50. Solicitor,

Writer & Architectural Historian. Published "Robert Adam and His Circle", "Penguin Dictionary of Architecture". *Travellers' Club.* Fellow of Royal Society of Literature.

FLEMING, Major Richard Wallace, M.B.E., b. 24 Oct. 14, s. of G. N. Fleming, O.B.E. W, 28³–32¹. Magdalene, Cambridge, B.A. Batten Memorial Sword of Honour, 35. Gazetted to Black Watch, 35. ✕ Bde. Major, 14th Inf. Bde., Crete, 41. Dispatches. Staff College, Haifa, 41–42. G.S.O.2, Op. H.Q., M.E.F., 42; G.S.O.2 Trg., E. African Command & O.C., E. African O.C.T.U.,43–45. M.B.E. G.S.O.2, 51 Div., Germany. Retired as Major, 48. Now farming in Rhodesia.

FLEMING, William Launcelot Scott, b. 7 Aug. 06, 4th s. of late R. A. Fleming, M.D., LL.D., F.R.C.P.E. W, 20²–25². Trinity Hall, Cambridge, M.A. Yale University (Commonwealth Fund Fellowship in Biology), M.S. Westcott House, Cambridge. Ordained, 33. D.D., 49. F.R.S.E. Chaplain & Fellow, Trinity Hall, 33–49, Dean, 37–49; Hon. Fellow, 56. Expedition to Iceland, 32. Spitsbergen, 33. British Graham Land. Expedition to Antarctic, 34–37, as Chaplain & Geologist. Hon. Vice-Pres., Royal Geographical Society, 61. ✕ Chaplain, R.N.V.R , 40–44. Hon. Chaplain, R.N.V.R. (now R.N.R.) from 50. Dir., Scott Polar Research Institute, Cambridge, 47–49. Chrmn., C. of E. Youth Council, 50–61. Chrmn., Archbishop's Advisers on Needs and Resources, from 63. Bishop of Portsmouth, 49–59; Norwich, 59–71. Dean of Windsor from 71. Royal Commission on Environmental Pollution from 70. Vice-Chrmn., Parliamentary Group for World Government, 69–71. Polar Medal (Antarctic). Register, Order of the Garter from 71. Domestic Chaplain to Queen from 71. *Brooks's, Leander, Jesters.*

FLEMING-BERNARD, John Fishe (formerly Fleming, J. F.), b. 26 May 98, s. of Dr. A. M. Fleming, C.M.G., C.B.E. W, 12²–16²; Levée; XV, 15; R. VIII, 15–16 (Capt.); Cadet Officer; Boxing Lightweight, 15; Welterweight, 16. R.M.A., Woolwich. XV. ✕ "U" Battery, R.H.A., 17–18. Lt. Dispatches. Magdalen, Oxford. Rhodes Scholar (Rhodesia), B.A. Ranching & Tobacco Growing in Rhodesia, 22–37. F.L.A.S., 42. Practising Land Agent in Britain, 37–63. Retired, 63. *Vincent's. Farmers' Club, Royal Perth Golfing Society,* Pres., Land Agents Society, 52–53.

FLEMMING, Cecil Wood, C.B.E., M.D., M.Ch., F.R.C.S., b. 20 Aug. 02, 2nd s. of late P. Flemming, F.R.C.S. SH, 15³–20²; Scholar; Head of House. Trinity, Oxford, B.A., D.M. University College Hospital, M.R.C.S., L.R.C.P., F.R.C.S., M.Ch. Orthopaedic Surgeon, retired. ✕ R.A.F.V.R. (Medical Branch). Air Commodore. O.B.E., C.B.E. *Reform Club.* Brothers, Sir G. N. Flemming, K.C.B. & P. H. Flemming. Sons, 800 & 1695.

FLEMMING, Sir Gilbert Nicolson, K.C.B., b. 13 Oct. 97, eldest s. of late P. Flemming, F.R.C.S. SH, 11³–16²; Scholar. Trinity, Oxford. ✕ 7th Bn., Rifle Bde. Lt. Wounded. Ministry of Education (Board of Education), 21–59. (Permanent Sec. to the Minister.) Member Restrictive Practices Court, 60–64. Brothers, C. W. & P. H. Flemming. Sons, 483 & 1095. K.C.B. (Civil), 53.

FLEMMING, Percy Henry. SH, 17³–22¹.*

FLETCHER, Prof. Geoffrey Bernard Abbott, b. 28 Nov. 03, s. of J. A. Fletcher. Tu, 17³–22²; Major & Minor Exhibitioner. Senior Scholar of King's, Cambridge, B.A. Asst. Lecturer in Classics, Univ. of Leeds, 27–28. Asst. Lecturer in Greek, Univ. of Liverpool, 28–36. Prof. of Latin, Univ. of Durham, King's College, Newcastle-upon-Tyne from 37.

FLETCHER, Major John, M.B.E., b. 25 Mar. 17, eldest s. of late Major E. Fletcher (OR K 95). K, 30³–35². Corpus Christi, Cambridge, B.A. Royal Agricultural College, Cirencester, 54–55. Regular Army Officer. p.s.c. ✕ Royal Engineers, 38–49, then 16th/5th Queen's Royal Lancers to 54. Palestine, Italy, wounded (Anzio). M.B.E. Major. Korea (Dispatches). Retired, 54. Royal Agricultural College, Cirencester, 54–55. Co. Dir. & Financial Adviser. *Cavalry Club.* R.P.S.

FLETCHER, Richard John. M, 42²–47².*

FLINT, Algernon Horace. SF, 96²–00².*

FOA, Francis Raoul Osborne, b. 19 May 28, s. of late A. M. Foa (OR W 04). W, 42¹–45³; Levée; Head of House; Cap; XXII. ✕ Regular Soldier, King's Dragoon Guards. Resigned, 49. Farmed for 10 years on getting married. Steel Industry. *Cavalry Club.*

FOLEY, The Rev. Peter David. K, 46^3–52^1.*

FOLKES, John Joseph, b. 8 May 31, eldest s. of Lt.-Col. P. L. Folkes. St, 45^2–48^2. Hotelier. *R.A.F. Club.*

FOOKS, Henry Raymond Harvey, b. 29 June 26, s. of Sir R. Fooks, C.B.E. SH, 40^2–44^2. Exeter, Oxford. Gazetted to 1st King's Dragoon Guards, 46. Retired, 52. Farmer & Distributive Trades. *Cavalry Club.*

FOOKS, Thomas Courtenay. C, 17^3–18^2.*

FORD, John. K, 43^2–46^3.*

FORREST, Martin Nicholas. C, 26^2–30^3.*

FORRESTER, Alexander Fleming Campbell. W, 15^3–18^2. Son, 1035.*

FORSTER, Alan Douglas, M.B.E. b. 17 Oct. 05, 2nd s. of late J. C. Forster. St, 19^3–23^3. Pembroke, Oxford, B.A. Purely Commercial. Retired. M.B.E.(Mil.) *Jesters' Squash Club.*

FORSTER, Alan Phter, W, 34^1–38^3*

FORRESTER, John Alexander Leckie, b. 30 May 12, 4th s. of late R. Forrester. SH, 26^1–30^2; S. VIII, 27–30 (Capt.). Trinity, Cambridge, B.A. Birmingham University (Coal Mining Diploma). Colliery Manager's Certificate. Mining Industry, 35–46. Farming from 47. Highland Gathering. Brother, B. T. C. Forrester.

FORSTER, Alan Douglas, M.B.E. b. 17 Oct. 05, 2nd s. of late J. C. Forster. St, 19^3–23^3. Pembroke, Oxford, B.A. Purely Commercial. Retired. M.B.E. (Mil.). *Jesters' Squash Club.*

FORSTER, Alan Peter. W, 34^1–38^3.*

FORSTER-COOPER, Anthony. St, 31^1–36^1.*

FORSTER-COOPER, John, b. 19 Apr. 14, elder s. of late Sir C. Forster-Cooper, Sc.D., F.R.S. (OR St 94). St, 27^3–32^1. Gonville & Caius, Cambridge, M.A. Birmingham Commercial College. ✕ R.A., 39–45. Major. T.D. Production Engineer. Dir., Ducellier et Cie, Paris. Son, 2250.

FORSYTH, Philip Athelstone, M.R.C.S., L.R.C.P. SF, 22^3–26^2. Son, 2389.*

FORT, Thomas Cocker. B, 29^1–34^2.*

FOSTER, David Aubrey Clarence, b. 11 May 30, eldest s. of late C. H. M. Foster. M, 43^3–48^2. Member of Lloyd's. Dir., Bland, Welch & Co. Ltd., London.

FOSTER, Henry Evans, b. 29 Jan. 89, s. of late F. W. Foster. W, 02^3–07^2; Walrond Scholarship; Head of House; Head of School. Scholar of Trinity, Cambridge, M.A. Craven Scholar & Chancellor's Classical Medal. Half Blue in Chess. ✕ A.S.C. Pte. Staff of University College, London, 20; later, Registrar. Retired, 54. Member of Fauna Preservation Society. For 39 years, Sec. of the P.C.C. of Holy Trinity, Northwood.

FOSTER, Kenrie Hewitt. W, 37^1–41^3.*

FOSTER, The Hon. Sir Peter Harry Batson Woodroffe, Q.C., M.B.E., T.D., b. 5 Dec. 12, s. of late F. Foster. B, 26^3–31^2; Levée; XI; Cadet Officer. Corpus Christi, Cambridge, B.A., LL.B. Bar, 36. ✕ Fife & Forfar Yeomanry. Col. M.B.E. Dispatches thrice. T.D. Member, General Council of the Bar, 56–60. Q.C., 57. Bencher, Lincoln's Inn, 63. Member of Senate, 66–69. Judge of Chancery Div. of the High Court of Justice, 69. Steward of the B.B.B. of Church Commissioners. Chrmn., Performing Rights Tribunal, 65–69. Kt., 69. *White's, R. & A., Hawks.* Son, 740.

FOWLER, Stanley Grant, M.B.E., b. 23 Mar. 19, s. of late T. G. Fowler. B, 32^3–37^2; Tom Hughes Prize; XV, 36; XI, 37; Shared Athletic Cup, 37. Gonville & Caius, Cambridge, B.A. Half Blue for Athletics, 39. ✕ R.N.V.R. Lt.-Cdr. M.B.E. Dispatches. Fellow, Chartered Institute of Transport. Dir., Wm. Cory & Son Ltd., London. *Hawks.* R.O.R.C.

FOX, Ashton Raynor, b. 14 Sept. 09, s. of late M. J. Fox. K, 23^2–27^2. ✕ R.A.S.C. Lt.-Col. Queen's Coronation Medal. Chrmn. & Man. Dir., Ashton R. Fox Ltd.

FOX, John William Rawson, b. 4 July 30, s. of T. R. Fox, D.F.C. (OR B 13). B, 44^1–48^2. University College, Oxford, M.A. Bar, Middle Temple, 55. Senior Administrator, University of London. *Ski Club of Great Britain, Austrian Alpine Club.*

FOX, Thomas Rawson, b. 1 Jan. 00, s. of late W. Fox. B, 13^3–17^2. ✕ R.F.C., 18. Flight Cadet. University College, Oxford. ✕ R.A.F.V.R., 39–45. F/Lt. D.S.C.

Mohair Merchant, retired. Son, J. W. R. Fox.

FOX-EDWARDS, Gerald Norman, b. 15 Mar. 10, s. of Dr. N. Fox-Edwards. K, 23^3–27^1. Magdalene, Cambridge, B.A. ✕ R.N.V.R. Lieut. Various Directorships. Owns a fishing hotel, The Arundell Arms, Lifton, Devonshire. *Flyfishers' Club.*

FRANCE, Simon John, b. 27 Mar. 32, s. of P. E. France. St, 45^3–50^3; Levée; Head of House; XV, 50; XXII, 49–50; Fives IV, 50. St. John's, Cambridge, M.A. Provincial & District Administration, H.M.O.C.S., Nyasaland, 55–64. Ministry of Defence from 64.

FRANCIS, Francis. SH, 20^1–23^2. Sons, 15 & 451.*

FRANCIS, John Harvey, M.B., B.Ch., b. 29 Oct. 98, eldest s. of late Dr. H. Francis. SF, 12^3–17^1. ✕ R.G.A. 2nd Lt. St. John's, Cambridge, B.A., M.B., B.Chir. St. Mary's Hospital, M.R.C.S., L.R.C.P. General Medical Practitioner, 26–66. Part-time only since 66. Brother, R. H. Francis. Son, 628.

FRANCIS, Reginald Harvey. SF, 19^3–23^2.*

FRANK, Charles James, M.R.C.V.S., b. 31 Oct. 26, 2nd s. of late J. Frank. Tu, 40^3–45^3. Cadet Officer. Royal Veterinary College, London University, M.R.C.V.S. Senior partner in firm of Thoroughbred Horse Practitioners. *East India, Sports & Public Schools Club.* Son, Nigel James, Tu, 71^2–.

FRANKAU, Anthony MacDougall, M.I.Mech.E., b. 24 Mar. 21, 2nd s. of late Sir C. Frankau, C.B., D.S.O., M.S., F.R.C.S. (OR M 96). M, 34^3–39^2. ✕ R.A.F., 41–46. Specialist Signals Officer on Radar. Sqn. Ldr. Gonville & Caius, Cambridge, M.A. Chartered Mechanical Engineer. British Iron & Steel Research Assoc., 47–55. Dir., Huntington Heberlein & Co. Ltd., 55–71. Dairy Farmer.

FRANKAU, Col. John Howard, M.C., b. 23 Sept. 18, s. of late G. N. Frankau (OR M 95). M, 32^1–36^3; Levée; Head of House. R.M.A., Woolwich. Gonville & Caius, Cambridge. The Staff College, Haifa. The Joint Services Staff College, Latimer. B.A. (War Degree). p.s.c. j.s.s.c. ✕ Royal Engineers & Staff, 38. Retired, 73. Colonel. Ministry of Defence. Inst. of Royal Engineers. M.C. Son, 2604.

FRANKLAND, Thomas Smith, b. 10 June 26, s. of C. H. Frankland. SH, 40^1–44^3; Paddison Art Prize, 42–44. Trinity, Cambridge, M.A. N/S. R.A.F., 49–51. P/Officer. Fellow, Royal Society of Arts; Fellow, Linnean Society. Chrmn. or Hon. Treas. of several charitable organisations and institutions. A Financial Consultant, & Chrmn. of a number of companies. Advised some forty bodies, including The Lord Mayor of London's Appeal for Youth, The Royal College of Art, The Royal Society of Medicine. Currently Chrmn. of Charity Consultants Ltd. F.R.S.A., F.L.S.

FRANKS, Arthur Temple, C.M.G., b. 13 July 20, younger s. of A. Franks. B, 34^2–38^1. Queen's, Oxford, B.A. ✕ Hertfordshire Regt., 40. Libyan Arab Force, 42–43. S.O.E., 43–45. Control Commission, 45–46; Dispatches. Major. Journalism, 46–49. H.M. Diplomatic Service, 49. British Middle East Office, 51–53. Tehran, 53–56. Bonn, 62–66. F.C.O. C.M.G. *Travellers' Club, Sunningdale G.C.* Son, 2278.

FRASER, The Rev. Alastair Garden, b. 2 June 02, eldest s. of late Rev. A. G, Fraser, C.B.E. SH, 17^2–21^2. Queen's, Oxford, M.A. Colonial Education Service. 24–54. Schoolmaster, Achimota College, Gold Coast, 24–37. Headmaster, Munro College, Jamaica, 37–45. Ordained, 39. ✕ Hon. Chaplain to the Forces, attd. N. Caribbean Command, and later King's African Rifles. Asst. Dir. of Education, Nyasaland, 45; Deputy Dir., 46–54. Bishop's Chaplain for Youth, Chichester Diocese, 54–56. Overseas Sec., National Council of Y.M.C.A.s, 56–68. Retired, 68. Chatham House. Royal Commonwealth Society. Brother, A. R. B. Fraser.

FRASER, Andrew Robert Bruce, b. 16 Nov. 03, 2nd s. of late Rev. A. G. Fraser, C.B.E. SH, 17^2–22^2; XXII, 22. Queen's, Oxford, B.A. Retired. Brother, Rev. A. G. Fraser.

FRASER, Arthur, b. 18 Feb. 05, younger s. of J. C. Fraser. B, 19^1–21^2. Lyceum Alpinum, Zuoz, Switzerland. Dir., Tozer Kemsley & Millbourn (Holdings) Ltd. ✕ R.A.F., 40–45. Sqn. Ldr.

FRASER, Major Michael Quintin, b. 8 July 29, youngest s. of late Lt.-Col. Sir D. Fraser, K.C.V.O., C.S.I., C.I.E. (OR St 03). St, 44^3–47^2. Rackets Pair, 46–47 (Capt.). R.M.A. Sandhurst. Capt. of Rackets. Gazetted to 7th Queen's Own

Hussars, 50. Retired, 73, as Major. Farming in Aberdeenshire. *Cavalry Club.* Overseas League. British Horse Society.

FRASER, Patrick Shaw. B, 06³–10².*

FRASER-CAMPBELL, Evan James, T.D., b. 31 Aug. 18, s. of late E. Fraser-Campbell. SH, 32¹–36². ✕ Argyll & Sutherland Highlanders, 39–45. Capt. Wounded. T.D. Norwegian Liberty Medal. U.S. Army Certificate of Merit. British Steel Corporation. *Caledonian Club, London; Prestwick G.C.* Sons, 1696 & William Patrick, SH, 67³–71³.

FREEMAN, Brian Sidney, B.M., B.Ch., b. 25 Jan. 26, s. of Capt. S. Freeman, C.B.E. Sh, 39³–43³; Cadet Officer; Holder of Bigside Bags. Brasenose, Oxford, M.A., B.M., B.Ch. House Officer, St. Thomas Hospital & Rowley Bristow Orthopaedic Hospital, Byfleet. Dir. of Companies, including Irish Hospitals Sweepstakes Organisation. Member, Council of World Health Foundation (Geneva) not actively practising medicine at present time. *Royal St. George Yacht Club.*

FREEMAN, Donald Eric, b. 8 Feb. 33, elder s. of E. H. R. Freeman (OR B 17). B, 46³–50³; XV, 49–50; XI, 50; H. XI, 50. With Chrysler Motors, Adelaide, S. Australia.

FREEMAN, Edward Hugh Ramsden, b. 9 Feb. 04, 2nd s. of J. E. Freeman, M.A. B, 17³–22²; Scholar; Levée; Head of House; Cap, 21; Cadet Officer. Solicitor, 26. Now consultant with former firm of Freeman, Daly & Jacks, of Darlington. Sons, D. E. Freeman, 1869 & 2805.

FREEMAN, Sir John Keith Noel, Bt. C, 37²–41².*

FREEMAN, John Oliver, b. 8 Oct. 10, 3rd s. of late D. G. Freeman. W, 24³–28³. ✕ R.A.F., 41–46. F/Sgt. Retired. Son, 1544.

FREKE, John Henry, b. 2 May 25, s. of C. G. Freke, C.I.E. B, 40³–43³. ✕ R.E., 44–47. Lt. St. John's, Cambridge, M.A. C.A. (Canada). Dir., Toronto Region, Audit Services Bureau, Dept. of Supply & Services, Toronto, Ont., Canada.

FRENCH, Lt.-Col. Henry John Sawyer, O.B.E., B.C.L., b. 7 Jan. 13, s. of Dr. H. S. French, C.V.O., C.B.E., M.D., F.R.C.P. B, 26³–31²; Exhibitioner; S. VIII, 29–31. Christ Church, Oxford, M.A.,

B.C.L. Bar, Gray's Inn, 35. City Editor, "Sunday Times", 38–39. ✕ Army, 39–41. Lt.-Col. R.A. O.B.E. Officer U.S. Legion of Merit. Dir., London & Yorkshire Trust Ltd., 46–69. Dir. of other companies. Chrmn., Issuing Houses Assoc., 59–61. *Boodle's; Flyfishers; Pilgrims;* Pres., *Bishopstoke Fishing Club.* Son, 899.

FRENCH, Peter Reginald, F.R.C.S., b. 22 July 21, eldest s. of late Rev. R. French, M.C., M.A. (OR B 97). Tu, 35³–39². St. Thomas's Hospital, L.R.C.P., F.R.C.S. ✕ R.N.V.R., 45–47. Surg.-Lt. Orthopaedic Surgeon, St. George's Hospital, London. Royal Masonic Hospital. *Naval Club, London; Hurlingham; Berkshire G.C.* Worshipful Society of Apothecaries. British Orthopaedic Assoc.

FRESTON, Major Richard Lloyd, M.B.E., T.D., b. 1 Mar. 03, younger s. of late H. W. Freston. SH, 16³–20². ✕ R.A., 39–45. Major. M.B.E. Dispatches. T.D. Company Dir. Textiles. Retired, 64. *Ski Club of Great Britain.*

FREUND, Peter Hans, b. 7 Apr. 28, younger s. of O. Freund. SH & St, 42¹–46¹; Capt. of Fives, 45; Tennis Team. Hartwick College, Oneonta, N.Y. B.A. Tennis Team, 49–50 (Capt.). U.S. Marine Corps., Sgt., 51–53. Master of Business Administration. Computer Auditor, Marine Midland Bank, N.Y.

FRIEND, Herbert John, B.S., D.R.C.O.G., b. 16 Dec. 16, s. of H. J. Friend. T, 30³–35²; Levée; Head of House. Entrance Scholarship to St. Mary's Hospital, M.B., B.S., M.R.C.S., L.R.C.P., D.Obst.R.C.O.G. ✕ R.A.M.C., 40–46. Capt. General Practitioner, 46–48. Medical Officer, Unilever Ltd., from 48. Present appointment, Senior Medical Officer. Royal Society of Medicine.

FRISWELL, John Keith, b. 23 Feb. 27, elder s. of A. Friswell. T, 40³–44². Dalton Hall, Manchester Univ., B.Sc., C.Eng., F.I.M.A., A.F.R.Ae.S. Joined Scientific Civil Service, 52. Now Superintendent, Instrumentation Div., Royal Aircraft Establishment, Farnborough.

FRITH, Michael Rex, b. 21 Oct. 17, s. of late W. R. Frith (OR C 99). C, 31³–36²; Levée; XV, 35. Exhibitioner of Pembroke, Cambridge, M.A. ✕ R.A. (Field), 39–46. Major. Schoolmaster since 46, 5 years at Bilton Grange. Headmaster of a Prep. School, 54–69. Now Asst. Master at another. Son, 2042A.

FROOMBERG, John Simon, b. 7 Aug. 31, eldest s. of A. Froomberg. K & C, 44³–49²; Scholar; Levée; Head of House; Cap; Sw. VIII, 49 (Capt.). N/S. Eaton Hall & Royal Warwickshire Regt. 2nd Lt. 16 years in family Textile business. Now Partner in firm of Textile Manufacturers' Agents. *Hendon R.F.C.* London Society R.F.U. Referees. Brothers, 81 & 538. Son, Peter Mark, C, 72²–.

FRYER, John Denny, b. 5 Oct. 22, s. of late Sir J. C. F. Fryer, K.B.E. (OR C 01). C, 36³–41²; Levée; Cap; XXII. Gonville & Caius, Cambridge, M.A. Frank Smart Prize for Botany. M.A. (Oxon.). ✗ Commissioned, R.E., 44. Transferred to Indian Army Ord. Corps, 45, Capt. Joined Plant Protection Ltd., Fernhurst, Haslemere, Surrey, 47. i/c Botany Section. Agricultural Research Council Unit of Experimental Agronomy, 50; A.R.C. Weed Research Organisation, Yarnton, Oxford, 60. Dir. since 64. Member of Assoc. of Applied Biology. *Farmers' Club.*

FULLER-QUINN, Gerald Arthur (formerly Quinn, G.A.F.). W, 25³–29³.*

FURNESS-SMITH, John Gerald. SF, 37³–42².*

FURNIVALL, Cecil Gerald (formerly C. G. F. Salinger). SH, 15¹–19².*

G

GAASTRA, John Newhouse, b. 21 June 18, 2nd s. of late B. Gaastra. Sh, 31³–36². University of London. A.T.D. ✗ Inns of Court Regt., 39–46. Capt. Dir. of Art, St. Peter's School, York.

GADDUM, Edward Walter, b. 19 June 06, 3rd s. of late H. E. Gaddum. K, 20²–24². Wye College, London University, B.Sc. Imperial College of Tropical Agriculture, Trinidad, A.I.C.T.A. Kenya Agricultural Service, 29–52. Now Company Dir./Sec. Brother, P. W. Gaddum.

GADDUM, Peter William, b. 29 Dec. 02, 2nd s. of late H. E. Gaddum. K, 16³–21². With H. T. Gaddum & Co., Silk Merchants, Manchester. ✗ King's Own Scottish Borderers. Commissioned, 40. Later transferred to Ministry of Supply for work in M.E., Italy & Far East. Merchant. *Ancoats Lads & St. James's, Manchester.* Brother, E. W. Gaddum. Son, 839.

GAIR, Edward Coleridge. K, 18¹–21².*

GALE, David Newlyn, b. 6 Oct. 32, s. of late A. Gale. SH, 46²–50³; Leader of School Orchestra. N/S. Oxford & Bucks L.I., 51–53. Trinity, Oxford, B.A. Manchester Univ., Diploma in Drama. Actor & later Director. Teaching English & Drama at Exeter School to 73. Coopers Co. & Coborn School, Upminster, from Sept. 73.

GALES, David Russell. M, 31³–33³.*

GALES, John Denys, b. 5 Feb. 22, 2nd s. of late J. R. Gales (OR M 04). M, 35³–39². ✗ R.N.V.R. Lieut. Dispatches. Design Manager, Associated Biscuits Ltd., Reading. R.N.R. Brother, D. R. Gales. Son, Andrew John, 67³–72².

GALLIA, Godfrey Eugen Hugo, b. 17 June 32, s. of E. E. H. Gallia. K, 45³–50³; Levée; Head of House; Water-polo Team. Christ Church, Oxford, M.A. Water-polo Blue. Schoolmaster at Sherborne School, Dorset; and Farmer.

GALLOWAY, Alexander Hugh, b. 10 Oct. 07, 2nd s. of late Sir J. Galloway, K.B.E., C.B., M.D. C, 21²–25². Octavius Steel & Co., East India Merchants, from 25. Dir., 45 & Man. Dir., 48. ✗ R. Signals in India, 41–44. Capt. Chrmn., Indian Tea Assoc., Calcutta, 51. Chrmn., Indian Tea Assoc., London, 63–65. Retired, 72. Chrmn., Octavius Steel & Co. Ltd., Calcutta, 54–58. Dir., Octavius Steel & Co. (London) Ltd., 59–72. Dir., Walter Duncan & Goodricke Ltd., London, 66–72. *City of London, Oriental.*

GANDERTON, Martin Noel. T, 02¹–04².*

GARDENER, Geoffrey Chase. K, 36³–40².*

GARDINER-HILL, Col. Robin Clive, O.B.E., R.E., b. 25 July 24, 2nd s. of late Dr. C. Gardiner-Hill. M, 37³–42²; Sw. VIII, 40–42 (Capt.). Gazetted to Royal Engineers, 45. ✗ R.E. Capt. Pembroke, Cambridge, B.A., 50. Standing Sub-Committee of British National Committee for Geography. Colonel, currently serving as Dep. Dir., Ordnance Survey. O.B.E. (Mil.). F.R.G.S. Rear Commodore of

Royal Southampton Yacht Club. The Photogrammetric Society, British Cartographic Society.

GARDNER, Prof. Arthur Duncan, D.M., F.R.C.S., F.R.C.P., b. 28 Mar. 84, younger s. of late J. W. Gardner (OR St 64). St, 97³–02²; XV, 01; G. VIII, 01–02 (Capt.); Gym Pair, winner of Public Schools Shield at Aldershot, 02. University College, Oxford, M.A., M.B., B.Ch., D.M. Blue for Hockey, 06. St. Thomas' Hospital (London), F.R.C.S., F.R.C.P. ✕ Red Cross Surgeon with Army in France, 14. Bacteriological Supplies & Research under the Medical Research Council in Oxford, 15–36. 30 or 40 original contributions to Medical Scientific journals. Member of Oxford Team which discovered the healing powers of penicillin, 40. Prof. of Bacteriology, Oxford, 36–48. Regius Prof. of Medicine, 48–54. Now Prof. (Emeritus), Oxford University. Retired since 56. Hon. Fellow, University Coll., Oxford. Student of Christ Church, 48–54. Hon. Consultant, Radcliffe Infirmary, Oxford. Rede Lecturer, Cambridge, 53. Lichfield Lecturer, Oxford, 54. Son, A. M. N. Gardner. Grandson, Andrew David, Sh, 72³–.

GARDNER, Arthur Michael Newsam, D.M., M.Ch., F.R.C.S., b. 15 Aug. 19, eldest s. of Prof. A. D. Gardner, D.M., F.R.C.S., F.R.C.P. (OR St 97). SF, 33³–37³. University College, Oxford. Theodore Williams Scholar in Pathology, M.A., D.M., B.Ch. Radcliffe Infirmary, Oxford. Oxford Medical School, D.M., M.Ch., F.R.C.S.(Eng.). ✕ R.A.F.V.R. Dispatches. Surgeon, 44. Hunterian Prof., Royal College of Surgeons, 70. Consultant Surgeon (General & Vascular), Torbay Hospital, Torquay. Royal Society of Medicine. Corresponding Fellow, Academy of Medicine, Toronto. Son, Andrew David, Sh, 72³–.

GARDNER, Charles Frederic, b. 4 Feb. 04, eldest s. of late C. F. Gardner. B, 17³–22². Trinity Hall, Cambridge, B.A. United Shoe Machinery Corporation, 26–69. ✕ R. Norfolk Regt., 40–45. Seconded to Gold Coast Regt., R.W.A.F.F. Major. Brother, L. R. Gardner.

GARDNER, John Jotham, b. 15 Aug. 31, 2nd s. of R. Gardner, M.C., M.A. Sh, 45²–49³; XV, 48–49; XI, 48–49; H. XI, 49. Emmanuel, Cambridge, M.A. F.C.I.I. Asst. Gen. Man., Orion Insurance Co. Ltd. *M.C.C. Harlequins F.C.* Brother, R. Gardner.

GARDNER, Lyman Ruediger, B.Chir., M.R.C.S., L.R.C.P., b. 10 June 10, 2nd s. of late C. F. Gardner. W, 23³–29². Trinity Hall, Cambridge, M.A., B.Chir. Middlesex Hospital Medical School, M.R.C.S., L.R.C.P. Asst. Pathologist, Reading Royal Infirmary. House Physician, Middlesex Hospital. Hon. Physician, Victoria Cottage Hospital, Barnet. Clinical Asst., Barnet General Hospital. Casualty Officer, Finchley Memorial Hospital. Registered General Medical Practitioner in National Health Service. Brother, C. F. Gardner.

GARDNER, Richard, R.I.B.A., b. 2 Oct. 28, eldest s. of R. Gardner, M.C., M.A. Sh & C, 42³–47¹; Scholar; Levée; XV, 45–46 (Capt., 47); H. XI, 46–47. Exhibition to Emmanuel, Cambridge, M.A. R.I.B.A. Architect, Private Practice, 61–68. Now, Under-Secretary, R.I.B.A. Brother, J. J. Gardner.

GARDNER, Stanley York Preston. Tu, 08³–10¹.*

GARFORTH, Major William Sealey Herbert, b. 8 June 14, s. of late Col. W. Garforth, D.S.O., M.C. (OR SH 96). SH, 28¹–31¹. R.M.A., Woolwich. R.M.A. XI & H. XI, 33. Army Staff College. Gazetted to Royal Artillery, 34. Regular Soldier. ✕ War Office. Iceland, att. R.A.F. N. Africa (Gen. Staff). Comd. Field Battery, Italy, wounded, 43. Major. Retired, 44. Personnel Dir. Administration Man. Company Sec. Brewery. *M.C.C., A. & N. Club.*

GARFORTH-BLES, Lt.-Col. George David, b. 5 Oct. 09, eldest s. of late Capt. G. M. Garforth-Bles (OR SF 91). SF, 23³–27³; XV, 27; H. XI, 27. Jesus, Cambridge, B.A. Cadet Officer. Played polo for Cambridge. Gazetted to The Guides Cavalry, Frontier Force, 30. ✕ India, Burma. Dispatches. Lt.-Col., retired, 47. In business with brother, M. W. Garforth-Bles (OR SF 27). Business Investments Co. of London. Brothers, M. W. & J. M. Garforth-Bles. Son, 1220. Nephew, David James, SF, 67¹–71³.

GARFORTH-BLES, John Marcus. SF, 27²–31¹.*

GARFORTH-BLES, Michael William, b. 28 July 13, younger (twin) s. of late Capt. G. M. Garforth-Bles (OR SF 91). SF, 27²–31¹. A.C.A., 39. ✕ R. Signals, 39–45. Major. Retired. *E.S.U.* Brothers, G. D. & J. M. Garforth-Bles. Sons, 2390 & 2688. Nephew, David James, SF, 67¹–71³.

GARLAND, Adrian Edgar. T, 42^3-46^2.*

GARLAND, Francis Le Manquais. T, 41^1-41^3.*

GARNER, Frederic Francis, C.M.G., b. 9 July 10, s. of late F. H. Garner. B, 24^3-28^2. Worcester, Oxford, B.A. Joined H.M. Foreign Service, 32. Interned in Japan, 42–45. H.M. Ambassador to Cambodia, 58–61. H.M. Ambassador to Costa Rica, 61–68. Retired. C.M.G., 59.

GARNETT, Jan Nicholas Palmer. SH, 43^3-47^2.*

GARNETT, Michael Ronald Kenneth. SH, 33^3-37^2.*

GARNETT, Peter Henry Milcrest. Tu, 38^1-41^3.*

GARNETT, William John Poulton Maxwell, C.B.E., b. 6 Aug. 21, 2nd s. of J. C. M. Garnett, C.B.E., Sc.D. SH, 35^3-39^2. Kent School, U.S.A. Trinity, Cambridge. Won Freshman's Sculls, 41. University Sculls, 46. Double Sculls, 47. B.A. ✕ R.N.V.R., 41–46. Lt. I.C.I., 46–62. Dir. Industrial Society from 62. C.B.E., 69. *Athenæum, Leander.* Brothers, M. R. K. & J. N. P. Garnett.

GARNONS-WILLIAMS Peter Boleyn, b. 22 Apr. 29, 3rd s. of late Major R. F. Garnons-Williams. T & Sh, 43^1-46^3. 10 years Royal Navy to rank of Lt. Retired into Horticulture, now running own nursery.

GARRARD, Frank Rochfort, b. 9 Nov. 01, younger s. of late F. R. Garrard. St, 16^1-19^3; XV, 19; S. VIII, 19. Trinity, Cambridge, M.A. Chartered Accountant—A.C.A., 27 (not followed after 35). Retired Farmer.

GARRATT, David Jon, b. 7 Jan. 33, eldest s. of Alderman A. L. Garratt, J.P. K, 46^3-51^2. N/S. 13/18 Royal Hussars, 52/3. 2nd Lt. Served in Malaya, 53. London Polytechnic. National Bakery Diploma. Bakery. Sales Dir., Sunshine Bread Co. (Norwich) Ltd. J.P., 71. Chrmn., British Chapter of American Society of Bakery Engineers. *Cruising Assoc., Junior Chamber of Commerce, Pinmill Sailing Club.*

GARRETT, Michael. SF, 23^2-27^2.*

GARRETT, Philip Arthur, b. 27 Jan. 23, s. of late W. B. Garrett. T, 37^1-41^3. Birmingham Univ., B.Sc. Dudley Docker Research Scholarship. Hockey Colours. ✕ R.E., 44–47. Capt. Appointed Asst. Lecturer, Dept. of Geology, Birmingham University, 48 (now Senior Lecturer). F.G.S.

GARRETT. Roderick Paul Agnew, b. 27 Dec. 08, s. of late D. T. Garrett. SH, 22^3-27^3. Trinity Hall, Cambridge, B.A. Solicitor, 34. ✕ R.N.V.R. (Minesweepers), 41–46. Partner, Parker Garrett & Co., Solicitors in London, 39–70. Now parttime on own a/c. Law Society.

GARRETT, Victor Richard, b. 21 Oct. 87, 4th s. of late F. Garrett (OR SF 60). SF, 01^3-05^3; XV, 05. Pembroke, Cambridge, M.A. Business in England and South Africa (retired). *Hawks Club, St. Stephens, R.A.C.*

GARRETT-JONES, Charles. M, 26^1-30^1.*

GARRETT-JONES, Ronald. SH, 28^3-33^1.*

GASKELL, William Harriman Craig, b. 11 June 14, s. of W. Gaskell, C.I.E. B, 27^3-32^3; XV, 32; Cadet Officer. St. John's, Cambridge, B.A. ✕ R.A.S.C. Capt. Dir., W. H. Everett & Son Ltd. (18 years). Retired.

GASKELL, William Roscoe, M.C. SF, 07^3-11^1.*

GATLIFF, Herbert Evelyn Caulfeild, b. 21 Sept. 97, elder s. of late Rev. J. F. Gatliff. W, 11^3-16^2; Scholar; Head of School; Exhibitioner, 16. ✕ 5th Coldstream Guards. 2nd Lt. Resigned, illhealth, 17. Scholar of Balliol, Oxford (Lit. Hum.), 20. Asst. Principal, H.M. Treasury, 17–19 & 20–32 (Principal, 32–44); Treasury Representative on Nat. Savings Committee, 34–38; Asst. Secretary, Min. of Town & Country Planning, 44–52. Retired. Exec. Committee, Commons & Footpaths Society, 42. Estates Committee, Nat. Trust, 44–62. Youth Hostels Assoc. Nat. Exec., 34–66; Vice-Pres., 66.

GAUNT, David Philip Keppel. Sh, 46^3-51^2.*

GAUNT, The Rev. Roger Cecil, b. 13 July 30, eldest s. of H. C. A. Gaunt. Sh, 44^2-49^2; Levée; Head of House; Minor Scholar of King's, Cambridge, B.A. Jasper Ridley Music Prize. Westcott House, Cambridge. Ordained, 55, Durham Cathedral. Rector of Limpsfield, Surrey. Dir. of St. Endellion Music Festival, Cornwall. Brother, D. P. K. Gaunt.

GAVIN, Alexander Giraud, b. 16 May 13, s. of E. Gavin. Tu, 26³–30³. Trinity Hall, Cambridge, B.A. A.R.I.B.A. Architect (Private Practice—Man., Gavin & Associates). J.P.

GEARY, Colin Garton. W, 44²–49².*

GEDDES, Sir Anthony Reay Mackay, K.B.E., b. 7 May 12, 3rd s. of late Sir E. C. Geddes, G.C.B., G.B.E., P.C. SF, 25³–30². Magdalene, Cambridge, B.A. ✕ R.A.F. Group-Capt. O.B.E. Chrmn., Dunlop Holdings Ltd. K.B.E., L.R.D., D.Tech.

GEDDES, The Rt. Hon. Lord (Geddes, R. C.), K.B.E., b. 20 July 07, eldest s. of late The Rt. Hon. Sir Auckland Geddes, 1st Lord Geddes, G.C.M.G., K.C.B., M.D. SH, 21¹–26¹; Cadet Officer. Gonville & Caius, Cambridge, M.A. Shell Group of Companies, 31–46. Chrmn., Navy Dept., Fuels & Lubricants Advisory Cttee., 51–57. Pres., Institute of Petroleum, 56–58. Chrmn., British Travel Assoc., 64–69. Pres., Chamber of Shipping of the U.K., 68. Chrmn., Westminster Medical School Council from 68. Dir., P. & O. Steam Navigation Co., 57–72. Chrmn., Trident Tankers Ltd. Clerical, Medical & General Life Assurance Society. Monks Inv. Trust, Linner Holdings Ltd., 64–71. Dir., Foseco-Minsep Ltd. Brixton Estate Ltd. Technology Inv. Trust. C.B.E., 58. K.B.E., 70. *White's, Royal Lymington Yacht Club.* Succeeded father, 54. Son, 632.

GEE, Hugh Michael. St, 32³–36².*

GEE, Robert George, b. 16 Oct. 31, s. of G. Gee. SH, 45²–50¹. Cap. Oriel, Oxford, B.A. N/S. & T.A., Argyll & Sutherland Highlanders, 50–64. Solicitor. Company Sec., The Rugby Portland Cement Co. Ltd.

GEFFEN, John Lionel Henry, O.B.E. b. 10 May 25, eldest s. of D. H. Geffen. K, 40¹–40². Went to America. New College, Oxford, M.A. Capt. of Tennis. Capt. of Hockey. ✕ The Buffs, 44–47. Staff Capt. O.B.E. England & Middle East. Group Man. Dir. & Chief Executive, Bersons Hosiery Holdings Ltd. Group Man. Dir., Wharf Holdings Ltd. Dir., Gardner Merchant (Trust Houses). Man. Dir., Hide & Co. (Calico Printers). *Army & Navy Club, Hurlingham, M.C.C.* Son, Robin John Henry, K 71²–.

GEMMELL, John Alexander, b. 30 Sept. 98, eldest s. of late J. Gemmell. B, 12³–17¹. ✕ 3rd Bn. York & Lancaster Regt. 2nd Lt. Emmanuel, Cambridge, M.A. Dir. of Balmer Lawrie & Co. Ltd., Calcutta, 23–35; Chrmn., 34–35. Dir., Alex Lawrie & Co. Ltd., for 35 years, now retired. Dir., Royal Caledonian Schools, Bushey, Herts, & of the Royal Scottish Corp. from 33. Capt., 3rd Finchley Company of the Boy's Brigade, 21–22. Member of the Gen. Assembly of Presbyterian Church of England. Central Council of the Leprosy Mission and many other Philanthropic Boards. Member of the General Assembly of the Church of Scotland, 32. Author & Composer of Music. Liveryman of the Leathersellers Co. Vice-Pres. of the London Y.M.C.A. *Oriental Club, R.S.A.C., Northwood Golf Club.*

GEMMILL, Hugh Mure. Sh, 33³–38¹.*

GEMMILL, James Alistair, b. 21 Aug. 14, 2nd s. of late W. Gemmill, F.I.A. W, 28³–33²; Cap; XI, 30–33 (Capt.); Sw. VIII, 30–33. University College, Oxford, M.A. Athletics Blue, 36. Bar, Middle Temple, 38. ✕ S. African Artillery, 41–45. 2nd Lt. Gen. Man., National Labour Organisation of the Transvaal Chamber of Mines, Johannesburg. *Junior Carlton Club; Rand Club, Johannesburg, S.A.* Brother, W. R. M. Gemmill. Son, 1179.

GEMMILL, William Richard Muir, b. 9 June 18, youngest s. of late W. Gemmill, F.I.A. Sh, 32²–37¹. Peterhouse, Cambridge, B.A. ✕ R.A.F.V.R., 39–40. King's African Rifles, 41–45, Africa, India, Ceylon, Burma. Capt. Man. of M.L.O., Botswana & Malawi. *Junior Carlton Club; Country Club, Johannesburg, S.A.* Brother, J. A. Gemmill.

GERMAN, Col. Guy Johnson, D.S.O., T.D., b. 17 June 02, eldest s. of Col. G. German, D.S.O., T.D., D.L. SH, 15²–20¹; XV, 19; Boxing Welterweight, 19. Magdalen, Oxford, M.A. Rugby Football Blue, 22. Gazetted to 5th Bn. Leicestershire Regt. (T.A.), 21. Senior Partner of John German & Son, Chartered Surveyors, Ashby-de-la-Zouch. ✕ Lt.-Col. R. Leicestershire Regt. P.O.W. D.S.O., T.D., F.R.I.C.S.

GERRARD, Peter Noel, b. 19 May 30, s. of Sir D. Gerrard, Q. C. W, 43³–48²; Scholar; Levée; Head of School; Exhibitioner. Scholar of Christ Church, Oxford, M.A. N/S. 12 Royal Lancers, 53–54. 2nd Lt. Solicitor.

GIBB, Charles Oliver. K, 33¹–37².*

GIBB, Hugh James. K, 28³–32³.*

GIBB, James. K, 30²–34³.*

GIBB, Jocelyn Easton, C.B.E., b. 18 May 07, 2nd s. of late Sir A. Gibb, G.B.E., C.B., F.R.S. (OR St 86). St, 21¹–24². Pembroke, Cambridge, M.A. Man. Dir., Geoffrey Bles Ltd., Book Publishers, 54–71. Chrmn., Land Settlement Assoc. from 54. ✕ R. Wiltshire Yeomanry, R.A.C., 39–45. Lt.-Col. C.B.E. *Athenæum, Cavalry, Pratt's.* Son, 874.

GIBB, Richard Wilson. K, 31¹–35¹.*

GIBB, William Brian, D.F.C. K, 33²–37³.*

GIBB, William Eric, D.M., F.R.C.P., b. 30 Apr. 11, only surviving s. of late J. G. Gibb, F.R.C.S. C, 25¹–30¹. Oriel, Oxford, M.A., B.M., B.Ch., D.M. St. Bartholomew's Hospital, London, F.R.C.P. (London). ✕ R.A.F.V.R., 41–46. Wing-Cdr. (Medical Specialist). Physician, St. Bartholomew's Hospital. Fellow, Royal Society of Medicine. Sons, James Christopher, SF, 67³, & William Richard Glenny, SF, 69²–.

GIBBINGS, James Frankling, b. 5 Sept. 26, 2nd s. of late W. W. Gibbings. B, 40³–44². New College, Oxford (Army short course). International Scholarship. College of Business & Public Administration Graduate College, Arizona. Spec. Cert. in Electromagnetism & High Frequency Oscillations, Oxford, 44. B.Sc. Industrial Management, 49. M.A., Economics, 50, University of Arizona. R.C.A. Corp. (Corporate Staff) Man. Systems Projects, David Sarnoff Research Centre, Princeton, N.J., U.S.A. Brother, P. W. Gibbings.

GIBBINGS, Peter Walter, b. 25 Mar. 29, youngest s. of late W. W. Gibbings. B & C, 42³–47¹; Levée; Head of House; XV, 46; H. XI, 47; Major Classics Scholar of Wadham, Oxford, M.A. N/S. 9th Queen's Royal Lancers, 51–52. 2nd Lt. Barrister, 53. Trinidad Oil Co. Ltd., 55. Associated Newspapers Ltd., 56–60. The Observer Ltd., 60–67; Dir. & Deputy Man., 65–67. Man. Dir., "The Guardian", 67; Deputy Chrmn., "The Guardian" & "Manchester Evening News" from 72. Member of the Press Council. Brother, J. F. Gibbings.

GIBBONS, Major Leonard John, D.L., J.P., b. 23 Mar. 03, 2nd s. of L. P. Gibbons. Tu, 16³–21². Keble, Oxford, B.A. Solicitor, 28. J.P., County of Worcester, 46, & Deputy Chrmn. of Quarter Sessions. ✕ 53rd Anti-Tank Regt. (Worcestershire Yeomanry), R.A., 39–42; Major & Sqn. Ldr. in R.A.F. Regt. Now retired. D.L. for the County of Worcester.

GIBBS, Christopher Lawrence. T, 42³–47².*

GIBBS, David Stormont, O.B.E., b. 9 July 26, s. of C. C. S. Gibbs. SF, 40³–44²; Scholar; Levée; Head of House; XV, 42–43; H. XI, 44. Exhibitioner of Clare, Cambridge, B.A. N/S. Commissioned in R.E., 47–49. A.M.I.C.E., 52. Consulting Engineer, 49–55. Asst. Master, Repton School, 55–64. Rector, St. Paul's School, Darjeeling, 64–72. Asst. Master, Rugby School from 73. O.B.E., 73. Headmaster, St. Columba's College, Dublin, 74.

GIBSON, Alexander Brian Forsyth, M.R.C.S., L.R.C.P., b. 7 Mar. 09, eldest s. of late Dr. A. G. Gibson, D.M., F.R.C.P. SH, 22³–27². Gonville & Caius, Cambridge, B.A. St. Thomas's Hospital, London, M.R.C.S., L.R.C.P. ✕ R.A.M.C., 39–45. General Medical Practitioner Brother, W. M. Gibson.

GIBSON, Cullen Barnes, b. 11 May 25, s. of late C. T. Gibson. W, 38³–42². King's, Cambridge. ✕ 11th Hussars (P.A.O.), 43–49. Lt. Chrmn., A. B. Gibson Ltd. (Wholesale & Retail Grocery) from 49, also Chrmn., Makro (Cash & Carry) Ltd. *Cavalry Club.*

GIBSON, Lt.-Cdr. The Hon. Edward Barry Greynville, R.N., b. 28 Jan. 33, s. of Vice-Admiral Lord Ashbourne, C.B., D.S.O. St, 46³–50³. Graduate, Royal Naval Staff College, 65. Naval Officer, 51–72, retired as Lt.-Cdr. Associate Member, British Institute of Management, 70. Stockbroker. *United Service Club, St. Moritz Tobogganing Club.*

GIBSON, John Atkinson, b. 12 June 12, 3rd s. of late Sir H. J. Gibson, K.C.B. M, 26³–29². Barclays Bank Ltd., 30–34. Boustead & Co. Ltd., 35–63 (Singapore & Malaya), now retired. Dispatches. Royal Commonwealth Society. Natal Senior Golfers' Society. *Durban Country Club & Klouf Country Club.*

GIBSON, John Colin. T, 36¹–39³.*

GIBSON, William Martin, B.M., B.Ch., b. 14 Dec. 12, 2nd s. of late Dr. A. G. Gibson, D.M., F.R.C.P. SH, 26³–31². Christ Church, Oxford, M.A., B.M., B.Ch. St. George's Hospital, London. ✕ R.A.M.C., 40–46. Dispatches. Capt. General Medical Practitioner. Brother, A. B. F. Gibson.

GIDLOW JACKSON, Charles William. B, 01²–04².*

GIDLOW JACKSON, Col. Sir Francis James, M.C. (formerly Jackson, F. J. G.), b. 16 Sept. 89, 2nd s. of late C. Gidlow Jackson. K, 03³–07². Solicitor, 12. ✕ 2nd East Lancashire Bde., R.F.A. (T.F.) M.C. Colonel. Practised as Partner in Denham & Jackson of Manchester. Kt., 55. M.C., T.D. Brother, C. W. Gidlow Jackson.

GIELGUD, Val Henry, C.B.E., b. 28 Apr. 00, 2nd s. of late F. Gielgud. SF, 14¹–18². Exhibitioner of Trinity, Oxford. ✕ Grenadier Guards, 18. Novelist & Playwright (21 Novels & 3 Volumes of Autobiographies). Head of Radio Drama, B.B.C. (sound), 29–63. Retired. C.B.E., 58. *Savile.*

GIFFARD, David Campbell Walter, b. 3 Nov. 31, s. of late C. W. Giffard (OR M 01). M, 45²–49²; XV, 48. N/S. The Queen's Royal Regt., 50. Slade School Fine Art, Diploma in Fine Art. Co. Dir. in C.I.E. Ltd., a company dealing with the marketing of products for the building trade.

GILBERT, James Elton, M.D., b. 8 June 16, eldest s. of J. Gilbert. T, 29³–34³. Guy's Hospital, M.B., B.S.; Hammersmith Postgraduate Hospital; Diploma Obstetrics, R.C.O.G.; Maudsley Hospital; McGill University. Board Certified by Royal College of Physicians & Surgeons (Canada), 52. M.D. (S. Dakota), S. Carolina. Assoc. Prof. in Psychiatry, Tulane University, New Orleans, 65. Chief of Staff, Veterans' Administration Hospital, Canandaigua, New York, 71. Fellow of Royal College of Physicians & Surgeons (Canada), 72. Lt.-Col., U.S. Army Medical Corps. Member, British Medical Society, American Medical Society. Brother, R. B. W. Gilbert.

GILBERT, John Douglas. T, 39³–40².*

GILBERT, Robert Bloye Wanstall, b. 14 June 23, 2nd s. of J. Gilbert. T, 37¹–42²; Minor Foundationer; Head of School Music, 42. ✕ R.N.V.R , 42–45 S/Lt (A).

L.R.A.M., 50. Principal, The Harrow School of Music. Incorporated Society of Musicians. Music Teachers' Assoc. Brother, J. E. Gilbert.

GILBERT, Robert (took additional Christian name of Greenway), b. 9 Jan. 25, s. of late Rev. G. A. Gilbert. M, 38²–42³. ✕ Merchant Navy. Radio Officer, 43–45. St. John's, Cambridge, M.A. Mansfield, Oxford. Bar, Lincoln's Inn, 50. Practised, 50–53. Member of Lincoln's Inn.

GILCHRIST, Robert Adam Sampson, b. 19 Jan. 33, elder s. of late A. Gilchrist. Sh, 46³–51². Scholar of Trinity Hall, Cambridge, M.A., M.B., B.Chir. St. Thomas's Hospital, London, D.(Obst.) R.C.O.G., M.R.C.G.P. General Medical Practitioner, Banbury. Member of B.M.A. College of G.P.s, Galpin Society.

GILKS, Major John Allen, R.M., b. 21 Feb. 16, s. of A. Gilks. T, 30¹–34²; R. VIII, 34 (Capt.); Athletics Cup. Gazetted to Royal Marines, 34. ✕ Mediterranean, Arctic, S. Atlantic, Far East (Commando Brigade). Dispatches. Divisional Field Officer. M.A.F.F. Retired, 58. Mammal Society. British Deer Society (Sec. of N.E. Branch). *Civil Service Club.*

GILLESPIE, Lt.-Col. Robert Rollo, O.B.E., M.C., b. 11 Oct. 00, s. of late Major R. W. Gillespie. Tu, 14³–18²; Scholar. R.M.A., Woolwich. Commissioned in R.E. Reported for Gallantry by G.O.C. in Ireland, 20. Wounded. Capt., 30; Major, 38; Lt.-Col., 41–54. Served in West Africa, Hong Kong. ✕ Served in Flanders, 39–40. Wounded. M.C. Western Desert, Malta, France/Germany, 44/45 (wounded). Later, Malaya. Now retired. Institute of R.E. Royal British Legion. O.B.E., 45.

GILLETT, Vivian. SF, 31³–36¹.*

GILLIATT, Prof. Roger William, M.C., D.M., F.R.C.P., b. 30 July 22, s. of late Sir W. Gilliatt, K.C.V.O. SF, 36²–40²; Exhibitioner. Magdalen, Oxford, M.A., D.M. Middlesex Hospital Medical School, F.R.C.P. Prof. of Clinical Neurology, University of London. ✕ K.R.R.C., 42–45. M.C. Dispatches. Lt.

GIVATOVSKY, Nicholas Leonid. T, 19³–22³.*

GLAZEBROOK, John Rimington, b. 3 Dec. 29, s. of late W. R. Glazebrook. SF, 43³–48²; XV, 47; XXII, 46–48. Trinity, Cambridge. Company Director.

GLEDHILL, Prof. Alan, b. 26 Oct. 95, eldest s. of late O. Gledhill. Tu, 10^3–14^2; Scholar; Exhibitioner in Natural Science, 14. Corpus Christi, Cambridge, M.A. Gray's Inn. ✗ 2nd Bn. Monmouthshire Regt. Lieut. Wounded. LL.D.(Lond.). Barrister-at-Law. I.C.S., 20; District & Sessions Judge, Burma, 27; Judge, High Court, Rangoon, 45; Lecturer in Indian Law, S.O.A.S., 45; Prof. of Oriental Laws, University of London, 53. Emeritus Prof., 65. Royal Commonwealth Society. Sons, Capt. H. Gledhill & Rev. P. Gledhill.

GLEDHILL, Capt. Hugh, R.A.E.C. Tu, 40^2–44^1.*

GLEDHILL, The Rev. Peter, b. 7 Dec. 29, younger s. of Prof. A. Gledhill (OR Tu 10) Tu, 42^3–47^3; Scholar; Exhibitioner. Scholar of Balliol, Oxford, 1st Cl. Lit. Hum.; 2nd Cl. Theology, Cuddesdon, Oxford. Deacon, 56. Priest, 57. Priest-in-charge, Kingstone-with-Gratwich, Uttoxeter, Staffs. Brother, Capt. H. Gledhill.

GLEGG, Robert Francis Pillans, b. 14 Sept. 03, s. of late A. H. Glegg, W. S. K, 17^2–22^1; Cap, 21. Oriel, Oxford. Rubber Planter in Malaya till 32. Hospital Secretary, 35. Eastbourne Hospital Group Secretary from 48. F.H.A. Retired.

GLENDINNING, George Stewart. SH, 32^1–36^2.*

GLOAG, Julian. SF, 44^2–49^1.*

GLOVER, Jocelyn Howard, b. 14 May 24, eldest s. of late C. H. Glover (OR SH 06). SH, 38^1–42^2; Fencing Team, 42. Balliol, Oxford. ✗ R. Welch Fusiliers. Major, 43–46. Underwriting Member of Lloyd's. Dir. of F. Bolton & Co. (Foreign) Ltd.; Bolton Ingham Agencies Ltd.; Glover Bros. (London) Ltd. *City Club*, *M.C.C.* Cercle Royale Gaulois Artistique et Litteraire. Liveryman of the Coopers & Gold & Silver Wyredrawers. Brother, M. H. Glover.

GLOVER, John Richard, M.B., B.Chir., b. 18 May 25, eldest s. of late J. C. Glover. SH, 39^1–43^2. Exhibitioner of Queens', Cambridge, M.A., M.B., B.Chir. Middlesex Hospital, 46–51. Physician. Diploma of Industrial Health. Member of Faculty of Community Medicine. Occupational Medicine. Senior Lecturer in Occupational Medicine, Welsh National School of Medicine, Cardiff. Royal Society of Medicine.

GLOVER, Myles Howard, b. 18 Dec. 28, 2nd s. of late C. H. Glover (OR SH 06). SH, 42^2–46^2. Balliol, Oxford, M.A. Bar, Lincoln's Inn, 54. Clerk to the Skinners' Company & to the Governors of Tonbridge School since 59. Honorary Secretary of the Association of Governing Bodies of Public Schools (the G.B.A.) since 67. Member of the Horatian Society. Brother, J. H. Glover.

GLOVER, Roderick Lewis. SH, 20^3–25^2.*

GLYNN, Thomas Hugh. Tu, 46^3–51^2.*

GOATLY, John, O.B.E., b. 22 Nov. 17, eldest s. of late C. R. A. Goatly. Sh, 31^3–36^2; Scholar; Levée; Exhibitioner; Cap. Scholar of Corpus Christi, Oxford, M.A. ✗ Sherwood Foresters, 39–46. Lt. Wounded. Japanese P.O.W., 42–45. British Council since 46; Administrative Officer, Egypt; Representative, Sarawak; Regional Representative, West & Central India; Representative, Malaysia. O.B.E., 64. *Travellers' Club.* Sons, 2322, 2487 & 3012.

GODLEY, Major Maurice. Tu, 16^1–18^1.*

GODLEY, The Hon. Wynne Alexander Hugh. K, 40^2–43^3.*

GODSELL, Robert James Pool. Tu, 36^2–39^3.*

GOING, Alexander Thomas. T, 37^1–42^1.*

GOING, Charles Hardinge, M.B., B.Chir., b. 23 Oct. 20, elder s. of Rev. T. H. Going. T, 34^2–39^2. London Hospital Medical College, M.B., B.S. ✗ R.N.V.R. Surg.-Lt. Miscellaneous hospital posts. General Practitioner.

GOLDSMITH, William Noel, F.R.C.P. (formerly Goldschmidt, W. N.), b. 26 Dec. 93, elder s. of late E. Goldschmidt. B, 07^3–12^2. Pembroke, Cambridge, M.A., M.D. University College Hospital, London, F.R.C.P. ✗ R.A.M.C., 18–20. Capt. Chief Appointments: Consultant in charge of Dermatological Dept., University College Hospital, London. Chief Editor, "British Journal of Dermatology". Studied dermatology at Vienna & Breslau on a travelling Scholarship, 24–25. Pres., British Assoc. of Dermatology. Author "Recent Advances in Dermatology", 36 & 54. Now retired. *Hurlingham Club.* Fellow of Royal Society of Medicine.

GOMPERTZ, Richard Humfrey Litton. B, 13³–17³.*

GOOD, Christopher James, B.M., B.Ch., b. 24 May 28, s. of late J. P. Good. SF, 41³–46²; Hulme Exhibition to Brasenose, Oxford, M.A., B.M. University Scholarship to St. Thomas's Hospital, M.R.C.P. Subsequently various postgraduate institutions of University of London, University of Newcastle-upon-Tyne, University of Michigan. Consultant Physician, Hastings, 66–69. Principal Physician & Head, Dept. of Medicine, Addington Hospital, Durban. Hon. Senior Lecturer, Dept. of Medicine, University of Natal. R.S.M., B.M.A., M.A.S.A. Airborne Medical Society. Brompton Hospital Assoc.

GOODBODY, Gerald Maurice. SF, 19²–23². Son, 1600.*

GOODBODY, Gen. Sir Richard Wakefield, G.C.B., K.B.E., D.S.O., b. 12 Apr. 03, eldest s. of G. E. Goodbody. SH, 17²–21². R.M.A., Woolwich. Commissioned R.A., 23. Col. Commandant R.A., 57–68. H.A.C., 59–66. R.H.A., 60–68. Adj.-Gen. of the Forces, 60–63. A.D.C.-Gen. to the Queen, 61–63. Retired from Army, 63. Bath King at Arms since 65. G.C.B., 63; K.B.E., 58; D.S.O. *Naval & Military Club.* Brother, G. M. Goodbody.

GOODHART, Sir John Gordon, Bt., M.B., B.Chir., b. 14 Dec. 16, s. of late G. W. Goodhart, M.D., F.R.C.P. M, 30³–35². Trinity Hall, Cambridge, M.A., M.B., B.Chir. Guy's Hospital Medical School, M.R.C.G.P. ✕ R.N.V.R., 42–45. Surg.-Lt. General Practitioner from 47. Succeeded Uncle, 61. Son, 2313.

GOODWYN, Paul Allen, b. 22 June 15, younger s. of J. A. Goodwyn. Tu, 29¹–33²; Lees Knowles Exhibition. Trinity, Cambridge, M.A. ✕ R.A.F., 40–45. F/Lt. P.O.W., 41–45. Civil Service (Ministry of Defence) since 68.

GORDON, Alexander Grant. Tu, 44²–49².*

GORDON, The Rev. Canon Archibald Ronald McDonald, b. 19 Mar. 27, eldest s. of Sir A. Gordon, C.M.G. M, 40³–45²; Scholar; Levée; Head of House; Leaving Exhibition. Organ Scholar of Balliol, Oxford, M.A. Organ Scholar of Cuddesdon Theological College, Oxford, 50–52. Ordained Deacon, 52. Ordained Priest, 53. Curate, Stepney Parish Church, 52–55. Chaplain, Cuddesdon Theological College, 55–59. Vicar, St. Peter, Birmingham, 59–67. Canon Residentiary, Birmingham Cathedral, 67–71. Vicar, University Church of St. Mary the Virgin, and St. Cross with St. Peter in the East, Oxford, from 71. Brother, D. S. Gordon.

GORDON, Charles Grant, b. 21 Aug. 27, eldest s. of W. G. Gordon. Tu, 40²–44³; Sw. VIII, 44. ✕ R.N., 45–48. A.B. Chartered Accountant. Scotch Whisky Distiller. R.O.R.C. Brother, A. G. Gordon. Gordon. Sons, Grant Edward, Tu, 69²–; Grant Glenn, Tu, 71¹– & Peter Grant, Tu, 72³–.

GORDON, Duncan Silvester, b. 21 Nov. 28, 2nd s. of Sir A. Gordon, C.M.G. M, 42³–47²; Scholar; Levée; Head of House; Head of School; XV, 45–46; XI, 47; H. XI, 46–47. Scholar of Corpus Christi, Oxford, M.A. Teaching, 52–56. Bar, Gray's Inn, 57; practised to 62. Lord Chancellor's Office, Legal Asst., 63; Senior Legal Asst., 67; Asst. Solicitor from 72. Brother, A. R. McD. Gordon.

GORDON, Gavin Muspratt (formerly Gordon-Brown, G.M.). SH, 15²–18³.*

GORDON, James Edgar, b. 14 June 86, elder s. of late J. E. Gordon. SF, 99³–05²; XI, 04–05 (Capt.); Cap, 03–04. Exhibitioner of Oriel, Oxford. ✕ 7th Bn. Argyll & Sutherland Highlanders. Lt. Produce Broker, 08–69, now retired. *Vincent's Club, Oxford.* Brother, S. E. Gordon. Son, J. G. Gordon.

GORDON, James Gifford, b. 6 Jan. 17, s. of J. E. Gordon (OR SF 99). SF, 30³–34³; Scholar; Head of House; Levée. ✕ Cheshire Regt. P.O.W. Legal Staff, War Criminals Trial, Nuremburg, 45–46; T.D. Solicitor, 39. Member of the Council of the Law Society from 62. Member of the Council of Benenden School from 71. Solicitor, Senior Partner in Hill, Dickinson & Co., London & Liverpool. *Australian Club.* Member of Kennet Committee (Customs & Excise), 50.

GORDON, Michael, b. 3 June 94, 3rd s. of late Rev. C. J. Gordon, M.A. K, 08³–11². ✕ 11th Bn. Border Regt. Later Indian Army. Capt. Wounded. Farming at Gisborne, New Zealand. ✕ R.A.F. (Ground Staff). Sqn. Ldr. Retired.

GORDON, Robin Stephen, b. 28 June 32, s. of Lt.-Col. S. E. Gordon, M.C., T.D. (OR SF 04). SF, 45³–50². N/S R.A., 51–52. Lt. Oriel, Oxford, M.A. With

Unilever Ltd., 55–71. With Tilney & Co. (Stockbrokers) from 71. T.D.

GORDON, Lt.-Col. Stanley Edgar, M.C., T.D., b. 7 Mar. 90, younger s. of late J. E. Gordon. SF, 04²–08². ✕ 6th Bn. Liverpool Regt. Major. Wounded. M.C. Commanded 6th (Rifle) Bn., The King's Regt., Liverpool T.A., 28–32. T.D. Hide Broker, retired. Brother, J. E. Gordon. Son, R. S. Gordon.

GORDON, Lt.-Col. William Howat Leslie, C.B.E., M.C., b. 8 Apr. 14, eldest s. of F. L. Gordon, F.I.C.E. St, 28¹–32²; XI, 30. R.M.A., Woolwich; Cricket, Squash Rackets & Running Teams. Gazetted to Royal Signals. ✕ 39–45. Lt.-Col. M.B.E., M.C. Dispatches thrice. Retired, 49. Chief Executive, The Uganda Co. Ltd., 49–60. Man. Dir., John Holt & Lonrho Ltd., 60–71. Adviser on Private Investment, Foreign Office, O.D.A., from 71. C.B.E. (Civil). *M.C.C., White's, Royal Commonwealth Society.* Son, 2333.

GORDON, William Roger. SH, 38¹–42¹.*

GORDON BROWN, Timothy Patrick. Sh, 31¹–34². Sons, 2451, 2771 & Nicholas Charles, Sh, 69³–.*

GORDON-SMITH, David Gerard, C.M.G., b. 6 Oct. 25, 3rd 's. of late F. Gordon-Smith, Q.C. M, 39³–42². ✕ R.N.V.R., 44–46. Sub-Lt. Trinity, Oxford, B.A. Bar, Inner Temple, 49. Legal Depts., Colonial Office & Commonwealth Relations Office, 50–66. Legal Counsellor, Commonwealth Office & subsequently Foreign & Commonwealth Office, 66–72. Deputy Legal Adviser, F.C.O., from 73. C.M.G., 71.

GORE, Ralph. W, 07²–10².*

GORE BOOTH, Sir Michael Savile, Bt. M, 22²–26².*

GOSLETT, Graham Johnstone, b. 28 July 08, eldest s. of late W. B. Goslett (OR St 88). St, 22¹–26². ✕ R.A., 39–45. Lt. Consultant to A. Goslett Furniture Co. *Bath Club, London.* Nephews, 1357 & 1994.

GOSLETT, John Harington, b. 22 Feb. 23, 2nd s. of late R. G. Goslett, M.C. (OR St 98). St, 36³–40². ✕ Oxford & Buckinghamshire Light Infantry, 42–46. Lt. Served in India & Burma. Invalided, 46. With Goslett Ltd., London. *Light Infantry*

& Green Jackets Clubs. Brother, P. G. Goslett.

GOSLETT, Patrick Gwyn, b. 20 Jan. 21, elder s. of late R. G. Goslett, M.C. (OR St 98). St, 35¹–39². ✕ R. Signals, 40–46. Capt. C.Eng., M.I.E.E. Dir., Rashleigh Phipps & Co. Ltd., Electrical Engineers, since 55. Institution of Electrical Engineers. Brother, J. H. Goslett.

GOSLETT, Wallis Maynard, b. 1 Aug. 12, s. of late G. M. Goslett (OR St 88). K, 26²–30². Man. Dir. of Goslett Ltd., London. *Bath Club.*

GOSS, Arthur Bertram Massey. B, 32¹–35¹.*

GOSSAGE, Stevenson Milne, b. 6 Dec. 05, s. of A. M. Gossage, M.D. SF, 19³–23². University College, London, B.Sc. Yale University, New Haven, Conn. (M.Sc. in Trans.). Member, Board of Governors, Bishops University, Lennoxville, Quebec, Canada. Clerk with Canadian Pacific Rly. Co., Canada. M.Sc. (Transportation), Yale, 34. Asst. to Gen. Man., Eastern Lines, C.P.R., 41; Asst. Man. of Personnel, 45; Asst. Vice-Pres., Personnel, 57; Vice-Pres. & Gen. Man., 58; Vice-Pres., Co. Services, 64; Vice-Pres., Dir. & Member Executive Committee, 66. Retired, 71. Chrmn., Metric Commission (Govt. of Canada), 71. *University Club, Montreal; National Club, Toronto.*

GOTTO, Claude Corry. St, 06³–09².*

GOULD, Alan Clive, Vet. M.B., M.R.C.V.S. Tu, 45³–50³.*

GOULD, Colin Michael, B.Sc., M.R.C.V.S. Tu, 43³–48².*

GOULD, Geoffrey Windham, O.B.E., M.C., b. 17 June 24, s. of late M. R. Gould, C.I.E. K, 38²–42²; XI, 42; Leaving Exhibition. Brasenose, Oxford, B.A. ✕ 43–47. Lt. 8th K.R.I. Hussars, 49–65. Wounded. M.C. Malaysian Civil Service. B.P. Chemicals International Ltd., from 65. O.B.E., K.M.N. Son, 2818.

GOULDING, Lt.-Cdr. Brian Henry, R.N., b. 13 Mar. 28, s. of late Rev. H. Goulding, M.A., R.N. SH, 41³–45². Royal Navy, 45. Lt., 50. H.M. Ships *Alliance, Token, Sidon, Tally-Ho!, Brinkley* (in command), *Whirlwind*—Lt.-Cdr., 58, H.M.S. *Blackwood.* Staff College, Staff of Commodore Hong Kong, H.M.S. *Maid-*

stone, Staff of Commander Far East Fleet. Retired, 68. I.B.M. (UK) Ltd., from 68. Member of Royal Institute of Navigation. Member of Royal United Service Institute. Associate Member, British Institute of Management.

GOVER, John Eric Bruce. St, 08³–11³.*

GOW, Andrew Sydenham Farrar, b. 27 Aug. 86, eldest s. of late Rev. J. Gow. SH, 00³–05². Scholar of Trinity, Cambridge, Porson Prize, 06–07; Browne Medal, 07–08; M.A. Charles Oldham Classical Scholar, 09–10. Fellow of Trinity, 11. Asst. Master at Eton College, 14. Fellow & Lecturer of Trinity from 25. Retired from Teaching.

GOWAN, Antony Campbell, O.B.E., b. 17 Apr. 18, 3rd s. of late Sir H. C. Gowan, K.C.S.I., C.I.E., I.C.S. (OR B 92). SF, 31³–36²; S. VIII, 36. Hertford, Oxford, B.A. The Burmah Oil Co. Ltd., from 39. ✕ Burma Army, 41–45. F.R.H.S. M.I. Petroleum. O.B.E. *Travellers' Club.* Brothers, J. H. B. & C. D'O. Gowan.

GOWAN, Lt.-Col. Christopher D'Olier, b. 4 Aug. 10, 2nd s. of late Sir H. Gowan, K.C.S.I., C.I.E., I.C.S. (OR B 92). SF, 24³–29²; Head of School; Holder of Bigside Bags; R. VIII, 27, 28 & 29; XV, 28; XXII, 29; S. VIII, 26–27; Capt. of Swimming, 29; H. XI, 29; Major Exhibitioner and Minor Modern Languages, 29. Exhibitioner of Hertford, Oxford, M.A. Athletics Half-Blue. Asst. Master, Eton College, 32–70; Housemaster, 47–64; Head of Modern Languages Dept., 59–70. ✕ Intelligence Corps, 40–46. Dispatches. p.s.c. Lt.-Col. Author of "The Background of the French Classics" & "France from Regent to Romantics". Brothers, J. H. B. & A. C. Gowan.

GOWAN, James Hyde Bowie, b. 24 Nov. 07, eldest s. of late Sir H. Gowan, K.C.S.I., C.I.E., I.C.S. (OR B 92). SF, 21³–26²; S. VIII, 25. I.P.M. Course No. 1, Manchester College of Science & Technology. Maidenhead College of Art. Liverpool Cotton Exchange. Goodyear Tyre & Rubber Co. Ltd. Gowan's Paints Ltd. ✕ R.A., 40–46. Major. Staff Superintendent, B.E.A. Textile (Foreign) Manufacturers' Agent. Artist—present employment. Brothers, A. C. & C. D'O. Gowan.

GRAHAM, Allan Ralph, b. 27 May 31, s. of late R. L. Graham. SF, 44³–49². Gonville & Caius, Cambridge, M.A. Deputy Chrmn., Thomas Salter Ltd., Toy Manufacturers. *R.A.C.* Commission, R.A.

R.R.W.W.—4*

GRAHAM, David Maurice, b. 16 Aug. 11, s. of late Sir L. Graham, K.C.S.I., K.C.I.E. SH, 25²–30¹; Levée; Head of House. Balliol, Oxford, B.A. Jenkyns Prize, 32. Secretary & Librarian, Oxford Union, 32–33. Polytechnic of Central London—courses in Arabic and Polish languages. British Broadcasting Corporation, 38–71 (Asst. Head, East European Service, 49–58; Central Research Organiser, External Services, 62–71). Retired from B.B.C., 71. Present occupation, studying Polish language and literature. Oxford Union Society. *The Bushmen.*

GRAHAM, Edward John. Tu, 18¹–21³.*

GRAHAM, Ian Michael. B, 45¹–49².*

GRAHAM, Michael Garrett. T, 37³–42².*

GRAINGER, Anthony John, b. 6 Jan. 10, elder s. of late A. E. Grainger. B, 23³–28³; Levée; Head of House; Cap; Gym VIII; Cadet Officer. Harvard University. Graduate School of Business Administration, A.M.P. Entire career in roller-bearing industry. Present employment: Dir. Gen., Timken France & Timken Rollenlager. Union Interalliée, Paris. Iron & Steel Institute, London. Brother, M. M. Grainger.

GRAINGER, Michael Mytton. B, 34³–40¹.*

GRAND, Keith Walter Chamberlain, b. 3 July 00, younger s. of late D. H. Grand. W, 14³–18³. Joined Great Western Rly., 19. In U.S.A., 26–29. Gen. Man., Great Western Railway, 48–59. Member, British Transport Commission, 59–62. Chrmn., Coast Lines, 68–71. Director of Companies. Commander, Order of St. John. U.S. Medal of Freedom with Gold Leaf. *Carlton Club, Royal Thames Yacht Club.* Brother, L. D. Grand.

GRAND, Major-General Laurence Douglas, C.B., C.I.E., C.B.E., b. 10 Aug. 98, elder s. of late D. H. Grand. W, 12³–16². R.M.A., Woolwich. Christ's, Cambridge. ✕ R.E. 2nd Lt. Lt., 19. N. Russia, 384th Field Co., Grogan's Bde., 19. N.W. Frontier, India, 20. Iraq Rebellion, 20. Iraq Army, 23–28. M.B.E. ✕ 39–45. C.B.E., 43. C.I.E., 46. Chief Engineer, IV Corps, 42–43. Dir. of Engineer Resources, India, 43–45. Dir. of Fortifications & Works, 48–52. F.I.C.E. R. Institute International Affairs, 29. R. Central Asian Society. C.B. *U.S. Club.* Brother, K. W. C. Grand.

GRANDAGE, Christopher Landale, M.B., B.Chir., b. 16 Aug. 16, s. of late W. B. Grandage, M.D. W, 30^2–35^2. Clare, Cambridge, M.B., B.Chir. St. Bartholomew's Hospital, D.C.H. ✕ R.A.M.C. Dispatches. Hospital Appointments, 42–46. General Practice from 50. Son, Timothy William, W, 71^1–.

GRANT, Douglas Marr Kelso, b. 5 Apr. 17, 2nd s. of late J. M. Grant. Tu, 30^3–35^2; S. VIII, 35; Capt. Fives, 34–35. Peterhouse, Cambridge, M.A., LL.B. ✕ Kenya Regt. & King's African Rifles. Colonial Administration Service, Uganda, 39–46. Colonial Legal Service, 46. Bar, Gray's Inn, 46. Scottish Bar, 59. Legal & Judicial Depts., Federation of Malaya, 46–57. Scots Bar, 59–66. Sheriff of Ayr & Bute at Ayr since 66. *Public Schools Club; County Club, Ayr.*

GRANT, Ian Cecil, b. 3 Aug. 30, s. of J. J. Grant. T, 44^1–48^2; Exhibitioner. Man. Dir., Computers for Industry, Software House—Systems, Programming, Consultancy.

GRANT, John Richards. Tu, 32^2–35^2.*

GRANT, William Arthur. C, 28^3–31^3.*

GRANTHAM, Admiral Sir Guy, G.C.B., D.S.O., b. 9 Jan. 00, s. of late C. F. Grantham. C, 14^1–18^1; XV, 17. Pembroke, Cambridge. Naval Course, R.N., 18. ✕ 39–45. Dispatches twice. D.S.O., C.B., C.B.E. Chief of Staff to C.-in-C. Med., 46–48. Naval A.D.C. to King, 47–48. F.O., Submarines, 48–50. F.O., 2nd in Command Med., 50–51. Vice-Chief of Naval Staff, 51–54. C.-in-C. Med. & Allied Forces Med., 54–57. C.-in-C. Portsmouth, Allied C.-in-C. Channel & Southern North Sea, 57–59. Retired List, 59. G.C.B., 56. Hon. Freeman of Haberdashers Company.

GRANTHAM, James Michael. B, 38^1–41^2.*

GRANTHAM, John Peter. B, 35^2–39^2.*

GRAY, Antony Thomas Arnold, b. 18 Sept. 18, eldest s. of late Rev. P. Gray. SH, 32^3–36^3; Scholar. Organ Scholar of Gonville & Caius, Cambridge, M.A. ✕ Queen's Royal Regt., 41. King's African Rifles in E. Africa & S.E.A.C., 44–46. Major. Royal College of Music. Professional Musician. Examiner for the Associated Board of the Royal Schools of usic. Music Teacher at various estab-

blishments including R.C.M. Junior Dept. and St. Paul's School. Free-lance player. Brother, P. S. Gray.

GRAY, Peter Henry, T.D., b. 25 June 12, eldest s. of late H. B. Gray. T, 26^1–30^2; Cap, XXII; H. XI, 29–30; Rackets Pair, 29–30 (Capt.); Capt. of Squash & Fives. Rackets, Squash & Tennis Professional to Rugby School. Sports Retail Business. Chrmn., Tennis & Rackets Assoc. ✕ R.A. Major. T.D. Son, 1709.

GRAY, Philip Stephen, b. 11 Mar. 23, 2nd s. of late Rev. P. Gray.,SH, 36^3–41^2; Exhibitioner. Foreign Office, 42–46. Trinity, Oxford, M.A. Bank of England, 49. Gen. Man., Royal Liverpool Philharmonic Society. Brother, A. T. A. Gray.

GRAY, Ronald Albert, b. 30 Aug. 14, 2nd s. of late H. B. Gray. T, 28^2–33^2; Cadet Officer; Rackets Pair, 31–33; Winner with R. F. Lumb of Public School Doubles, 33. Birmingham University. Silver Medal for Conservation Dentistry, 37. L.D.S., R.C.S.(Eng.)., L.D.S.(Birm.). Dental Surgeon. Brother, P. H. Gray.

GRAY, Ronald Walpole. SF, 20^3–25^2.*

GREANY, Hugh Wingate, C.B.E., b. 13 June 00, younger s. of Surgeon-General J. P. Greany, I.M.S. W, 14^3–19^2; XV, 18; Levée; Head of House. Queen's, Oxford, B.A. London & North Eastern Railway, 22–35. Tyne Investment Commission (Asst. Sec.), 35–36. The Shipping Federation (Dir., 62–65), 36–65. Retired. C.B.E. Sons, 146 & 1661.

GREANY, Willoughby Hugh, M.C., D.M., B.Ch., b. 20 Apr. 06, s. of late Lt.-Col. H. Greany, M.D., I.M.S. W, 20^1–24^2; XV, 23; H. XI. Queen's, Oxford, M.A., D.M., B.C.L. Guy's Hospital Medical School, M.R.C.S., L.R.C.P., D.T.M. & H. Medical Officer in Sudan Government Medical Service, 33–53. ✕ R.A.M.C., 40–45. Lt.-Col. M.C. Lately, Medical Officer with Shipping Federation in London & Southampton. Now retired.

GREEN, Anthony Arthur Ramsay, b. 8 June 26, eldest s. of Capt. W. D. T. Green, M.B.E. Sh, 40^1–43^3; Sw. VIII, 43 (Capt.). ✕ Scots Guards, 43–47. Capt. Dir., United Wire Group Ltd. Advisory Committee on Business Studies (Edinburgh Univ.). F.R.Z.S. (Scotland). Scottish Wildlife Trust. Brother, M. R. Green. Son, Ramsay Laurence, Sh, 68^3–72^3.

GREEN, David John, F.R.I.B.A., b. 11 Sept. 12, s. of J. T. Green. SH, 26^2–29^2. Architectural Assoc. School of Architecture, London. A.A. Dipl. Partner in Messrs. Tayler & Green. F.R.I.B.A.

GREEN, George. W, 15^3–19^3.*

GREEN, James Maurice Spurgeon, M.B.E., T.D., b. 8 Dec. 06, 3rd & youngest s. of late Col. J. E. Green. SH, 19^3–25^2; Scholar; Exhibitioner. Scholar of University College, Oxford, M.A. Editor, "Financial News", 34–38. Financial & Industrial Editor, "The Times" from 38. ✕ R.A., 39–44. Major. M.B.E., T.D. Asst. Editor, "The Times", 51–61. Deputy Editor, "Daily Telegraph", 61–64. Editor, "Daily Telegraph" from 64. Sons, 604 & 1851.

GREEN, Michael Ramsay. Sh, 42^2–48^3.*

GREEN, Peter Michael Arthur, O.B.E., b. 22 July 04, eldest s. of A. A. Green. C, 18^3–21^3; Minor Exhibitioner. Member of the London Stock Exchange from 30. Stockbroker. ✕ R.A.F. (Intelligence Branch), 40–45. Coastal Command. Wing-Cdr. O.B.E. Dispatches twice. *Bath Club*. Brother, R. A. Green.

GREEN, Richard Arthur, b. 26 May 06, 2nd s. of A. A. Green. SH, 20^1–22^3. Studied in Lausanne. Paper Stock Merchant. ✕ R.A.F.V.R., 40–45. Wing-Cdr. Chevalier Légion d'Honneur. Retired. *Bath Club, London*. Brother, P.M.A. Green.

GREEN, Walter Lyall Hennis. SF, 15^3–19^2.*

GREENSTED, Leslie Bryan, M.B.E., b. 8 Dec. 15, s. of L. Greensted. SF, 29^3–33^2. College of Air Training, 33–36. F.R.G.S., F.R.Met.S., A.F.R.Ae.S., A.F.B.I.S., M.R.I.N., M.I.M. Flying Instructor, 36–40. Chief Test Pilot, 40–48. Chief Pilot, Skyways Ltd., 52. Operations Dir., Hunting Clan Air Transport, 60. Consultant to date. M.B.E. *United Services & Royal Aero Club*.

GREENSTREET, Peter Anthony Reginald. St, 45^3–50^2.*

GREENWAY, Peter Alfred, b. 1 Apr. 15, 3rd s. of late G. Greenway, St, 28^3–33^1. London University, B.Sc.(Eng.), F.I.C.E., M.I.Struct.E. Articled pupil to Sir Alexander Gibb, Consulting Civil Engineer, 38–41. Employment with Sir Alexander

Gibb & Partners from 41. ✕ R.E., 43–47. Major. Brother, R. Greenway.

GREENWAY, Richard, b. 20 Mar. 21, youngest s. of late G. Greenway. St, 34^3–39^1. ✕ R. Signals, 39–45. Articled to Chartered Accountants. A.C.A., 49. Gained first place in Institute of Taxation Associateship Examination. Chartered Accountant & Member of Institute of Taxation. Practising Accountant (sole practitioner). *Sheringham Golf Club*. Brother, P. A. Greenway. Son, Christopher Richard, St, 72^1–.

GREENWOOD, Basil, b. 30 July 14, eldest s. of late R. Greenwood (OR SH 98). SH, 28^1–32^1. Trinity, Cambridge, M.A. Cotton Manufacturer, retired. ✕ Duke of Lancaster's Own Yeomanry, 39–41. Anti-Tank Regt., R.A., 41–44. Trans-Jordan Field Force, 44–45. Major. T.D.

GREENWOOD, Geoffrey Martin, b. 30 Nov. 08, eldest s. of M. Greenwood. B, 21^3–26^3; Scholar; XV, 24–26 (Capt.); XXII, 26. Exhibitioner of Christ's, Cambridge, M.A. Rugby XV, 29–30. Colonial Administrative Service from 31; Uganda, 31–35 & 48–55; Cyprus, 35–40 & 45–47. ✕ Cyprus Regt., 40–45. P.O.W., 41–45. Asst. Secretary, General Commission for Technical Co-operation in Africa, 56–60. Teaching since 60. Son, 2029.

GREER, Samuel Francis, b. 25 Feb. 00, s. of Sir F. N. Greer, K.C.B., K.C. SF, 13^2–18^2; Cap, 17–18. Trinity, Cambridge, B.A. Man. Dir., John J. Hopper Ltd., Cleveland Property, Thornaby-on-Tees, Teeside, now retired. Chrmn., Federation of Wire Ropemakers of G.B., 46–48. J.P., 55.

GREG, Alexander Carlton, b. 24 Apr. 01, 3rd & youngest s. of late Col. E. W. Greg, C.B., V.D. (OR K 76). K, 15^2–19^2. Trinity, Cambridge, M.A. Landowner, Farmer, J.P. *Carlton Club*.

GREG, Henry Gair. C, 15^3–19^2.*

GREGORY-SMITH, Henry Graham, b. Mar. 99, s. of Prof. G. Gregory-Smith, LL.D.(Hon.). St, 13^1–15^2. R.M.C., Sandhurst. ✕ 1st Bn. Black Watch. Lt. Wounded. A.D.C. to H.E. The Viceroy of India, 21. Capt. A.D.C. to Governor of Southern Rhodesia, 26–28. District Officer, Kenya, 28–46. Commissioner of the Interior, British Guiana, 46. Resident Commissioner, British Solomon Islands Protectorate, 50. Retired, 53. ✕ King's African Rifles, 41–43.

GREGSON, Anthony Kirkes. W, 26²–29¹.*

GREGSON, Brig. John Henry, C.B.E., A.D.C., b. 8 Nov. 03, s. of late Col. H.G.F.S. Gregson, C.M.G. (OR W 87). W, 17³–21³; Cadet Officer. R.M.A., Woolwich. Staff College, Camberley. Gazetted to R.A., 24. Commands: British & Indian Field Artillery Regts.; C.R.A., 17 Indian Div.; Commander, Army Group, R.A.; Commander, Western A.A. Defences, London, 52; B.R.A., Middle East, 53–56; Egypt & Cyprus. Staff employment, Northern Command & War Office, G.H.Q., India. Instructor, Staff College, Camberley. Retired, Feb. 57, Brigadier. Commander, Oranje Nassau, C.B.E. A.D.C. to the Queen. Brother, M. I. Gregson. Son, 1545.

GREGSON, Col. Martin Innes. W, 24¹–28².*

GREIG, Charles Lawrence, M.C. SH, 10³–13³.*

GRENSIDE, John Peter, O.B.E., b. 23 Jan. 21, s. of late H. C. Grenside (OR SH 93). SH 34³–39³; XXII. ⚔ R.A., 41–46. Capt. Fellow of Institute of Chartered Accountants in England & Wales (admitted, 48); Member of Council, 66; Chrmn., Parliamentary Law Committee, 72; Member of Council with special responsibility for E.E.C. matters, 71. Partner in Peat, Marwick, Mitchell & Co., since 60. O.B.E. *M.C.C., Queen's, Hurlingham.* Son, Mark Nicholas, SH, 70³–.

GRESFORD-JONES, The Rt. Rev. Edward Michael, K.C.V.O., D.D., b. 21 Oct. 01, eldest s. of late Rt. Rev. H. Gresford-Jones, D.D. SH, 15²–20². Trinity, Cambridge, M.A. Ordained, 26. Vicar of Holy Trinity, South Shore, Blackpool, 33–39. Vicar of Hunslet, 39–42. Bishop Suffragan of Willesden, 42–50. Lord Bishop of St. Albans, 50–69. D.D. (Lambeth), 50. Lord High Almoner, 53–70. Chrmn. of C. of E. Youth Council. Hon. Asst. Bishop of Monmouth since 70. K.C.V.O., 68. *United University.*

GRETTON-WATSON, Bernard Gordon, M.R.C.S., L.R.C.P., b. 5 June 15, s. of late Dr. B. Gretton-Watson. St, 29¹–29³. K.E.S., Birmingham. Gonville & Caius, Cambridge, M.A., M.B., B.Chir. St. Bartholomew's Hospital, M.R.C.S., L.R.C.P. London School of Hygiene, D.P.H. Bar, Inner Temple, 55. (Foundation) Fellow, Faculty of Community Medicine (Royal College of Physicians, United Kingdom), 72. Various Hospital Appointments, 39–41. ⚔ R.A.F., 41–46. Sqn. Ldr. Deputy M.O.H., Dudley, 47–48; and Cheshire, 48–67. M.O.H. & Principal School M.O., Cheshire C.C., from 67. *R.A.F.* Assoc. of County M.O.s.

GRIBBON, Major-General Nigel St. George, O.B.E., b. 6 Feb. 17, eldest s. of late Brig. W. H. Gribbon, C.M.G., C.B.E. (OR B 94). SH, 30³–34². R.M.C., Sandhurst, 35–36. Army Staff College, Quetta, 43. R.A.F. Staff College, 52. National Defence College, Canada, 65. Commissioned into King's Own Royal Regt., 37. Commanded 5th Bn. King's Own Royal Regt., 58–60. Commanded 161 Infantry Brigade, 63–65. Dir., Military Co-ordination, Ministry of Defence, 66. Asst. Chief of Staff (Intelligence), S.H.A.P.E., 70–72. Retired as Major-General, Nov., 72. O.B.E. *Army & Navy Club, Little Ship Club.* R.Y.A. Army Sailing Assoc. Army Ski Assoc. Sons, 1936 & 2733.

GRIER, John Lyndon, b. 12 May 18, s. of late J. A. B. Grier, C.I.E. Sh, 31³–36²; Cap., 35. King's, Cambridge, M.A. ⚔ R.A.S.C., 39–46. Major. Dispatches (Burma, 44). Gen. Man., Jeremiah Ambler (Ulster) Ltd., 47–51. Present employment, Headmaster, Arundel House School, Surbiton. *Leatherhead Golf Club.*

GRIERSON, Charles Douglas. Tu, 11²–15¹.*

GRIFFITH, Edward Peter Leigh. Sh, 43³–47¹.*

GRIFFITH-JONES, Philip Pigott. M, 34¹–36².*

GRIFFITHS, Barry Charles Roger, M.R.C.V.S., b. 2 May 28, elder s. of H. W. Griffiths, M.R.C.V.S. Tu, 42²–46². Royal (Dick) Veterinary College, Edinburgh, B.Sc., M.R.C.V.S. In Practice. Son, Philip William Kinsman, Tu, 70²–.

GRIFFITHS, John Emerson, b. 1 Nov. 23, s. of W. L. Griffiths. T, 37²–42²; Foundationer; Cap, XI, 42. Queen's, Cambridge, B.A. C.Eng., M.I.Mech.E., M.I.E.E. ⚔ R.N., 44–47. Mechanical Engineer in the Turbine Dept. of the English Electric Co. Ltd. London Sales Man., G.E.C. Turbine Generators Ltd. *M.C.C., Roehampton Club.*

GRIMWOOD-TAYLOR, Col. James Richard Sancroft, LL.B., T.D., D.L., b. 8 Sept. 16, eldest s. of S. Grimwood Taylor. St, 30^2–35^2; Cadet Officer; Nat. Sc. Exhibitioner. Corpus Christi, Cambridge, M.A., LL.B. ✕ R. Signals, 39–46. Major. T.D. Solicitor, 47, Partner (now senior) in Taylor, Simpson & Mosley of Derby. Registrar, Diocese of Derby, 61; Clerk to Commissions of Taxes; Under-Sheriff of Derbyshire; Member of the Council of the Law Society, 69. D.L. (Derbyshire). Hon. Colonel, 38, Signal Regt., T.A. *County Club, Derby.* Brother, C. B. G. Taylor. Sons, 2937 & James Lawrence, St, 70^2–.

GRISSELL, Major Michael, b. 30 Mar. 13, s. of late Lt.-Col. B. S. Grissell, D.S.O. SH, 26^3–30^3; S. VIII, 30. Germany, France. Trinity, Cambridge. Commissioned 10th Royal Hussars (P.W.O.), 35. P.O.W., 40–45. Retired, 47, as Major. Farmer & Landowner. High Sheriff of Sussex, 67. *Boodle's.*

GROOM, Arthur Howard Victor, M.C., T.D., b. 21 Oct. 18, eldest s. of late A. W. Groom. K, 32^2–35^3. Associate of the Chartered Insurance Institute (A.C.I.I.). ✕ R.A., 39–45. Dispatches. M.C. Wounded. Major. T.D. Marine Underwriter at Lloyd's, and Chrmn. of A. W. Groom & Co. Ltd. Underwriting Agent at Lloyd's. Brother, J. Groom. Son, Christopher Howard, K, 71^3–.

GROOM, John. K, 38^2–42^1.*

GROS, Edward Hamilton Falkenberg, b. 7 Oct. 08, s. of late E. F. Gros. M, 22^3–25^3. Jesus, Cambridge, M.A. Schoolmaster till 39. ✕ Dorset Regt. (T.A.). Seconded to Gold Coast Regt., R.W.A.F.F., 40–45. Major. Now at Price's School, Fareham. Retired, 73. *Hawks, Cambridge; M.C.C.*

GROSCH, Major Antony John Peter, b. 27 June 28, s. of A. Grosch. SH, 42^3–46^2. R.M.A., Sandhurst. Boxing Half-Blue. Gazetted to Durham Light Infantry, 48. Lt., 50. Major. Garrison Adjutant, Colchester. Master, Colchester Garrison Beagles.

GROVE-WHITE, Charles William. M, 27^2–31^2.*

GROVE-WHITE, James Herbert, M.D., b. 23 Nov. 89, 4th s. of late W. Grove-White. Tu, 03^3–07^2. Trinity College, Dublin, B.A., M.B., B.Ch., B.A.O., M.D. Fellow, Royal College, General Practice. ✕ Indian Medical Service. South Persia Rifles. Capt. Invalided, 21. Physician. Radiologist, Memorial Hospital, Cirencester, Glos., 22–54. Practising still as Physician. *Army & Navy Club; University Club, Dublin.* Son, P. A. Grove-White.

GROVE-WHITE, Patrick Alexander. Tu, 34^3–38^3.*

GROVE-WHITE, Robert John, M.D., F.R.C.P., b. 15 Feb. 16, 2nd s. of late G. E. Grove-White. M, 29^3–32^3; Cap. Trinity College, Dublin, B.A., B.C.H., B.A.O., M.D., M.R.C.P.Ed., F.R.C.P.Ed. Colonial Medical Service. F.M.S. & Singapore, 39–58, formerly Senior Chest Physician, Singapore. Now in General Medical Practice. Royal Society of Medicine. *Flyfishers' Club.* Brother, C. W. Grove-White. Sons, 906 & 2123.

GRUBB, Cedric Alexander, b. 16 Feb. 02, 2nd s. of late L. H. Grubb, D.L., J.P. (OR St 81). St, 15^3–20^2; Winner of the Crick. Citrus Farming at White River, E. Transvaal, 21–45. ✕ Q Services Corps (Mechanical Transport), S.A. Defence Force, 39–45. Capt. Deputy Sheriff of County Tipperary.

GRYLLS, Shadwell Harry, C.B.E., s. of late H. B. Grylls (OR SH 94). SH, 23^1–27^1. Exhibitioner of Trinity, Cambridge, B.A. Chief Engineer, Motor Car Div., Rolls-Royce, 52. C.B.E. Son, 1523.

GUEDALLA, Francis Basil, b. 9 Sept. 04, s. of late F. M. Guedalla (OR SH 87). SH, 18^1–20^3. Solicitor, 28, of Bartlett & Gluckstein of Piccadilly, London. Inns of Court O.T.C. ✕ Rifle Bde. & Staff, 39–45; Staff Capt. & D.A.A.G., M.E.F. & A.F.H.Q. T.D. *M.C.C., Pilgrims, Devonshire, Green Jackets.* Son, 1853.

GUERRIER, Kenneth Joynson, b. 29 Sept. 98, eldest s. of late Rev. W. J. Guerrier. B, 13^2–17^1; R. VIII, 16. ✕ 6th Bn. K.R.R.C.; 5th Bn. Rifle Bde. 2nd Lt. Wounded twice, 18. Balliol, Oxford, M.A. University of London, B.A. Asst. Master, Dame Allen's Endowed School, Newcastle-upon-Tyne; Raynes Park County School, Surrey; Grammar School, Goole, Yorks.; City of Bath Boys' School; at present Barfield Prep. School for Boys, Farnham, Surrey.

GUEST, Gordon, b. 1 June 23, younger s. of G. Guest. M, 37^3–41^2. ✕ Yorkshire Hussars. Lt. Staff Capt., G.H.Q., 2nd

Echelon, B.A.O.R. Trinity Hall, Cambridge, M.A., LL.B. Solicitor, 51. Town Clerk's Office, Leeds, 48–54. Town Clerk's Office, Nottingham, 54–68. Town Clerk & Chief Executive Officer, Southampton, from 68.

GUETERBOCK, Brig. Ernest Adolphus Leopold, b. 24 June 97, 3rd s. of late A. Gueterbock. B, 11^3–16^2; Scholar; S. VIII, 13–16 (Capt.); Cadet Officer; Levée; Head of House. Scholar of Trinity, Cambridge, M.A. R.M.A., Woolwich (Sword of Honour). Royal Engineers. p.s.c. One of the interservice team who in 41 made the first plan for the D-Day landing of June 44. Retired in 47 as Brigadier. Secretary, University College, London, 47–64. Past Pres., Ski Club of Great Britain. Founder Chrmn. of Council, National Ski Federation of G.B. *Alpine Club, United Service Club.*

GUETERBOCK, Cmdr. William Stanley, R.N., b. 26 Aug. 30, s. of late Col. Sir P. Gueterbock, K.C.B., D.S.O., M.C. Sh, 44^2–48^2. R.N.C., Dartmouth, 48. Lt., 53, Lt.-Cdr., 61, Cdr., 66. C.O., H.M.M.L. 6013, 52–53. C.O., H.M.S. *Wotton*, 59–61; *Russell*, 64–65; *Aisne*, 66–68. Executive Officer, H.M.S. *Ark Royal*, 71–72. Son, Richard Stanley, Sh, 71^1–.

GUILD, Ivor Reginald, b. 2 Apr. 24, 2nd s. of late A. M. Guild. SF, 37^3–42^2; Scholar. Exhibitioner of New College, Oxford, M.A. Edinburgh University, LL.B. Writer to the Signet, 49. Procurator-Fiscal to the Lyon Court. Partner in firm of Shepherd & Wedderburn, W.S., Edinburgh. *New Club, Edinburgh; Hon. Company of Edinburgh Golfers.* Brother, N. C. M. Guild.

GUILD, Nigel Cox Marjoribanks, b. 23, Apr. 23, eldest s. of late A. M. Guild. SF, 37^1–41^2. New College, Oxford, part only Hon. Degree in French. ✕ Black Watch & King's African Rifles, 43–48, also 54–56. Various Commercial Cos. in Kenya. Presently, Collins (Publishers) representative in E.A. *R. & A. Golf Club; Muthaiga Country Club, Nairobi; Mombasa Club; Kenya Golfing Society.* Brother, I. R. Guild.

GUIMARAENS, Leonard John, b. 15 Apr. 31, s. of late G. P. Guimaraens. K, 45^2–49^1. N/S. Commissioned to 7th Queen's Own Hussars. 42nd R. Tank Regt., T.A. Man. Dir., G. E. Hudson (Pty.) Ltd. Member of Barlow Rand Group of Cos., Johannesburg, South Africa. *Country Club, Johannesburg.*

GUINNESS, Brian Cecil. SH, 17^2–21^2. Sons, 802 & 1044.*

GUINNESS, Edward Douglas, C.B.E., R.D., b. 19 Apr. 93, 2nd s. of late H. R. Guinness. SH, 07^3–11^3; XV, 11; Sw. VIII. Banker, Partner in Guinness, Mahon & Co., 23–48. ✕ ✕ Royal Navy, 1st and 2nd World Wars. Capt. R.N.R. Retired. C.B.E. (Mil.). *Brooks's, Kildare St., Dublin.* Brothers, F. R. & B. C. Guinness. Son, 333.

GUINNESS, Frederick Roberts. SH, 14^2–17^2.*

GULLAND, Derrick, b. 9th Feb. 04, 2nd s. of late H. C. Gulland. W, 17^3–22^2; XXII, 21–22. Trinity Hall, Cambridge. ✕ R.A.S.C., 40–45. Major. N. Africa & France. Lloyd's, 25. Dir. of own firm, Gardiner & Gulland, stainless steel fabricators. Retired. *Senior Golfers Soc.* Brother, H. M. Gulland.

GULLAND, Herbert Miles, b. 1 Nov. 01, eldest s. of late H. C. Gulland. W. 15^3–20^2. Clare, Cambridge, B.A. Coffee Planting in Kenya, 25. Partner, Kinloch & Co., Merchant Bankers, 34–39. ✕ Welsh Guards, 39–45. Capt. Dir., Adria Hotels Ltd. Retired. Brother, D. Gulland.

GURDON, Lt.-Col. Adam Brampton Douglas, O.B.E., b. 4 May 31, elder s. of late Major-General E. T. L. Gurdon, C.B., C.B.E., M.C. (OR St 10). SF, 44^3–49^1; Rackets Pair, 47–49 (Capt.). ✕ Black Watch (R.H.R.). Korea, 52. Lt. Now Lt.-Col. O.B.E., 73. *Army & Navy Club.* Brother, R. T. T. Gurdon.

GURDON, Lt.-Col. Robert Temple Thornhagh, b. 23 June 32, younger s. of late Major-General E. T. L. Gurdon, C.B., C.B.E., M.C. (OR St 10). St, 45^3–50^2. R.M.A., Sandhurst. Gazetted to Black Watch, 52. p.s.c. Major. Lt.-Col., 73. Chief Instructor, R.M.A., Sandhurst. Brother, A. B. D. Gurdon.

GUTHRIE, Allan Cochrane, b. 30 Apr. 25, s. of T. C. Guthrie. SF, 39^1–43^2; XI, 41–43; Cap, 42. ✕ Rifle Bde., 43–47. Capt. F.C.A. With Thomson McLintoch & Co., London, 51–56. With Gallaher Ltd., London & Belfast, Gen. Man., 56–68. Dir., Westminster Trust Holdings Ltd., 68–71. Deputy Chrmn., Primographic Co. Ltd., Wembley, from 68. *M.C.C.; I.Z.; Swinley Forest Golf Club; Royal Thames Yacht Club.*

GUTHRIE, Sqn. Ldr. David, b. 26 May 28, elder s. of R. Guthrie, B.Sc. T, 41^3–46^2; Exhibitioner. R.A.F. College, Cranwell. Commissioned as Pilot Offr., R.A.F., 49. Flying appointments in Transport, Coastal & Flying Training Commands, & R.A.F., Germany. R.A.F. Staff College, Bracknell, 62. Staff appointments in Flying Training Command & H.Q., A.F.C.E.N.T., Fontainebleau. Retired List, Sqn. Ldr., 66. Joined British European Airways, 66. Qualified Commercial Pilot, 67; Airline Transport Pilot, 68. Now First Officer, Trident Flight, Heathrow. *R.A.F. Club, Newark Town & District Club.*

GUTT, Etienne. K, 40^2–42^2.*

GUTTERIDGE, Frank, b. 5 Sept. 20, eldest s. of late N. Gutteridge. W, 34^1–38^3. Trinity Hall, Cambridge, M.A., LL.B. ✕ R.A.C., 41–46. Dispatches. Bar, Middle Temple, 48. British Employers' Confederation, 47–48. World Health Organisation, now Dir., Legal Div., from 48. *International Lawyers Club (Geneva).* Son, 2870B.

GUY, Trevor Maurice Buckley, b. 13 Apr. 29, younger s. of S. S. Guy. SF, 42^3–47^2; Cap, 46; XI, 45–47; Sw. VIII, 44. Courses in Electrical & Mechanical Engineering. N/S. 10th Hussars (P.W.O.), 2nd Lt., 49–51. Experience in Engineering, Manufacturing & Operating of Commercial Vehicles. Asst. Sales Man. of Guy Motors Ltd., 56–58; Service Dir., 58–61. Now Farming in Shropshire & on Executive Committee of Pig Health Control Assoc. *M.C.C., R.A.C.*

H

HADDEN-PATON, Major Adrian Gerard Nigel, D.L., J.P., b. 3 Dec. 18, s. of the late N. F. Paton. SF, 32^3–37^2. Worcester, Oxford, B.A. ✕ 1st Dragoon Guards, 40–45. Major. Dispatches. Instructor, R.M.A., Sandhurst, 47–50. Retired, 50. Member, Estates Committee of Nat. Trust, 56; & Properties Cttee., 70; & Finance Cttee., 73. Member, Executive Cttee., 59; & Finance Cttee., 61 (Chrmn., 62–68) of Country Landowners' Assoc. Underwriting Member of Lloyd's. Chrmn., Holland Ltd. Chrmn., Hertfordshire Agric. Soc., 61–69. Past Pres., Hertfordshire & Middlesex Trust for Nature Conservation. Chrmn. of Governors, Berkhamsted School, & Berkhamsted School for Girls, 73. Chrmn., Home Counties Division, Royal Forestry Soc., 72. J.P., 51. D.L., 62. Herts. High Sheriff, 61. *Cavalry Club.*

HADEN, Charles Lancelot Ingham, b. 16 Aug. 01, s. of the late C. I. Haden. SF, 15^2–18^2. Harper Adams Agricultural Coll. (N.D.A.). Retired Sheep Farmer in New Zealand.

HADLEY, Christopher John, b. 2 Mar. 29, s. of G. H. Hadley. B, 42^3–47^2. St, John's, Oxford, M.A. Forest Officer, British Solomon Islands, 53–58; and Tanzania, 58–64. Forestry Consultant, S.W. England, 64–65. Warden Naturalist i/c Upper Teesdale National Nature Reserve, 65–71. Higher Scientific Officer responsible for Nature Conservation in Surrey from 71. Royal Forestry Society. The Nature Conservancy. *Oxford Univ. Mountaineering Club.* Sons, Michael John, B, 68^3– and James Merlin, B, 70^3–.

HADRILL, Christopher Hardy, b. 13 Mar. 24, 2nd s. of the late H. C. Hadrill. M, 37^3–41^3. Exhibitioner of Trinity, Cambridge, B.A. ✕ R.A., 43–46. Capt. & 50–51 (Korea). Man. Dir., Drynamels Ltd. (subsidiary of Tube Investments Ltd.). Son, David John, Tu, 73^1–.

HADWEN, Gerald Dorrington, b. 22 Nov. 03, s. of the late H. S. Hadwen (OR C 90). SF, 17^3–21^1. Merton, Oxford. Commercial Career of 32 years with Thos. Parsons & Sons, Paint Manufacturers. ✕ Sqn. Ldr., Royal Auxiliary Air Force with 17 years service. Air Efficiency Award. *R.A.F. Club, R.A.F. Reserves Club.*

HAGUE, Michael Taylor. M & St, 42^3–47^2.*

HAIG, Robert Wolseley, b. 15 Dec. 02, s. of the late Lt.-Col. Sir W. Haig, K.C.I.E., C.S.I., C.M.G., C.B.E. W, 16^3–19^3. Studied Arabic & Persian in the Middle East, & passed exams therein. Staff of the Imperial Bank of Persia, 24–52. Deputy Chief Man., 51–52. Retired, 52. *United Service & Royal Aero Club, London; Highland Club, Inverness.*

HAIGH, Anthony Irvin, b. 13 Sept. 28, s. of V. Haigh. T, 42^1–46^2. Commercial Engineer.

HALEY, Donald John, b. 26 Aug. 28, elder s. of Sir W. J. Haley, K.C.M.G. K, 42^2–46^2. Christ Church, Oxford, M.A. Member of Institute of Transport. N/S. R.N., 49–51. Shipping Industry thereafter. Dir., Walter Runciman & Co. Ltd. *Western Club, Glasgow; Royal Northern Y.C.* Brother, 33. Son, Stephen John, K, 72^2–.

HALL, E. E. D. (see Dawson Hall, E. E.).

HALL, Ernest Nicholas. M, 22^1–25^3.

HALL, Frederick McDonald, b. 24 Feb. 11, elder s. of the late Dr. D. G. Hall, M.D., F.R.C.P. C, 25^1–28^2. A.C.A., 34. F.C.A., 42. Partner in Tansley Witt & Co., London, with T. G. Harding (OR Sh 33). Brother, R. C. Hall.

HALL, Lt.-Col. James Aylmer, O.B.E., b. 30 June 11, 2nd s. of the late N. A. Hall. K, 25^1–28^2. Gazetted to 4th King's Own Royal Regt., 33. ✕ Africa & Italy. Major, 46. Dispatches. Lt.-Col. O.B.E., 48. p.s.c. Now retired. Brother, R. A. Hall.

HALL, Michael John, b. 20 Aug. 32, s. of the late W. F. Hall. W, 46^2–50^3; XV, 50. Trinity, Cambridge, M.A. Bar, Inner Temple. F.C.I.S. Secretary, Institution of Highway Engineers since 64.

HALL, Robert Aylmer, b. 22 Jan. 14, 3rd s. of the late N. A. Hall. K, 27^3–32^2; Cadet Officer. Clare, Cambridge, M.A. B.Sc.(Econ.) London. A.C.I.S. Dep. Man. Dir., The Sanitas Trust Ltd. Brother, J. A. Hall. Son, 1130.

HALL, Rowland Colman, F.C.A., b. 16 Apr. 13, younger s. of the late Dr. D. G. Hall, M.D., F.R.C.P. C, 27^3–31^2. Leaving Exhibition. Exhibitioner of Emmanuel, Cambridge, M.A. F.C.A. Coal Commission, 37–39. ✕ R.A., 39–45. Lt.-Col. Dispatches. Rickett Cockerell & Co. Ltd., 46, Dep. Chrmn. & Man. Dir., 68, Finance Director Charrington Gardner Locket & Co. Ltd. *St. George's Hill G.C.* Squash Rackets Assoc. Salmon & Trout Assoc. Brother, F. M. Hall. Son, Andrew Rowland, C, 67^3–70^2.

HALL, Stephen Hargreaves, F.C.A., b. 30 Apr. 33, s. of W. B. Hall. Sh, 46^3–51^2. N/S. K.O.Y.L.I. Att. 1st Bn. Durham L.I., 51–53. ✕ Korea, 2nd Lt. Dispatches. Served 4th Bn. K.O.Y.L.I. (T.A., 53–66).

Major. T.D. Christ's, Cambridge, M.A. F.C.A. Partner, Buckley, Hall, Devin & Co. Chartered Accountants, Hull & London.

HALLETT, Michael Hillersden George Heys. Sh, 43^3–48^2.*

HALLIDAY, Michael Alexander Kirkwood. W, 38^3–42^1.*

HALLIFAX, Cdr. James Cunningham, R.N. B, 37^3–41^1. Son, 2697.*

HALPIN, William Richard Crozier, b. 28 June 12, 2nd s. of the late W. H. Halpin. M, 26^1–30^1; Cap. Corpus Christi, Cambridge, M.A. ✕ R.A.S.C., 39–46. Major. Seconded to the Treasury, 43–45. F.C.A. Dir., John Lewis Partnership, 46–52. Sec., Lobitos Oilfields, 52–57. Chrmn., Premier Consolidated Oilfields, 57–62. Finance Controller, Assoc. British Foods, 62–68. Man. Dir., Knight-Wegenstein, 68–70. Dep. Chrmn., S. & K. Holdings, 70–72. From 70, Dir., Knight-Wegenstein, Pricerite, & Francis Industries. *Junior Carlton.* Royal Institute of International Affairs. *Hurlingham.*

HAMBLEN-THOMAS, Edwin Oliver, b. 31 Jan. 28. s. of C. Hamblen-Thomas. M & St, 41^3–46^2. Cadet Officer. Pembroke, Cambridge, M.A. C.Eng., M.I.C.E., D.M.S. With Central Electricity Generating Board.

HAMBLIN, Air-Commodore Richard Kaye, C.B.E., b. 16 Dec. 06, s. of R. E. Hamblin. SF, 20^3–24^2. R.A.F. Cadet College, Cranwell. Air Commodore, R.A.F. Retired. C.B.E. Son, 1951.

HAMEL, Geoffrey Fergus Wynn (see Wynn-Hamel, G. F.).

HAMILTON, Hamish (formerly James Hamilton), b. 15 Nov. oo, s. of the late J. N. Hamilton. B, 14^3–18^3. Gonville & Caius, Cambridge, M.A., LL.B. Bar, Inner Temple, 26. Publisher. ✕ Army, 39–41. Seconded to American Division, Min. of Information, 41–45. Légion d'Honneur. Clubs—*Whites, Garrick & Leander.*

HAMILTON, James Dundas, b. 11 June 19, s. of the late A. D. Hamilton. C, 33^2–38^2; Levée; Head of House. Exhibitioner of Clare, Cambridge. ✕ R.A., 39–46. Lt.-Col. Member of the Council of the London Stock Exchange; the Industrial Society; the E.E.C. Sub-Committee of the Committee of Invisible Exports. Chrmn., City & Industrial Liaison Council. Joined Carroll & Co., Stockbrokers, 46; Partner, 48. Partner in Fielding, Newson-Smith & Co. from 51. Dir., Bluemel Bros. Ltd. & Richard Clay & Co. Ltd. *City of London Club, All England Tennis & Croquet Club.* Publications: "The Erl King" (Radio Play), "Lorenzo Smiles on Fortune", "Three on a Honeymoon" (T.V. Series), "Six Months Grace" (Play jointly with Robert Morley), and "Stockbroking Today".

HAMILTON-GRIERSON, Philip John, b. 10 Oct. 32, s. of the late P. F. Hamilton-Grierson. St, 46^2–51^1; Levée; Head of House; Hands Prize; Buxton Divinity Prize. N/S. R.A.F., 51–53. Pilot Officer. Corpus Christi, Oxford, B.A. Sec. to Liberal Parliamentary Party, 62–65. Gallaher Ltd.—Gen. Man., Corporate Planning and Dir. of Dollond International Ltd. since 66.

HAMPTON, Philip George, b. 11 June 15, eldest s. of the late G. C. Hampton. K, 29^1–33^1. Gazetted to R.A. (T.A.), 34. ✕ R.A. (T.A.). M.C. Wounded. Major. T.D. & Bar. P. & O. Group of Companies, 34–72. Management, Company Sec., Exec. Dir. Retired, 72. Brother, R. L. Hampton. Son, 1587.

HAMPTON, Richard Latham. K, 39^3–41^2.*

HAMSHAW THOMAS, Christopher John, b. 26 Sept. 30, s. of H. H. Thomas, M.B.E., F.R.S. W & St, 43^3–49^2. King's, Cambridge, M.A. Chartered Engineer. Assoc. Fellow, R. Aeronautical Society. Joined Vickers Armstrong (Aircraft) Ltd. as Aerodynamicist. Technical Sales Engineer, Development Asst. & Man., Market Development. Now Public Affairs Executive, British Aircraft Corp. *East India, Sports & Public Schools.*

HANCOCK, Francis William, b. 19 Nov. 09, s. of the late Dr. E. D. Hancock. SH, 23^3–28^1; XV, 27. Trinity, Cambridge, B.A. Engineer, Aviator, Operations Staff, Min. of Civil Aviation from 35. ✕ R.Aux.A.F., 39–43. Sqn. Ldr. Air Efficiency Award. Dep. Dir., Flight Safety Dept. of Civil Aviation, B.O.T. Commercial Pilot/Navigator/Radio Operator/Ground Engineer. Chief, Aerodromes, International Civil Aviation Organisation. Retired, 69. *R.A.F. Club.* Sons, 1550 & 2008.

HANCOCK, Wilfrid Leuchars, b. 31 Dec. 05, s. of the late G. C. Hancock. K, 19^3–24^3. New College, Oxford, B.A. Joined Hunt, Leuchars & Hepburn, S. African Merchants. ✕ S.A.N.F.(V.), 39–45. Lt. Presently retired in Durban, S. Africa. *Royal Thames Y.C., Durban Club.*

HANDFIELD-JONES, Francis Valentine. St, 22^1–24^1.*

HANKEY, The Hon. Christopher Alers, O.B.E., b. 27 Apr. 11, 2nd s. of the late The Rt. Hon. Lord Hankey, G.C.B., G.C.M.G., G.C.V.O. (OR K 90). K, 24^3–29^2. New College, Oxford, M.A. University College, London, B.Sc. Tilbury Contracting & Dredging Co. Ltd., 33. R.E., 40. ✕ Royal Marines, 41–46. Major. Min. of Labour, 46. Dept. of Technical Co-operation, 61. Min. of Overseas Development, 64. Foreign & Commonwealth Office (Overseas Development Admin.), 70. Council for Technical Education & Training for Overseas Countries, 72. O.B.E., 58. Brothers, The Rt. Hon. Lord Hankey & H. A. A. Hankey.

HANKEY, The Hon. Henry Arthur Alers, C.M.G., C.V.O. K, 28^3–32^2. Sons, 1588, 1887 & 2819.*

HANKEY, Lancelot Hugh Alers, O.B.E., b. 11 Feb. 09, s. of the late Capt. C. T.A. Hankey (OR K 89). K, 22^3–27^2; XI, 27. Balliol, Oxford, M.A. Half Blue Lawn Tennis, 31. Asst. Master, Clifton College Prep. School, Bristol, 32–35. Housemaster, Giggleswick School, Yorkshire, 35–46. Headmaster, Clifton College Prep. School, 46–67. Sec., Inc. Assoc. of Preparatory Schools & of Common Entrance Board from 67. O.B.E., 74. Brother, O.C.A. Hankey.

HANKEY, Oliver Clement Alers, b. 19 Apr. 12, younger s. of the late Capt. C. T. A. Hankey (OR K 89). K, 26^1–30^2. College of Aeronautical Engineering, Chelsea. Air Service Training Ltd., Hamble. Held professional qualifications in Flying, Air Navigation and Air Radio. Civil & Service Air Pilot, Jersey Airways Ltd.; Imperial Airways Ltd. ✕ 7 years service as Pilot in F.A.A. Lt.-Cdr. British Aircraft Corp. Brother, O. C. A. Hankey. Son, 1737.

HANKEY of the Chart, The Rt. Hon. Lord, K.C.M.G., K.C.V.O. (Hankey, Robert Maurice Alers), b. 4 July 05, eldest s. of the late The Rt. Hon. Lord Hankey, G.C.B., G.C.M.G., G.C.V.O. (OR K 90). K, 19^2–23^2; Levée; Head of

House. New College, Oxford, B.A. Laming Travelling Fellowship, Queen's Coll., 26. Bonn Univ., Sorbonne, Paris. Entered H.M. Diplomatic Service, 27. Served Berlin, Paris, Warsaw, Bucharest, Cairo, Teheran & Madrid. Private Sec. to Rt. Hon. Anthony Eden, M.P. H.M. Minister to Hungary, 50–53. H.M. Ambdr., Stockholm, 54–60. Official Chrmn., O.E.E.C., 60–61. U.K. Delegate, O.E.C.D., 61–65. Retired from Diplomatic Service, 65. Member, International Council of United World Colleges since 66. Member, Council International Baccalaureate, Geneva. Hon. Vice-Pres., European Institute of Business Administration, Fontainebleau. Dir., Alliance Building Society. Royal Commonwealth Soc. Anglo-Swedish Soc. (President). K.C.M.G., 55. K.C.V.O., 56. Succeeded father, 63. Brothers, C. A. & H. A. A. Hankey. Sons, 774 & 2146.

HANN, Kenneth Graeme, b. 30 Aug. 12, 3rd s. of the late G. G. Hann. M, 26^2–31^1; XV, 30; H. XI, 31. Trinity, Cambridge, B.A. Jt. Man. Dir., G.K.N. Rolled & Bright Steel Ltd. Chrmn., G.K.N. Somerset Wire Co. *Royal Ocean Racing Club.* Brother, M. G. Hann.

HANN, Menteith Graeme, M, 23^3–28^2. Son, Michael Menteith, M, 67^3–.*

HANNAY, Thomas Scott, b. 5 Apr. 14, s. of the late W. S. S. Hannay. SF, 28^1–31^2. From 31–39, Liverpool Cotton Market. Broken war service owing to ill-health. Market Gardening, 45–58. Asst. Master at Leas School, Hoylake, 58–71. Now retired for health reasons. *Old Hall Club, Liverpool; Royal Liverpool G.C.* Son, 1601.

HANSON, William Gordon, O.B.E., b. 25 Sept. oo, elder s. of W. B. Hanson. M, 15^1–19^1. Hansons Ltd.; Hardy's Kimberley Brewery Ltd., Man. Dir., 38–70; Chrmn., 48. ✕ Commandant, Midland Area, Royal Observer Corps, 40–50. At present Chrmn., Hardys & Hansons Ltd. O.B.E. *Notts County Club.*

HANSON-LAWSON, John Gordon. SH, 28^1–32^2. Son, 2298.*

HARBORD, John Gilbert, b. 2 Jan. 04, younger s. of F. W. Harbord, C.B.E. St, 16^3–22^1; Scholar; Minor Exhibitioner. King's, Cambridge, B.A. Branch Man., Metal Traders Ltd., 27–33. Commercial Man., Imperial Smelting Corp. Ltd., 34–45 and London & Scandinavian Metallurgical Co. Ltd. from 45. Now retired. *North Devon Y.C.* Son, 407.

HARDCASTLE, Antony Roderick Kenyon. B, 44^3–49^2.*

HARDEN, Charles Gerald, b. 27 Sept. 04, s. of the late C. Harden. SH, 18^2–23^2. ✕ R.A., 39–40. Home Guard, 40–45. Retired. Farmer. Sons, 1524 & 1968.

HARDEN, Major Richard Wallace, M.C. St, 34^3–39^1.*

HARDIE, Henry David Stewart, O.B.E., LL.B., b. 15 Apr. 25, s. of J. S. Hardie. O.B.E. SH, 38^3–43^2. Aberdeen Univ. Army Short Course. Senior Scholar, Emmanuel, Cambridge, M.A., LL.B. Royal Tech. Coll., Salford, 50–51. City & Guilds Textile Technology. ✕ 3rd Indian Field Regt., 43–47. Capt. Wounded, Java, 45. A.D.C., Governor of Assam, 46. A.D.C., Governor of Bombay, 47. Forbes, Forbes, Campbell & Co. Ltd., Bombay, 51–57. Gen. Man., Gokate Mills Ltd., 55–57. Turner & Newall Ltd. Group since 57 (Man. Dir., Asbestos Cement Ltd., India, 62–66; Man. Dir., Asbestos Magnesia & Friction Materials Ltd., 63–66; Man. Dir., Hindustan Ferodo Ltd., India, 64–66). Pres., Bombay Chamber of Commerce & Industry, 65–66. Deputy. Pres., Assoc. Chamber of Commerce & Industry of India, 65. Since 69, Overseas Cttee., C.B.I. Chrmn., Asbestos Information Cttee. since 71. Manchester District Cttee., Inst. of Directors since 72. O.B.E. (Civil), 67. *Caledonian Club, London; Western Club, Glasgow; Royal Clyde Y.C.; Royal Bombay Y.C.* Son, James Henry Smyth, SH, 70^2–.

HARDIE, Ian William. SH, 45^3–49^2.*

HARDING, George Eric. W, 20^2–24^3.*

HARDING, Major George Roland, T.D., b. 9 May 15, elder s. of R. C. Harding. Tu, 29^1–33^2. Exhibitioner of Corpus Christi, Cambridge, B.A. F.I.Mech.E., F.I.E.E. Commissioned in R.E. (T.A.), 37. ✕ R.E., 39–44. R.E.M.E., 5th Indian Div., 44–45. Major. T.D. Retired, 51. English Electric Co., 36–69. Lanchester Polytechnic, Senior Lecturer. Brother, H. A. Harding. Sons, 2717 & Robert John Bruce, Tu, 67^3–72^2.

HARDING, Gerald O'Brien, b. 30 Nov. 23, elder s. of L. O'B. Harding (OR W 07). W, 37^3–42^2; Cap, XXII; H. XI, 41–42 (Capt.); Cadet Officer, 41–42. King's, Cambridge. Wartime Short Course. R.E. Univ. Hockey XI. ✕ R.E., 42–47. Capt. Partner, Bibby Bros. & Co. Managers of

Bibby Line Ltd., Shipowners. *R.O.R.C.* Brother, P. L. Harding.

HARDING, Hugh Alastair, C.M.G., b. 4 May 17, younger s. of R. C. Harding. Tu, 30³–35²; Scholar; Levée; Exhibitioner. Senior Scholar of Trinity, Cambridge, B.A.✕R.A., 39–45. Capt., Colonial Office Asst. Principal, 39; Principal, 45. Dep. Sec., West African Council, 48–50. Asst. Sec., Colonial Office, 50–61. C.M.G., 58. Treasury, 61–62. Under-Sec., 62. Minister, U.K. Delegation to O.E.C.D., 64–67. Under-Sec., Dept. of Education & Science, 67. Brother, G. R. Harding. Son, 1777.

HARDING, John Grosvenor Laurance. M, 22³–26².*

HARDING, Kenneth Gillison Mosford, b. 17 Nov. 99, elder s. of the late G. Harding. W, 13³–18¹; S. VIII, 16–17; Cadet Officer. ✕ 6th Bn. K.R.R.C. 2nd Lt., 19. Queen's, Oxford, B.A. Chartered Accountant. A.C.A., 26. With Ministry of Food, 39–45, as Area Meat & Livestock Officer, North Western Area. Partner in Harmood Banner & Son, Chartered Accountants, of Liverpool. Now retired, Consultant. J.P. for City of Liverpool from 48.

HARDING, Leslie O'Brien, b. 16 July 93, eldest s. of Sir C. O'B. Harding. W, 07²–12²; XI, 12; Cap, 11. ✕ Rangoon Mounted Rifles, I.A.R.O., att. 70th Burmese Rifles. Lt. Shipowning. Now retired. *Oriental Club, Royal Liverpool G.C.* Sons, G. O'B. & P. L. Harding. Grandson, David Charles Robert, W, 72³–.

HARDING, Peter Leslie, b. 22 Sept. 26, younger s. of L. O'B. Harding (OR W 07). W, 40²–44². King's, Cambridge. F.I.C.S. Shipbroker. Senior Partner, J. E. Hyde & Co. Dir., Baltic Mercantile & Shipping Exchange Ltd. and Seabridge Shipping Ltd. *R.A.C.* Brother, G. O'B. Harding. Son, David Charles Robert, W, 72³–.

HARDING, Thomas Garrard, F.C.A., b. 8 Jan. 20, s. of the late P. E. Harding, O.B.E., M.C. Sh, 33²–37²; Levée; Head of House. Exhibitioner of Brasenose, Oxford, M.A. ✕ Commissioned, South Lancashire Regt., 39. Trans. to Frontier Force Regt., 41. Dispatches, 42. Retired as Major, 46. A.C.A., 50. F.C.A., 55. Practising Chartered Accountant. Partner in firm since 50. Now Tansley Witt & Co. with F. M. Hall (OR C 25). *R.A.C. Cruising Assoc., Royal Yachting Assoc., Bexhill G.C.*

HARDWICK, Prof. James Leslie, M.D.S., Ph.D., b. 27 Mar. 13, s. of G. H. Hardwick. T, 27¹–31²; Major Foundationer. Birmingham Univ., L.D.S., B.D.S., M.D.S., Ph.D., 50. M.Sc.(Manch.), F.D.S., R.C.S.(Eng.). Private Dental Practice, 36–39. ✕ R.A.D.C., 39–45. Capt. Lecturer, and later Senior Lecturer & Reader in Dental Surgery, Univ. of Birmingham, 45–60. Professor of Preventive Dentistry, Univ. of Manchester from 60. Sec. General, European Organisation for Cancer Research.

HARDY, Brig. Arthur John, C.B.E., b. 19 Aug. 18, eldest s. of the late H. H. Hardy, C.B.E., M.A. (OR M 95). C. 32³–37²; Scholar; Levée; Head of House; Leaving Exhibition. Hulme Exhibition to Brasenose, Oxford, M.A. Army Staff College, 45. Imperial Defence College, 67. M.B.I.M., 71. Commissioned King's Shropshire Light Infantry, 39. Commanded 1st Bn. K.S.L.I., 58–60. G.S.O.1, 17 Gurkha Div., 60–62. Commander, Kenya Army, 64–66. Dep. Dir. of Manning (Army), 68–71. Dir. of Equipment Management (Army) from 71. Dispatches, 46. M.B.E., 53. C.B.E., 67. Dep. Colonel, K.S.L.I., 68. A.D.C. to H.M. The Queen, 70. *Army & Navy Club, Ski Club of G.B.* Brothers, R. H. & T. S. R. Hardy.

HARDY, Richard Henry, D.M., B.Ch., b. 11 June 21, 2nd s. of the late H. H. Hardy, C.B.E., M.A. (OR M 95). C, 35³–40¹; Scholar; Stovin Exhibition; Levée; Head of House. New College, Oxford, D.M., B.Ch., M.A. University College Hospital. Magrath Scholarship in Surgery. Satra Research Fellowship, 48–50. M.R.C.G.P. N/S. R.A.M.C., 51–52. Major. General Medical Practice, 53–71. Accident Dept., Hereford General Hospital. Fellow, Royal Society of Medicine. Brothers, A. J. & T. S. R. Hardy.

HARDY, Timothy Sydney Robert, b. 29 Oct. 25, 3rd s. of the late H. H. Hardy, C.B.E., M.A. (OR M 95). M, 39³–44¹. Levée. ✕ R.A.F.V.R. Sgt. Demy of Magdalen, Oxford. Actor & Writer. Worshipful Company of Bowyers. *Bucks.* Royal Toxophilite Society. Brothers, A. J. & R. H. Hardy.

HARE, The Hon. Richard Gilbert. SH, 20³–24¹.*

HARE, Prof. Richard Mervyn, b. 21 Mar. 19, 3rd s. of the late C. F. A. Hare. K, 32³–37²; Scholar; Levée; Head of House; Head of School. Balliol, Oxford,

M.A. Senior Domus Scholar, 37. ✕ Royal Artillery in France, India, Malaya. 4 (Hazara) Mtn. Bty., Indian Artillery. Lt. Captured Singapore, 42, and Japanese P.O.W. in Singapore & Siam, 42–45. Fellow, Balliol, 47–66. Fellow of British Academy, 64. White's Professor of Moral Philosophy & Fellow of Corpus Christi, Oxford, from 66. Son, 2430.

HARGREAVES, The Rev. Arthur Cecil Monsarrat. K, 32^3–38^1.*

HARGREAVES, Gordon Frank, M.B., B.Ch., b. 19 July 26, 2nd s. of the late Canon W. F. C. Hargreaves. SF, 40^3–44^2; Scholar; Cadet Officer. Trinity Hall, Cambridge, M.A., M.B., B.Chir. Middlesex Hospital, London. After qualifying in medicine, hospital appointments, service with R.A.F. (N/S.), and general practice, have had 18 years in pharmaceutical industry. Now Chrmn. & Man. Dir. of Boehringer Ingelheim Ltd., the U.K. subsidiary of large international pharmaceutical company. British Medical Assoc. Royal Society of Medicine. Brother, S. C. Hargreaves.

HARGREAVES, The Rev. Herbert Price, M.C., b. 29 Mar. 90, 5th s. of the late J. P. Hargreaves. W, 05^1–09^2; Cap, 08. Pembroke & Ridley Hall, Cambridge, M.A. Ordained, 14. Curate of Bradford, Yorks., 14–17. ✕ Temp. Chaplain to the Forces, 17–19. M.C. Wounded. Curate of West Ham, 19. C.M.S. Missionary in Nigeria, 21. Supervisor of C.M.S. Schools, Dio. Lagos, 28–29. Chaplain of Wellington Coll., 29. Vicar of Ripley, Derby, 34. Vicar of Newtown Linford, Leicester, 49. Retired, 68. Son, T. H. Hargreaves.

HARGREAVES, Stephen Carlile, b. 4 Sept. 24, elder s. of the late Canon W. F. C. Hargreaves. SF, 38^3–42^2. Trinity Hall, Cambridge, M.A. ✕ R.N., 44–46. Sub. Lt. (E). J.P., C.Eng., M.I.Mech.E. Engineering, Dir., Baker Perkins Holdings Ltd. Peterborough. Brother, G. F. Hargreaves.

HARGREAVES, Theodore Henry, b. 10 Feb. 30. s. of the Rev. H. P. Hargreaves, M.C., M.A. (OR W 05). SF, 43^3–47^3. ✕ R.A., 48–49. Malaya. 2nd Lt. F.C.A. Man., South West Area, Industrial & Commercial Finance Corp. Ltd. (I.C.F.C.).

HARKER, John Frederick. SH, 10^2–14^2.*

HARMAR, Leslie Charles D'Oyly, b. 17 Nov. 03, eldest s. of the late Col. C. D'O. Harmar, D.S.O., R.M.L.I. B,

17^3–21^2. A.C.A., 27. Whinney, Murray, Baguley, Berlin, 27–29. Whinney, Murray, Paris, 30–31. Deloitte Plender Binder & Co., Vienna, 31–39, and Belgrade from 38. S.O.E., Belgrade, Istanbul, Jerusalem, Cairo, 39–41. Braithwaite & Co. Ltd., Istanbul & Iskenderun, 41–43. British Member, Finance Control Cttee. of Spears Mission, Damascus, 43–44. P.A. to Dir., Rice Procurement Agency, Bengal, 44–45. Financial Controller, Mitchell Cotts, Khartoum, 45–50. Man. of Buildmore & Co. Ltd. Khartoum, 50–52. Now living in Portugal. *Royal British Club, Lisbon.* Hon. Treas., St. George's Church, Lisbon. Brothers, V. D'O. & N. D'O. Harmar.

HARMAR, Nigel D'Oyly, b. 6 Jan. 15. 3rd. s. of the late Col. C. D'O. Harmar, D.S.O., R.M.L.I. B, 28^3–33^2. Peterhouse, Cambridge, M.A. Joined Sudan Plantations Syndicate, Blue Nile Province, Sudan, 37. ✕ Sudan Artillery Regt., Sudan Defence Force. Major. Modern Language Master at King's School, Worcester, 49. Brothers, L. C. D'O. & V. D'O. Harmar.

HARMAR, Vincent D'Oyly, Lieut.-Col., b. 8 Dec. 08. 2nd s. of the late Col. C. D'O. Harmar, D.S.O., R.M.L.I. B, 22^3–27^2. Gym VIII, 27. R.M.A., Woolwich. Gazetted to R.A., 29. ✕ Special Appts., Palestine & Istanbul. Asst. Military Attaché, Ankara. B.M.R.A., 3rd Div., 83rd Field Regt., R.A. Military Attaché, Damascus & Beirut, 48–50. Attaché, Mexico City, Havana, Guatemala City, San Salvador. Interpreter in Russian, French, Turkish & Spanish. p.s.c. Retired, 58. Lt.-Col. Now owner of Panorama Motel, Bay of Islands, New Zealand. British Mexican, Anglo-Turkish, Anglo-Thai & Anglo-Florentine Societies. Brothers, L. C. D'O. & N. D'O. Harmer.

HARPER GOW, Leonard Maxwell, M.B.E., b. 13 June 18, eldest s. of the late L. Harper Gow. SF, 32^2–36^3. Cap. Corpus Christi, Cambridge, B.A. ✕ Commissioned into R.A., 40. Major. M.B.E. Apptd. Member of the Queen's Bodyguard for Scotland, The Royal Company of Archers, 51. Apptd. Hon. Norwegian Consul, 58. Dir. of Christian Salvesen Ltd. & other companies incl. The Royal Bank of Scotland Ltd., Edinburgh Investment Trust Ltd., The Scottish Widows' Fund & Life Assur. Soc., & The Burmah Oil Co. Ltd. *New Club, Edinburgh, Caledonian Club, London.* Sons, 1829 & Leonard Paul, SF, 69^2–.

HARRIS, Alan Martin, O.B.E., b. 4 July 99, younger s. of the late Sir C. Harris, G.B.E., K.C.B. K, 13³–17²; Scholar; Exhibitioner. ✕ R.G.A., 18–19. 2nd Lt. Domus Exhibitioner of Balliol, Oxford, B.A. Asst. Lecturer in Classics, Univ. College, London, 24–27. Publishing, 27–46; Dir., Gerald Duckworth & Co. Ltd. from 37. Temporary Civil Servant (War Office), 41, established 46, retired as Asst. Sec. Royal Hospital, Chelsea, 65. O.B.E. *Savile Club.*

HARRIS, Richard George. T, 39³–44³.*

HARRIS, Lt.-Col. William Arthur Brooke, M.C., b. 14 May 12, s. of the late Sir D. G. Harris, K.B.E., C.S.I., C.I.E. (OR B 97). B, 25³–29³; R. VIII, 29; Cadet Officer. R.M.C., Sandhurst. p.s.c. Camberley, 46. Gazetted 2nd Lt., Royal Fusiliers, 31. Sudan Defence Force, 38–42. Commanded 12 Parachute Bde., Normandy, 44; Somaliland Scouts, 53–54; and 1 Bn. Royal Fusiliers, 54–55. Retired from Regular Army, 55. Farming in Kenya from 55. Twice wounded: Abyssinia, 41; Normandy, 44. M.C. (Abyssinia, 41). *Army & Navy Club.*

HARRISON, Alfred Chase, b. 1 Nov. 24, 3rd s. of the late A. B. Harrison (OR K 88). K, 38³–42³; R. VIII. ✕ K.R.R.C., 44–47. Lt. Brothers, F. E. M. & C. L. S. Harrison.

HARRISON, Charles Lyndon Samuel b. 29 Apr. 19, 2nd s. of the late A. B. Harrison (OR K 88). SH, 32³–37³. 1½ years in City Bank. ✕ R.A. 6½ years in Ranks. Wounded, Normandy, 44. Dispatches. Growing things, mainly trees, since demobilisation in 46. Royal Forestry Soc. National Rose Soc. D-Day Group. Brothers, A. C. & F. E. M. Harrison.

HARRISON, Desmond Roger Wingate. K, 46³–52¹.*

HARRISON, Francis Edward Michael. K, 31³–35².*

HARRISON, William Simpson Nicoll, b. 9 Jan. 15, s. of W. Harrison, LL.D. SH, 28²–31³. King's College, London, LL.B. Solicitor, 37–45. ✕ R.A., 39–45. Major. T.D. Bar, Inner Temple, 46. A Senior Lecturer in Law at Bristol Polytechnic.

HARRISON-HALL, Michael Kilgour, b. 20 Dec. 25, younger s. of the late A. Harrison-Hall, M.B., M.R.C.P. C & Tu, 39³–44¹; Cap, 43; Sw. VIII, 43. Trinity,

Oxford. Bar, Inner Temple, 49. Dep. Chrmn., Warwickshire Quarter Sessions, 68. Recorder of Crown Court, 72. Circuit Judge, 72. Midland & Oxford Circuit. *Leander; Union Club, Birmingham.* Brother, P. Harrison-Hall.

HARRISON-HALL, Peter, B.M., B.Ch., b. 19 May 24, elder s. of the late A. Harrison-Hall, M.B., M.R.C.P. C & Tu, 37³–42¹. Trinity, Oxford, B.M., B.Ch., M.A. Middlesex Hospital. General Practitioner. Brother, M. K. Harrison-Hall.

HART, William Douglas, b. 10 Nov. 29, eldest s. of Sir W. O. Hart, C.M.G. (OR B 17). B, 44¹–48¹; Scholar. Exhibitioner of New College, Oxford, B.A. Mobil Oil Ltd., 52–66. Mobil Oil Corp. Inc. (U.S.A.), 66–69. Haverly Systems Inc. (U.S.A.) from 70 (Position: Technical Director). *R.A.C.* Mathematical Programming Society. Institute of Petroleum. Brothers, 237 & 1265.

HART, Sir William Ogden, C.M.G., J.P., b. 25 May 03, s. of Sir W. Hart, O.B.E. B, 17¹–21². New College, Oxford, B.C.L., M.A. Bar, Lincoln's Inn, 27. Member, Social Service Research Council, 65–70. Member, National Bus Co., 68–71. Fellow & Tutor of Wadham, Oxford, 26–47. Ministry of War Transport, 40–46. British Merchant Shipping Mission, Washington, 42–46. Gen. Man., Hemel Hempstead Development Corp., 47–55. Clerk of L.C.C., 56–65. Dir. General & Clerk to G.L.C., 64–68. Chrmn., Northampton Development Corp. from 68. C.M.G., 46. Knight Bachelor, 61. *United Oxford & Cambridge Universities Club.* Sons, W. D. Hart, 237 & 1265.

HARTCUP, Roderick Edward. K, 02³–07².*

HARTLEY, Cecil Rycroft. Tu, 38³–42¹.*

HARTNOLL, Amyas Victor, M.C., b. 17 May 97, 5th s. of the late Sir H. S. Hartnoll. SH, 11³–14³. R.M.A., Woolwich. ✕ Commissioned, 15, in Royal Field Artillery. A/Capt. M.C. Wounded, 18. Provincial Administration, Tanganyika Territory, 20–49. Retired with rank of Provincial Commissioner.

HARVEY, Bernard George. T, 33²–37².*

HARVEY, Gordon Columba. C, 35²–39³.*

HARVEY, Prof. John Wilfred. W, 03³–17².*

HARVEY, Rudolf Pogson, b. 11 May 99, elder s. of the late Sir E. M. Harvey, K.B.E. W, 13³–17². ✕ R.A.S.C., 18–19. Lt. Partner in Allen, Harvey & Ross, Bill Brokers, London. ✕ Suffolk Regt., 39–40. Capt.

HARVEY, Thomas Colin, b. 19 July 31, s. of T. B. G. Harvey. K, 45³–50²; Scholar; Levée; Head of House; Tom Hughes Prize; Rackets Pair, 47 & 48–49 (Hon.). Trinity, Oxford, B.A. Edin. Univ., Dip. Soc. Stud. L.S.E., Cert of Appl. Social Studies. 10 years in Social Work in London & Manchester. Lecturer in Social Work, Jordanhill College of Education, 69. Cert. Ed., 70. Curriculum Team. Dunbarton C.C. from 72. Member, British Assoc. of Social Workers. Pres., Scott Minority Group from 69. Founded History of Social Work Society. Founder of Colin Harvey Library of Social Work (Incl. "History of Public Schools").

HARVEY, Thomas Gourlay, F.R.C.S., b. 25 Dec. 10, 2nd s. of the late W. Harvey. St, 24²–28¹. Chelsea Polytechnic, Intermediate B.Sc. St. Thomas's Hospital, M.R.C.S., L.R.C.P. London Univ., M.B., B.S., F.R.C.S.(Eng.). ✕ R.A.M.C., 43–46. Major. Registrar, E.N.T. Dept., St. Thomas's Hospital, 49–51. Consultant Surgeon (E.N.T.), Royal Berkshire Hospital, Newbury District Hospital and Townlands Hospital, Henley, from 51. Royal Society of Medicine. *Berkshire G.C.*

HASLAM, The Rev. James Alexander Gordon, M.C., D.F.C., b. 24 Sept. 96, 3rd s. of the late J. B. Haslam (OR T 57). W, 10³–15²; Scholar; Levée; Head of House; Exhibition to Corpus Christi, Cambridge, 14 (not taken up). R.M.A., Woolwich, 15–16. ✕ 125th Bde., R.F.A., No. 8 (Tank) Squadron, R.F.C., 16–18. Wounded. M.C., D.F.C. R.A.F., 19–27 and ✕ 39–45. Corpus Christi, Cambridge (Fellow Commoner), 27–30, M.A. Aviation Dept., Asiatic Petroleum Co. Ltd. (Shell) London, 30–32. Research & Teaching in Aeronautics Sub-Dept., Cambridge Univ., 33–39 & 45–52. Fellow of Corpus Christi, 49–52. St. George's, Windsor (Training for Ordination), 53. Ordained Deacon, 54; Priest, 55. Parish Ministry, C. of E., 54–64. Retired. Sons, 149 & 733.

HASLAM, Col. John Patrick Mac-Dougall, b. 30 Jan. 08, s. of the late Lt.-Col. B. J. Haslam, D.S.O., R.E. (OR T 88). SH, 21³–26²; Scholar. R.M.A., Woolwich. Gazetted to R.A., 2nd Lt., 28. Retired as Lt.-Col. (Hon. Col.), 58. Appeals Sec., Cancer Research Campaign. Royal Archaeological Institute.

HASSAN, Clement, b. 3 Sept. 24, s. of the late V. Hassan. W, 37³–41³. King's, Cambridge, M.A. Chrmn. & Man. Dir., family business, Victor Hassan Ltd., engaged in Textiles & other allied interests. *R.A.C.* Chrmn., Assoc. of Spanish & Portuguese Jewish Congregation of U.K. & Commonwealth. Son, 2620.

HASWELL, Gordon Thrale, b. 6 Aug. 26, eldest s. of the late Dr. R. E. Haswell. Sh, 40²–44². Oxford Univ., 44–45. Durham Univ., 47–48. ✕ R.N., 44–47. Dep. P.R.O. & P.O., Northern Region, National Coal Board.

HATCH, Col. Keith, O.B.E., b. 23 Oct. 96, 2nd s. of the late Lt.-Col. W. K. Hatch. M, 10³–13². Staff College, Quetta. ✕ 34th Poona Horse, Capt., 19. 17th Q.V.O. Poona Horse, Bannu, N.W.F.P., India. Colonel, Indian Army. Retired. O.B.E. *Civil Service Club, Cape Town; Muthaiga Country Club, Nairobi.*

HATT, Thomas Montagu David. C, 21³–25¹.*

HAUGH, Norris King, b. 15 Nov. 29, s. of Major-General J. W. N. Haugh. SF, 43³–48²; R. VIII, 47–48; Leaving Exhibition. Scholarship (Mawson) to Corpus Christi, Cambridge, M.A., Cert. Ed. N/S. R.E.M.E., 48–50. 2nd Lt. Chemistry Master, Malvern College, 54–59; then Bec School, Tooting, 59–70. Asst. Sec., The Queen's Club, Baron's Court, from 70. Fellow of the Chemical Society. *All England Lawn Tennis Club, The Queen's Club.* Represented Worcestershire at Lawn Tennis.

HAUGHTON, William Theodore Hoghton, b. 14 June 86, s. of the late W. H. Haughton. SH, 00²–03². Trinity, Cambridge, B.A. Landowner & Artist. ✕ Experimental Camouflage, Scots Guards. Pte.

HAVARD, John Kenneth Holmes, b. 7 June 31, 2nd s. of Rt. Rev. W. T. Havard, M.C., T.D., D.D., Bishop of St. Asaph. B, 44³–49²; XXII. Christ Church, Oxford. Solicitor. Partner in firm of Amery Parkes & Co., London.

HAVELL, Charles Cedric Walter, M.C., b. 10 June 95, s. of the late Dr. C. G. Havell. C, 09³–13³; Cap, 12. Exhibitioner elect of Pembroke, Cambridge. ✕ 4th Bn. Suffolk Regt. Divnl. Trench Mortars. Capt. M.C. Dispatches twice. Dir., Imperial Tobacco Co. Ltd. Retired.

HAVILAND, Denis William Garstin Latimer, C.B., b. 15 Aug. 10, s. of the late W. A. Haviland. M, 24^2–28^2. St. John's, Cambridge, M.A. A.M.Inst.T. Imperial Defence Col. (i.d.c.), 50. Member, Court, Cranfield Institute of Technology. Member, Council, B.I.M., from 67. Member, Council, C.B.I., 68–70. F.B.I.M. L.M.S. Railway, 34–39. ✕ R.E., 40–46. Col. Civil Service, 46. Principal Control Officer for Germany & Austria, 47. Asst. Sec. to Foreign Office (G.S.), 47. Ministry of Supply, 51. Under-Sec., 53. Dep. Sec., 59. Ministry of Aviation, 59. Joint Man. Dir., Staveley Industries Ltd., 64. Chrmn. & Man. Dir., 64–69. Dir., Short Bros. & Harland from 65, & other Directorships. F.R.S.A. C.B., 58. *Bath Club.*

HAWARD, Ashley Gordon, b. 21 Apr. 04, s. of the late Sir H. Haward. St, 18^2–23^1. University College, Oxford, B.A. Man., British Aviation, France & Canada (founder). Original Member, O.U.A.S. & 601 Sqn., R. Aux. A.F., 25 & 26. ✕ R.A.F.V.R., 39–42. F/Lt. Founder & Man., Aviation Dept., Sedgwick Collins & Co. Ltd., Insurance Brokers, 49–59. Retired. *R. Aero Club.*

HAWKESWORTH, Charles Peter Elmhirst, b. 14 Aug. 10 elder s. of the late C. E. M. Hawkesworth, M.A. (former Housemaster of Tudor House). Tu, 24^2–29^2. Corpus Christi, Oxford, M.A. Asst. Master at Shrewsbury School, 35–62. ✕ The Rifle Bde., 40–45. Major. Retired. *Greenjackets.* Brother, J. W. C. Hawkesworth. Sons, 1539 & 2482.

HAWKESWORTH, John Stanley, b. 7 Dec. 20, s. of Lt.-Col. J. L. I. Hawkesworth. M, 34^3–39^1. Queen's, Oxford. ✕ Grenadier Guards, 40–46. Capt. Joined London Films, 46. Art Director & Designer. Now Free-lance.

HAWKESWORTH, John Walter Cooper, T.D., b. 15 July 17, younger s. of the late C.E.M. Hawkesworth, M.A. (former Housemaster of Tudor House). SF, 31^2–36^2; Scholar; Levée. Scholar of Queen's, Oxford, B.A. ✕ R.A.(Field), 39–45. Capt. Solicitor, 49. Partner in Soulby & Co. of Malton & Pickering, Yorks. Capt. 12th (Yorks.) Bty., The Parachute Regt. (T.A.). T.D. Brother, C. P. E. Hawkesworth.

HAWKINS, Arnold Caesar, O.B.E., b. 30 May 09, s. of the late T. H. Hawkins. Bt 22^3–28^2; Levée; Head of House; Cade, Officer; Major & Minor Leaving Exhibitions. Trinity, Cambridge, M.A. Exchange Student (1 year), Berlin Technical Univ. College Apprentice, Metropolitan-Vickers, 32–35. Employed in wine firm, Valente Costa e Cie Ltda, Oporto, to 40. British Council, 40. Founded British Institute, Oporto, 43. Served in Czechoslovakia, Oxford (Area Officer), France, Belgium (Representative), London (Commonwealth Div.), Austria (Representative), Retired, 71. O.B.E., 69. O.M., Portuguese Red Cross, 46. *Savile Club, Royal Commonwealth Society.*

HAWKINS, George Charles, b. 19 June 02, elder s. of the late H. C. Hawkins. B, 16^2–21^1. Dir., Hawkins & Tipson Ltd. Rope Trade in U.K. & Durban. Chrmn. of Manilla Rope Assoc. & London Sisal Assoc. Now retired. Dir., Addington G.C., Beckenham C.C. (Chrmn., 68–72). Blackheath F.C. (Player). *R.A.C., Kent C.C.C.* Sons, 891 & 1230.

HAWKINS, Gordon Frank, M.B., Ch.B., D.A., F.F.A.R.C.S., b. 14 Apr. 21, s. of the late F. J. Hawkins, T, 35^1–39^2. Edinburgh Univ., M.B., Ch.B., D.A., F.F.A.R.C.S.(Eng.). ✕ R.N.V.R. Surg.-Lt. Consultant Anæsthetist, Bradford Royal Infirmary.

HAWKINS, William Francis Spencer, C.B., b. 13 Feb. 96, eldest s. of the late F. W. Hawkins. M, 10^1–14^2. ✕ 4th Bn. Devonshire Regt., 27th Divnl. Signals, R.E., 15–19. Lt. Dispatches twice. Solicitor, 21. Partner in the firm of Bird & Bird, Grays Inn, 28–32. Master of Supreme Court (Chancery Div.), 33–69. Chief Master, 59–69. Admin. Head, Chancery Judges Chambers & Chancery Registrars Office, 60–69. Retired, 69. Senior Trustee, United Law Clerks Society since 53. J.P. for Surrey since 47 (now on Supplemental List). Chrmn., Wallington, Surrey, Petty Sessional Div. Bench, 57–59. Pres. O.R. Society, 57–58. Member of Coulsdon & Purley U.D.C., 45–47. C.B., 68. A past member of the Magistrates' Assoc. The Middlesex & Surrey Society. *The Surrey Magistrates Club.*

HAWORTH, Sir Arthur Geoffrey, Bt., b. 5 Apr. 96, s. of the late Sir A. Haworth, Bt. (OR B 79). St, 10^2–14^3. New College, Oxford, M.A. ✕ 3rd Bn. Royal West Kent Regt. 10th Bn. Machine Gun Corps. Lt. Dispatches. Retired Farmer. J.P., F.R.S.A., Hon. M.A., Manchester Univ. *Farmers' Club.*

HAWORTH, Arthur Maurice, b. 4 Oct. 06, 2nd s. of the late J. G. Haworth (OR B 84). M, 20²–25²; Levée; Head of House; H. XI, 25. New College, Oxford, M.A. Hockey Blue, 26–28. Stockbroker of Manchester. Nat. Fire Service, 39–44, Divisional Officer. ✗ Army Special List, 44–45. Major. J.P., Manchester City, 49. Retired. Brother, S. A. Haworth.

HAWORTH, Christopher William, b. 22 Nov. 04, eldest s. of the late F. A. Haworth. SF, 18³–23²; Scholar; XI, 23. H. XI, 23. New College, Oxford, M.A. Partner in family firm of cotton yarn agents & merchants of Manchester. ✗ Intell. Corps., 39–45. Major. Retired from business, 70. *Leicestershire Club, Butterflies C.C., Gentlemen of Cheshire C.C., Gentlemen of Leics. C.C.* Court of Worshipful Company of Framework Knitters. Brother, F. A. Haworth. Son, 2391.

HAWORTH, Frank Alexander. SF, 23³–27².*

HAWORTH, Stephen Alexander, b. 8 Nov. 03, eldest s. of the late J. G. Haworth (OR B 84). M, 17³–22²; Cap. New College, Oxford, B.A. Partner, James Dilworth & Son, Yarn Agents, Manchester, from 30. Dir., Goyt Mills Mfg. Co. Ltd. & Abraham Haworth Ltd. Semi-retired. ✗ R.A. (Searchlights), 39–45. Major. T.D. *St. James's Club, Manchester.* Brother, A. M. Haworth. Son, 428.

HAWTHORNE, John Greenfield, b. 6 June 15, 2nd s. of the late W. Hawthorne. M, 29³–33²; Scholar; Levée; Athletic Cup, 33. Exhibition to Corpus Christi, Cambridge, M.A. Harvard Univ., Cambridge, Mass., M.A. Univ. of Chicago, Ill., Ph.D. Pres., Illinois Classical Conference, and Chicago Society of the Archaeological Institute of America. Instructor at Harvard & Radcliffe. Principal, South African Govt. Mission, Washington, D.C. 1st Sec., Anglo-American Mission, Dakar, F.W.A.; British Embassy, Brussels, Belgium. Asst. Sec. & Treas., Consolidated Gold Fields of South Africa, New York Office. Associate Professor of Classics, Univ. of Chicago. *Harvard; N.Y. Univ.; Washington, D.C.* Field excavator in Greece, from 57–68.

HAY, Anthony Malcolm. C, 32²–36³.*

HAY, Donald Molson, b. 12 July 15, eldest s. of the late Capt. A. C. Hay (OR Tu 02). C, 29²–33¹. Dir., Naylor, Benzon & Co. Ltd. of London. ✗ 1st King's Dragoon Guards, 40–46. Capt. *City of London & Cavalry Clubs.* Brothers, A. M. & R. A. Hay.

HAY, Ian Bruce David Erroll, b. 4 June 16, s. of the late E. G. Hay. W, 30²–33². Trinity Hall, Cambridge, B.A. ✗ R.A.F., 39–45. 611 Squadron. Wing-Cdr. Dispatches. Director of Companies. *R.A.F. Club, Durban Club.*

HAY, John Macalister. M, 38²–42³.*

HAY, Michael King, b. 8 May 31, s. of the late Dr. W. K. Hay. K, 45²–49²; Tennis Cup, 49. Trinity College, Dublin, M.B., B.Ch. Medical Practitioner.

HAY, Robert Alan, b. 31 Mar. 21, 3rd s. of the late Capt. A. C. Hay (OR Tu 02). C, 34³–38³. Northamptonshire Institute of Agriculture, Moulton, Northants, Diploma. 1st Prizeman, Macdonald College, McGill Univ., Montreal, Diploma. ✗ 16/5th Lancers. Lt. Wounded (lost right eye at Tunis). Invalided, 43. Farming own farm, 47–66. Apptd. Exec. Dir., Ontario Hospital Assoc., from 66. Knight, Order of Chivalry of St. Lazarus of Jerusalem. *Cavalry Club; York Club, Toronto.* Brothers, D. M. & A. M. Hay.

HAYBURN, Lt.-Col. Edward Francis, b. 29 Oct. 07, elder s. of the late E. G. Hayburn. Tu, 21³–26¹. St. John's, Cambridge, B.A. Gazetted to R.A., 29. Retired, 52, as Lt.-Col. Dispatches.

HAYCOCK, Col. Michael Brian, T.D., B.Sc., b. 10 May 29, s. of H. J. Haycock. W, 43²–47¹. N/S. Commissioned in 10th Royal Hussars (P.W.O.), 47–49. Univ. of Aston, B.Sc., C.Eng., M.I.Mech.E., 49–52. Technical Asst., 54–59. Technical Dir., 59–68. Chrmn. & Man. Dir. of Haycock Gauge & Tool Co. Ltd. from 68. Served in Queen's Own Warwickshire & Worcestershire Yeomanry, T.A., 49–69. C.O., 67–69. T.D. Apptd. Dep. Commander, T.A.V.R. in the West Midlands, 72, in the rank of Colonel. *Cavalry Club.*

HAYDON, Thomas Henry Vernon, b. 21 Sept. 99, elder s. of the late His Honour Judge Haydon, K.C. W, 13¹–16³. ✗ R.F.C. & R.A.F., 17–19. Pilot Lt. Past Pres., Bournemouth & District Licensed Hotels & Restaurants Assoc. & Fellow of the Hotel & Catering Institute. Retired. *Parkstone G.C., Royal Southampton Y.C.*

HAYLEY, George Gilbert, b. 29 July 17, 2nd s. of the late F. A. Hayley, D.C.L.,

Q.C. Tu, 31¹–35². Exeter, Oxford. Commerce, Colombo, Ceylon, from 37–61. Presently a Rubber Broker in London. ✕ R. Signals, 42–46. Major. D.A.A.G., G.H.Q., India, New Delhi. Brother, J. F. Hayley.

HAYLEY, John Frederic, O.B.E., b. 16 Apr. 16, eldest s. of the late F. A. Hayley, D.C.L., Q.C. Tu, 29³–34²; XXII; Cap; Tennis, Squash, Fives. Exeter, Oxford, M.A. Played Rugby Fives for Oxford, 35–37, & Squash Rackets, 36–37. Colonial Administrative Service, 38–64, serving in Nigeria, N. Rhodesia, Bechuanaland, United Nations, Dir., 64–70. Retired (temp. employment, F.C.O.). O.B.E. *East India, Sports & Public Schools Club.* *M.C.C.* Brother, G. G. Hayley.

HAYNES, Lt.-Col. Basil Britain, b. 25 Sept. 99, s. of the late F. Haynes. T, 13²–17². R.M.C., Sandhurst. Gazetted to Indian Army, 19. ✕ Royal Indian Army Service Corps, in India, U.K., Iraq, Persia, Burma & Malaya, 39–45. Dispatches. Retired as Lt.-Col., 48.

HAYS, Geoffrey Richard. Tu, 32³–36¹.*

HAZEL, William Broxholme. B, 05³–08³.*

HEAD, Robert George, b. 17 Apr. 10, s. of the late R. G. Head. T, 23³–27². Birmingham Univ., B.Sc. (Mining). H. XI, 28–30. Fellow, Institute of Mining & Metallurgy. Mining Engineer in Spain, Gold Coast, Yugoslavia, Colombia & N. Rhodesia, 30–51. ✕ Major, General List, 40–44. Invalided. Temp. 3rd Sec., H.B.M. Embassy, Madrid, 45–46. Head of Mining Dept., Camborne School of Mines, Cornwall, 52–54. Mining Engineer, Rhodesian Selection Trust, N. & S. Rhodesia, 54–65. Selection Trust Ltd., London, from 65. *Mining Club, London; Special Forces Club.* Son, 2739.

HEAFIELD, Philip John, b. 21 Oct. 14, elder s. of the late S. Heafield. T, 28¹–32². Borough Road College, Isleworth, B.A. Cert. Ed. King's College, London, LL.B. Lecturer in Law, Harrow College of Technology. Brother, S. Heafield.

HEAFIELD, Lt.-Col. Samuel, b. 30 Dec. 17, younger s. of the late S. Heafield. T, 31³–35². Borough Road College, Isleworth. Loughborough College, Leics. Diploma in Physical Education. ✕ 5th Gurkha Rifles, 41–46. Major. Hon. Lt.-Col., R.A.R.O. Staffordshire Organiser of

Phys. Ed. for 11 years. Head of Phys. Ed. Dept. at Madeley College from 59. Brother, P. J. Heafield.

HEALD, John Marsden. St, 28²–32².*

HEALD, Michael, D.S.O., b. 6 Mar. 16, 2nd s. of W. M. Heald. St, 29³–33³. East India Merchant, & Company Dir. for over 30 years. Now retired. ✕ 40–45, 3rd (Peshawar) Mountain Bty., 23rd Indian Mountain Regt. Major. D.S.O. Dispatches. Brother, J. M. Heald.

HEALE, John Lawson. St, 37²–41².*

HEAP, Derek Clifford, M.B., B.Chir., b. 23 Apr. 31, s. of Dr. C. Heap. B, 44³–49². Queens', Cambridge, M.A., M.B., B.Chir. St. Thomas's Hospital, D.Obst. R.C.O.G., M.R.C.G.P. General Medical Practitioner.

HEAPE, Brian Peere. SF, 36³–41³.*

HEAPE, Charles Herbert. K, 06³–10³.*

HEAPE, Richard Samuel, M.C. SF, 11¹–15².*

HEARN, Lt.-Col. John Neill Whitcombe, b. 1 Aug. 13, eldest s. of the late J. W. Hearn, C.S.I., C.I.E. Tu, 27²–31³. R.M.A., Woolwich. Gazetted to R.A., 32. India, 33–39. Staff College, 42. ✕ Middle East & Normandy, 39–44. Dispatches twice. Wounded. Retired, Lt.-Col., 60. Dir. of Brooker & Gatehouse Ltd. *Army & Navy Club, Royal Lymington Y.C.* Brother, R. F. Hearn. Sons, 1090 & 1540.

HEARN, Lt.-Col. Richard Francis, b. 14 Apr. 21, 3rd s. of the late J. W. Hearn, C.S.I., C.I.E. Tu, 35¹–40²; XV, 39; H. XI, 38–40 (Capt.); Squash, 39–40 (Capt.); Tennis, 39–40 (Capt.). ✕ Intell. Corps from 41. Lt.-Col. Dispatches (Cyprus), 58. *Army & Navy Club.* Brother, J. N. W. Hearn. Son, 2777.

HEASLETT, Eric Arthur, M.R.C.S., L.R.C.P. W, 26¹–30². Son, 1204.*

HEATH, Denis William. M, 19¹–22³. Son, 724.*

HEATH, The Rev. George Nicholas, b. 8 Feb. 24, 2nd s. of R. Heath. C & Tu, 37³–41². Gonville & Caius, Cambridge, M.A. The Admiralty. Translation of German War Documents, 47. Caledonian Insurance Co., Foreign Dept., 47–49. Lincoln Theological College, 49–51. Ordained Deacon, 51; Priest, 52. Curate of

St. Mary & St. Nicholas, Spalding, 51–55. Priest-in-charge, St. Andrew, Bedwell, Stevenage, 55–60. Vicar, St. Alban's, Acton Green, London, 60–70. Vicar, St. Stephens, Hounslow, Middlesex, from 70. Hon. Chaplain to the Knights of St. George. Brother, M. Heath.

HEATH, Martin, b. 22 Feb. 20, eldest s. of R. Heath. C, 33³–38²; Scholar. English Speaking Union. Exchange Scholarship to U.S.A. Hill School, Pottstown, Pa., U.S.A. Trinity Hall, Cambridge, M.A. ✕ Essex Regt., 40–46. Wounded, 45. Major. Fellow of the Institute of Purchasing & Supply. Member of the Transport Users Consultative Cttee., W. Region. Employed by Procter & Gamble Ltd., 48–57. Avon Rubber Co. Ltd. since 57 as Supplies General Manager. *United Oxford & Cambridge Univ. Club;* Wiltshire Beekeepers Assoc.; *Shearwater Sailing Club.* Brother, G. N. Heath.

HEATON, David, b. 22 Sept. 23, s. of Dr. T. B. Heaton, O.B.E., M, 37³–42¹. Christ Church, Oxford. ✕ R.N.V.R., 42–46. Colonial Administrative Service, Ghana, 47–58. Ministry of Defence, 59–61. Cabinet Office, 61–69. Home Office from 69.

HEATON, Lt.-Cdr. David John, R.C.N., b. 23 Apr. 31, s. of T. Heaton. Tu, 45¹–49¹. R.N. Engineering College, Keyham. R.N., 49–56. Lt.-Cdr. (E.) Royal Canadian Navy, 56–70. Univ. of Western Ontario, London, Ontario, Canada. Diploma in Business Admin. Stockbroker from 70. *Bath Club.*

HECHLE, Herbert Rea, b. 12 Mar. 00, eldest s. of the late J. H. Hechle, C.I.E. (OR M 79). M, 14¹–18²; Cadet Officer; Head of House. ✕ R.A.F. Cadet, 18. With Bird & Co., East India Merchants, London & Calcutta, 20–36. Thereafter own business in England except for war years, when with M.O.F. & R.A.F. (3 years). Retired, 68.

HEDDERWICK, Peter David Nelson. K, 45³–50².*

HEIGHT, Laurence Desmond. T, 44³–48³.

HELLAWELL, Henry Swindells, b. 27 Oct. 85, younger s. of the late T. Hellawell. C, 99³–03³; Cap, 03. Of Hall & Hellawell, Cotton Yarn Merchants & Exporters, Manchester. ✕ 6th Bn. Manchester Regt. Capt. Wounded. Resigned: Wounds, 18.

HELLAWELL, Thomas Anthony, b. 29 Sept. 20, s. of the late J. H. Hellawell (OR C 96). C, 34³–38². Cotton Yarn Merchant. ✕ R.A. Wounded, 42. Major. Company Director. Son, Richard Bridson, C, 73²–.

HELME, Alexander. C, 28¹–32². Sons, 1395 & 2162.*

HELME, James Milner. B, 03²–07². Son, 2814.*

HELME, Wing-Cdr. James Michael, D.F.C., A.F.C., b. 1 Oct. 19, younger s. of the late J. Helme. C, 33³–38². Trinity, Cambridge, M.A. ✕ 40–58, R.A.F.; A.F.C., 45; D.F.C., 51. Dir., The Expanded Metal Co. Ltd. from 59. Brother, A. Helme. Son, 2814.

HENDERSON, Hamilton Brown Lord, M.B. Tu, 03¹–07².*

HENDERSON, Ian Nigel. SF, 44³–48³.*

HENDERSON, John, D.F.C., b. 14 Oct. 19, elder s. of the late W. T. Henderson (OR SF 99). SF, 33²–38². ✕ R.A.F., 39–45. D.F.C. Member of Inst. of Chartered Accountants of Scotland. Dir., Bass Charrington Services Ltd. Brother, W. T. Henderson. Son, 2839.

HENDERSON, Lt.-Col. John, T.D. SF, 43³–48².*

HENDERSON, Keith. St, 27³–31³.*

HENDERSON, Michael. K, 43³–48³.*

HENDERSON, Richard Yates, T.D., D.L., b. 7 July 31, 2nd s. of the late J. W. Henderson. SF, 45²–49². N/S. R. Scots Greys. Hertford, Oxford, B.A., LL.B. (Glasgow). Solicitor. T.D., D.L. *Western Club, Glasgow.* Brother, Lt.-Col. J. Henderson. Son, Charles Richard, SF, 72²–.

HENDERSON, Thomas Beveridge, C.A., b. 9 July 21, eldest s. of T. B. Henderson. St, 35²–39². Glasgow Univ. ✕ R.N. & F.A.A., 40–46. Lt., R.N.V.R. C.A. A.T.I.I. Dir. & Sec., Fleming Bros. (Structural Engineers) Ltd. *Scottish Ski Club.* Loch Lomond Angling Improvement Assoc. Brother, M. Henderson.

HENDERSON, William Antony, F.R.I.B.A., b. 13 July 14, s. of the late J. A. Henderson (OR St 96). St, 28²–32². Liverpool Univ. School of Architecture. Honan Scholar. John Rankin Prize. A.R.I.B.A. ✕ R.E., 39–46. Major. Senior

Asst. (Schools) Herts. C.C., 46–52. Farmer & Dark, Architects, London. Partner from 54. F.R.I.B.A., 65. Consultant Arch. to the Univ. of Kent, at Canterbury, since 66. Architectural Assoc. Anglo-Turkish Society.

HENDERSON, William Thomson, b. 28 Jan. 25, 2nd s. of the late W. T. Henderson (OR SF 99). SF, 38^2–43^2; Levée; Leaving Exhibition. Exhibitioner of Clare, Cambridge. (6 months under R.A.F. Scheme.) ✕ R.A.F., 43–47. Aircrew Sgt. Became partner in Rowe & Pitman, Stockbrokers, 50–68. J.P., 70. Brother, J. Henderson. Son, Michael Thomson, SF, 67^3–.

HENDLEY, Lt.-Col. Charles Gervase, D.S.O. B, 20^3–24^2.*

HENDRY, Albert Gilbert, T.D. B, 21^3–24^3. Sons, 2463 & David Robert Charles, B, 69^2–.*

HENDRY, Alexander Mitchell, b. 29 Nov. 11, s. of the late J. Hendry, M.C. W, 25^2–29^2. ✕ Middlesex Regt. & R.A. Chartered Accountant in practice throughout. At present, Partner, Ball Baker Carnaby Deed, London. J.P.

HENDRY, Charles William Righton, b. 14 Apr. 22, s. of C. Hendry, F.C.I.I. B, 35^3–40^2. Trinity Hall, Cambridge. ✕ 98th (S.P.) Field Regt., R.A., 41–46. Major. Member of London Stock Exchange. *M.C.C.* Son, Charles, B, 72^3–.

HENNESSY, George Peter, b. 10 July 16, eldest s. of the late Capt. G. T. Hennessy (OR Tu 04). Tu, 30^1–32^3. F.R.P.S., 40. Film director/cameraman. Man. Dir., Screen Locations Ltd. *Savage, Oriental, Arts Theatre, Island Sailing, Royal Photographic.* Brother, J. M. Hennessy.

HENNESSY, James Mitchell, M.C., b. 5 Oct. 17, 2nd s. of the late Capt. G. T. Hennessy (OR Tu 04). Tu, 31^3–35^2. ✕ 2nd N.Z.E.F., 40–45. M.C. Lt. Reserve List. 1st Canterbury Regt. Sheep Farmer, Canterbury, N.Z. *Christchurch Club.* Brother, G. P. Hennessy.

HENNY, Victor Edward, b. 30 Dec. 24, s. of the late V. Henny, D.Sc. W, 38^3–40^2. ✕ Ensign. U.S. Naval Air Force. Montezuma Mountain Ranch High School, 40–41. Stanford Univ., California, U.S.A., 41–43. U.S. Naval Aviation Pilot, 43–45. Univ. of Calif., 46–48. Geneva Univ., Switzerland, 48–49. Birmingham Univ.,

50–52. B.A.(Chem.), Diplome d'Ingenieur Chimiste. Ph.D. (Chemical Engineering). Fellow I.P. Member, A.C.S. R. & D. Universal Oil Products, Chicago, 52–57. Commercial Developments, U.O.P., London, 54–60. Senior Adviser, Institut Français du Petrole, Paris, 60–62. Directeur Industriel from 62. Consultant to World Bank, O.E.C.D. Development Centre, U.N.I.D.O., Greek Govt., Indian Govt. *American Club, London; Roehampton, London; Yacht Club Ile de France.*

HENRIQUES, Lionel Reginald Quixano, b. 10 May 10, 3rd (younger twin) s. of the late J. Q. Henriques. W, 24^2–28^2; S. VIII, 27–28. New College, Oxford, B.A. ✕ Hon. Capt., R.E. Farmer, Rhodesia. *Ex. Ayrshire & Mashonaland Flying Club.* Winner, 1st Rhodesian National Air Race.

HENSON, Brig. Robert Kent, M.C., b. 17 July 97, youngest s. of the late F. B. Henson. B, 11^2–14^3. Quetta Cadet College (Indian Army). ✕ 25th Punjabis att. 45th Sikhs. Capt. Wounded. M.C., 15–18. Instructor, Small Arms School, India, 24–27. N.W.F., India, 30–31. ✕ Commandant, 3rd Bn. 11th Sikh Regt. (Rattray's), Iraq, Syria & Iran, 40–44. Commandant, 2nd Reinforcement Group. Altsea, 46. Retired. Retired Officer (Civilian), Lowland District, Scotland, 51–58.

HEPBURN, John Malcolm, b. 13 Aug. 14, s. of the late J. P. Hepburn (OR C 92). C, 28^3–32^1. Magdalene, Cambridge, B.A. Solicitor, 38. Partner in Kitson Dymond & Easterbrook of Torquay since 46. Notary Public, 53. J.P., 67. T.A. (Royal Devon Yeomanry Artillery), 38–50. ✕ R.A., 39–45, incl. East Africa, Ceylon, India & Burma. Dispatches. T.D. Royal Philatelic Society.

HEPPEL, Richard Purdon, C.M.G., b. 27th Oct. 13, 2nd s. of the late Engineer Rear-Admiral W. G. Heppel. K, 26^3–31^2; Scholar; Levée; Head of School; Sw. VI, 31; Exhibitioner. Balliol, Oxford (Domus Scholar), B.A. Laming Travelling Fellow, The Queen's, Oxford. H.M. Diplomatic Service, 36–69. Served Foreign Office, Rome, Tehran, Athens, then as Private Sec. to Minister of State, and later to Parliamentary Under-Sec. of State for Foreign Affairs, & as Sec. of the U.K. Delegation to the United Nations; 1st Sec. at Karachi, Counsellor at Saigon, H.M. Ambassador at Phnom-Penh, Minister-Counsellor at Vienna, Head of S.E. Asia Dept., Foreign Office, later Head of

Consular Dept. & M.O.I. Consul General at Stuttgart. Administrative Officer, Graduate Business Centre, The City Univ., 69–70, & since 70, Appeals Sec. for Beds., Bucks. & Herts. Cancer Research Campaign. C.M.G., 59. Liveryman, Skinners Company.

HEPWORTH, Alfred Dalton, T.D., LL.B., b. 6 Dec. 15, eldest s. of the late E. A. Hepworth. SH, 29¹–34². Trinity Hall, Cambridge, M.A., LL.B. ✕ R.A.S.C., 39–46. Major. Solicitor, 46. Notary Public, 49. Provincial Notaries Society. T.D. Past President of Provincial Notaries Society. *St. James's Club, Manchester; Wilmslow G.C.* Brother, R. V. Hepworth. Son, 2461.

HEPWORTH, Robert Vincent, b. 17 Aug. 20, 2nd s. of the late E. A. Hepworth. SH, 34²–39¹. Trinity Hall, Cambridge, M.A. ✕ R.E., 42–46. Major. F.R.I.C.S. Chartered Surveyor. Partner since 50 in Messrs. W. H. Robinson & Co., Chartered Surveyors, Manchester. Also Dairy Farmer. *St. James's Club, Manchester.* Manchester Soc. of Land Agents & Surveyors (Past President). Brother, A. D. Hepworth.

HERBERT, David Mark. SH, 40³–45².*

HERBERT, William Denys Blyth, b. 27 June 15, s. of the late W. H. Herbert (OR St 94). St, 29²–33². Headmaster of Bickley Park School, Bickley, Kent, 40–63. Now Farmer. Son, 2081.

HERON, John. B, 44¹–46¹.*

HETHERINGTON, Thomas Chalmers, T.D., b. 18 Sept. 26, eldest s. of W. M. Hetherington, M.B., LL.B. C & Tu, 40³–44³; Scholar; Levée; Head of House. Scholar of Christ Church, Oxford, M.A. ✕ R.A., 45–48 (Commissioned, 47). R.A. (T.A.) (Palestine, 47–48). Wounded. T.A., 48–67. Major. T.D. Barrister, 52. Legal Sec. to the Law Officers of the Crown from 66. C.B.E.

HETT, Lt.-Cdr. Keir Stewart, R.N., b. 20 Sept. 26, eldest s. of the late A. I. Hett, J.P. (OR C 05) C & W, 40³–44². R.N. College, Dartmouth (1 term). ✕ Lt., 47. In H.M.S. *Scorpion.* Dispatches, 48. In H.M.S. *Amethyst,* Yangtse River, 49. Lt.-Cdr. Uncle, L. K. Hett. Son, Charles Stewart, W, 71³–.

HETT, Leonard Keir, F.R.I.B.A., b. 9 Sept. 87, 2nd s. of the late H. H. Hett.

C, 02¹–05¹. Architectural Assoc. (School Architecture). Travelling Scholarship. ✕ R.E. Signals, 53rd Div. Lt. Invalided. F.R.I.B.A. in Private Practice. Nephew, K. S. Hett.

HEWITT, Major Frederick Eardley Walker. Tu, 26²–30².*

HEWITT, Peart Derek, b. 12 Feb. 27, s. of the late A. E. Hewitt. SF, 40³–45¹; Cap. Exhibitioner of Clare, Cambridge, M.A., LL.B. Solicitor, 53. Sons, 3007, James Neil Terry, SF, 72²–, & Charles Derek Mortimer, SF, 73²–.

HEY, Peter Wilson, b. 28 Dec. 22, 2nd s. of W. H. Hey, F.R.C.S. C, 36³–40². Trinity Hall, Cambridge, M.A., LL.B. ✕ R.N.V.R., 42–46. Lt. Bar, Inner Temple, 48. Brother, T. W. Hey.

HEY, Thomas Wilson, b. 19 July 21, elder s. of W. H. Hey, F.R.C.S. C, 35²–39². King's, Cambridge, M.A. Manchester Univ., M.Sc. Engineer with Metropolitan Vickers Elec. Co. Ltd., 42–47. M.I.E.E., 48. Consulting Engineer since 61. Brother, P. W. Hey.

HEYWORTH, Peter Stuart Arthur, b. 25 Feb. 13, 2nd s. of the late Dr. F. A. F. Heyworth. SF, 26³–30³; H. XI, 29–30. Christ's, Cambridge, M.A. London Hospital. Liverpool United Hospitals, M.R.C.S., L.R.C.P., D.A. ✕ R.A.F.V.R. Sqn. Ldr. Senior Anaesthetist, R.A.F. Hosp., Cosford. Hon. Medical Officer, Princess Elizabeth Hosp., Guernsey and General Practice. *Royal Channel Islands Y.C., Guernsey Y.C.*

HICHENS, Humphrey Bain, M.B.E., b. 26 Mar. 03, s. of the late F. Hichens. M.D. SH, 17¹–21²; S. VIII, 19–20. Trinity, Cambridge, M.A. F.I.Mech.E. ✕ S. African Engineers Corps, 42–45. Capt. M.B.E. Chrmn. of certain S. African Engineering Companies. Otherwise retired. *United Oxford & Cambridge Club; Rand Club, Johannesburg.*

HICKINBOTHAM, The Rev. Canon James Peter, b. 16 May 14, elder s. of the late F. J. L. Hickinbotham, J.P. M, 27³–32²; Scholar. Exhibitioner of Magdalen, Oxford, M.A. Wycliffe Hall. Ordained, Deacon, 37, Priest, 38. Curate of St. Paul, S. Harrow, 40–42. Chaplain of Wycliffe Hall and Acting Chaplain of Wadham, Oxford, 42–45. Vice-Principal of Wycliffe Hall, 45–50. Examining Chaplain to the Bishop of Manchester and to the Bishop of Leicester, 47–50. Prof. of Theology, Univ. Coll. of the Gold Coast, 50. Principal of Wycliffe Hall from 70. Brother, P. F. J. Hickinbotham.

HICKINBOTHAM, Paul Frederick John, Ch.M., F.R.C.S., b. 21 Mar. 17, younger s. of the late F. J. L. Hickinbotham, J.P. M, 30³–34². Birmingham Univ., M.B., Ch.M., F.R.C.S.(Eng.). Consultant Surgeon to Leicester Group of Hospitals. Brother, J. P. Hickinbotham.

HIGGINBOTHAM, Major Ian Ker, b. 23 Nov. 98, 3rd & youngest s. of the late R. K. Higginbotham (OR SH 79). SH, 12¹–15²; G. VIII, 14–15. R.M.C., Sandhurst. ✕ 8th Bn. Black Watch, 16–18. Lt. Wounded twice. Reserve of Officers. Military Attaché accredited to Ecuador, Colombia & Venezuela, 43–45. Sales Executive with Stewart and Lloyds Ltd., 46–63. Retired. *Hove Club, Sussex.*

HIGGINBOTHAM, Richard Henry C.B.E., b. 4 Dec. 02, s. of C. J. Higginbotham. SH, 16³–21¹. Chartered Accountant of Scotland after apprenticeship in Glasgow, 28. Practised in London, 29–39. Joined B.O.T. Food Defence Plans, 39. Established in Civil Service, 46. Retired, 68. C.B.E., 53. *Civil Service Club.*

HIGGINS, John Denis Pearce (see Pearce-Higgins, J. D.).

HIGGS, John Richard Cole, b. 19 Sept. 20, s. of R. D. Higgs, M.C. W, 34²–38². St. John's, Oxford, B.A. ✕ R.A., 40–46. N.C.O. with 1st R.H.A. in Egypt, Libya, Palestine and Italy. Solicitor, 50.

HIGHLEY, Arthur Stansfield. W, 15³–20².*

HIGHTON, Lt.-Col. Ernest Newlands, O.B.E., T.D., b. 8 June 01, 3rd s. of R. E. Highton. Tu, 15¹–19¹. Trinity, Cambridge, M.A. Sheffield Univ., B.Met. Dorman Long, 26–66. ✕ R.A.O.C. Lt.-Col. O.B.E., T.D. Retired, 66.

HIGHTON, Ross Digby Charles. SH, 08²–11².*

HIGNETT, Lt.-Col. John Derrick. K, 14³–17¹.*

HIGSON, Aubrey Wilson, b. 16 Feb. 95, 4th s. of the late J. Higson. SH, 08³–13²; Cap, 12. ✕ Motor Transport, A.S.C.

R.F.C., 14–18. Lt. (Pilot). Bolckow Vaughan & Co. Ltd., Middlesbrough, 19–25. Man., Engineering Dept., National Benzole Co. Ltd., 25–60. Retired. M.I.Mech.E.

HIGSON, Lt.-Col. Frank, O.B.E., b. 25 May 81, s. of the late F. S. Higson. K, 95³–99². Jesus, Cambridge. Gazetted to the Northumberland Fusiliers, 01. ✕ 2nd Bn. Norfolk Regt. Lt.-Col. O.B.E. Dispatches. Retired. *Naval & Military Club.*

HILBERY, George Patrick Moncaster, T.D., b. 16 Mar. 09, s. of the late F. C. Hilbery. SH, 23¹–26³. Trinity Hall, Cambridge, M.A. Solicitor, 34. ✕ 1/6 Bn. East Surrey Regt., France. Evacuated from Dunkirk. R.E. (Burma, India & Ceylon), 39–45. Major. T.D. Legal Adviser to the Belgian Govt., Chrmn., Anglo-Belgian Union. In active practice. Officier de l'Ordre de la Couronne (Belgium). *Garrick Club, Anglo-Belgian Club.* Son, 545.

HILDYARD, Robert Christopher Thoroton, M.C., b. 7 Nov. 12, s. of Brig.-Gen. H. Hildyard, C.M.G., D.S.O. SH, 26²–30³. Trinity, Cambridge, B.A. Business Admin. at L.S.E., Univ. of York, Cert. Ed. Part-time teacher, York College of Further Education. Rural District Councillor, 60–72. Buyer, Harrods Ltd., London. ✕ R.A. Major. M.C. Dispatches. Now Farmer. Chrmn., Friends of York Art Gallery.

HILL, Major Henry Hubert, M.C., b. 15 Sept. 19, s. of B. H. Hill. SH, 32³–37². R.M.C., Sandhurst. Gazetted to the Royal Fusiliers, 39. ✕ Middle East, Greece, Korea. Capt., 46. T/Major, 46. Knight's Cross of George I of Greece (with swords). p.s.c., 48. Major, 52. Retired, 57. Bar, Inner Temple, 60. Practised from 61. M.C. *Special Forces Club, Hurlingham, R.A.C.*

HILL, Ian Cameron Miller, O.B.E., b. 11 July 02, younger s. of R. A. Hill, S.S.C. C, 16¹–19². Trinity, Cambridge, B.A., LL.B. Member of the Stock Exchange, London, 27–70. Partner, McAnally Montgomery & Co. Deputy Dir., General Materials Production, Ministry of Aircraft Production, 40–45. Retired. O.B.E., 46. *Reform Club.*

HILL, Peter Mace, b. 22 Oct. 29, 2nd s. of T. G. Hill (OR M 13). M, 43³–48². St. John's, Oxford, B.A. Management Trainee, Clarks Ltd., Street, Somerset. Now Secretary, Walter & Son, Shoe Retailers, Folkestone and Branches. Brother, T. G. Hill, jnr.

HILL, **Thomas Gray,** b. 14 Dec. 98, eldest s. of the late T. G. Hill. M, 13¹–16¹. Dir. of Thos. G. Hill & Co. Ltd., Textile Manufacturers & Merchants from 25 till about 7 years ago. Retired. *St. James's Club, Manchester; Wilmslow G.C.* Brother, V. G. Hill. Sons, T. G. & P. M. Hill.

HILL, **Thomas Gray, jnr.,** b. 27 Apr. 26, elder s. of T. G. Hill (OR M 13). M, 39³–44²; Scholar; Levée; Head of House. Scholar of St. John's, Oxford, M.A. ✕ Intell. Corps, 44–47. W.O.II. Production Manager, English Calico Ltd. Brother, P. M. Hill.

HILL, **Vivian Gray,** b. 9 Dec. 02, 2nd s. of the late T. G. Hill. M, 17¹–21²; R. VIII, 21. ✕ R.A.F. F/Lt. Textile Manufacturer & Merchant. Retired. Brother, T. G. Hill.

HILLIER, **Harley Hirst Shuttleworth,** b. 2 June 02, 2nd s. of the late S. Hillier, M.D. Tu, 16¹–19¹. Gonville & Caius, Cambridge, B.A. Chartered Accountant, A.C.A., 26. Retired. *Hawks Club.*

HILLS, **George Ker,** b. 5 Feb. 06, 4th s. of the late R. S. Hills (OR B 56). K, 19³–24¹. With Binney & Co., Madras, 26–31, and General Accident Fire & Life Assce. Corp. Ltd., 33–53. ✕ R.A.F., 40–44. Insurance Underwriter. Retired. Brothers, J. & R. S. Hills.

HILLS, **Brig. James,** D.S.O., b. 9 May 03, 2nd s. of the late R. S. Hills (OR B 56). K, 16³–21². R.M.A., Woolwich. Gazetted to R.A., 23. Lt. 25. ✕ Waziristan, 35–37. Dispatches twice, 39–45. D.S.O. Wounded T/Brigadier. p.s.c. Retired Regular Officer. *Army & Navy Club.* Brothers, R. S. & G. K. Hills. Sons, 1529 & 2050.

HILLS, **Robert Savi,** b. 16 Apr. 02, eldest s. of the late R. S. Hills (OR B 56). K, 15³–20³; Cap, 20. ✕ R.A.O.C., 40–53. Capt. Ministry of Defence. Brothers, J. & G. K. Hills.

HILTON, **Sir Derek Percy,** M.B.E., b. 11 Apr. 08, s. of the late P. Hilton. SH, 21³–26¹. Trinity Hall, Cambridge, B.A. Solicitor, 32. In private practice until retired in 70. Pres., Manchester Law Soc., 57. Pres., Law Society, 65–66. ✕ 39–45, Manchester Regt., seconded 41 to Special Operations Executive. Major. Pres., Immigration Appeals Tribunal since 70. M.B.E. Norwegian Liberty Cross, 45. Kt., 66. *St. James's Club, Manchester; Special Forces Club, London.*

HILTON, **Robert Antony.** SH, 17³–20¹.*

HILMAT, **Singhi Kumar Shri.** T, 16³–18².*

HINDLEY, **Charles Edward Hugh.** W, 06¹–10².*

HINDLEY, **Christopher Paton,** M.B., B.Chir. M, 41³–46².*

HINDLEY, **Peter John Howitt,** J, 44³–49³.*

HINDLEY, **William Hugh.** W, 39³–40².*

HINE, **John Richard.** W, 33²–37².*

HINES, **James Wilfred,** b. 31 Mar. 21, s. of H. J. Hines. W, 35¹–39¹. ✕ Suffolk Regt., 40–46. St. John's, Cambridge, M.A. (Agric.). Farmer.

HINGLEY, **Anthony Capper Moore,** C.V.O., b. 28 Nov. 08, eldest s. of Lt.-Col. S. H. Hingley. SF, 21³–27²; Scholar. Scholar of Trinity, Oxford, B.A. Ceylon Civil Service, 31–47. Colonial Admin. Service (Kenya), 47–49. Nyasaland (Chief Establishment Officer), 49–50. Sec. to Governor-General of Ceylon, 50. Establishments Adviser, Seychelles, 65. Hon. Sec., Somerset Trust for Nature Conservation. C.V.O., 54. *East India, Sports & Public Schools Club; Somerset County Club.* Son, 2392.

HINITT, **Harold Wilfrid,** b. 11 Apr. 08, eldest s. of the late F. C. Hinitt. T, 22¹–24³. Articled pupil of City Engineer of Coventry, 25–28. C.Eng., M.I.Mun.E. ✕ R.E., 39–45. Major. Dispatches (Italy). Service with City of Coventry, Hampshire C.C. & Northampton C.C. until retirement, 68, from post of Asst. County Surveyor with latter Authority.

HINTON, **William Patrick Crane,** b. 28 May 31, s. of W. K. Hinton. M, 44³–49²; R. VIII, 48–49; Athletics Cup. St. John's, Cambridge. Yorkshire Hussars, T.A. 2nd Lt. Director, Grocery Company. Son, William James, M, 71³–.

HIPPISLEY, **Claude Francis Baynton.** St, 24²–28².*

HIRSCHFELD, **Major Max Anthony,** R.A. Tu, 43³–48².*

HIRST, **Gerald Scott.** M, 02¹–06².*

HIRST, John Boyce. SH, 21¹–23².*

HIRTZEL, Michael Arthur Frederick, O.B.E. M, 18³–23².*

HITCHINS, Guy Vivian Savile. Tu, 29³–34².*

HOARE, Julian, b. 25 Apr. 05, s. of the late C. N. Hoare. SH, 18²–23². Chartered Accountant. F.C.A. ✕ R.A.O.C., 39. Invalided, 42. Capt. Company Director- ships. Member of Coventry Cathedral Reconstruction Cttee., 47–63. Retired. Son, 952.

HOBBS, John Michael. Tu, 29³–32¹.*

HOBSON, Brian Hugh, b. 15 May 15, 4th s. of R. L. Hobson, C.B. St, 28³–33¹; Tennis VI. Corpus Christi, Cambridge, B.A. Lawn Tennis Half-Blue, 37. ✕ R.E., R.A. & East African Intell. Corps, 39–45. Capt. Kenya's Rep. on the International Centre for Settlement of Investment Dis- putes since 63. Chrmn., Kenya Export Promotion Council since 66. Man. Dir., East African Breweries Ltd. Group since 72. Apptd. International Master at Con- tract Bridge in 71. Represented Kenya in Bridge Olympics in 68 at Deauville. *Muthaiga Country Club, Nairobi; Nairobi Club.* Brother, J. W. Hobson. Sons, 2411 & 2614.

HOBSON, John Waller. St, 22³–27². Sons, 573, 939 & 2557.*

HODDER-WILLIAMS, Lt.-Col. Paul, O.B.E., T.D., b. 29 Jan. 10, s. of the late Very Rev. Dean Garfield Hodder-Williams, LL.D. SH, 23³–28²; XV, 27; XI, 27–28; H. XI, 27–28; Cadet Officer. Gonville & Caius, Cambridge, M.A. Commissioned in H.A.C., 39. ✕ 39–45. Lt.-Col. Command- ing 99th (London Welsh) H.A.A. Regt., R.A., 43–45. M.B.E., 41. O.B.E., 44. Dispatches. T.D. Joined Hodder & Stoughton Ltd., 31. Dir., 36. Chrmn., Matthew Hodder Ltd. since 60. *Hawks Club.* Sons, 803 & 1403.

HODGART, Prof. Matthew John Cald- well, b. 1 Sept. 16, s. of the late Major M. Hodgart, R.E. W, 30³–35¹; Scholar. Scholar of Pembroke, Cambridge, M.A. Jebb Studentship, 38–39. ✕ Argyll & Sutherland Highlanders, 39–45. Major. Dispatches. Asst. Lecturer, Cambridge, 45–49; Lecturer in English, 49–64; Fellow of Pembroke, 49–64; Prof. of English, Sussex Univ., 64–70; Prof. of English, Sir George Williams Univ., Montreal,

Canada from 70 (part-time). Chevalier de la Légion d'Honneur & Croix de Guerre.

HODSON, Christopher, b. 17 June 23, eldest s. of the late J. Hodson. Tu, 37²– 41³. ✕ R.N.V.R. N. Atlantic Convoys & East Indies Fleet, 42–46. Lt. Sudan Plan- tations Syndicate, 46–48. Later tobacco farming in Rhodesia. 12 years dairy farm- ing in U.K. At present, farming at Donny- brook, W. Australia. Donnybrook Rotary & R.S.L. Brother, J. W. Hodson.

HODSON, John Walter. Tu, 39³–44².*

HODSON-MACKENZIE, Kenneth John. M, 22²–26². Sons, 995 & 1349.*

HOGG, Brig. Dudley William Bruce Trower, C.B.E., b. 14 Nov. 03, eldest s. of the late J. M. T. Hogg. Tu, 17³–21²; XI, 21. R.M.C., Sandhurst. Cadet Scholar. Gazetted to Royal Berkshire Regt., 23. C.S. 1st Class Interpreterships, French & German. Instructor, St. Cyr, 32–35. Army Staff College, 38–39. ✕ France & Middle East. Colonel, Royal Berkshire Regt., 56–59. Retired. Modern Langs. Master, Dragon School, Oxford, 60–62, and at Bradfield College, 63–67. C.B.E.

HOLDEN, Antony Charles Shuttle- worth, b. 16 Mar. 08, s. of the late E. C. Holden. M, 22¹–25³. Pembroke, Cam- bridge, B.A. Gazetted to 12th Royal Lancers, 30. ✕ 12th R. Lancers. Major. Wounded. T.D. Alderman, Norfolk C.C. Farmer.

HOLDEN, John Langdale Ainsworth, b. 20 Mar. 26, s. of the late R. A. Holden. SF, 39³–43³. ✕ R.E., 44–48. Sgt. Asst. Chief Engineer, De Havilland Propellers Ltd. Gen. Man., Lakeland Electric Ltd. Man. Dir., Ambleside Engineering Co. Ltd. Now self employed. Proprietor of Caravan Park.

HOLDEN, John Vernon. St, 45³–39³. Son, Jonathan Mark, St, 72¹–.*

HOLE, Charles Samuel Faulkner, A.C.A., b. 21 Jan. 06, eldest s. of the late C. H. Hole. B, 20¹–23². Chartered Ac- countant. Now retired from a life in Industry. Member of Lloyd's. Son, 669.

HOLEY, John Walton, b. 15 Apr. 18, s. of the late A. W. Holey. Sh, 31³–36³; Cap. ✕ Royal Indian Navy Volunteer Reserve. Lt. F.C.A. Sec., Doxford & Sunderland Ltd. *Sunderland Club.*

HOLFORD, Richard Edward, b. 15 May 09, eldest s. of the late C. F. Holford (OR SH 93). SH, 23^1–27^2; XI, 27. Trinity, Oxford. Farmer. Retired.

HOLKAR, Shripat Rao. T, 20^2–23^2.*

HOLLAND, Franklin Denton. W, 41^1–44^3.*

HOLLAND, John Peter, b. 29 Mar. 25, s. of the late W. R. Holland. T, 38^3–43^2; Foundationer; Levée; Head of House. Open Scholar of Queens', Cambridge, M.A. Member of the British Computing Society. Mathematician in Research Dept. of Central Electricity Authority, 51–55. Design Engineer in Computer Dept. of Ferranti Ltd., later I.C.T. Ltd., 55–66. Senior Systems Engineer in Group Dev. Dept. of Tunnel Cement Ltd. since 66.

HOLLAND, Prof. Walter Werner, M.D., B.Sc., b. 5 Mar. 29, s. of the late H. J. Holland. T, 42^3–47^2; Minor Foundationer. St. Thomas's Hospital Medical School, B.Sc., M.R.C.P., M.B., B.S., M.D., F.F.C.M. Professor of Clinical Epidemiology and Social Medicine, St. Thomas's Hospital Medical School. Soc. of Scholars Johns Hopkins Univ., Baltimore.

HOLLICK, Major John Phillips Holioake. Tu, 24^1–28^3.*

HOLLIDAY, Peter, M.R.C.S., L.R.C.P., b. 11 Apr. 19, younger s. of the late H. Holliday. B, 33^1–37^2. Gonville & Caius, Cambridge, M.A. Middlesex Hospital, M.R.C.S., L.R.C.P. Major. R.A.M.C., 47–49. General Practitioner. B.M.A.

HOLLINS, Timothy Allatt. W, 43^3–47^1.*

HOLLOND, Prof. Henry Arthur, D.S.O., O.B.E. B, 98^3–03^2.*

HOLMAN, David McArthur, b. 11 Dec. 28, youngest s. of A. M. Holman. Sh, 42^3–46^2. N/S. R. Horse Guards, 48–49. Chrmn., John Holman & Sons Ltd. *Cavalry & City of London Clubs.*

HOLMAN, Harold Spurway, b. 7 May 98, 3rd s. of the late F. Holman. Tu, 12^3–15^2. ✕ R.N.A.S. & R.A.F., 16–19. Capt. (Pilot). Dispatches. Exhibitioner of King's, Cambridge, M.A. Headmaster, Lime House Prep. School, Cumberland, 31–48. Chrmn., Dulverton R.D.C., 63–73.

HOLMAN, James Frederick, C.B.E., b. 11 Mar. 16, s. of J. L. Holman. SH, 29^3–33^3. Trinity Hall, Cambridge, M.A. ✕ R.A.F. Sqn. Ldr. F.I.Mech.E., F.I.Prod.E., F.B.I.M. Chrmn., International Compressed Air Corp. Ltd. of London. C.B.E. *R.Y.S., R. Cornwall Y.C., Bath Club.*

HOLMAN, Michael Robert. Tu, 35^2–39^2.*

HOLMAN, Peter Paul Dixon. Tu, 32^2–36^3.*

HOLME, Hugh Christopher, b. 20 Oct. 07, s. of the late H. B. Holme, I.C.S. (OR St 92). St, 21^3–26^2; Scholar; Minor Exhibitioner; Head of House. Scholar of Oriel, Oxford, B.A. Reuters, 31–39 (Special Correspondent, Germany, Austria, Abyssinia, Spain; Chief Corres., Balkans). Poet & Translator. Palestine Govt. Ass. Public Information Officer, 39. Public Info. Officer, 40–46. Editor of the "Observer" Foreign News Service, 46–47. Dir. of Information Services, Chatham House. Chief Asst., B.B.C. Third Programme, 48, and Asst. Head of Features, then Drama. Retired, 68. Producer, still active. British Ornithological Union.

HOLMES, Brian, M.B.E., b. 5 Aug. 26, s. of W. Holmes. T, 39^3–44^2; Exhibitioner. Scholar of Queens', Cambridge, B.A. R.N.C., Greenwich. Royal Corps of Naval Constructors (R.C.N.C.). Admiralty, 51–56. Atomic Power Div., English Electric Co. Ltd., 56–65. Permutit Co. Ltd., 65–67. Bovis Holdings Ltd., 67–70. Deputy Chief Executive, Marryat Group Ltd. since 70. M.B.E.

HOLMES, Dennis Patrick, M.B.E., b. 15 Dec. 11, 2nd s. of the late Rev. R. Holmes. Tu, 25^3–30^1. Christ's, Cambridge, B.A. Bachelor Scholar. Solicitor, 37. Partner in Messrs. Francis & Crookenden of London since 47. ✕ 39–45, Adj., 70th Bn. The Rifle Bde. War Course, Staff College, Camberley. G.S.O.2, War Office M.O.5 and G.S.O.2, Joint Planning Staff, War Cabinet Offices. Major. M.B.E. *City University Club, Royal Green Jackets Club.*

HOLMES, John Nicholas, b. 16 Jan. 26, elder s. of G. N. Holmes, J.P. SH, 39^3–44^2; XXII. ✕ R.N., 44–47. A.B. Corpus Christi, Cambridge, B.A.(Ag.). Farmer. Chrmn., Suffolk A.E.C., 66–72. Chrmn., Sugar Beet Research and Education Cttee.

since 70. *Royal Norfolk & Suffolk Y.C.,
Farmers' Club.* Brother, P. G. Holmes.

HOLMES, Peter Geoffrey. SH, 41²–46².*

HOLMES, Peter Robert Campbell. SH, 38¹–42².*

HOLT, Alan Thomas Selborne, M.C., b. 25 May 95, 2nd s. of the late E. Holt. M, 09³–12³. Articled clerk to Solicitor, 13. ✕ 17th Bn. Manchester Regt. Lt. Wounded twice. M.C. P.O.W., 17. Solicitor, 20, of Edwyn Holt & Co. of Manchester. Retired, 65. Hon. Treas., Ancient Monuments Society, 24–49. *Hon. Member of the Manchester Club.* Vice-Pres., The Manchester Regt. Officers' Assoc. and The Ancient Monuments Society. Brother, F. A. Holt.

HOLT, Brian Alfred, b. 23 Sept. 17, eldest s. of the late G. M. W. Holt. Sh, 31³–36²; H. XI, 35–36. ✕ Duke of Wellington's Regt., 39–46. Dispatches. Solicitor, 47. In law, 47–56. Martin Baker Aircraft Co. Ltd., 56–59, in Canada. Ronaldsway Aircraft Co. Ltd., Isle of Man, since 59. Gen. Man. Brother, P. F. Holt.

HOLT, Charles Edwyn Geoffrey. M, 37³–40².*

HOLT, Frederic Appleby, O.B.E. M, 02¹–06¹.*

HOLT, James Alwyn, b. 7 Nov. 04, s. of A. E. Holt. W, 18³–22³. New College, Oxford, B.A. ✕ R.A. Capt. Wounded. Hampshire County Councillor. *Brooks's, R.Y.S.*

HOLT, Peter Fox. Sh, 34³–38³.*

HONE, Oliver Blunden, b. 27 May 17, s. of the late W. P. Hone. B, 31¹–34³. Trinity College, Dublin, B.A. Fellow, Chartered Institute of Transport (London). Joined Imperial Airways, 39 (later B.O.A.C.) as Management Trainee. Served in U.K., Middle East, Iraq, South Africa, Sudan and Ireland. Joined Aer Lingus, 47. Apptd. Traffic Manager in 52 and Customer Standards Manager since 66.

HOOLEY, Charles Purnell. SF, 41²–44³.*

HOOLEY, Robert Patrick, b. 25 Aug. 30, 2nd s. of the late Lt.-Col. R. Hooley. SF, 44³–49¹; Levée; Head of House; R. VIII;

48–49. Exhibitioner of Christ's, Cambridge, M.A. Asst. Master (former Housemaster) at Malvern College. N/S. 49–50. 2nd Lt. R.A. *Victory Club.* Brother, C. P. Hooley.

HOPE, Lt.-Col. Arthur Henry Cecil, O.B.E., T.D., b. 18 July 96, eldest s. of the late J. A. Hope, LL.B., W.S. M, 11¹–14². ✕ 4th Bn. Seaforth Highlanders, 14–16. A.D.C. to G.O.C., 17th Army Corps. Balloon Commander, R.F.C., 16–18. Capt. Dispatches twice. Edinburgh Univ. B.L. Writer to the Signet, 22. Notary Public. Law Agent to the Royal Infirmary of Edinburgh. Session Clerk of St. George's Parish Church, Edinburgh, from 29–70. C.O., 4/5th (Queen's, Edinburgh) Bn. Royal Scots, 37–41. ✕ War Office, Movement Control. O.C. Troopships. O.B.E. (Mil.), T.D. (Four Bars). *New Club, Edinburgh.* Brother, J. L. Hope. Sons, 744 & 2152.

HOPE, John Charles. K, 11³–15¹.*

HOPE, James Louis, LL.B., T.D. b. 31 Jan. 06, 3rd s. of the late J. A. Hope, LL.B., W.S. M, 19³–24². Edinburgh Univ., M.A., LL.B. Writer to the Signet, 30. Partner in Messrs. Gillespie & Paterson, W.S., and Messrs. Hope, Todd & Kirk, W.S. Lt.-Col. The Royal Scots (T.A.). ✕ Served with the Royal Scots, H.L.I. & R.W.A.F.F., 39–45. T.D. Scottish Amateur Fencing Union (Pres., 49–58). *New Club, Edinburgh.* Brother, A. H. C. Hope. Sons, 995 & 1452.

HOPE, Owen Morley. St, 01²–02³.*

HOPE-MURRAY, Major Henry Cecil. W, 14¹–15².*

HOPE SIMPSON, James Russell, b. 17 Aug. 01, younger s. of Sir James Hope Simpson. C, 15³–20²; Scholar; Levée; Head of House. Scholar of Queen's, Oxford, M.A. Housemaster, School House, Shrewsbury School. Retired, 65. Lakeland Horticultural Society (Council).

HOPKIRK, Kenneth Dewar, M.R.C.S., L.R.C.P., b. 13 Aug. 20, eldest s. of the late K. R. Hopkirk. T, 33³–39²; Levée; Head of House; Warwickshire County Major Exhibition. Major Scholar of Emmanuel, Cambridge, M.A. University College Hospital, London, L.R.C.P., M.R.C.S. Univ. of Melbourne (Postgraduate) D.P.M. Consultant Children's Psychiatrist, Leicester. A.N.Z. Coll. of Psychiatrists. Royal Coll. of Psychiatrists. I.S.T.D. Brother, 815.

HORNBY, Edward Windham, J.P., b. 15 Apr. 95, 4th s. of the late Archdeacon P. J. Hornby (OR K 66). W, 09^3–13^1; R. VIII, 13. ✕ Lancashire Hussars. Capt. Farming, 22–53.

HORNE, Ian Lionel Spencer (now Inigo-Jones, I. L. S.). B, 45^2–49^3.*

HORTON, Klaus George (formerly Hornstein, K. G.). M, 40^3–42^2.*

HORTON, Kevan William, b. 16 Sept. 12, s. of W. S. Horton. B, 27^1–30^3. Accountant, 36. F.C.A., 44. Partner, P. & J. Kevan, Chartered Accountants, Bolton, 37–68. Dir., Horton's Estate Ltd., Birmingham. *Royal Windermere Y.C.* (Past Commodore). *R. Birkdale G.C.*

HORTON, Robert George Chandler, b. 18 May 14, s. of the late D'A. R. G. Horton. M, 28^3–31^3. Chartered Accountant, 38. F.C.A. R.A. (T.A.), 37. ✕ R.A. Lt.-Col. Senior Partner, Williams Stoker & Co., Chartered Accountants. Warden, Worshipful Company of Gold & Silver Wyre Drawers. *Oriental Club.*

HOSKYNS, David Charles Benedict. SH, 44^1–47^3.*

HOSKYNS, The Rev. John Algernon Peyton, b. 11 May 20, s. of O. P. L. Hoskyns. SH, 34^1–38^2; XV, 37–38. Pembroke, Cambridge, M.A. Westcott House. ✕ Major, Royal Signals, 40–46, N. Africa, N.W. France. Ordained Deacon, 49; Priest, 50. Asst. Curate, Eastleigh Parish Church, 49–52. Holy Trinity, Brompton, 52–54. Vicar of Hartley Wintney with Elvetham, 54–62. Rector of Worplesdon since 62. Parish Priest licensed to the Archdeacon of Hereford working in S. Herefordshire.

HOTTOT, Alfred Louis Ernest Hubert, b. 25 Aug. 13, s. of the late R. Hottot. B, 27^1–32^2. Exeter, Oxford, M.A., B.Litt. Head of Modern Langs. Dept., The Woodlands Comprehensive School, Coventry. E.S.U.

HOUGHTON-BROWN, Geoffrey, b. 12 Apr. 03, eldest s. of the late P. Houghton-Brown, LL.D. Tu, 17^2–20^2. Studied painting in Paris and at Slade School, London. Decorative painting, decoration and restoration of many houses in England, also in Jamaica and Canary Islands & France. Active defence of the Tridentine site of the Mass during the last seven years. *Travellers'*. Georgian Society.

HOULBROOK, Group Capt. William Leigh, O.B.E. C, 22^3–25^3.*

HOUSE, Harry Wilfred, D.S.O., M.C., b. 26 Sept. 95, 2nd s. of H. H. House. K, 09^3–14^2; Scholar; Cap, 12; Head of House. Scholar of Queen's, Oxford. ✕ 7th Bn. East Lancashire Regt. 6th Bn. Wiltshire Regt. Staff Capt. 58th Infantry Bde. Major. Wounded. Italian Silver Medal. M.C., D.S.O. Dispatches. Queen's, Oxford. Sorbonne, Paris. Fellow of Queen's, 23. Laming Resident Fellow, 24–41. Junior Proctor, 31–32. ✕ Ox. & Bucks. L.I. & War Office, 39–41. Appointed Master of Wellington College, 41–56. Supernumerary Fellow, Queen's Coll. from 53. *Vincent's Club.*

HOUSLEY, John. B, 21^2–24^3.*

HOVENDEN, Anthony Lennox, b. 24 Oct. 31, 2nd s. of Capt. R. C. Hovenden, R.N. Sh, 45^2–50^2; Scholar. N/S. R. Corps of Signals, 51. 2nd Lt. Pembroke, Cambridge, M.A., M.B., B.Chir., M.R.C.S., L.R.C.P., D.A., D.M.R.T., F.F.A.R.C.S.(Eng.), F.F.R. Consultant Radiotherapist, Newcastle Regional Hospital Board. Brother, P. L. Hovenden.

HOVENDEN, Patrick Lennox. Sh, 42^1–46^2.*

HOWARD, Major Ewen Storrs, M.B.E., b. 16 Apr. 03, 2nd s. of the late J. Howard. SH, 17^1–21^3. Clare, Cambridge, B.A. ✕ R.E. (seconded from S. African Engineers Corps). M.B.E. Dispatches twice. Chrmn., H. H. Robertson (Africa) Pty. Ltd. *Rand Club, Johannesburg; City Club, Cape Town; Royal Cape G.C.*

HOWARD, John James, b. 9 Mar. 23, 2nd s. of the late Sir H. F. Howard, K.C.I.E., C.S.I. SH, 36^3–41^2. Trinity Hall, Cambridge, M.A. ✕ R.A.F.V.R., 42–46. Pilot. F/Lt. F.C.I.I., Royal Insurance Co. from 47. Dir. & Gen. Man. since 70. *St. George's Hill G.C.* Son, 2488.

HOWARD, John Liddon. M, 16^2–20^1.*

HOWARD, Michael Henry Samuel, b. 26 May 26, s. of the late A. E. S. Howard. Tu, 40^2–44^2; Jex-Blake Leaving Exhibition; Cadet Officer; H. XI. Mod. Langs. Exhibition to Peterhouse, Cambridge, M.A. ✕ Rifle Brigade, 45–47. Capt. W. R. Grace & Co., New York, London, Guatemala & El Salvador, 50–63. Project Finance Man., Lloyds & Bolsa International Bank Ltd. and Balfour Williamson & Co. Ltd.,

63–73. *C.U. Wanderers.* Sons, Rohan Michael, Tu, 68²–72³, and Aubyn Edward, Tu, 71³–.

HOWARD, Robin Somervell. C, 38³–41².*

HOWARD, Roger Alexander. St, 33³–36³.*

HOWARD-JONES, John. K, 45²–49³.*

HOWARTH, Godfrey David Greenwood. M, 43²–47².*

HOWARTH, Patrick John Fielding, b. 25 Apr. 16, 2nd s. of the late F. F. Howarth. K, 29³–33³; Levée. Scholar of St. John's, Oxford, M.A. ✕ Special Forces, 40–45. Major. Author & Civil Servant. Sometime Editor of "Baltic and Scandinavian Countries"; Foreign Correspondent in Danzig & Gdynia; Sub-Editor in B.B.C. monitoring service. First Sec., British Embassy, Warsaw and official in Min. of Town & Country Planning. Official of R.N.L.I. Company Dir. Author of "The Year is 1851", "Special Operations", many other books and "Play up and Play the Game" to be published in 74. Brother, T. E. B. Howarth.

HOWARTH, Thomas Edward Brodie, M.C., b. 21 Oct. 14, eldest s. of the late F. F. Howarth. K, 28³–32³. Exhibitioner of Clare, Cambridge (Scholar). Research student, 37. M.A. ✕ King's (Liverpool) Regt., 39–45. Bde. Major, 207 Inf. Bde. M.C. Personal Liaison Officer to Field-Marshal Lord Montgomery. Asst. Master, Winchester College, 38–39 & 46–48. Headmaster, King Edward's School, Birmingham, 48–52. Second Master, Winchester College, 52–62. High Master, St. Paul's School, 62–73. Senior Tutor, Magdalene College, Cambridge since 73. Trustee, Imperial War Museum since 64. Chrmn., Headmasters' Conference, 69. *Savile, Athenæum.* Brother, P. J. F. Howarth. Son, 1589.

HOWCROFT, John Burdett, b. 15 Dec. 31, s. of Lt.-Col. G. B. Howcroft. K, 45³–50²; Sw. VIII, 50. Manchester Univ., Dip. Arch. Univ. Squash Team, 52–53 (Capt.). Architect, A. J. Howcroft & Son. A.R.I.B.A.

HOWE, Arthur, O.B.E., LL.D., b. 19 July 21, 2nd s. of the late Rev. Dr. A. Howe. C, 38³–39²; E.S.U. Scholar; XV, 38; Sw. VI, 39. Yale Univ., B.A. Oxford Univ. Graduate study, 50–51. ✕ Major,

C.O., 567 (A.F.S.) Amb. Car Co., R.A.S.C., 42–44 (N. Africa & Italy). Teacher, The Hotchkiss School, Conn., 45–50. Dean of Admissions & Student Appts., Yale Univ., 51–64. Pres., American Field Service International Scholarships, 64–72. Dir., Riegel Textile Corp., R.D.C. Inc. Educational Consultant. Chrmn., Board of Trustees, Hampton Institute. O.B.E., 44. LL.D., 58. *New Haven Lawn Club.* The Century Assoc. (N.Y.C.). Son, 3039.

HOWELL, Owen Bulmer. B, 96¹–99².*

HOWES, Jack Foster Wyndham, F.R.G.S., b. 19 June 18, s. of the late S. Howes. C, 32²–36². St. Catharine's, Cambridge, M.A. T.Eng.(C.E.I.). M.I.M.I., F.R.G.S. on Court of Assistants, Wor. Company of Coachmakers and Coach Harness Makers of London. Chrmn. & Jt. Man. Dir., Howes & Sons Ltd., Motor Engineers, Norwich. Chrmn., Carley Motors Ltd., Fakenham, Norfolk. Dir., Woodbridge Garages (Suffolk) Ltd. *R.A.C., City Livery Club,* 20 *Ghost Club.*

HOWKINS, Col. Walter Ashby, T.D., b. 9 Aug. 10, s. of W. G. Howkins. T, 23³–28². College of Estate Management. R.I.C.S. Special Prizeman, 30. Own practice, St. James's St., 32–39. ✕ 31–46, Northamptonshire Yeomanry. Military Asst. Sec., War Cabinet Offices, 41. British Joint Staff Mission, Washington, D.C., 43. New York, 48. Partner, firm of Consulting Engineers, 54. Colonel. T.D. U.S. Legion of Honor. *Bath Club, M.C.C.* Sons, 1383 & 1830.

HOWORTH, John Henry Ellicott, O.B.E., b. 5 June 10, s. of the late Sir R. B. Howorth, K.C.M.G., K.C.V.O., C.B. K, 23³–28³; Levée; Cap. New College, Oxford, B.A. Bar, Inner Temple, 33. ✕ R.A., 38–40. 2nd Lt. Joined the Fire Offices Cttee. as Asst. Sec., 34. Sec., 51. Dep. Chrmn., 59. Chrmn., 63–72. Chrmn., British Insurers European Cttee., 68–72. O.B.E., 71. *Oriental Club.* Chartered Insurance Inst. Son, 688.

HOY, The Rev. Trevor Austin, b. 17 Dec. 21, twin s. of A. Y. Hoy. SH, 35³–39³. Williams College, Williamstown, Mass., B.A. ✕ Air Corps U.S. Army Navigator, Rome-Arno service, Army Commendation Ribbon. Capt. Episcopal Theol. School, Cambridge, Mass. Master of Divinity. Ordained, 50. Chaplain, Ohio State Univ., 50–54. Rector, St. Michael's, Ligonier, Pa., 54–58. Dir. of Education and Program, Dio. of California, 59–65. Exec.

Dir., Berkeley Center for Herman Interaction since 66. Hon. Canon of Grace Cathedral, San Francisco. *San Francisco Univ. Club.*

HOYSTED, Brig. Desmond St. John, C.B.E., b. 10 Feb. 06, eldest s. of the late Col. D. M. F. Hoysted, C.B.E., D.S.O. (OR M 89). M, 19^3–24^2. R.M.A., Woolwich. Gazetted to Royal Corps of Signals, 26. Seconded Indian Signal Corps, 32–38. p.s.c., 39. ✕ R. Signals Staff & Regimental Appts., 39–58, including France & Germany, 44–45. G.H.Q., India, 46–47. Middle East, 50–52. Brig., 52. A.M.I.E., 59. Chief Training Officer, Essex County Civil Defence H.Q., 59–69. Resigned, 69. C.B.E. (Mil.), 56. Son, 1139.

HUDSON, Major Francis Edward, b. 10 June 12, eldest s. of the late E. Hudson. C, 26^1–29^2. Engineering. ✕ Yorkshire Hussars, 39–45. Major. T.A. Dir., United Newspapers Ltd. Chrmn., Doncaster Newspapers Ltd. and Bradford Power Systems Ltd. Dep. Chrmn., Yorkshire Post Newspapers Ltd. Brother, M. Hudson.

HUDSON, Havelock Henry Trevor, b. 4 Jan. 19, elder s. of the late S. E. Hudson. SF, 32^3–37^2; Holder of Bigside Bags; R. VIII, 36–37. Middlesex Hospital, 36–37. Merchant Service, 37–38. ✕ R. Hampshire Regt., 39–42. Parachute Regt., 42–44. Capt. A.C.I.I. Lloyd's underwriter from 46. Member of Lloyd's, 52. Dep. Chrmn., Lloyd's, 68, 71 & 73. Cttee., Lloyd's, 65–68, 70–73. Cttee., Lloyd's Underwriters Assn. since 63. Exec. Board, Lloyd's Register of Shipping since 69. Gen. Cttee. since 66. *Boodle's, R.A.C.*

HUDSON, Malcolm, b. 12 July 13, 2nd s. of the late E. Hudson. C, 27^3–30^2. ✕ R.A.F. F.O., 39–45. Engineering & Farming now retired (ill-health). Brother, F. E. Hudson.

HUDSON, Richard Guy Ormonde, D.S.C. SH, 34^2–38^3.*

HUGHES, Cyril Johnston Cresswell, b. 16 Mar. 08, s. of Major F. C. Hughes, T.D., D.L. K, 22^1–26^1. Sidney Sussex, Cambridge, B.A. ✕ R.A.F. Company Director, retired. Son, 988.

HUGHES, David Anthony, b. 22 Aug. 25, 2nd s. of the late T. G. Hughes (OR K 00). SF, 39^2–43^1; Paddison Art Prize. ✕ R.N.V.R. S/Lt., 43–45. Trinity, Cambridge, M.A., Asst. Headmaster, Rose

Hill School, 50–52. Asst. Master, Abberley Hall, Worcs., 52–56. Housemaster, Stamford School, Lincs., since 56. *C.U. Wanderers H.C.* Asst. Member, S.A.T.I.P.S.

HUGHES, Edward Godfrey. K, 31^3–35^2.*

HUGHES, John. M, 10^3–14^2.*

HUGHES, Major John Herbert Bristow, b. 14 Aug. 20, eldest s. of E. H. B. Hughes. T, 34^2–38^3; Exhibitioner. Gazetted to Royal Marines, 38. ✕ R.M. Wounded. Combined Ops. Staff Course. Higher interpreter (French), R.N. Retired as Major. Agronomist, qualified in Honduras. Joined United Fruit Co. (Boston); Vice-Pres. in Europe. Now Dir., Central & South African Operations. I.M.T. (Geneva) S.A. British West India Cttee. *United Hunts Club.* Brother, T. B. Hughes.

HUGHES, John Michael Duckworth, b. 10 Jan. 32, s. of the late H. G. Hughes. SF, 45^3–50^2. Scholar of Oriel, Oxford, M.A. F.R.I.C. N/S. 54–56. Guinness (Ireland, Nigeria, U.K.) since 57.

HUGHES, Michael Tancred. Sh, 42^3–46^2.*

HUGHES, Thomas Bartley, b. 23 Nov. 21, 2nd s. of E. H. B. Hughes. T, 35^2–39^2. Liverpool Univ. Sidney Sussex, Cambridge, M.A. C.Eng., M.I.Mech.E., M.I.E.E. ✕ R.A.F., 40–45. Pilot. Wounded. P.O.W. A.E.I. Ltd., Pilkington Brothers Ltd., Ronson Products Ltd. *United Service & Royal Aero Club.* Brother, J. H. B. Hughes.

HUGHES-D'AETH, Narbrough Michael. St, 44^3–49^3.*

HUGH-JONES, Michael Llewelyn Herbert, b. 14 July 28, eldest s. of the late L. A. Hugh-Jones (OR SH 01). SH, 41^3–46^2. Scholar. Scholar of Jesus, Oxford, M.A. N/S. R.A.F., 48–51. Schoolmaster, 51–64. County Council Town Planner, 64–73. Hon. Sec., Oxford Branch, United Nations Assoc. Hon. Sec., Dorchester on Thames Society. Editor & Publisher of "Dorchester Times" monthly.

HULL, Adin, M.B.E. B, 22^3–26^2.*

HULL, Wing-Cdr. David Hugill, M.R.C.P., b. 21 Aug. 31, 2nd s. of the late T. E. O. Hull. C, 45^2–50^2. Exhibitioner of Trinity Hall, Cambridge, M.A., M.B., B.Chir. Cressingham Prize, 51. St.

Thomas's Hospital, M.R.C.P. Consultant in Medicine, R.A.F. Wing-Cdr. Consultant Physician in charge of Medical Div., R.A.F. Hospital, Cosford. *R.A.F. Club.* Brother, J. G. Hull.

HULL, John Grove, b. 21 Aug. 31, eldest s. of the late T. E. O. Hull. C, 45²–50¹; Scholar; R. VIII, 50. Scholar of King's, Cambridge, M.A., LL.B. Bar, Middle Temple, in private practice. Brother, D. H. Hull.

HUMBERT, Gordon Johnston, b. 3 Nov. 82, eldest s. of the late E. Humbert. C, 96³–99². Trained with the L.M.S. Railway. ✕ Railway Operating Div., R.E.Capt. Dispatches. Railway Official, Man. of Traffic & Transportation in Argentine & Cuba. Retired, 47.

HUMBLE, The Rev. Joseph Francis, b. 29 Nov. 24, s. of J. H. M. Humble. Tu, 38³–43². ✕ R.N.V.R., 43–46. Lt. University College, Oxford, M.A. Cuddesden College. Ordained, Deacon, 56; Priest, 57. Curate of Rugby, 56–61. Vicar of Thurcroft, 61–66. Vicar of Lillington, Leamington Spa, since 66.

HUME-GORE, Lt.-Col. Gavin Robert Vernon, M.C. Tu, 02³–06¹.*

HUMPHRY, Alexander Murchison, M.D., b. 17 Sept. 88, 3rd s. of the late A. P. Humphry (or SH 63). W, 02³–07²; S. VIII, 04–07 (Capt., 06, 07). Won Fry Competition, Bisley, with record score, 05. Team won Ashburton Shield, 07. Trinity, Cambridge. Univ. Shooting VIII, 08–10 (Capt.). Winner, St. George's Vase & Gold Cross, Bisley, 10. Shot for England, 09. St. Bart's Hospital, M.R.C.S., L.R.C.P. ✕ R.A.M.C., 15–18. Major. Norfolk War Hospital. Dispatches. Retired.

HUNKIN, The Rev. Oliver John Wellington, b. 7 Apr. 16, eldest s. of the late Rt. Rev. J. W. Hunkin, Bishop of Truro. T, 29³–34³; Levée; Head of House. Gonville & Caius, Cambridge. Wycliffe Hall, Oxford. Asst. Master, Eton College. Staff Writer, Ealing Studios. Producer, B.B.C. Head of Religious Programmes, B.B.C. Television.

HUNT, Roland Charles Colin, C.M.G., b. 19 Mar. 16, 3rd s. of the late C. B. Hunt. C, 29³–34²; Scholar; Levée; Head of House; Jex-Blake Prizeman; Exhibitioner. Scholar of Queen's, Oxford, B.A. Indian Civil Service, 39–47. In South India. Joined Commonwealth Relations Office,

48. Served Pakistan & S. Africa. Dep. High Commissioner in Malaya. High Commissioner, Uganda, 65–67. C.M.G., 65. Trinidad & Tobago since 70. *United Oxford & Cambridge Club.*

HUNTER, Sqn. Ldr. Basil Victor, b. 19 Dec. 21, 2nd s. of the late T. H. V. Hunter (or T 01). W, 35³–40¹; R. VIII, 39–40; Crick Winner, 39. Gazetted to R.A.F., 41. ✕ Bomber Command Pilot, 41–42. Commendation. P.O.W., Germany, 42–45. Dispatches twice. Resigned, 58, as Sqn. Ldr. Commissioned in T.A. (Special Air Service), 59–72. T.D. Now, Civil Airline Pilot, Monarch Airlines. Lloyd's Underwriter, 71. *Special Forces Club.* Brother, I. W. Hunter.

HUNTER, David Ian, b. 13 Nov. 29, 2nd s. of the late J. Hunter. M, 43³–47³. Member of the Council of the Stock Exchange. Dir., The Halifax Building Society. Stockbroker. *Manchester Tennis & Racket Club; St. James's Club, Manchester.*

HUNTER, Fred. T, 09³–14¹.*

HUNTER, Ian Wilfred, b. 5 Sept. 25, 3rd s. of the late T. H. V. Hunter (or T 01). W, 39³–43¹; R. VIII, 43. ✕ R.A.F.V.R., 43–47. F/Sgt. (Air Gunner). Company Dir. in the retail side of the Motor Trade. Brother, B. V. Hunter.

HUNTER, The Hon. Lord (Hunter, John Oswald Mair), b. 21 Feb. 13, s. of J. M. Hunter, K.C. Tu, 26³–31². New College, Oxford, B.A., LL.B.(Edin.). Bar, Inner Temple, 37. Member, Faculty of Advocates, 37. Q.C. (Scotland), 51. Home Advocate-Depute, 55–57. Sheriff of Ayr & Bute, 57–61. Senator of H.M. College of Justice in Scotland since 61. Chrmn., Scottish Law Commission since 71. Dep. Chrmn., Boundary Commission for Scotland since 71. Chrmn., Scottish Council on Crime since 72. V.R.D. *New Club, Edinburgh.*

HUNTER, Michael James, M.B., B.Chir., b. 1 Feb. 25, s. of the late W. J. H. Hunter. SH, 38³–43². St. John's, Cambridge, M.A., M.B., B.Chir. Guy's Hospital, D.(Obst.).R.C.O.G. N/S. Capt. R.A.M.C. Japan & Korea, 51–53. General Medical Practitioner, Jersey, C.I. Sons, Simon James, SH, 69²– & Hugh Robin, SH, 73¹–.

HUNTER, Samuel Arthur. T, 03²–06³.*

HUNTER-JONES, Lt.-Col. Hugh Edward (formerly Jones, H. E. H.), M.C., T.D., D.L., b. 20 July 15, eldest s. of the late S. Hunter Jones (OR St 89). St, 29¹–33³. Corpus Christi, Cambridge, M.A. A.D.C. to the Queen, 66–70. D.L., Essex, since 61. J.P. since 65. Yeomanry, T.A., 38. ✕ Essex Yeomanry, 39–46. M.C. Dispatches. Staff College, 43. Retired Acting Brig. T.D. Bass Charrington, Dir. of Licensed Houses. Court of the Merchant Taylors Company. *Cavalry Club.* Brother, M. S. Hunter-Jones. Son, Nicholas Richard, St, 67³–71³.

HUNTER-JONES, Michael Stanley, b. 30 July 16, 2nd s. of the late S. Hunter-Jones. St, 30¹–35²; Scholar; Levée;.Head of House; Leaving Exhibition. Scholar of Exeter, Oxford, M.A. ✕ Essex Regt. & Staff, 39–45. Major. Solicitor, 48. Senior Partner, Blyth Dutton Robins Hay of London. *Hurlingham. M.C.C., Essex Hunt Club.* Brother, H. E. Hunter-Jones.

HUNTING, Charles Patrick Maule, b. 16 Dec. 10, eldest s. of Sir P. L. Hunting. SF, 24³–29²; XI, 27–29 (Capt.). Trinity, Cambridge, B.A. A.C.A., 36. ✕ R.A.O.C., 40–46. R. Sussex Regt. Dispatches. Belgian Croix de Guerre with Palms. Chevalier of the Order of Leopold II with Palms. Served in France, Belgium & Western Desert. p.s.c. Major. T.D. Joined Hunting Group of Companies, 37. Chrmn. since 60. *Bath Club, M.C.C., R. Ashdown Forest G.C.* Court of The Ironmongers Company. Sons, 1904 & 2393.

HUNTSMAN, John Harold, b. 19 Nov. 23, 2nd s. of the late H. Huntsman. K, 37²–41³. ✕ Commissioned in the Rifle Brigade, 42. Dispatches. Wounded. American Silver Star. F.C.A. Dir. & Investment Man., Provincial Insurance Co. Ltd. Brother, P. W. Huntsman.

HUNTSMAN, Peter William, b. 29 May 18, eldest s. of the late H. Huntsman. K, 31³–36². ✕ R.A. Solicitor, 47. M.I.M.C. Private practice in Basildon, Essex. Royal Commonwealth Society. Brother, J. H. Huntsman.

HURRELL, Geoffrey Taylor, O.B.E., b. 12 Mar. 00, elder s. of the late A. Hurrell (OR B 74). B, 14¹–17³. R.M.C., Sandhurst. ✕ 17th Lancers. 2nd Lt. Lt., 20. ✕ 17th/21st Lancers, 39–45. Colonel, O.B.E., retired. Lord Lieutenant, Cambridgeshire & Isle of Ely. K. St. J. *Cavalry Club.*

HURST, Edward Graham. Sh, 40³–45².*

HURST, Peter Graham. Sh, 43²–47³.*

HUSSEY, Marmaduke James, b. 29 Aug. 23, eldest s. of the late E. R. J. Hussey, C.M.G. C & Tu, 37¹–41³; Levée; XV, 40–41 (Capt.); XI, 40–41. Scholar of Trinity, Oxford, M.A. Played Rugby Football & Cricket for Univ., 42. ✕ Grenadier Guards. Wounded. P.O.W., 44. Associated Newspapers, 47–70. Man. Dir. & Chief Executive of Times Newspapers Ltd. and Thomson Organisation Board. *Brooks's.*

HUTCHINGS, Bryan John. T, 43³–47².*

HUTCHINSON, Frederick Heap, C.I.E., b. 16 Oct. 92, s. of the late W. H. H. Hutchinson. B, 06²–07³. Oundle School, 08–10. City & Guilds College, London Univ., A.C.G.I., B.Sc. P.W.D. India, Irrigation Branch, 14. ✕ F.A.R.O. Temp. Capt. O.C., 120th Labour Corps. Executive Engineer, 10th Saida Div., Lucknow.

HUTCHINSON, John Charles Duncan, b. 3 June 09, s. of the late H. N. Hutchinson. SH, 23¹–28¹; XV, 26–27. Clare, Cambridge, M.A. and A.R.C. Studentship in Animal Health, 34–36. Held appointments with M.R.C., A.R.C. and Cambridge Univ. Research Scientist,C.S.I.R.O. Div. of Animal Physiology. Physics Soc. Australian Physical & Pharmaceutical Soc.

HUTCHINSON, Ralph Maurice James, b. 25 Apr. 30. s. of the late G. G. S. Hutchinson (OR B 16). C, 46²–48². Magdalene, Cambridge, M.A. Barrister & Solicitor, British Columbia. Partner, Heath, Hutchinson & Taylor of Nanaimo. Law Soc. of B.C., Canadian Bar Assoc., Inner Temple. *Alpine Club of Canada.*

HUTCHINSON, Thomas Heap. SF, 41³–45².*

HUTCHISON, William Henry Oliphant, b. 25 Sept. 27, elder s. of R. G. O. Hutchison. SH, 41³–45². Trinity Hall, Cambridge, B.A. ✕ 1st The R. Dragoons, 48–50. 2nd Lt. Dir., Robert Hutchison & Co. Ltd., Kirkcaldy, Fife. T.D. J.P. *R. & A. Golf Club, Cavalry Club, Leander.*

HUXLEY, Michael Heathorn, b. 9 Aug. 99, 2nd s. of the late H. Huxley, F.R.C.S. St, 13²–16²; Scholar; Minor Exhibitioner. Trinity, Cambridge. ✕ Grenadier Guards.

2nd Lt. Diplomatic Service from 22. Served at Teheran, Washington and in the F.O. 2nd Sec., 25. 1st Sec., 34. Resigned, 34, in order to launch and edit "The Geographical Magazine". Resigned editorship, 59. ⚔ Recalled to F.O., 39–45. *National Liberal Club.*

HYDE, Christopher Grimshaw. W, 44¹–48².*

HYDE, John William, T.D., b. 9 Nov. 09, 2nd s. of J. E. Hyde. W, 23²–27². Exeter, Oxford. Fellow, Inst. of Chartered Shipbrokers. ⚔ H.A.C., att. R.A. Major.

T.D. Served Norway, Holland & Germany. Joined J. E. Hyde & Co., Shipbrokers and Agents, 29. Partner, 35. Senior Partner, 50 and 66–71. Chrmn. & Man. Dir., J. E. Hyde & Co. Ltd., 54–66. *R. Thames Y.C.* Brother, R. E. Hyde.

HYDE, Robert Evelyn, b. 24 May 21, 3rd s. of J. E. Hyde. W, 35¹–38³. Exeter, Oxford, M.A. ⚔ Coldstream Guards, 41–46. Capt. Wounded. Bar, Inner Temple, 47. Director, Trinder, Anderson & Co. Ltd., Shipowners & Shipbrokers. Member, Baltic Mercantile & Shipping Exchange. *R. Thames Y.C.* Brother, J. W. Hyde.

I

IGGLESDEN, Michael Stewart, b. 31 Aug. 23, s. of late C. H. Igglesden. SH, 37²–41². ⚔ R.A.F.V.R., 41–46. Corpus Christi, Cambridge. R.A.F. Short Course. B.A., 49; C.Eng.; A.F.R.Ae.S. Civil Service (Scientific) from 49. Dept. of Trade & Industry (Research Requirements Div.). Son, Charles Edwin, SH, 68²–.

ILES, Edward Charles, b. 12 Oct. 99, s. of C. H. Iles. SH, 13³–17³. ⚔ R.F.C. Cadet, 18. R.A.F. 2nd Lt. Engineer. Retired.

INGE, Charles Hamilton, b. 31 Oct. 09, younger s. of late Rev. C. C. Inge. M, 23³–28². Oriel, Oxford. Fellow of the Society of Antiquaries. Wellcome Marston Archæological Expedition to the Near East, 32–40. Political Officer, Aden Protectorate, 40–62.

INGLIS, Lt.-Col. Ernest John D'Oyly. 13³–17². Son, 42.*

INGLIS, Robert Alexander, LL.B. C, 31³–33³.*

INGLIS, Robert John Evelyn, b. 5 Apr. 19, 2nd s. of late W. W. Inglis. W, 32³–37²; XI, 36–37; Cap; Sw. VIII, 35. R.M.A., Woolwich. Clare, Cambridge, B.A. ⚔ R.E., 39–45. Member, Institute of Management Consultants. Self-employed. *Royal Automobile Club, Itchenor Sailing Club.* Brother, W. M. Inglis.

INGLIS, Brig. William Murray, C.B.E., b. 20 Jan. 15, eldest s. of late W. W. Inglis. W, 28³–33²; Levée; Head of House; XV, 31–32 (Capt., 33); Sw. VI, 30–32 (Capt., 33); Tom Hughes Prize. R.M.A., Woolwich. Sword of Honour, 34. XV, 33–34

(Capt.). Clare, Cambridge, B.A. University XV, 35–36. School of Military Engineering, Chatham, 35–37. Scotland XV, 37–38. Commissioned into Royal Engineers, 35. p.s.c. Military Attaché, Rome, 61–64. Commandant, Royal School of Military Engineering, 67–70. Retired as Brigadier. C.B.E. (Mil.), 69. Brother, R. J. E. Inglis. Sons, 1334 & 1781.

INGRAM, John Rutherford, T.D., b. 24 Feb. 16, eldest s. of late C. W. Ingram. C, 29³–32². ⚔ R.A. Major. 657 Air Observation Post Squadron. T.D. F.R.I.C.S. Partner of Bell-Ingram, Chartered Surveyors, Estate Agents & Valuers, Edinburgh, Perth, Monkton & Irvine. *New Club, Edinburgh.* Edinburgh Merchant Company. Brothers, P. A. & W. D. M. Ingram.

INGRAM, Paul Alexander, b. 19 June 21, 2nd s. of late C. W. Ingram. C, 34³–38². ⚔ R.A., West Africa, India & Burma, 39–45. F.R.I.C.S. Sporting Consultant to Secretary of State for Scotland. Partner in C. W. Ingram & Sons, Chartered Surveyors, 51–71. Bell-Ingram & Co., Edinburgh, from 71. *New Club, Edinburgh.* Brothers, J. R. & W. D. M. Ingram.

INGRAM, Walter David Markham. St, 45¹–48².*

INIGO-JONES, Ian Lionel Spencer (formerly Horne, I. L. S.). B, 45²–49³.*

INIGO-JONES, Ralph William (see Neeld, R. W.).

INNES, Lt.-Col. Berowald Alfred, b. 22 July 04, eldest s. of late Col. S. A. Innes, D.S.O. (OR K 92). B, 18²–21². R.M.C.,

Sandhurst. The Black Watch, 24–48. Retired as Lt.-Col. *Farmer's Club, London, R. & A. Golf Club.*

INNES, David John Lockhart, b. 14 Feb. 23, 3rd s. of J. L. Innes. St, 36^3–41^2. Balliol, Oxford, M.A. ✕ R.A., 42–47. Lt. T.D. Man. Dir., N. & N. Lockhart Ltd., Kirkcaldy. Brother, M. W. Innes.

INNES, John Nicholas, b. 9 Oct. 13, s. of late E. A. Innes. B, 27^2–30^3. Grenoble University, France. Studying French. Chartered Accountant. A.C.A., 37. Farmer from 46. Compulsorily retired 5 years ago through ill-health.

INNES, Michael Wemyss, b. 14 Oct. 24, 4th s. of J. L. Innes. St & K, 38^3–43^1; Scholar. Balliol, Oxford, B.A. ✕ R.A.F.V.R., 43–46. Writer to the Signet, 50. Partner, A. & J. L. Innes, Solicitors, Kirkcaldy, from 51. *R. & A. Golf Club.* Brother, D. J. L. Innes.

IREDALE, Henry Cecil, b. 22 Apr. 90, s. of late J. H. Iredale. SH, 04^3–09^2; Scholar; Minor Exhibitioner. Scholar of Christ's, Cambridge, M.A. ✕ 6th Bn. Bedfordshire Regt. Lt. Wounded twice. Teacher. Felsted School, 20–30. Charterhouse, 30–50.

IRVIN, Ardern Douglas. W, 03^1–05^3.*

IRWIN, Major-Gen. Brian St. George, b. 16 Sept. 17, s. of Lt.-Col. A. P. B. Irwin, D.S.O. K, 31^3–35^3; Levée; Head of House. R.M.A., Woolwich. Gazetted to Royal Engineers, 37. Trinity Hall, Cambridge, M.A. ✕ 39–45, Egypt, Libya, Sicily, Italy, Greece. Dispatches twice. Major, 41. Specialist in Survey. F.R.I.C.S. Serving Army Officer with the rank of Major-General. Now, Director-General, Ordnance Survey. *Army & Navy Club.* F.R.G.S. Sons, 1132 & 2051.

IRWIN, Kenneth Gordon Fenwick. SF, 39^3–43^2. Son, 2691.*

IRWIN, Patrick Hugh. K, 02^2–05^3.*

ISAACS, Kenneth Martin Nugent, M.B., B.S., b. 13 Dec. 98, youngest s. of late Rev. W. H. Isaacs (OR SH 80). SH, 12^3–15^3; G. VIII, 15. London Hospital, M.B., B.S., 26. In General Practice.

ISHAM, Sir Gyles, Bt., b. 31 Oct. 03, younger & only living s. of late Sir V. Isham, Bt. SH, 17^3–22^2. Demy of Magdalen, Oxford, M.A. Pres. of O.U.D.S. & Oxford Union. Professional Actor, 29–39. Succeeded father as 12th Baronet, 41. ✕ London Irish Rifles. K.R.R.C. & Staff, 39–47. Lt.-Col. Served under Foreign Office, 46–48. D.L. (Northants.), 52. High Sheriff, 58. C.C., 55–64. Trustee, National Portrait Gallery, 64–71. Fellow of Society of Antiquaries. Farms 500 acres in Northamptonshire. *Beefsteak Club.*

IVESON, Richard James Anthony. Sh, 44^3–49^1.*

IVIMEY, William Maitland. C, 13^2–17^1.*

IVIMEY-SIMMONDS, Dick. C, 20^2–24^2.*

IVY, Geoffrey Sutcliffe, Ph.D., b. 15 Mar. 23, 2nd s. of M. H. Ivy. Sh, 36^3–41^2; Scholar; Exhibitioner. Scholar of Trinity, Cambridge, M.A. Princeton, U.S.A. (Procter Fellow), M.A. Asst. Lecturer in English, University College, London, 50–54. Ph.D.(Lond.), 54. Lecturer in English at Durham University, 54–64. Senior Lecturer from 64. Son, Michael Robert Norman, Sh, 67^2–71^3.

IZARD, Gerald John, b. 29 Apr. 25, s. of C. G. Izard. Sh, 38^3–43^1. Farmer. *1st Guards Club.*

J

JACK, Major Archibald Frederick Maclean. Tu, 26^3–32^3.*

JACK, Douglas John, b. 9 May 23, eldest s. of J. Jack, M.C. B, 36^3–40^3. Exhibitioner of Trinity Hall, Cambridge, M.A. ✕ R.N.V.R. Sub-Lt. Dir. & Sec., Callard & Bowser Ltd.

JACK, Evan Stuart Maclean, b. 17 Jan. 10, elder s. of late H. S. M. Jack. SH,

23^3–28^1. Trinity, Cambridge, B.A. Solicitor, 37. Partner in Sydney, Merse & Co. *Garrick.* T.D. Brother, T. A. M. Jack. Son, 1390.

JACK, Thomas Anthony Maclean. SH, 28^3–33^3.*

JACK, William Alastair, b. 7 June 16, 2nd s. of late J. S. M. Jack. C, 30^2–34^1; Sw. VI. ✕ Ayrshire Yeomanry, 39–42.

R.A.F., 42–45. Dispatches. French Croix de Guerre. Dir., Stoddard Holdings Ltd.

JACKSON, Prof. Derek Ainslie, O.B.E., D.F.C., A.F.C., F.R.S., b. 23 June 06, younger (twin) s. of Sir C. J. Jackson. Scholar of Trinity, Cambridge, M.A. (Cantab. & Oxon.). Balliol, Oxford, D.Sc. ⋈ R.A.F.V.R., 40–45. Wing-Cdr., O.B.E., D.F.C., A.F.C. Officer, Legion of Merit (U.S.A.). Chevalier de la Légion d'Honneur, France. F.R.S., 47. Prof. of Spectroscopy, Oxford Univ. Visiting Prof., Ohio State Univ., Dept. of Physics. At present, Research Prof., C.N.R.S. II Faculté des Sciences, 91-Orsay, France. *Travellers', London; Travellers', Paris; Polo, Paris.*

JACKSON, Francis Bertrand Hart, b. 27 Mar. 08, eldest s. of R. B. Jackson. B, 21^3–26^2. Trinity Hall, Cambridge, M.A. Solicitor, 32. ⋈ R.A.F.V.R. (A. & S.D.) F/O. Private Practice. *Royal Thames Yacht Club.* Brother, L. S. H. Jackson. Son, 670.

JACKSON, George Julius. SH, 98^1–99^3.*

JACKSON, Lt.-Col. Guy Leslie, O.B.E., b. 21 Feb. 05, s. of H. Jackson. SF, 18^3–22^1. R.M.A., Woolwich. Gazetted to R.A. Lt., 27. ⋈ Served in M.E., Italy & Germany, 39–45. O.B.E. Lt.-Col., retired, 50. *Monday Club.*

JACKSON, Herbert Frederick. SF, 14^3–18^2.*

JACKSON, Humphrey Foster, b. 19 Aug. 08, s. of F. J. Jackson. C, 22^2–26^2. Formed Sea Insurance Co. Ltd., Liverpool, & after service in S. America & Army Service became Gen. Man. in 49. Retired, 69. ⋈ R.A., 39–45. Major. Chrmn. of the Management Committee of Liverpool Univ. Botanic Gardens, Noss, Wirral. *Old Hale Club, Liverpool.* Son, 770.

JACKSON, John Walter, b. 27 July 29, s. of W. D. Jackson. Tu, 43^2–47^3; Cap, 47; XXII, 47. Chrmn. & Man. Dir. of family Jewellery business, P. F. Jackson Ltd. Past Capt. of *Handsworth Golf Club.* Son, David Swinburne, Tu, 67^2–72^2.

JACKSON, Kenneth Leslie Tattersall, T.D., b. 17 Nov. 13, 2nd s. of late Dr. J. W. Jackson. C, 27^2–32^2; XV, 29–31 (Capt.); XI, 29–32 (Capt., 31 & 32); H. XI, 30–31. Trinity, Oxford, M.A. Rugby Football Blue, 32, 33 (Capt.). Cricket Blue, 33. Scottish Cap, 33–34. Asst.

Master, Wellington College, 36. ⋈ Duke of Wellington's Regt., Welch Regt., & R.W.A.F.F. Major. Headmaster, Repton Prep. School, 47–60. Headmaster, Cargilfield School, Edinburgh, 60–71. Regional Dir., I.S.I.S.—South & West. Son, 1496.

JACKSON, Lowry Stephen Hart, b. 13 Mar. 13, 2nd s. of R. B. Jackson. B, 26^3–31^2. Trinity Hall, Cambridge, B.A. Bar, Gray's Inn, 35, Northern Circuit. ⋈ R.A. Lt. *St. James's Club, Manchester.* Brother, F. B. H. Jackson.

JACKSON, Robert Francis Anthony, M.B.E. B, 32^3–36^2.*

JACKSON, William Dugdale. W, 10^1–13^2.*

JACOBS, Edwin Cyril. W, 29^1–32^3.*

JACQUES, Christopher Baldwin. St, 46^3–50^3.*

JACQUES, David Baldwin. St, 44^3–49^1.*

JAFFÉ, Alexander Macrae, b. 5 Oct. 25, elder s. of late W. Jaffé. K, 39^2–41^3. Trinity, Cambridge, M.A. F.C.A. Mining, Contracting, etc., Britannia Lead Co. Ltd. *Hurlingham.*

JAFFÉ, Peter John, b. 19 Apr. 14, elder s. of A. D. Jaffé, O.B.E. SF, 29^2–32^2. King's, Cambridge, M.A. Represented C.U. Chess Club. Employed by London Stockbroker, 36–39. Ministry of Information, Psychological Warfare, S.H.A.E.F. Financial Journalism, including "The Economist", Control Commission, Germany. B.B.C., Overseas Listening. Partner, Wm. Noall & Son, Melbourne Shareholders, 61. Fellow, Royal Philatelic Society, London. Royal Philatelic Society of Victoria (Pres., 72).

JAMES, Edward. W, 23^2–26^3.*

JAMES, John Hubert, b. 5 June 06, s. of J. James, J.P. K, 20^3–22^3. Private Land Agent (Managing Estate of 2,000 acres— also a Farmer on own account).

JAMES, Meyrick, b. 17 Mar. 11, 2nd s. of C. E. James. W, 24^3–28^1. Farmer. Pupil farmer in Worcestershire & then in S.Africa. Fruit grower in Elgin, S. Africa. Chrmn., Elgin Fruit Packers Cooperative. Farmer, Somerset West, S. Africa,

Dir., Leasing & Finance Co., Credfin (Pty.) Ltd., Trust Bank Centre, Cape Town. *Kelvin Grove, Western Province C.C.; Royal Cape G.C.; Durban Country Club & Kloof G.C.*

JAMES, Ralph Trevor, E.R.D., F.L.A., b. 13 June 19, s. of late W. T. James. T, 32^3-37^2. ✕ Gloucestershire Regt., 39–42. R.A.S.C., 42–46. Capt. Chartered Librarian. Fellow of the Library Assoc., 56. Army Emergency Reserve R.A.S.C./ R.C.T. Retired as Major, 67. Public Library Service, Rugby, Coventry & Liverpool. Head of Co-Ordination, Liverpool City Libraries. Committee Member, Liverpool Centre, National Trust. Emergency Reserve Decoration.

JAMES, Robert Henry Fitzgerald, M.R.C.S., L.R.C.P., b. 12 Mar. 20, s. of late Dr. H. H. James. K, 33^2-37^2. St. John's, Oxford, B.A., M.R.C.S., L.R.C.P., B.M., B.Ch. ✕ R.A.M.C., 46–49. Capt. Medical Practitioner.

JAMES, Thurstan Trewartha, b. 7 May 03, eldest s. of late A. James. W, 17^3-19^2. Royal School of Mines. After mining in Portugal & studying General Engineering, joined Short brothers to work on all-metal flying-boats, 26. Joined Technical Staff of "The Aeroplane", 29, founded first gliding weekly, "The Sailplane & Glider", 30. Editor, "The Aeroplane", 45–65, now retired. Air Ministry, Min. of Aircraft Production, 39–45. Liveryman, Coach Makers & Coach-Harness Makers Co. *United Service & Royal Aero Club; R.A.F. Reserves Club.* Honorary Companion, Royal Aeronautical Society.

JAMIESON, Kenneth Douglas, C.M.G., b. 9 Jan. 21, s. of late Rt. Hon. Lord Jamieson, P.C. St, 34^3-39^2; Scholar; Levée; Head of House; Leaving Exhibition. Balliol, Oxford, Domus Exhibitioner, 39. Interrupted by War Service, 40, after Honour Mods. and did not return. ✕ 5th Regt. R. Horse Artillery, 39–45. H.M. Foreign Service, 46. Present employment, Deputy Permanent Representative, U.K. Mission to the United Nations, N.Y. C.M.G., 68. *St. James's Club.* Son, 2892.

JARROLD, Comdr. David John Esmond, R.N., b. 21 Aug. 28, s. of late E. V. Jarrold (OR Tu 01). Tu, 42^2-46^1; R. VIII; Crick Winner, 46. Trained as a Naval Officer in Marine Engineering at R.N.E.C., Manadon, Plymouth. Subsequently, trained as Weapons & Electrical Officer at H.M.S. *Collingwood, Excellent*

& *Vernon.* M.I.Mech.E. Served as Cadet in H.M.S. *Frobisher,* 46; Midshipman in H.M.S. *Newcastle,* 48–49; S/Lt. in H.M.S. *Warrior,* 50–52; Lt. in H.M.S. *Eagle,* 54–56; Lt.-Cmdr. in H.M.S. *Tiger,* 61–62; Cmdr. in H.M.S. *Devonshire,* 70–73.

JARVIE, John Robert Thomas Gibson. Sh, 35^1-37^1.*

JAYNE, Col. Ronald Francis Garland, D.S.O. SH, 16^1-18^3.*

JEFFERSON, Antony Andrew, F.R.C.S., b. 13 June 22, younger s. of late Prof. Sir G. Jefferson, F.R.S., F.R.C.S. M, 36^3-39^2. Manchester Univ. Scholar of Oriel, Oxford, M.A., B.Sc., B.M., B.Ch. McGill Univ., M.D., C.M. F.R.C.S. (Eng.), 50. Consultant Neurological Surgeon to the United Sheffield Hospitals. Royal Society of Medicine. Holder of Hunterian Professorship, Royal College of Surgeons of England, 57. Nuffield Foundation Fellow, 53–56. Brother, J. M. Jefferson.

JEFFERSON, John Michael, D.M., F.R.C.P., b. 9 Dec. 16, elder s. of late Prof. Sir G. Jefferson, F.R.S., F.R.C.S. M, 30^3-35^1. Magdalen, Oxford, B.Sc., M.A., B.M., B.Ch., D.M., M.R.C.P., F.R.C.P. ✕ R.A.M.C., 42–47. Major. Consultant Neurologist, Queen Elizabeth Hospital, Birmingham. Adviser in Neurology, Birmingham Regional Hospital Board. Member, Assoc. Brit. Neurol.; Assoc. Phys. G.B. & Ireland etc. *The Bath Club.* Brother, A. A. Jefferson.

JEFFREYS-JONES, Llewellyn Hyslop, b. 30 May 03, younger s. of D. Jeffreys-Jones. St, 17^1-21^1; Cap, 21. Magdalen, Oxford, M.A. Schoolmaster, Summer Fields, Oxford, 27–35. Headmaster, Wolborough Hill School, Newton Abbot, S. Devon, 35–50. Retired. O.U. Occasionals Hockey. Played Hockey for Devon.

JELLY, George Oliver. K, 23^1-27^2.*

JENKINS, The Rev. David Noble, b. 20 Oct. 25, s. of late Brig.-Gen. N. F. Jenkins, C.M.G., C.B.E. (OR K 74). K, 39^2-43^2. ✕ R.N.V.R., 44–46. S/Lt. Corpus Christi, Cambridge, M.A. Cuddesdon College, Oxford. Ordained Deacon, 50; Priest, 51. Chaplain to Eastbourne College, Sussex.

JENKINS, Sir Evan Meredith, G.C.I.E., K.C.S.I., b. 2 Feb. 96, 2nd s. of late Sir J. L. Jenkins, K.C.S.I., I.C.S. W, 09^3-14^3; Scholar; Head of House. Balliol,

Oxford, Domus Exhibitioner, 13. ✕ H.A.C., 2nd Bn. Duke of Cornwall's Light Infantry. I.A.R.O., att. 91st Punjabis. Capt. Wounded. Indian Civil Service, 20. Under-Secretary to Punjab Government. Chief Commissioner, Delhi, 37. Private Sec. to Viceroy & Sec. to Governor-General (Personal), 43–45. Governor of Punjab, 46–47. Retired. K.C.S.I., 45; G.C.I.E., 47. *Travellers' Club.*

JENNINGS, Sir Raymond Winter, Q.C., b. 12 Dec. 97, s. of late Sir A. O. Jennings. M, 11^3–15^3. R.M.C., Sandhurst. Oriel, Oxford, M.A., B.C.L. Bar, Inner Temple, 22. Queen's Counsel, 45. Bencher of Lincoln's Inn, 51. Master, Court of Protection, 56–70. Retired. Knighted, 68. *Athenæum Club.*

JERWOOD, Major Harold Peter, b. 7 June 16, s. of Rev. F. H. Jerwood. C, 29^3–35^2; XV, 33–34. Jesus, Cambridge, B.A. ✕ R.E., 40–45. Joined The British United Shoe Machinery Co. Ltd., Leicester, 38. Export Dir. Retired, 72. *Hawks, Cambridge.* Barbarian Rugby Football, England Trial, 47.

JESSEL, Ernest Anthony. SF, 21^3–25^2.*

JESSEL, Oliver Richard, b. 24 Aug. 29, elder s. of Cdr. R. F. Jessel, D.S.O., D.S.C., R.N. M, 43^2–47^2. Chrmn., Jessel Securities Ltd. *Garrick Club.*

JEVONS, Philip John, b. 26 Apr. 30, s. of late J. C. Jevons, M.A., A.R.I.B.A. K, 44^1–48^2. R.A.F. College, Cranwell; Under-Officer; Hockey XI. R.A.F. Officer, 51–59, F/Lt. Man. Dir., Rudolf Wolff & Co., Metal Brokers & Merchants. Founder Members, London Metal Exchange. Son, Philip Mark Sebastian, K, 69^3–.

JEWELL, Charles John Samuel, b. 6 Nov. 92, s. of late C. Jewell, F.R.G.S. SF, 06^3–09^3. Trinity, Cambridge. Agriculturalist. ✕ 2nd Home Counties Bde., R.F.A. Capt. Man. Dir., Estancia Property Co. Ltd., 22–71.

JEWITT, David Dennis Ernest, b. 11 July 20, elder s. of late D. D. E. Jewitt. T, 33^1–35^1. Leicester College of Technology. University College Hospital Medical School, London, M.R.C.S., L.R.C.P. House Surgeon, Botleys Park Hospital, 45. N/S. R.N.V.R., 46–47. Surg.-Lt. Registrar, Bristol Royal Infirmary, 48–49. General Medical Practitioner in Chatham. B.M.A. Chatham R.N.V.S.R. Officers Assoc. Brother, R. H. Jewitt.

JEWITT, Ross Herman. T, 38^1–43^2.*

JEWSON, Charles Boardman, J.P., F.C.A., b. 23 Oct. 09, elder s. of late P. W. Jewson, J.P. C, 23^3–27^1. F.C.A. ✕ R.A.F.V.R., 40–45. Sqn. Ldr. J.P. for City of Norwich, 51. Dir., Horsley Smith & Jewson Ltd. Fellow of the Society of Antiquaries. Lord Mayor of Norwich, 65–66. *Lansdowne Club; Norolk Club, Norwich.* Brother, G. M. Jewson. Sons, 1431 & 1648.

JEWSON, Gerald Maurice, M.R.C.S., L.R.C.P., b. 16 Oct. 14, younger s. of late P. W. Jewson, J.P. W, 28^3–32^3. Queens', Cambridge, M.A. St. Bartholomew's Hospital, M.R.C.S., L.R.C.P. ✕ Merchant Navy, Surgeon. Medical Practitioner. Brother, C. B. Jewson.

JOHNSEN, Robert Oscar Claridge, b. 12 Dec. 25, s. of late O. C. Johnsen. Sh, 39^3–43^3. ✕ R.N.A.S. Man. Dir., Johnsen & Jorgensen (Holdings) Ltd. & West Pharmarubber Ltd.

JOHNSON, Alfred Henry, b. 11 July 12, s. of late A. G. Johnson. B, 26^1–29^2. Tile Manufacturer, 29–37. Poultry Farmer since 37.

JOHNSON, Christopher Frank, b. 23 May 17, younger s. of late F. G. Johnson (OR C 96). C, 31^2–35^3. Earthenware Manufacturer. F.I.D. ✕ R.A. (Field), 39–46 N.W. Europe. Capt. Dispatches. T.D. Dir., Johnson Bros., Hanley, Stoke-on-Trent. Brother, P. C. Johnson. Son, 2976.

JOHNSON, Ernest James, J.P., b. 20 Feb. 13, 2nd s. of late Sir E. Johnson (OR C 95). C, 26^3–30^3. Earthenware Manufacturer. ✕ R.A.S.C. Lt. F.I.Ceram. J.P. Dir., Messrs. Johnson Bros. & Josiah Wedgwood & Sons Ltd. Brothers, F. S. & S. B. Johnson. Sons, 741 & 985.

JOHNSON, Frederick Shepard. C, 23^3–27^3.*

JOHNSON, Major Gordon Saffery, D.S.O., M.B.E., b. 4 Nov. 90, eldest s. of late G. Johnson. SH, 04^3–08^2. Pembroke, Cambridge. Gazetted to 61st K.G.O. Pioneers, Indian Army, 12. ✕61st Pioneers. Intelligence, Gen. Staff. Capt. M.C. N.W. Frontier, Afghanistan, 19–20. Waziristan, 22–25. M.B.E. Staff Capt., Southern Command, India, 26. Transferred to 1st Bn. Baluch Regt., 32. With 7 Bn. R. Norfolk Regt., France, 40. P.O.W. D.S.O. *Junior Army & Navy Club.* Master, Worshipful Company of Pewterers, London, 57–58.

JOHNSON, Henry Leslie, b. 4 Mar. 04, eldest s. of H. Johnson, O.B.E., J.P. SF, 18¹–22². Joined Courtaulds Ltd., 22. Dir., 33–68 (Man. Dir., 33–47). Fellow of Textile Institute & Pres., 42–44. Chrmn., Offchurch, Bury Farms Ltd. Farmer & Thoroughbred Stockbreeder. Liveryman of Worshipful Company of Farmers. Member of Warwickshire County Council, 64; Vice-Chrmn., 74. Chrmn., Mid-Warwickshire Education Executive from 70. Son, Henry Edward, SF, 69³–.

JOHNSON, Hubert Bryan. C, 09³–13².*

JOHNSON, Michael Henry. W, 43³–48³.*

JOHNSON, Peter Cayme, b. 16 Jan. 11, eldest s. of late F. G. Johnson. C, 24³–29¹. ✕ R.N.A.S., 43–46. Earthenware Manufacturer. Retired. Brother, C. F. Johnson. Sons, 485 & 679.

JOHNSON, Peter Fordham, M.B., M.R.C.S., L.R.C.P., D.P.M., b. 9 Dec. 15, s. of O. F. Johnson. C, 29³–34²; Cap; R. VIII. St. Bartholomew's Hospital, M.B., D.P.M., M.R.C.Psych. Consultant to Adolescent & Family Unit, Longrove Hospital, Epsom. Assoc. Chief Asst. & Psychotherapist, St. Bartholomew's Hospital. Part-time Private & Hospital Consultant. Gaskell Gold Medal & Prize in Psychiatry. Publication, "Poetry Now". R.S.M. Royal College of Psychiatry. *M.C.C.*

JOHNSON, Peter Saffery, b. 9 Feb. 31, 2nd s. of Major G. S. Johnson, D.S.O., M.B.E., M.C. SH, 44³–49¹. Royal Marines, 49–54. Lt. Various firms in business systems, now working for Alacra Ltd. (Computer Form Printing). *M.C.C.* Kennet & Avon Canal Trust.

JOHNSON, Stephen Boote, b. 4 Apr. 19, 3rd s. of late Sir E. Johnson (OR C 95). C, 32³–37²; Levée. Pottery Manufacturer. Jt. Man. Dir., Johnson Bros., Hanley. Man. Dir. of wholly-owned Australian branch of this firm. Dir. of Josiah Wedgwood (Australia) Pty. Ltd. & of H. & R. Johnson (Australia) Pty. Ltd. R.A.C.V., Melbourne. J.P. Brothers, F. S. & E. J. Johnson.

JOHNSON, William Guy Denbigh. Tu, 45³–49³.*

JOHNSON-GILBERT, Ronald Stuart. W, 38³–43².*

JOHNSON-GILBERT, Thomas Ian. W, 37³–41³. Son, Christopher Ian, W, 68³–.*

JOHNSON-HILL, Cyril, b. 14 Nov. 08, 2nd s. of late K. Johnson-Hill. T, 22¹–26³; Benn Scholar. ✕ Intelligence Corps, 41–43. R.A.O.C., 43–46. Capt. Cert. A.I.B. Banking. Retired, 69, as Man. of Barclays Bank Ltd., Felpham & Middleton. Brothers, K. C., G. M. & D. R. Johnson-Hill.

JOHNSON-HILL, Derek Royce, b. 22 Mar. 19, 4th s. of late K. Johnson-Hill. T, 32²–33³. Cranbrook School. Played Cricket, Rugby & Hockey for School. School Teaching, 37–39. ✕ R. West African Frontier Force, 39–47. Capt. Tobacco Statistician with Gallaher Ltd., in Nyasaland from 48–57 and in Salisbury, Rhodesia, from 58. Brothers, K. C., C. & G. M. Johnson-Hill.

JOHNSON-HILL, Gerald Martin, b. 11 July 14, 3rd s. of late K. Johnson-Hill. T, 28²–31¹. Administration Officer, Colonial Service. ✕ Kedah Volunteer Force (Malaya), 39–45. Lt. Brothers, K. C., C. & D. R. Johnson-Hill.

JOHNSON-HILL, Kenelm Clifton, J.P., b. 4 June 06, eldest s. of late K. Johnson-Hill. T, 19²–22³; Benn Scholar. With Barclays Bank Ltd., 23–25. British American Tobacco Co. (Hong Kong) Ltd., from 51. ✕ R.A. Capt. P.O.W., Singapore, 42–45. Brothers, C., G. M. & D. R. Johnson-Hill. Sons, 940, 1358 & 1995.

JOHNSTON, Colin McKenzie (see McKenzie, Johnston C.).

JOHNSTON, Dudley David Cameron, b. 22 June 29, s. of late D. H. Johnston. W, 43²–47². Civil Engineer. C.Eng., M.I.C.E. Managing Director. Son, David Anthony, W, 68³–.

JOHNSTON, Major Francis James, b. 26 Aug. 28, eldest s. of late F. B. Johnston, M.A. B, 42³–47¹; R. VIII, 47. R.M.A., Sandhurst. 1st Whip R.M.A. Beagles. Gazetted to Coldstream Guards, 48. Served in Malaya, 49–50. Staff H.Q. 1st (Br.) Corps, 55. Retired, 59. Major. Underwriting Member of Lloyd's since 54. Attached to Hedderwick Borthwick & Co. (Stockbrokers), 60–69. Dir., M. B. P. Russell & Co. Ltd. (Private Bankers), 69–71. Investment Man., English Transcontinental Ltd., 71–72. Dir., Anglo Overseas Engineers & Merchants Ltd., from 73. *Buck's, Guards, Pratt's, City of London.* Brother, I. B. M. Johnston.

JOHNSTON, Ian Benjamin Murray, b. 19 Jan. 30, 2nd s. of late F. B. Johnston, M.A. B, 43³–48¹; R. VIII, 48. R.M.A., Sandhurst. Commissioned into Coldstream Guards, 49. Resigned, 54. Associate of The Chartered Insurance Institute. Fellow of the Corp. of Insurance Brokers. Underwriting Member of Lloyd's. Associate Member of Liverpool Underwriters Assoc. Employed at Lloyd's of London. 54–60. Dir. of Brodrick Leitch & Kendall Ltd., Insurance Brokers, Liverpool, from 60. Veteran Member of H.A.C. Dir. of Old Hall, Exchange & Palatine Club Ltd., Liverpool. *Nulli Secundus Club.* Member of Council of The Liverpool School of Tropical Medicine. Vice-Pres. of Liverpool Branch of Coldstreamers Assoc. Brother, F. J. Johnston.

JOHNSTON, Kenneth James Ross, b. 28 May 29, 2nd s. of Col. R. H. Johnston, O.B.E., F.I.Mech.E. K, 43³–47¹. Engineering.

JOHNSTON, Kenneth Robert Hope, b. 18 June 05, eldest s. of late Dr. J. A. H. Johnston. M, 19³–24²; Cap, 24; XXII; Leaving Exhibition. Scholar of Sidney Sussex, Cambridge, M.A. Harvard Univ., U.S.A. (Davison Scholar). Bar, Gray's Inn, 33. Practised, 33–39 & 45–67. Q.C., 53. Bencher, Gray's Inn, 58. Retired. ⚔ R.A.F.V.R., 39–45. Wing-Cdr. *M.C.C.* Son, 848.

JOHNSTON, Patrick Nigel. K, 45²–50².*

JOHNSTONE, Alastair Montague (formerly A. Montague Johnstone). M, 42³–46³.*

JOHNSTONE, Charles Malcolm, b. 28 Mar. 05, elder s. of C. G. Johnstone. St, 19¹–23². Pembroke, Cambridge, B.A. ⚔ R.A.F., 40–45. Sqn. Ldr. Dispatches. Served on Godstone Bench, 53–64. Dir., Hogg, Sons & J. B. Johnstone Ltd., of London.

JOHNSTONE, Conrad Powell, C.B.E., b. 19 Aug. 95, eldest s. of late W. Y. Johnstone. St, 10¹–13²; XI, 12–13; Rackets Pair, 13. ⚔ 1st Bn. Highland Light Infantry, Att. 17th Bn. Lancashire Fusiliers, 14–19. Lt. Wounded twice. Pembroke, Cambridge, B.A. Cricket Blue, 19–20. Branch Man., Messrs. Burmah-Shell,

Madras, India. Now retired. C.B.E. *M.C.C.; Senior Golfing Society; East India, Sports & Public Schools Club.*

JOHNSTONE, Edward Tremlett (see Tremlett-Johnstone, E.).

JONES, Christopher Maurice, b. 17 May 19, s. of late S. E. Jones (OR SH 72). SH, 32³–36³. Trinity, Cambridge, M.A. ⚔ R.A. Captured at Singapore, 42. P.O.W., 42–45. Lt. In Agriculture. Man. Dir., Leckford Estate Ltd., Hants. *M.C.C., Farmers'.* Son, 2905.

JONES, Edward Ellis, M.B., B.Chir., D.R.C.O.G. B, 29²–34².*

JONES, George Thomas. W, 43³–47².*

JONES, Hugh Edward Hunter (see Hunter-Jones, H. E.).

JONES, Philip Rufus, b. 6 Feb. 10, s. of H. C. Jones. M, 23³–28². In Textile Industry, 28–39. ⚔ R.A., T.A., 39–45. Major. (In T.A., 38–51.) T.D. Farmer from 45. Northants County Councillor, 56–65.

JONES, Robert William Raines. W, 44³–49².*

JORDAN, Robert Byrt. St, 28²–32².*

JOSEPH, Pater Nathaniel Waley. K, 27³–32².*

JUBB, Charles Patrick, b. 18 May 14, elder s. of E. C. Jubb, C.B., O.B.E. Tu, 28²–32²; Levée; Head of House; XXII. Corpus Christi, Oxford, B.A. ⚔ R.E., later seconded to Foreign Office. Lt.-Col. Allied Commission for Austria, 45–46. B.B.C., 36–72. Dir. Gen., Kenya Broadcasting Corporation, 59–63. Retired. Royal Overseas League. *M.C.C.*

JURY, Peter Charles Cotton, b. 30 Aug. 19, s. of late Col. E. C. Jury. St, 33²–37³. King's, Cambridge. ⚔ 13th/18th Royal Hussars, 38–47. Capt. Chrmn., Irish Hotel & Restaurant Assoc., 48–56. Pres., Irish Hotel Federation, 59–70. Chrmn., Trust Houses Forte (Ireland) Ltd. Vice-Pres., International Hotel Assoc. Chrmn., International Airport Hotel, Dublin. *Cavalry Club; Kildare St. Club, Dublin.*

K

KAHN, Cecil Harry Benedict, b. 10 May 01, s. of the late H. J. Kahn. St, 15²–18². Trinity, Cambridge, M.A. Chrmn., Adamite Co. Ltd., Hertford. A.M.Inst.Struct.E. Master, W. Company of Paviors, 73.

KARMINSKI, The Rt. Hon. Sir Seymour Edward, P.C., b. 28 Sept. 02, younger s. of E. Karminski. B, 15³–20². Christ Church, Oxford, M.A. Bar, Inner Temple, 25; Midland Circuit. ✕ R.N.V.R., 40–50. Lt.-Cdr. K.C., 45. High Court Judge, 58–69. Lord Justice of Appeal, 69–73. Retired, 73. Privy Council, 67. Treasurer, Inner Temple, 73. *Garrick Club*.

KARNEY, The Rev. Gilbert Henry Peter, b. 30 Sept. 09, eldest s. of the Rt. Rev. A. B. L. Karney, Bishop of Johannesburg. SH, 23³–28²; R. VIII, 28. Trinity, Cambridge, M.A. Cuddesdon Theological Coll., Oxford. Ordained Deacon, 34; Priest, 35. Curate, Newcastle Cathedral, 34–36. Chaplain, Trinity, Cambridge, 36–40. ✕ Chaplain, R.N.V.R., 40–46. Rector of Godstone, Surrey, 46–54. Vicar of Embleton, with Craster & Newton from 54. Chaplain to High Sheriff of Northumberland, 62–63. International Assoc. of Master Mariners, Cape Horners. Sons, 1244 & 1553.

KAULBACK, Lt.-Col. Roy James Alfred, D.S.O., F.R.G.S., b. 11 May 11, 2nd s. of the late Lt.-Col. H. A. Kaulback, O.B.E. W, 25²–29²; Shooting, Laurie Cup, 26–28; XV, 27–28. Pembroke, Cambridge, M.A. Gazetted Royal Irish Fusiliers, 31. Inter-Services Light Heavyweight Boxing Champion, India, 32. Travelled Central-Southern Tibet, 33. Own expedition on camels to explore S. Libyan Desert, 34. Regtl. Adjutant, 36–39; Capt., 39. ✕ Staff College, Camberley, 40–41. Major, 41. p.s.c. Lt.-Col. Commanding 1/6th Queen's Royal Regt. in 7th Army Div., Western Desert, 42–43. Wounded. Dispatches twice. Commanded 1st Yorks. & Lancs. Regt. in 5th Infantry Div., Italy & W. Europe, 44–45. D.S.O. Chief of Staff, 1st Infantry Div., 46. R.N. Staff College, Greenwich, 46. Jt. Services Staff College, 47. Retired at own request, 47. Executive with Iraq Petroleum & Shell Oil Companies, 47–60. Member, Institute of Petroleum, 57. Man. Dir., Fenja Properties Ltd., from 60. Author of "The Post-War Army", "Army Training", "Value

for Money", & "The Regiment". *Pitt Club, United Services Club*. Member of Brit. School of Archaeology in Athens. F.R.G.S. Brother, R. J. H. Kaulback. Son, 917.

KAULBACK, Lt.-Col. Ronald John Henry, O.B.E., F.R.G.S., b. 23 July 09, eldest s. of the late Lt.-Col. H. A. Kaulback, O.B.E. W, 23³–27²; XV, 26; Athletics Cup, 26; S. VIII, 25–27 (Capt.); Cadet Officer. Pembroke, Cambridge. Exploration in S.E. Tibet, 33 & 35–36. In Upper Burma, 38–39. ✕ Instructor & Chief Instructor, Small Arms School, Netheravon, 39–45. Force 136, Burma, O.B.E. Lt.-Col. R.A.R.O., F.R.G.S. Now Publican in S.W. Eire. *United Service & Royal Aero Club; Special Forces Club*. Brother, R. J. A. Kaulback.

KAY, William Reid. Tu, 36³–41¹.*

KAYE, Norman Henry, b. 23 Jan. 04, s. of the late T. Kaye. W, 17³–21². Queens', Oxford, M.A. Kaye & Stewart Ltd., Fine Cloth Manufacturers, Huddersfield, 24–40. Man. & Dir., 30–40. ✕ 40–62, R.A.F. Sqn. Ldr. Retired, 62. Dispatches, 42. Civil Service, Min. of Health & Social Security, 62–71. Retired.

KAYE, Major Ronald Leslie Downing, T.D., b. 13 June 99, eldest s. of the late R. W. Kaye. B, 13²–17². ✕ R.F.A. 2nd Lt. Army of the Rhine, 17–19. Lt. 239th (Leicester) Bty., R.F.A. (T.A.). Major, 29. R.A.R.O., 32. Queens', Oxford. Joined T. H. Downing & Co. Ltd., Hosiery Manufacturers, Leicester. ✕ R.A., 39–45, T.D.

KEANE, Denis Michael. SF, 34³–39¹.*

KEARNS, Henry John Denis, b. 20 Jan. 09, elder s. of the late W. E. Kearns. B, 22³–27²; Exhibitioner. Scholar of Christ's, Cambridge. M.I.Mech.E. H. W. Kearns & Co. Ltd., Machine Tool Making, 30–69. Boat Operator & Hirer on Canals, 71. Manchester Association of Engineers. Grand Cross of Merit, Lower Saxony. Brother, W. D. Kearns.

KEARNS, Stephen Henry Lumsden. B, 45³–50¹.*

KEARNS, Walter Donald, b. 22 Sept. 23, younger s. of the late W. E. Kearns.

B, 37^3–41^2. ⋇ R.A.F. F/Lt. Cotton yarn dyer, bleacher & doubler. Brother, H. J. D. Kearns.

KEATINGE, Sir Edgar Mayne, C.B.E., b. 3 Feb. 05, s. of the late G. F. Keatinge, C.I.E. SH, 19^1–23^3; XV, 23; R. VIII, 23. School of Agriculture, Natal, S. Africa. Dept. of Agriculture, S. Africa, 26–29. County Councillor, West Suffolk, 33–45. ⋇ R.A., 39–45. Lt.-Col. M.P. (Conservative), Bury St. Edmunds, 44–45. J.P., Wilts., from 45. Governor, Sherborne School. Royal African Society. C.B.E., 54. Kt., 60. *Carlton Club.* Son, W. R. Keatinge.

KEATINGE, William Richard, M.B., B.Chir., Ph.D., b. 18 May 31, s. of Sir E. M. Keatinge, C.B.E. (OR SH 19). St, 45^1–49^3. Exhibitioner. Scholar of Pembroke, Cambridge, M.A., M.B., B.Chir., Ph.D. St. Thomas's Hospital Medical School. Director of Studies in Medicine, Pembroke, Cambridge & Fellow in Physiology, Pembroke, Oxford. Now Professor of Physiology, London Hospital Medical College. Member of Physiological Society. Fellow, Royal Society of Medicine.

KEAY, Capt. Thomas Alan Colin, R.N.R., b. 19 June 21, s. of Capt. W. F. Keay, O.B.E., V.R.D., D.L., R.N.V.R. Tu, 35^2–39^2. ⋇ R.N.V.R., Tay Div., 39–45. Dispatches. Lt.-Cdr. Retired, 69, as Capt., R.N.R. In Command, Tay Div., 63–66. V.R.D. & Clasp. President, Engineering Employers, Dundee & District Assoc., Member Management Board, Engineering Employers Federation from 61. Chrmn., Dundee Branch, R.N.L.I., from 67. Chrmn. & Man. Dir., Thomas C. Keay Ltd., Dundee and Keay-Turner Ltd., Dundee. Chrmn., Convertapak Machines Ltd., Gt. Yarmouth. *Naval & Military, R. & A. G.C., Royal Tay Y.C.*

KEAY, William Arthur, b. 30 Sept. 27, s. of Major G. A. Keay, M.C. (A), T, 40^3–46^2; Levée; XV, 45; XI, 46; H. XI, 46; Cadet Officer. Scholar of Trinity, Oxford, M.A. N/S. 5th Regt. R.H.A. Commissioned, 50. Teaching at Haileybury College.

KEEF, Denis Clissold, b. 28 June 99, elder s. of H. W. Keef. Tu, 13^3–17^3; Scholar; won Crowdy Cup, 13. Scholar of Gonville & Caius, Cambridge, M.A. ⋇ 51st Siege Bty., R.G.A. 2nd Lt., 18–19. Schoolmaster. ⋇ R.A., 40–45. Lt. Master, Millfield School, Street, Somerset, from

45. Somerset Trust for Nature Conservation.

KEELE, Stephen Clare Kennedy. St, 46^2–50^2.*

KEEN, Gerald Ian. T, 44^3–49^1.*

KEEP, Alfred Lawrence. Tu, 09^2–13^2.

KEITH, Sir Kenneth Alexander. C, 30^1–30^3.*

KELLAR, David Crawford. SH, 45^3–50^2.*

KELLETT, Oswald Bainbridge, M.B.E., b. 20 June 06, eldest s. of the late W. O. Kellett, J.P. Tu, 20^3–23^1. Wigan Mining & Tech. Coll. Attended various courses in Radio Communications & Staff Management. C.Eng., F.R.I.E.R.E. Manchester City Police, Radio Technician, 36–39. Home Office, Nottingham, Radio Experimental Technician, 39–42. Home Office, Newmarket, Chief Wireless Technician, 42–45. Home Office, Newcastle-on-Tyne, Regional Wireless Eng., 45–72. Retired, 72. Late, Regional Wireless Eng., Directorate of Telecommunications, Home Office, 39–72. Newcastle-on-Tyne Photographic Socy. Ass. Royal Yachting Assoc. M.B.E., 69.

KELLOCK, Thomas Donald, M.B., F.R.C.P., b. 15 Apr. 17, eldest s. of the late T. H. Kellock, F.R.C.S. Sh, 30^3–35^3. Exhibition to Clare, Cambridge, M.A., M.B., B.Chir. Middlesex Hospital Medical School, M.R.C.S., F.R.C.P. ⋇ R.A.M.C. Major. Consultant Physician, Central Middlesex Hospital. Medical Officer, Sun Life Assurance Society. Chairman of Children Cttee., British Diabetic Assoc. Member of the Dietician Board. Medical Socy. of London. Royal Socy. of Medicine. Socy. of Apothecaries of London. Brother, T. O. Kellock.

KELLOCK, Thomas Oslof, Q.C., b. 4 July 23, 2nd s. of the late T. H. Kellock, F.R.C.S. Sh, 37^2–42^2. Clare, Cambridge, B.A. ⋇ R.N.V.R. (Special Branch), 44–46. S/Lt. Bar, Inner Temple, 49. Q.C., 65. Director, Legal Div., Commonwealth Secretariat, 69–72. Contested (L.) Torquay, 59; S. Kensington, 66 & 68. *Reform Club.* Brother, T. D. Kellock.

KELLY, Brig. Theodore Edward Dudley, C.B.E., K. St. J., b. 24 Feb. 03, s. of the late Brig.-Gen. H. E. T. Kelly, C.B., C.M.G. (R.A.). Tu, 17^1–20^3. R.M.A., Woolwich. Gazetted R.A. p.s.c., 35. Capt.,

36. ⚔ R.A. & Staff, 39–45. G.S.O., G.H.Q., Home Forces, 40. E. Command, 41. Deputy Dir., Operations G.H.Q., India, 40–42. Brig.-Gen., Staff 11 Army Group, 42–43. Commd. R.A., 26 Ind. Div., 43–44. j.s.s.c., 49. Commd. A.A. Brigade, 49–52. Principal Admin. Officer, Far East, 52–55. Defence Secretary, East African High Commission & at H.Q. E. Africa Command, 56–60. Commission, St. John Ambulance Brigade, Berks.; Commander, 65–72. C.B.E., 46. K. St. J., 72. *Army & Navy Club*. Son, J. E. T. Kelly, Tu, 45. Killed by terrorists in Cyprus, 55.

KEMSLEY, Michael Unwin Stirling. SH, 25³–29².*

KENNARD-DAVIS, Lt.-Col. Frank Edward. B, 10³–13².*

KENNEDY, Bruce Bingham, T.D., b. 10 July 20, elder s. of the late Col. N. Kennedy, C.B.E., D.S.O., D.L., J.P. (OR SF 95). SF, 33³–38²; Scholar; S. VIII, 38; won Heavyweight Boxing, 38. Scholar of Hotchkiss Univ., U.S.A., Graduated "Cum Laude". ⚔ Ayrshire (E.C.O.) Yeomanry, 39–46. Wounded twice. Major (D.A.Q.M.G.). T.D. Chrmn., James Kennedy & Co. Ltd. and Turners & Kennedy Ltd. Formerly Pres., Timber Trades Fed. of U.K. & Home Timber Merchants Assoc. of Scotland. Formerly Chrmn., Timber Development Assoc., now Chrmn., Ayr Area, N.F.U. of Scotland. *Cavalry Club; Western Club, Glasgow; Prestwick G.C.* Brother, J. H. B. Kennedy. Sons, 1385, 2394 & 2692.

KENNEDY, James Hugh Bingham. SF, 42³–46³.*

KENRICK, Hugh, b. 12 Aug. 13, 3rd s. of the late W. B. Kenrick (OR M 87). M, 27¹–31². Balliol, Oxford, M.A. ⚔ 69th H.A.A. Regt., R.A. (T.A.). L/Sgt. 110th H.A.A. Regt., R.A. Capt. Archibald Kenrick & Sons Ltd., Hardware Manufacturers, West Bromwich; Director from 45. High Sheriff of Warwickshire, 69–70. Brothers, W. E. & J. B. Kenrick. Son, John Alan, M, 67²–.

KENRICK, John Byng. M, 25¹–29².*

KENRICK, William Edmund, b. 21 Sept. 08, eldest s. of the late W. B. Kenrick (OR M 87). M, 22¹–27¹. Balliol, Oxford, M.A. Chrmn., Archibald Kenrick & Sons Ltd., Hardware Manufacturers, West Bromwich. Commissioner of Taxes. Guardian, Birmingham Assay Office. Pres., Birmingham Chamber of Commerce, 62. Vice-Pres., Assoc. British Chambers of Commerce. Life Governor, Birmingham Univ. Governor, City of Birmingham Polytechnic. Member of Convocation, Aston Univ. Hon. LL.D., Birmingham, 72. Brothers, H. & J. B. Kenrick. Sons, 996 & 2220.

KENT, Adrian Arnold, b. 20 Sept. 03, 2nd s. of the late S. Kent, M.D. (OR SF 80). K, 17³–21²; Scholar. Central School of Arts & Crafts & Slade School of Art, London. Art Master, Darlington Hall, 31–36. St. Marylebone Grammar School, 37–39. Head of Dept., Christ's Hospital, Horsham, 39–52. Retired. Now painting or teaching mainly for pleasure. Inverness Art Society (Committee Member). Brothers, C. H. I. & S. G. Kent.

KENT, Alan Hugh, b. 1 Nov. 11, eldest s. of the late H. B. Kent, M.S., F.R.C.S. St, 25³–29³. Solicitor, 38. ⚔ R.A., 39–41. Asst. Treasury Solicitor, 48–65. Partner, Hill Dickinson & Co. of London & Liverpool from 65. Brother, R. C. Kent.

KENT, Christopher Howard Irving, b. 19 Oct. 00, eldest s. of the late S. Kent (OR SF 80). K, 14³–19²; Head of House. Exhibitioner of Trinity Hall, Cambridge, B.A. ⚔ Pte., Straits Settlements Volunteer Forces, 40–42. P.O.W., Singapore & Siam, 42–45. Merchant, Singapore & Malaya, 22–54; London, 54–65. Retired, 65. *East India, Sports and Public Schools Club*. Brothers, A. A. & S. G. Kent.

KENT, Major Geoffrey Harcourt, b. 19 May 87, eldest s. of the late H. H. Kent. K, 02¹–05². R.M.C., Sandhurst. Gazetted to King's Own Yorkshire Light Infantry, 06. ⚔ 2nd Bn. Yorkshire Light Infantry. Capt. Dispatches. Belgian Croix de Guerre Wounded at Hill 60, Ypres. Retired, 32. ⚔ 39–45, Home Guard. The Officers' Christian Union.

KENT, Sir Harold Simson, G.C.B., Q.C., b. 11 Nov. 03, 2nd s. of the late P. H. B. Kent, O.B.E., M.C. (OR St 91). St, 17³–22²; Scholar. Merton, Oxford. Postmaster. M.A. Bar, Inner Temple, 28. Parliamentary Counsel to the Treasurer, 40. C.B., 46. Procurator-Gen. & Treasury Solicitor, 53–63. K.C.B., 54. G.C.B., 63. Standing Counsel to Church Assembly, 64. Q.C., 73. Dean of the Arches Court of Canterbury; Auditor of the Chancery Court of York; Vicar Gen. of the Province of Canterbury; Master of the Faculties. *Oxford & Cambridge United Univ. Club*. Brother, L. H. Kent. Son, 127.

KENT, Lionel Horace, b. 9 Sept. 02, eldest s. of the late P. H. B. Kent, O.B.E., M.C. (OR St 91). St, 16³–21²; Cap, 20; XXII, 21; Head of House; Minor Exhibitioner. Corpus Christi, Oxford, M.A., B.C.L. Bar, Lincoln's Inn, 25. ⋊ M.G. Bn., IX Jat Regt., Indian Army, 41–45. Arakan, 42–43, with 14th Indian Div. Practised in China where the British Crown enjoyed extra-territorial jurisdiction to 41. Legal Adviser to Electricity Council, 65–67, after 17 years in Legal Dept. *United Oxford & Cambridge; Royal Commonwealth Socy.; R.A.C. Country Club.* Brother, Sir H. S. Kent. Son, 442.

KENT, Ronald Clive, C.B., St, 30³–35².*

KENT, Sydney Graham, b. 11 Feb. 05, 3rd s. of the late Dr. S. Kent (OR SF 80). K, 19¹–23². Stockbroker from 32. *Flyfishers' Club, London; Hurlingham Club.* Brothers, C. H. I. & A. A. Kent.

KENTFIELD, Frederick Ronald. St, 23³–27².*

KENTISH, John William, b. 21 Jan. 10, elder s. of the late O. Kentish. Tu, 23³–28¹; XV, 26, 27 (Capt.); Cadet Officer. Oriel, Oxford. ⋊ R.N.V.R., 41–45. Lt. Opera Tenor, at present Director of Studies, London Opera Centre. *Savile Club.* Son, 2592.

KER, Charles Murray, O.B.E. SH, 20³–25².*

KER, Charles Paton, M.C. SH, 10¹–14².*

KERR, Robert Michael Thomas, b. 6 Nov. 19, s. of the late Major R. Kerr, D.S.O. St, 33³–37². Stock Exchange, 37–39. ⋊ R.E., R. Fusiliers & Parachute Regt., 39–46. Major. Wounded twice. Vice-Chrmn., Packaging Company. *R.N.V.R. Club; St. James's Club.*

KERR WILSON, David Alexander, b 8 Sept. 21, 4th s. of Major H. K. Wilson, J.P. Sh, 35²–39¹. Trinity Hall, Cambridge, M.A. ⋊ Coldstream Guards, 42–46. Capt. Chrmn., Deeside Merchants Ltd. High Sheriff, Flintshire, 69. J.P. *Guards Club.*

KERRY, Michael James, b. 5 Aug. 23, s. of R. Kerry. W, 37¹–41³; Levée; Scholar, 40; XV, 40, 41. Scholar of St. John's, Oxford, B.A. ⋊ 42–46, R.A.F.V.R., F.O. Bar, Lincoln's Inn, 49. Legal Asst., B.O.T. (now D.T.I.), 51. Senior Legal Asst., 59. Asst. Solicitor, 65. Principal Asst. Solicitor, 72.

KERSHAW, Peter, b. 31 May 15, eldest s. of the late H. S. Kershaw. C, 29²–34²; XI, 34; Rackets Pair, 34; winner with R. F. Lumb of Public School Rackets, 34. Worcester, Oxford, B.A. Represented Oxford at Rackets, 35, 37, 38; Tennis, 36–38 & Squash, 37–38. Old Boys Public Schools Rackets Championship. Winners for Rugby, 36–38 & 46–51. Amateur Champion, Singles, 39 & 48–51. Old Boys Public Schools Tennis Championship. Winners for Rugby, 50–51. Represented England, Bathurst Cup, 50. ⋊ R.N., 39–45. Lt. Brewer. Chrmn., Joseph Holt Ltd., Brewers. Director, Bridgewater Estates. *Vincent's Club, Oxford.* Hon. Sec., *Manchester Tennis & Racquets Club.* Son, Richard Peter, K, 68³–.

KERSHAW, Simon Alexander, b. 13 Sept. 23, s. of Capt. C. A. Kershaw, R.N. (Retired). Sh, 37²–41²; Cap, 40. ⋊ R.N. & R.N.V.R., 42–46. Lt. Member, Society Film & Television Arts also British Kinematograph Sound Television Society. Tea Boy to Asst. Gen. Man., Ealing Film Studios. Director, Film Producers Guild. Gen. Man., Granada T.V. Centre, Manchester. *Bath Club.*

KETTLE, Alan, SF, 35³–40².*

KETTLE, Capt. Alan Stafford Howard, R.N., b. 6 Aug. 25, s. of the late A. S. Kettle. T, 38²–42³. Three years' professional Engineering Training. R.N. Engineering College. Nuclear Engineering Training, R.N. College, Greenwich. Industrial Management, Strathclyde Univ. Royal Navy. Chief Staff Officer (Technical) to Flag Officer, Medway.

KETTLE, John, b. 3 Apr. 17, eldest s. of the late Sir R. Kettle. SF, 31¹–35²; XI, 34 & 35. Clare, Cambridge, B.A. ⋊ The Queen's Royal Regt. (T.A.), Iraq, Middle East, Italy. Wounded & P.O.W. Solicitor, 48. Partner in Ernest Bird & Sons of London, from 54. Brother, R. Kettle.

KETTLE, Richard. SF, 32³–37².*

KEUN, George Benjamin Edward, b. 29th Mar. 81, s. of the late A. A. Keun. B, 96²–00¹; Cap, 99; G. VIII, 99. Merchant. Partner in Keun Missir & Co., Smyrna and Summa & Keun, Constantinople. Retired to South of France.

KEW, Richard Colin Mercer, M.B., B.Chir., D.(Obst.)R.C.O.G., b. 24 Oct. 30, s. of the late J. M. Kew. W, 44³–49². Trinity Hall, Cambridge, M.A., M.B.,

B.Chir. St. Thomas's Hospital, M.R.C.S., L.R.C.P., D.(Obst.)R.C.O.G. Medical Practitioner. House Surgeon, Essex County Hospital, Colchester. House Physician in Medicine & Paediatrics, Black Notley Hospital. Senior House Officer in Casualty & Radiotherapy. Medical Registrar, Essex County Hospital. Obstetric H.P., St. Thomas's Hospital. Clinical Asst., St. Mary's Hospital, Manchester. Medico-Ethical Socy.

KEYMER, Eric William Langston, M.C., b. 10 Sept. 21, 2nd s. of the late S. L. Keymer. W, 35^3–37^1. London Univ., B.Sc. ✕ R.A., 40–46. M.C. Wounded. Civil Service. Dept. of Health & Social Security. *M.C.C.*

KEYNES, Sir Geoffrey Langdon, M.D., LL.B., D.Litt., F.R.C.P., F.R.C.S., F.R.C.O.G., b. 25 Mar. 87, s. of the late J. N. Keynes, Sc.D. SF, 01^3–05^3. Foundation Scholar. Pembroke, Cambridge, M.A., M.B., B.Chir., M.D. & Hon. Fellow. Open Entrance Scholar, St. Bartholomew's Hospital, London. Brackenbury Surgery Scholar, M.R.C.S., L.R.C.P., F.R.C.S., F.R.C.P., F.R.C.O.G., F.R.C.S. (Canada), Hon. Member American Assoc. of Surgeons. Sims Commonwealth Professor of Surgery, 56 (Africa, Canada). (Retired.) ✕ 14–18, Major, R.A.M.C. Surgical Specialist. Dispatches. Asst. Surgeon, St. Bartholomew's Hospital, 29. ✕ 39–45, Snr. Consulting Surgeon, R.A.F. Acting Air Vice-Marshal. Snr. Surgeon, St. Bartholomew's Hospital, 45–51. Hon. Fellow, Royal Socy. of Medicine. Hon. Member, Mod. Languages Assoc. of America. Gold Medal, R.C.S. Kt. Bachelor, 55. Harveian Orator, R.C.P., 58. Osler Orator, R.C.P. Gold Medal, 68. Hon. D.Litt. Oxford, Cambridge, Sheffield, Birmingham and Reading Universities. LL.D. Edinburgh Trustee, National Portrait Gallery, 42–66. Chrmn., 58–66. Lit. Trustee, Rupert Brooke. *Roxburghe Club.*

KHILKOFF - CHOUBERSKY, André (formerly Shoubersky, A.), b. 5 Sept. 07, s. of the late V. Choubersky. T, 21^2–23^2. Lycée Janson de Sailly, Paris. Strasburg Univ., graduated, 30. Mining Geologist. Exploring Lake Tilsed and Tibesti Mountains, 30–32. Mining exploration, French West Africa, 33–36. Mining in French N. Africa, 36–42. British Forces & Government Service in N. Africa, 42–48. British Steel Federation, in Guinea & Mauretania, 48–64. Consultant to British Steel Federation (now Confederation), to United Nations Development Programme, 64–72.

Now Consultant, British Steel Confederation. Fellow, Institute of Mining & Metallurgy of G.B. American Institute of Mining Engineers. Canadian Institute of Mining Engineers. Society of Economic Geologists.

KHOO, Teng Keat. K, 30^3–33^3.*

KIDNER, Harold John, b. 19 June 07, s. of the late C. Kidner. K, 21^2–25^3. ✕ Admiralty. Ferry Crew Service & Lt., 9th Bn. Norfolk Home Guard. Farmer, now retired. Rhodesia Wild Life Society. Son, 840.

KILPATRICK, Wilbert James, b. 22 Dec. 23, s. of the late J. Kilpatrick, C.A. SF, 37^3–42^1. Scholar of Corpus Christi, Oxford, M.A. ✕ The Royal Scots attached K.O.S.B., 45. Wounded. Lt. C.A., 52. With Messrs. Deloitte, Plender, Griffiths & Co., Chartered Accountants, 48–58. With Gillett Bros. Discount Co. Ltd. from 59. Director, 65. Man. Dir., 69. *The Royal Scots Club, The Lowland Brigade Club, The City University Club.* Son, Robert William Auld, SF, 70^1–.

KING, Francis William, b. 31 Mar. 07, 3rd s. of Rev. H. R. King. B, 20^3–25^2; Scholar; Head of School. Exhibition to Balliol, Oxford, B.A. Asst. Master, Manchester Grammar School, 29–35. Winchester College, 35–41, 45–69. ✕ R.A.F., 41–45. Wing-Cdr. (Retired). Son, 1373.

KING, John Wills. M, 18^3–22^2.*

KING, Peter Bryan Charles, T.D., b. 13 May 09, eldest s. of the late L. D. King. C, 23^3–26^2. Downing, Cambridge, B.A. ✕ R.A. (T.A.). Lt. P.O.W., Malaya, 42–45. Farmer. Son, Thomas Walter Bullard, C, 68^2–.

KING, Philip Walter Brunskill, b. 19 June 27, s. of the late C. A. King (OR Tu 09). Tu, 41^2–45^1. ✕ Essex Regt., 45–48. Lt. Publisher—Philip King Ltd., International Hospital Equipment & Services. Son, Philip Simon Cotman, Tu, 70^1–.

KING, Robert Launcelot. W, 14^1–18^1.*

KINGDOM, Thomas Doyle, C.B., b. 30 Oct. 10, elder s. of the late T. Kingdom. SH, 25^3–29^2; Scholar; Exhibitioner. Scholar of King's, Cambridge, M.A. Royal Institute of Public Administration. Chrmn., Executive Council, 65–66. Chrmn., Research Board from 70. Controller of Government Social Survey Dept., till 70. Now Chrmn. of a Supplementary Benefit Appeal Tribunal. Work for the National Council of Social Service. C.B. Author of Report to U.N. on "Improvement of Organisation & Management in Public Administration".

KINGSLEY, John Stewart, b. 7 Jan. 23, 2nd s. of G. H. Kingsley. C, 36^3–40^3. Clare, Cambridge. $\times$ R.E., 43–47. Member of the London Stock Exchange.

KINGSTON-upon-Thames, The Rt. Rev. The Bishop of (see Montefiore, H. W.).

KINMAN, Thomas David, b. 10 Aug.28, 2nd s. of T. H. Kinman, M.B.E. T, 41^3–46^2; R.VIII, 44–46 (Capt.); Exhibitioner; Exhibitioner of Magdalen, Oxford. M.A., D.Phil. Astronomical positions at Oxford, Pretoria & Cape Observatories, S. Africa, and at the Lick Observatory at California University. Presently employed as Astronomer at the Kitt Peak National Observatory, Tucson, Arizona, U.S.A.

KINROSS, Robert Ivor, b. 5 Dec. 08, s. of the late Charles Kinross. SH, 22^2–25^3. Chartered Electrical Engineer. F.I.E.E. Director of Research, Rediffusion Engineering Ltd. Member of Royal Television Society.

KIRK, Geoffrey Peter. C, 25^3–29^2. Son, 1048.*

KIRK-GREENE, Anthony Hamilton Millard, M.B.E., b. 16 May 25, elder s. of the late L. Kirk-Greene. Tu, 38^3–43^2; Scholar; Levée; Head of House; H. XI, 41–43 (Capt.); XXII, 42, 43; Exhibitioner. Scholar of Clare, Cambridge, M.A. $\times$ Royal Warwickshire Regt., 43–44. 8th Punjab Regt., 44–47. Capt. & Adjutant. H.M. Col. Admin. Service (Nigeria), 50–57. Senior Lecturer, Institute of Admin., Zaria, Nigeria, 57–61. Harkness Fellowship, North-western Univ. & California Univ., Los Angeles, 58–59. Reader in Pub. Admin., Ahmadu Bello Univ., 61–66. Author of numerous books, articles, reviews on African History & Politics. Snr. Research Fellow, African Studies, St. Antony's College, Oxford, from 67. M.B.E., 63. *Hawks; United Oxford & Camb. Univ.* Brother, C. W. E. Kirk-Greene.

KIRK-GREENE, Christopher Walter Edward, b. 19 July 26, 2nd s. of the late L. Kirk-Greene. Tu, 40^2–45^2; Levée; Exhibitioner; Capt. of Fencing, 43–5.

Christ Church, Oxford, M.A. Dukes (French) Prize (Christ Church). Won Freshman's Foil Cup; Half Blue for Epée Match, 46–48. Hon. Sec., O.U.F.C., 46. Asst. d'Anglais, Lycée Berthollet, Annecy, France, 48–49. Asst. Master, Eastbourne Coll. from 49. (Head of Modern Languages Dept. since 62.) *East India, Sports & Public Schools Club.* Committee, Public Schools L.T.A. Publications, various books on French language. Brother, A. H. M. Kirk-Greene.

KIRKWOOD, Lord (Kirkwood, David Harvie), b. 24 Nov. 31, eldest s. of the late Rt. Hon. Lord Kirkwood. W, 45^2–50^1. Trinity Hall, Cambridge, M.A., Ph.D. Research Fellow, M.I.T., Mass. Research Scientist, U.S. Steel Corporation, Pittsburgh. Lecturer, Sheffield Univ. Brother, 630.

KIRWAN, Brig. Rudolph Charles Hogg, D.S.O., O.B.E., b. 22 May 03, s. of the late Gen. B. B. Kirwan. Tu, 17^3–20^3; XXII, 20; Rackets Pair, 20 (Capt.). R.M.A., Woolwich. Gazetted to R.A., 23. Lt., 25. Capt., 36. Major, 39. $\times$ France, 39–40. O.B.E. India & Persia, 42–43. M.E., Sicily, Italy & Greece, 43–46. Brigadier, C.R.A., 4th Div., 44. D.D. Military Ops., War Office, 46–49. Retired, 49. D.S.O.

KISCH, John Marcus, C.M.G. SH, 29^3–35^2.*

KITCHEN, Stanley, b. 23 Aug. 13, eldest s. of the late P. I. Kitchen. T, 27^1–31^2; Major Foundationer. $\times$ R.A.S.C. Major. A.C.A., 37, F.C.A., 53. Member of Council of Institute of Chartered Accountants in England & Wales from 66. (Chrmn., Parliamentary & Law Committee, 69–72.) President, Birmingham & West Midlands Society of Chartered Accountants, 57–58. Partner, Touche Ross & Co., Birmingham, from 48. *Union Club & Chamber of Commerce Club, Birmingham; Copt Heath G.C.*

KITOVITZ, Lionel. St, 39^2–40^3.*

KITSON, Richard Inglis, b. 17 Jan. 25, elder s. of the late Cdr. E. H. Kitson, R.N. SF, 38^3–43^2; XI, 43; Cadet Officer; Exhibitioner. $\times$ R.N.V.R., 44–46. S/Lt. Trinity, Cambridge, B.A. Schoolmaster, Prep Schools. Deputy Headmaster, The Pilgrims' School, Winchester. For some years Hon. Secretary of Rugby Meteors.

KITTERMASTER, David Darlington, b. 6 May 07, 4th s. of the late F. J. Kittermaster (A). SH, 21¹–26²; XXII, 26. Trinity, Oxford, B.A. Schoolmaster from 34. Headmaster, Framlingham College Junior School, 48–68. Retired. *Vincent's Oxford.* Brothers, M. R. & N. C. Kittermaster.

KITTERMASTER, Maurice Radcliffe, b. 7 Aug. 05, 3rd s. of the late F. J. Kittermaster (A). SH, 19²–24²; XI, 24; H. XI, 24; Cap. Queen's, Oxford, B.A. Retired. Brothers, D. D. & N. C. Kittermaster. Son, 54.

KITTERMASTER, Norman Colley, b. 7 Aug. 09, 5th s. of the late F. J. Kittermaster (A). SH, 23²–27¹. Asst. Manager, Theatre Royal, Brighton, 37–41. ⚔ Lt. & Paymaster, R.A.P.C., 42–45. Lt., R.A.S.C./ E.F.I., 45–46. Asst. Manager, Queen's Hotel, Cardiff, 47–49. Librarian, Rugby School, 53–72. Brothers, M. R. & D. D. Kittermaster.

KITWOOD, Peter, b. 24 June 06, younger s. of the late T. Kitwood. SF, 20²–24². Studied languages in Germany & France privately, 24–25. ⚔ Lincolnshire Regt., 40–41. R.A.O.C., 41–45, Capt. Director, T. Kitwood & Sons, Wholesale Grocers & Wine Merchants, till 69. Part-time Accountant from 69 with firm of Wholesale Grocers in Boston, Lincs. Brother, R. T. S. Kitwood. Son, 561.

KITWOOD, Col. Reginald Thomas Slator, b. 8 Oct. 97, elder s. of the late T. Kitwood. SF, 12¹–16¹. Gazetted to the R.A., 17. ⚔ 114 Battery, R.F.A. "J" Battery, R.H.A. Lt., "L" Battery, 21. Transferred to Duke of Cornwall's Light Infantry, 29. ⚔ Commandant, Depot, Corps of Military Police, 40–41. O.C., 70th Bn. Royal Inniskilling Fusiliers, 42. Lt.-Col. Commandant, 10 Holding & Selection Centre. Col., 45. Commandant, College of the Rhine Army, 45–46. Dispatches. P.C.O., Penal Branch, Legal Div., C.C.G., 47–48. Retired from Army, 49. Brother, P. Kitwood.

KLEIN, John Victor, b. 2 July 08, youngest s. of the late C. Klein. C, 22²–27²; Head of House; Cap; Sw. VI, 26–27 (Capt.). Clare, Cambridge, M.A. ⚔ R.A.S.C., 40–45. Major. Company Director (Retired). Ex-Managing Director, Associated Tube Co. Ltd. *R.A.C.*

KNEESHAW, Richard. Tu, 26³–28³.*

KNIGHT, Claude Leonard. T, 30³–34².*

KNIGHT, Francis Cecil Corbet. W & M, 23¹–26².*

KNOWLES, Robert Bernard. SH, 33¹–37².*

KNOX, Collie, b. 13 Mar. 97, 2nd s. of the late E. F. V. Knox, K.C., M.P. St, 11¹–14³. R.M.C., Sandhurst. ⚔ R.F.C. & Queen's Royal Regt. Wounded. Capt. on Staff, War Office. P.A. to G.O.C., London Air Defences, 17. Staff of Governor of Bombay, Uganda & Governor-General of Sudan. Entered Fleet Street in 28 on "Daily Express". Joined "Daily Mail" as Special Columnist, 38. Rejoined "Daily Mail" as Columnist in 45. Resigned, 55. Joined Newnes Pearson Publications. Author & Free-lance Journalist. European Columnist & Critic on "The Morning Telegraph", New York, from 55. Was first Radio Columnist-Critic in Fleet Street. Director of Public Relations, E.N.S.A., at Drury Lane Theatre. Joined "The Star" as Feature Writer. Author of 14 books. First book, "It might have been You", was Book Society's Choice, 38.

KNOX, George Lathan. W, 13³–18².*

KNOX, John, M.B.E., T.D., b. 8 Mar. 10. elder s. of the late J. Knox. SF, 23³–28²; XV, 27; XI, 28. Clare, Cambridge, M.A. Textile Manufacturer. 121 Field Regt., R.A. (T.A.). ⚔ R.A. Brigade Major. H.Q., R.A., 52nd Lowland Division. M.B.E., p.s.c. Dispatches. T.D. Man. Dir., Family Firm. *Golfers' Club.*

KNYVETT, Lt.-Col. John Lefroy, M.B.E., M.C., b. 26 Nov. 19, s. of Major J. S. Knyvett, Royal Warwickshire Regt. Tu, 33³–37³; Levée. R.M.A., Woolwich. Gazetted to R.A., 39. ⚔ 8th Army & N.W. Europe. M.C. Major. Seconded, Nigerian Army, 61–63; N.A.T.O. Staff, 64–66 (Oslo) & 70–72 (S.H.A.P.E.) M.A., Warsaw, 67–69. Now on Defence Policy Staff, Defence Ministry, retiring Nov., 74. M.B.E. *Army & Navy Club.*

KOPPEL, John Patrick, b. 17 Nov. 13, eldest s. of the late P. A. Koppel, C.M.G., C.B.E. SH, 27²–32¹. University of Freiburg-im-Breisgau, Magdalen, Oxford, B.A. Chartered Textile Technologist. ⚔ Welsh Guards, 41–45, N.W. Europe. Capt., 45. Allied Commission for Austria i/c Secretariat, Economic Directorate. Major, 46. Director, Courtaulds Ltd., 61. Deputy Chrmn. from 68. Member of Council, Institute of Directors. *Guards Club, Army & Navy Club.*

KUENSTLER, Peter Harold Keith, b. 12 Dec. 19, 3rd s. of G. Kuenstler. W, 33³–38²; Scholar; Levée; Head of House; Head of School; Exhibitioner. Scholar of Oriel, Oxford, M.A. Oxford House in Bethnal Green, 40–48. Research Fellow, University of Bristol Institute of Education, 48–55. Secretary, African Development Trust, 56–64. Social Development Officer, United Nations, since 64. Society for International Development. Author of various publications.

L

LACEY, David Charles, M.B., M.R.C.P., b. 17 Sept. 25, 2nd s. of W. G. Lacey, C.S.I., C.I.E., I.C.S. (Rtd.). SH, 39³–40². Diocesan College, S. Africa. King's, Cambridge, B.A., and St. Thomas's Hospital, London, 47–50. M.B., B.Chir., M.R.C.P. House Appointments, St. Thomas's, 51–52. R.A.F. Medical Branch (Sqn. Ldr.), 53–54. General Practitioner in Chichester, Sussex, since 55. Brother, M. G. Lacey.

LACEY, Major Desmond Ralph. T, 28³–33¹.*

LACEY, Michael Graham, b. 16 July 21, elder s. of W. E. Lacey, C.S.I., C.I.E., I.C.S. (Rtd.). SH, 35²–40². King's, Cambridge, M.A., F.I.Mech.E. Consultant, Water & Effluent Treatment. Brother, C. D. Lacey.

LAIDLAW, Christopher Charles Fraser, b. 9 Aug. 22, s. of the late H. A. L. Laidlaw. SF, 36³–40². St. John's, Cambridge, M.A. ✕ R. Fusiliers, 40–41. Intelligence Corps, 41–46. Major. Man. Dir., The British Petroleum Co. Ltd. *The Bath Club.*

LAING, George Davys, M.B., M.R.C.S., L.R.C.P., b. 23 July 16, 2nd s. of Dr. G. D. Laing. St, 30¹–34²; Head of School Music. Corpus Christi, Cambridge, M.A., M.B., B.Chir. St. Thomas's Hospital, London, M.R.C.S., L.R.C.P. House Surgeon & Physician, St. Thomas's, 40–41. ✕ R.A.F.V.R. (Medical Branch), 41–46. Sqn. Ldr. Dispatches. General Practitioner. Brother, S. R. S. Laing. Sons, 2252, Richard George, St, 67³–71³ & Andrew Marcus K., 68³–.

LAING, Stephen Rea Stuart, M.R.C.S., L.R.C.P., b. 7 Dec. 18, 4th s. of Dr. D. G. Laing. St, 32³–36¹. Corpus Christi, Cambridge, M.A., M.B., B.Ch., D.Obst. R.C.O.G. ✕ R.E., 40–45. Capt. Working mostly abroad in sixteen different countries. B.M.A. Brother, G. D. Laing.

LAIRD, Graeme Stuart, b. 12 Apr. 17, 2nd s. of the late J. Laird, I.S.O. M, 30³–35¹. ✕ R.E. Lt.-Col. then R.E. (T.A.). Man. Dir., Scottish Brick Co. Ltd., Glasgow. *The Western Club, Royal Northern Yacht Club.*

LAMB, Philip Sherard, b. 3 Jan. 16, s. of the late J. Lamb (OR M 94). M, 29³–34²; Cap, 33; H. XI, 32–33. With Charringtons, Fuel Merchants, London, 34–35. Joined Imperial Tobacco Group's Rhodesian Branch, 36. Now Chrmn. & Man. Dir. of Commercial Union Assurance Company's Rhodesian Company. ✕ 39–45, 2nd E. Yorks. Regt., S. Rhodesian Armoured Car Regt., 6th S. African Armoured Div. Capt. *Salisbury Club, Rhodesian Pioneers Society, Mashonaland Turf Club.*

LAMBERT, George Byron, b. 29 July 22, s. of G. L. Lambert. W, 36¹–41¹; Cadet Officer. Peterhouse, Cambridge. R.M.C., Sandhurst. Gazetted to the Buffs, 42. ✕ Seconded to King's African Rifles. Lt. Royal Agricultural College, Cirencester. Now Farmer & Land Owner. *Farmers' Club.*

LAMBERT, George Ronald. M, 45²–49³.*

LAMBERT, Sir Greville Foley, Bt., M.C. St, 14²–19².*

LAMBERT, Capt. Geoffrey Thornton, D.S.C., R.N., b. 4 Oct. 03, eldest s. of the late Sir G. B. Lambert, K.C.S.I. Tu, 17¹–21². Joined R.N., 21 (Public School Entry–Cadetship). Executive Branch of R.N. Various appointments from Cadet to Capt. Rtd., 57. D.S.C. *United Service & Royal Aero (Pall Mall).* Son, G. R. Lambert.

LAMBERT, James Dewe, D.Sc., b. 9 Oct. 12, eldest s. of the late B. Lambert, O.B.E., D.Sc. SH, 26³–30¹; Scholar. Exhibitioner of Trinity, Oxford, M.A., D.Sc. Fellow & Tutor of Trinity, Oxford, 38. University Lecturer in Physical Chemistry. ✂ R.E. Technical Staff Officer, 41–45. S.E. Asia, 42–45. Major.

LAMBIE, John Edward. C, 13³–16³.*

LANCASTER, John Evelyn Hogg. SF, 22²–25².*

LANDAU, Stefan Witold, b. 5 Feb. 19, s. of the late S. J. Landau. St, 32³–36³; Lawn Tennis VI. Trinity, Cambridge. Caen University, France. ✂ R.A.F. Bomber Pilot. Sqn. Ldr., 40–46. Dispatches. Officer of Official Operations Executive. Bar, Lincoln's Inn, 47. Practising Barrister. Legal Adviser, Govt. of Libya. Senior Legal Officer, United Nations Organisation. *Junior Carlton, Special Forces Club.*

LANE, Thomas Ernest, b. 27 Mar. 33, 2nd s. of E. A. Lane. Sh, 46³–51³; XXII; Fives IV, 50–51. N/S. 13/18 Royal Hussars (Q.M.O.). ✂ Malaya, 52–53. 2nd Lt. Farmer.

LANG, John Hamish Michael Gordon, b. 3 July 24, s. of the late J. G. Lang. Tu, 38²–42¹; Cap; H. XI, 42. ✂ R.N. Engineering College, 42. Administrative Staff College, Henley. Retired as Lt.-Cdr., R.N., 54. M.B.I.M. In Industry, manufacturing Machine Tools and Land Boilers, as Director, 54–68. Farmer from 68. Son, Mark Harvey Gordon, Tu, 72²–.

LANGFORD, Col. Richard Crawford, M.R.C.S., L.R.C.P., b. 28 May 07, s. of the late Major C. Langford, D.S.O. C, 21²–25¹; Littleboy Exhibitioner. Queens', Cambridge, B.A. St. Thomas's Hospital, London, M.R.C.S., L.R.C.P., D.A.(Ire.). Commissioned, R.A.M.C., 31. Retired as Col., 55. Specialist Anaesthetist. Served in India, E. Africa, Burma (Dispatches, 44), Germany. Director of Chamber of Commerce, Limerick, 61–63. Man. Dir., 57–67, J. Metterson & Sons, Limerick. Now retired. *Army & Navy Club.*

LANYON, John Charles. St, 35³–39².*

LARN, The Rev. Nigel, b. 4 Jan. 21, s. of Capt. S. C. Larn, M.C. W, 34³–39²; Waring Exhibitioner; Levée; Head of House. Scholar of Keble, Oxford, M.A. Parish Priest (R.C.), Sydenham. *Linguists' Club, London.*

LARRETT, John Humphrey, b. 3 May 33, s. of the late Rev. S. A. Larrett. SH, 46³–51¹. N/S. R. Fusiliers. ✂ Korea, 52. 2nd Lt. Dispatches. Wounded. Scholar of

Lincoln, Oxford, B.A. Studied Japanese at International Christian University, Tokyo. Now studying pottery at West Surrey College of Art & Design. Shell, 56–63, mostly in Japan. Present employment—Petit Entrepreneur and Potter.

LASDUN, Denys Louis, C.B.E., F.R.I.B.A., b. 8 Sept. 14, s. of the late N. Lasdun. W, 28²–32². Architectural Association. ✂ R.E., 40–45. Major. M.B.E., F.R.I.B.A., 47. Architect. C.B.E.

LASSETTER, Frederic Joseph, b. 23 May 31, younger s. of the late F. M. Lassetter. SH, 45²–49². R.M.A., Sandhurst. Gazetted to the 3rd Carabiniers (Prince of Wales Dragoon Guards), 51. Regular Army to 67. (A.D.C. to Gen. Speidel, 57–60.) Liverpool University, 67–72, B.A. Schoolmaster at St. Richard Gwyn R.C. High School, Flint. *Cavalry Club.*

LATHAM, Lt.-Col. Christopher, b. 14 Nov. 96, 5th s. of the late W. Latham, K.C. St, 10³–14³. King's, Cambridge, M.A. C.Eng. F.I.Mech.E. ✂ 14–19. 2nd Lt. 2/5 Hampshire Regt., India and Palestine. Lt., 72, Punjabi Regt. Seconded to 3rd Kashmir Rifles on Special Service. Mather & Platt Ltd., Apprentice, 21–24. Pulsometer Eng. Co. Ltd., Pump Dept., Manager, Filtration Dept., 24–39. ✂ Capt. R.A., A.A. Home Command, 39–43. R.E., S.H.A.E.F. Planning for Operation Overland, 43. Lt.-Col. Staff Officer, R.E., H.Q., 21 Army Group. Dispatches. Lt.-Col., 43–45. *Athenæum.* Son, J. S. Latham.

LATHAM, Ian Russell Andrews, b. 10 Feb. 28, eldest s. of R. Latham. SF, 41³–46²; Scholar; H. XI, 46. Exhibitioner of Balliol, Oxford, B.A. N/S. Somaliland Scouts, 49–51. 2nd Lt. Member of French Religious Order, "Les Petits Frères de Jesus".

LATHAM, Jeremy Stuart, b. 20 June 26, elder s. of Lt.-Col. C. Latham (OR St 10). M, 40²–43². King's, Cambridge, B.A. ✂ Attd. Madras Sappers & Miners, 45–48. 2nd Lt. Farmer. *Farmers' Club.*

LATHBURY, Robert James, b. 11 Mar. 94, s. of the late R. Lathbury. M, 08²–11³. Emmanuel, Cambridge, M.A. ✂ 14–19, Artists Rifles, 6th London Regt. Capt. Wounded twice. Colonial Agricultural Service, Tanganyika & Kenya, 21–47. *Lansdowne Club.*

LATIFI, Danial. W, 30^3–34^2.*

LATIMER, Sir Courtenay Robert, C.B.E., b. 13 Jan. 11, elder s. of the late Sir Courtenay Latimer, K.C.I.E., C.S.I. St, 25^2–30^2; Exhibitioner; R. VIII, 29–30; Levée; Head of House. Scholar of Christ Church, Oxford, M.A. Indian Civil Service & Indian Political Service, 35–47. H.M. Overseas Service (Southern Africa), 47–64. With Foreign Office (Southern Africa), 64–66. Registrar, Kingston Polytechnic, from 67. Knight. C.B.E. Brother, G. D. Latimer. Son, 2163.

LATIMER, Geoffrey Denis, b. 20 Nov. 14, younger s. of the late Sir Courtenay Latimer, K.C.I.E., C.S.I. St, 28^3–33^2; Rupert Brooke Prize; Canon Evans Ecclesiastical History Prize. Exhibitioner of Christ Church, Oxford, M.A. Gladstone Memorial Exhibitioner, 37. Unilever, 38–56 (served in India, Argentine & Uruguay). Beechams, 56–59. British Tobacco (Australia) from 59. *R.A.C. of Australia.* Brother, C. R. Latimer. Son, 1359.

LATTA, Gordon Cuthbertson. W, 18^3–23^2.*

LAURANCE, John Bidwell. W, 03^3–08^1.*

LAURIE, Frederick Grieve, M.C., b. 20 Dec. 93, elder s. of the late H.M. Laurie, I.C.S. C, 07^3–12^2. Gonville & Caius, Cambridge, B.A. ✕ 9th. Bn. Loyal North Lancashire Regt., att. 7th Bn. Durham Light Infantry. Capt. Wounded twice. M.C., Order of St. Anne. With Shaw, Wallace & Co., Merchants, Bombay. Retired. Brother, H. C. Laurie.

LAURIE, Herbert Crawford, b. 14 Apr. 95, younger s. of the late H. M. Laurie, I.C.S. C, 08^3–13^1. Gonville & Caius, Cambridge. ✕ 1st Bn. Cambridgeshire Regt., 3rd Bn. K.R.R.C., att. 80th Trench Mortar Bty. Lt. Solicitor, 24. With Robins, Hay, Waters & Hay of London. Retired. Brother, F. G. Laurie.

LAVER, George Harrison. B, 37^3–42^2.*

LAW, Donald William. Tu, 25^3–30^1.*

LAWRENCE, Denys Antony Lyndon, b. 13 May 16, 2nd s. of the late B. L. Lawrence (OR SH 97). SH, 30^1–34^2. Trinity, Cambridge, B.A. Won C.U.B.C. Pairs. Took up Engineering on leaving University. ✕ Grenadier Guards, 40–46. Wounded.

Capt. Insurance Broker, Lloyd's. *Leander.* Brother, O. L. Lawrence.

LAWRENCE, Lt.-Col. Edward Lafone Graham, D.S.O., M.C. C, 04^3–09^2.*

LAWRENCE, John Cecil, b. 31 May 02, 2nd s. of the late H. R. Lawrence. Tu, 16^2–20^2. Oriel, Oxford, B.A. Bar, Inner Temple, 27. ✕ R.A., 39–45. Lt.-Col. Dispatches. Barrister. *Bath Club.*

LAWRENCE, Oliver Lyndon, C.B.E., b. 27 Feb. 11, eldest s. of the late A. L. Lawrence. SH, 24^3–29^2. Trinity, Cambridge, B.A. Member, Institute of Management Consultants. ✕ 39/45, Foreign Office & Ministry of Economic Warfare, C.B.E. Stevenson Jordan & Harrison Ltd. (Director), Management Consultants, London, from 64. Brother, D. A. L. Lawrence.

LAWSON, Major Alexander David Duncan, M.B.E., b. 31 Mar. 04, s. of W. Lawson. Tu, 17^3–22^2. Trinity Hall, Cambridge, B.A. Farmer in Western Australia, 29–37, & in Scotland from 38. Now retired. ✕ R.A. (T.A.), 39–45. Major. M.B.E. *New Club, Edinburgh; R. & A. G.C.; United Oxford & Cambridge Club.* Son, 883.

LAWSON, Donald Michael Brook (see Brook-Lawson, D. M.).

LAWSON, James Stewart, b. 19 Sept. 20, s. of the late J. Lawson, M.D., F.R.C.P.(E.), LL.D. K, 34^3–39^2; Scholar; Levée; Head of House; Cap, 39; Tom Hughes Prize. Scholar of Trinity, Oxford. ✕ 1st Fife and Forfar Yeomanry, 40–45. Capt. Administrative Officer Class II, Colonial Service. Service in Gold Coast, 47–56 (Asst. District Commissioner), District Commissioner/Government Agent, Clerk to Cabinet. Asst. Man. Dir., Lawsons Ltd., 57–64. Asst. Secretary, The Institute of Chartered Accountants of Scotland, 65–71. *R. & A. G.C.; The Hon. Company of Edinburgh Golfers; The Oxford & Camb. Golfing Society.* Chairman, Rules of Golf Committee (R. & A.), 68–72.

LAWSON, Prof. John Bateman, M.B., B.Chir., F.R.C.O.G. Sh, 35^3–39^3.*

LAYCOCK, Richard Tempest, b. 27 July 30, s. of G. K. Laycock. W, 44^2–48^3; Exhibitioner; Leaving Scholarship. Scholar of King's, Cambridge, M.A. Certificate of Competent Knowledge in Swedish, 53. N/S. R.A., 49. 2nd Lt. A.C.A., 56. Price Waterhouse & Co.,

Chartered Accountants, from 53. Audit Manager since 61.

LEA, The Rev. Arthur Blackwall, b. 31 Oct. 06, 3rd s. of the late J. Lea (OR SF 75). C, 20^3–24^3; XV, 24. In the Bank of England, 25–39. Univ. of Emmanuel College, Saskatoon, Canada, 39. Graduated Testamur with Great Distinction, 42. Ordained Deacon, 41; Priest, 42. Rector of Breamore. Fordingbridge, Hants. Brothers, R. S. & G. H. C. Lea. Son, 2117.

LEA, George Holden Clark. C, 25–29^3.*

LEA, Robert Simcox, b. 26 Nov. 97, eldest s. of the late J. Lea (OR SF 75). C, 11^3–16^1; XV, 15. Brasenose, Oxford, M.A. ✕ The Rifle Brigade, 16–19. Salonica & A. of O., Germany. Lt. ✕ Middlesex Regt. and R. Signals, 40–45. Paiforce, M.E.F. & B.L.A. Capt. Preparatory Schoolmaster, Lindley Lodge, Nuneaton, 24–35. Asst. Editor, the "Complete Peerage" till 59. Asst., History of Parliament Trust, 59–70. Brothers, A. B. & G. H. C. Lea.

LEACH, Arthur Croome, T.D., b. 26 Jan. 95, s. of the late A. S. Leach. SH, 09^1–13^2. St. John's, Oxford, M.A. ✕ A.S.C., R.F.A. Lt. T.D. Asst. Master, Clifton College. Retired. Son, J. C. Leach.

LEACH, Eric Rivington, b. 7 Aug. 05, s. of the late R. E. H. Leach, O.B.E. (OR W 88). W, 19^3–23^1. Tea Planter, 27–40. ✕ 2nd Royal Lancers (G.H.) Indian Army, 40–46. Capt. P.O.W., 41–45. District Manager, Group of Tea Estates, Nyasaland, 47–51. Son, 2595.

LEACH, John Croome, b. 4 June 26, eldest s. of A. C. Leach (OR SH 09). SH, 40^1–44^2. St. John's, Oxford. ✕ R.N.V.S.R. 44–48. S/Lt. Member, Institute of Petroleum. Oilbroker. *Naval Club.*

LEACOCK, Aubrey Gordon, C.B.E., F.R.C.S., b. 27 Oct. 18, 2nd s. of Sir Dudley Leacock. B, 32^2–35^3. Scholar. Exhibitioner of Gonville & Caius, Cambridge. Surgical Brackenbury Scholar of St. Bartholomew's Hospital, London. M.A., M.B., M.Chir., F.R.C.S.(Eng.). Various appointments in England. Senior Surgeon, Queen Elizabeth Hospital, Barbados. Royal Society of Medicine. Association of Surgeons of G.B. & I. C.B.E., 62. Lately, President, W. Indies Yachting Association. *Yacht Club, Barbados.* Brother, D. G. Leacock.

LEACOCK, Dudley Gordon. B, 21^3–26^2. Son, 73.*

LEADER, The Rev. Robert, M.C., b. 7 Nov. 11, s. of R. Leader. SF, 25^3–30^2; Cap, 29; XI, 29–30. Christ's, Cambridge, M.A. Asst. Manager, Rugby Club, Notting Hill, 33–35. Bishop's Hostel, Lincoln, 36–37. Ordained, 37. Curate, St. Paul's, Jarrow-on-Tyne, 37–40. ✕ Royal Army Chaplains Dept., 40–46. C.F. 4th Class. Vicar of St. Peter's, Abbeydale, Sheffield, 46–54. Vicar of Breedon-on-the-Hill, Leics., 54–59. Vicar of Ashby Folville, Twyford and Thorpe Satchville, Leics., from 59. Rural Dean from 60. M.C. Commendation.

LEAPINGWELL, Robert Edward. St & W, 40^3–43^1.*

LEARMOUNT, Capt. Dennis Kenelm Leonard, D.S.C., R.N., b. 11 Sept. 19, s. of the late Major L. W. Learmount, D.S.O., M.C., C.M.G. B, 33^3–37^2; XV, 36; Athletics Cup; Water Polo Team. Civil Service Commissioners Exam. for entry into R.N. Joined R.N., 38. ✕ Lt.-Cdr., R.N., D.S.C. & Bar. Capt., R.N., Director of Naval Manning & Training. M.B.I.M. *Army & Navy Club.* Sons, 2111 & 2807.

LEATHES Cdr. John Alexander de Mussenden, O.B.E., R.N., b. 12 May 28, 2nd s. of the late Lt.-Cdr. J. D. de M. Leathes, R.N. SH, 41^3–45^2. Joined Navy, 45. Served mainly at sea. Since then in Far East, Mediterranean, Atlantic, W. Indies & Home Waters in a variety of ships. Promoted Lt. 50, Lt.-Cdr. 58, Commander, 65. Qualified professional Navigating Officer, 55. Commanded H.M. Ships, *Briton*, 56; *Lewiston*, 64; *Picton*, 66; *Sirius*, 68–70, & Senior Officer of the 2nd M/S Sqn., 64, & 11th M/S Sqn., 65–66. Saw service in Malayan Campaign, 49–50; Korea, 50–51; Indonesian Confrontation (Malaysia & Borneo), 65–66. O.B.E. At present employed by the Ministry of Defence. Member of the Royal Institute of Navigation. Additional Officer of the O.B.E., 66. Brother, R. E. de M. Leathes.

LEATHES, Capt. Robert Edwards de Mussenden, R.N., b. 5 Jan. 24, elder s. of the late Lt.-Cdr. J. D. de M. Leathes, R.N. SH, 37^3–42^1. R.N. Special Entry, 42. ✕ Served in the Mediterranean & N. Atlantic & Channel. Lt., 45. Specialist in Navigation & Direction. Capt., R.N. Commanded H.M. Ships *Alert* & *Nubian*. Brother, J. A. de M. Leathes.

LEAVER, John David Almond, b. 10 Mar. 26, elder s. of the late J. B. Leaver. SH, 39³–44². ✕ R.N.V.R., 45–47. S/Lt. Trinity Hall, Camb., M.A., LL.B. Solicitor. *Royal Thames Y.C.* Brother, W. A. J. Leaver.

LEAVER, William Anthony James, b. 20 Mar. 30, 2nd s. of the late J. B. Leaver. SH, 43³–48³; Levée; Head of House; XV, 48; H. XI, 48. Trinity Hall, Cambridge, B.A. Solicitor, 56. Partner, Norton, Rose, Botterell & Roche. Member of the Law Society. Brother, J. D. A. Leaver.

LEDINGHAM, John Gerard Garvin, b. 19 Oct. 29, s. of the late J. Ledingham. K, 43³–48²; XXII. New College, Oxford, M.A., B.Ch., D.M., Hockey Blue. Middlesex Hospital Medical School, M.R.C.S., F.R.C.P. Consultant Physician, United Oxford Hospitals; Lecturer in Clinical Medicine, University of Oxford. Member, Association of Physicians of Gt. Britain & N. Ireland. Scottish H. XI, 55–57. *Vincent's Club, Oxford.*

LEDWARD, Philip Archibald, M.C., b. 6 May 91, s. of the late A. P. Ledward. W, 05³–10²; Cap, 09; XXII, 09–10. Christ Church, Oxford, M.A. ✕ 2nd Bn. H.A.C. 9th (att. 14th & 15th) Bn. Hampshire Regt. Staff Capt. Capt. Wounded. M.C. Dispatches. Cotton Manufacturer till 35. Bursar of Harrow School till 51. Retired.

LEE, Douglass Boardman, b. 22 Aug. 03, eldest s. of the late D. C. Lee, LL.B. B, 17²–21³; S. VIII, 20–21; R. VIII, 20–21; Crick Winner, 21. Cornell University, New York. Oriel, Oxford, B.A. Bar, Middle Temple, 28. In practice of Law, New York City, 29–32. Ithaca, N.Y., since 32, except in Govt. Service, Washington, D.C., 42–46. Brother, H. C. Lee.

LEE, Hardy Campbell, b. 15 July 10; 2nd s. of the late D. C. Lee, LL.B. B, 24¹–28². Clare, Cambridge. Cornell University, U.S.A., LL.B. Bar, Middle Temple, 39. ✕ R.A.S.C., 39–46. Major. Brother, D. B. Lee.

LEE, John Robert Carne, b. 14 July 21, s. of R. H. Lee. K, 35¹–40²; Jex-Blake Exhibitioner. Balliol, Oxford, M.A. Bar, Inner Temple, 48. Solicitor, 57. ✕ 10th R. Hussars (P.O.W.). Partner in Ellis Peirs & Young Jackson of London. *Bath Club.*

LEE-SMITH, Major Cyril (formerly Smith, C. L.). T, 18²–21¹.*

LEECH, Ralph Bosdin, b. 22 Nov. 11, 2nd s. of the late A. J. Leech, C.I.E., M.B.E. B, 25³–29². Christ's, Cambridge, M.B., B.Chir. London Hospital Medical College, M.R.C.S., L.R.C.P., T.D.D. (Wales). Medical Officer, Church Missionary Socy., at Mengo Hospital, Uganda, 38–46. Medical Superintendent, Maseno Hospital, Kenya, 47–62. Now, General Practitioner. Lay Reader, Church of England.

LEEDHAM-GREEN, Hugh Lascelles, b. 8 Mar. 08, 3rd s. of the late Prof. C. A. Leedham-Green, Ch.M., F.R.C.S. C, 22¹–26²; XI, 25–26. Balliol, Oxford, M.A. Solicitor, 34. ✕ 40–45, R.A.F. Sqn. Ldr. Dispatches twice. Solicitor. Partner in Sole Sawbridge & Co., London. *M.C.C., Bath.* President, *Hampstead C.C.* since 67. President, *Rugby Meteors C.C.*, 73. Vice-Chrmn., British Tunisian Socy. since 71. Brothers, J. C. & R. G. Leedham Green.

LEEDHAM-GREEN, John Charles, F.R.C.S., b. 30 Oct. 02, eldest s. of the late Prof. C. A. Leedham-Green, Ch.M., F.R.C.S. C, 16³–21¹. Balliol, Oxford, M.B., B.M., B.Ch. Middlesex Hospital, F.R.C.S., F.R.C.G.P. President, East Suffolk Branch, B.M.A., 71–72. ✕ R.A.M.C. Lt.-Col. Mainly General Practice. Excursions into Surgery. Brothers, R. G. & H. L. Leedham-Green.

LEEDHAM-GREEN, Richard Garth, b. 6 Jan. 05, 2nd s. of the late Prof. C. A. Leedham-Green, Ch.M., F.R.C.S. C, 18³–22². Birmingham University. Man. Dir., J. B. & S. Lees Ltd., Albion Strip Mills, West Bromwich. ✕ G.S.O.2, F6 Sector, Birmingham Home Guard. Major. *Little Aston G.C.* Brothers, J. C. & H. L. Leedham-Green. Son, 1497.

LEES, Stanley Lawrence, M.V.O., b. 2 Mar. 11, 2nd s. of C. Lees, M.R.C.S., L.R.C.P. W, 24³–29². Scholar. New College, Oxford. Solicitor, 36. Inland Revenue, 36–46. M.V.O., 52. H.M. Treasury, 46–66. Ministry of Transport (and Environment Dept.), 67–70. Retired through ill-health, 70. *E.S.U.*

LEES-JONES, John Richard, b. 20 Nov. 22, eldest s. of J. Lees-Jones, J.P. W, 36³–40¹. King's, Cambridge, B.A. ✕ R.N.V.R. Lt. (A). Brewer. Director of Operations—South & East and Staff Director—Bass Production Ltd. Member of the Bass Charrington Group. Game Conservancy. Fleet Air Arm Officers' Assoc. Worshipful

Company of Brewers. Guild of City Freemen. King's College Assoc.

LEESON, Alister Curtis, b. 25 July 12, s. of the late I. A. Leeson. Tu, 26^2–29^1. University College, Oxford, M.A. Price, Waterhouse & Co. ✕ R.A.F.V.R., 41–46. Sqn. Ldr. Director, Philip Morris & Co. Ltd., 36–52. Solent Carpet Co. Ltd., 52–63, and Brickfield Engineering Ltd., 65–67. Retired. *Army & Navy Club; M.C.C.; Vincent's, Oxford; Rye, Stoneham & Ampfield G.C.s.* Son, 586.

LEESON, Maxted Reynolds, b. 19 May 31, s. of the late A. E. Leeson. T, 45^1–49^2. King's College, London, B.Sc.(Eng.). C.Eng., M.I.Mech.E. University Lecturer in Mechanical Engineering. University of Technology, Loughborough. University Leave, 64. Ricardo & Co., Shoreham-by-Sea. *Various University Clubs.*

LEGG, Brian Bolton, b. 22 Mar. 32, s. of K. B. Legg, F.R.I.C.S. Tu, 45^2–49^1. Trailer Manufacturer.

LEGGATT, Edward Wilmer, M.C. M, 06^2–08^1.*

LEGGE, John Anthony, b. 14 Sept. 29, elder s. of W. H. Legge. Tu, 43^3–47^3. N/S. R.A.F. Chrmn. & Man. Dir., J. Legge & Co. Ltd., Willenhall, Staffs. (Lock Manufacturers). *Llanbear–Pensarn Y.C.; Albrighton Hunt.*

LEGGETT, Douglas Malcolm Anfrère, Ph.D., b. 27 May 12, 4th s. of G. M. K. Leggett. Tu, 25^3–30^1; Scholar; Levée; Head of House. Edinburgh Univ. Exhibitioner of Trinity, Cambridge. Senior Scholarship, 34. Rayleigh Prize, 36. Fellow of Trinity, 38. Ph.D., 39. M.A., D.Sc., F.R.Ae.S., F.I.M.A. University Lecturer in Mathematics, Queen Mary College, London, 37–39. Reader in Applied Mathematics, King's College, London, 50. Royal Aircraft Establishment, Farnborough, 39–45. Vice-Chancellor, Surrey Univ., Guildford.

LE GROS, Lt.-Col. Philip Walter, b. 3 Oct. 92, eldest s. of the late C. W. Le Gros. B, 06^3–10^3; XI, 10; Cap, 10; Fives Pair. École de Commerce, Neuchâtel, Switzerland. Henderson & Liddell, Merchants, London. ✕ 4th Bn. Royal Warwickshire Regt. Major. Wounded twice. With Frame & Co. Ltd., Merchants. Retired. *M.C.C.* Vice-President, *Queen's Club.* Past President, Squash Rackets Assoc.

LEIDY, Joseph, SH, 46^3–47^2.*

LE MARCHANT, Major Gaspard St. John. C, 20^1–24^2.*

LEMIEUX, Joseph Noel Victor Alphonse. St, 30^3–34^2.*

LEONARD, David Hare, b. 13 Feb. 32, s. of the late H. R. Leonard (OR SH 01). K, 36^1–40^2. Imperial College of Science & Technology, City & Guilds College, 41–42. Royal College of Science, 46–47. Petroleum & Coal Tar Refiner. ✕ R.A.F., 42–45. F.O. Commercial Director, Carless Capel & Leonard Ltd., London. *R.A.C.* Sons, Hugh James Hare, K, 67^1–72^2 & Ian David Robert, K, 71^3–.

LEONARD, John Thirlestane, b. 10 July 22, s. of the late J. G. Leonard. SF, 36^2–40^2. ✕ R.N., 41–46. Lt. R.N.V.R. F.C.A. Man. Dir., Carless, Capel & Leonard Ltd., London. *Royal Solent Y.C., The Naval Club.*

LE QUESNE, Prof. Leslie Philip, D.M., M.Ch., F.R.C.S., b. 24 Aug. 19, 2nd s. of the late C. T. Le Quesne, K.C. Tu, 32^3–37^2. Exeter, Oxford, B.M., B.Ch. Middlesex Hospital Medical School, F.R.C.S., D.M., M.Ch. Professor of Surgery, Middlesex Hospital Medical School. Consultant Surgeon, Middlesex Hospital, London. Former President of the Surgical Research Socy. Chrmn. The British Journal of Surgery.

LERRIGO, John Michael, b. 30 Jan. 27, 2nd s. of J. H. Lerrigo. T, 39^3–45^2. Exhibitioner. Jesus, Cambridge, M.A., Cert. Ed. Intelligence Corps, 45–48. Teaching. Eton College, 50. Lycée de Garçons, Le Mans, France, 51–53. Bloxham School, Banbury, Oxon, from 53 (Senior Modern Language Master since 56). Author of "Love is Never Wasted". Cadet Force Medal, 67. Brother, P. M. Lerrigo.

LERRIGO, Peter Morgan, T. 36^3–42^2.*

LESLIE, Benjamin Stewart. St, 34^1–37^3. Sons, 1918 & 2253.*

LESLIE, Hubert Graham, b. 24 May 17, elder s. of H. J. Leslie. SH, 31^2–34^3. Bank Official.

LESLIE, Hubert John, b. 8 Sept. 90, elder s. of the late Col. J. H. Leslie, R.A., D.L. SH, 04^2–08^3; G. VIII, 08. Sheffield School of Art, Slade School of Art, Westminster School of Art. Entertainer &

Artist. ⚔ 187 & 118 Siege Bty., R.G.A. Capt. Wounded. Retired.

LESLIE, John Falkiner. SH, 38³–42³.*

LESLIE, Kenneth Alexander Stewart, b. 21 June 14, 3rd s. of Col. A. S. Leslie, C.M.G., T.D. SH, 28¹–32². Sidney Sussex, Cambridge, B.A. Edinburgh Univ., LL.B. ⚔ R.A.F., 39–45. Sqn. Ldr. Writer to the Signet, 46. Director: Life Assoc. of Scotland Ltd., Exacta Circuits Ltd., and Highland Home Industries Ltd. Partner in Gillespie & Paterson, W. S., from 45. *New Club, Edinburgh; H.C.E.G.; Senior Golfers Society.* Air Efficiency Award. Brother, N. D. Leslie. Sons, 2009, 2339 & 2785.

LESLIE, Col. Norman David, O.B.E., b. 1 Oct. 10, eldest s. of Col. A. S. Leslie, C.M.G., T.D. SH, 24²–28². R.M.C., Sandhurst. Commissioned to Queen's Own Cameron Highlanders, 30. ⚔ N. Africa & N.W. Europe. O.B.E. Dispatches. Post-war, served in Gibraltar, Germany & Hong Kong. Retired as Col., 57. Dir., Scottish Country Industries Development Trust (Edin.), 57–67. *New Club, Edinburgh.* Brother, K. A. S. Leslie. Son, Andrew David, SH, 67¹–71³.

LESLIE, Major Peter, R.E., M.C., B.Sc., b. 2 Nov. 21, 3rd s. of the late F. S. Leslie. St, 35²–40¹; XV, 38–39 (Capt.); R. VIII, 40; Cadet Officer. ⚔ Gazetted to R.E., 41. Served N.W. Europe, 44–45, and Korea 50–51. Retired, 62. Major. London University (External), 48, B.Sc.(Eng.). Now Technical Director, British Quarrying & Slag Federation. Granite Guild. Son, John Stewart, St, 72³–.

LESLIE-SMITH, Anthony, b. 21 Oct. 99, 2nd s. of the late Major J. Leslie-Smith (OR C 75). C, 13³–17³; Cap, 17. ⚔ R.M.A., Woolwich, Cadet. University College, Oxford, B.A. Solicitor, 26. Retired. Police, Special Constabulary, Long Service Medal. Brother, L. C. Leslie-Smith.

LESLIE-SMITH, Luke Corbett, b. 23 Nov. 96, eldest s. of the late Major J. Leslie-Smith (OR C 75). C, 10³–14²; XXII, 12. ⚔ R.M.A., Woolwich. 51st Bde., R.F.A. Lt. Wounded. Dispatches. In Mesopotamia during Arab rising, 21. Capt. Reserve of Officers, R.A. Retired to farm, 21. Brother, A. Leslie-Smith.

LEUCHARS, Alexander George. M, 24³–29².*

LEUCHARS, John Noel. M, 29³–34². Son, Nicholas John, M, 68³–.*

LEUCHARS, William Sidney, b. 4 Feb. 08, eldest s. of the late W. W. Leuchars. M, 21³–26²; XV, 25. Hertford, Oxford, B.A. ⚔ Bedfordshire & Hertfordshire Regt., 39–46. Major. Dispatches. In Publishing business. Retired. *Vincent's, M.C.C.* Brothers, A. G. & J. N. Leuchars.

LEVENS, Robert Graham Cochrane, b. 14 Jan. 01, elder s. of Rev. J. T. Levens, M.A. B, 14³–19²; Scholar; Levée; Major & Minor Exhibitioner; Capt., Fencing. Scholar of Balliol, Oxford. Craven Scholar, 20. Chancellor's Prize for Latin Verse, 21. Gaisford Prize for Greek Verse, 22. M.A. Sixth-Form Master, Haileybury College, 24–27. Fellow & Tutor of Merton, Oxford, 28–67. Emeritus Fellow since 67. ⚔ N.I. Div., Admiralty, 42–45. Founder of *Barnacles C.C.* & Capt., 29–52. Publication: "A Book of Latin Letters".

LEVETT, Geoffrey Lewis, M.C., b. 5 Apr. 19, s. of the late N. L. Levett. M, 32³–36². Clare, Cambridge, M.A. ⚔ D.C.L.I. (att. Gold Coast Regt.) Lt. M.C. Chrmn. & Man. Dir., Pict Ltd.; Man. Dir., Wattie-Pict Ltd., Frozen Vegetable Professors, Melbourne, Australia. *Naval & Military Club, Melbourne; Lansdowne Club, London.*

LEVICK, Rodney Beeton Murray, b. 8 Dec. 20, s. of the late Surg.-Cdr. G. M. Levick, R.N. (Rtd.). Sh, 34³–39². Scholar. ⚔ R.E., 39–47. Capt. Resigned, 47. Working & Campaigning in: Physics (Demolishing the theory of Relativity & Developing a New Foundation), mostly lectures, 45–54. Meteorology (Mapping the weather of the British Isles in terms of weather types; Analysis of forecasting errors). Current Affairs (Recent history; original solutions to outstanding world problems). The Royal Meteorological Socy. (Fellow since 50). *Royal Commonwealth Socy., E.S.U.* British Schools Exploring Socy.

LEVITT, Bryan Philip, b. 2 June 31, s. of the late P. I. Levitt, M.B. W, 44³–49²; Leaving Exhibition. Corpus Christi, Cambridge, M.A., Ph.D. Lecturer in Chemistry, Imperial College, London University.

LEVY, Bernard Frederick Goodman, Ph.D., b. 28 Jan. 11, eldest s. of Dr. A. G. Levy. SF, 25¹–29². St. Catharine's, Cambridge, B.A. Reading University, Cert. in Horticulture. R. VIII. London

University, East Malling Research Station,
Ph.D. East Malling Research Station, 35–
48. ✕ 39–41, R.A. Royal Marines, 41–46.
Ministry of Agriculture (Horticultural
Adviser), 48–71. Retired, 71. Brother,
H. D. G. Levy.

LEVY, Hugh David Goodman, b. 15
Nov. 15, younger s. of Dr. A. G. Levy.
SH, 29^2–35^2. Reading University. Cert. of
Commerce. Royal College of Music.
Studied Clarinet & Cello. ✕ Intelligence
Corps (Field Security Wing), 39–41.
L/Cpl. Invalided out. With ENSA Con-
cert Parties for 5 yrs. at home & overseas.
Copenhagen, to teach English and continue
to teach in other European cities, 46.
Opened own school in London for teaching
languages, 49. Went to live in Morocco, 54.
At present semi-retired. *Subud.* Brother,
B. F. G. Levy.

LEWIS, Sir Edward Roberts, b. 19 Apr.
00, s. of Sir A. E. Lewis. Tu, 14^1–18^2;
Head of House; Cap, 17. ✕ R.F.A., Cadet.
Trinity, Cambridge. Stock Exchange, 23.
Partner, E. R. Lewis & Co., Members of
the London Stock Exchange. Chrmn.,
Decca Ltd. Knight Bachelor, 61. Gov-
ernor, Rugby School, 64. Albert Medal,
R.S.A., 67. *United University Club.* Son,
R. A. Lewis. Two Grandsons in Tu.

LEWIS, Richard Alfred, b. 2 Mar. 28,
s. of Sir E. R. Lewis (OR Tu 14). Tu, 42^1–
46^1; Cap, 44; Sw. VIII, 44–45. Member
of the London Stock Exchange. Partner,
Messrs. E. R. Lewis & Co. Sons, David
Edward Noel, Tu, 70^2– & Christopher
John Alfred Noel, Tu, 71^3–.

LEWIS, The Rev. Roger Edward, b. 7
June 24, s. of the late H. Lewis. C & Tu,
38^1–42^2. Queens', Cambridge. Ridley
Hall, Ordained, 49. Curate, Handsworth
Parish, Birmingham, 49–52. Rector, Had-
leigh, Essex, 52–8. Vicar, St. James's,
Clacton-on-Sea, 58–71. Vicar, St. Matthew,
Surbiton, from 71.

LEWIS-CROSBY, Robert Cornwall,
M.C., b. 1 May 15, eldest s. of Very Rev.
E. H. Lewis-Crosby. Tu, 28^3–33^3. Corpus
Christi, Oxford, M.A. ✕ R.A. (H.A.A. &
Medium), 40–46. Capt. M.C. Chartered
Accountant, 47. Director of Bank of Ire-
land, 57; Deputy Governor from 70.
Chartered Accountant in practice in Dub-
lin with Stokes Kennedy Crowley & Co.,
Peat Marwick Mitchell & Co. *University
Club, Dublin; Royal Irish Y.C.* Son, 2094.

LEWIS-DALE, Ellis Henry. W, 25^3–
30^2.*

LEWTHWAITE, Brig. Rainald Gilfrid,
M.C., b. 21 July 13, 2nd s. of the late Sir
W. Lewthwaite, Bt. (OR M 96). M, 27^1–
31^2; XV, 29–30 (Capt.); Cadet Officer;
Tom Hughes Prize. Trinity, Cambridge,
B.A. 2nd Lt., Scots Guards, 34. ✕ G.S.O.1,
H.Q. 21 Army Group, 44. Commanded
1st Bn. Scots Guards, 45. M.C., 43. Dis-
patches twice. p.s.c. Defence & Military
Attaché, Paris, 64–68. Retired from Army,
68, as Brig. Director of Protocol, Hong
Kong Govt., from 69. *Guards Club,
Pilgrims.* Croix de Guerre with Palm.
Brother, Sir W. A. Lewthwaite, Bt. Son,
997.

LEWTHWAITE, Sir William Anthony,
Bt., b. 26 Feb. 12, eldest s. of the late Sir
W. Lewthwaite, Bt. (OR M 96). M, 26^1–
30^2; H. XI, 29–30; Rackets Pair, 29–30.
Trinity, Cambridge, B.A. Capt. University
Squash Rackets Club. Succeeded father as
3rd Bt., 33. Solicitor, 37. ✕ R. Signals.
Signalman. Grenadier Guards. Lt. Coun-
try Landowner and Solicitor in Private
Practice. Member, Country Landowners'
Assoc., 49–64. Member, Committee West-
minster Law Society. *Brooks's.* Brother,
R. G. Lewthwaite.

LEYLAND, William Stewart, J.P., b. 23
May 22, 2nd s. of the late R. Leyland. C,
35^3–40^2. F.R.I.C.S. (Chartered Land
Agent). J.P. (Bucks). ✕ R.N.V.R., 41–46.
Lt. (A). Managing Director, Aylesbury
Brewery Co. Ltd. *Naval & Parkstone
Yacht Clubs.* Son, Jeremy Francis Wil-
liam, C, 70^2–72^2.

LIDDELL, Sqn. Ldr. Harry Mitford,
R.A.F., b. 27 Sept. 24, eldest s. of Prof.
E. G. T. Liddell, F.A.S. K, 38^3–42^2. ✕
R.A.F., 42–46. Trinity, Oxford, M.A.
Rejoined R.A.F. in 49. Now on staff of
No. 46 Group Air Transport Examining
Unit as VC10 Pilot Examiner. Son,
Charles Edward, K, 72^3–.

LIDDINGTON, Ian, M.C. T, 28^1–32^1.*

LIDDINGTON, Peter, b. 23 Feb. 21,
2nd s. of H. Liddington. T, 34^3–38^2.
Birmingham Univ., LL.B. Solicitor, 47.
✕ Inns of Court Regt. & 1st Derbyshire
Yeomanry. Wounded. Clerk to Gover-
nors of Lawrence Sheriff School.

LIGHTFOOT, Anthony, b. 10 Apr. 21,
adopted s. of K. Lightfoot, O.B.E. K,
34^3–38^2. Architectural Assocn. School of
Arch. Slade School of Fine Arts. ✕
R.A.F.V.R., 40–45. P.O.W. in Japanese
hands, 42–45.

LILIENFIELD, C. W. C. (see Lynfield, C. W. C.).

LILLIE, Walter Hamilton. W, 09²–12¹.*

LINDLEY, Duncan William Burns. Tu, 46³–50³.*

LINDLEY, William. SH, 41³–45².*

LINDOP, Lt.-Cdr. Geoffrey Cecil, R.N., b. 21 Mar. 19, youngest s. of the late C. H. Lindop. T, 31³–36². Royal Navy, 37–58. Cadet to Lt.-Cdr. (S). Retired voluntarily, 58. Joined Jones, Lang, Wootton, London Chartered Surveyors, 58. Currently Partner in charge of administration. F.C.I.S., M.Inst.A.M., M.H.C.I. *Lansdowne, Little Ship Club.* Brother, J. L. Lindop.

LINDOP, John Llewellyn, b. 8 Apr. 15, 2nd s. of the late C. H. Lindop. T, 28³–32². Royal Navy, 32–58. Lt.-Cdr., R.N. Bursar, Trinity College School, Port Hope, Ontario, from 58. A.C.I.S. Brother, G. C. Lindop.

LINDSAY, Major-General Courtenay Traice David, C.B., b. 28 Sept. 10, s. of the late C. T. Lindsay (OR T 88). B, 24²–28³; Cap, 28. R.M.A., Woolwich. 2nd Lt., R.A., 30. Member, Ordnance Board (Col.), 52. Director of Munitions, British Staff, Washington (Brig.), 59. Director General of Artillery (Major-General), 61–64. Retired, 64. C.B., 63. *R.A.C., Rye Golf Club.* Sons, 399 & 825.

LINDSAY, Noel Patrick. SH, 20¹–21¹.*

LINDSEY-RENTON, Ian Peter, M.B.E., b. 10 Jan. 13, elder s. of L. S. Lindsey-Renton. B, 27¹–30¹; XI, 29. ✕ R.A., 39–45. Major. M.B.E. Chairman, Burt Boulton & Haywood Ltd., Timber Importers, Chemical Manufacturers & Tar Distillers, 66–70. Now retired. Lloyd's Underwriter. Committee, *Surrey C.C.C.*

LINNELL, Arthur John, b. 7 Aug. 97, eldest s. of J. Linnell. M, 11³–15². ✕ 19th Bn. Manchester Regt. Lt. Wounded twice. Dispatches. Exhibitioner of Trinity, Cambridge. Managing Director, Wallis and Linnell Ltd., Kettering, Clothing Manufacturers. *Royal Aero Club, R.A.C.*

LINNELL, Derek Childs. T, 26¹–30³.*

LINNELL, John Maxwell, A.I.A., b. 9 Jan. 10, 2nd s. of the late W. H. Linnell (OR T 94). T, 22³–27³. Minor Founda-

tioner. Institute of Actuaries, London. Fellow of the Canadian Institute of Actuaries. A.I.A. Joined the Standard Life Assurance Company, London, 28. At present still with Company. Calcutta, 33–38. Edinburgh, 39–47 and 49–52. Montreal, 47–49 and from 52. *United Services Club, Montreal.* Brothers, R. H. & D. C. Linnell.

LINNELL, Richard Henry. T, 20³–24³.*

LINTON, Robert Desmond Fox, b. 6 Dec. 21, 3rd s. of Dr. S. F. Linton. B, 35³–40². Trinity Hall, Cambridge, M.A. ✕ The R. Scots Greys. Capt. Senior Lecturer, Royal Military Academy, Sandhurst. Brother, S. G. F. Linton.

LINTON, Surg. Lt.-Cdr. Stanley Geoffrey Fox, M.B.E. B, 27³–32².*

LISTER, Edward Carson, b. 26 Dec. 15, s. of the late A. A. Lister. Tu, 29³–34¹; Scholar. Classical Scholar of Worcester, Oxford, B.A. ✕ South Lancashire Regt., 39–45. Capt. Wounded, Burma, 45. Bar, Lincoln's Inn, 46. R. A. Lister & Co. Ltd., Dursley, Glos., 46–52. R. A. Lister y Cia., Buenos Aires, 52–56. Executive, Bryant & May Ltd., from 61. Chrmn., Guildford Conservative Assoc., 66–69.

LISTER, Rupert Pickslay, b. 30 Aug. 27, eldest s. of the late W. E. Lister. T, 41¹–44². Harper Adams Agricultural College. Dip.Ag. In Agriculture. Currently in Sales Management, Agricultural Feeds. Royal National Rose Socy. Brother, W. M. Lister.

LISTER, Thomas Guy Kirkby, b. 21 Nov. 08, eldest s. of J. M. S. Lister. C, 22³–26³. Clare, Cambridge, M.A. Worsted Spinner (Wool), 31–64 (Partner in family business of Lister Brothers & Co.). Retired.

LISTER, William Mark, b. 1st Mar 31, 3rd s. of the late W. E. Lister. T, 44³–49²; County Major Scholar; Levée; Head of House; Exhibitioner; Cadet Officer. Queens', Cambridge, M.A. Export Marketing Manager with Beecham Group Ltd. Brother, R. P. Lister.

LITLER-JONES, Robert Clouston Martland. St, 29³–31².*

LITTLE, Patrick Hugh. M, 25³–29².*

LITTLE, Wilfrid Lawrence, b. 30 July 01, 2nd s. of W. G. Little. T, 15^2-18^3. Entered Bank of England, 20. Principal rank, 49. ✕ R.A., T.A., 38-45. Capt. Adjutant of Territorial Regt., R.A. Served in Norway. Retired from B. of E., 60. Publication, "Staffordshire Blue". Member of the English Ceramic Circle.

LITTLEBOY, Charles Graham, b. 3 Feb. 28, eldest s. of the late C. N. Littleboy (OR SH 08). SH, 41^3-46^2; S. VIII, 45-46. Trinity, Cambridge, M.A. Farmer. *Farmers' Club*. Brother, P. E. E. Littleboy. Son, Charles Kevin Irving, SH, 70^3-.

LITTLEBOY, Peter Evelyn Eldon, b. 26 Aug. 30, 2nd s. of the late C. N. Littleboy (OR SH 08). SH, 44^2-49^2; Cap. Trinity, Cambridge, M.A. Banana Grower, Teacher and now Dept. Chrmn., adult educational upgrading, Vancouver City College. Brother, C. G. Littleboy.

LIVINGSTON, Charles Geoffrey Shannan, b. 16 June 20, s. of the late C. S. H. Livingston. St, 34^2-38^2; S. VIII, 36-37. ✕ R.N.V.R., 41-46. Acting Lt.-Cdr. Senior Officer, M.T.B. Flotilla. Retired, after working mostly for Encyclopaedia Britannica. Owned and ran Boat Yard for the last ten years. Now handed over to eldest son, 1620. Commodore, *Royal Anglesey Yacht Club, Royal Dee Yacht Club*.

LLEWELLIN, Major Thomas Caradoc Trevor. SH, 09^3-13^3.*

LLEWELLYN, Lloyd Wynne Llewellyn. M, 24^1-26^2.*

LLOYD, Anthony Fetherston, b. 4 Oct. 14, 2nd s. of the late H. D. L. Lloyd. Tu, 28^3-33^1; Scholar. Clare, Cambridge, B.A. ✕ R.E. Major. Solicitor, 46. Retired from Private Practice, 72. Now employed by United Kingdom Provident Institution, London. *East India, Sports and Public School Club*.

LLOYD, Christopher, b. 2 Mar. 21, 5th s. of N. Lloyd. St, 34^2-39^1. ✕ R.A. (Field), 41-46. King's, Cambridge, M.A. Wye College, London Univ., B.Sc.(Hort.). Author of Gardening Books, "The Well-Tempered Garden", etc. Regular contributor to "In My Garden" in "Country Life" and occasionally to other horticultural journals, T.V., "Gardening Spot" (S.T.V.). Director owner of Great Dixter Nurseries. Brother, O. C. Lloyd.

LLOYD, David Aubrey. Tu, 36^3-40^1. Son, 2329.*

LLOYD, Hugh Mark. B, 31^1-35^2.*

LLOYD, Jeremy Patrick. Sh, 42^3-46^3.*

LLOYD, Jeremy Sampson. SH, 44^3-48^3.*

LLOYD, Oliver Cromwell, M.D., b. 4 Aug. 11, 2nd s. of N. Lloyd. St, 25^2-30^2. King's, Cambridge, M.A., B.Chir., M.D. London Hospital, M.R.C.S., L.R.C.P. Research Student for Royal Society on Mammalian Malaria Enquiry, Kasauli, Punjab, 45-47. Lecturer in Pathology, Bristol Univ., 48. Brother, C. Lloyd.

LLOYD, Robert Edward. W, 39^2-43^2.*

LLOYD, Lt.-Col. William Anthony Sampson, M.B.E. SH, 14^1-18^2.*

LOGAN, James John Forbes Moffatt, R.A.S., b. 3 Mar. 24, s. of the late Sir W. M. Logan, K.B.E., C.M.G. Sh, 38^1-41^2; Cap, 40. St. Andrew's Univ. (R.A.F. Entry). Brasenose, Oxford. ✕ R.A.F. Pilot Officer. Royal Air Force. Retired, 68. Now Chief Flying Instructor, Oxford Air Training School. Upper Freeman. Guild of Air Pilots & Navigators. A.F.M.

LONG, Major Guy Frederick Downer, M.C., b. 30 Oct. 20, s. of the late R. F. Long, M.C. W, 34^3-38^3. R.M.A., Woolwich. ✕ Gazetted to R.A., 39. Transferred to R.A.P.C., 58. Lt.-Col., 68. M.C. Now Deputy Financial Controller, Headquarters, Northern Army Group. *Army & Navy Club*. British Horological Society, Royal United Service Institution.

LONG, Richard Samuel. SH, 21^3-26^1.*

LONGHURST, Mervyn Lyster, C.B.E., b. 9 Nov. 07, s. of the late C. Longhurst, C.B. SF, 22^1-25^2; XXII. St. John's, Oxford, B.A. Bar, Inner Temple, 29. Entered Legal Branch, Board of Education, 31. Retired as Chief Asst. Legal Adviser, Dept. of Education & Science. Sat on several Government Cttees. on Education & Charities. Retired, 68. C.B.E., 52.

LONGRIGG, Edmund Fallowfield, b. 16 Apr. 06, s. of the late G. E. Longrigg. SF, 20^3-25^2; XI, 22-25 (Capt.); H. XI, 21-25 (Capt., 24 & 25); Rackets Pair, 24 & 25; with D. S. Milford (OR) won Public

Schools Champ., 24. Pembroke, Cambridge, B.A.; Cricket Blue, 26 & 27. Solicitor, 32–72. Retired, 72. ✕ Sqn. Ldr., R.A.F., 40–45. Played Somerset County Cricket, 25–46 (Capt., 38–46). Chrmn. for 10 yrs., President, 3 yrs. *M.C.C.*, *Free Foresters*, *Bath G.C.*—President. Son, 1083.

LONGRIGG, John Stephen, C.M.G., O.B.E., b. 1 Oct. 23, eldest s. of Brig. S. H. Longrigg, O.B.E. SF, 37³–41²; Scholar; Levée; XV, 40; Exhibitioner. Demy of Magdalen, Oxford, B.A.; Rugger Blue, 41. ✕ Rifle Brigade, 42–45. Dispatches. Lt. Counsellor, H.M. Diplomatic Service. O.B.E., C.M.G., 73. *Reform Club, Royal Blackheath G.C.* Son, Stephen Hugo, SF, 68³–.

LONGWORTH - DAMES, Desmond Charles. B, 15³–16².*

LOOS, Major Frederick Charles. B, 27²–31³.*

LORD, David Anthony, b. 1 May 31, s. of F. Lord. B, 44³–49². N/S. R.A. T.A. Lt. Queens', Cambridge, B.A. General Manager since 66 of Reckitt & Colman (Ghana) Ltd., Accra. *Ikoyi Club (Lagos), Accra Club.*

LOVE, John Percy Roderick, b. 19 Jan. 28, s. of the late Major P. A. Love. K, 42¹–45³. N/S. Welsh Guards, 46–48. Lt. Member of Lloyd's. Director, Chandler Hargreaves Whittall (Life & Pensions) Ltd., London. *Guards Club.*

LOVELL, Frederick William, b. 17 May 29, eldest s. of H. O. Lovell (OR Tu 16). Tu, 43²–47². Brother, 173.

LOVELL, Lt.-Col. Harry Oswald, b. 7 Feb. 02, 3rd s. of W. G. Lovell, C.B.E. Tu, 16¹–18²; XXII, 18. R.M.C., Sandhurst. Gazetted to 1st Bn. Queen's Own Royal West Kent Regt., 21. Lt., 25. Retired, 28. President, River Plate Dairy Company, 30. Director, Lovell & Christmas Ltd., 34–65. ✕ 39–44 (Bn. Commander, 42). Lt.-Col. Wounded. Dispatches. Retired. *United Services Club.* Sons, F. W. Lovell & 173.

LOVELL-PANK, Roderick Guy. St, 24¹–27².*

LOVEROCK, Gerald. T, 05¹–08².*

LOW, Marcus Warren. St, 18²–22³.*

LOW, Robert Carmichael Stuart, M.C., b. 24 June 12, s. of the late R. S. Low. C, 26²–31¹; XV, 30; R. VIII, 29–30. Balliol, Oxford, B.A.; Rugger Blue. Chartered Engineer. F.I.Mech.E. ✕ R.E. Major. M.C. Wounded, 44. Recently retired as Engineering Director of British Rail Engineering Ltd. *Vincent's, Oxford.*

LOW, Thomas Patrick Corscaden. SF, 25²–29².*

LUCAS, Donald William, b. 12 May 05, younger s. of F. W. Lucas. K, 19³–24²; Scholar; Exhibitioner; King's Medal. Scholar of King's, Cambridge, B.A. Fellow of King's Coll., 29. University Lecturer in Classics, 33. Director of Studies in Classics, 36–65. Perceval Maitland Laurence Reader, 52–69. Retired. Son, 689.

LUCAS, Richard Freer. SH, 29³–34².*

LUCAS, William Samuel Ashburner, b. 18 May 17. Son of Rev. H. Lucas. Sh, 31¹–34². Entered R.N., 34. ✕ 39–45, R.N. Invalided out as Lt.-Cdr., 47.

LUCAS-LUCAS, Guy Bazalgette, b. 4 Apr. 94, 2nd s. of the late H. F. Lucas-Lucas. T, 08¹–09². ✕ 4th South Midland Bde., R.F.A. 240th Bde., R.F.A. Capt. Wounded. Dispatches. Grazier since 25 with Brownless & Lucas Polled Shorthorn Stud at "Broome", Jerilderie, N.S.W. *Retired Servicemen's Club, Central Riverina Race Club.* Brother, R. W. Lucas-Lucas.

LUCAS-LUCAS, Major Reginald Woolmer, eldest s. of the late H. F. Lucas-Lucas. T, 06¹–07³. ✕ 14–19, British Columbia Regt. 9th Bn. Royal Warwickshire Regt., Machine Gun Corps. Lt. ✕ 40–54, R.A.S.C., R.A.O.C., Commander Vehicles Depots, and for last 6 yrs. as A.A.G., Welfare, London District. Retired as Lt.-Col. Brother, G. B. Lucas-Lucas.

LUDLOW, Michael Richard, b. 30 Mar. 33, s. of the late Sir R. Ludlow. SH, 46³–51²; XV, 50; XI, 50–51; H. XI, 50–51. Trinity, Oxford, M.A. Solicitor. *United Service & Royal Aero Club, Grannies.*

LUMB, Charles Edward, b. 3 Dec. 10, eldest s. of the late C. F. Lumb. W, 24³–29²; Levée; Head of House; Cadet Officer; S. VIII, 29. Swiss Reinsurance Co., Zürich, 29–30. James Howden & Co. Ltd., Glasgow, 31–35. Diamond Blower Co. Ltd., London, 35–39. ✕ Royal Artillery (A.A.), 39–45. Lt.-Col. South American Traders Ltd., 47–48. B.O.E.C.C. Ltd., 48–57. Consolidated Foundry Plant Ltd., 57–67. Export Consultant, 67–72. *Boodle's, R.A.C.*

LUMB, Joseph Edward, b. 14 Aug. 06, s. of J. Lumb. M, 20^3–24^2; Cap; XXII, 24. Clare, Cambridge, B.A. Joined family firm Joseph Lumb & Sons Ltd., in 27. Became Man. Dir. and Chrmn. before merging with R. Beanland & Sons in 63 to form Allied Textile Cos. Ltd. Now Chrmn. ⋊ R. Observer Corps. Obs. Lt. *Huddersfield & Borough Club, Bath Club.*

LUMSDEN, George Ranald Campbell, M.B.E., J.P., b. 22 Mar. 17, younger s. of Sir J. R. Lumsden. SH, 31^1–36^1; XV, 35–36; R. VIII, 35, 36; Crick Winner, 35; Athletic Cup, 36. Corpus Christi, Cambridge, B.A. Sudan Political Service, 39 to 54. M.B.E. Farmer. J.P. Brother, J. A. Lumsden. Son, Nigel William, SH, 69^2–.

LUMSDEN, James Alexander, M.B.E., T.D., b. 24 Jan. 15, elder s. of Sir J. R. Lumsden. SH, 28^3–33^2; Scholar. Scholar of Corpus Christi, Cambridge, B.A. Glasgow University, LL.B. Solicitor (Scotland), 39. ⋊ Anti-Aircraft T.A. Major. M.B.E., T.D. Partner in Maclay, Murray & Spens, Solicitors, Glasgow. Chairman of The Burmah Oil Co. Ltd., 71. D.L. Director of Bank of Scotland and other public companies. *United Services, London; New, Edinburgh; Western, Glasgow.* Brother, G. R. C. Lumsden. Sons, 2272, 2632 & 2907.

LUNT, Michael John Winstanley, b. 23 Aug. 32, elder s. of J. W. Lunt. T, 45^2–50^3. N/S. R.N.V.R., 51–52. S/Lt. (S). Clare, Cambridge, M.A., F.C.A. Co. Secretary, Gordon Johnson-Stephens Group, Gloucester, 64–70. Co. Secretary, Andercroft Group, Westminster, since 71. City of Bath Bach Choir. Brother, 182.

LUPTON, Arthur Ralph Ransome, C & Tu, 37^3–42^2. Brother, G. C. M. Lupton. Son, William Francis, W, 72^3–.*

LUPTON, Geoffrey Charles Martineau, b. 20 Apr. 30, 3rd s. of H. R. Lupton. Tu, 44^2–48^2. Merton, Oxford, M.A. Bombay Burmah Trading Corporation, Bangkok, Thailand, 52–54. Hong Kong Government, 55–70. Home Civil Service from 71. Brother, A. R. R. Lupton.

LUSHINGTON, David Henry. K, 43^2–46^3.*

LUSHINGTON, Philip Michael, b. 12 Feb. 31, 2nd s. of P. J. Lushington. K, 44^3–49^3. Salesman. *Crowborough Squash Club.* S.R.A. Approved Coach. Brothers, D. H. Lushington & 89.

LUSTY, Alan Charles, b. 3 Dec. 10, 3rd s. of the late W. Lusty. SF, 24^3–29^2; Scholar; XV, 28; H. XI, 29 (Capt.); Major & Minor Exhibitioner. Scholar of Gonville & Caius, Cambridge, B.A. ⋊ R.A.O.C., 40–46. Dispatches. Belgian Croix de Guerre with Palms. Chevalier of the Order of Leopold II with Palms. Lt.-Col. Director of Aircraft Catering Company, Bonded Store & Company Bottling Specialised Foods. Sons, 2155 & 2843.

LUTYENS, John Leslie, b. 29 Dec. 17, eldest s. of the late W. F. Lutyens. SF, 31^3–36^2; Exhibitioner; R. VIII, 36. Exhibitioner of Clare, Cambridge, M.A. C.Eng. F.I.Mech.E. Man. Dir. & Chief Executive, George Kew Ltd. Sons, 2230 & 2449.

LYDE, Lionel Gildea. K, 18^3–23^2. Sons, 1406 & 1855.*

LYNAM, Jocelyn Humphrey Rickman, b. 27 June 02, s. of the late A. E. Lynam. M, 16^3–21^2; Scholar; Levée; Head of House; Cap, 20; XI, 21. Exhibitioner of Hertford, Oxford, M.A.; Hockey Blue, 25. Headmaster of Dragon School, Oxford, 40–65. Chrmn. of Council of Incorporated Association of Preparatory Schools, 41 and 42. Retired. *Vincent's, Oxford, Acrostics Hockey Club.*

LYNDON-SKEGGS, Peter (formerly Skeggs, P. L.), B.M., B.Ch., b. 26 Jan. 22, 2nd s. of B. Lyndon-Skeggs. St, 35^3–39^3. Oriel, Oxford, M.A., B.M., B.Ch. St. Bartholomew's Hospital, M.R.C.Path. General Practice, Alresford, Hants. *Lansdowne.* Son, 2413.

LYNFIELD, Clarence Walter Charles (formerly Lilienfeld, C. W. C.), b. 13 May 00, s. of A. Lilienfeld. C, 14^2–17^2. R.M.C., Sandhurst. Winner of Sabres, 19; & Foils, 19. Gazetted to 3rd (Prince of Wales) Dragoon Guards, 19. Reserve of Officers, 21. Changed name, 25. Man. Dir., Inter-Office Telephones Ltd., from 47. ⋊ France, 39–40. Home Forces, 40–44. Holland & Germany, 44–45. Major.

LYNN-ALLEN, Major Esmond Harcourt, M.C., b. 22 Aug. 03, s. of the late Major W. Lynn-Allen, D.S.O. (OR K 85).

B, 17²–20³; Hoyle Exhibitioner. Selwyn, Cambridge. Gazetted to the Gloucestershire Regt., 26. ⋈ With 2nd Bn. in France & Flanders, 39–40. Major. M.C. P.O.W., 40–44. Invalided out, 45. Author of "Rough Shoot", "Leaves from a Game Book", "The Way of a Gun", etc.

LYON, David Henry George, b. 1st Oct. 22, 3rd & youngest s. of the late Admiral Sir George Lyon, K.C.B. SH, 36³–41²; Cap, XXII; H. XI, 41. Pembroke, Cambridge, B.A. ⋈ Pilot in R.A.F., 42–46. F/Lt. Tube Investments, 47–55. British Aluminium Co. Ltd., 55–62. Joined Indalex Ltd., now part of R.T.Z. Ltd., 62. Sales Director from 65. *Royal Overseas League.* Savoyard Society.

LYON, Geoffrey Malcolm. SH, 29²–33³.*

LYON, Percy Hugh Beverley, M.C., b. 14 Oct. 93, s. of the late P. C. Lyon, C.S.I. St, 07³–12²; Scholar; XXII; R. VIII, 12; Head of House; Major & Minor Exhibitioner. Exhibitioner of Oriel, Oxford. (Headmaster of Rugby School. See details under Headmasters, Part III.)

LYONS, Brig. Richard Clarke, C.I.E.. M.C., b. 4 June 93, s. of the late R. Lyons, Tu, 07³–10³. R.M.A., Woolwich. Winner,

Middleweight Boxing. Gazetted to R.F.A., 14. Lt. ⋈ Z Bty., R.H.A., & 157th Bde., R.F.A. Capt. Wounded. M.C. Dispatches.

LYSTER, Anthony Lyttleton, b. 5 Mar. 30, elder s. of G. F. M. Lyster. B, 43³–48¹. Exhibitioner of Queens', Cambridge, B.A. A.C.A., 55. British Oxygen, 58–61. Albright & Wilson from 61.

LYSTER, George Francis Marsh, b. 5 May 02, s. of Very Rev. H. C. Lyster. B, 16³–21²; Scholar; Cap, 20; Cadet Officer; Minor Exhibitioner. Scholar of Queens', Cambridge, B.A. A.C.I.S. Formerly Director, Southalls (Birmingham) Ltd., Smith & Nephew Associated Companies Ltd., & Provincial Insurance Co. Ltd. Now retired.

LYSTER-TODD, Lt.-Col. George Kennett Chaworth, O.B.E., b. 16 May 14, elder s. of the late G. H. Lyster-Todd (OR St 99). B, 28²–32². R.M.C., Sandhurst. Army Staff College, Camberley. 25 yrs. service in the Durham Light Infantry, retiring as Lt.-Col. p.s.c. 14 yrs. with Pilkington Brothers Ltd., Glass Manufacturers, Production Manager. Now Manager in Technical Advisory Service. Retired List, St. John Ambulance Brigade. O.B.E., S.B.St.J.

M

MACARTHUR-ONSLOW, Denzil Ion, b. 25 Aug. 28, eldest s. of Maj.-Gen. Sir Denzil Macarthur-Onslow, C.B.E., D.S.O. W, 42²–46². Man. Dir., Macdonald Hamilton & Co. Ltd., Sydney, Australia. *Caledonian Club, London; Royal Sydney G.C.* Brother, N. G. Macarthur-Onslow.

MACARTHUR-ONSLOW, Neil Gordon, b. 21 Mar. 30, 2nd s. of Maj.-Gen. Sir Denzil Macarthur-Onslow, C.B.E., D.S.O. W, 44¹–47². Gen. Man., Denzil Macarthur-Onslow Pty. Ltd. E.D. *Imperial Service Club, Sydney; Australian Club, Sydney; Caledonian Club, London.* Brother, D. I. Macarthur-Onslow.

MACARTNEY, Thomas Lamont. Sh, 34²–38¹.*

MACASKILL, Major John Leonard Cameron, b. 15 Nov. 20, younger s. of D. C. Macaskill, M.A., M.D. B, 34³–38³. Gazetted to Royal Engineers. ⋈ R.E., 39–45. Lt. P.O.W. in Japanese hands,

42–45. B.Sc. Capt., 46. T/Major, 49. Lecturer in the Computing Science Dept., University of Adelaide, S. Australia.

MACAULAY, John David, b. 16 July 24, eldest s. of the late Lt.-Col. R. K. A. Macaulay, D.S.O., R.E. (OR SH 95). SH, 38²–41²; XI, 41. ⋈ Royal Navy, 42–47, Motor Gun Boats & Minesweepers, S/Lt., R.N.V.R. Chrmn., David Macaulay Advertising, London. *Royal Thames Yacht Club, Royal Ocean Racing Club.* Society of Postal Historians.

MACAULAY, Jasper Noel. SH, 05³–09².*

McBAIN, Frank Matheson, b. 4 Jan. 06, s. of the late J. A. D. McBain, C.I.E. SH, 20¹–23². Glasgow University. With British Linen Bank, Glasgow, 25–28, and Sun Life Assurance Co., of Canada. Served in branches in Montreal, Shanghai, Java, Singapore, Hong Kong, India & Burma from 28–41. Manager, Ceylon branch from 41–59. ✕ Ceylon, R.N.V.R., 43–46, Lt. (S). Retired. Hon. Schools Manager, Cross-in-Hand Primary School (Diocesan Rep. on Board of Governors). Clan Chattan Association. *R.A.C.*

McCALL-SMITH, Samuel, M.B., B.Ch., b. 14 Dec. 20, s. of Dr. B. McCall-Smith, O.B.E. M, 34²–38²; XXII. ✕ Cameronians (Scottish Rifles), 40–46. Capt. Dispatches. Edinburgh Univ., M.B., Ch.B., D.M.R.D. Consultant Radiologist, Borders Area, Peel Hospital, Galashiels, Selkirkshire.

McCALLUM, Alastair Ian. C, 17²–20³.*

McCANCE, Angus Joseph, b. 20 Sept. 23, s. of the late Brig. J. B. McCance (OR B 13). B, 42²–46³; Levée; XV, 46. R.M.A., Sandhurst. Junior Under-Officer. Commissioned Royal Scots Greys, 48. Retired, 57 as Major. Joined Scottish & Newcastle Breweries, 59. Director, Scottish Brewers, 66. At present Director, Scottish Brewers Ltd., and South England Regional Manager, Scottish & Newcastle Breweries. *Caledonian Club, Roehampton; Bosham Sailing Club.*

McCARTHY, Brig. Charles Henry Florence D'Arcy, O.B.E. M, 13³–17².*

MacCARTHY, Egerton Hedley Desmond. W, 28²–31¹.*

MacCARTHY, Peter Arthur Desmond, b. 9 May 12, eldest s. of the late E. H. D. MacCarthy. W, 26³–30³; Scholar. Scholar of Emmanuel, Cambridge, M.A. Asst. Master, Stowe School, 35–37. British Council Lecturer, 39–41. B.B.C. (European Div.), 42. Lecturer in Phonetics, School of Oriental & African Studies, London Univ., 43–48. Univ. of Leeds from 48, Head of Dept. of Phonetics. Brother, E. H. D. MacCarthy.

McCLEAN, Harry Philip. SF, 24²–28³.*

McCLEAN, John Newsam, b. 22 Mar. 08, 2nd s. of the late W. N. McClean (OR SF 87). SF, 22¹–26². Trinity, Cambridge, B.A.(Agric.). Farmer, Liss, Hampshire. Member Hampshire W.A.E.C. Represented Hampshire in N.F.U. Council, 44. Vice-President and then Deputy President. Member of Executive, Animal Health Trust to Sept., 72. Chrmn., Nuffield Farming Scholarship Scheme. Hampshire C.C.,

Petersfield R.D.C., Cirencester R.D.C. Greenwood Cttee. Governor of R.A.S.E. *Farmers' Club.* Brother, H. P. McClean. Son, 644.

McCLELLAND, George Melville. St, 33²–36¹.*

McCOLL, Lt.-Col. Alastair Wilson, b. 21 Mar. 17, s. of the late Sir A. L. McColl. B, 30³–35¹. Clare, Cambridge, M.A. Mobil Oil Corporation, N.Y., since 38. Worked in Colombia, Argentina, Brazil, France, U.S.A. & Chile. ✕ Royal Engineers in Middle East and N.W. Europe, 40–46, Lt.-Col. U.S. Bronze Star.

MacCOLL, David Ferguson, M.C., b. 30 Jan. 20, 4th s. of the late A. M. MacColl. St, 33³–38¹; XI, 37; Cap, 37; R. VIII, 37. ✕ 39–46, R.H.A. Capt. M.C. Anglo-American Corporation, Singapore, 46–58 (Director, 52). Director, Corrie MacColl & Son Ltd., London from 58. Appointed Chrmn., 66. Director, N.V. Deli Maatschappij, Amsterdam from 63. *M.C.C.* Brother, E. P. MacColl. Son, Peter David Archibald, St, 71³–.

MacCOLL, Evan Peter, M.C., T.D., b. 23 May 15, 3rd s. of the late A. M. MacColl. St, 28³–32³; R. VIII, 32. Boxing VIII, 31–32. ✕ 3/4th County of London Yeomanry, 39–45. Dispatches. M.C., T.D. Lt.-Col. Stockbroker, 45–65. Gillett Bros., Discount Co. Ltd., from 65. *St. James' Club, Beefsteak Club.* Brother, D. F. MacColl.

McCOLL, William Murray, b. 19 June 28, s. of the late T. McColl. W, 42³–46²; XI, 46 (Capt.). Trinity Hall, Cambridge, B.A., LL.B. Solicitor; Partner at Northampton in Private Practice. *Northampton County Club.*

McCOMB, Arthur Kilgore. SH, 10³–12³.*

McConnachie, William, M.B., B.Chir. T, 44³–50².*

McCOSH, David John, b. 15 Sept. 30, 3rd s. of A. K. McCosh, J.P., D.L. Sh, 44²–48²; Scholar; S. VIII, 48. Major Classical Scholar of Clare, Cambridge, B.A. N/S. R.E. 2nd Lt. Management Consultant, P.E. Consulting Group Ltd. Brother, E. H. McCosh.

McCOSH, Edward Henry, b. 28 Feb. 26, 2nd s. of A. K. McCosh, J.P., D.L. Sh, 39³–44¹. ✕ R. Signals, 44–48. Lt. Clare, Cambridge, B.A. C.A. Man. Dir., James Kerr & Co. Ltd., Glasgow. *Western, Glasgow.* Botanical Society of the British Isles. Brother, D. J. McCosh.

McCRONE, Alastair Keith Lyle, b. 9 Sept. 30, s. of the late J. L. McCrone. T, 44³–48². Corby Technical College. C. Eng., M.I.Mech.E. Services Manager, R. A. Lister & Co. Ltd., Dursley, Glos.

McCULLOCH, Colin James, b. 10 Mar. 08, s. of the late Maj.-Gen. Sir A. McCulloch, K.B.E., C.B., D.S.O., D.C.M. SH, 22¹–25². Balliol, Oxford, B.A. Sheep Farmer in New Zealand. Now retired. Brother, D. St. D. McCulloch.

McCULLOCH, Major David St. Denis, b. 4 July 19, 4th s. of the late Maj.-Gen. Sir A. McCulloch, K.B.E., C.B., D.S.O., D.C.M. W, 33³–37³; Cadet Scholar of R.M.A., Woolwich. Gazetted to Royal Artillery, 39. ✕ Major. Dispatches. Lt.-Col. R.A. *Naval & Military Club.* Brother, C. J. McCulloch.

McCULLOCH, Ian. Tu, 40²–44².*

McCULLOCH, Maxwell Forbes, b. 8 May 33, youngest s. of the late L. F. McCulloch, M.B.E. Tu, 46³–50². F.C.A. Financial Director, Chapman & Frearson Ltd., Grimsby. Honourable Society of Knights of the Round Table. Commissioned, The Royal Horse Guards (The Blues), 56. Brother, I. McCulloch.

McDANIEL, James Richard Lane. B, 01¹–04².*

MacDERMOT, Niall, O.B.E., Q.C. B, 29³–33³.*

MACDONALD, Coll, J.P. SF, 37³–42².*

MACDONALD, Donald Buchanan, b. b. 7 Mar. 08, 2nd s. of W. R. Macdonald. B, 21³–26²; Cap, 25; XXII, 26; Fives Team. Lausanne University. Chrmn., Donald Macdonald (Antartex) Ltd., Donald Macdonald (Lambskins) Inc., U.S.A. Antartex Sheepskin Shops of Canada Ltd. *Western Club, Glasgow; Feltmakers Riviera Country Club, Florida, U.S.A.*

MACDONALD, Duncan Brodie, b. 5th June 07, s. of Capt. J. D. Macdonald, M.C. SH, 21¹–25¹. Pembroke, Cambridge, M.A. Sh. Half Blue and Scottish Elco team, 28. Joined Imperial Tobacco Co. Ltd., 28. Chrmn., Darvel Tobacco Plantations Ltd., 57. ✕ R.A., 39–45. Major G.S.O.2. T.D. Retired. *Buck's, All England L.T. & C.C.*

MACDONALD, John Auld. Tu, 36¹–40². Son, 2749B.*

MACDONALD, John Neville Douglas, b. 2 July 07, eldest s. of the late Col. C. R. Macdonald, C.M.G. (OR SF 91). SF, 21³–24³. Victoria University, Wellington, N.Z. Entered Bank of New Zealand, Wellington, 25. Retired. *Wellesley Club, Wellington; Wellington G.C.* Brother, R. C. Macdonald.

MACDONALD, Maj.-Gen. Ronald Clarence, C.B., D.S.O., O.B.E., b. 1 Aug. 11, 2nd s. of the late Col. C. R. Macdonald, C.M.G. (OR SF 91). SF, 25³–28³. R.M.C., Sandhurst. Gazetted to Royal Warwickshire Regt., 31. ✕ France & Germany, 39–45. Lt.-Col. Commanded 1st & 2nd Bns. The Royal Warwickshire Regt., 6th Infantry Brigade. Chief of Staff, Middle East Command—Deputy Chief of Staff, Allied Land Forces, Central Europe. Col., R. Warwickshire Fusiliers. Deputy Col., Royal Regiment of Fusiliers. Appointed Maj.-Gen., 62. Director, Griffin Farms Ltd. C.B., D.S.O. (& Bar), O.B.E. *Army & Navy Club.* Brother, J. N. D. Macdonald.

McELHINNY, Geoffrey William, b. 16 Dec. 00, s. of Col. W. J. McElhinny, R.E. W, 14³–19¹; Scholar; Levée; Scholar of Corpus Christi, Oxford, B.A. I.C.S. Sec. to Govt. of Bombay for Education, 44. Chief Sec. to Govt. of Sind, 45. Revenue Commissioner for Sind, 46. Commissioner, Central Division, Bombay, 47. Retired, 47. Hon. Sec., Grahamstown Golf Club & of the South African Correspondence Chess Association. Senior Golfers Society of S. Africa.

McEVEDY, Brian Victor, M.Ch., F.R.C.S., b. 13 Dec. 23, 2nd s. of P. G. McEvedy, F.R.C.S. K, 37³–41³. Exeter, Oxford, M.A., B.M., M.Ch. Guy's Hospital, London, F.R.C.S. Surgical Training continued at Ancoats Hospital, Manchester and University College Hospitals, London and Ibadan, Nigeria. N/S. R.A.M.C., 48–50. Consultant Surgeon, Royal Victoria Infirmary, Newcastle-upon-Tyne. Association of Surgeons. North of England Surgical Society. *National Liberal Club.* Member of the Court of Examiners, Royal College of

Surgeons of England. Brother, M. B. McEvedy.

McEVEDY, Mark Beresford, B.M., B.Ch. K, 36^1–40^2.*

MacEWEN, Robert Begg. M, 13^3–17^1.*

McEWEN, Richie William Heywood Lachlan. SF, 33^3–36^3.*

McFADYEAN, Colin, b. 21 Sept. 14, s. of Sir A. McFadyean. SH, 28^3–33^2; Scholar; Levée; Head of House. Scholar of Brasenose, Oxford, B.A. ✕ R.N.V.R., 39–45. Lt.-Cdr. Solicitor, 46. Partner, Slaughter and May. *Garrick Club.*

MACFADYEN, John Langdon. C, 19^1–22^3.*

MACFARLANE, The Rev. Alwyn James Cecil, b. 14 June 22, s. of J. W. Macfarlane. St, 36^2–40^3. New College, Oxford, M.A. ✕ Black Watch, 40–46. Capt. Wounded. New College, Edinburgh. Ordained to the Ministry of the Church of Scotland, 52. Presently in Newlands South Parish Church, Glasgow.

MacGEORGE, Alastair William, b. 3 July 31, s. of the late Major W. B. Mac-George, M.C. (or M 03). M, 44^3–50^2; XXII, 49–50 (Capt.). Wadham, Oxford, M.A. Export Office Manager, Ivy Sullivans Ltd., (Greenock & London), 58–63. Asst. Director, Consumers' Association from 63.

McGLASHAN, Ian Fraser, b. 10 Oct. 08, eldest s. of the late J. McGlashan, C.I.E., M.Inst.C.E. W, 22^3–25^2; two yrs. in Gym VIII. C.A. Retired. Brother, K. McGlashan.

McGLASHAN, Kenneth, M.R.C.S., L.R.C.P., b. 8 Dec. 16, 2nd s. of the late J. McGlashan, C.I.E., M.Inst.C.E. Sh, 30^3–34^3; R. VIII, 34. Middlesex Hospital, M.R.C.S., L.R.C.P. Capt. Hospital H. XI, 40–43. ✕ R.A.M.C., 44–47. Medical Registrar, Central Middlesex Hospital, 47–49. General Practitioner in Watford, Herts. *Sandy Lodge G.C.* Brother, I. F. McGlashan. Son, 1610.

MACGREGOR, Thomas Roben, b. 28 Jan. 16, s. of the late T. L. Macgregor. B, 29^3–34^3; Levée; Head of House; Cap, 34. Sorbonne. Clare, Cambridge, M.A. Golf Blue. ✕ 135th (North Hertfordshire Yeomanry) Field Regt., R.A. Lt. P.O.W. Director & Manager of The Scottish

Investment Trust Co. Ltd., and of The Second Scottish Investment Trust Co. Ltd. Director of The Scottish Mortgage & Trust Co. Ltd. *New Club, Edinburgh; H.C.E.G.; Oxford & Cambridge Golfing Society.* Chrmn., Berwickshire & East Lothian Conservative Assoc., 66–68. Son, 2303.

McILWRAITH, Kenneth Douglas, b. 25 May 17, 2nd s. of the late W. N. McIlwraith (Canadian by birth). SF, 31^1–36^1; Cap, 36. Clare, Cambridge, M.A. 2nd Lt. (T.A.) C.U.O.T.C. ✕ R. Wiltshire Yeomanry, R.A.C., 40–46, Middle East, Norway. Capt. Canadian Foreign Service, 48. Canadian Ambassador to Norway & Iceland, 72. Brother, W. G. McIlwraith.

McILWRAITH, William Gordon, b. 30 Dec. 15, eldest s. of the late W. N. McIlwraith (Canadian by birth). SF, 29^3–34^2. XI, 34; H. XI, 34. Clare, Cambridge, M.A. ✕ 51 H.A.A. Regt., R.A. (T.A.), 39–41. Battery Capt. 2nd Cdn. H.A.A. Regt., R.C.A., 41–45. Capt. (Q.M.). Chrmn. & Technical Director, Shipelle Ltd., Haslemere, Surrey (Manufacturers of water-set Propulsion for Boats). Brother, K. D. McIlwraith. Son, 2128.

MacINNES, John Fletcher, b. 17 Mar. 32, eldest s. of Lt.-Col. I. D. MacInnes, D.S.O. K, 45^3–50^1. Royal Agricultural College, Cirencester. In Agriculture. *Cumberland County Club.*

MacINNES, Kenneth Lionel, C.B.E., J.P., D.L., b. 12 July 05, 3rd s. of the late Rev. J. MacInnes (or C 81). M, 19^1–23^2. Trinity, Cambridge, B.A. Joined the Burmah Oil Co. Ltd., 26–49. Retired. C.B.E., D.L., J.P. Brother, R. G. MacInnes. Sons, 263, 745 & 1797.

MacINNES, Richard Iain, M.R.C.S., L.R.C.P., b. 24 June 21, s. of the late J. MacInnes. M, 35^2–39^2. Brasenose, Oxford. Westminster Hospital, M.R.C.S., L.R.C.P. N/S. R.N.V.R. Surg.-Lt., 49–51. General Practice in Maidenhead. Son, 2928.

MacINNES, Ronald Grant, D.F.C., b. 10 Feb. 03, 2nd s. of the late Rev. J. MacInnes (or C 81). M, 17^1–21^2; Fives Pair; H. XI. Trinity, Cambridge, B.A. Hockey & Lawn Tennis Blues. In India, 24–37. ✕ R.A.F. Pilot, 40–45. F/Lt. D.F.C. *All England Lawn Tennis Club; Oriental Club.* Brother, K. L. MacInnes. Son, 998.

MACINTYRE, Col. Alastair Campbell, b. 26 Sept. 96, 4th s. of the late D. Macintyre. Tu, 11^3–13^3; Cap, 13. R.M.C., Sandhurst. ✕ 20th Hussars, Comdg. 2nd Signal Squadron, R.E. Capt. Dispatches. Cavalry School Course, 21. 16th The Queen's Royal Lancers, 22. Served in India, 22–24; Egypt, 24–25; U.K., 25–37; India, 37–39. Commanded 16/5 The Queen's Royal Lancers, 38–42. Deputy Military Governor North Rhine & Westphalia, 45–47. Col., 45. Retired, 47. *Cavalry Club, M.C.C., I Zingari, Free Foresters.*

MACK, Henry Patrick Bradshaw, b. 15 Oct. 22, s. of Sir H. Mack, G.B.E., K.C.M.G. B, 36^2–40^2. ✕ R.A.F. F/Lt., A.F.C. Trinity, Cambridge, I.C.I. Ltd., Plastics Div., 51–72.

McKELVIE, Peter, Ch.M., F.R.C.S., D.L.O., b. 21 Dec. 32, s. of W. B. McKelvie, M.D., Ch.M., F.R.C.S.Ed., D.L.O. C, 46^3–50^2; Sw. VIII. Manchester University Medical School. Junior Appointments: King's College, London; Manchester Royal Infirmary; St. Mary's Hospital, London; Institute of Laryngology & Otology—University of London. M.D., Ch.M., F.R.C.S., D.L.O. Late reader of Laryngology, University of London. Consultant, E.N.T. Surgeon, London Hospital. Royal National Throat, Nose and Ear Hospital. Royal Postgraduate Medical School and Hammersmith Hospital. Royal Society of Medicine.

MACKENZIE, Alastair Douglas. SH, 30^3–34^2.*

MACKENZIE, Hamish, b. 26 Feb. 12, s. of the late J. Mackenzie, O.B.E. Tu, 26^1–29^2. ✕ R.N.V.R., 39–45. Lt. Burma. Commerce, Burma (pre-war), Malaya & India. Retired. *Naval Club.*

MACKENZIE, Ian Carville Keith, T.D., M.D., F.R.C.P., s. of Dr. Ivy Mackenzie. M, 27^2–31^2. Trinity, Cambridge, B.A., M.B., B.Chir. Glasgow University, M.B., Ch.B. ✕ R.A.M.C., 39–46. Major. M.R.C.P. (London), M.D. (Cantab.). Son, 2675.

MACKENZIE, John Moncrieff Ord. SH, 25^2–30^1.*

MACKENZIE, Keith, b. 16 July 24, 4th s. of the late J. Mackenzie. W, 38^2–40^2. Left Rugby after serious illness. Chepping Wycombe School of Art, 41. ✕ R.N., 43–46. Slade School, 46–49. Diploma in Fine Art, London University. Art Editor, Associated Newspaper Group. *Savage, Chelsea Arts, Garrick.* Brother, N. Mackenzie.

MACKENZIE, Neil, b. 13 July 20, 3rd s. of the late J. Mackenzie. W, 34^2–38^2. ✕ R. Fusiliers & R. Norfolk Regt. Major. Dispatches. Chartered Surveyor. Partner in firm of Estate Agents & Surveyors. Brother, K. Mackenzie.

McKENZIE, JOHNSTON, Colin (formerly Johnston, C. M.), b. 31 Jan. 94, eldest s. of the late R. McKenzie Johnston, M.D., F.R.C.S.E. St, 07^3–12^1. Brasenose, Oxford. ✕ 8th Bn. Argyll & Sutherland Highlanders. Lt. Chartered Accountant, 22. Retired. Sons, H. B. & C. D. McKenzie Johnston.

McKENZIE JOHNSTON, Colin David, b. 21 May 29, 2nd s. of C. McKenzie Johnston (OR St 07). Sh, 42^3–47^3; Head of House. Major Scholar of Corpus Christi, Cambridge, M.A., C.Eng., M.I.E.E. Asst. Keeper in the Science Reference Library. Brother, H. B. McKenzie Johnston.

McKENZIE JOHNSTON, Henry Butler, b. 10 July 21, eldest s. of C. McKenzie Johnston (OR St 07). St, 35^2–40^1; R. VIII, 39–40. Brasenose, Oxford (1 term). ✕ The Black Watch (R.H.R.), 40–46. Private to Major. Wounded. Dispatches. Diplomatic Service since 46, in Athens, Paris, Bonn, Montevideo, Mexico City & Trinidad. Presently Consul-General, Munich, since 71. Seconded to the office of the Ombudsman from 73. *United Oxford & Cambridge University Club, Hurlingham Club.* Royal Geographical Society. Brother, C. D. McKenzie Johnston. Son, 2708.

MACKESON-SANDBACH, Capt. Graham Lawrie (formerly Mackeson, G. L.), b. 24 Jan. 07, younger s. of the late H. Mackeson. K, 21^1–24^3. ✕ Irish Guards. Capt. Chartered Surveyor. Farmer. *Guards Club.*

MACKESSACK, Douglas, M.B.E., b. 7 Oct. 03, younger s. of G. R. Mackessack. Tu, 17^2–21^2; XI, 21; Cap, 19–20. University College, Oxford, B.A. C.A. ✕ Seaforth Highlanders. Major. M.B.E. P.O.W., 40–45. Wounded & captured at St. Valery. Man. Dir., J. & J. Grant, Glen Grant, Rothes. D.L., J.P. Brother, K. Mackessack.

MACKESSACK, Col. Kenneth. Tu, 16^2–20^1.*

MACKIE, John Martyn, b. 21 Sept. 31, eldest s. of the late J. H. M. Mackie (OR W 07). W, 45³–50²; Levée; Leaving Exhibition. History Exhibitioner of Trinity Hall, Cambridge, M.A. Regular Commission, Royal Tank Regiment, 55–69. William Grant & Sons Ltd., Glasgow, from 69. *Army & Navy Club*. Brothers, 175 & 653.

McKINSTRY, Robert Archibald. St, 30³–33³.*

MACLACHLAN of MACLACHLAN, George Styles Rome (formerly Rome, G. H. S.), b. 15 July 21, s. of S. Rome. Sh, 36³–39¹; XV, 38–39; H. XI, 39. Trinity Hall, Cambridge. ⚔ Argyll & Sutherland Highlanders, 40–46. Major. Dispatches. Director, Geo. Rome & Co. (Glasgow) Ltd., Plastering & Ferro-Concrete Contractors. Farmer. *The Highland Brigade Club, H.C.E.G.*

MACLACHLAN, Thomas Kay, b. 21 Jan. 32, s. of Dr. T. K. Maclachlan. Sh, 45³–50². Edinburgh Univ., London Univ., M.B., Ch.B., M.R.C.P., M.R.C.Psych., D.P.M. Research Psychiatrist, Medical Research Council, 68–69. Director, Child Guidance Services, Worcestershire, 69–71. Consultant Child Psychiatrist, Addenbrooks Hospital, Cambridge, from 71. B.M.A. Royal College of Psychiatrists.

MACLAREN, Archibald Shaw, b. 18 Sept. 02, 3rd s. of the late J. F. Maclaren. C, 16³–20². St. John's, Cambridge, M.A., C.Eng., F.I.C.E. Civil Engineer to B.O.A.C., 39–45. Consultant specialising in airports. Retired, 71. *Army & Navy Club*. Brother, J. F. P. Maclaren. Son, 539.

MACLAREN, Col. John Frederick Peverell, b. 28 Jan. 96, eldest s. of the late J. F. Maclaren. C, 10¹–14¹. ⚔ Ayrshire Yeomanry & R.F.C.,14–20. Lt. Dispatches. Scholar of Pembroke, Cambridge, M.A. Sudan Political Service, 22–35. Bursar & Secretary, R. Veterinary College, London, 35–38. Bursar & Fellow, Exeter, Oxford, 39–48, M.A.(Oxon.), 39. Agent to the Duke of Devonshire (Sussex Estates), 49–53, and to the Earl of Faversham, 53–56. ⚔ Intelligence Corps, 40–45. Dispatches. Chief Secretary to Military Govt. of British Somaliland and to 10 British Military Administration, Cyrenaica. G.H.Q., Middle East (Colonel). Former Fellow of the Chartered Land Agents' Society. Order of the Nile. *Royal Over-Seas League, St. James's*. Brother, A. S. Maclaren.

McLAUGHLIN, Charles Redmond, M.B., F.R.C.S., b. 1 Oct. 09, s. of the late W. H. McLaughlin. W, 23³–28². Emmanuel, Cambridge, & Edinburgh University. M.B., B.Chir.(Cantab.), F.R.C.S.E. ⚔ R.A.F.V.R., 40–45. Wing.-Cdr. Plastic Surgeon. Retired. Naval Historian.

MacLEAN, Martin Bruce, b. 9 Nov. 19, s. of W. MacLean. C, 33³–37². Queens', Cambridge, B.A. ⚔ Intelligence Corps. Argyll & Sutherland Highlanders & Black Watch (R.H.R.). Major. Manager, Textiles.

MACLEHOSE, The Rev. Alexander, b. 20 Dec. 04, younger s. of J. Maclehose, LL.D. SH, 18²–23²; Scholar. New College, Oxford, B.A. Asst. Secretary, Scottish Home & Health Dept., 56–65. Vicar of Locherley-with-East Dean, 68. Also Vicar of East Tytherley and Rector of West Tytherley, 72.

MACLEHOSE, H. E. Sir Crawford Murray, K.C.M.G., M.B.E., b. 16 Oct. 17, 2nd s. of the late H. A. Maclehose (OR W 00). W, 31³–36²; XI, 35; Capt. of Fives. Balliol, Oxford, B.A. Malayan Civil Service, 39–46. ⚔ R.N.V.R., 42–45. Lt. Diplomatic Service since 47. Governor & Commander-in-Chief, Hong Kong. M.B.E.(M), K.C.M.G., Kt. of St. John. *Athenæum, Travellers', Royal Commonwealth Society*. Brother, N. D. Maclehose.

MACLEHOSE, Norman Donald, D.S.O. T.D. W, 28³–33². Sons, 1140 & 1985.*

MacLELLAN, Prof. George Douglas Stephen, Ph.D., b. 1 Nov. 22, elder s. of the late A. S. MacLellan. Tu, 36³–40³; Scholar. Pembroke, Cambridge, M.A., Ph.D. Major Scholarship in Mathematics, Massachusetts Institute of Technology, U.S.A. Chartered Engineer, F.I.Mech.E., F.I.E.E. Fellow, Pembroke, Cambridge, 44–59. Univ. Lecturer in Engineering, 52–59. Rankine Prof. of Engineering (Mechanics & Mechanism), Univ. of Glasgow, 59–65. Professor and Head of Department of Engineering, University of Leicester since 65. *Athenæum. Leander*.

McLELLAN, Hugh, b. 21 Nov. 95, s. of the late C. M. S. McLellan. B, 10²–14¹; Boxing—Represented Rugby School at Aldershot: Bantamweight, 12; Featherweight, 13. Trinity, Oxford. ⚔ 6th Bn. Durham Light Infantry. Att. R.E. Signals. 14–19. Lt. Retired Farmer. *Farmers' Club*, Trinity (Oxford) Society.

MacLEOD, Donald Norman. SH, 28³–34¹.*

MacLEOD, Major John Edmund Hardinge. SH, 26³–30².*

MACLEOD, Joseph Todd Gordon, b. 24 Apr. 03, younger s. of the late J. G. Macleod. K, 17¹–22²; Levée; Head of House. Balliol, Oxford, M.A. Bar, Inner Temple, 28. Lessee & Sole Director, Festival Theatre, Cambridge, 33–36. Announcer, B.B.C., 38–45. Man. Dir., Scottish National Film Studios, 46–47. Directed Festival of Britain production, Aberdeen, 51. Author, 8 volumes of verse, some under pseudonym Adam Drinan. Six works of Theatre History. Plays, Biography, Autobiography, Travel, etc. Lived in Italy since 55. Hon. Member, British Actors' Equity. Silver Medal, Royal Society of Arts, 44. Scottish Arts Council Award for a play.

MACLEOD, Col. Roderick, D.S.O., M.C., b. 13 Nov. 91, elder s. of the late R. H. Macleod, I.C.S. M, 06³–10². R.M.A., Woolwich. Gazetted to Royal Artillery 11. ✕ R.F.A. & R.H.A., 240th & 241st Bde. Major. Wounded. M.C., D.S.O. Dispatches. Staff College, Camberley, 26–27. Brevet Lt.-Col., 35; Colonel, 39. ✕ Military Assistant to C.I.G.S., 39–40. On Intelligence Staff at S.H.A.E.F., 44–45. Retired, 45. Now Hon. Sec., S.S.A.F.A., Uckfield area. *United Service Club.* Royal Artillery Historical Society, Senior Golfers. *E.S.U.*

McLINTOCK, Alastair George, b. 23 Apr. 17, eldest s. of the late C. H. McLintock, O.B.E. SF, 31¹–35². Articled to Partners of Thomson McLintock & Co., Institute of Chartered Accountants (Scottish), 35–39. ✕ War Office, London, 39–45. General Staff, 42–43 & 45. British Army Staff, Washington, D.C., 43–45. Demobilised, Lt.-Col. Worked with group of British Companies (principally Evans Thornton y Cia., S.A.) in Buenos Aires. Director of several of these, 52–62. Joined Channel Television, Jersey, C.I., 65. Company Secretary since 66. Brothers, T. G. & C. A. McLintock. Son, 2886.

McLINTOCK, Charles Alan, b. 28 May 25, 3rd s. of the late C. H. McLintock, O.B.E. SF, 39²–43². New College, Oxford (Army Short Course). ✕ R.A., 44–47, 6th Regt. R.H.A. Capt. Chartered Accountant. Partner in firm of Thomson McLintock & Co. Director of Woolwich Building Society, Lake View Investment Trust,

Grange Trust and other companies. Governor of Rugby School since 73. Brothers, A. G. & T. G. McLintock.

McLINTOCK, Thomson Graeme, M.B.E., b. 6 Mar. 20, 2nd s. of the late C. H. McLintock, O.B.E. SF, 33³–38²; Cap, 37; H. XI, 36–38; broke school record for long jump, 38; Leaving Exhibition. Clare, Cambridge, M.A. ✕ Indian Armd. Corps, 41–45. Major. M.B.E. With British Petroleum Co. Ltd. since 46. Man. Dir., B.P. Canada, 56–61. Now with European Directorate in Head Office, London. *Hawks Club, Hurlingham, Queen's.* Brothers, A. G. & C. A. McLintock.

MACLURE, Robert William Johnstone, M.B., B.Chir., M.R.C.S., L.R.C.P. C, 28³–32².*

McMILLAN, Anthony Stewart, b. 18 Nov. 98, s. of the late A. J. McMillan. C, 12³–14². Editor of "The Coventry Herald", subsequently General Diocesan Secretary and Secretary, Diocesan Board of Finance, St. Albans, Herts. Now retired.

McMILLAN, Robert Gordon Macleod, b. 3 Aug. 05, elder s. of the late Capt. W. M. McMillan. K, 19²–23¹. Chartered Accountant (Scotland), 30. Director of Wellings & McMillan Ltd., Travel Agents, London, from 32. ✕ R.A.O.C., 39–45. Capt. Now retired. *Reform Club.*

McMINNIES, John Gordon, O.B.E., b. 1 Oct. 19, s. of W. G. McMinnies. W, 33³–37²; Stovin Exhibitioner. Journalist, 38–39. ✕ R.A., 39–46. Wounded. Joined Foreign Service, 46. British Embassy, Athens, 46–49. Warsaw, 49. Now Foreign & Commonwealth Office. O.B.E.

McMULLEN, Launcelot, b. 29 Aug. 05, s. of the late A. McMullen (OR SF 86). King's, Cambridge Exhibitioner. M.A. ✕ R.N.V.R., 40–46. Lt. Norwegian Freedom Medal. Formerly Fellow, Royal Statistical Society, and Head Brewer of Guinness's Brewery, Dublin. Now retired. *Royal St. George Yacht Club.* Sons, 1602 & 2067.

McMULLEN, Lt.-Col. Robert Peter D.S.O., M.B.E., D.L., T.D., b. 18 Feb. 14, 2nd s. of the late Lt.-Col. O. R. McMullen, C.M.G., T.D., J.P., D.L. (OR SF 80). SF, 27³–31³. Career in Brewing Industry. Chrmn. & Man. Dir., McMullen & Sons Ltd., The Hertford Brewery. Gazetted to the Hertfordshire Regt., T.A., 32. M.B.E., 38. ✕ General Staff with Special Forces, 42–45. D.S.O. & Bar.

Lt.-Col. J.P., 48–70. High Sheriff (Herts.), 55. Now Chrmn., McMullen & Sons Ltd. D.L., T.D., U.S.A. Bronze Star. *United Services Club.* Sons, 1300 & 1753.

MACNAB, John Angus. W, 20³–24².*

MACNAIR, Alexander John, M.C., F.C.C.S. C, 37³–40³.*

McNICOL, Kenneth Martin, M.B., B.Chir. Sh, 37³–42². Sons, 2405 & Angus Martin, Sh, 68³–.*

McNICOL, Robert Stewart. Sh, 30³–35².*

McNISH PORTER, Robert Miles (see Porter, R. M. McN.).

MACPHERSON, Colin Archibald Ivor. SH, 41²–44³.*

MACPHERSON, Norman Charles. Tu, 01²–04¹.*

MACPHIE, Charles Stewart. SH, 43³–48¹.*

MACRAE, Charles Alexander Mackenzie. SH, 38³–41².*

MacROBERT, John Carmichael Thomas, b. 26 Apr. 18, s. of J. MacRobert. Tu, 31³–35³. Queens', Cambridge, M.A., & LL.B., Glasgow. ✕ R.A., 40–45. Dispatches. 10th Field Regt., Burma; 80th Field Regt., B.A.O.R. Solicitor, 48. Partner, MacRobert Son & Hutchison. Hon. Solicitor, Scottish Civic Trust. *Western Club, Glasgow; Royal Gourock Yacht Club.*

McROSTIE, John James, b. 30 Dec. 27, s. of J. McRostie. K & St, 41³–46²; XV, 45; Athletics Cup, 46. Went to South Africa. Director of Companies. *East London G.C.; East London Club; Rotary Club, Arcadia.*

MADDEN, John Franklin, J.P., b. 19 Sept. 01, elder s. of the late F. C. Madden, C.M.G., O.B.E., M.D., F.R.C.S. K, 14³–20²; Scholar; Exhibitioner. Demy of Magdalen, Oxford, B.A. Sudan Political Service, 24–51 (Governor, Northern Province, 48–51). The Magistrates Association Organising Secretary, 52–57. Secretary, 57–64. J.P. for W. Suffolk, 55. *Royal Over-Seas League, London.* Brother, W. E. Madden.

MADDEN, William Edmund, b. 5 Oct. 06, younger s. of F. C. Madden, C.M.G., O.B.E., M.D., F.R.C.S. K, 20–24².² Scholar of Royal School of Mines, London. Scholar of Institute of Petroleum. B.Sc., A.R.S.M. With "Shell" group of Oil Companies in Rumania, Holland, U.S.A., Mexico (Southern Area Gen. Manager), Venezuela (Asst. Gen. Manager), Trinidad (Gen. Manager), London (Manager of various depts.), 27–63. Retired. Fellow of Institute of Petroleum. *Oil Industries Club.* Brother, J. F. Madden. Sons, 842 & 1077.

MADDOCKS, Bertram Catterall, b. 7 July 32, 2nd s. of G. Maddocks. Sh, 45³–50³; Levée; Head of House; Fives IV, 50. N/S. R.A., 51–52. Trinity Hall, Cambridge. Barrister, Middle Temple. Practising in Manchester. Brother, D. C. Maddocks.

MADDOCKS, Denys Catterall. Sh, 43³–47³.*

MAFFEY, The Hon. Simon Chelmsford Loader. K, 32³–36².*

MAGILL, Dermot Bibby. SH, 36²–41¹.*

MAGILL, Denis Sandes, b. 4 June 25, 2nd s. of the late M. F. S. Magill. SH, 39¹–43². ✕ Grenadier Guards, 43–47. Retired with rank of Capt. Wounded, 45. Insurance Broker and Underwriting Member of Lloyd's, 49. *City of London Club.* Brother, D. B. Magill.

MAHON, Patrick MacMahon, T.D., b. 24 Oct. 10, 3rd s. of the late H. M. Mahon. M, 24³–28². Solicitor, 33. ✕ London Irish Rifles. Major. Wounded. P.O.W. Practising Solicitor. T.D. Brother, R. E. M. Mahon.

MAHON, Ronald Erskine MacMahon. M, 22³–27².*

MAIER, Alan John, b. 3 Jan. 23, s. of J. D. Maier. C, 36³–41²; Scholar; Exhibitioner; Cadet Officer. Scholar of Corpus Christi, Oxford, M.A. Capt. of Hockey. ✕ Commissioned 2nd Lt., The Rifle Brigade, 42. Served 2nd Bn. The Rifle Brigade, 44–45. North Africa, Italy (P.O.W., 44). Joined I.C.I. Ltd., 47. Various commercial appointments. P.A. to Chairman, 56–59. Appointed to Board of I.C.I. Plant Protection Ltd., 63. Currently Marketing Director. Also Director of: Sopra, France; Solplant, Italy; and Zeltia Agraria, Spain. Contemporary Arts Society. Son, 2970.

MAITLAND, Adam, b. 6 Sept. 13, s. of Lt.-Col. C. A. S. Maitland, D.S.O. SH, 27^3-32^2; R. VIII, 31 & 32; Cadet Officer. Trinity, Cambridge, M.A. President of the Magpie & Stump Debating Society. ⚔ Royal Armoured Corps. Major. Dispatches. Director of Eyre & Spottiswoode Ltd., St. Clements Press Ltd., & other printing companies to 65. Member of Queen's Bodyguard for Scotland, The Royal Company of Archers. The Scout Association: County Commissioner for the Stewardship of Kirkcudbright. County Councillor, 67–70. Sons, 2178, 2946 & Robert Forbes, SH, 68^3–.

MAITLAND, James, b. 3 Sept. 27, 3rd s. of the late Col. Sir G. R. Maitland, Bt., D.S.O., D.L. Sh, 41^2-45^1. Royal Agricultural College, Cirencester. Queen's Own Cameron Highlanders, 45–48. Lt. Farming Company Director. Brother, J. R. Maitland.

MAITLAND, James Anthony. Tu, 23^1-26^3.*

MAITLAND, John Ramsay, b. 11 Oct. 24, 2nd s. of the late Col. S. Ramsay Maitland, Bt., D.S.O., D.L. Sh, 38^3-42^3; XV, 42. ⚔ R.N.A.S., 42–43. R.A.F., 43–58. Sqn. Ldr. D.F.C. Airport Operation. Exhibition Organiser. Motor Trade, etc. Man. Dir. various Companies. *R.A.F., United Services & Royal Aero Club.* Brother, J. Maitland.

MALING, Robert William Maurice, b. 20 June 13, s. of R. W. Maling. St, 27^1-31^2. Corpus Christi, Cambridge. Manners Scholar. B.A. Mechanical Engineer with I.C.I. Ltd., Billingham, Teesside, 35–69. Retired, 69. Farmer in partnership with father at Fenwick Steads, Belford, Northumberland since 69. President, Durham County Rugby Football Union, 71–72.

MALTMAN, Donald. T, 23^3-26^1.*

MALTMAN, Peter. T, 21^1-25^2.*

MAN, John Henry Garnet, b. 14 Oct. 06, 2nd s. of the late E. J. F. G. Man. C, 20^2-25^1; Boxing, 23; Cap, 24. Employed by Anthony Gibbs, Chile. ⚔ K.O.Y.L.I., 40–45. Major. Dispatches. Farmer. Now School Bursar. Brother, L. G. Man.

MAN, Lt.-Col. Lionel Garnet, b. 11 July 03, eldest s. of the late E. J. F. G. Man. C, 17^2-21^3; Cadet Officer; Boxing, Lightweight, 20; Junior Athletics Cup, 19.

R.M.C., Sandhurst. Gazetted to the Indian Army, 24. Jat Regt. (Indian Army), 25, until retirement in 48. p.s.c. Staff College, Quetta, 38. Various Staff appointments in India, Basra & Baghdad, 39–42. Commanding various Battalions of the Jat Regt., 42, and again, 45–47. Farming, 48–61. Retired, 62. Brother, J. H. G. Man.

MAN, Major-Gen. Patrick Holberton, C.B., C.B.E., D.S.O., M.C., b. 17 Mar. 13, s. of Col. H. W. Man (OR C 90). C, 26^3-30^2. R.M.C., Sandhurst. Prize Cadet, 31. Leaving Scholar, 32. Gazetted to Hampshire Regt., 33. Capt., 39. ⚔ M.C., O.B.E., Bronze Star. A/Brigadier, 45. Lt.-Col., 1st Bn. The Royal Hampshire Regt., Malaya, 54. Imperial Defence College (Instructor), R.A.F. Staff College (Student), Army Staff College (Student, subsequently Instructor). Major-General (retired). Personnel Manager, Manganese Bronze Ltd., Ipswich. British Institute of Management. C.B., C.B.E., D.S.O., M.C.

MANCHESTER, The Rt. Rev. The Lord Bishop of (see Rodger, P. C.).

MANDERS, Richard George Cobbe. St, 15^3-18^3.*

MANGER, Alfred Stuart. SH, 03^3-07^2.*

MANN, Philip John, M.I.C.E., b. 14 Feb. 29, s. of F. J. Mann. T, 43^1-47^2. M.I.C.E. Associate Member, Institute of Highway Engineers. Director, Marley Homes Ltd., Guildford.

MANNERS, Charles Harrington, b. 29 July 18, s. of the late R. Manners. St, 32^3-36^2. Pembroke, Cambridge, B.A. Fellow, Institute of Materials Handling. Head of Materials Handling Section, The Metal Box Co. Ltd., London.

MANNING, Cecil John. SF, 13^3-18^2.*

MANSERGH, Brig. Patrick Ernest Shirreff, O.B.E., b. 9 July 17, s. of the late Brig. G. E. Mansergh, C.B., M.C. (OR C 06). C, 31^1-35^3; Cadet Officer; XV, 35. R.M.A., Woolwich. R.M.A., XV. Gazetted to Royal Signals, 37. ⚔ B.E.F., 39–40. B.L.A., 44–45. Major. O.B.E. p.s.c. T/Lt.-Col., 45–47. Military Asst. to Chief of General Staff, India, 46–47. Seconded to Royal Canadian Corps of Signals, 48–51. C.O., Hong Kong Signal Regiment, 58–60. A.A.G., Ministry of Defence (P.S.2), 60–62. Officer i/c R. Signals Records, 62–66. Chief Signal

President, Regular Commissions Board, 70–71. Brigadier (retired, 71). R.A.R.O. Security Officer, H.Q. Provost & Security Services, R.A.F. A.D.C. to H.M. The Queen, 70–71.

MANSFIELD, Major Geoffrey Edward, M.C., b. 18 May 91, elder s. of the late E. D. Mansfield. St, 04³–09²; Scholar. R.M.A., Woolwich. Commissioned into Royal Artillery. ✕ R.A. Major. Wounded three times. M.C. Dispatches. Retired, 36. Sons, J. E. & J. M. R. Mansfield.

MANSFIELD, James Edward. St, 37³–42³.*

MANSFIELD, John Michael Roger, b. 21 Mar. 31, 2nd s. of Major G. E. Mansfield (OR St 04). St, 44³–48³. University of Canterbury, Christchurch, New Zealand, B.A. Regular Commission in British Army, 54. Joined New Zealand Diplomatic Service in 57. Served in New Zealand Embassies or High Commissions in Bangkok (Second Secretary), Bonn (Counsellor), Apia, Western Samoa (Deputy High Commissioner). Present appointment: Deputy Permanent Representative, New Zealand Permanent Mission to the United Nations. Brother, J. E. Mansfield.

MANSON-BAHR, Philip Edmund Clinton, M.D., F.R.C.P., b. 5 May 11, eldest s. of the late Sir P. Manson-Bahr (OR SF 96). SF, 24³–29²; S. VIII, 28, 29. Trinity, Cambridge. London Hospital, M.D., F.R.C.P. ✕ 39–46, 1st E. African Field Ambulance & Medical Adviser, E. Africa Command, Abyssinia & Kenya. Lt.-Col. Professor, Tropical Medicine, New Orleans, U.S.A.; Senior Lecturer, London School of Hygiene & Tropical Medicine. Consultant, Seamen's Hospital, Greenwich. *Hurlingham Club.* Son, 1987.

MANZONI, Michael Victor, b. 4 Sept. 28, youngest s. of the late Sir Herbert J. Manzoni. SH, 42²–46². Trinity Hall, Cambridge, M.A., F.I.C.E. Director, R.M. Douglas Construction Ltd.

MARCH, George Frederick, C.M.G., M.C., b. 6 July 93, s. of the late F. J. March. K, 07³–11¹; Cap, 10; Boxing Heavyweight, 11. Wye College, Dip. Agric. ✕ 2nd & 10th Bns. Sherwood Foresters, 14–21. Capt. Wounded thrice. M.C. Dept. of Agriculture & Forests, Sudan Govt., 21–47. Member of Governor General's Council, 44–47. Agricultural Consultant on mission to Swaziland by Colonial Development Corporation, 50. Manager & Secretary, Flishinghurst Farms Ltd., 50–52. Now farming on own account in Kent. C.M.G., 46. Sons, 487 & 690.

MARCUS, Hans Herbert, b. 18 July 21, s. of the late O. Marcus. C, 39¹–40². Manchester University, B.A. Grotius Prize for International Law. Solicitor, 48. Sons, Thomas Alexander James, C, 68³– & Robert Paul Andrew, C, 71¹–.

MARKLAND, Alfred King, b. 1st Jan. 20, younger s. of the late A. D. Markland. T, 32³–38²; Levée; XI, 36–38; Tom Hughes Prize, 38. Science Exhibitioner of Queen's, Oxford, M.A. Represented Oxford v. Cambridge at cricket, 41, & squash, 40–41. ✕ R.N.V.R., 41–45. Lt. Sudan Political Service, 46. District Commissioner, 52. Joined U.A.C. International Ltd. as Staff Manager of subsidiary Company in Kenya, 54. Head of Group Personnel, U.A.C. International (London) Ltd., 67. Member of the Institute of Personnel Management. *Royal Commonwealth Society.*

MARKS, Ian Roy, b. 15 Oct. 32, 3rd s. of Lt.-Col. S. J. Marks. W, 46²–49³. N/S. R.E., 50–52. 2nd Lt. Clare, Cambridge, M.A. Man. Dir., Trebor Sharps Ltd.

MARLING, Major Erskine Macdonald, T.D., A.M.I.E.E. SH, 25²–28².*

MARPLES, Walter Keith, b. 6 Aug. 07, eldest s. of the late S. A. Marples. B, 21³–24². M.I.C.E., 34. ✕ R.E. Resident Engineer supervising Civil Engineering Schemes (dams, drainage & water supply). *Climbers' Club.* English Folk Dance & Song Society.

MARQUIS, Geoffrey Frederic, b. 11 Oct. 24, eldest s. of G. C. Marquis. Tu, 38³–40². ✕ R. Aust. Air Force, 43–46. F.O. University of Sydney, Australia. Bachelor of Architecture. Fellow, Royal Australian Institute of Architects. Partner, Peddle Thorp & Walker, Architects, Sydney. *Union Club, Royal Prince Alfred Yacht Club, Sydney Club.*

MARR, David Lawrence. B, 45²–49³.* Officer, Eastern Command, 66–67. Chief Signal Officer, B.A.O.R., 68–69. Vice-

MARRIAGE, James, b. 23 Jan. 11, elder s. of the late H. J. Marriage, F.R.C.S. C, 24³–29². Emmanuel, Cambridge. ✕ R.A. Capt. Underwriting member of Lloyd's. Brother, P. Marriage.

MARRIAGE, Peter, T.D., LL.B., b. 15 May 15, 2nd s. of the late H. J. Marriage, F.R.C.S., C, 28³–32³; Levée; Emmanuel, Cambridge, B.A., LL.B. ✕ Artists Rifles. Commissioned in Northamptonshire Regt., Burma. Various Staff appointments with Army & 33 Indian Corps. Lt.-Col. Dispatches. T.D. Solicitor, 46. Senior Partner, Slaughter & May. *Army & Navy, Worplesdon G.C.* Brother, J. Marriage. Son, 2043.

MARRIOTT, George Geoffrey Hall, M.C. C, 35¹–39².*

MARRIOTT, Lt.-Col. Ian Arthur, T.D., b. 25 Mar. 11, s. of the late H. F. Marriott. W, 25¹–29²; S. VIII, 28–29 (Capt.). New College, Oxford. Staff College, Camberley, 40. C.Eng., F.Inst.Prod.E., F.B.I.M. ✕ R.E. (T.A.), 32–45. Lt.-Col. G.S.O.1 at War Office, A.F.H.Q., & S.H.A.E.F. T.D. At present London Office Manager, Thomas French & Sons Ltd. Previously Sales Director of Chaseside Engineering Ltd., G. A. Harvey & Co. Ltd., Brush Group, W. G. Bagnall Ltd. Man. Dir., Parsons Engineering Ltd. *Army & Navy Club.* Sons, 1182 & 1231.

MARRIOTT, Peter Armstrong Hartley. C, 32¹–36³.*

MARRIOTT, Richard Hampden Micklethwaite. C, 34²–37³. Son, Hampden Charles, C, 67¹–71².*

MARRIOTT, Rowland Wilkieson. C, 32³–36³.*

MARRIOTT, William Gordon, B.Sc. C, 31²–35².*

MARSH, Philip Ernest Harley, b. 24 July 04, eldest s. of the late Dr. E. L. Marsh. K, 18²–22¹; XV, 20–21. Brasenose, Oxford, M.A., F.C.A. Pre-war: In practice. Post-war: United Nations, Geneva. At present practising as Financial Consultant. *Bath Club.* Oxford Society.

MARSH, Peter John, b. 10 Nov. 17, s. of the late A. C. Marsh. C, 31³–36². London Univ. City & Guilds College, B.Sc., A.C.G.I. Associate, Chartered Institute of Patent Agents. Fellow, Institute of Patent Attorneys of Australia. Patent Attorney, Sydney, Australia. *University Club, Sydney.* President, Squash Rackets Association of Australia.

MARSHALL, Charles John Evelyn, b. 29 May 11, elder s. of the late V. E. Marshall. K, 25¹–29²; Art Prize, 28. Architectural Diploma, 34. A.R.I.B.A., 35. Art. Brother, R. V. A. Marshall.

MARSHALL, The Rev. Godfrey Hibbert. SF, 19²–23².*

MARSHALL, Henry Bruce, b. 19 Oct. 24, elder s. of the late Major J. R. Marshall. Sh, 38³–42². Appointed to Metropolitan Vickers Electrical Co. Ltd. N/S. Q.O. Cameron Highlanders, 45–48. Lt. Trinity, Oxford and Edinburgh University, B.Sc. Electronic Engineer with Ferranti Ltd. Member of Royal Company of Archers, Queen's Bodyguard for Scotland. Brother, P. B. Marshall.

MARSHALL, Hugh Kinsman, b. 9 Apr. 25, eldest s. of W. K. Marshall, M.C. (or C 02). C & Tu, 38³–43²; XI, 43. Corpus Christi, Cambridge (R.A.F. Short Course). ✕ R.A.F., 44–47. F.R.I.C.S. Partner in firm of W. K. Marshall. *The East India, Sports & Public Schools Club.* Brother, L. H. Marshall.

MARSHALL, Ian, b. 27 Nov. 26, elder s. of H. P. Marshall. W, 42³–44². Army Service, 45–48. Asst. to Artistic Director, Edinburgh Festival, 49–51. Asst. to General Manager, Ealing Film Studios, 52–55. Advertising Writer & Agency Director, 55–67. Insurance Underwriter from 67. *Harlequins, Savile Club.*

MARSHALL, John Campbell, b. 30 Jan. 29, elder s. of Dr. G. G. Marshall, M.B., Ch.B. M, 42³–47²; XV, 46; XI, 45–47 (Capt.); H. XI, 47. N/S. 47–49. Brasenose, Oxford, M.A. Cricket Blue, 53. Greyhounds R.F.C. Capt., 52. Five Rugby Caps for Scotland, 54. Manager, Wagtails C.C. tour to Canada, 46. Asst. Master at Dragon School, Oxford, 53–59. Asst. Master at Rugby School, 59. Housemaster of School House, 69. *Vincent's Club.*

MARSHALL, Lewis Henry, b. 19 July 27, 2nd s. of W. K. Marshall, M.C. (or C 02). C & Tu, 40³–45²; Scholar; XV, 44. ✕ Rifle Brigade, 45–48. Lt. Exhibitioner of Clare, Cambridge, M.A. F.R.I.C.S. Partner, Vaughan & Marshall, Chartered Surveyors. Director, Welsh Tree Services Ltd. Brother, H. K. Marshall. Sons, Robin Lewis, Tu, 69³– & Christopher Kinsman, Tu, 71³.

MARSHALL, Patrick Bruce, b. 9 Oct. 27, 2nd s. of the late J. R. Marshall. Sh, 41^3–45^2. N/S. Q.O. Cameron Highlanders, 45–48. Lt. Trinity, Oxford. M.A. in Agriculture. Hill Farmer. Brother, H. B. Marshall.

MARSHALL, Robert MacKenzie, M.B., B.Ch., b. 11 Feb. 06, s. of the late R. J. Marshall, M.D. C, 20^1–24^1; XV, 23. Oriel, Oxford, B.A., B.M., B.Ch. St. Bartholomew's, London (H.P. to Lord Horder). ✕ R.N.V.R., 39–45. Surg. Lt.-Comdr. General Practice in Brockenhurst, 33–68. *Vincent's, The Naval Club.* Son, 540.

MARSHALL, Richard Vernon Antony. K, 32^3–36^3.*

MARSHALL, Prof. Thomas Humphrey, C.M.G., b. 19 Dec. 93, elder s. of the late W. C. Marshall (OR SH 65). SF, 07^3–12^2; Scholar. Exhibitioner of Trinity, Cambridge, M.A. Civilian Prisoner of War, Ruhleben Camp, 14–18. Fellow of Trinity, Cambridge, 19–25. London School of Economics, rising to Professor of Sociology, 26–56. Educational Adviser to U.K. Commissioner in Germany, 49–50. Director, Social Services Dept., U.N.E.S.C.O., 56–60. C.M.G. Hon. Doctor of Southampton, Leicester & York.

MARSHALL, Trevor McLean. SF, 33^1–37^2.*

MARSHALL, Col. Vivian James Chaworth, T.D., b. 11 June 04, s. of C. E. Marshall. B, 18^1–21^3. Clare, Cambridge, B.A. In Sudan, 26–30. Fruit Farmer & Company Director since 32. ✕ Hampshire Carabiniers Yeomanry, 39–45. Lt.-Col., T.D. Col. Member of the R.N. Auxiliary Service. *R.N.Y.C. of England.* Sons, 312 & 671.

MARSHALL, Walter Kinsman, M.C., b. 26 Mar. 88, s. of the late Dr. L. W. Marshall. C, 02^3–05^3; Cap, 05. ✕ 4th P.S. Bn. Royal Fusiliers. 4th Bn. West Yorkshire Regt. Capt. Wounded twice. M.C. (2 Bars). Chartered Surveyor. Retired. *Public Schools Club.* Sons, H. K. & L. H. Marshall.

MARSHALL, William Martin Walter, b. 11 Nov. 02, eldest s. of the late W. H. Marshall. SF, 17^3–19^3. Faraday House Electrical Engineering College, London. Engineer.

MARSHALL-CORNWALL, Gen. Sir James Handyside, K.C.B., C.B.E., D.S.O., M.C., b. 27 May 87, s. of the late J. Cornwall. SF, 01^3–05^2; XV, 04–05. R.M.A., Woolwich. R.M.A. XV, 06. Gazetted to the R.F.A., 07. ✕ R.A. Gen. Hdqrs. Staff. G.S.O.3, 2nd Corps. G.S.O.2, Gen. Hdqrs. G.S.O.1, War Office. Lt.-Col. Wounded. M.C., Brevet Major. D.S.O. Army of Black Sea, 20–23. Shanghai Defence Force, 27. Mil. Attaché in Berlin, Stockholm, Oslo & Copenhagen, 28–32. C.R.A., 51st Div., 32–34. Chief of Brit. Mil. Mission, Egyptian Army, 37–38. D.C.G.S., War Office, 38–39. G.O.C., III Corps, 40. G.O.C. Brit. Troops in Egypt and G.O.C. in C., Western Command, 41–42. Retired, 43, as General. Author of six books on military subjects. F.R.G.S. (Past President, 54–58). F.S.A. K.C.B., 40, C.B.E., 19. Légion d'Honneur, Belgian Ordre de la Couronne & Croix de Guerre. American D.S.M. & Legion of Merit. Order of the Nile. *Brooks's, Beefsteak & Geographical.*

MARTIN, Denis Hemmant Rolleston, b. 22 Dec. 06, elder s. of A. W. Martin. St, 20^3–25^3; Scholar; Levée; Head of House; XV, 24. Oriel, Oxford, B.A. Played golf for Oxford v. Cambridge, 27–28. Stockbroker. ✕ City of London Yeomanry, R.A., 39–45. Major. Brother, M. H. A. Martin. Son, Robert Jasper, St, 68^1–72^1.

MARTIN, Dennis Stanley, b. 21 Apr. 33, s. of R. I. Martin. T, 46^3–51^2; Paddison Art Prize; Baines Exhibition. N/S. R.E., 52. 2nd Lt. Queens', Cambridge, M.A. Technical Director, The Sankey Sugar Co. Ltd., Lancs. *Mid-Surrey Hockey Club.*

MARTIN, Henry Arthur North. W, 16^3–21^1.*

MARTIN, Jean Rémi, b. 24 June 06, s. of the late E. Martin. C, 20^3–24^1. Royal School of Mines, London. A.R.S.M., B.Sc. London (Mining Engineering). ✕ R.E., 40–45. Major. Commercial, principally property. Founder of Carbon Dioxide and Crown Cork Industries in East Africa. Now retired. *Karen Country Club, Nairobi* (Founder, 36); *Muthaiga Country Club; Royal Nairobi G.C.* Son, P. V. Martin.

MARTIN, Maurice Hemmant Alford, b. 19 Apr. 11, 2nd s. of the late A. W. Martin. St, 24^3–29^2; XV, 28; XXII. Oriel, Oxford, B.A. With Alexanders Discount Co. Ltd., 33–71. Cripps, Warburg Ltd. since 71. ✕ City of London Yeomanry, R.A. (T.A.), 39–45. P.O.W. in Germany, 40–45. *Bath Club, M.C.C., Royal St. George's G.C.* Brother, D. H. R. Martin. Son 1919.

MARTIN, Philip Vale, F.C.A., b. 5 Aug. 31, s. of J. R. Martin (OR C 20). Tu, 45²– 49². F.C.A. Kenya Regiment, 55/56. Hartwells Group Ltd., Oxford. Man. Dir., Oil Companies Division.

MARTINEAU, Alan Denis. C, 34¹–38². Son, Jeremy John, C, 68³–.*

MARTINEAU, Bernard Gaston, b. 23 Nov. 95, younger s. of the late Col. E. Martineau, C.M.G. (OR C 76). C, 10³– 14². ✕ 6th Bn. Royal Warwickshire Regt. Capt. Wounded twice. Trinity Hall, Cambridge, M.A. Teacher Training Cert. Schoolmaster at Ashford Grammar School, Kent, & at Oldfield Co-educational School, Swanage, Dorset, 21–28. Poultry Farmer at South Rookery, Lowsonford, Henley-in-Arden, 28–49. Retired. Now living in Gloucestershire.

MARTINEAU, The Rev. Christopher Lee, b. 28 Nov. 16, eldest s. of the late Sir Wilfred Martineau (OR C 04). C, 30³– 35²; S. VIII, 34–35. Trinity Hall, Cambridge, M.A. Scholae Cancellarii, Lincoln, 39–41. Ordained Deacon, 41; Priest, 42. Curate of St. Mary, Hinckley, 41–43. ✕ Chaplain, R.N.V.R., 43–46. Curate, St. Albans Abbey, 46–48. Vicar, St. Paul's, Balsall Heath, Birmingham, 48–54. Vicar, All Saints, Shard End, Birmingham, 54–65. Rector, Holy Trinity, Skipton, from 65. B.S.E.S. Hon. Canon of Bradford Cathedral, 72. *Rotary.*

MARTIN-HURST, John Forrest, b. 11 Oct. 10, younger s. of W. Martin-Hurst, M.A., F.R.G.S. K, 24³–29². New College, Oxford, M.A. Elstree School, Elstree & Woolhampton, 33–43. ✕ R.A.F.V.R., 43–46. F/Lt. (Photographic Intelligence). Man. Dir. of Photographic Library, 46–53. Headmaster of Tower House, London, S.W.15 (Boys' Preparatory School) from 53. Member of Incorporated Association of Preparatory Schools since 57. Brother, W. F. F. Martin-Hurst.

MARTIN-HURST, William Frederick Forrest, b. 20 Oct. 03, elder s. of W. Martin-Hurst, M.A., F.R.G.S. B, 17³– 21³. City & Guilds Engineering College, South Kensington. Ch.Eng., F.I.Mech.E. Associate Fellow, Royal Aeronautical Society. With Lightfoot Refrigeration Co.

Ltd., London, 25–31. British Thermostat Co. Ltd., Sunbury-on-Thames, 31–45— Joint Man. Dir., 37–45. Teddington Aircraft Controls Ltd., Merthyr Tydfil, 46–60, Man. Dir. The Rover Company Ltd., Solihull, 60–70. Appointed Man. Dir., 62–69. Consultant Engineering Director, 70. Retired, 70. Director of Royal British Legion Cambrian Factory Ltd., Breconshire, since retirement. *Royal Aero Club.* Brother, J. F. Martin-Hurst. Son, 1198.

MARTLEY, John Francis. SH, 07²–09³.*

MARTYN, Edward Owen. SH, 16²– 20³.*

MARTYN, Graham Reed, b. 20 May 08, younger s. of W. E. Martyn. SH, 22¹–26². Brasenose, Oxford, B.A. Solicitor, 34. Partner in Bolton & Lowe, London. Retired, 73. ✕ Royal Observer Corps, 40–45. *United Service & Royal Aero Club, M.C.C.* Brother, E. O. Martyn.

MARTYN, Gian Timothy. Tu, 43³–48².*

MARTYN, Loel Fellowes. Tu, 42¹–46¹.*

MARX, Robert Ian, b. 13 Jan. 23, 2nd s. of H. Marx. St, 36³–41². Trinity, Cambridge, M.A. ✕ R.N.V.R. (F.A.A.) S/Lt. (A). Member of Stock Exchange, London (Vickers da Costa & Co.) since 47. S.B.St.J. *R.A.C.* Son, 2709.

MASLIN, Raymond Charles John. K, 21³–26².*

MASON, Gerald Finch, b. 26 Oct. 51, 4th s. of G. H. Mason. C, 33²–38². Magdalene, Cambridge, M.A. ✕ R.A.F., 40–46. Asst. to Sales Manager, Ruberoid, London, 48–52. Emigrated to Canada, 52. Various jobs. Manager of an Import Agency from 66. *Toronto Cricket, Skating & Curling Club.* Imperial Officers Association of Canada.

MASON, Major Humphrey Francis, D.S.O., J.P., b. 8 Mar. 84, elder s. of the late F. W. Mason. St, 98²–01³. King's College, London—Engineering. ✕ H.A.C., 43rd Siege Bty., R.G.A. Major. D.S.O. Dispatches. Member, Institution of Civil Engineers. Retired. J.P., Woodbridge.

MASON, Major Hugh Francis Ross, R.E., b. 23 Feb. 26, s. of F. E. Mason. St & W, 39³–44¹. Peterhouse, Cambridge (R.E. Short Course). Gazetted to R.E., 46. T/Capt., 47. Royal Corps of Transport.

M.C.I.T., A.M.B.I.M. Man. Dir. (Technical), British Steel Corp.

MASON, Philip Fairfan. K, 26^3–31^2.*

MASON, Stephen Parsons, b. 19 Nov. 98, eldest s. of the late D. M. Mason. SH, 12^3–17^2. ✕ 72nd Bde., R.F.A. 2nd Lt. Queen's, Oxford, M.A. ✕ R.A., 39–42. Accountant, retired 62. Social Member, *Piltdown G.C.*

MASON, William Richard. SF, 43^3–48^2.*

MASSIE-BLOMFIELD, Hugh, T.D. B, 97^3–00^2.*

MATHESON, Henry Greville, b. 3 July 10, eldest s. of the late J. F. Matheson. K, 24^2–28^2. Sorbonne & New College, Oxford, M.A. Imperial Airways Ltd., 32–39. ✕ R.A.F., 39–47. Wing-Cdr. Dispatches twice. Civil Aviation, 47–58. Management Consultant, 58–72 (Rtd.). Member of the Institute of Marketing, Institute of Export & Institute of Management Consultants. *United Service & Royal Aero Clubs.* Brother, O. R. Matheson. Sons, 2053 & 2824.

MATHESON, Oliver Rayner, D.F.C., b. 2 Aug. 16, 3rd s. of the late J. F. Matheson. K, 30^3–34^3. Underwriter at Lloyd's. ✕ R.A.F.V.R. Sqn. Ldr. D.F.C. & Bar. Shot down while leading a Pathfinder Mission over the Ruhr, 42, escaped through France & Spain & returned to active service within two months. Retired. *P.F.F. Club.* Brother, H. G. Matheson.

MATHIESON, George, b. 23 Feb. 09, eldest s. of the late J. G. Mathieson. St, 22^3–28^2; Levée. Scholar of Sidney Sussex, Cambridge, B.A. ✕ R.A., 40–46. P.O.W., 42–43. Council Member, Cocoa Chocolate & Confectionery Alliance, 60–69. Chrmn. of Council, British Food Manufacturing Research Assoc., 67–69. Clarke Nickolls & Coombs Ltd. Director, 35. Chrmn., 57. (Confectionery manufacture till 69 when subsidiary, Clarnico Ltd., acquired by Trebor Sharps Ltd., thereafter in property.) *United Oxford & Cambridge.* Brothers, T. & J. Mathieson. Son, 1165.

MATHIESON, James, b. 12 June 19, 3rd s. of the late J. G. Mathieson. St, 32^3–38^1. Choral Scholar of King's, Cambridge. ✕ R.E., 40–46., Capt. (mainly in India & Burma with Indian Army). Short period with W. H. A. Robertson & Co.

Ltd., Engineers, of Bedford, then joined family Company, Clarke Nickolls & Coombs Ltd., Confectionery Manufacturers, till 69. Now Property Management & Development. Brothers, G. & T. Mathieson. Sons, Christopher James, St, 69^2– & Robert Alexander, St, 71^3–.

MATHIESON, The Rev. Theodore, b. 2 June 13, 2nd s. of the late J. G. Mathieson. B, 27^1–32^1. Sidney Sussex, Cambridge, M.A. Cuddesdon College, Oxford. General Ordination Exam. Ordained Deacon, 37; Priest, 38. Curate of Elland, Yorks., 37–42. Curate of Greenford, Middlesex, 42–46. Oxford Mission Brotherhood of the Epiphany, Calcutta, from 46. Brothers, G. & J. Mathieson.

MAUDE, Col. Alan Hamer, C.M.G. D.S.O., T.D., D.L., b. 18 Aug. 85, elder s. of the late E. Maude, J.P. (OR T 69). St, 99^3–04^3; Scholar; S. VIII, 03–04 (Capt.). Exhibitioner of Oriel, Oxford, M.A. University S. VIII & Humphry Cup IV, 05–08. (Capt.). Editor, "Isis". Sub-Editor, "Daily Chronicle", 12–14. Editorial staff of "The Times", 20–50 (Chief Sub-Editor; Editor, Special Numbers). Commissioned A.S.C. (T.A.), 09. ✕ Colonel commanding 47th Divnl. Train, R.A.S.C., 14–18. ✕ 39–45, Colonel, A.Q.M.G. & Controller, Central Purchase Board, G.H.Q., B.E.F., 39–40. C.R.A.S.C., Borden District, 40–43. C.R.A.S.C., Kent District, 43–45. President, O.R. Society, 52/3. Edited "Rugby School Register", 11–46, & "War History". C.M.G., D.S.O., T.D. Dispatches twice. Hon. Col., 56 (London) Armd. Div. Column, R.A.S.C. D.L., Greater London. Brother, R. E. Maude. Son, A. E. U. Maude.

MAUDE, Angus Edmund Upton, T.D., M.P., b. 8 Sept. 12, s. of Col. A. H. Maude, C.M.G., D.S.O., T.D., D.L. (OR St 99). St, 25^3–30^2; Scholar. Oriel, Oxford, M.A. ✕ R.A.S.C. (T.A.), 39–49. P.O.W., 42–45. Major. T.D. M.P. (Cons.), Ealing (S.), 50–58, & Stratford-upon-Avon from 63. Author & Journalist.

MAUDE, Derek Ronald, b. 13 June 25, s. of Col. R. E. Maude, O.B.E., T.D. (OR St 03). St & K, 39^2–43^2. Magdalene, Cambridge. (Army Short Course.) ✕ R.A.S.C., 43–47. Capt. Joined Standard & Triumph Sales Ltd., 47. Director, 52–53. Asst. London Manager, The Standard Motor Co. Ltd., from 54; Sales Manager, University Motors of Kingston-on-Thames.

MAUDE, Evan Walter, C.B., b. 11 Feb. 19, s. of the late Sir E. J. Maude, K.C.B., K.B.E. (OR W 97). Sh, 32²–36³. New College, Oxford, B.A. ✕ R.N.V.R. (Fleet Air Arm), 40–45. Lt. (A). Dispatches. Civil Service, H.M. Treasure, 46–70. Ministry of Agriculture, Fisheries and Food from 70, Deputy Secretary. C.B., 68. *United Oxford and Cambridge University Club.*

MAUDE, Col. Ronald Edmund, O.B.E., T.D., b. 5 Nov. 88, younger s. of the late E. Maude, J.P. (OR B 69). St, 03¹–04². General Engineering College, 04. With Deasy Motor Manufacturing Co. Ltd., 06 & Austin Motor Co. Ltd., 11–14 and 18–20. ✕ 47th (London) Divnl. Train, A.S.C. Major. O.B.E., T.D. Dispatches twice. British Motor Trading Corporation Ltd., 20. London Manager, Bean Cars Ltd., 22; Director, 26. The Car Mart Ltd., London, Director. Dagenham Motors Ltd., Director. Standard & Triumph Cars Ltd., Man. Dir. *Oriental Club, London.* Brother, A. H. Maude. Son, D. R. Maude.

MAVOR, Richard Edward, b. 15 May 31, s. of the late E. I. Mavor. B, 44³–49²; S. VIII, 48. N/S., 49–51, Coldstream Guards. Lt. Trinity, Oxford, M.A. Merchant Banker. *Caledonian & Oriental Clubs.*

MAXWELL, Col. Arthur Terence, T.D., b. 19 Jan. 05, s. of the late Brig.-Gen. Sir Arthur Maxwell, K.C.B., C.M.G., D.S.O., T.D. SH, 18³–23²; XV, 22; Cadet Officer; G. VIII, 22. Trinity, Oxford, M.A. Bar, Inner Temple, 29. Man. Dir., Glyn Mills & Co., Bankers, till 45. Fellow Institute of Bankers. ✕ K.R.R.C., 40. Capt. Staff College, 41. Col., Gen. Staff, A.F.H.Q., 43–44. Deputy Chief, Military Govt. Section att. S.H.A.E.F. T.D. Director of many Companies. Governor of Rugby School, 36–73. *Carlton Club.* Sons, 605 & 1699.

MAXWELL, The Rev. John Francis, b. 17 Apr. 18, s. of the late Lt.-Col. D. W. Maxwell (Indian Army). W, 31³–36¹; Cap. ✕ R.N.V.R., 41–46. Lt. Cambridge & London Universities. Ordained Roman Catholic Priest, 54. Engaged in research and writing on moral and industrial questions. London Circle, Newman Association.

MAY, Barry William N. St, 45³–50².*

MAYBERRY, Robert Gerald, b. 7 Mar. 19, 2nd s. of Dr. R. J. Mayberry. M, 32³–36². ✕ R.A., 39–46. Capt. Dispatches.

Solicitor, 46. Practising Solicitor. Partner in Reynolds Porter Chamberlain & Co., London. Law Society.

MAYHEW, Evelyn Hill, M.D. SH, 93³–98².*

MAYNARD, Frederick Roy Macfie. C, 20²–23².*

MAYNE, David Roger, b. 5 May 29, 2nd s. of the late A. B. Mayne. K, 42³–47². Brackenbury Scholarship to Balliol, Oxford, B.A. Photographer, illustrating a number of books. Taught at Bath College of Art, Corsham, 66–69. Edited "Great Victorian Photographs". Held numerous one-man Exhibitions.

MAYO, Francis Carbutt, M.R.C.S., L.R.C.P., T.D., D.L., b. 21 Apr. 05, s. of the late Dr. F. H. Mayo. St, 19²–23²; XV, 20–22; XXII; Junior Athletics Cup, 21. Pembroke, Cambridge, B.A. Burney Yeo Scholarship to King's College Hospital. University Relay Team, 25. M.R.C.S., L.R.C.P. ✕ R.A.M.C., 39–45. Lt.-Col. Dispatches. T.D. General Medical Practitioner (Retired). D.L. *Alpine Club.* Son, 579.

MAYS-SMITH, Lt.-Col. Robert Shankland, M.B.E., b. 30 Oct. 02, eldest s. of Sir Alfred Mays-Smith. Tu, 16³–20². Trinity, Cambridge, M.A., F.C.A. ✕ R.A.P.C., 39–45. Lt.-Col. M.B.E. Retired. *O. & C. Golfing Society., M.C.C.*

MAYTHAM, Alan Kent, b. 31 Aug. 20, 2nd s. of the late A. A. Maytham. W, 34³–37². Trinity, Cambridge. Engineering Studies, 39–41. ✕ R.E., 41–46. Att. Indian Army. Major. Spicers Export, 47–61. Man. Dir., Spicer Cowan (Ireland) Ltd., from 62. *United Service Club, Dublin; Fitzwilliam L.T. Club, Dublin.* Administrative Staff College, Henley, 58.

MEADE, Ronald Clanwilliam Alwyne. St, 29³–33².*

MEADON, John Percival, b. 7 Apr. 13, s. of the late Sir Percy Meadon, C.B.E. C, 26³–31². University College, Oxford, B.A. Solicitor. Local Govt. Deputy Clerk to Surrey C.C. Now retired.

MEAGEEN, Thomas, b. 17 Nov. 23, 2nd s. of the late T. Meageen. K, 38²–41³; XV, 41; XXII, 41. ✕ Rifle Brigade, N. Africa, Italy & N.W. Europe, 42–46. Wounded. Business of Cumberland Motor Services. Subsequent to nationalisation acquired hotel, "Castle Inn", Bassen-thwaite. Retired to Isle of Man in 65.

MEAKIN, Cyril Alfred, b. 26 June 02, s. of the late A. J. Meakin (OR K 90). W, 16²–20¹. University College, London. In business in Ceylon till 51. Then with the Ceylon & Eastern Agency Ltd., London. *Oriental Club.* Sons, 596 & 1232.

MEDEN, Alexander Peter (formerly Van der Meden). W, 15³–20¹.*

MEEK, Richard Ombler, b. 23 Oct. 08, s. of the late J. B. L. Meek. SH, 22³–25³. St. John's, Cambridge, M.A. ✕ R.E., 42–45. Capt. F.I.C.E., A.M.I.Mun.E. Chief Sewerage and Drainage Engineer, City of Swansea, City Engineer and Surveyor's Dept.

MEGGITT, Stephen Michael Anselm. K, 43³–48².*

MELLAND, Roger Birley, b. 26 Nov. 08, s. of Dr. C. H. Melland. K, 22²–27². Corpus Christi, Oxford, M.A. Solicitor, 34. ✕ R.N.V.R., 39–45. Lt. Practised as Solicitor from 34–69, in Manchester (now retired). General Commissioner for Income Tax. Charities Review Officer for Wiltshire. Son, 1443.

MELLOR, Walter John. M, 36³–41².*

MELLY, Edward Travers, b. 17 Sept. 22, s. of the late Rev. C. T. Melly (OR K 01). K, 36²–41³; Levée; Head of House; XV, 40; XXII. Trinity, Oxford, M.A. Dip Ed., Brit. Col. (U.B.C., Vancouver). ✕ R.N.V.R., 41–46. Lt. Schoolmaster, Maidstone Grammar School.

MELLY, Capt. Peter Emerson, R.N., b. 12 Feb. 23, eldest s. of the late E. E. Melly. K, 36³–40². Scholar. Royal Naval Engineering College, Plymouth. Passed 1st Class. ✕ H.M.S. *Unicorn*, 44–45. R.N. College, Greenwich, 45–47. Lt. (E), F.I.Mech.E. Member of the Institute of Marine Engineers. Capt. R.N. Deputy Director of Marine Engineering in the Ship Dept. of the Procurement Executive of the Ministry of Defence.

MENELL, Clive Sydney, b. 13 June 31, eldest s. of S. G. Menell. C, 45³–49²; Sw. VIII, 47, 48; XXII, 49 (Capt.). Trinity, Cambridge, M.A. Wharton School. Univ. of Pennsylvania, M.B.A. Deputy Chrmn., Anglo-Transvaal Consolidated Investment Co. Ltd. Chrmn., Auglovaal Holdings Ltd. Chrmn., Middle Witwatersrand

(Western Areas) Ltd. and Consolidated Glass Works Ltd. *M.C.C., Sky Club (N.Y.).* Member of Governing Council of the Univ. of the Witwatersrand. Son, Richard Peter, C, 69¹–72³.

MENNEER, Stephen Snow, C.B., b. 6 Mar. 10, 4th s. of Dr. S. C. Menneer, LL.D. M, 23³–29²; Scholar; Levée; Exhibitioner. Scholar of Oriel, Oxford, M.A. Schoolmaster, 33–39. Ministry of Information, 39–48 (Established Civil Servant from 46). Ministry of National Insurance from 48. Retired, 70. C.B., 67.

MENZIES, William Allan, T.D. St, 24³–27³.*

MEREDITH, Thomas Keven, J.P., b. 3 May 14, s. of T. Meredith, J.P. K, 27³–32². Exhibitioner (Nat. Sc.). Clare, Cambridge, B.A. ✕ R.A., 39–46. Capt. Wounded. Dispatches. Farmed, 46–53. Partner, Meredith & Hill, Coventry, 54–68. Retired. J.P., 62. *Flyfishers'.*

MERIVALE, John Herman. SH, 31³–36².*

MERRIAM, Antony Brooke, b. 15 Dec. 22, 3rd s. of the late C. F. Merriam. SH, 36²–40³. ✕ 19th K. G. V's O. Lancers, Indian Army. Capt. Corpus Christi, Cambridge, B.A. Chartered Engineer. Fellow, Institute of Production Engineers. Halex Division, The British Xylonite Co., 48–67 (Man. Dir., 63). Man. Dir., Spearwell Tools Ltd., 67–72. Director, Mason Cash & Co. Ltd. from 73. Brothers, J. F. P., H. K. & D. C. Merriam. Son, Mark Richard, SH, 68³–.

MERRIAM, David Charles, b. 29 Nov. 30, youngest s. of the late C. F. Merriam. SH, 44³–48². Royal Agricultural College, Cirencester. 358 (Suffolk Yeomanry) Medium Regt., R.A. (T.A.). Lt. F.R.C.I.S., M.R.A.C. Farmer. Chartered Surveyors, Strutt & Parker, Ipswich. *Royal Harwich Yacht Club.* Brothers, J. F. P., H. K. & A. B. Merriam.

MERRIAM, Major Hugh Kenneth, M.C. SH, 33²–36².*

MERRIAM, John Franklin Pearse. SH, 26²–30³.*

MEYJES, The Rev. Walter Alexander. W, 19¹–22¹.*

MICHELMORE, Col. James Franck Godwin, T.D., b. 15 Feb. 24, 2nd s. of Sir

W. G. Michelmore, C.B., D.S.O., M.C., T.D., D.L., LL.B. (OR St 08). SH, 37³–41³; Cap, 41. Balliol, Oxford, M.A. ✕ 6th Regt., R.H.A., 43–46, India. Capt. Solicitor, 50. Notary Public. Registrar & Bishop's Legal Secretary, 63. 296th (Royal Devon Yeomanry) Field Regt., R.A., T.A., 47–66. Cmdg., 62–66. T.A. Col. T.A.V.R., 68–73. Hockey for Devon, 47–59. West of England, 54. T.D., A.D.C. *Army & Navy Club, Exeter Golf & Country Club.* Sons, Robert James Godwin, SH, 71¹– & William Franck, SH, 72³–.

MICHELMORE, Ralph Godfrey, M.D., b. 23 July 92, 2nd s. of the late H. W. Michelmore (OR C 78). St, 06³–09³. London Hospital, London University, M.R.C.S., L.R.C.P., M.B., B.S., M.D. ✕ R.A.M.C., 16–20. Capt. India. Medical Practitioner, Sidmouth, Devon, 23–61. Brother, Sir W. G. Michelmore.

MICHELMORE, Major-Gen. Sir (William) Godwin, K.B.E., C.B., D.S.O., M.C., T.D., D.L., b. 14 Mar. 94, 3rd s. of the late H. W. Michelmore (OR C 78). St, 08²–12³; Cap, 12. ✕ Comdg., 32nd Divnl. Signal Company, R.E. Major. Wounded. M.C., D.S.O. London University, LL.B. Solicitor, 20, & Notary Public of Michelmore's of Exeter. Major-Gen. (T.A.) A.D.C. to H.M. The King, 42–47. Mayor Exeter, 49–50. Vice-Chrmn., Council, T. & A.F.A., 56–59. Chrmn., Governors of St. Luke's Coll., Exeter. Governor of Blundell's School. Member Council of Exeter Univ. K.B.E., 53; C.B., 45; T.D., D.L., J.P. *Army & Navy Club.* Brother, R. G. Michelmore. Son, J. F. G. Michelmore. Grandsons, Robert James Godwin, SH, 71¹– & William Franck, SH, 72³–.

MICHIE, Donald, b. 11 Nov. 23, eldest s. of the late J. K. Michie. W, 37²–42¹. Open Classical Scholarship to Balliol, Oxford, M.A., D.Phil., D.Sc. Fellow of British Computer Society. Fellow of Royal Society of Edinburgh. Personal Chair of Machine Intelligence in Edinburgh Univ. from 67. F.Z.S.

MICKLEM, The Rev. Nathaniel, D.D., LL.D., C.H., b. 10 Apr. 88, eldest s. of the late N. Micklem, Q.C. St, 01³–06³; Head of House; XXII, 05. Marburg Univ. Scholar of New College, Oxford, M.A. Mansfield College, Oxford. Ordained Congregational Minister, 14. Principal, Mansfield College, Oxford, 32–53. Wilde Lecturer in Natural & Comparative Religion, Oxford, 48–51. President of Liberal Party, 57–58. Select Preacher, Univ. of Oxford, 60.

Authors' Club. Hon. D.D. Glasgow & Queen's Univ. of Canada. Hon. LL.D. Queen's Univ. of Canada. C.H., 74. Brother T. E. Micklem. Nephew, 99.

MICKLEM, Thomas Esmond, M.B., b. 24 May 90, 2nd s. of the late N. Micklem, Q.C. St, 03³–09²; Cap, 08; R. VIII, 08. New College, Oxford, M.A., M.B., B.Ch. Guy's Hospital. ✕ R.A.M.C. Capt. Medical Practitioner (Retired). Brother, Rev. N. Micklem. Nephew, 99.

MIDDLETON, Alfred. Tu, 99¹–01¹.*

MIDDLETON, Charles Tyson, b. 7 Mar. 05, 2nd s. of the late T. T. Middleton. K, 19¹–23²; XXII, 22–23. Trinity, Cambridge, B.A. Malayan Civil Service, 29–35. British Council (Overseas Service), 42–61 (Retired). *Royal Commonwealth Society.* Brother, T. R. T. Middleton.

MIDDLETON, Herbert Douglas. Tu, 97³–99².*

MIDDLETON, Thomas Robert Tyson, b. 20 Aug. 03, eldest s. of the late T. T. Middleton. K, 17³–21¹. University College, London University, B.Sc., M.I.C.E. With Civil Engineering Contractors, 24–62. Consultant, 62–70. ✕ R.E. & att. Indian Army, 43–46. Capt. Retired, 70. *Royal Commonwealth Society, Huntercombe G.C.* Member (Veteran) of H.A.C. Brother, C. T. Middleton.

MIDGLEY, The Rev. Arnold Spencer, b. 25 Aug. 95, eldest s. of the late A. W. Midgley. W, 10²–12². ✕ 140th & 97th Field Ambulance, R.A.M.C., 14–18. Pte. Leeds Univ., B.A. Ordained, 23. St. Hilda's, Leeds, 25 yrs. King's, Sutton, 16 yrs. Retired, 61.

MILES, Rev. Archibald Geoffrey, b. 1 May 22, 2nd s. of Admiral Sir Geoffrey Miles, K.C.B., K.C.S.I. C, 36²–40³. New College, Oxford. "War" Degree in Modern History. Hons. Degree (2nd Class Theology). ✕ R.A., 42–46. Theological College, Chichester. Ordained Deacon, 50; Priest, 51. Parish Ministry, Northampton, England; Bulawayo, Rhodesia; Bentley, England. Rector of Riverside, Bulawayo, from 63.

MILES, Frank Ronald, b. 30 Sept. 20, younger s. of T. Miles. C, 34²–39². Queens', Cambridge, B.A. Asst. Director, Open Cast Coal Mining, Indian Govt., 44–46. Senior English Master, King's Coll. School, Wimbledon. Author: "Catalogue

Raisonné"; "Samuel Laurence"; "Critical Edition Doctor Johnson". Brother, T. E. Miles.

MILES, Henry John Christopher, b. 16 Jan. 13, s. of the late H. R. Miles. St, 26³–31²; Cap, 30. Peterhouse, Cambridge, M.A. Solicitor & Commissioner for Oaths, 38. Partner, Bevan Hancock & Co., of Bristol, from 50. Vice-President, *Clifton R.F.C.* The Weavers Company. Son, Robert John Jeffrey, St, 69³–.

MILES, Thomas Edward. C, 31³–35³.*

MILFORD, David Sumner, b. 7 June 05, younger s. of the late Sir Humphrey Milford. SF, 18³–24²; Rackets Pair, 21–24 (Winners, Queens, 23–24); XI, 23–24; H. XI, 23–24; Head of House. New College, Oxford, B.A. Hockey Blue, 26–28. Rackets Half Blue, 25–28. Lawn Tennis Half Blue, 26. Amateur Rackets Champion, 30, 35–38, 50, 51. Open Champion, 36. World Champion, 37–45. Amateur Doubles Champion eleven times. Hockey International for England, 30–37 (25 Caps). Asst. Master, Marlborough College, 28–65. Retired, 65.

MILLAR, Gerald Arthur, M.C., b. 31 Aug. 95, 4th s. of the late C. C. H. Millar. K, 09³–13³; Cap, 12; XXII, 13. With William Heinemann Ltd., Publishers, London, till 26, then in organisation associated with P.R. side of Brewing Industry. ✗ R.M.A., Heavy Howitzer Battery. 202nd Siege Battery, R.G.A. Major. M.C. Author of "Part-time Countrymen". Sons, O. N. Millar & 468B.

MILLAR, Sir Oliver Nicholas, K.C.V.O., b. 26 Apr. 23, elder s. of G. A. Millar (OR K 09). SF, 36³–40²; Paddison Art Prize; Exhibitioner. London Univ. Courtauld Institute of Art. (Academic Diploma, History of Art). Fellow of British Academy, 70. Trustee of National Portrait Gallery. Asst. Surveyor of the King's Pictures, 47–49; Deputy Surveyor, 49–72; Surveyor since 72. Published numerous Art Historical Books & Articles. Fellow of Society of Antiquaries. M.V.O., 53; C.V.O., 63; K.C.V.O., 73. Brother, 468B.

MILLER, Sqn. Ldr. Arthur William Darley. B, 28³–33².*

MILLER, Cecil John Whitworth. C, 04³–07².*

MILLER, Cyril Thomas Risch. K, 13³–17¹. Sons, M. D. & P. N. Miller.*

MILLER, Douglas James Birkmyre. Tu, 39³–44². Son, Robert Alexander Mark, Tu, 73¹–.*

MILLER, Ian Gerald, b. 23 May 17, elder s. of G. E. Miller. Sh, 31¹–35². Gonville & Caius, Cambridge, M.A. Dip. Ed. ✗ H.A.C. (12th Regt., R.H.A.), 39–45. Capt. Asst. Master, Royal Lancaster Grammar School, 48–50, & Rugby School from 50. Brother, T. B. C. Miller. Son, 2242.

MILLER, Ian Mitchell, b. 29 June 23, eldest s. of the late G. W. M. Miller, M.C. Sh, 37²–41². Trinity, Cambridge. ✗ Royal Scots. Seconded King's African Rifles, 42–46. Capt. Chrmn., Scottish Tea & Lands Company of Ceylon Ltd.; Partner, Bell, Lawrie Robertson & Co., Stockbrokers, Edinburgh. *H.C.E.G.; New Club, Edinburgh.* Son, 2849.

MILLER, John Bryan Peter, G.C. SF, 16³–22².*

MILLER, John Dawson. SH, 33¹–37³. Son, 2576.*

MILLER, Michael Dawson, b. 12th Mar. 28, elder s. of C. T. R. Miller (OR K 13). SH, 41³–45³. Practising Solicitor. Manager, Shipowners Marine Insurance Mutual Association. Professional Airline Passenger. *Hurlingham Club, H.A.C.* London Maritime Arbitrators Assoc. Brother, P. N. Miller.

MILLER, Peter North, b. 28 Sept. 30, 2nd s. of C. T. R. Miller (OR K 13). SH, 44²–48³; Holder of Bigside Bags; XV, 48; R. VIII, 47–48 (Capt.); Winner of Crick. Lincoln, Oxford, M.A. Blue, Cross-country, 52. Half Blue, 1 Mile, 53. Barrister. Member of Lloyd's, 59. Joined Thos. R. Miller & Son, Insurance at Lloyd's, 53. Senior Partner, 71. Chrmn., "Miller" Group of Insurance Organisations, Triport Shipping Ltd., & Morton Insurance Co. Ltd. Life Member of the Chief Pleas, Sark, 70. *Vincent's & Gresham.* Brother, M. D. Miller. Son, Andrew Henry Benedict, SH, 72³–.

MILLER, Thomas Basil Crisp, D.S.C. b. 4 Dec. 20, 2nd s. of G. E. Miller. Sh, 34³–39²; XXII. ✗ R.N.V.R., 41–46. Lt. D.S.C. Director, Lambert Bros. Oil Co. Ltd. *R.A.C. ,Petroleum Industries Club.* Brother, I. G. Miller.

MILLER, Thomas Robert Sinclair, b. 30 Oct. 22, s. of the late T. Miller. B,

36^3–39^2; Sw. VIII, 39. London University (External) LL.B., 43. Solicitor, 47. In practice at Hythe & Folkestone.

MILLER, William McCrum, R.M., b. 25 Nov. 03, 3rd s. of Rev. D. Miller, B.A. C, 17^3–21^1. Magdalene, Cambridge, B.A. Barrister. Northern Ireland, 27. Resident Magistrate, Omagh, Co. Tyrone. *Tyrone County, Armagh County Clubs.*

MILLER, William Mitchell, M.V.O., b. 15 Sept. 27, 2nd s. of G. W. M. Miller. Sh & St, 41^1–45^3; Cap; Tom Hughes Prize. Regular Army, Grenadier Guards, 45–54 (Palestine & Middle East, 48–52). Capt. M.V.O. Apprentice Stockbroker, 55–58. Member of Stock Exchange from 58. Partner, Bell, Lawrie, Robertson & Co., Edinburgh. *R. & A. Golf Club; H.C.E.G.; New Club, Edinburgh;* Member of the Queen's Bodyguard for Scotland (Royal Company of Archers).

MILLETT, Stansbury Girtin. B, 18^3–21^3.*

MILLIGAN, John Stowell, b. 28 Feb. 23, s. of the late H. S. Milligan. Sh, 36^3–41^2; Levée; Head of House. Corpus Christi, Cambridge, M.A. ⚔ Commissioned 5th Royal Inniskilling Dragoon Guards, 43. Normandy, 44. G.3(Ops.), Southern Command, 45. Capt. Schoolmaster at Heatherdown, Ascot, now retired. *Junior Carlton Club.* F.R.M.S., N.R.S., B.A.R.C., C.U.A.C.

MILLIKEN, Michael. SH, 42^3–48^1.*

MILLWARD, Charles Geoffrey, b. 1 Sept. 04, 2nd s. of the late G. Millward. C, 18^3–20^2. Pembroke, Cambridge, B.A. Joined Dunlop Rubber Co. (Far East) Ltd., Kobe, Japan. Retired. *Bath Club.*

MILNER, Guy Chandley, M.D., b. 30 July 01, 3rd & youngest s. of the late E. T. Milner, M.B. T, 15^2–20^1; XV, 19. King's, Cambridge, B.A. The London Hospital, M.R.C.S., L.R.C.P., 26. M.A., B.Chir., M.B. ⚔ 39–45, M.O. i/c Pettswood F.A.P. & R.N.V.R. Surg.-Lt. Independent Parliamentary Candidate for Orpington, 46. Retired from N.H.S. and general practice, 57. M.O., Kidbrooke Government Training Centre till 62. Author of "Some of the Answers". Brother, S. M. Milner.

MILNER, Silvanus Mottram, F.R.C.S., b. 21 Jan. 01, 2nd s. of the late E. T. Milner, M.B. T, 15^2–18^3; Head of House.

King's, Cambridge, & Manchester, M.A., M.B., B.Ch., L.R.C.P., F.R.C.S. Consulting Orthopaedic Surgeon. Brother, G. C. Milner. Son, 205.

MILNES, Harold Tetley, b. 3 Mar. 15, s. of H. Milnes. B, 28^3–33^2. Trinity, Oxford, M.A. ⚔ Ox. & Bucks. Light Infantry, 39–45. Major. Solicitor. Secretary & Solicitor to the Boots Company Ltd., from 47. Chrmn., *Notts. C.C.C.,* 64–70. *M.C.C., Lansdowne (London), United Services (Notts.).*

MILNES, John Harvey Charlton, b. 16 Aug. 19, s. of the late C. Milnes, F.R.I.C.S. (OR C 02). C, 33^3–35^1. ⚔ M.E.F. Wounded. F.R.I.C.S. (Building). Building Surveyor.

MILROY, Charles Patrick, b. 16 Sept. 13, s. of the late G. W. W. Milroy (OR W 00). W, 27^3–32^2; Levée; Head of House; XV, 31; Tom Hughes Prize. Emmanuel, Cambridge, M.A. London University Institute of Education. Teachers Dip. ⚔ R.A., 40–46. Capt. Member of Teachers Training Enquiry (James Committee), 71. Member of Agricultural Training Board since inception, 67. Now Chief Education Officer, Gloucestershire. Society of Education Officers. *Farmers' Club.*

MILWARD, Sir Anthony (Horace), C.B.E., b. 2 Mar. 05, 3rd s. of the late H. T. Milward. K, 18^3–23^2. Clare, Cambridge, Foundation Scholar, B.A. With Manchester Textile Company, 26–40. ⚔ Fleet Air Arm, R.N.V.R., as Pilot, 40–45. With British European Airways, 46–70, in various capacities. Last 14 yrs. as Chief Executive and finally Chrmn. Retired, 70. Presently part-time Chrmn., London Tourist Board. Clare Association, O.B.E. (Military), C.B.E. Knight Bachelor, 64. *Royal Automobile Club.* Brothers, H. G. V. & F. J. Milward. Son, 90.

MILWARD, David Victor, M.B., B.Ch., K, 30^3–34^3.*

MILWARD, Francis John, M.Ch., F.R.C.S., b. 5 Apr. 03, 2nd s. of the late H. T. Milward. K, 16^3–21^2. Clare, Cambridge, M.A., M.Ch. St. Thomas's Hospital, F.R.C.S. Surgeon to the Chesterfield & Mansfield Hospitals. Retired. Member, B.M.A. & B.A.U.S. Fellow, R.S.M. Brothers, H. G. V. & A. H. Milward. Son, 618.

MILWARD, Col. Henry Gerard Victor, T.D., D.L., b. 27 Dec. 00, eldest s. of the late H. T. Milward. K, 14^3–19^2. Clare, Cambridge. Henry Milward & Sons Ltd., Needle & Fishing Tackle Manufacturers from 21. ✕ R.A., 39–45. Lt.-Col. T.D. Hon. Col., T.A., 51. Retired, 65. Chrmn., Association of Fishing Tackle Makers, 46–62. Asst. Court of Worshipful Company Needlemakers. D.L., Worcestershire, 52. *Midland Flyfishers' Club.* Brothers, F. J. & A. H. Milward.

MITCALFE, Capt. John Stanley, O.B.E., V.R.D., b. 27 Feb. 27, eldest s. of the late W. S. Mitcalfe. B, 40^3–44^3; Cap, 44. ✕ R.N. Able Seaman (Y). Brasenose, Oxford, M.A. O.B.E., V.R.D., A.D.C., 70–71.

MITCHELL, Charles William Errington. W, 31^1–33^2.*

MITCHELL, George Abercromby, C.B.E., b. 20 June 99, s. of G. A. Mitchell. St, 13^3–17^3; Head of House; XV, 16–17; R. VIII, 16–17; Cadet Officer. ✕ 1st Bn. Rifle Brigade. 2nd Lt. Queen's, Oxford, M.A. Engaged in Banking, City of London, 23–45. Retired and took up Public & Social work. Member, London County Council, 49–55. Vice-Chrmn., University College Hospital, 51–63. Queen Charlotte's Hospital, Chrmn., 61–70. London Council of Social Service, Chrmn., 46–63. C.B.E., J.P. *Garrick, Alpine.*

MITCHELL, Gordon Valentine Kay. SF, 28^1–32^2. Son, 1149.*

MITCHELL, Henry Gordon, b. 14 Jan. 26, s. of the late Capt. G. Mitchell. Sh, 39^3–44^2. Peterhouse, Cambridge, B.A. N/S. R.E., 48–49. 2nd Lt. Engineer, Ransome Hoffman Pollard Ltd.

MITCHELL, James Gordon. M, 13^1–16^3.*

MITCHELL, Leonard Foster, M.C. Tu, 08^1–11^3.*

MITCHELL, Michael John. SF, 46^3–51^3.*

MITCHELL, Ronald, b. 15 Dec. 25, s. of the late A. C. Mitchell (OR SF 96). Sh, 39^3–43^2. ✕ R.A.F., 43–47. King's, Cambridge, B.A. University College, London (Dip. Surveying). With Hunting Aerosurveys Ltd., 51–56. With B.E.A. from 57. Now Training Capt., Trident Flight, B.E.A.

MITCHELL, Major Ronald Douglas. SF, 29^3–34^2.*

MITRA, Satyendra Nath. W, 33^3–38^2.*

MOIR, Sir Ernest Ian Royds, Bt., b. 9 June 25, s. of the late Sir Arrol Moir, Bt. St & K, 39^2–43^2. Gonville & Caius, Cambridge, B.A. ✕ Served in R.E. Manager & Director of Metropolitan Construction Co. Ltd. (a Management Company in the Balfour Beatty Group). *R.A.C.* Succeeded father as 3rd Bt., 57.

MOLLER, Peter Severin Crawford. B, 22^2–26^2.*

MOLLISON, Prof. Patrick London, F.R.S., b. 17 Mar. 14, eldest s. of the late W. M. Mollison. K, 27^3–31^3. Clare, Cambridge, M.B., M.D. St. Thomas's Hospital, M.R.C.P., F.R.C.P., F.R.C.Path. ✕ Blood Transfusion Service, London, 39–43. R.A.M.C., 43–46. Lt.-Col. Director, M.R.C. Experimental Haematology Unit from 46. Professor of Haematology (Univ. of London) at St. Mary's Hospital Medical School from 62. F.R.S., 68. Author "Blood Transfusion in Clinical Medicine".

MOLONY, Patrick Harry, b. 27 July 26, s. of the late Canon B. C. Molony (OR K 05). K, 40^2–45^1; Levée; Head of House. Trinity, Cambridge, M.A. Housemaster, Ardingly Coll., Sussex.

MOLTENO, Malcolm Francis Christian. B, 18^1–21^3.*

MONCK, Peter Christopher, b. 19 June 28, s. of C. J. H. Monck. T, 42^2–44^3. H.N.C. in Electrical Engineering, 52. Chief Service Engineer, G.E.C. Machines Ltd., Blackheath.

MONCKTON, Robert Timothy. B, 32^1–37^2.*

MONIER-WILLIAMS, Craufurd Stephen. St, 36^2–40^2.*

MONKHOUSE, John Mowbray. Sh, 22^3–27^2.*

MONKHOUSE, Patrick James, O.B.E., b. 18 Apr. 04, elder s. of A. N. Monkhouse. SH, 17^3–22^2; Scholar; Head of House; Major & Minor Exhibitioner. Scholar of Trinity, Oxford, B.A. Employed as Journalist, "Manchester Guardian", 27–36 & 46–69; Asst. Editor, 48–60; Northern Editor, 60–65. "Evening Standard", 36–40. Retired, 69. ✕ Royal Ulster Rifles, 40–46. Lt.-Col. A.A.G., G.H.Q., Middle East. Member (52–72) Peak National Park Planning Board; Vice-

Chrmn., 52–66. J.P., Manchester, from 52. O.B.E., 72. *Manchester Press Club.* Brother, J. M. Monkhouse.

MONROE, Hubert Holmes, Q.C., b. 2 July 20, s. of J. H. Monroe, K.C. SF, 34³–39²; Levée; Exhibitioner; Cap, 39; Cadet Officer, 38–39. Scholar of Corpus Christi, Oxford, M.A. ✕ 6th Punjab, L.A.A. Regt. R.I.A., Major. Harmsworth Scholar, Middle Temple, Bar, 48. Q.C., 60. Executive Director, S. G. Warburg & Co. Ltd. *Island Cruising Club, Salcombe.* Bencher, Middle Temple.

MONTAGUE, Aubrey. K, 20³–25².*

MONTAGUE, Francis Arnold, C.M.G., b. 14 June 04, 2nd s. of the late C. E. Montague. K, 17³–22²; R. VIII, 21–22 (Capt.); Crick Winner, 22. Exhibitioner of Balliol, Oxford, B.A. Cross-country Half Blue, 23. Colonial Administrative Service, 25–57. Re-employed, 58–63. Now in Local Government (Oxford C.C.) since 69. C.M.G. *Lansdowne Club.*

MONTEFIORE, Hugh William, The Rt. Rev. The Bishop of Kingston (formerly Sebag-Montefiore, H. W.), b. 12 May 20, s. of the late C. E. Sebag-Montefiore, O.B.E. SH, 34¹–38³; Levée; Head of House; XV, 38. Scholar of St. John's, Oxford, M.A. ✕ Royal Bucks. Yeomanry (R.A.), 39–45. Capt. 1st Class Theology, 47. Westcott House, Cambridge, M.A., B.D. Ordained, 49. Vice-Principal, Westcott House, 52–53. Fellow & Dean, Gonville & Caius, Cambridge, 54–63. Univ. Lecturer, 59–63. Canon Theologian, Coventry, 59–70. Hon. Canon, Ely, 69–70. Vicar of Gt. St. Mary's, Cambridge, 63–70. Bishop of Kingston-on-Thames from 70. *Royal Commonwealth Society.*

MONTGOMERY, James Graham. SF, 27¹–30².*

MONTGOMERY, John Matthew, b. 22 May 30, eldest s. of late Prof. G. A. Montgomery, Q.C. SH, 44¹–49¹; Levée; Head of House. Exhibitioner of Trinity Hall Cambridge, B.A. First National City Bank. *United Oxford & Cambridge University Club.* Liveryman, Grocer's Company.

MOON, Arthur Graham, b. 28 Oct. 01, eldest s. of the late Rev. C. G. Moon, M.A., Hon. C.F. Tu, 15³–17³. Pilot, R.A.F., 23. Reserve of R.A.F. Officers, 28. Relinquished commission, 32.

MOON, Michael Scott, b. 14 July 26, elder s. of the late E. J. Moon. SF, 40²–44². ✕ R.A., 44–48. Lt. T.D., F.C.A. Practising Chartered Accountant.

MOORCROFT, Walter, b. 12 Feb. 17, elder s. of W. Moorcroft. Sh, 30³–35². ✕ Intelligence Corps, 39–45. Sgt. Man. Dir. & Art Director, Moorcroft Ltd., producing Moorcroft Pottery. F.R.S.A.

MOORE, Antony Ross, C.M.G. St, 32³–36².*

MOORE, Basil Oates, M.C., b. 19 Jan. 90, eldest s. of the late E. H. Moore. W, 04¹–07³; XV, 06–07; XXII, 07. Rubber Planter in Straits Settlements, 10. ✕ King Edward's Horse, 149 Bde., R.F.A. Major. M.C., Belgian Croix de Guerre. Dispatches. In Kenya, Farmer & Planter, Agriculturist. Retired.

MOORE, Harry John Bradley, b. 5 Dec. 29, s. of Rear Admiral H. J. B. Moore, C.B.E. (OR SF 11). SF, 43³–47³; XV, 47. N/S. R.N., 48–9. Naval Airman (Met.). S.E. Essex Technical College. C.Eng., M.I.Mech.E. Sales Engineer, British Steel Corporation.

MOORE, Rear-Admiral Humfrey John Bradley, C.B.E., b. 16 May 98, eldest s. of the late H. F. B. Moore. SF, 11³–16²; XV, 15; Cadet Officer, 15. R.N.C., Keyham. ✕ R.N., H.M.S. *Resolution,* S/Lt. Lt., 19; Lt.-Cdr. (E.), 27; Cdr. (E.), 30; Capt. (E.), 42; Rear Admiral (E.), 49. Retired, 52. M.I.Mech.E. ✕ Cmdr. (E.) for Armament work, Devonport, 40–41. Gunnery Engineer Overseer, 41–43. Deputy Chief Inspector of Gun Mountings, Admiralty, 43–45. Manager, Engineering Depot, H.M. Dockyard, Rosyth, 45–46 & Devonport, 46. Elected to Royal Institute of Painters in Water Colours, 56. C.B.E., 51. *Arts Club.* Son, H. J. B. Moore.

MORGAN, Hugh Treharne, T.D. SH, 24²–27².*

MORGAN, Llewellyn Rees. M, 99³–02².*

MORGAN, Prof. Thomas Hubert, M.D. F.R.C.S., b. 23 Apr. 23, s. of T. P. Morgan, B.Sc. St, 36³–40²; Scholar. Trinity, Cambridge. M.B., B.Chir. University College Hospital, London, L.R.C.P., F.R.C.S. ✕ R.N.V.R. Surg.-Lt. Professor & Head, Division of Orthopaedic Surgery, University of Maryland

Hospital, Baltimore, Maryland. Fellow, American Academy of Orthopaedic Surgery. Member, British Orthopaedic Association.

MORGAN EDWARDS, Quentin, b. 9 May 31, s. of the late A. Morgan Edwards, M.C. SH, 45^1–49^2. Oriel, Oxford. In Wine Trade.

MORISON, Major, Frank Dalcour, M.C. St, 33^3–37^3.*

MORISON, John Miller, b. 1 May 03, s. of the late W. Morison. St, 17^1–20^1. Glasgow Univ. B.Sc. Eng. Farmer. Son, 1769.

MORISON, John Patrick Cecil Morgan. Tu, 26^1–29^3.*

MORISON, Peter Hugh. M, 43^3–48^2.*

MORLEY, Cornelius William, M.R.C.S., L.R.C.P., b. 22 Feb. 04, eldest s. of the late C. C. Morley. Tu, 17^3–22^2. Trinity, Cambridge, B.A., M.R.C.S. (Eng.), L.R.C.P. (London). Founder Fellow, Royal College of Pathologists. Clinical Pathology, E.M.S. Director, Clinical Bacteriology, St. Mary's Hospital, London. Clinical Pathologist (Consultant), Western Ophthalmic Hospital & Samaritan Hospital for Women. Now retired.

MORLEY, John Stanley James, F.R.C.S., b. 2 Mar. 18, eldest s. of Prof. J. Morley, Ch.M., F.R.C.S. K, 31^3–36^2. University College, Oxford. Half Blue O.U.A.C., M.R.C.S., L.R.C.P., 43. F.R.C.S., F.R.A.C.S. ✕ R.N.V.R., 44–46. Surg.-Lt. Orthopaedic Surgeon, Alfred Hospital, Melbourne & Royal Children's Hospital, Melbourne. *Vincent's*. Brother, T. P. Morley.

MORLEY, Richard. W, 45^1–47^2.*

MORLEY, Thomas Paterson, F.R.C.S., b. 13 June 20, 2nd s. of Prof. J. Morley, Ch.M., F.R.C.S. K, 34^3–38^2; R. VIII, 37–38 (Capt.). University College, Oxford, B.A., B.M., B.Ch., A.I.A. ✕ R.A.F.V.R., Medical Branch, 44–47. F/Lt. F.R.C.S. (Eng.), F.R.C.S. (Canada). Associate Professor, Dept. of Surgery, Toronto Univ. & Chrmn., Division of Neurosurgery, Toronto Univ. Head, Div. of Neurosurgery, Toronto Gen. Hospital. *University Club of Toronto*. Brother, J. S. J. Morley.

MORRIS, Arthur Henry, T.D., b. 25 Feb. 08, s. of H. M. Morris. K, 21^3–25^3; Scholar. Lausanne Univ. Scholar of Hertford, Oxford, B.A. ✕ Hertfordshire Regt., 39–45. Major. T.D. Member, London Stock Exchange, 34–51. Man. Dir., own Engineering business, Bury St. Edmunds, Suffolk, since 51. Son, 1530.

MORRIS, Charles Evan Henry, b. 7 May 26, s. of T. S. Morris. M.C. (OR St 08). St & W, 39^3–44^2; Scholar; Levée; Head of House. Clare, Cambridge, B.A. C.Eng. F.I.Mech.E. N/S. Royal Navy, 47–49. Instructor Lt. Steel Company of Wales Ltd., 49–67. British Steel Corp. since 67. Present position, Man. Dir. Technical. Vice-President, Iron & Steel Institute. Sons, Martyn, St, 69^3– & Stephen, St, 72^3–.

MORRIS, John Peter, b. 22 Nov. 18, eldest s. of the late W. L. Morris. St, 32^2–35^2. ✕ Queen's Own West Kent Regt., 39–46. Director, Priday's, Hardwood Importers.

MORRIS, Philip Edward, b. 18 Apr. 32, s. of the late M. Morris. SH, 45^3–50^1. N/S. Commission, R.A. Director of various enterprises.

MORRIS, Thomas Silvan, M.C., b. 11 Apr. 95, 2nd s. of Rev. S. Morris, M.A. St, 08^3–14^2; Scholar; Head of School; Major Exhibitioner. Exhibitioner of Trinity, Cambridge. ✕ 6th (att. 4th) Bn. Rifle Bde., 80th Co. Machine Gun Corps. Major. M.C. Dispatches. Colliery Proprietor& Man. Director's. Asst., Thomas Williams & Sons Ltd., Llangennech, 22. Retired. J.P. for County of Glamorgan (now supplementary list). *Hawks' Club, Oxford & Cambridge Golfing Socy*. Son, C. E. H. Morris.

MORRIS-DAVIS, Edward James. W, 29^2–33^3.*

MORRISON, Cyril Sanderson, b. 19 Jan. 07, 2nd s. of the late D. Morrison. C, 21^1–24^1. Born in Chile & lived there all his life except for 15–24. Served in Chilean Army, 27–28, then farmer. Founder & Director of Rotary Club of Casablanca, 36–51 (President three times). Director of Milk Assoc. & President for 1 yr. Hon. Director of Agricultural Society of Los Angeles, 57. Hon. Director of the biggest irrigation scheme in the country. Hon. Member of the *Club de Viña del Mar* after 40 yrs. Brother, D. G. Morrison.

MORRISON, Donald Grace, b. 1 Apr. 01, eldest s. of the late D. Morrison. C, $15^2–18^2$. Went to Chile straight from Rugby and worked for a British firm for 10 yrs. Returned to England. ✕ A.F.S. & A.R.P., became A.R.P. Officer for Rugby & rural areas. After war, Buyer for a Chilean firm in London. Then retired to Chile and moved to Spain when Chile went Communist. Brother, C. S. Morrison.

MORRISON, Gordon Macgregor, b. 2 Aug. 21, eldest son of F. Morrison. B, $35^3–40^2$. Trinity, Cambridge, M.A. Member, Institute of Linguists. ✕ R.E.M.E., 43–47. Capt. With three Industrial firms, 48–57. With Barr & Stroud Ltd. since 58 (Joint Man. Dir. & Alternate Chrmn. since 68). *Royal Over-Seas League, Royal Scottish Automobile Club, Chatham Dining Club.*

MORRISON, The Rev. Leonard Haslett, b. 29 Dec. 16, s. of the late Lt.-Col. R. V. Morrison. Tu, $30^3–35^2$; XV, 34; Sw. VI, 33–35 (Capt.). Corpus Christi, Cambridge, M.A. Malay Civil Service, 38. P.O.W. in Japanese hands for $3\frac{1}{2}$ yrs. Resigned from Colonial Civil Service, 46. Bar, Gray's Inn, 47. Cuddesden Theological College, 47. Ordained Deacon, 49; Priest, 50. Curate, Leckhampton. Chaplain, Cheltenham Coll., 51. Housemaster, 55–62. Chaplain, Rugby School, 62–69. Chaplain, Charterhouse, since 69. *Harlequins R.F.C.*

MORRISON, Peter Francis, b. 22 Jan. 28, younger s. of F. Morrison, B.Sc. B, $41^3–46^2$. Cambridge Univ., M.A. C.A., M.I.M.C. Partner, Brown Fleming & Murray, Whinney Murray & Co., from 61–71 (Chartered Accountants). Director, Denys Wrey Ltd. (Antique Dealers) since 69. *Royal St. George's G.C.; R.C.P. G.C.; Hanstown Club.*

MORSE, Lt.-Col. Lionel Henry, M.C. W, $99^1–03^3$.*

MORTON, Brig. Alan Handfield, M.C. K, $04^3–08^2$.*

MORTON, Michael Ernest, b. 26 Apr. 28, 2nd s. of W. E. Morton. Sh, $41^3–46^2$; Scholar; Cap, 46. Peterhouse, Cambridge, B.A. Manchester Coll. of Technology, M.Sc.Tech. Technical Management with Stone-Platt Industries Ltd., to 64. Manager, Textile Div., Barber & Colman Ltd. since 64.

MORTON, Michael Mainwaring, b. 8 Aug. 26, s. of the late G. M. Morton (OR Tu 10). M, $39^3–44^2$; XI, 43–44; Cap. ✕ Grenadier Guards, 44–47. Lt. Classical Exhibitioner of Brasenose, Oxford, M.A. Tennis Half Blue, 50. Solicitor. Son, Jeremy David Mainwaring, C, $70^1–$.

MORTON, Peter Harlow. B, $41^3–46^2$.*

MORTON, Major Philip Peter Handfield, b. 19 May 20, s. of Brig. A. H. Morton. K, $34^1–39^2$. Sidney Sussex, Cambridge, B.A. ✕ R. Signals from 40. Regular Commission, 41. Capt., 45. Major, 51.

MOSLEY, Major Edward Heathcote, b. 25 Apr. 99, 2nd s. of the late Sir Oswald Mosley, Bt. St, $13^1–16^3$. R.M.C., Sandhurst. ✕ Commissioned in Royal Dragoons, 17. Retired with rank of Major.

MOSS, David George Wood, F.C.A., b. 24 Apr. 30, younger s. of S. H. Moss, J.P. Sh, $43^3–48^2$. N/S. Royal Leicestershire Regt. Trinity, Cambridge, M.A. Articled, qualified & became partner in present firm of Chartered Accountants in Derby. F.C.A. Brother, J. W. Moss.

MOSS, John Walys, b. 4 May 27, elder s. of S. H. Moss, J.P. Sh, $40^3–45^2$; Scholar; Exhibitioner. Scholar of Trinity, Cambridge, M.A. N/S. Commission R.A.F. (Education Branch), 48–50. Solicitor. Senior Partner in Jackson & Moss, Ilkeston, Belpar, Ripley. *Erewash Valley G.C., Ockbrook & Borrowash L.T.C.* Brother, D. G. W. Moss.

MOSS-BLUNDELL, The Rev. Richard Henry, b. 22 Dec. 21, s. of H. S. Moss-Blundell, C.B.E., M.A., LL.D. C, $35^3–40^2$. Heythrop Coll., Chipping Norton. Campion Hall, Oxford. Theology Faculty, Lyons, France. Clerk in Holy Orders in Society of Jesus. Qualified Teacher, M.A. (Oxon.). Licencié en Théologie, Facultés Catholique, Lyons, France. Senior History Master, Mount St. Marys, Derbyshire. Asst. Master, St. Aloysius Coll., Glasgow. Senior History Master, S.F.X. Coll., Liverpool. Asst. Master, Wimbledon Coll.

MOSTYN, Leonard Arthur. K, $40^3–44^2$.*

MOTHERSILL, Gerald Rivaz, b. 8 Apr. 09, 2nd s. of the late H. J. Mothersill (OR B 14). B, $23^1–27^3$; XXII, 27. Joined Ralli Bros. Ltd. in 28. Served them in India

& Pakistan, 31–63, apart from service in Indian Army, 40–46. ⚔ Saw active service in N. Africa, Italy and N.W. Frontier. Now retired. *East India, Sports & Public School Clubs.*

MOULE, Gerard Elliot, b. 3rd Dec. 15, younger s. of the late H. E. Moule. K, 29³–33¹. ⚔ Somerset Light Infantry. Major. Son, Douglas Elliot, K, 70³–.

MOUSLEY, James Arthur, b. 20 Feb. 31, s. of the late Lt.-Col. J. H. Mousley. Tu, 44³–49². Pembroke, Cambridge. A.M.B.I.M. Transparent Paper Ltd.

MOWER WHITE, Anthony Peter Wolfe, b. 15 Mar. 15, younger s. of the late G. B. Mower White, M.B., B.S., F.R.C.S. K, 28³–33¹. Brasenose, Oxford, B.A. Solicitor, 39. ⚔ 60th Rifles, 39–45. Capt. Asst. Secretary, Wellcome Foundation, 46. Chief Solicitor, Fisons Ltd., 52–70. Chief Solicitor, E.M.I. Ltd., since 70. *Oriental Club.* Brother, G. J. Mower White.

MOWER WHITE, Gilbert John, b. 5 July 02, elder s. of the late G. B. Mower White, M.B., B.S., F.R.C.S. K, 16²–21¹; XV, 19–20; Sw. VI, 18–19; Athletics Cup, 20. Brasenose, Oxford, B.A. Rowing Blue, 23–25. President, O.U.B.C., 25. Headmaster, Imperial Service Coll., Windsor, 28–42. ⚔ Pioneer Corps, 42–43. R.E., 43–46. Capt. Deputy Secretary, National Federation of Young Farmers' Clubs since 47. Brother, A. P. W. Mower White.

MOYERS, Henry Wilson, b. 22 June 17, 3rd & youngest s. of the late W. W. Moyers. Sh, 30³–35¹. Trinity Hall, Cambridge, B.A. ⚔ R.A., 39–42. Seconded to Iraq Levies Habbaniya, 42–46. Intelligence Officer. Capt. Sudan Political Service, 47–51. Retired from Farming. Brother, W. G. Moyers. Son, 2243.

MOYERS, William Gerald, b. 3 Oct. 08, eldest s. of the late W. W. Moyers. W, 22²–26³. Joined family business, H. A. Watson & Co. Ltd., Mineral & Metal Brokers, and retired, 67, after selling business in 64. *Boodle's.* Brother, H. W. Moyers.

MOYLAN, Lt.-Col. Edmund Walter Patrick. M, 26³–30³.*

MUIR, Basil James, M.B., B.Chir., F.F.A.R.C.S., eldest s. of J. Muir. W, 39³–44². Gonville & Caius, Cambridge, B.A., M.B., B.Chir. St. Bartholomew's Hospital, F.F.A.R.C.S. Consultant Anaes-

thetist, Royal Devon Infirmary, Barnstaple. T.A.V.R. Lt.-Col. R.A.M.C. (V.). T.D.

MUIR, John Gerald Grainger, O.B.E., b. 19 Jan. 18, s. of the late G. B. F. Muir, I.C.S. (OR SH 95). SH, 31³–36²; Levée; Cap; R. VIII, 35; S. VIII, 34 (Capt.). Corpus Christi, Oxford, M.A. ⚔ R.N.V.R. Lt. D.S.C. Joined British Council, 46. Now representative, Spain. Royal Institute of International Affairs. Royal Asiatic Society. Society for Nautical Research. O.B.E. *Naval Club.*

MUIRHEAD, John Denis. W, 42²–46³.*

MUNBY, Denys Lawrence, b. 9 Oct. 19, 2nd s. of the late W. M. Munby. M, 33²–37²; Scholar; Levée; Exhibitioner. Scholar of Wadham, Oxford, B.A. Lecturer at Christ's Church, Oxford, 48–49, also Aberdeen Univ., 49–58. Reader in Economics of Transport, Oxford Univ. & Fellow of Nuffield College since 58.

MUNN, Col. James Walter, C.B.E., b. 1 May 08, s. of the late W. Munn. Tu, 22²–26². R.M.A., Woolwich. Commissioned R.A., 28. ⚔ 39–45, Col. O.B.E., Belgian Order of Leopold. Retired, 49. C.B.E. *Royal Cruising Club, Royal Ocean Racing Club.*

MUNNS, Lewis Oliver Gatty. B, 45²–48².*

MUNRO, Hector Campbell, b. 24 Oct. 20, s. of C. C. Munro. SF, 34³–39²; XI, 38–39 (Capt.). Trinity, Oxford, B.A. ⚔ R.A., 42–45. Capt. Rubber Broker. Director of Wm. Jas. & Hy. Thompson (Rubber) Ltd., London. *Vincent's, Oxford; Rye G.C.*

MURDOCH, William Francis Patrick. K, 43³–48².*

MURIEL, William Granville, b. 7 July 94, elder s. of the late W. D. Muriel. T, 08³–11². Training with the British Thompson Houston Co. Ltd., in electrical engineering, 12–14. ⚔ Capt. & Adjutant, Ox. & Bucks. Light Infantry, 14–19. Director, Findley Durham & Brodie. Sales Ltd., of London. *Danish Club.*

MURRAY, Col. Adair, b. 5 June 00, eldest s. of Col. H. W. Murray. SF, 14³–18²; XI, 17–18 (Capt.); XV, 17; Cadet Officer. R.M.A., Woolwich. Gazetted to R.E., 19. Lt., 21. Capt., 31. Adjutant, R.E., Aldershot, 32–35. Major, 38. ⚔

Burma & North Africa, 39–45. Dispatches twice. Lt.-Col., 41. Col., 47. Military Attaché in Madrid, 49–53. Retired, 54. Alderman, Hampshire C.C.

MURRAY, David, b. 4 May 10, elder s. of the late A. S. Murray. SH, 23³–28². Glasgow Univ., M.A., LL.B. Solicitor, 36. Notary Public. Member of the Royal Faculty of Procurators, 39. ✕ R.A., 39–45. Major. Partner in Maclay Murray & Spens, Solicitors, Glasgow. *Western Club, Gldsgow; Prestwick G.C.* Son, 1972.

MURRAY, David Hugh. B, 20¹–23².*

MURRAY, John Douglas Ridout, F.R.C.S., b. 24 May 99, s. of the late J. Murray, F.R.C.S. St, 13³–17². ✕ 226th Field Company, R.E. 2nd Lt. Wounded. Hon. Exhibitioner. King's, Cambridge, M.A. Middlesex Hospital, London, M.R.C.S., L.R.C.P., F.R.C.S., M.B., B.Chir., H.P., H.S. Casualty Surgical Officer, Middlesex Hospital, 23–26. Bolingbroke Hospital, R.S.O., 27–28. General Practice, Exmouth, 28–55. S.H.M.O., Exmouth Hospital, 48–55. Clinical Asst., Accident & Emergency Dept., Lymington Hospital, since 62. Fellow B.M.A., *Royal Lymington Yacht Club.*

MURRAY, James Iain, b. 12 Nov. 32, s. of J. I. Murray. C, 46²–51¹. N/S. Royal Signals. Sgt. Corpus Christi, Cambridge, M.A. Solicitor. Partner, Linklaters & Paines. *City of London & New Clubs.*

MURRAY-HUDSON, Gordon Alan (formerly Hudson, G. A. M.). SH, 13²–17¹.*

N

NANCE, Arthur Trengove. W, 34³–35².*

NANCE, Air Commodore, Charles Trengove, O.B.E. SF, 32³–37².*

NAPIER, Sir Joseph William Lennox, Bt., O.B.E., b. 1 Aug. 95, eldest s. of the late Lt.-Col. Sir W. L. Napier, Bt. W, 09³–12³; Cap, 12. Jesus, Cambridge, 13–14. ✕ South Wales Borderers, Gallipoli & Mesopotamia, 15–18. Lt. Wounded thrice, and P.O.W., Turkey. Succeeded to Baronetcy, 15. Capt., Richmond R.F.C. Member of Lloyd's since 21. Director of Public Companies. Member of Council of Institute of Directors. ✕ Lt.-Col. (A.Q.M.G.(M.)). Chairman of Guide Dogs for the Blind.

MUSGRAVE, James, b. 24 Oct. 07, eldest s. of the late J. F. Musgrave. B, 21²–25². Cotton Spinner. ✕ R.A.F.V.R. F/Lt. Company Director, Company Secretary, Management Consultant. Son, 826.

MUSGRAVE, Peter. B, 27³–32¹.*

MUSGRAVE-HOYLE, Lt.-Col. Walter, M.C., T.D. SF, 09³–14¹.*

MUSSON, Eric Methven. Tu, 02²–05³.*

MUSSON, Peter Runciman. Tu, 29³–33³.*

MYRDDIN-EVANS, George Watkin, b. 26 Mar. 24, 2nd s. of Sir G. Myrddin-Evans, K.C.M.G., C.B. SH, 38¹–42¹; XV, 41; Draper English Literature Prize. Christ Church, Oxford, M.A. Rugby football v. Cambridge, 42–43. Athletics v. Cambridge, 42 & 47. ✕ Coldstream Guards, 43–46. Capt. Entered Lloyd's, 48. Underwriting Member of Lloyd's, 51. Conservative Member, St. Pancras Borough Council, 53–56, and 59–61. Deputy Mayor & Chrmn. of Libraries Committee. Director of Hogg Robinson & Gardner Mountain Ltd., Gardner Mountain d'Ambrumenil and Rennie Agencies Ltd., Hogg Robinson & Capel Cure (Underwriting Agencies) Ltd., O.A.Z. Ltd. *White's, Pratt's, Guards, M.C.C.* Brother, T. O. W. Myrddin-Evans.

MYRDDIN-EVANS, Towy Owen Watkin. SH, 34¹–38².*

Chelsea Arts Society. O.B.E. (Mil.), 44. *Alpine, Leander.*

NASH, Cdr. Jeremy, O.B.E., D.S.C., b. 12 Sept. 20, s. of Capt. W. M. Nash, O.B.E., R.N. SF, 34²–37³. Royal Navy, joined, 38; commissioned, 40. Qualified to command H.M. submarines, 42. Commander various submarines from 43. Promoted Commander, 54. Served mainly at sea until 60, then Ministry of Defence till 70. Retired, 70, and since then employed as S.W. Regional Organiser for National Society for Cancer Relief. A.R.N.O., O.B.E., D.S.C. Dispatches twice.

NASH-WILLIAMS, Crispin St. J. Alvah, b. 19 Dec. 32, elder s. of the late Dr. V. E.

Nash-Williams. B, 45³–50¹; Scholar; Exhibitioner. Scholar of Trinity Hall, Cambridge, M.A., Ph.D. Princeton Univ., U.S.A. Aberdeen Univ., Asst. Lecturer, Mathematics, 57–58; Lecturer, 58–63; Senior Lecturer, 64–67. Mathematics Professor, Waterloo Univ., Canada, 67–71. Mathematics Prof., Aberdeen Univ., since 72. Elected F.R.S.E., 68. Cambridge. Philosophical Society. London, Edinburgh & American Mathematical Societies. Brother, 400.

NATHAN, Matthew Lewis, b. 28 Dec. 07, 3rd s. of the late Sir F. L. Nathan, K.B.E. K, 21²–25³. Gonville & Caius, Cambridge, B.A. Univ. College, London. Research Engineer, Woodall-Duckham Co., 31–34. Gas Turbine Combustion Engineer, Power Jets Co., 41–48. Consulting Engineer.

NAYLOR, The Rev. Canon Charles Basil. T, 25³–30². *

NAYLOR, John Malcolm Proctor. M, 45³–49². *

NEAL, Nigel Thomas, b. 9 June 32, s. of H. A. Neal. C, 45³–50³; Scholar. N/S. Grenadier Guards, 51–52. Scholar of Clare, Cambridge, M.A. M.I.B. At present Man. Dir., Caxton Reinforced Concrete Ltd. Director, Harry Neal Ltd., & Wm. Verry Ltd. *Royal Thames Yacht Club, Rye G.C.*

NEELD, Ralph William (formerly Inigo-Jones, R. W.), b. 2 Nov. 28, s. of R. C. Inigo-Jones. B, 42³–46³. N/S. R.A.S.C., 46–48. 2nd Lt. Brasenose, Oxford, B.A. A.R.I.C.S. Colonial Service, Singapore. 51–58. Chartered Land Agent, 62–70, Managing own estates since 70. R.I.C.S. C.L.A.

NEGUS, Lt.-Col. Robert Essington. C, 98³–01³. *

NEILL, Lt.-Col. Frederick Henry. SH, 12³–16². Son, 155. *

NEILL, James Hugh, C.B.E., T.D., b. 29 Mar. 21, s. of Col. Sir F. Neill, C.B.E., D.S.O., T.D., D.L. Tu, 34³–39¹; Scholar. ✕ R.E. & R. Bombay Sappers & Miners. Norway, 40. India & Burma, 42–45. Germany, 45–46. Dispatches. Major. T.D. Chrmn. & Chief Executive, James Neill Holdings Ltd. Master Cutler of Hallamshire, 58–59; High Sheriff of Hallamshire, 72–73. C.B.E. *R. & A. G.C.*

NEILL, John Miller. Tu, 34¹–38². *

NEILL, Robert James Robertson. B, 32¹–36². *

NEILSON, Drevor Frederick Acton, F.R.C.S. K, 05³–08². Son, 928. *

NEILSON, Henry John Tullis, b. 28 May 94, 2nd s. of the late Dr. H. J. Neilson. K, 07³–10²; XI, 10; G. VIII, 08–10. Trinity, Cambridge, B.A. Half Blue Golf, 14. ✕ 1st Life Guards, 14–15. R.A.M.C. & A.S.C., 15–19. Lt. ✕ R.A.S.C., 40–45. Refrigerating Engineer now retired. *O. & C. G.C., Pitt, Cambridge; R.A.C.* Brother, D. F. A. Neilson. Nephew, 928.

NELSON, Dudley. K, 99²–01¹. *

NELSON, Ian David, b. 23 Apr. 31, s. of R. E. D. Nelson. Tu, 44³–48³. Chartered Accountant. C.A. in practice. Partner, Jennings Johnson & Co., Sunderland.

NELSON, Ronald Blyth. Tu, 17²–20¹. *

NETTLETON, John Oldfield, b. 1 Dec. 26, eldest s. of the late J. Nettleton (OR Tu 11). Tu, 40³–44³; Cap (Capt., 2nd XV); Cadet Officer; H. XI. F.C.A. Now Financial Director, Ogilvy Benson & Mather Ltd., Advertising Agents. Brothers, J. S. & T. Nettleton.

NETTLETON, Jeremy Shaw. Tu, 43³–47³. *

NETTLETON, Timothy. Tu, 46³–50². *

NEWBOUND, Peter. T, 39¹–42². *

NEWCOMBE, Francis William, b. 4 Dec. 29, s. of W. Newcombe. T, 43³–48²; Foundation Scholar; Levée; Head of House. N/S. Somerset L.I., 48–50. 2nd Lt. Civil Servant since 48. Now Asst. Secretary, Board of Inland Revenue, Somerset House, London.

NEWMAN, Anthony Gerald, L.R.A.M., b. 20 May 28, s. of F. E. Newman. T, 42¹–46³; Minor Scholar. N/S. Royal Signals, 46–48. Signalman. Coventry Coll. of Education, L.R.A.M. (Mime), 51. Professional Theatre. Teaching. Commerce.

NEWMARK, Peter Paul. W, 30¹–34². *

NEWSUM, Neil Henry Hillas. SH, 40³–44³. Son, Jeremy Henry Moore, Sh, 68³–72³. *

NICHOLAS, John William Robert Charles. W, 46¹–49³. *

NICHOLLS, Henry Arthur Ben, B.Chir. M, 31^2–35^2.*

NICHOLSON, John Frederick, b. 20 July 11, elder s. of the late A. F. Nicholson. SH, 25^2–29^2. Cambridge Univ. ✕ Ox. & Bucks. Light Infantry, 39–45. Wounded. Major. Farmer. Brother, M. Nicholson.

NICHOLSON, Michael, b. 3 Jan. 22, younger s. of the late A. F. Nicholson. SH, 35^3–40^1; H. XI. Trinity, Cambridge, M.A. Dip. Agric. ✕ R.A.F., 42–46. Pilot. F.O. ex N.F.U. County Chrmn. Member, Oxford Diocesan Synod. Member, Ministry of Agriculture's Farm Animal Welfare Committee. Farmer. Company Director. R.A.S.E., N.I.A.B. Brother, J. F. Nicholson.

NICHOLSON, Robert Keith. C, 27^1–31^1.*

NICHOLSON, William Archer. M, 17^2–21^2.*

NICKOLS, Major Noel Fraser. SF, 99^3–02^3.*

NICOL, Henry James. St, 17^2–20^3.*

NICOL, Neil MacGregor. SH, 45^2–50^2.*

NICOLLS, Jasper Henry, D.S.O. W, 12^1–15^2.*

NIGHTINGALE, Edward Humphrey, C.M.G., b. 19 Aug. 04, s. of E. C. Nightingale. W, 18^2–23^1; S. VIII, 22. Emmanuel, Cambridge, B.A. Sudan Political Service, 26–54. Deputy Civil Secretary, Sudan Government, 51–52. Governor, Equatorial Province, Sudan, 52–54. Farmer in Kenya since 54. Order of the Nile (4th Class). C.M.G., 55. *Rift Valley Sports Club.* Sons, 1934 &2573 & Richard Mervyn, W, 68^1–72^2.

NIMMO, John Atholl Duncan, b. 15 Apr. 06, 2nd s. of the late J. D. Nimmo. B, 20^1–24^2; Cap, 22; Exhibitioner. Emmanuel, Cambridge, B.A. East India Merchant with Duncan Bros. & Co. Ltd., Calcutta, 28–48; Director, 40–48. Scottish Council (Development & Industry), Edinburgh, from 49. Now retired. ✕ Lt., Indian Engineers, 42–43. Staff Capt. (Docks) H.Q., D.D. Tn. Calcutta, 43–46. *Caledonian Club, Edinburgh & London.* Sons, 1116, 1268, 1872 & 2364.

NISBET, Brian Callaway. Tu, 22^2–24^3.*

NISBET, Robert Anthony Bruce, b. 31 Jan. 29, s. of R. A. Nisbet (OR SH 14). SH, 43^3–45^3. N/S. Fleet Air Arm, 47–49. Company Secretary. *London Rowing Club, Molesley Boat Club.*

NISBET, Robert Archibald, O.B.E., b. 23 Nov. 00, younger s. of the late H. B. Nisbet (OR St 77). SH, 14^3–18^2; S. VIII, 17–18. ✕ R.A.F., 18. Pembroke, Cambridge, B.A., LL.B. Solicitor, 26. Partner in H. B. Nisbet & Co., of London. ✕ R.N.V.R., 40–45. Lt.-Cdr. O.B.E. Law Society. *London Rowing Club.* Son, R. A. B. Nisbet.

NOBLE, John Douglas Carmichael, b. 1 Dec. 31, s. of J. H. Noble, M.D. W, 45^3–49^2. Solicitor. Partner in Bartlett & Gregory, Bromley, Kent. Law Society. Town & Country Planning Association.

NORMAN, Major Ralph Oliver Geoffrey, M.B.E., M.C., b. 30 July 11, s. of R. Norman, M.D. SF, 25^2–29^2; XI, 28–29; H. XI, 29. Clare, Cambridge, M.A., M.B., B.Ch. The London Hospital, M.R.C.S., L.R.C.P. General Medical Practitioner. ✕ R.A.M.C., 39–45. R.M.O., 8th Bn. The Rifle Brigade, 39–42. D.A.D.M.S., 11th Armoured Div. D.A.D.M.S., 2nd Army, 43–45. M.B.E. Dispatches. J.P. *London Hospital Medical Club,* British Medical Assoc.

NORMAN, Theodore Vassie, B. 08^2–10^1.*

NORRIS, Francis Edward Bashear, C.B.E. W, 99^3–02^1.*

NORTH, The Hon. Charles Frederic John, b. 14 Sept. 87, elder s. of the late F. D. North, C.M.G. (OR SH 80). SH, 01^3–06^1. Oriel, Oxford, B.A. Bar, Middle Temple, 12. Barrister & Solicitor, W. Australia, 13–56. ✕ R.A.F. & R.F.C., 15–19. Capt. Member for Claremont, W.A., State Parliament, 24–56. Speaker, 47–53. Retired, 56. Appointed by Her Majesty "The Hon.".

NORTH, Eric Harrison, b. 8 Mar. 91, younger s. of the late A. North. SF, 05^3–09^1. St. John's, Oxford, M.A. ✕ Private, Inns of Court O.T.C., 14–15. 4th Hussars, Lt., 15–19. Bar, Inner Temple, 17. North Eastern Circuit. Duff Development Co. Ltd., Chrmn., 46–61. Master Turners Co., 34. Retired. *Cavalry Club, Oxford & Cambridge Univ.* Oriental Ceramic Socy.

NORTH, John Gamble, b. 25 July 21, s. of Major J. T. North. Tu, 35¹–39³. ✕ The Queen's Bays, Capt., 42–46. Horticulture Diploma. Own Flower Nursery. *Cavalry Club.*

NORTH-LEWIS, Philip Henry, b. 4 Jan. 10, eldest s. of the late H. North-Lewis. St, 23³–27¹. Solicitor, 33. Commissioner for Oaths. Examiner in Admiralty. Senior Partner, Middleton, Lewis & Co., of London, Solicitors. *M.C.C.* Empire Lodge 2108, O.R. Lodge 3551.

NORTON, Sir Clifford John, K.C.M.G., C.V.O., b. 17 July 91, younger s. of the late Rev. G. Norton. T, 04³–10²; Exhibitioner. Scholar of Queen's, Oxford, M.A. ✕ Capt. General Staff, Suffolk Regt. Political Officer, Damascus, Deria, Haifa, Cairo, 14–20. Wounded twice. Diplomatic Service, 21–51. Counsellor, Warsaw, 37–39. Minister, Switzerland, 42–46. Ambassador, Greece, 46–51. Anglo-Hellenic, Anglo-Swiss, Anglo-Polish Societies. K.C.M.G., 46. C.V.O., 37. Hon. Fellow, Queen's, Oxford, 63. Hon. Citizen of Athens.

NORTON, Major-General Cyril Henry, C.B., C.B.E., D.S.O., Tu, 12³–15². Son, 1961.*

NORTON, David Edward Pepler, b. 29 Oct. 24, eldest s. of D. G. Norton. SH, 38¹–42²; Cap, 41; Sw. VIII, 41–42. Trinity, Cambridge, B.A. ✕ R.N., 44–46. S/Lt.(E). M.I.Mech.E., M.I.C.E. Man. Dir., Sir James Farmer Norton & Co. Ltd., Salford. Freeman, the City of Salford. *Royal Ocean Racing Club, Royal Thames Yacht Club, Royal Dee Yacht Club* (Commodore).

NOURSE, William Stuart Wilfred. T, 20³–24².*

NOVIKOFF, Mazimilian. B, 01³–04¹.*

NOWILL, Sydney Edward Payn, b. 29 Aug. 21, s. of the late S. J. P. Nowill (OR K 09). K, 35³–39²; Scholar. Attached British Embassy, Ankara & Istanbul, 39–45. Partner, Sidney Nowill & Co., Istanbul, 46–57. Director, Catalmaya Ambalaj A.S., 57–67. Director, Istiropor Ambalaj A.S. since 67. Economic Adviser to Shell (Turkey) since 71. Sometime Chrmn., now Vice-Chrmn., British Chamber of Commerce of Turkey Inc. Currently Chrmn. (since 60) of the Governing Body of the English High School for Girls, Istanbul. *Alpine Club, Travellers' Club.* F.R.G.S. Published "The Mountains of My Life". Written numerous articles in Blackwood's Magazine under pen name of "Ashenden".

NUNN, Lt.-Col. James Edward, R.A., D.F.C., b. 26 July 28, s. of the late J. N. Nunn. SH, 42¹–46³; Cadet Officer. R.M.A., Sandhurst; Scholar; H. XI, 47–48 (Capt.). Gazetted to 33rd Airborne Light Regt., R.A., 48. Lt. p.s.c. Pilot, light aircraft, helicopter. Parachutist. Lt.-Col., Army Air Corps., till June 73. British Liaison Officer, U.S. Army Aviation Centre, Fort Rucker, Alabama. D.F.C., Malaya, 57. Son, James William, SH, 73¹–.

NUTHALL, Barry Wathen, b. 6 Aug. 07, eldest s. of the late A. W. Nuthall. W, 21¹–25². Joined R. W. Eaton & Co., Stockbrokers, London. Now in Government service, Dept. of Trade & Industry, Export House, London. *Civil Service Club, Whitehall.*

NUTTALL, Christopher George Falkiner. W, 45¹–49³. Sons, Robert Christopher Falkiner, W, 69³ and Alexander Falkiner, W, 72¹–.*

NUTTALL, George Robert Falkiner Hans, b. 24 July 96, eldest s. of the late G. H. F. Nuttall, F.R.S. W, 11¹–14². ✕ A.S.C. att. R.G.A. Lt. Magdalene, Cambridge, M.A. Post-Graduate, Technical High School, Zürich. C.Eng., M.I.C.E. Consulting Engineer on own account. Many large projects abroad. Nephew, C. G. F. Nuttall.

O

OAKSHOTT, The Hon. Anthony Hendrie, b. 10 Oct. 29, elder s. of the Rt. Hon. Lord Oakshott, M.B.E. (OR C 18). SF, 43²–47¹. Farmer. *Turf Club.* Brother, M. A. J. Oakshott.

OAKSHOTT of BEBINGTON, The Rt. Hon. Lord, M.B.E. (Oakshott, H. D.), b. 8 Nov. 04, 2nd s. of A. J. Oakshott, J.P. C, 18¹–22². Paris & Trinity, Cambridge, B.A. ✕ Middle East, Italy, War Office.

Dispatches. M.B.E. Invalided, 44. M.P. (C.) for Bebington, Cheshire, 50–64. Government Whip. Lord Commissioner of the Treasury, 52–55. Comptroller of Royal Household, 55–57, and Treasurer, 57–59. Private Sec. to Foreign Secretary, 59–60, and Chancellor of the Exchequer, 60–62. Director of Liverpool Timber Company. Member of Totalisator Board. Baronet, 59, Life Peer, 64. *Boodle's, Pratt's & Turf Clubs.* Sons, A. H. & M. A. J. Oakshott. Grandson, Thomas Hendrie, C, 72³–.

OAKSHOTT, Major The Hon. Michael Arthur John, b. 12 Apr. 32, younger s. of the Rt. Hon. Lord Oakshott (OR C 18). St, 45³–49³. Cirencester Agricultural College. Farmer. *Turf Club.* Brother, A. H. Oakshott. Son, Thomas Hendrie, C, 72³–.

OASTLER, Eric Gordon, T.D., M.B., F.R.C.P., F.R.C.P.S., b. 6 Nov. 03, s. of the late J. Oastler, M.D. C, 17²–21¹. Glasgow University, M.B., Ch.B.; Balliol, Oxford, M.A. F.R.C.P. (London), (Edinburgh) and (Glasgow). Rockefeller Medical Fellowship at Harvard and Massachusetts Gen. Hospital, U.S.A., 34–35. ✕ R.A.M.C., 39–44. Lt.-Col. T.D. Senior Consulting Physician, Southern General Hospital, Glasgow, 47–56. Consulting Physician and Endocrinologist, Glasgow Royal Infirmary, 56–67 (Retired). Hon. Lecturer in Clinical Medicine, Glasgow Univ., 47–67. Hon. Consulting Physician to Scottish Command, 55–68. Retired, 67. Now, Hon. Consulting Physician, Glasgow Royal Infirmary. Chrmn., Scottish Health Services Council, 63–67. Sons, 831 & 1578.

O'BRIEN, Donough, M.B., b. 9 May 23, s. of the late A. J. R. O'Brien, C.M.G., M.C., F.R.C.S. C, 36³–41²; Scholar; Levée; Head of House; XV, 40. Exhibitioner of Clare, Cambridge, M.D. St. Thomas's Hospital Medical School, F.R.C.P. N/S. R.A.M.C., 48–49. Major. Prof. of Pediatrics, University of Colorado Medical Center, Denver, Colorado. American Pediatric Society.

O'BRIEN, Col. Henry William, M.C., T.D., b. 25 Aug. 93, eldest s. of the late H. O'Brien. St, 07³–11². Of O'Brien, Thomas & Co., Wholesale Ironmongers, etc., London & Rotherham. ✕ 1st Bn., H.A.C. Capt. Wounded. M.C. Commanded H.A.C. Inf. Bn., 34–38. T.D. Master of Ironmongers Company, 32. Retired.

ODGERS, Charles Norman Fellows, O.B.E., b. 14 Oct. 12, elder s. of the late Sir C. Odgers. St, 26³–31¹. Lincoln, Oxford, M.A. With United Steel Companies, 36–37, & British Cellophane Ltd., 38–39. ✕ Rifle Brigade, 40–46. Lt.-Col. H.M. Colonial Service since 46. Administrative Officer, Nigeria, now Government Service. O.B.E. *Royal Commonwealth Society.*

ODGERS, Lindsey Noel Blake, M.C., b. 21 Dec. 92, 4th s. of the late W. B. Odgers, K.C., LL.D. W, 07³–11². Scholar of St. John's, Cambridge, M.A. ✕ 14–18, 2nd Lt. 12th Bn. Middlesex Regt., 2nd Field Survey Bn., R.E. Capt. Wounded thrice. M.C. Civil Service, 19–54. Asst. Principal, Home Office, 19; Dublin Castle, 20; and Home Office, 22. Principal, 26. Asst. Secretary at Home Office, 41. Asst. Under Secretary of State, Home Office, 51. Retired, 54.

ODGERS, Paul Randell, C.B., M.B.E., T.D., b. 30 July 15, eldest s. of the late P. N. B. Odgers, D.M., F.R.C.S. Tu, 29³–33²; Levée; Head of House; Major & Minor Exhibitioner. Scholar of New College, Oxford, M.A. Administrative Class, Home Civil Service since 37. ✕ 39–45, Major, Ox. & Bucks. Light Infantry. M.B.E. Asst. Secretary, Ministry of Education, 48. Under-Secretary, 58. Deputy Secretary, Department of Education & Science, 71. C.B., T.D. *United Oxford & Cambridge University Club.* Brother, R. M. D. Odgers. Son, 2300.

ODGERS, Richard Michael Douglas, D.F.C., b. 11 Jan. 20, 2nd s. of the late P. N. B. Odgers, D.M., F.R.C.S. Tu, 33²–38¹. New College, Oxford, M.A. ✕ R.A. Capt. D.F.C. (651 A.O.P. Sqn., R.A.F.). Director, Curtis Brown Ltd. (Literary Agents). *Travellers' Club, Royal Lymington Yacht Club.* Brother, P. R. Odgers. Son, James Richard Blake, SH, 67³–71³.

ODLING, Thomas George. C.B. SH, 25³–30². Son, William, SH, 70¹–71³.*

OFFICER, Adam Cairns. Tu, 95³–96³.*

OGDEN, Alex Cyril. K, 16³–20².*

OGILVIE, Bruce Mortimer, B.M., B.Ch., b. 16 Jan. 21, 2nd s. of the late Lt.-Col. S. S. Ogilvie, C.B.E., D.S.O. (OR M 98). M, 34³–38³. Grenoble University, France, 39. University College, Oxford, M.A., B.M., B.Ch. ✕ Grenadier Guards. Lt.

Wounded. Dispatches. Middlesex Hospital. Doctor. *Naval & Military Club.* Son, Robert Bruce Challinor, M, 67^3–71^2.

OGILVIE, David Alexander, b. 2 Aug. 27, 2nd s. of the late Sir F. W. Ogilvie. SH, 40^2–46^2; Scholar; Levée; Head of House; Exhibitioner. Scholar of St. John's, Cambridge, M.A. N/S. 3rd R. Tank Regt., 46–48. 2nd Lt. C.Eng., M.I.Mech.E. H.M. Overseas Civil Service, Northern Rhodesia, 52–54. Director and Manager, Baker Perkins Ltd., Peterborough, 55–66. General Manager, Small Industries Council for Rural Areas of Scotland, Edinburgh, since 66. Brother, R. M. Ogilvie.

OGILVIE, Douglas Farquhar, b. 5 Feb. 26, eldest s. of the late D. D. Ogilvie (OR B 01). B, 39^3–44^1; Cap, 43. Edinburgh University, B.Sc. (Agric.). ✕ Army Officer Cadet, 44–45. Disabled 44 & invalided out. F.R.I.C.S. Chartered Land Agent & Farmer. *New Club, Edinburgh; Royal Perth Golfing Socy.* Brother, G. H. Ogilvie.

OGILVIE, Gavin Harry, b. 2 June 29, 2nd s. of the late D. D. Ogilvie (OR B 01). B, 43^2–47^2; Cap, 46. N/S. 2nd Lt. (Emergency Commission) Black Watch, Seconded Gold Coast Regt., 48–49. Dundee Technical College. Silver & Bronze Medals for City & Guilds Jute Weaving & Spinning, 51. Chrmn., British Jute Trade Federal Council, 62–63. Chrmn. & Man. Dir. of Malcolm Ogilvie & Co. Ltd., Dundee; Buckhaven Textiles Ltd., Dundee. Director, Dens Metals Ltd., Dundee. Brother, D. F. Ogilvie.

OGILVIE, Robert Maxwell, D.Litt, b. 5 June 32, 3rd s. of the late Sir F. W. Ogilvie. SH, 45^3–50^2; Scholar; Levée; Head of House; Head of School; Exhibitioner. Warner Exhibitioner of Balliol, Oxford, D.Litt., F.S.A., F.S.A.(Scot.), Fellow of Clare, Cambridge, 55–57. Fellow of Balliol, 57–70. Headmaster of Tonbridge School since 70. F.B.A. *Athenæum.* Brother, D. A. Ogilvie.

OGLE, John. Tu, 25^3–29^2.*

OGLE, William Maurice, b. 14 Jan. 90, younger s. of the late W. S. Ogle. W, 03^3–08^2; R. VIII, 07–08. Corpus Christi, Oxford, M.A. ✕ 3rd Bn. Royal West Kent Regt. Capt. Wounded. Dispatches. Retired through wounds, 18. Chartered Accountant, F.C.A. Partner in W. S. Ogle, Sons & Porter, London. Retired, 60.

OGLETHORPE, James Kenneth, M.C., T.D., b. 3 May 21, s. of C. O. Oglethorpe. SH, 35^2–39^3; Cap, 39. ✕ 1st Derbyshire Yeomanry. Major. M.C., T.D. Chartered Accountant, 49. P.A. to Man. Dir., Mackenzie Engineering Ltd., 49–52. Sec. & Man. Dir., John Cartmel & Sons (1947) Ltd., 52–59. Sec., Aire Wool Co. Ltd., 59–66. Fin. Dir., Ralli Brothers & Coney Ltd., & Ralli Brothers (Trading) Ltd., & Sec., Ralli International Ltd., since 66. *E.S.U.* Sons, 2909 & Miles Kenneth, SH, 71^1–.

OGLETHORPE, Nicholas Ralph. B, 46^2–50^3.*

O'HAGAN, Brian Denis. B, 32^3–37^2.*

O'HAGAN, Denis Shaftesbury, M.C. B, 11^3–14^1.*

O'HANLON, Geoffrey, M.C., T.D., b. 2 Aug. 85, 5th s. of the late W. O'Hanlon. B, 99^3–04^2; Major Exhibitioner; XXII, 04; Cadet Officer. Scholar of Corpus Christi, Oxford, M.A. Asst. Master, Sherborne School, 08. ✕ 6th Bn. Dorsetshire Regt., 17th Divnl. & 17th & 8th Corps Schools, 14–18. Capt. M.C., T.D. Retired from teaching, 45. Governor of Sherborne School & twice acting for Headmaster. Son, 672. Nephew, W. D. O'Hanlon.

O'HANLON, The Rev. William Douglas, b. 6 May 11, s. of the late A. O'Hanlon (OR B 92). B, 24^3–29^3; Levée; Head of House. Peterhouse, Cambridge, M.A. Ordained Deacon, 37; Priest, 38. ✕ Chaplain, R.A.F.V.R., 39–45. Canon of Salisbury. The Rectory, Studland, Dorset. *Parkstone & Poole Yacht Clubs.* Author "Features of the Ethiopian Church".

OKELL, Charles Edwin Frederick. B, 09^2–12^3.*

OKELL, David, T.D., b. 8 June 20, eldest s. of the late Bishop F. J. Okell. B, 34^2–38^3; XV, 38. Gazetted to Royal Artillery (T.A.), 39. ✕ 59th Medium Regt., R.A., 39–46. Capt. Dispatches. T.D. Wool Broker. Senior Partner, H. W. Hammond & Co., Birkenhead. *Royal Liverpool G.C.; Old Hall, Exchange & Palatine Club.* Son, Philip Charles, B, 68^3–.

O'KELLY, Desmond Lawrence Fitzgerald, b. 8 Feb. 23, s. of L. O'Kelly. Sh, 37^1–41^2; Capt. of Tennis, 41. ✕ 4th P.W.O. Gurkha Rifles, 41–47. Major.

Trinity, Cambridge, B.A. Bar, Lincoln's Inn, 50. Cholmely Scholar, 51. Chrmn., Albany Fund Limited. Man. Dir., Company & Individual Financial Planning Services Ltd. Man. Dir., Capital Advisory Services Ltd. *Special Forces Club; R.A.C.; Pitt Club*. Sons, Martyn Charles Fitzgerald, K, 68³–72² & Sebastian Michael Fitzgerald, K, 71³–.

OLDLAND, Michael John, b. 14 Mar. 28, s. of V. U. Oldland. SH & St, 41³–46²; Exhibitioner; Cap, XXII. Oriel, Oxford, B.A. Lancs. County Major Scholar. Chrmn., Group of Companies. J.P. Son, David Antony, St, 67–71¹.

OLIPHANT, John Laurence. Sh, 43¹–47².*

OLIPHANT, Trevor. St, 06³–11².*

OLIVER, Col. Claude Danolds, O.B.E., T.D., D.L., b. 29 Dec. 03, 3rd s. of the late Col. Sir F. Oliver, T.D., D.L. (OR K 84). St, 18¹–20³; Cap, 20. Gazetted to 4th Bn. Leicestershire Regt. (T.A.), 22. Man. Dir., George Oliver (Footwear) Ltd., Braunstone, Leicester. ✕ R.A. Lt.-Col. O.B.E., T.D., County Cadet Commandant, Leicestershire & Rutland A.C.F. D.L., Leicestershire, 50. *Army & Navy Club*. Brothers, G. B. & Sir F. E. Oliver.

OLIVER, Sir Frederick Ernest, C.B.E., T.D., b. 31 Oct. 00, 2nd s. of the late Sir F. Oliver, T.D., D.L. (OR K 84). St, 14²–19¹; Cap, 18. Gazetted to 4th Bn. Leicestershire Regt. (T.A.), 22. Chrmn., George Oliver (Footwear) Ltd., Braunstone, Leicester. ✕ R.A., 39–45. T.D. Member, Leicester City Council since 33. D.L., Leicestershire. Lord Mayor, 50–51. Knt., 62. C.B.E., 55. J.P. *Leicestershire Club*. Brothers, G. B. & C. D. Oliver.

OLIVER, George Barry, M.C., b. 16 Dec. 96, eldest s. of the late Col. Sir F. Oliver, T.D., D.L. (OR K 84). St, 10³–14³; Cap, 14; G. VIII, 14. ✕ 4th Bn. Leicestershire Regt. Capt. M.C. With George Oliver, Boot Factor, of Leicester, now retired. Brothers, Sir F. E. & C. D. Oliver.

OLIVER, Admiral Sir Geoffrey Nigel, G.B.E., K.C.B., D.S.O., b. 22 Jan. 98, eldest s. of the late Prof. F. W. Oliver, F.R.S. SF, 11³–15²; Cadet Officer. R.N. Coll., Keyham (sp. entry cadet), 15–16. ✕ Midn., 16 (H.M.S. *Dreadnought* & *Renown*). S/Lt., 17. Courses (Cambs. & Portsmouth), 20. Goodenough Medal for

Gunnery. Qual. Gunnery Officer, 23 (Cdr. Egerton Prize). Cdr., 32; Capt. 37. ✕ H.M.S. *Hermione*, 40–42; Commodore, 42; R.-Adl., 45; V.-Adl., 49; Adl., 52. Retired list, 55. D.S.O. (2 Bars). Dispatches twice. C.B., 44. K.C.B., 51. G.B.E., 55. U.S. Legion of Merit, Officer, 43. Commander, 44. Brother, P. D. Oliver. Son, 167.

OLIVER, Harold Gordon, M.B., B.Ch. SF, 03³–05³.*

OLIVER, Ian Maurice Lomas. SF, 12³–15².*

OLIVER, Capt. Philip Daniel, R.N., C.B.E., b. 20 July 00, 2nd s. of the late Prof. F. W. Oliver, F.R.S. SF, 14²–18²; Cap, 16; Cadet Officer. R.N. College, Keyham, 18. Specialised in Engineering, 23. Pilot in Fleet Air Arm, 26. ✕ Admiralty Aircraft Maintenance & Repair Dept., 39–41. H.M.S. *Unicorn*, 41–44. Capt. (E.), 45. M.I.Mech.E. F.E.O. (Home Fleet), 47–49. Superintendent, R.N. Aircraft Repair Yard, Belfast, 51–53. Principal of "The West Down Tutors" (now the Mill, Clymping), 58–62. Retired. C.B.E. *Army & Navy Club*. Brother, G. N. Oliver. Son, 763.

OLIVER, Stanley Blues, b. 14 May 27, s. of the late C. L. Oliver. K, 43¹–44³. ✕ Royal Marines, 42; Commando, 45–47. Journalist. Deputy Editor, "Shields Gazette" (Evening).

OLIVIER, Lt.-Col. Henry Alfred Arnould, b. 21 Oct. 03, s. of the late Col. H. D. Oliver, R.E. SH, 17²–21². Brasenose, Oxford, M.A. Gazetted to S. Staffordshire Regt., 24. Lt., 28. ✕ 39–45. Posted to Command 1st North Staffordshire Regt., 45. Lt.-Col. (Retired).

ORLEBAR, Richard Astrey Bourne. SH, 08³–12².*

ORMEROD, Charles Maurice, b. 27 Aug. 04, elder s. of C. Ormerod. B, 18³–23²; Scholar; S. VIII, 21–23 (Capt.); R. VIII, 22, 23; Cadet Officer. Scholar of King's, Cambridge, M.A. C.U. Shooting VIII, 25–26. Indian Civil Service, 27–47 (Service terminated on transfer of power). Bar, Inner Temple, 40. Voluntarily disbarred, 51. Solicitor, 51, with Clifford Turner & Co. Retired, 70. *East India, Sports & Public Schools Club*.

ORMEROD, Thomas Laurence, M.B. SH, 06³–10².*

ORR, David James Campbell. SH, 42¹–46².*

ORTMANS, Derrick Horace. M, 36²–40². Sons, 2314* and 2607*.

OSBORN, John Holbrook, M.P., b. 14 Dec. 22, eldest s. of the late S. E. Osborn (OR Tu 05). Sh, 36³–41². Trinity Hall, Cambridge, M.A. ⚔ R. Signals, 43–47. Major. R.A. (T.A.), 47–55. National Foundry College, Wolverhampton. Dip. Foundry Practice. M.P., Hallam Division of Sheffield, 59. Director, Steelworks. *Carlton, Sheffield Club, R. & A. G.C.* Brother, P. L. Osborn.

OSBORN, Peter Leslie, b. 24 July 25, younger s. of the late S. E. Osborn (OR Tu 05), SH, 39²–43². Trinity Hall, Cambridge, M.A. ⚔ R.N., 45–47. S/Lt. (E.). Post-Graduate Engineering Course with Davy United Engineering Co. Ltd., Sheffield, 47–49. Various executive jobs with Samuel Osborn & Co. Ltd., Sheffield, makers of high speed steel & cutting tools, since 49. *R. & A. G.C., Oxford & Cambridge Golfing Society, The Sheffield Club.* Brother, J. H. Osborn. Son, Charles Eric, Sh, 68³–72³.

OSBORNE, Lt.-Col. George Edward Ross Coke, b. 11 Sept. 99, s. of the late G. E. Osborne. Tu, 13²–18¹; Cadet Officer. R.M.C., Sandhurst. Gazetted to 1st Bn. K.R.R.C., 19. Lt., 21. Capt., 28. Major, 38. ⚔ Lt.-Col., 41. Retired.

OSBOURNE, Roger Bruce (formerly Oppenheim, R. B.), b. 2 Aug. 17, elder s. of the late E. F. Oppenheim, I.C.S., C.I.E. (OR SH 89). SH, 31²–36¹; R. VIII, 34–36 (Capt.). Corpus Christi, Cambridge, M.A. Oxford Dip.Ed. Principal, Cambridge Tutors of Croydon (one of only 6 colleges recognised by Dept. of Education & Service as an efficient College of Further Education specialising in G.C.E. & Oxbridge entrances). Secretary of the Conference for Independent Further Education. *Croydon Press Club.* Oliver Prior Society (Modern Languages).

OSMOND, Eric Alexander. SF, 04¹–06².*

OSWALD, John George Devereux. B, 18²–21³.*

OSWALD, Major-General Marshall St. John, C.B., C.B.E., D.S.O., M.C., b. 13 Sept. 11, 2nd s. of W. W. Oswald. C, 25³–29³; XV, 28–29 (Capt.); XI, 28–29; H. XI, 28–29; Cadet Officer. R.M.A., Woolwich. Senior Under-Officer. Sword of Honour. King's Medal. Capt., Cricket & H. XIs; 1st XV. Gazetted to Royal Artillery, 31. ⚔ Battery Commander, R.H.A. and Staff Officer, Egypt & Western Desert, 39–43. 2 i/c, Field Regt., Italy, 43–44. C.O., South Notts. Hussars in W. Europe, 44–45. p.s.c., j.s.s.c. Instructor, Staff College, 50–52. C.O., 19 Field Regt., Germany & Korea, 53–55. Chief of Staff, 1st Corps, 59–62 (Brigadier). I.D.C. Director of Military Intelligence (Major-General), 62. Retired, 66. C.B., C.B.E., D.S.O., M.C. Council Member of Salmon & Trout Assoc. *Army & Navy Club.* Brother, W. A. H. Oswald. Son, 1016.

OSWALD, Lt.-Col. William Alexander Hugh, b. 3 July 05, elder s. of W. W. Oswald. C, 19³–23². Jesus, Cambridge, M.A. Commissioned in Queen's Own Royal West Surrey Regt. (T.A.), 23. ⚔ R.A.S.C., 38–46. Lt.-Col. A.D.S. & T. at Naples, 45. Anglo-American Oil Co. Ltd., London, Asst. Chief Chemist, 26–39. Sales Manager, Foster Wheeler Ltd., London, 46–70; Man. Dir., Foster Wheeler Française, Paris, 50–70. Retired. Brother, M. St. J. Oswald.

OTTEWILL, Major Walter Kirby. B, 31³–36¹.*

OVER, Lt.-Col. Dennis Spencer, O.B.E., T.D., D.L., b. 22 May 99, 2nd s. of the late S. Over (OR T 84). T, 12³–16³. R.M.C., Sandhurst. ⚔ 1st Bn. Royal Warwickshire Regt. Seconded to R.A.F. as Pilot, 19–24. Retired from Regular Army, 37. In T.A., 37–47. ⚔ Lt.-Col. M.B.E., T.D., Hon. Colonel. Secretary, County of Surrey Territorial & Auxiliary Forces Assoc., 47–64. Appeals Sec., Star & Garter Home, Richmond-upon-Thames, 64–67. Hon. Sec., Army Benevolent Fund, Surrey. D.L., Surrey, 58. O.B.E., 58.

OWEN, John Howell, b. 11 Feb. 30, 2nd s. of the late H. Owen, M.C. Sh, 43³–48²; XV, 46–47; Rackets Pair, 48; Fives IV, 47–48 (Capt.); Capt. of Lawn Tennis, 48. N/S. 78 H.A.A. Regt., R.A., 48–51. 2nd Lt. Magdalene, Cambridge, B.A. J. & P. Coats Ltd., P.A. Management Consultants. Duncan Fox & Co. Ltd., Lima, Peru. Now Unicorn Estate Agency, Mallorca, Spain. Son, Peter Howell, Sh, 72–.

OWEN, John Roger Gordon. St, 44³–49².*

OWEN, Noel Richard Holmes, b. 11 Dec. 25, s. of M. Owen. SF, 39³–44¹; Levée; Head of House; XV, 42, 43. (Capt.); XXII, 43. Scholar of Clare, Cambridge, M.A. Schoolmaster at Harrow & Hilton College, Natal, S. Africa, 48–52. Partner with Capel-Cure, Carden & Co., Stockbrokers. *Hawks.*

OWEN, Trevor Bryan, b. 3 Apr. 28, 2nd s. of the late L. Owen. SH, 42¹–46³; Levée; XV, 46. N/S. R.A., 47–49. 2nd

Lt. Scholar of Trinity, Oxford. Personnel Officer.

OWSTON, Clifford Scott. Tu, 02³–06² *

OWTRAM, Thomas Cary, M.B.E., M.C., b. 18 Apr. 93, eldest s. of the late H. H. Owtram. B, 06³–10³; Scholar. Christ Church, Oxford, M.A. ⚔ 5th Bn. Royal Lancaster Regt. Capt. Wounded twice. M.C. Bar, Inner Temple, 25. Retired. M.B.E. *Travellers' Club.*

P

PADMORE, Neville Thomas, b. 25 May 25, s. of the late E. H. Padmore. B, 39¹–42²; Sw. VIII, 42. Aberdeen University (Inter B.Sc.); Univ. Sw. VIII. ⚔ R.A. & attd. Indian Army. Capt., 44–47. Man. Dir., Thos Padmore & Sons Ltd. (Billiard Table Manufacturers), of Birmingham. *Kings Norton R.F.C.* (Past President).

PAGET, John Francis, b. 6 Aug. 03, s. of M. J. Paget. B, 17²–20³. In Bank of England, 22–27. Joined London Office of Australian Mercantile Land & Finance Co. Ltd., 27. ⚔ R. Signals, 39–45. Major. Public Company Registrar. Retired.

PAIGE, Arnold Henry. W, 37³–41³.*

PAIGE, John Friend, M.C., b. 31 July 92, 3rd s. of the late H. Paige. W, 06³–10². Gonville & Caius, Cambridge, B.A. ⚔ Royal Engineers (Gallipoli, Mesopotamia), 14–19. Lt. M.C. Dispatches. Works Manager, Birmingham Corrugated Iron Co. Ltd., Widnes, 19–20. Asst. to Commercial Man., Pearson & Knoles Coal & Iron Co. Ltd., Warrington, 20–27. Gen. Man., William Mills & Co., Wednesbury, 27–44. Man. Dir., 44–57. Retired, 57. Sons, A. H. & J. P. Paige.

PAIGE, John Phillips. W, 41³–45².*

PAIN, Trevor Gordon, b. 19 Jan. 19, s. of G. H. Pain. Sh, 32³–37²; S. VIII, 36–37; (Cadet Pair). Peterhouse, Cambridge. 1st Class in Estate Management. ⚔ R. Signals. Invalided. Capt. A.R.I.C.S., 47. Land Agent for G. H. Pain, and Farming. Sons, 2700 & James Andrew, Sh, 67²–.

PAINE, Michael Cleverly, b. 11 Nov. 20, 2nd s. of the late F. E. Paine. SF, 34²–38². Jesus, Cambridge. ⚔ R.A., 41–45. Capt. Diploma Member, Institute of Practitioners in Advertising. Director,

Benton and Bowles Ltd. Now Marketing Consultant. *R.A.C.*

PALCA, Henry, b. 23 Sept. 19, s. of the late J. Palca. SH, 33¹–37³. Oriel, Oxford, M.A. Civil Servant (Government Statistic Service), Ministry of Agriculture, 41–60. Chief Statistician at British Egg Marketing Board, 60–67. Post Office, 67–70. Department of Environment since 70.

PALMER, Brian Dudley Buller. SH & C, 43³–47².*

PALMER, John Antony St. John. C, 30³–35².*

PALMER, John Elliott George. St, 18³–22².*

PALMER, The Rev. John Michael Joseph, V.R.D., R.N.R. Tu, 32¹–35³.*

PALMER, Lt.-Col. Kenneth Randall, D.L., b. 4 Apr. 91, s. of the late F. R. Palmer. SH, 05³–09². Trinity, Cambridge. Polo Half Blue, 11–13. ⚔ 2nd Life Guards. Capt., 19. Retired, 22. ⚔ Re-employed, 39, as Major, R.A. Lt.-Col. Comdg. 1st Caithness Bn. Home Guard, 43. Retired. D.L. (1946), Caithness. *Boodle's.*

PALMER, The Rev. Neville William Jarvis, b. 14 Sept. 06, s. of W. J. Palmer. W, 20²–24¹. Witwatersrand Univ., Johannesburg, B.Sc. Licentiate in Theology, 34. Ordained, 35. Asst. Curate, Benoni, Transvaal, 35–41. ⚔ Chaplain to the Forces, 41–46. P.O.W., 42–43. Chaplain, St. John's College, Johannesburg, from 46. Canon of St. Mary's Cathedral, Johannesburg, 72. *Rand Club, Johannesburg.*

PALMER, Olaf Barwell, M.C. M, 04³–08³.*

PANK, John Dudley, b. 30 Apr. 05, eldest s. of the late J. R. Pank (OR St 87). St, 19²–20³. University of London. Senior Supervision Officer, Children's Branch, Home Office Approved School Service. Secretary, Mount Grace Comprehensive School, Potters Bar, Herts. Honorary Commissioner, Hertfordshire Boy Scouts Assoc. Author "The Order of the Court", "The Man and the Boy", "The Scouter's Job" and many short stories.

PARGA, Rafael. W, 13³–18¹.*

PARGITER, Major.-Gen. Robert Beverley, C.B., C.B.E., b. 11 July 89, s. of the late F. E. Pargiter. St, 03³–07². R.M.A., Woolwich. Staff College, Camberley. p.s.c. Imperial Defence College. Royal Artillery. Served 35 yrs. in Army, 09–44. Commissioner, Red Cross & St. John's War Orgn. Middle East, 45. Malaya, 46., ✕ N.W. Frontier, India, France & Belgium, 14–18. Dispatches. Brevet Major. ✕ 39–45, France, N. Africa, Italy. Dispatches. C.B., C.B.E. American Legion of Merit.

PARHAM, John Carey, b. 13 June 28, s. of Admiral Sir Frederick Parham, G.B.E. W, 42²–46³; Levée; Head of House Magdalen, Oxford, M.A. A.I.B. Local Director, Barclays Bank, Windsor. *Travellers'.*

PARK, John Mungo, b. 1 Sept. 20, s. of Capt. C. T. Park. Tu, 34²–38³; XV, 38; XI, 38. Exhibition to Brasenose, Oxford. Attended Heidelberg & Sorbonne, 39. ✕ Irish Guards, 39–44. Capt. Wounded in N. Africa & invalided out. In Kenya, 47–53. Member of Irish Stock Exchange, Dublin, since 54. Trustee, Irish Hospitals Trust Board. Governor, Rotunda, Simpson & King's Hospitals (Blue Coat). *Royal Yacht Squadron, Royal Irish Yacht Club, Royal Alfred Y.C.* (Commodore).

PARKER, Francis Timothy. Tu & C, 43³–46².*

PARKER, Robin James, b. 11 May 31, elder s. of the late J. S. Parker. W, 45²–49². N/S. R.A.F. Pilot Officer. B.Sc. (Edinburgh). (Eight U.S. Patents.) Manager, Catalyst Development. Universal Oil Products Co., U.S.A. Member, *Catalysis Club.* American Chemical Socy., American Institute of Chemical Engineers.

PARKINSON, Harold Jackson. SH, 33¹–36².*

PARMITER, Hugh Clavell, b. 3 Jan. 03, s. of the late Rev. S. C. Parmiter. SH, 16³–21²; Cap, 20; S. VIII, 19–21 (Capt.). Oriel, Oxford. Joined Joseph Crosfield & Sons Ltd., Soap Manufacturers, Warrington. Retired.

PARNELL, Richard William, D.M., B.Ch., F.R.C.P., b. 2 Oct. 11, 2nd s. of W. C. Parnell. T, 25¹–30²; Cadet Officer; XI, 29, 30. Exhibitioner of St. John's, Oxford, M.A., B.Ch., D.M. The London Hospital, F.R.C.P. Consultant Physician in Geriatrics, North Birmingham Hospital. ✕ R.A.F.V.R., 43–47. No. 65 Mobile Field Hospital, Burma. Sqn. Ldr. Physician, Institute of Social Medicine, Oxford, 47–51. Research Physician, Medical Research Council, Warneford Hospital, Oxford, 51–62. Assoc. of Physicians of Gt. Britain. Author of "Behaviour and Physique".

PARRY, David Knollys Heber, b. 14 Nov. 24, s. of R. H. Parry. St, 38³–40². Completed school at Michaelhouse, Natal. ✕ R.A.F., 42–46. F/Lt. Served 44 Rhodesian Squadron. With Mann, George & Co. Ltd., Shipping Agents, Durban. The firm merged to form Freight Services in 68. Since 46 (became Freight Services Ltd. 68), Manager at Cape Town. *R.A.C.; Durban Club; Johannesburg Country Club.*

PARRY, Geoffrey Norman, b. 13 Apr. 17, youngest s. of the late E. A. Parry (OR Tu 93). Tu, 30³–35³; H. XI; Leaving Exhibitioner (History). Exhibitioner of King's, Cambridge. ✕ Colonial Administrative Service. King's African Rifles, 39–46. Bar, Inner Temple, 47. *Flyfishers' Club.* Brother, J. E. Parry. Sons, 2940 & James G., Tu, 68²–.

PARRY, John Butler, O.B.E., b. 30 Dec. 05, s. of the late E. C. M. Parry, O.B.E. St, 19³–24². London University, B.A., Ph.D. John Stuart Mill Scholar. Asst. Chief Scientist, Ministry of Defence (Air). Fellow, British Psychological Society. Retired, Civil Service, 71. Publications: "Personnel Selection in the British Forces", "The Psychology of Human Communication". O.B.E., 60. *Pen Club.*

PARRY, John Edward, M.C., b. 5 Mar. 14, 2nd s. of the late E. A. Parry (OR Tu 93). Tu, 27³–32². Magdalene, Cambridge. B.A. ✕ R. Tank Regt. Lt. M.C. 2 yrs. London Stock Exchange. At present farming in S. Africa. Brother, G. N. Parry.

PARRY-EVANS, The Rev. Cuthbert John, b. 11 Aug. 05, s. of Canon A. B. Parry-Evans. SH, 19²–22². Sidney Sussex, Cambridge, M.A. Ordained, 32. Curate of St. Mary, Gateshead, 32–38. Vicar of Fatfield, Co. Durham, 38–54. Vicar of Hognaston with Kniveton, Derbyshire, 54–68. Retired, 68.

PARSONS, Arthur. T, 05³–08².*

PARSONS, Major Anthony Dallin, M.B.E., M.C., b. 24 Sept. 17, s. of the late W. H. Parsons (OR SH 88). SH, 31²–36¹. Corpus Christi, Cambridge, B.A. Gazetted to Wiltshire Regt. ✕ 39–45. M.C. Wounded, 45. Regular Commission, 46. p.s.c., 48. Retired, 72, as Major. M.B.E. *Army & Navy Club.*

PARSONS, Paul Edward. T, 44³–48².*

PARTINGTON, James Foster Edge. K, 01²–05¹.*

PASCOE, James Sherard Harding. M, 19¹–22¹.*

PASKIN, Philip Wallgrave. W, 07³–11².*

PASSEY, David Anstruther, b. 28 Feb. 27, eldest s. of the late Prof. R. D. Passey, M.C., M.D., D.P.H. K, 40³–45¹; Cap; Cadet Officer, 43–45. Oriel, Oxford, B.A. N/S. 13/18th Royal Hussars (Q.M.O.) 2nd Lt. Industry—Manager in I.C.I. *United Oxford & Cambridge Club.* Salmon Trout Assoc. Brother, R. D. C. Passey.

PASSEY, Richard Douglas Cook, b. 18 Mar. 31, 2nd s. of the late Prof. R. D. Passey, M.C., M.D., D.P.H. K, 44³–49². Bristol University, B.Sc. (Aero Eng.), A.F.R.Ae.S., P.Eng. Canadair (Montreal), Rolls-Royce (Aero Div.) Derby, I.C.I. (Fibres Div.), Bristol Siddeley Engines. Now Senior Reliability Engineer, Rolls-Royce (1971) Ltd., Derby, specialising in reliability analysis, fatigue, stress criteria, fail safe design and economical testing. Royal Aeronautical Socy. Brother, D. A. Passey.

PATERSON, Aylmer John Noel, C.B.E., b. 16 Apr. 02, s. of Rev. H. D. N. Paterson. K, 16¹–20³; Scholar; Levée; XV, 20. Scholar of Clare, Cambridge. Foundation Scholar, 22. B.A., LL.B. Bar, Middle Temple, 26. Oxford Circuit. Private Secretary to the Lord Chancellor & Deputy Sergeant-at-Arms in House of Lords, 30–34. Legal Asst., Lord Chancel-

lor's office, 34–39. Chief Clerk, Judicial Committee of Privy Council, 39–54. Registrar of Privy Council, 54–63. C.B.E., 63. *Athenæum, Hawks.*

PATERSON, Edward Gordon, b. 15 Aug. 25, younger s. of C. J. Paterson, M.A., LL.B. M, 39²–39³ & 42¹–42². Educated in Scotland, 40–41. Officer in Scots Guards discharged as W/S Lt., 43–47. Apprentice, Chartered Accountant, 48–52. Now self-employed as Travel Agent with branches in Aberdeen, Glasgow and Edinburgh. B.L.A.C. Numerous Flying and Motor Sporting Clubs.

PATRICK, Felix Faris. K, 16³–20².*

PATRICK, Sir Paul Joseph, K.C.I.E., C.S.I., b. 6 Oct. 88, s. of the late the Rev. J. A. Patrick, M.A. B, 02³–07²; Head of House. Scholar of Corpus Christi, Oxford, M.A. Home Civil Service. India Office and Commonwealth Relations Office, 12–50. Retired, 50, as Asst. Under Secretary of State. ✕ 3rd Gurkha Rifles & 39th Garhwal Rifles, Indian Army, 16–19. Staff Major. K.C.I.E., C.S.I., Comdr. of St. J. *Travellers' Club.*

PATTERSON, Kimball George, b. 20 Oct. 21, s. of the late G. H. Patterson of Sydney, N.S.W. W, 35¹–38²; Sw. VIII, 37–38. St. Paul's College, Univ. of Sydney. ✕ R.A.N.V.R., 41–45. P.O.W., 44–45. Lt. Wounded. Dispatches. Farmer & Grazier. Agricultural Engineer. Edzell Div. of Petersville Limited, Bathurst, N.S.W. *Royal Sydney G.C.; Bathurst Club; Naval Officers Club, Sydney.*

PATTINSON, John Lawrence, b. 17 June 26, s. of the late Air Marshal Sir L. A. Pattinson, K.B.E., C.B., D.S.O., M.C., D.F.C. Sh, 40¹–44²; Sw. VIII, 43–44; Cadet Officer; Tom Hughes Prize. ✕ R.A. 44–48. Short Course, Aberdeen Univ., 44–45. Lt. Jesus, Cambridge, M.A. Farming, 51–54. International Harvester, 54–58. Agricultural Marketing, 58–62. Sun Life of Canada, 62–64. Formed own Broking Company. Life Assurance Broker since 64. A.M.I.B. F.R.S.A. *Army & Navy Club.*

PATTINSON, John Mellor, C.B.E., b. 21 Apr. 99, eldest s. of the late J. P. Pattinson (OR SH 75). SH, 13²–17¹; Cap, 16. R.M.A. Woolwich. ✕ R.F.A. 2nd Lt., 18–19. Jesus, Cambridge, M.A. Joined Anglo-Persian Oil Co. in Persia, 22. Gen. Man., 37–46. Appointed Head Office, British Petroleum Co., 46. Director, 52.

Deputy Chrmn., 60–65. Director, Chrmn., Associated Companies. Now Director, Chartered Bank. Fellow, Institute of Petroleum. F.R.G.S. Iran Society. Central Asian Society. Member, Council Overseas Development Institute. C.B.E., 43. *East India, Sports and Public Schools.*

PATTINSON, Mark b. 13 May 30, 2nd s. of G. P. Pattinson. M, 44^2–49^2; XI, 49. Trinity, Cambridge, M.A. F.C.A. Director, Manchester Liners Ltd.

PATTISSON, Gilbert Richard, b. 22 Aug. 08, s. of the late R. M. Pattisson, M.A. M, 22^2–26^2. Emmanuel, Cambridge. F.C.A. Retired Chartered Accountant. *East India, Sports & Public Schools.*

PATTISSON, Hoël Carlos, b. 3 Sept. 05, eldest s. of C. H. Pattisson. W, 19^3–24^2; XV, 22 & 23; XI, 22 to 24 (Capt., 23 & 24); G. VIII, 21–22; Athletics Cup (Junior) 22, (Senior) 23–24. London Stock Exchange, 24–39. ⚔ Rifle Brigade, 40–46. Major. Hotelier, 46–56. Retired, 56. *M.C.C., Free Foresters, I.Z., Harlequin F.C., Rye G.C.* The Medical Society. Brother, R. G. Pattisson. Son, 734.

PATTISSON, Patrick Henry, M.B., B.S., b. 21 Dec. 32, elder s. of R. D. M. Pattisson (OR Tu 22). Tu, 46^3–51^2; Cap. King's College, London. St. George's Hospital, M.B.B.S., F.R.C.S.(Eng.), F.R.C.S.(Ed.). Consultant General & Vascular Surgeon, West Middlesex Hospital, Isleworth. Brother, 589.

PATTISSON, Richard Duke Merriman. Tu, 22^3–27^1. Sons, P. H. Pattisson & 589.*

PATTISSON, Rupert George, b. 10 Nov. 09, younger s. of C. H. Pattisson. W, 23^3–27^2; XXII, 26; G. VIII. Stock Exchange, London, 28–51. ⚔ R.A., 39–45. Staff Capt. C.B.I., 51–71. Now retired. *Walton Heath G.C.* Army Ski Assoc. Brother, H. C. Pattisson.

PATTULLO, Charles Peter Norman. C, 46^3–48^2.*

PATTULLO, Major (James) Neil (Ballingal), b. 26 Sept. 03, elder s. of the late C. M. Pattullo. Tu, 17^3–21^1. Brasenose, Oxford. With the Powell River Paper Mills Co., British Columbia. ⚔ Canadian Army, 39–45. Major. J.P., 53. D.L. (Angus), 60. *New Club, Edinburgh.* Brother, N. A. Pattullo.

PATTULLO, Norman Adam, b. 29 Nov. 05, younger s. of the late C. M. Pattullo. Tu, 19^3–24^1. Brasenose, Oxford, B.A. Writer to the Signet. Partner in Edinburgh firm, 34–46. ⚔ 1st Lothian & Border Yeomanry, 39–45. Lt. Captured at St. Valéry, 40. P.O.W., 40–45. Hon. Sheriff Substitute (Angus). J.P. Member of the Royal Company of Archers. *Cavalry Club; New Club, Edinburgh.* Brother, J. N. B. Pattullo.

PATTULLO, Ronald William, b. 11 Nov. 01, 2nd s. of J. D. Pattullo. SH, 15^3–20^2. Queens', Cambridge, M.A. ⚔ R.N.V.R. Lt. Preparatory Schoolmaster. Headmaster, King's House, Richmond, Surrey. Retired.

PAUL, Major Peter Graham. M, 26^2–29^3. Son, 1826.*

PAUL, Thomas Neil. M, 23^2–26^3. Son, 2530.*

PAUL, William Derrick, b. 13 Jan. 08, eldest s. of T. W. Paul. M, 21^3–25^1. Gonville & Caius, Cambridge, B.A. For 30 yrs., Chrmn. of Directors, William Paul Ltd., Leather Manufacturers, Leeds. Now retired. Brother, T. N. Paul.

PAUL, William Kelso, T.D., b. 29 June 09, elder s. of the late J. A. Paul, T.D. (OR M 85). M, 23^2–26^3. Language Course in Germany. Director of William Paul Ltd., Leather Mnfrs., from 30. Retired, 67. ⚔ R.A. (Field), 39–45. Lt.-Col. T.D. *Army & Navy; The Club, Harrogate, Yorks.* Brother, P. G. Paul. Son, 695.

PAWLING, Major Claud Heaton. St, 02^1–06^2.*

PAWSON, Kenneth Vernon Frank, b. 24 Sept. 23, s. of the late A. G. Pawson. Sh, 37^2–41^2; S. VIII. Trinity Hall, Cambridge, M.A. ⚔ Rifle Brigade & Staff, 42–47. Capt. Bar, Gray's Inn, 49. Man. Dir. of family Brewery and various Wine & Spirit, Printing, Plant Hire, Quarrying, Property & Investment Companies. Deputy Chrmn. of Gale Lister & Co. Ltd. *Aire Fishing Club.* Son, 2850.

PAYEN-PAYNE, James Bertrand Guy. B, 24^3–27^3.*

PAYNE, Edwin Rowland. W, 34^3–39^2.*

PAYNE, The Rev. Frederick Gates, H.C.F., b. 24 Apr. 19, s. of the late Dr. A. G. Payne. SF, 32^2–37^2. Jesus, Cambridge, M.A. London College of Divinity. Ordained, 42. H.C.F., 48. Curate of St. James' & later of Walcot, Bath, 42–45. Chaplain to the Forces (Ethiopia & Kenya), 45–48. Head of Mission to the Felasha Jews, Ethiopia, 48–67. South Western Secretary on Home Staff of the Church's Ministry among the Jews based at Weston, Bath. Bath Philatelic Socy. Author of "Ethiopian Jews".

PAYNE, John Charles Rowland, M.B., Ch.B. Tu, 31^3–35^2.*

PAYNE, Roger Lewin. M, 28^3–32^3. Son, 1512.*

PAYNE, Lt.-Col. William Melville, b. 28 Aug. 29, younger s. of Dr. T. M. Payne. W, 43^2–47^2. Jesus, Oxford. Manchester University. Diploma in Industrial Management. Lt.-Col. in Army. Now self-employed. O.S.L.

PAYTON, Stanley Charles. T, 27^1–32^1.*

PEAK, John Ashbrooke, b. 20 Apr. 29, s. of the late Capt. C. A. Peak. SF, 43^3–47^1; Rackets, 2nd Pair, 46–47. N/S. 22nd (Cheshire) Regt., 47–49. 2nd Lt. Clare, Cambridge, M.A. A.R.I.C.S. Industrial Development Officer, Skelmersdale New Town. T.D. *West Lancashire Y.C.*

PEARCE, Arthur Peter. K, 31^2–35^2.*

PEARCE, Major Edward Augustus, b. 3 Nov. 04, 2nd s. of Capt. J. J. Pearce. C, 18^3–22^2; XI, 22. Trinity, Oxford. Worked in Real Estate, New York, 26. Joined 3rd/6th Dragoon Guards, 27, through Supplementary Reserve and retired, 29. Held Racehorse Trainer's Licence. ✗ Rejoined Regt., 40, in India, attd. R.A.F., serving in Burma & M.E. Major. Retired, 46, to live in Southern Ireland and became an Irish citizen. *R.I.A.C.*

PEARCE-HIGGINS, The Rev. Canon John Denis (formerly Higgins, J. D. P.), b. 1 June 05, younger s. of Dr. A. P. Higgins, LL.D., F.B.A., C.B.E. B, 19^3–23^2; Scholar; Head of House. Scholar of Gonville & Caius, Cambridge. Scholar & Prizeman, Warr Scholar, M.A. Ripon Hall, Oxford, 34. Ordained, 37; Priest, 38. ✗ Chaplain, R.A., Ch.D., 40–45. Invalided, 45. Vicar of Hagley Castle, Worcs., 45–53. Lecturer at City of Worcester Training College, 46–53. Vicar of Putney, 53–63. Residentiary Canon & Vice-Provost of Southwark Cathedral from 63, & Canon Emeritus from 71. Member of the Society for Psychical Research. Vice-Chrmn., Churches Fellowship for Psychical & Spiritual Studies. Lecturer & Broadcaster. Editor of Symposium, "Life, Death and Psychical Research".

PEARMAN, Paul Beningfield. B, 42^3–45^2.*

PEARSON, Edward Arthur, b. 1 July 24, 3rd s. of the late Lt.-Col. N. G. Pearson, D.S.O., M.C. SF, 38^3–42^3; Scholar; Levée; Head of House; Cap; Cadet Officer, 42. Corpus Christi, Oxford. ✗ 11th Hussars, 43–45. Sudan Political Service, 45–53. A.D.C. to Governor-General of Sudan, 49–50. Foreign Service, 54–62. Bursar Aysgarth School since 63. *E.S.U.* Royal Central Asian Socy. Brother, M. Pearson. Son, Christopher Michael Standish, SF, 67^2–72^2.

PEARSON, John Erskine Grayhurst, D.M., F.R.C.P., b. 14 Sept. 08, s. of the late Sir H. G. Pearson. SF, 22^3–27^2; Scholar; Cap, 25; XI, 26–27; H. XI, 26–27. University College, Oxford. Middlesex Hospital, London, D.M.(Oxon.), F.R.C.P. (Lond.). Consultant Physician, United Bristol Hospitals. Clinical Teacher, University of Bristol. *R.A.F. Club.*

PEARSON, Mark, M.C., b. 18 June 15, eldest s. of the late Lt.-Col. N. G. Pearson, D.S.O., M.C. SF, 29^2–33^2; Cap, 32. Director, Beeston Boiler Co. Ltd., 40. ✗ 15th/19th The King's Royal Hussars, 40–45. M.C. Brother, E. A. Pearson. Sons, 1754, 2129 & 2744.

PECK, Dennis Ralph, b. 12 Aug. 14, eldest s. of the late R. D. Peck. B, 28^2–31^2. London School of Printing. Writer & Composer. Publications: "Bess, The Story of a Horse", "Suzanne the Elephant". Sons, 1477 & 2476.

PEMBERTON, Derek John. St & W, 41^3–45^2.*

PEMBERTON, Nigel Digby, b. 15 Oct. 32, 2nd s. of R. T. Pemberton. W, 46^3–50^3. Trinity, Cambridge, B.A. N/S. 13/18 Royal Hussars (Q.M.O.) 2nd Lt. ✗ Malaya, 51–53. Chrmn., Graham Associates Ltd., Montego Bay, Jamaica, W.I. *Cavalry Club; Royal Thames Y.C.; Knickerbocker Club (New York).*

PENRUDDOCKE, Thomas Beresford, b. 18 Apr. 06, s. of the late Capt. H. B. Penruddocke (R.N.R.). T, 20^1–21^2. Rugby Technical College. Electrical Engineer. A.M.I.E.E. Retired, 71.

PERCIVAL, Charles Kenneth Moreland, b. 6 May 20, s. of the late C. A. E. Percival (OR SH 02). SH, 34¹–38²; Sw. VIII, 38. Corpus Christi, Cambridge, M.A., C.E., M.I.C.E. ⋊ R.E., Middle East & Europe, 40–46. Capt. Family business, Moreland Hoyne & Co. Ltd., London, Structural Steelwork. Director, 46–66. Asst. Master, Grammar School, 66–70. Devonport Dockyard, Planning, 71–72. Manager, Boatyard, Salcombe, since 72.

PERCIVAL, Philip Robin, b. 28 Jan. 30, s. of the late F. N. Percival (OR SH 01). SH, 43³–48²; Scholar; XXII, 46–48 (Capt.); H. XI, 48. Scholar of Queens', Cambridge.

PERCY, Jervis Joscelyn, b. 21 July 28, eldest s. of the late J. E. S. Percy, D.S.O., M.C. (OR K 11). K, 42²–46². R.M.A., Sandhurst. Gazetted to the Durham Light Infantry, 48. Man. Dir., Draeger Normalair Ltd. *Derwent Reservoir Sailing Club.* Brother, R. J. Percy.

PERCY, Richard Joscelyn, b. 22 Nov. 32, younger s. of the late Col. J. E. S. Percy, D.S.O., M.C. (OR K 11). K, 46²–50³; XV, 50. R.M.A., Sandhurst (R.M.A., XV). Gazetted to the Durham Light Infantry, 53–55. The Parachute Regt., 55–58. Now Sales Director of Raisby Quarries Ltd., Coxhoe, Co. Durham. M.I.M. Brother, J. J. Percy.

PERCY-JONES, Col. Donald. W, 12³–15³.*

PERRIN, John, M.D., M.R.C.P. St, 31⁵–35². Son, 1662A.*

PERRY, John Maddock Thorpe, b. 7 Oct. 04, s. of R. T. Perry. Tu, 18³–22³; XI, 21–22. Hertford, Oxford. ⋊ R. Signals, Middle & Far East, 39–45. 40 yrs. with Thomas Forman & Sons Ltd., Nottingham (Printers). Now retired. *Junior Carlton Club, Denham G.C.*

PETERS, Francis Raymond. Tu, 36³–40³.*

PETERS, Cdr. Gordon Hamilton, R.N., b. 1 Apr. 19, s. of K. K. Peters. SH, 32³–36³. Pembroke, Cambridge, M.A. Royal Navy, 40–58. Staff College, 49. Commander, 52. Retired (own request), 58. Man. Dir., Rhodesian Alloys Ltd., Gwelo, Rhodesia. *United Service & Royal Aero; Bulawayo; Ruwa Country.*

PETERS, Rudolph Verel, M.B., D.P.H., b. 7 Sept. 18, elder s. of Sir R. A. Peters. Tu, 32³–37³. Gonville & Caius, Cambridge, M.B., M.A., D.P.H. ⋊ R.A.M.C., 44–46. Capt. Medical Officer of Health of the St. Lawrence & Ottawa Valleys. Health practising at Cornwall, Ont., Canada. Brother, F. R. Peters.

PETERSON, Ian William Drummond, b. 26 Aug. 28, eldest s. of the late Sir M. D. Peterson, G.C.M.G. (OR W 04). SH, 41³–46². N/S. Army, 46–48. Trinity, Cambridge, M.A. H.M. Colonial Administrative Service, Kenya, 52–56; Zambia, 56–64 (District Commissioner in last year). Registrar, Barnet College of Further Education since 65. *Corona Club.* Passed Inst. of Linguists, Associate Stage Examination—French, Oral, 68. Brother, R. M. Peterson.

PETERSON, Richard Maurice. SH, 43²–47².*

PETTIGREW, Andrew Hislop. SH, 36²–40¹. Son, Andrew Hamish Hewitt, SH, 70³–.*

PETTIGREW, Campbell Manners MacLeod, b. 15 Jan. 20, elder s. of the late Sir A. H. Pettigrew, D.L., J.P. SH, 33³–38¹. Magdalen, Oxford, B.A. ⋊ Queen's Own Royal Glasgow Yeomanry, R.A., 40–44. King's Own Yorkshire L.I., 44–46. Italy. Wounded. Capt. Fruit Grower. Chrmn., Elpaco (Pty.) Ltd. Dir., Elgin Fruitpackers Co-operative Ltd. *Jockey Club of South Africa; S. African Turf Club; Weskin Province C.C.; City Club, Cape Town.* Brother, A. H. Pettigrew.

PETTIT, Cecil Stone, b. 20 May 03, s. of the late C. E. Pettit. SH, 17²–21². Magdalene, Cambridge, M.A. Unilever in Argentina, Sales Director, 29. Chrmn., 33. In India, Man. Dir., 40. Chrmn., 47. In Belgium, Chrmn., 53–63. ⋊ R.I.N.V.R., 42–45. Hon. Lt. Officer of the Order of the Crown, Belgium, 56. Officer of the Order of Leopold, 63. Sons, J. K. H. Pettit & 178.

PETTIT, John Kenneth Humphrey, b. 14 Sept. 29, eldest s. of C. S. Pettit (OR SH 17). SH, 44³–48². Magdalene, Cambridge. N/S. 60th Rifles. 2nd Lt. Dunlop Ltd. *Royal Thames Y.C., Bembridge Sailing Club.* Brother, 178. Son, Timothy John, SH, 72³–.

PHARAZYN, Charles Martin. St, 36³–40².*

PHAYRE, Col. Robert Desmond Hensley, R.A., b. 1 Oct. 15, s. of Lt.-Col. R. B. Phayre, M.C., F.L.S. SH, 29¹–33³; S. VIII, 31–32 (Capt.). R.M.A., Woolwich. Army Staff College & Royal Naval Staff College, French École Supérieure de Guerre. Senior Officer's War Course. Commissioned as 2nd Lt., R.A., 35. Promoted Col., General Staff, 63. Retired List, Oct., 70. ✕ Served in India, Burma and in War Office, London. Later in Palestine, 47–48. Dispatches. Cyprus, 56. Asst. Mil. Attaché, Helsinki, 49–50. Athens, 51–53. Mil. Attaché, Tehran, 57–60. Defence Mil. & Air Attaché, Amman, 63–66. Sec. of the Staff, H.Q. Allied Forces Central Europe (N.A.T.O.), 67–70. R. Central Asian Socy. Iranian Order. Son, 2492.

PHELPS, Norman Bayles, b. 27 Apr. 05, s. of the late L. Phelps. B, 18³–22². Man. Dir., Arthur Phelps & Co. Ltd., Lace Mnfrs., Nottingham. ✕ R.A., 39–45. Major. Retired.

PHILIP, Norman Littlejohn. Tu, 39³–44².*

PHILLIPS, Colin McNair. T, 41³–44¹.*

PHILLIPS, David Charles Serille, b. 26 June 27, elder s. of F. S. Phillips. W, 41³–45²; Scholar. Exhibitioner of Magdalene, Cambridge, M.A. Preparatory Schoolmaster. Headmaster of Nevill Holt, Market Harborough. *M.C.C., I.A.P.S.* Son, Simon Frederick Serille, W, 69³–72².

PHILLIPS, Frank Ryder. K, 28²–33¹.*

PHILLIPS, Sir (John) Raymond, M.C., Q.C., b. 20 Nov. 15, 2nd surviving s. of the late D. R. Phillips. K, 29³–33³. Balliol, Oxford, B.C.L., M.A. Bar, Gray's Inn, 39. Q.C., 68. Judge of the High Court, 71. Knighted, 71. ✕ 3rd Medium Regt., R.A. Dispatches. M.C. Major. *Oxford & Cambridge, Cardiff & County.* Sons, 2988 & Richard Anthony Rupert, K, 68³–.

PHILLIPS, Kenneth McNair, b. 24 Dec. 98, 3rd s. of the late J. A. Phillips. T, 12³–17²; Scholar; XXII, 16; Head of House. ✕ 3rd Bn. Royal Northumberland Fusiliers, att. 5th Durham Light Infantry. Wounded & P.O.W., 18. Lt. Schoolmaster, 19–23. Trainee Accountant, 24–29. Director & Secretary, Lennon Bros. Ltd., Rugby, 29–67. Retired, 67. Son, C. McN. Phillips.

PHILLIPS, Louis Patrick Charles. Tu, 02²–04¹.*

PHILLIPS, Thomas Brian Warrington, M.R.C.S., L.R.C.P., b. 5 Aug. 16, s. of W. Phillips. K, 30¹–34²; S. VIII, 32–34. Emmanuel, Cambridge, M.A. St. Thomas' Hospital, London, M.R.C.S., L.R.C.P. ✕ Indian Medical Service, 41–46 (Specialist in Pathology). General Medical Practice since 46. *Ski Club of Gt. Britain.*

PHILLIPS, Thomas James. K, 30³–36¹.*

PHYSICK, Frank David, b. 12 July 15, eldest s. of F. S. Physick. SF, 29²–34¹; H. XI. Corpus Christi, Oxford, M.A. Golf Blue, 37 & 38. Bar, Inner Temple. Colonial Administrative Service, Nigeria, 38–47. ✕ R.W.A.F.F. (Capt., Nigeria Regiment), 39–43. A.D.C. to Governor of Nigeria, 46. Chrmn. & Joint Man. Dir., Searcy Tansley & Co. Ltd., since 62. *Vincent's, Oxford; Oxford & Cambridge Golfing Society; R. & A. G.C.* President, O.R. Socy., 70–72. Governing Committee of Rugby Clubs since 50. Capt. of *Worplesdon G.C.,* 69.

PICKARD, Aveling Jocelyn. C, 35³–40².*

PICKARD, Thomas Arthur, b. 14 Oct. 17, s. of the late A. G. Pickard. B, 31³–36¹; Levée; Head of House; XXII. Exhibitioner of Hertford, Oxford, M.A. ✕ 40–46. Major. Instructor of Gunnery, School of A.A. Artillery, Pembrokeshire. Asst. Master, Liverpool College, 46–70. 46–70. Second Master, 70.

PICKIN, Col. Joseph, T.D., b. 18 June 01, eldest s. of the late J. Pickin. SH, 15³–19². Emmanuel, Cambridge, B.A., C.Eng., M.I.Mech.E. Positions with various firms in Machine Tool Industry, 24–39 and 45–63. Service in T.A. and T.A.R.O., 24–58, retiring with rank of Colonel. T.D. Brother, J. E. Pickin.

PICKIN, John Edmondson, b. 2 Aug. 05, 2nd s. of the late J. Pickin. SH, 19²–24¹; XV, 22–23; R. VIII, 24; G. VIII, 23; Cadet Officer. Emmanuel, Cambridge, M.A. ✕ R.A.F.V.R., Technical Branch (Armaments), 41–45. F/Lt. Asst. Master at Ampleforth College, York. Brother, J. Pickin.

PIERSON, Lt.-Col. Hugh Timothy, b. 15 Aug. 17, s. of the late H. K. Pierson. Tu, 31²–36²; Levée; Head of House. Woolwich Polytechnic. Royal Military College of Science. Engineering, 36–42. ✄ Northamptonshire Yeomanry, R.A.C., 42–44. 8th King's Royal Irish Hussars, 44. Brig., 68. *Cavalry Club*. Vice-President, *Ski Club of Gt. Britain*.

PIERSON, Michael Kirshaw, b. 27 Dec. 22, s. of R. K. Pierson, C.B.E. Tu, 36³–40³. Clare, Cambridge, M.A. Imperial College, London (Post-Grad. Course). D.I.C. ✄ R.A.F. F.O. Production Controller, British Aircraft Corporation, Weybridge, Surrey.

PIERSSENÉ, Andrew Stephen David, b. 17 Mar. 29, eldest s. of the late Sir S. H. Pierssené. M, 43³–48¹. Exhibitioner of Worcester, Oxford, M.A. Head, Cambridge University Mission, 55–60. Warden, Oxford-Kilburn Club & Secretary, Oxford Boys' Club Trust, 60–63. Field Officer, Norfolk Youth Service, 64–72. Freelance since 72. British Trust for Ornithology. Society for Bibliography of Natural History. Chrmn., Youth Committee of Council for Nature. Brother, J. A. R. Pierssené.

PIERSSENÉ, The Rev. Jeremy Antony Rupert, b. 24 June 31, 2nd s. of the late Sir S. H. Pierssené. M, 45²–50²; Levée; Head of House; XI, 50; Stovin Exhibition. Corpus Christi, Cambridge, M.A. Ridley Hall. Ordained Deacon, 58; Priest, 59. Curate, Christ Church, Cockfosters, 58–61. Scripture Union Staff Worker, 61–69. Chaplain, Rugby School, since 69. Brother, A. S. D. Pierssené.

PILKINGTON, Edward Cecil Arnold, b. 1 Nov. 07, s. of the late A. C. Pilkington. Tu, 21³–26²; XV, 25; XXII. New College, Oxford, M.A. O.U. Athletics Relay Team, 29. Asst. Master & Head of Modern Studies at Merchant Taylors' School, Northwood. ✄ R.A.F., 41–45. F/Lt. Retired. *Vincent's & Achilles Clubs*. Author of "The Economic Problem in Outline".

PILKINGTON, The Rev. John Rowan, b. 15 Mar. 32, s. of the Rt. Hon. Lord Pilkington. M, 45³–50²; R. VIII. Magdalene, Cambridge, M.A. Ordained (C. of E.), 59. Rector of Newhaven.

PILKINGTON, Major Richard William, b. 3 Oct. 01, eldest s. of the late Major E. S. Pilkington. C, 15³–19³. R.M.C., Sandhurst. Gazetted to the 9th Lancers, 22. Lt., 24. A.D.C. to C-in-C., India (Lord Birdwood), 30. ✄ Combined Ops., 40–45. Army of Occupation, Germany, 45–47. Major. Retired, 47. *Travellers' Club*.

PILKINGTON, Roger Windle, Ph.D., b. 17 Jan. 15, 3rd s. of R. A. Pilkington. W, 28³–33¹. Freiburg Univ. Magdalene, Cambridge, M.A., Ph.D. Author. Numerous publications. Brother, The Rt. Hon. Lord Pilkington. Son, 1233.

PILKINGTON, The Rt. Hon. Lord (William Henry), b. 19 Apr. 05, eldest s. of R. A. Pilkington. C, 19²–23². Magdalene, Cambridge, B.A. Glass Manufacturer. President, F.B.I., 53–55. Council of European Industrial Feds., 54–57. Chrmn., Pilkington Brothers Ltd., since 49. President, British Plastics Federation, and British Shippers Council. Chancellor, University of Loughborough. Hon. LL.D., Manchester, 59; Liverpool, 63. Kt., 53. Life Peer, 68. D.L. *Oxford & Cambridge Club*. Brother, R. W. Pilkington. Son, J. R. Pilkington.

PILLMAN, Joseph Robert, T.D. SF, 28³–33². Sons, 2844 & Rowland Henry Meirion, SH, 67¹–70³.

PIM, Michael Robert Gerald. SH, 43¹–45².*

PINNELL, Henry Anthony. W, 27²–31³.*

PIPER, David James Michael. W, 43³–47².*

PITT, Lt.-Col. Richard Jacomb, M.B.E. St, 35³–38³. Sons, 2084, 2558 & 2859.*

PITT, Col. Robert Brindley, C.B.E., M.C., T.D., D.L., b. 18 Apr. 88, s. of the late W. Pitt. St, 02²–07¹. Scholar of Clare, Cambridge, B.A. ✄ 1st Wessex Field Co., R.E. (T.). Lt.-Col., M.C. Order of the Redeemer, Greece. Dispatches thrice. M.I.Mech.E., M.I.C.E. (Retired). Man. Dir. of Stothert & Pitt Ltd. (Retired.) C.B.E. (Mil.), T.D., D.L., J.P. Sons, R. J., S. W. & W. R. Pitt.

PITT, Simon Walter, b. 6 Apr. 24, 2nd s. of Col. R. B. Pitt, C.B.E. (OR St 02). St & W, 38¹–42². Brothers, R. J. & W. R. Pitt. Son, 2559.

PITT, William Robert, b. 23 Dec. 26, 3rd s. of Col. R. B. Pitt, C.B.E. (OR St 02). St & K, 40²–44². Clare, Cambridge (R.A.F. Short Course). Engineer. Brothers R. J. & S. W. Pitt.

PITTS, John Elliott, M.B., B.Chir., b. 27 Jun. 21, younger s. of the late R. E. Pitts. Tu, 34³–39². Gonville & Caius, Cambridge, M.B., B.Chir. Wartime Golf Blue. Middlesex Hospital. London Univ. Hockey Team. General Medical Practitioner. *Hawks Club, Oxford & Cambridge Golfing Socy., O.R. Golfing Socy.* (Capt., 72–73). Brother, R. M. Pitts.

PITTS, Robert MacLaren, M.R.C.S., L.R.C.P., b. 23 Sept. 17, eldest s. of the late R. E. Pitts. Tu, 31³–35². Middlesex Hospital, M.R.C.S., L.R.C.P. House Surgeon, Orthopaedic Dept. ✗ R.N.V.R., 43–46. Surg.-Lt. Gynaecological Registrar, Southend-on-Sea General Hospital, 46. Medical Practice (General), Diss, Norfolk, from 47. Brother, J. E. Pitts.

PLACE, Peter John Milner. B, 43³–47².*

PLACE, Ullin Thomas, b. 24 Oct. 24, eldest s. of the late T. Place. B, 38³–42³. ✗ Friends Ambulance Unit. Scholar of Corpus Christi, Oxford, M.A. Diploma in Anthropology (Oxford), 50. D.Litt. (Adelaide), 72. Univ. Lecturer in Psychology, 51–54 & 67–69. Clinical Psychologist, N.H.S., 60–66. Lecturer in Philosophy, Dept. of Philosophy, Univ. of Leeds since 70. British Psychological Society. Associate, Royal Archaeological Institute.

PLATTS, Alfred William, b. 20 Mar. 09, s. of the late A. Platts. St, 22³–27². University College, Oxford, M.A. Solicitor, 34. ✗ R.N., 41–46. Lt. On Leeds Local Board, Royal Exchange Assurance, 6 yrs. Retired, 69. Son, 2560.

PLUMB, Charles Theodore, b. 4 Dec. 05, s. of Rt. Rev. C. E. Plumb, D.D. SH, 19³–24²; Levée; Head of House. Brasenose, Oxford, B.A. Some years in Civil Service. Author of "Walking in the Grampians", "Paradise Rejected". Poet & Painter. *Authors' Club.*

PLUMPTRE, John Huntingdon, b. 25 Jan. 10, s. of H. W. Plumptre. K, 23³–28²; Rackets Pair, 25–28 (Capt.). Hertford, Oxford & Birmingham Joint Diploma in Coal Mining. F.I.Min.E. National Coal Board. Divisional Manager, Kent. Deputy Director-General, Planning Headquarters. *Junior Carlton.* Sons, 2466 & Paul Huntingdon, K, 68³–.

POGSON-SMITH, John Edward, b. 15 Dec. 94, s. of the late W. G. Pogson-Smith. M, 09³–13²; Cap, 13; XXII, 13. One yr. at Trinity, Oxford, prior to 1st war.

✗ 2nd P.S. Bn. Royal Fusiliers, 8th Bn. Ox. & Bucks. Light Infantry. Lt. Dispatches. ✗ Retired with rank of Capt. Stockbroker (Retired).

POLITZER, Herbert Edwin. Tu, 98³–01³.*

POLLOCK, Kelvin Alexander, A.C.A., b. 22 Oct. 29, s. of K. C. Pollock. M, 43³–47². F.C.A. Partner in Tribe Clarke Darton & Pollock, Rochester, Kent. *M.C.C., R.A.C.*

POLLOK-MORRIS, James Allan, b. 31 Jan. 24, s. of A. G. Pollok-Morris. Sh, 37³–42². ✗ R.N.V.R. Lt. Peterhouse, Cambridge, M.A. Overseas Civil Service, Nigeria. Imperial Chemical Industries— Marketing Work.

POMEROY, Arthur John Cinnamond, b. 20 May 07, eldest s. of the late F. K. Pomeroy. SH, 21¹–23². Pupil, Shipbuilding & Naval Architecture, Harland & Wolff Ltd., Belfast. Student of Naval Architecture, Belfast College of Technology, 23–30. Harland & Wolff B.C.T. Diploma. Member, American Society of Naval Architects & Marine Engineers. Harland & Wolff, Liverpool, 30–34. I.C.I. Ltd., Northwich, 34–39. ✗ R.N., 39–46. Cdr. Dispatches thrice. I.C.I. Ltd., 46–49. H.M. Treasury, 49–50. West Indies, 50–52. Canadian Govt., Dept. of Defence Prodn., 52–69. R. Canadian Mint since 69. *Naval & Military Club.* Brother, J. F. B. Pomeroy.

POMEROY, Jocelyn Francis Brian, b. 24 Mar. 12, younger s. of the late F. K. Pomeroy. SF, 26¹–29¹. ✗ R.A.F.V.R. F/Lt. Man. Dir., Smith St. Aubyn & Co. Ltd., London, 57–72. Retired. Bank Director. Brother, A. J. C. Pomeroy.

PONCIA, Major Peter John Richard, b. 17 Aug. 29, s. of the late J. Poncia. B, 43²–46²; XI, 46. Army, South Wales Borderers, 49–69. Fund-raising Consultant, Hooker Craigmyle & Co. Ltd., since 69. *Free Foresters C.C., United Hunt Club.*

POOL, William Eden. T, 42³–47².*

POOLE, Alexander Geoffrey Bruce, M.B., Ch.B., b. 12 Sept. 25, younger s. of the late Major-General L. T. Poole, C.B., D.S.O., M.C. W, 39²–42². University of Edinburgh, M.B., Ch.B. Rugby Football Blue, 45–46. M.R.C.G.P., M.R.C.S., D.A. N/S. R.A.M.C., 48–50. General Medical Practice, Kelso.

POOLE, Lt.-Col. Arthur Eric Croker. C, 14^2–18^1. Son, 469 .*

POOLE, Geoffrey Sandford, b. 29 Oct. 01, 3rd s. of the late W. S. Poole. St, 15^3–18^2. Pembroke, Cambridge, M.A. Retired. Capt., 14th/20th King's Hussars.

POOLE, Giles Anthony St. George. St, 45^1–45^3.*

POOLE, John Sanderson, D.S.O., O.B.E., M.C. St, 10^3–14^2.*

POOLE, Thomas Hugh Ruscombe, T.D., b. 11 July 32, s. of the late Lt.-Col. G. S. Poole, D.S.O. (OR SH 97). St, 46^2–50^2. N/S. 5th Royal Inniskilling Dragoon Guards. Korea, 51–52. 2nd Lt. Territorial Service with North Somerset Yeomanry, 52–67. Major. T.D. Solicitor. Under-Sheriff of Somerset since 60. Fellow of Woodard Corpn. Chairman of Church of England Men's Society, Diocese of Bath & Wells. Law Society. Somerset Law Society. *Somerset County Club.*

POOLEY, John Michael Bright, M.R.C.S., L.R.C.P., b. 3 Feb. 17, eldest s. of the late J. S. Pooley. Sh, 30^3–34^1. Trinity, Cambridge, B.A., M.R.C.S., L.R.C.P., D.A., F.F.A.R.C.S. ✕ R.A.M.C. Capt. Wounded, 45. Consulting Anaesthetist, Veenendaal, Holland. R.S.M.

POPE, Brig. Philip William Gladstone, D.S.O., M.C. K, 26^3–31^2.*

POPKISS, Richard Barclay, b. 6 Oct. 02, s. of the late R. Popkiss. B, 16^3–21^2; Jex-Blake Exhibition. Trinity, Oxford, M.A. Solicitor, 28. ✕ Royal Berkshire Regt., 40–45. Major. Dispatches. Partner, Bischoff & Co., London, 37–73. Consultant, 73. *United Oxford & Cambridge University Club.*

PORTER, Arthur Digby, M.B., Ch.B., b. 27 June 97, younger s. of the late T. S. Porter. SH, 11^2–15^2. Pembroke, Cambridge. Burney Yeo Scholar, 18. M.A., M.D. King's College Hospital, London, F.R.C.P. Medical Consultant (Retired).

PORTER, David Latham, b. 30 Mar. 31, 2nd s. of T. L. Porter. M, 44^3–48^3. N/S. R.E. École Hotelière, Lausanne, Switzerland. Member of Hotel and Catering Institute. Man. Dir. for four Holiday Centres and Motel Inn Company.

PORTER, Lt.-Col. James Douglas, O.B.E., D.L., b. 26 Nov. 91, s. of the late J. Porter. SH, 05^3–10^2. St. John's, Oxford, M.A. ✕ 6th Bn. Royal Welch Fusiliers. Staff Capt. 158th Infantry Bde. D.A.A.G., 21st Corps & Northern Force. Major, O.B.E. Order of the Nile. Dispatches thrice. Bar, Inner Temple, 17. Disbarred at own request, 20. Solicitor, Commissioner of Oaths & Notary Public. Clerk to the Justices, Conway, Llandudno and Nant Conway Divisions, 40 yrs. Clerk to Commissioners of Taxes, Conway/Colwyn Bay Divisions, 40 yrs. Partner in Porter & Co., Solicitors, Conway, since 22. D.L., County of Caernarvon.

PORTER, John Latham. M, 41^2–45^2.*

PORTER, Lt.-Col. Robert Miles Mac-Nish, O.B.E. Assumed surname of McNish Porter. C, 28^3–31^3.*

PORTER, Walter Stanley, T.D., F.R.S.A., b. 28 Sept. 09, s. of the late W. Porter. T, 23^1–28^2; Exhibitioner. Gonville & Caius, Cambridge, M.A. ✕ Major, T.A. General List. T.D. Schoolmaster. Asst., Trent College, Felsted School and Radley College, 33–55. Headmaster, Framlingham College, Suffolk, 55–71. F.R.S.A., 64. Retired, 71.

POTTER, Francis Malcolm. SH, 45^3–50^2.*

POTTER, Major Richard James Keith. Tu, 96^3–00^1.*

POTTS, Timothy Cyril, D.Phil., b. 23 Aug. 29, s. of the late R. Potts. B, 43^2–47^2. University of Liverpool, School of Architecture. Ushaw College, Durham (Philosophy). Oscott College, Sutton Coldfield (Theology). St. Benet's Hall & Balliol, Oxford (Exhibitioner, 57–62), M.A., D.Phil. Asst. Lecturer in Philosophy, The University of Leeds, 62–63. Lecturer since 63.

POULSOM, Edward Douglas, b. 19 July 02, younger s. of the late F. A. J. Poulsom (OR M 83). M, 16^3–20^1. Retired. Farmer. Son, 1142.

POULTON, Edward MacLean, D.M., M.R.C.P., D.P.H. C, 27^2–31^2. Sons, 1943 & 2921.*

POULTON, Eustace Christopher, M.B., B.Chir., b. 23 Aug. 18, 3rd s. of the late Dr. E. P. Poulton (OR B 97). B, 32^2–37^2. Levée; Head of House; Jex-Blake Exhibition. Exhibitioner of Trinity Hall, Cambridge. Guy's Hospital, M.B., B.Chir. (Cantab.). Research Fellow, Harvard University, 53–54. Medical Research Council, Applied Psychology Unit since 47. Asst. Director since 58. Member, Experimental Psychology Society. Fellow, British Psychological Society. Publications: "Environment and Human Efficiency", "Tracking Skill and Manual Control". Brothers, E. M. & R. W. Poulton.

POULTON, Ronald William, b. 7 May 17, 2nd s. of the late Dr E. P. Poulton (OR B 97). SH, 30^3–35^2; Scholar; H. XI, 34–35. Scholar of Trinity Hall, Cambridge, M.A. ✕ R. Corps of Signals, 39–46. Capt. F.C.A. Chartered Accountant in London Professional Firm. Brothers, E. M. & E. C. Poulton. Son, 2493.

POUNTNEY, Cyril Graham, b. 12 Jan. 06, s. of the late Dr. W. E. Pountney. W. 20^1–23^3. Faraday House Electrical Engineering College, London. Diploma. Associate Member, Electrical Engineers. ✕ Fleet Air Arm, 39–46. Lt.-Cdr. R.N.V.R. Electrical & Mechanical Engineering. Retired. *All England Lawn Tennis & Croquet Club.*

POWELL, Edward Oliver Prince. T, 24^3–28^3.*

POWELL, John Astell, b. 14 Mar. 22, 2nd s. of the late Rt. Rev. G. E. Powell (OR K 97). K, 35^3–40^2. University College, Oxford, B.A. ✕ R.A.F., 42–46. Sgt. General Secretary, The John Lewis Partnership, London.

POWELL, Laurence, M.C. W, 02^3–07^2.*

POWELL, Thomas Charles Michael. K, 32^2–37^2.*

POWELL-BRETT, Col. Francis Bernard, b. 16 Sept. 16, eldest s. of the late B. Powell-Brett. C, 30^2–34^2; XV, 32, 33. Gazetted to Royal Artillery, 36. ✕ R.A., 39–45. Capt. Major, 49. p.s.c. Son, 1214.

POWER, Vice-Admiral Sir Arthur (Mackenzie), K.B.E., b. 18 June 21, 2nd s. of the late Admiral of the Fleet, Sir A. J. Power, G.C.B., G.B.E., C.V.O. Tu, 35^1–38^2. Joined R.N., 38. ✕ Commissioned, 41. Lt. R.N. M.B.E., 53. Cdr., 53. Vice-Admiral—still serving. Flag Officer, First Flotilla. As from Mar., 73, Flag Officer, Plymouth, K.B.E. 74. *United Services Club.* Brothers, J. D. & M. G. Power.

POWER, Major Edward George Hugh, O.B.E., b. 23 July 87, eldest s. of the late E. J. Power (OR W 73). W, 01^3–05^3. R.M.C., Sandhurst. Gazetted to the Gloucestershire Regt., 08. ✕ 2nd Bn. Gloucestershire Regt., commanding Machine Gun School. Major. Brevet Major, 16. Croix de Guerre. Dispatches thrice. Retired, 23. O.B.E. ✕ Air-Raid Precautions Officer, Norfolk County, 38–45. *Royal Norfolk & Suffolk Y.C., Norfolk Broads Y.C.*

POWER, Major Edward William Alec, b. 5 Sept. 24, eldest s. of the late Lt.-Col. F. T. Power, M.B.E. (OR W 06). Tu, 38^3–42^3; Cap; Cadet Officer. ✕ Enlisted in the Rifle Brigade, 43. Emergency Commission, 44. Gazetted to Regular Commission in the Royal Norfolk Regt., 45. Served with 2nd Gurkha Rifles, N.W. Frontier, India, 45–46. Capt. Staff College, Camberley, 56. United States Staff College, 60. Retired from Army, 66. Sales Officer, Hartmann Fibre Ltd. Brother, J. T. Power. Son, 2565.

POWER, Gerald Christopher. B, 46^3–51^2.*

POWER, Col. Herbert Raphe, C.B.E., M.C. W, 09^2–13^3.*

POWER, Lt.-Col. John David, b. 28 Oct. 19, eldest s. of the late Admiral of the Fleet, Sir A. J. Power, G.C.B., G.B.E., C.V.O. Tu, 33^2–37^3. R.M.A., Woolwich. Gazetted to Royal Artillery, 39. ✕ 39–45. Dispatches. Wounded twice. Capt. Parachutist. p.s.c. Colonel at N.A.T.O., Brussels—still serving. *Army & Navy Club, Royal Artillery Y.C.* Brothers, A. M. & M. G. Power.

POWER, John Thornburn. Tu, 43^2–46^3.*

POWER, Michael George, b. 2 Apr. 24, 3rd s. of the late Admiral of the Fleet, Sir A. J. Power, G.C.B., G.B.E., C.V.O. Tu, 37^3–42^1; Levée; Head of House; XV, 41. Corpus Christi, Cambridge. ✕ The Rifle Brigade, 42–47. Italy, Germany & Palestine. Capt. Wounded. Colonial Service, Kenya, Malaya, 47–63. Home Civil Service since 63. At present Director of Resources, Naval Weapons Dept., Ministry of Defence. *Royal Commonwealth Society.* Brothers, J. D. & A. M. Power.

POWER, Nigel Raphe, b. 18 May 25, elder (twin) s. of Col. H. R. Power, C.B.E., M.C. (OR W 09). W, 38^3–43^2; Levée;

Head of House; XV, 42. Oriel, Oxford (Army Short Course), 43–44. ✕ Royal Artillery, 44–47 (U.K., India). Scholar of Jesus, Cambridge, B.A. British Foreign Service, 49–54. British Petroleum Co. Ltd., since 54. Brother, R. H. G. Power.

POWER, Richard Herbert Guy, b. 18 May 25, younger (twin) s. of Col. H. R. Power, C.B.E., M.C. (OR W 09). W, 38³–43²; XV, 42. ✕ R.N.V.R., 44–47. S/Lt. Exhibitioner of Worcester, Oxford, M.A., A.C.I.S. Barrister. Courtaulds Ltd., Coventry. Brother, N. R. Power.

POWNALL, Henry Charles, LL.B., Q.C., b. 25 Feb. 27, elder s. of the late J. C. G. Pownall, C.B. (OR St 04). St & K, 40³–44³. Served R.N., 45–58. Palestine, 45–48. Clasp. Trinity, Cambridge, M.A., LL.B. Bar, Inner Temple, 54. Fourth Junior Prosecuting Counsel to the Crown at the Central Criminal Court, 64; Third Junior, 64; Second Junior, 69; First Junior, 69. Fourth Senior since 71. A Recorder since 72. Member of Committee of Management of the National Benevolent Institution since 64. Member of the Committee of the Orders & Medals Research Society, 61–71; President since 71. *United Oxford & Cambridge University, Hurlingham.* Brother, J. L. Pownall. Son, Nicholas Charles Deverell, St, 73²–.

POWNALL, Col. John Lionel, O.B.E., b. 10 May 29, younger s. of the late J. C. G. Pownall, C.B. (OR St 04). K & St, 43¹–47². R.M.A., Sandhurst. Gazetted to 16th/5th Lancers, 49. Served in Egypt, North Africa, Germany & Hong Kong. Staff College, 60. Joint Services Staff College, 68. Commanded 16th/5th The Queen's Royal Lancers, 69–71. O.B.E., 72. Promoted Col., 73. *Cavalry Club.* Brother, H. C. Pownall.

POYSER, Eric Stanley, J.P., F.C.A., b. 22 May 24, s. of E. S. Poyser. B, 37³–42²; Scholar; Levée. Scholar of Trinity Hall, Cambridge, M.A. ✕ R.N.V.R., 43–46. Lt. (Ex. Sp.) F.C.A., J.P. Man. Dir., E. S. Poyser & Sons Ltd. *Nottinghamshire Club.*

PREST, Edward Charles, D.F.C., b. 11 May 20, younger s. of G. S. Prest. SF, 34¹–38². R.M.A., Woolwich. Gazetted to Royal Artillery, 39. ✕ 39–46. D.F.C. Capt. Since 46 with Slag Reduction Co. Ltd. (now Chrmn. & Man. Dir.). F.C.I.S. *Army & Navy Club, Seaview Y.C., St. Stephens Club, Royal Ashdown Forest G.C.* Son, 1906.

PRESTON, David Christopher, b. 21 Oct. 18, 2nd s. of I. K. Preston (OR C 98). C, 32²–37². Oriel, Oxford, M.A. ✕ Green Howards. Lt. Taken prisoner near Arras, 40. Solicitor, 48. Partner, Preston & Redman, Solicitors, Bournemouth.

PRESTON, Francis Richard Walter. M, 27²–31³. Son, 1291.*

PRESTON, Frank Matthew. K, 94³–97¹.*

PRESTON, Ivor Kerrison, b. 21 May 84, s. of the late D. W. Preston. C, 98³–02². ✕ 28th Bn. London Regt., R.G.A. 2nd Lt. Family Solicitor, Bournemouth, 09–49. Writer on Blake. Gave Blake Library to City of Westminster. *Authors' Club, Arts Theatre.* Son, D. C. Preston.

PRESTON, Sir Kenneth Huson, b. 19 May 01, eldest s. of the late Sir W. R. Preston. M, 15²–19¹; XV, 16–18 (Capt.); Athletics Cup, 18–19. Trinity, Oxford. Chrmn., Platt Brothers & Co. (Holdings) Ltd. & J. Stone & Co. (Holdings) Ltd. Director, Midland Bank Ltd. Retired all executive duties. Kt, 59. *Royal Yacht Squadron, Royal Thames Y.C.* Brother, F. R. W. Preston. Son, 422. Grandson, Giles Kenneth Huson, M, 73²–.

PRICE, David William Tudor (see Tudor Price, David William).

PRICE, Group-Capt. Derek, b. 2 Aug. 08, 2nd s. of the late S. M. Price. B, 22²–26². Emmanuel, Cambridge, M.A. Apprentice, Aircraft Industry & R.A.F. Reserve, 28–33. R.A.F. from 33. ✕ R.A.F. Wing-Cdr. Retired with rank of Group-Capt., 62. M.I.Mech.E., F.R.Ae.S. Civil Defence Officer (Water Industry), 64–69. *Naval & Military Club.*

PRICE, Michael Wheatley, B.M., B.Ch. (see Wheatley Price, M.).

PRIDEAUX, John Kenneth Reginald, b. 22 Nov. 16, elder s. of the late W. R. B. Prideaux. M, 30²–34³. St. John's, Cambridge, B.A. Student Surveyor, 38–39. ✕ R.A.F.V.R., 39–40. Farming from 40–62. Law & Commerce Lecturer at Cornwall Technical College since 62. N.F.U. *Royal Fowey & Mylor Yacht Clubs.*

PRIDHAM, Michael James, b. 18 Apr. 29, s. of Lt.-Col. J. E. Pridham. K, 43¹–47¹. N/S. Army, 47–49. Staff Controller, The Hong Kong and Shanghai Banking Corporation, Hong Kong. *The Hong Kong Club, Hong Kong G.C.*

PRIDMORE, Charles Atton. T, 26³–31². Sons, 819 & 1110.*

PRIDMORE, William Henry, b. 17 Aug. 10, 2nd s. of the late W. H. Pridmore (OR T 85). T, 24²–29²; Scholar; Levée; Head of House; Exhibitioner. Queen's, Oxford, B.A. Indian Service between 33 & 48, ranged from Asst. Magistrate to District Magistrate, including 2 yrs. as Civil & Sessions Judge, mostly in the United Provinces. Held several educational posts, including 5 yrs. at Westminster School, before resuming legal career. Judge of H.M. Courts in the Persian Gulf, 63–67. Registrar of the Foreign Compensation Commission since 68. Brother, C. A. Pridmore.

PRIMROSE, Sir John Ure, Bt., b. 15 Apr. 08, eldest s. of the late Sir W. L. Primrose, Bt. Tu, 22¹–26²; Cap. R.M.C., Sandhurst. Gazetted to Q.O. Cameron Highlanders, 28. Retired, 33. Planter in Argentine, being Mayor of his locality for 14 yrs. Served with Intelligence Service in U.K. during the war. Administrator for plantation of the Tornquist Bank in Buenos Aires. Hon. Rep. of the British Embassy. St. Andrew's Scottish Society in the Argentine. Succeeded father as Baronet.

PRINGLE, Arthur Michael, b. 11 Feb. 14, 2nd s. of Dr. J. Pringle. C, 28¹–32². ✕ R.A.S.C. Dispatches. T.D. & Clasp. Major. Company Director, 54–61. Now Farmer.

PRINS, Vivian George. W, 33³–38².*

PRIOR-WANDESFORDE, Major Ferdinand Charles Richard, D.S.O., b. 23 Oct. 97, 2nd s. of the late R. H. Prior-Wandesforde, D.L. W, 11³–14²; S. VIII, 13–14. ✕ 76th Bde., R.F.A., 16–19. Major. D.S.O. Dispatches. Christ's, Cambridge, B.A. Resigned Commission, 22. Farmer. Retired. *Royal Irish Automobile Club, Dublin.* Brother, R. C. Prior-Wandesforde.

PRIOR-WANDESFORDE, Richard Cambridge, b. 24 Jan. 02, 3rd s. of the late R. H. Prior-Wandesforde, D.L. W, 16¹–19³. Trinity, Cambridge, B.A. Orange-growing and farming in E. Transvaal, S. Africa, 23–34. ✕ Intell. Corps, 40–45. Capt. Dispatches. Studied coal mining and business. Joined Board of Private Mining Co. in Ireland and became Man. Dir. One-time M.F.H. of local hunt. Brother, F. C. R. Prior-Wandesforde.

PROCTOR, William John Westley, b. 20 June 09, s. of W. H. W. Proctor. B, 22³–27³; Cap; Gym. VIII, Studied Accountancy, afterwards training as Engineering Apprentice & joined Follsain-Wycliffe Foundries Ltd., in 37. Sales Dir. from 49. M.I.B.F., A.M.I.Q., M.I.C.T. *Devonshire Club, Coventry G.C.*

PROUDMAN, Richard Hamilton. C, 45³–48².*

PUGH, Bryan Butler, M.C., b. 10 Feb. 21, eldest s. of Professor Sir W. J. Pugh, O.B.E., D.Sc., F.R.S. SH, 35¹–39²; R. VIII, 39. Exhibitioner of Trinity, Cambridge, M.A., LL.B. Half Blue Squash, 40. ✕ 3rd Bn. Welsh Guards, N. Africa & Italy. Wounded twice. M.C., 44. Solicitor, 49. With Grundy, Kershaw, Farrar & Co., of Manchester till 58. Commercial Director, Hardman & Holden Ltd., 59–63. Director, Hill Samuel & Co. Ltd. since 67. Director, Joseph Holt Ltd., Brewers, Manchester & Bridgewater Estates Ltd., Worsley. *St. James's Club, Manchester; Manchester Tennis & Racquet Club.* Brothers, D. R. & C. M. Pugh.

PUGH, Colin Moore, b. 4 Apr. 26, 4th s. of Professor Sir W. J. Pugh, O.B.E., D.Sc., F.R.S. SH, 39³–44². ✕ R.N., 44–47. A.B. Exhibition to Pembroke, Cambridge, M.A. Headmaster of Moor Allerton School since 62. *E.S.U.* Brothers, B. B. & D. R. Pugh. Son, David Henry, SH, 69³–.

PUGH, Cyril James Cunliffe (see Cunliffe, James).

PUGH, David Robert, M.B., B.Chir. SH, 37¹–41².*

PUGH, Michael Arthur. B, 19²–21³.*

PUMFRETT, David George, b. Feb. 09, elder s. of the late L. R. H. Pumfrett. Tu, 22³–26¹. Stock Exchange, 27–34. Laundry Proprietor, 34–69. Winchester R.D. Councillor since 53. Hampshire County Councillor since 56. *Royal Commonwealth Society, Hampshire Club.* Brother, H. L. Pumfrett.

PUMFRETT, Harold Lesley. Tu, 24¹–27³.*

PUREFOY, Geoffrey Purefoy, b. 3 Mar. 29, elder s. of Rev. B. Purefoy. SF, 42³–47¹. École Hotelière de la Société Swisse des

Hotelièrs, 49–51. N/S. 1st Bn. R. Innis-killing Fusiliers. 2nd Lt. Farmer.

PUTNAM, Penry Edward, b. 24 Aug. 29, s. of S. A. Putnam. SH, 43²–48². Trinity, Cambridge, M.A., M.B., B.Chir. The London Hospital, L.R.C.P., M.R.C.S., M.R.C.G.P. General Practitioner, Upper Hutt, New Zealand.

PYBUS, Michael Anthony. SF, 28³–32¹. Son, 1988.*

PYMAN, Michael Francis, b. 22 Apr. 25, 2nd s. of the late F. C. Pyman. Sh, 39¹–43²; XV, 42; XI, 41–43; H. XI. Trinity Hall, Cambridge, B.A. Ship repairing. Man. Dir., The Mercantile Dry Dock Co. Ltd.

Q

QUAYLE, John Anthony, C.B.E., b. 7 Sept. 13, s. of A. Quayle. Tu, 27²–30³. Actor and Play Producer. ✕ R.A., 39–45. Major. Dispatches. Dir., Shakespeare Memorial Theatre, Stratford-upon-Avon, from 49. C.B.E., 52. *Garrick Club.*

R

RACKOWE, Robin Beril Edward Bul-kyn, b. 28 Jan. 33, eldest s. of the late Major S. S. A. B. Rackowe. M, 46³–51²; XV, 50; H. XI, 50–51. N/S. R.N.V.R., 51–53. Midshipman. Pembroke, Cambridge. Antarctic Whaling & Fishmeal Production in Peru. (Chrmn., Salvesen, Leith), 56–66. Fishmeal Production in Peru, latterly as Gen. Man. (Gloucester Peruvian S.A.), 66–73. Brothers, 555 & 1434.

RADICE, Roger Neill Ponsonby, b. 24 July 25, 3rd s. of F. R. Radice, C.B.E. SH, 39³–43². Music Scholar. ✕ R.A.F., 3½ years. Brasenose, Oxford, B.A. Diploma in Music. Music Master, Bryanston, 51–53. Embley Park, 53–57. Brummana High School (Lebanon), 57–58. Brandeston Hall (Framlingham Junior Sch.), 59–73. Boundary Oak Prep. School. Senior Master, Arnold Lodge Prep. School, Leamington Spa. *Bath Club, E.S.U., M.C.C.*

RAE, David Alastair. Sh, 40³–44². Son, David Mitchell, Sh, 72³–.*

RAE-SCOTT, Philip Samuel, b. 30 May 21, s. of the late M. W. Rae-Scott. W, 35¹–39¹. Worcester, Oxford, M.A. ✕ R.A., 41–44. Bar, Inner Temple, 47. Barrister.

RAILTON, Reid Antony, b. 24 June 95, 2nd s. of the late C. W. Railton. B, 09³–12². Manchester Univ. B.Sc., F.I.Mech.E. Consulting Engineer. R.Ae.C. Pilot's Certificate, 15. Apprenticed to Leyland Motors. Man. Dir., Arab Motors Ltd. Motor Car Designer, incl. John Cobb's "Railton", which held World Speed Record for 25 years. As Engineering Consultant, responsible for Sir Malcolm Campbell's "Blue Bird II", & John Cobb's "Crusader".

RAISMAN, John Michael, b. 12 Feb. 29, eldest s. of Sir J. Raisman, G.C.M.G., G.C.I.E., K.C.S.I. SH, 44²–47²; Levée; Head of House. Scholar of Queen's, Oxford, B.A. President, Shell Sekiyu K.K., Tokyo, Japan.

RAIT KERR, Brig. Edmund, M.C., b. 5 Oct. 95, 4th s. of the late S. Rait-Kerr, D.L. B, 09²–13³. R.M.A., Woolwich. ✕ R.E., 14. G.S.O.3, War Office. Capt. M.C. (Bar). Wounded. Dispatches. Served in France in both wars. Retired as Brigadier, 49. American Bronze Star. *Army & Navy Club, M.C.C.*

RAMSAY, William Reid. C, 26³–31¹.*

RATCLIFF, Charles Milner, b. 15 Mar. 00, s. of the late W. M. Ratcliff (OR C 82). C, 14²–18². Trinity, Cambridge, M.A. Chrmn. & Man. Dir., Ratner Safe Co. Ltd. & Griffiths Safe Co. Ltd. Dir., Brine Veneer Mills. Retired. Current, Chrmn., Saw Mills Co. Ltd. *United Oxford & Cambridge University Club.*

RATHBONE, Robert Kennedy, b. 17 Oct. 10, s. of the late M. P. Rathbone (OR St 80). K, 24¹–28³; XV, 28. Trinity, Cambridge, B.A. Stockbroker, Liverpool Stock Exchange, since 36. ✕ 10 Bn. The King's Own Royal Regt., 40–42. 107 Regt., R.A.C. (King's Own), 43–45. Capt. *Royal Liverpool G.C. Hittite Golfing Society.*

RATHBONE, Sebastian David, b. 6 Jan. 32, 2nd s. of the late R. R. Rathbone. W, 45²-50¹; Scholar; Cap; H. XI, 49-50 (Capt.). Scholar of Trinity, Cambridge, B.A. N/S. Royal Signals, 50-51. 2nd Lt. Chartered Accountant (place 2nd with Hons. in finals). Rathbone Bros. & Co., Liverpool, Financial Consultant. *Oriental Club.*

RAVENSCROFT, Anthony. Sh, 43³-47².*

RAWDON SMITH, Alexander Francis, Ph.D. W, 26¹-30². Brother, 373.*

RAWSON, John Edwy. T, 38²-42².*

RAWSTRON, Edward Stanley Pickup. K, 29³-32¹.*

RAWSTRON, George Ormrod. K, 22¹-25².*

RAYMOND, Piers, b. 12 Mar. 21, s. of H. Raymond, O.B.E., M.C. SF, 34³-39²; Exhibitioner. New College, Oxford. ✕ Indian Army, 40-45. Publishing thereafter. Now Man. Dir. of J. M. Dent & Sons, Publishers. Sons, 2317, 2693 & Giles Antony, SF, 67³-71³.

RAYNOR, Henry Peter, b. 6 May 25, s. of K. Raynor. Sh, 38³-43²; Scholar; Levée; Head of House; XXII; Open Athletics Cup, 43; Exhibitioner. Scholar of St. John's, Oxford, M.A. ✕ R.A.F., 43-47. F.O. Lecturer at Peterhouse, Cambridge, 61-63. Farmer & Company Dir. in Rhodesia. Past Chrmn., Nat. Dairy Cttee. of the Rhodesia National Farmers' Union.

READ, The Rev. Francis Richard Waller, b. 2 July 18, s. of the late E. O. Read. T, 31²-37²; Stovin Exhibition. Exhibitioner of Selwyn, Cambridge, M.A. Ridley Hall, Cambridge. Ordained Deacon, 42; Priest, 43 (Bris.). Curate of Stratton St. Margaret, Swindon, 42; Walcot, Bath, 46-47; Holy Trinity, Cheltenham, 47-49; Rector of Kingswood, Wotton-under-Edge, 49-60 (also p.-in-c. Charfield, 55-57); Vicar of Holy Trinity, St. Philip's, Bristol, 60-66 (also p.-in-c. of St. Philip & St. Jacob, 60-64); Vicar of St. Budeaux, Plymouth, since 66.

RECKITT, David Francis, b. 31 Mar. 29, eldest s. of the late G. L. Reckitt. SF, 43¹-47¹. St. Martin's School of Art. M.I.P.A., Dip. Cam. Director, Wasey-Quadrant Ltd. (Advertising Agency). T.D. (Parachute Regt.).

REDDIE, Major Robert Alexander, M.B.E., M.C. Tu, 97³-00².*

REDDISH, Sir Halford Walter Lupton. T, 12²-14³.*

REDPATH, John Watson. St, 15¹-17².*

REECE, Sir Gerald, K.C.M.G., C.B.E.,b. 10 Jan. 97, s. of the late E. M. Reece. SH, 10³-14². ✕ 16th Bn. Sherwood Foresters, 15-18. Lt. Wounded thrice. Solicitor, 21. Kenya Administration, 25-48. H.B.M.'s Consul for S. Ethiopia, 34. Governor & Commander-in-Chief, Somaliland Protectorate, 48-53. Now, Chrmn. of Managers, Loaningdale Approved School. Hon. Sheriff in E. Lothian. D.L., East Lothian. Chrmn., Howard League for Penal Reform, Scotland. K.C.M.G., C.B.E. Councillor, *Royal Commonwealth Society*, Scotland.

REED, Barry St. George Austin, M.C., b. 5 May 31, eldest s. of D. A. Reed. St, 45²-49². ✕ Korea. The Middlesex Regt. (D.C.O.). M.C., 51. Man. Dir., Austin Reed Group Ltd. *Bath Club, M.C.C., Hurlingham, Royal Society of Arts.*

REES, Lt.-Col. John Gordon, D.S.O. K, 98¹-00³.*

REES, Richard Leventon. T, 19³-22¹.*

REEVE, Markway Roope, b. 24 Feb. 10, 2nd s. of the late R. R. Reeve. M, 23³-27². Oriel, Oxford, B.A. Bar, Lincoln's Inn, 35. Dir., Tube Investments Ltd.; Westminster Bank; Mercantile Credit Ltd. Now retired. *Boodle's.* Son, 930.

REEVES, Benjamin Anthony. Tu, 26¹-30².*

REEVES, Frederick Ernest. W, 36³-42².*

REFORD, Lewis Eric, b. 12 Dec. 00, 2nd s. of the late R. W. Reford. K, 14³-17³. R.M.C., Kingston, Canada. McGill Univ., Montreal, B.A. New College, Oxford, B.A. President of the Shipping Federation of Canada, 43-45. Councillor, City of Montreal, 44-54. Joined The Robert Reford Co. Ltd., Shipping Cargo Agents, in 24, becoming Vice-Pres., 29, Pres., 46, and Chrmn. of the Board, 72. Pres. of the Mount Royal Rice Mills, both firm's Head Offices in Montreal, Canada. *Mount Royal, University & Mount Stephen Clubs, Montreal.*

REGAN, John Michael Ernest, b. 19 May 32, s. of the late M. A. Regan. Sh, 46^1–50^2. Corpus Christi, Oxford, M.A. Man. Dir., Architectural Press Ltd. Publishers of "The Architectural Review" & "The Architects' Journal". *United Oxford & Cambridge University Club.*

REID, David Gildart, M.B.E., b. 31 Dec. 11, 3rd s. of the late N. Reid (OR St 87). St, 25^3–30^3; Levée; Head of House. ✗ R. Signals, 39–45. Forty years with John Bedford & Sons Ltd. Lion Works, Sheffield (Steel & Tool Manufacturers). (At present Joint Man. Dir.) The Cutlers Company, Sheffield. M.B.E. *Sheffield Club; East India, Sports and Public Schools Club.* Brother, N. Reid. Son, 1957.

REID, Edward John Carroll. SF, 26^3–30^3. Son, Ian Mark, SF, 67^3–72^2.*

REID, Kenneth Mason. SF, 34^1–38^3.*

REID, Leslie Hartley, b. 17 Nov. 95, elder s. of the late R. N. H. Reid. C, 09^3–14^1. ✗ R.F.A., Att. Trench Mortar Bty. Lt. Wounded. Toronto Univ., Canada, B.Sc.F. Univ. of London, B.A. Ontario Forestry Service, 22–28. Teaching, Stowe School, 43–56. Retired, 56. Author of "Cauldron Bubble", "The Sociology of Nature". Contributor to various papers. C.P.R.E., local secretary. Conservation Society. Toilhard Assoc.

REID, Major Nevile, b. 1 Mar. 06, eldest s. of the late N. Reid (OR St 87). St, 19^3–24^2. Brasenose, Oxford, B.A. College Athletics Colours. ✗ Served London Scottish, 29–45. Major. T.D. G.S.O.2 (Training), Eastern Command. Wine Trade—Partner in Reid, Pye & Campbell, 29–66. Chrmn., Port Wine Trade Assoc. & others. Now retired. Vice-Chrmn., Ross & Cromarty Conservative Assoc. Chrmn., Ross & Cromarty War Blinded Cttee. Brother, D. G. Reid. Son, 130.

REID-KAY, Alan Drummond, B. 19 July 26, younger s. of the late Sir J. Reid-Kay. Tu, 39^3–44^2; XV, 43. Peterhouse, Cambridge (Naval Short Course). ✗ R.N. Stores Asst., 44–47. C.A., 42. Financial Dir., Ross Chemical & Service Co. Ltd., Falkirk. *Prestwick G.C.*

REILLY, Edwin Alan. St, 23^3–27^2.*

RELTON, Bernard Cleather. C, 06^1–10^3.*

REMER, The Rev. Geoffrey. K, 94^1–97^1.*

RENDALL, Peter Godfrey, b. 25 Apr. 09, s. of the late G. A. H. Rendall (OR W 81). SF, 22^3–27^2; Scholar. Scholar of Corpus Christi, Oxford, M.A. ✗ R.A.F. Intell., 43–46. F/Lt. Asst. Master, Housemaster, Felsted, 31 & 35–43. Asst. Master, Upper Canada College, 34–35. Second Master, St. Bees School, 46–48. Headmaster, Achimota School, Ghana. Asst. Master, Lancing Coll. Now Headmaster, Bembridge School, I.O.W. Coronation Medal. *Royal Commonwealth Society.*

RENDEL, Major Alexander Meadows, M.B.E., b. 14 May 10, s. of the late H. Rendel. C, 24^3–29^2; Levée; Head of House; XI, 29; H. XI, 29. Scholar of Corpus Christi, Oxford. Solicitor with Parker Garrett, 34–38. ✗ R.A. & in Force 133 (Crete), 39–45. Major. M.B.E. Second Secretary, H.M. Embassy, Athens, 46–49. "The Times" Diplomatic Correspondent since 49. *Travellers' Club.* Son, 1166.

RENDEL, James Meadows, b. 16 May 15, s. of the late Col. R. M. Rendel. C, 29^2–32^3; S. VIII; Cadet Pair. University College, London, B.Sc., Ph.D. Chief of C.S.I.R.O. Division of Animal Genetics, Sydney, N.S.W. New York Academy of Science. Fellow, Australian Academy.

RENDEL, William Vincent, b. 21 Jan. 98, 3rd & youngest s. of the late J. M. Rendel. C, 11^3–16^3; Head of House; Head of School. ✗ General List. G.S.O.3, G.H.Q., Archangel. Capt. M.B.E. Order of St. Anne & St. Stanislas, Orange Nassau. Temp. Clerk, H.M. Treasury, 17. Solicitor, 28. Partner in Parker, Garrett & Co. *Reform Club.* Vice-Pres., Romney Sheep Breeders Society. Reduced to wheel chair by Lewisham train crash, 4 Dec. 57.

RENNOLDSON, Henry Francis, b. 5 Sept. 87, s. of the late J. H. Rennoldson. SH, 01^3–06^2. Trinity, Cambridge, B.A., LL.B. Solicitor, 12. Notary Public. Gazetted to the 4th Northumbrian Bde., R.F.A. (T.F.), 09. ✗ 63rd (R.N.) Div., R.F.A. 317th Bde., R.F.A. Capt. Wounded. Dispatches. R.F.A. (T.F.) Reserve, 22. Retired 71 from Legal Work. Chrmn., Sunderland & South Shields Water Co., Shields Commercial Building Society & South Shields Trustee Savings Bank. *Constitutional Club, St. James, S.W.1.*

REPARD, Hugo William Arbouin, b. 15 May 11, 2nd s. of the late W. J. Repard. M, 24^2–28^3. St. John's, Cambridge, B.A. Solicitor, 35. ✗ R.A., 39–45. Capt. Dispatches. The Legal Adviser, Rio Tinto-Zinc Corp. Ltd., London. The Law Society. Brother, J. D. L. Repard.

REPARD, Cdr. John David Latimer, R.N., O.B.E., D.S.C. M, 35^1–39^1.*

RETTIE, Cartmell John Alexander. St & W, 39^3–44^1.*

REYNELL, Antony Charles, b. 10 June 30, 3rd s. of Dr. W. R. Reynell, F.R.C.P. K, 43^3–49^1; Levée. Scholar of New College, Oxford, B.A. N/S. R. Tank Regt., 49–50. 2nd Lt. Head of Classics, Sedbergh School, 54–58. Head of Classics, Marlborough College, since 58. Brother, P. C. Reynell.

REYNELL, Peter Carew, D.M., F.R.C.P., b. 12 Sept. 17, eldest s. of the late Dr. W. R. Reynell, F.R.C.P. K, 31^2–35^2; XI, 35. Scholar of Balliol, Oxford, M.A., D.M., F.R.C.P. Lawn Tennis v. Cambridge, 41. ✕ R.A.M.C., 43–47. Capt. Rockefeller Fellow in Medicine, 52. Medical Tutor, Radcliffe Infirmary, Oxford, 53. Now Consultant Physician, Bradford Hospitals. Assoc. of Physicians of G.B. & I. Brother, A. C. Reynell.

REYNELL, Richard Harry Courtnay. SH, 43^3–47^2.*

REYNOLDS, Basil John. Sh, 40^3–45^2.*

REYNOLDS, Christopher Duffes. K, 39^2–41^3.*

RHODES, Anthony Richard Ewart, b. 24 Sept. 16, eldest s. of the late Col. G. E. Rhodes, C.B.E. St, 30^3–35^2; Cap; R. VIII, 34–35 (Capt.); Holder of Bigside Bags, 35. R.M.A., 35–37. Trinity, Cambridge, M.A. Asst. Prof., Geneva Univ., 52. Author of many books—Biography, Travel & Novels. Special Correspondent of the "Daily Telegraph" in Eastern Europe, 56–62; also there on behalf of Amnesty International & "Encounter Magazine", 61. Brother, J. D. E. Rhodes.

RHODES, John David Ewart, b. 1 Dec. 21, 2nd s. of the late Col. G. E. Rhodes, C.B.E. St, 35^3–39^3; XV, 39. Trinity, Cambridge, B.A. Owner of companies in Switzerland & Belgium. Live in Paris. *Travellers' Club, Paris; St. James' Club, London.* Brother, A. R. E. Rhodes.

RICARDO, Sir Harry (Ralph), LL.D., F.R.S., b. 26 Jan. 85, s. of the late H. R. Ricardo (OR K 69). W, 98^3–03^1. Trinity,

Cambridge, B.A. Consulting Engineer. Pres., Ricardo & Co. of Shoreham-on-Sea (retired). F.R.Ae.S., 26. F.R.S., 29. Hon. Mem., Netherlands Inst. of Engineers, 34. Mem., German Academy of Aviation, 38. Hon. Mem., American Soc. of Mechanical Engineers, 42. Pres., Inst. of Mechanical Engineers, 44–45. Knighted, 48. Hon. Degree, Turin Univ., 60. Hon. Fellow, Trinity, Cambridge, 67. Hon. D.Sc., Sussex Univ., 70. Many awards between 17 & 55, and Memorial Lectures given between 30 & 55. Author of "Memories & Machines—The Pattern of My Life" and "The High Speed Internal Combustion Engine". *United University & Athenæum Clubs.*

RICE, Lt.-Col. Charles Wilfrid Hammond, b. 26 Sept. 05, 2nd s. of the late Rev. W. A. Rice, M.A. C, 19^3–24^2; XV, 23; S. VIII, 22–23, Capt., 24. Commissioned 2nd Lt. R. Tank Corps, 29. ✕ 39–45. Lt.-Col. p.s.c., 41. Retired, 49.

RICHARDS, Chaud Irvine Whitmore, b. 3 Sept. 09, eldest s. of the late W. L. Richards (OR C 84). C, 23^2–28^2; XXII. Trinity, Oxford. Schoolmaster, 28–39 & 45–47. ✕ R.A. Lt.-Col. Dispatches twice. Market Gardener since 48. Son, 2742A.

RICHARDS, Geoffrey Charles. T, 35^1–39^2.*

RICHARDS, James Peel. SF, 17^1–21^1.*

RICHARDS, John Dermot. SH, 29^2–32^3.*

RICHARDS, Michael Rupert, b. 29 June 20, eldest s. of C. G. Richards. T, 34^1–38^1. Civil Engineer. ✕ R.E. attd. Indian Engineers. Capt. M.I.C.E., F.I.Mun.E., C.Eng. Engineer & Surveyor, Braintree & Bocking U.D.C., Essex, 60–67. Dep. Dir. of Technical Services, Rugby, 67–70. Borough Surveyor, Loughborough, 70–73.

RICHARDSON, Dudley Ernest Edgar. SF, 08^3–12^2.*

RICHARDSON, Edward Theodore Haughton. SF, 00^1–03^3.*

RICHARDSON, Geoffrey Nigel. SH, 38^2–41^3.*

RICHARDSON, Sir George Wigram, Bt., b. 12 Apr. 95, younger s. of the late Sir P. Wigham Richardson, Bt. (OR C 78). C, 09^1–12^2. ✕ 3rd Bn. Cheshire Regt.,

Capt. Wounded. Dispatches. Underwriting Member of Lloyd's from 20. Shipowner & Shipbuilder. Pres., Wigham Richardson & Bevingtons Ltd. & Dir. other Companies. Fellow of Institute of Insurance Brokers. Prime Warden of Shipwrights Company, 43. Royal Greek Maritime Gold Medal. Succeeded as 3rd Baronet, 73. *Carlton, Constitutional & City of London Clubs.*

RICHARDSON, Jocelyn Arthur St. Clair, b. 15 June 96, 3rd s. of the late Lt.-Col. A. J. Richardson. T, 11^3–14^3. At Rugby School. Housemaster & Tutor to 4 Tibetans, 14–15. ✕ 10th Bn. East Yorkshire Regt., 15–19. Lt. Wounded. Corpus Christi, Cambridge, B.A. Engineer, English Electric Co., 20–26. C.Eng., M.I.E.E. Westinghouse Elec. & Mfg. Co., U.S.A., 26–31, & with English Electric Co. Ltd., 31–62. Retired. *Gen. Electric Overseas Club, Mountain Club, Woodlands Health Club.* Tibet Society of U.K.

RICHARDSON, Leo Aylwin, b. 13 May 02, s. of the late H. L. S. Richardson, LL.D. B, 15^3–20^2. King's, Cambridge, M.A., M.B., B.Ch. St. Thomas's Hospital, M.R.C.S., L.R.C.P., F.R.C.S. Consulting Surgeon. Retired. Son, 978.

RICHARDSON, Michael Finch Wigham, b. 2 July 05, elder s. of the late G. B. Richardson (OR C 86). C, 19^3–23^3; Scholar. Gonville & Caius, Cambridge, M.A. Tanner. Underwriting Member of Lloyd's. Chrmn., Downtown Tanning Co. Ltd. Liveryman, Leathersellers Company. *Lansdowne & Farmers' Clubs.* Son, 1944.

RICHARDSON, Michael Ruskin, b. 17 Aug. 30, s. of B. V. Richardson. Tu, 43^2–49^2. Oriel, Oxford. In Theatre Design. Now B.B.C.

RICHARDSON, Philip Arthur, C.B.E., b. 16 Feb. 18, s. of the late A. G. Richardson. W, 31^3–36^2; Levée; Head of House; R. VIII, 36. Queens', Cambridge, M.A. Bar, Middle Temple, 39. Colonial Administrative Service (now Administrative Branch of H.M.O.C.S.), 40–72. Served in Nigeria, 40–47; Tonga, 47–50; Br. Solomon Is. Protectorate, 51–53; Colonial Office, 53–55; Nyasaland/Malawi, 55–72. Sec. for External Affairs, Malawi, 64–67. Chargé d'Affaires, Malawi Legation, S. Africa, 67–71. Retired, 72. C.B.E., 67. *Ski Club of Great Britain.* Son, 1785.

RICHARDSON, Philip Sewell. Tu, 31^3–35^2.*

RICHARDSON, Roger Hart, b. 13 Aug. 31, s. of J. Richardson, O.B.E. SH, 45^3–50^2; S. VIII, 49–50. N/S. R.N., 50–52, S/Lt. Served in R.N.R. till 71. R.D. Christ's, Cambridge, M.A. Man. Dir., Beaver & Tapley Ltd. (Furniture Manufacturers). Liveryman, Worshipful Company of Furniture Makers. *Island Sailing Club.*

RICKETT, Sir Denis (Hubert, Fletcher) K.C.M.G., C.B. Tu, 20^3–25^2.*

RICKWOOD, John Rendall Trezise. B, 40^1–44^2.*

RIDDOCK, Peter Anthony. Sh, 36^2–39^1.*

RIDEAL, Edmund John Killick. W, 34^3–39^2.*

RIDGE-JONES, Thomas. SH, 05^3–09^2.*

RIE, John Lewis, b. 24 Nov. 06, 2nd s. of the late P. Rie of France. C, 20^3–22^2. Pres. of Cresthill Industries Inc., Yonkers, N.Y. Pres. of Ets. Paul Rie, C.E.P. Thiers 63, France. Mother of Pearl Merchants. Brother, P. A. Rie.

RIE, Paul Alexander, b. 8 Sept 97, eldest s. of the late P. Rie of France. C, 11^3–14^2. Fencing, 14. ✕ American Ambulance Field Service. U.S.A. Ambulance Service. Sgt. 1st Class. Croix de Guerre. Importer of Mother of Pearl Shells. Retired. Presently Chrmn. of Chester County (Pennsylvania) Housing Authority. Brother, J. L. Rie.

RIGBY, Sir (Hugh) John (Macbeth), Bt., b. 1 Sept. 14, elder s. of the late Sir H. M. Rigby, Bt., K.C.V.O., F.R.C.S. K, 28^3–33^2; Scholar; Levée. Magdalene, Cambridge. M.A. Univ. Relay Team, 35. ✕ R.E. Major, D.A.D. in War Office, 42. Lt.-Col., A.Q.M.G. (Mov. & Tn.). H.Q., S.A.C.S.E.A., 44. Lt.-Col. R.C.T.(A.E.R.). Retired, 67. Dir., Exors of James Mills Ltd. (Steelworks). Succeeded father as 2nd Bt., 44. E.R.D. & 2 Clasps. Sons, 2054, 2215, 2380 & 2825.

RILEY, Peter. SF, 44^3–49^2.*

RILEY, Peter Lawrence Cole. M, 42^2–46^2.*

RILEY, Major William Pridmore, M.C., b. 21 Apr. 18, s. of W. L. Riley. K, 31^3–36^2; XV, 34–35; S. VI, 34–36. R.M.C., Sandhurst. Riding Blue. Gazetted to 4/7th Royal Dragoon Guards. ✕ M.C., 44. Major. Retired, 53. Farmer.

RINGROSE, Basil John, D.S.O., T.D., b. 15 July 04, s. of E. Ringrose, M.D., J.P. C, 18²–21²; Cap, 21. In the Nitrate Business. ✕ Notts. (Sherwood Foresters) Yeomanry, Cavalry & R. Armd. Corps, 39–45. Lt.-Col. D.S.O., T.D., Belgian Croix Militaire, 1st Class, Ethiopian Medal of St. George with Palm. Wounded. Merchant Banker, now retired.

RINGROSE, Thomas Leonard, M.B., B.Chir., D.M.R.T., b. 20 Sept. 27, s. of the late H. T. Ringrose, B.Sc. B, 41³–45². St. John's, Cambridge, M.A., M.B., B.Chir. Middlesex Hospital, London, D.M.R.T., D.A.C.R. Therapeutic Radiologist. Upstate Medical Centre, Syracuse, N.Y., U.S.A. British Institute of Radiology, American Medical Assoc.

RINTOUL, Charles Jeffrey Vere. C, 31³–36¹.*

RINTOUL, John Vere, O.B.E., b. 6 Oct. 12, 2nd s. of A. J. Rintoul. C, 26³–30². Brasenose, Oxford, B.A. Chartered Accountant, 37. ✕ Sudan Defence Force, 40–44. Dispatches. Sudan Civil Service, 39–55, finishing as Deputy Financial Sec. O.B.E. *Fly Fishers' Club.* Brothers, R. H. V. & C. J. V. Rintoul.

RINTOUL, Robert Humphrey Vere. C, 24³–29².*

RIPLEY, Oswald Harbord, M.C. M, 01³–05².*

RIPMAN, Hujohn Armstrong, F.R.C.S., F.R.C.O.G., b. 3 Jan. 18, s. of C. H. Ripman, M.D., M.R.C.P. SH, 31³–36²; XV, 35; R. VIII, 35–36; Crick. Winner, 36; Cadet Pair, 34; S. VIII, 35–36. Guy's Hospital, London. Treasurer's Gold Medal in Surgery. M.R.C.S., L.R.C.P., M.B., B.S. ✕ R.A.M.C., 42–46. Regtl. Med. Off., 2nd Bn. Irish Guards. Dispatches. Croix de Guerre (Fr.). M.R.C.O.G., F.R.C.S., F.R.C.O.G. Obstetric & Gynaecological Registrar, Guy's Hosp., 46–50; Consultant Obst. & Gyn., St. Alfege's Hosp., London, 50–52; Consultant Obst. & Gyn., Ipswich & E. Suffolk from 52. *M.C.C.* Royal Soc. Med. Sons, 1701, 2735, 2949 & James Jervis Hugo. SH, 72³–.

RIPMAN, Peter Hugo, M.C., b. 6 June 18, s. of the late H. A. Ripman. SH, 32²–37²; Scholar; Levée. Cadet Officer. Major Scholar, King's, Cambridge, B.A.

✕R.A., 40–46. Capt. M.C. Dispatches. Bar, Inner Temple, 47. *United Oxford & Cambridge University Club.*

RIPPON, Clive Langley, D.F.C. SH, 34³–39².*

RITCHIE, Major Edward Neish, b. 26 June 14, s. of the late A. L. Ritchie. SH, 28¹–31³. R.M.C., Sandhurst (Hockey XI). Gazetted to Suffolk Regt., 34. ✕ India, U.S.A., Egypt, Syria & Palestine. Major. p.s.c. Retired, 54. Dir., Export/Import Business, & Building Restoration Company. Now retired. Author of "The Winds of Grief" & "The Dodo's Nest".

RITCHIE, Lt.-Col. Sir James (Edward Thomson), Bt., T.D., eldest s. of the late Sir J. W. Ritchie, Bt., M.B.E. C, 16¹–19². Queen's, Oxford. London Stock Exchange, 27–35 & 45–46. Joined Inns of Court Regt., 36, commissioned, 38. ✕ Lt.-Col., 45. Command 44 (Home Counties) Div., 49. Retired, 53. Lt.-Col. T.D. (2 Clasps). Chrmn., M. W. Hardy & Co. Ltd. Dir., William Ritchie & Son (Textiles) Ltd. Retired. F.R.S.A., F.I.D. Master, Merchant Taylors Company, 63–64. Succeeded father as Bt., 37. *Army & Navy Club.*

RITCHIE, John Alexander, b. 7 Feb. 26, younger s. of the late R. J. H. Ritchie. SF, 39³–44¹. Durham University. Salesman to Export Manager. Now self-employed running firm known as "Unitables" Manufacturing Furniture. Brother, P. Ritchie.

RITCHIE, Peter, T.D., b. 18 Dec. 17, elder s. of the late R. J. H. Ritchie. C, 31³–34²; S. VIII, 32–34. King's College, Durham, B.Sc. ✕ R.E., 39–46. Solicitor, 49. Major, R.A. (T.A.). T.D. Company Sec., Darchem Ltd., Darlington. Brother, J. A. Ritchie. Sons, 2160 & 2694.

RITSON, Robert. SH, 98³–02¹.*

ROBERTS, Charles Collingwood, b. 6 July 00, elder s. of the late A. Roberts. SH, 14²–18². Queen's, Oxford, B.A. Formerly with John Swire & Sons Ltd. in the Far East & London. Dir., 52–68. Now retired. *City of London Club, Junior Carlton Club.* Sons, 478 & 1067.

ROBERTS, Denis Michael. C, 24²–27².*

ROBERTS, Sir Frank (Kenyon), G.C.M.G., G.C.V.O., b. 27 Oct. 07, s. of the late H. G. Roberts. B, 21³–26²;

Levée; Head of School; Head of House; XV, 25; XI, 25–26. Scholar of Trinity, Cambridge, M.A. H.M. Diplomatic Service, 30–68. Ambassador to Yugoslavia, 54–57; the Soviet Union, 60–62; the German Federal Republic, 63–68; & British Permanent Representative on the North Atlantic Council. Now Advisory Dir. of Unilever Ltd. Dir. of Dunlop Co. Ltd. & Adviser on International Affairs to Lloyd's of London. Pres. of the Atlantic Treaty Assoc., 69–73, & of the British Atlantic Cttee.; Chrmn. of the European Atlantic Group. Member of the Governing Board of the Atlantic Institute & of the Royal Institute of International Affairs. Pres. of the German Chamber of Commerce in the U.K. Chrmn. of the Governing Body of Bedales School, & of the East-West Relations Section of the Centre for Contemporary Studies at the Univ. of Sussex. Vice-Pres. of the G.B.-U.S.S.R. Society, & of the Anglo-German Assoc. Member of the Foreign & Commonwealth Secretary's Cttee. on British Overseas Representation, 68–69. G.C.M.G., 63; G.C.V.O., 65; Grand Cross German Order of Merit. Pres. O.R. Society, 74. *Brooks's Club & R.A.C.*

ROBERTS, George Rowland Lloyd. C, 31^2–35^2.*

ROBERTS, Col. James Ronald, O.B.E., M.C., b. 16 July 89, 2nd s. of the late D. T. Roberts. SF, 04^1–07^3; Scholar; Cap, 07; G. VIII, 06–07. R.M.A., Woolwich. Gazetted to the R.E., 09. India, 11. ✕ East Africa, 14–18. Indian State Rlys., 21–28. M.C. Dispatches twice. Major, 25. S.M.E., Chatham. R.T.C. Longmoor, 28–32. Singapore, 33–37. ✕ Recalled for Service, 39–43. Now retired. O.B.E.

ROBERTS, Norman Frederick Lloyd. C, 32^3–36^3.*

ROBERTS, Percival. T & W, 94^3–99^2.*

ROBERTS, Peter Patrick. T, 34^3–39^2.*

ROBERTS, Robert Thomas Francis Davies. Tu, 08^3–13^2.*

ROBERTS, Thomas Jones, b. 2 Sept. 24, s. of the late Sir W. Roberts, Kt., C.I.E., LL.D. (Wales). St & K, 38^2–42^2. Queens', Cambridge, M.A. British Columbia Univ. M.S.A. Apptd., 72, for 3-year term to Survival Service Commission of International Union for Conservation of Nature & Natural Resources. Man. Dir. own Cotton Ginning & Export Business, Roberts Cotton Associates Ltd., Pakistan. Author of "Mammals of Pakistan".

ROBERTS, William Antony Leslie, b. 15 Feb. 26, s. of Sir L. Roberts, C.B.E. B, 40^1–44^2; XV, 43; XXII. ✕ Grenadier Guards. Palestine, 44–48. Capt. Man. Dir., Manchester Liners Ltd. of Manchester. *St. James's Club, Manchester.* Son, Anthony Mark Leslie. B, 67^3–71^3.

ROBERTSHAW, William John. B, 46^3–51^2.*

ROBERTSON, Lt.-Col. Alan George, M.B.E., b. 27 Mar. 04, 2nd s. of the late W. B. Robertson. K, 18^1–22^1. Lloyd's Underwriter. Now retired. ✕ E. Lancashire Regt., 39–46. Lt.-Col. M.B.E. *Bath, Brooks's & City of London Clubs.*

ROBERTSON, David Bruce, L.D.S., b. 1 Feb. 32, s. of G. B. Robertson. T, 45^3–50^2. Birmingham Univ. L.D.S. Senior partner in general dental practice.

ROBERTSON, David Bruce. Sh, 41^3–45^2.*

ROBERTSON, David Lars Manwaring, b. 29 Jan. 17, 2nd s. of the late A. M. Robertson (OR B 96). B, 31^1–35^2; Cap, 34. University College, Oxford, B.A. ✕ Major, Welsh Guards, 39–45. Dispatches. With Charterhouse Finance Corp., 46. From 55, Dir. of Kleinwort Sons & Co., now Kleinwort Benson Ltd. Dir. other companies, incl. British Channel Tunnel Co., M.K. Electric Co. Ltd., Miles Druce Ltd., Provident Mutual Life Assur. Assoc. J.P. *Boodle's, M.C.C., Khandahar Ski Club.* Brother, S. M. Robertson.

ROBERTSON, Donald Russell. Tu, 21^3–24^1.*

ROBERTSON, David William. Tu, 18^1–21^2.*

ROBERTSON, Euan Macnab Lindsay, b. 19 June 23, 2nd s. of the late Col. W. A. Robertson, C.B.E., M.C., T.D., M.D. Sh, 37^1–41^2; XI, 40–41. ✕ R.A.F., 42–45. Navigator. Journalist.

ROBERTSON, Major Frank MacKenzie, M.C., b. 13 Mar. 14, 2nd s. of the late A. D. Robertson (OR C 98). Tu, 27^3–32^1. Gazetted to R.H.A., 34. ✕ Major. M.C. Wounded, 44. Brother, J. S. Robertson.

ROBERTSON, George Patrick, b. 11 July 29, 2nd s. of the late J. M. Robertson (OR C 87). SF, 42^3–47^3; Levée; Head of House. Scholar of Clare, Cambridge, B.A.

Housemaster of The King's School, Canterbury. Brother, J. D. Robertson.

ROBERTSON, Gordon Ross, b. 30 June 30, youngest s. of the late J. R. Robertson. Sh, 44²–48². Member of the Institute of Marketing. Advertisement & Marketing Dir., Thomson Regional Newspapers Ltd. *Woking G.C.*

ROBERTSON, James Cumming. C, 26²–31².*

ROBERTSON, James David, b. 13 Nov. 27, elder s. of the late J. M. Robertson (OR C 87). SF, 41³–46²; Scholar; Exhibitioner. Clare, Cambridge, B.A. Sandys Studentship in Classics, 49. Research Studentship, 51–52. N/S. Education Officer, R.A.F., 49–51. Management with W. D. & H. O. Wills from 52. Asst. Sec., Imperial Tobacco Co., 62–66. Now running own farm in Devon. Brother, G. P. Robertson.

ROBERTSON, Major James Sinclair, b. 16 Sept. 11, eldest s. of the late A. D. Robertson (OR C 98). Tu, 25²–29³. Peterhouse, Cambridge, M.A. Stockbroker. Gazetted R.A. (T.A.), 37. ✕ 110 Field Regt., R.A. (T.A.), 181 Field Regt., R.A. Major. Dispatches. Since war, Dairy Farmer. *Farmers' Club.* Brother, F. M. Robertson.

ROBERTSON, Robert Hugh Stannus, F.G.S., b. 17 June 11, s. of Sir R. Robertson, K.B.E., F.R.S. Tu, 25¹–28³. Gonville & Caius, Cambridge, M.A., F.G.S. Wiltshire Prize (Geology & Minerology), F.C.S., F.Eng.S., F.R.S.E. Consultant Mineralogist in Raw Material Development since 47. *Athenæum Club.*

ROBERTSON, Struan Manwaring, b. 5 Aug. 13, eldest s. of the late A. M. Robertson (OR B 96). B, 27³–32²; Levée; Head of House; Cap, XXII. University College, Oxford, B.A. British Metal Corp. Ltd., 37–39. ✕ 39–45. 17/21st Lancers & Intell. Corps. Major. Consolidated Tin Smelters Ltd. Asst. Man. Dir., 46–61. Dir., Sagit Trust Co. Ltd. & Assoc. Companies, 62–73. Master of the Mercers Company, 72–73. *Boodle's, M.C.C., Royal Institute of International Affairs, Australia Society.* Brother, D. L. M. Robertson.

ROBERTSON, William Moir, M.C., J.P., b. 24 July 19, elder s. of Col. W. A. Robertson, C.B.E., M.C., T.D., M.D. Sh, 33¹–37². Edinburgh Univ. Univ. XV,

39. ✕ The Seaforth Highlanders. Lt. M.C. Wounded. Textile Manufacturer, The Boase Spinning Co. Ltd., Dundee. J.P.

ROBINOW, Edmund, b. 29 Sept. 94, 3rd s. of the late M. E. Robinow. W, 08³–09³. ✕ 4th P. S. Bn. Royal Fusiliers. 4th Bn. Lancashire Fusiliers. Dunster Armoured Car Bde. Sgt. Wounded. F.C.A. from 23–70. Retired.

ROBINSON, Alfred Esmond, C.B.E., M.C., b. 1 May 98, s. of the late A. R. Robinson, J.P. SH, 12³–16²; XXII, 15. ✕ 29th Bty., R.F.A., 16–18. Lt. M.C. (Bar). Trinity, Oxford, M.A. Dir., British Oil & Cake Mills Ltd., 31. Chrmn. & Man. Dir., 59–63. Chrmn., Unilever Milling Group, 59–63. Chrmn., United Bristol Hospitals, 64–68. Master, Society of Merchant Venturers, 32–34. O.B.E. (Civil), 42. C.B.E. (Civil), 63. *Vincent's, M.C.C., Free Foresters, Oxford & Cambridge Golfing Society.*

ROBINSON, Andrew Moncrieff. C, 45³–47².*

ROBINSON, Christopher David. Sh, 46³–51².*

ROBINSON, David Mortimer. C, 39³–41².*

ROBINSON, Gerald, M.C. W, 09³–13¹.*

ROBINSON, The Rev. John Godfrey, b. 3 Oct. 27, eldest s. of G. Robinson, C.B.E., M.C. Sh, 41³–46²; Scholar; Levée; Cap, 45. Scholar of King's, Cambridge, M.A. N/S. Royal Armd. Corps., 49–51. Wells Theological College. Ordained Deacon, 53, Priest, 54. Served in Diocese of S. W. Tanganyika, 57–63. Now a member of a group ministry in Kingshurst & Castle Bromwich, Dio. of Birmingham.

ROBINSON, Col. John Peyton, O.B.E. Tu, 08¹–09².*

ROBINSON, Michael Finlay, B.Mus., D.Phil., b. 3 Mar. 33, elder s. of the Rev. A. G. Robinson. St, 46³–51²; Music Scholar; Levée. N/S. R.A., 51–53. 2nd Lt. Music Scholar, New College, Oxford, M.A., B.Mus., D.Phil. Lecturer in Music, Durham Univ., 61–65. Asst. Professor, 65–67, then Assoc. Prof. of Music, McGill Univ., Montreal, Canada, 67–70. Lecturer in Music, University College, Cardiff, from 70. Brother, 1059.

ROBINSON, Montague Lancelot Gaius, b. 28 Jan. 30, s. of C. G. Robinson. T, 43³–47³. R.M.A., Sandhurst. Gazetted to The Royal Welch Fusiliers, 49. Lt., 51; Capt., 55; Major, 62. Staff Officer at Ministry of Defence; in Army Public Relations from 74. *Nondescripts R.F.C. Nairobi, Kenya; London Rugby Union Referees Society.* Son, Martin Nicholas. SF, 72²–.

ROBINSON, Peter Bryan, b. 22 Oct. 31, eldest s. of Sir John Robinson. B, 45²–50². Manchester Univ. LL.B. Solicitor. Dir. of Frederic Robinson Ltd. Brewers of Unicorn Brewery, Stockport, Cheshire. Past Pres. of Macclesfield Junior Chamber of Commerce. F.R.H.S. On the Board of Management of Stockport & District Trustee Savings Bank. On Board of Governors of Sir Ralph Pendlebury Charity in Stockport.

ROBINSON, Patrick William, b. 23 July 27, eldest s. of L. B. Robinson. M, 41¹–45¹. Exhibitioner of Trinity Hall, Cambridge, B.A. N/S. R.A.F., 48–49. Pilot Offr. Employee of Rio Tinto Zinc Corp. & predecessor companies, 50–65. Dir., Rio Tinto Zinc Corp., 65–68. Dir., Kleinwort, Benson Ltd., 69–71. Chrmn., Herbert Morris Ltd. & assoc. companies since 69. *Boodle's; Lansdowne; Atheneum, Melbourne; University, & India House, N.Y.* Brothers, M. B. Robinson & 266, Son, Fletcher Freeland. SH, 67²–68¹.

ROBINSON, Richard John, b. 25 July 31, s. of F. J. Robinson. Tu, 44³–49²; XV, 48; H. XI, 49. N/S. R. Signals, 2nd Lt. (Contracted Polio while at Trieste.) Corpus Christi, Cambridge, M.A. F.C.A. With Associated Television Ltd., Pye Rentals Ltd. & C.B.S. Records. Now Vice-Pres. of European Manufacturing for C.B.S. International. Son, Timothy John Alan. Tu, 72³–.

ROBINSON, Lt.-Col. Robert Barnes, b. 13 May 12, eldest s. of H. Robinson, M.D., D.L., J.P. St, 26¹–29². R.M.A., Woolwich. Riding Prize. Gazetted to R.A., 32. ✕ Egypt & India, 39–45. T/Lt.-Col. p.s.c. Retired as Major (Hon. Lt.-Col.), 59. Self-employed since then as poultry producer. O. St. J. *Army & Navy Club, St. John Ambulance Bde., British Horse Soc., Royal Artillery Assoc.*

ROBINSON, Stanley, b. 22 Sept. 30, eldest s. of the late W. Robinson & Mrs. K. M. Tonkin. W, 44¹–49². Manchester Univ. LL.B. Solicitor of Supreme Court

of Judicature (Eng.); Barrister & Solicitor of Victoria, Australia. Senior Lecturer, Faculty of Law, Monash Univ., Clayton, Victoria. Author of "Principles of Drafting & Their Application to Conveyancing & Commercial Documents".

ROBINSON, Lt.-Col. William Moncrieff, b. 11 Feb. 91, s. of the late F. W. Robinson, M.D., F.R.C.S. C, 05³–10¹. Trinity, Oxford, B.A. ✕ 1st Bn. Sherwood Forresters, 15. Capt. Wounded thrice. Belgian Croix de Guerre. Attained rank of Lt.-Col. ✕ Worked for the Officers Association, 45–55. Retired. *Naval & Military Club.* Sons, D. M. & A. M. Robinson.

ROBSON, Christopher Brice. Tu, 42³–47¹.✳

ROBSON, David Cowen, b. 20 Aug. 29, elder s. of D. F. Robson. B, 43³–47²; XV, 46. N/S. R.A., 47–49. Solicitor, Notary Public & Commissioner for Oaths. Solicitor, Dir. & Sec., Walter Willson Ltd. The Incorporated Soc. of Provincial Notaries Public of England & Wales.

ROBSON, John Osborn, b. 6 June 94. eldest s. of the late J. A. Robson. Tu, 08³–11². ✕ London Scottish. 9th Bn. Gordon Highlanders. R.F.C. (Kite Balloon Observer). Lt. Wounded twice. Member of London Stock Exchange, 19–65. *Caledonian Club, R.A.F. Club.*

ROBSON, Piers Cowen, M.B., B.Chir., b. 1 July 32, 2nd s. of D. F. Robson. B, 46¹–50²; XV, 49. University College, Dundee. St. Andrews Univ. M.B., Ch.B., M.R.C.Psych., D.P.M. Consultant Psychiatrist, Newcastle Regional Hospital Board. The Soc. of Antiquaries of Newcastle-upon-Tyne.

ROBSON-SCOTT, Prof. William Douglas, Ph.D., b. 9 Aug. 01, 3rd s. of T. W. Robson-Scott. K, 15³–19². University College, Oxford, M.A. University Lecturer, Berlin, 33. Ph.D., Vienna, 38. Emeritus Prof. of German, Univ. of London. Hon. Dir., Institute of Germanic Studies, Univ. of London.

ROCHE, The Hon. John Fenwick Adair. C, 16³–21¹.✳

ROCHE, The Hon. Thomas Gabriel, Q.C., b. 11 May 09, 2nd s. of the late Lord Roche. C, 23²–27¹. Wadham, Oxford, B.A. Bar, Inner Temple, 32. ✕ R.A. (T.A.), 39–45, France. Dispatches. Lt.-Col. Q.C., 55. Recorder of Worcester, 59–71. Retired.

United Oxford & Cambridge Univ. Club.
Brother, J. F. A. Roche.

RODERICK, John Allan Buckley. K,
32^3–35^3.*

**RODGER, Patrick Campbell (The Rt.
Rev. The Lord Bishop of Manchester),**
b. 28 Nov. 20, younger s. of the late P. W.
Rodger. Sh, 34^3–39^2; Scholar; Levée;
Head of School, 38–39. Jex-Blake Exhi-
bition, 39. Scholar of Christ Church,
Oxford, M.A. ✕ R. Signals, 42–45. Lt.
Westcott House, Cambridge. Ordained
Deacon, 49; Priest, 50, Edinburgh. St.
John's, Edinburgh & Chaplain to Anglican
Students, 49–54. Student Christian Move-
ment, 55–58. Rector of St. Fillan, Kil-
macolm, 58–61. Exec. Sec. of Faith &
Order, World Council of Churches,
Geneva, 61–66. Vice Provost, then Provost
of St. Mary's Cathedral, Edinburgh, 66–
70. Bishop of Manchester since 70. *Royal
Commonwealth Society.*

RODGERS, Gerald Fleming, b. 22
Sept 17, s. of T. F. Rodgers. T, 31^1–
36^2; Levée. Cadet Officer, 35. Tom
Hughes Prize, 36. Queens', Cambridge,
M.A. ✕ Beds. & Herts. Regt., 39–46. Bde.
Major. H.M. Foreign Service, 47. Served
at Jedda, Cairo, Fayid, Peking, Paris &
Djakarta, & in the Foreign Office. Retired
as Counsellor (Economic), H.M. Embassy,
Paris, 67. Now teaching at the Rugby
High School for Girls. *R.A.C.*

RODOCANACHI, Ambrose John, b. 22
Oct 00, younger s. of the late J. M.
Rodocanachi. Tu, 14^2–17^3; Gym VIII, 16.
South-Eastern Agricultural College, Wye.
Obtained a Diploma. Farming, 23–67.
Presently retired. Sons, J. Rodocanachi &
369.

RODOCANACHI, Cdr. John, R.C.N., b.
10 June 30, eldest s. of A. J. Rodocanachi,
(OR Tu 14). Tu, 44^3–48^2. R.N.C., Dart-
mouth & Greenwich. Carleton Univ.,
Ottawa. Submarine Specialist. Com-
manded H.M.C. Submarines *Grilse* and
Ojibwa, & H.M.C.S. *Qu'Appelle* (DDE
264). Commander, 67. Dep. Chief of Staff
(Operations) to Maritime Commander,
Pacific. Canadian Forces Decoration.
Centennial Medal. Brother, 369.

ROE, Corrie Bernhard Castleman. Tu,
21^3–26^2.*

ROE, Robert Edward. M, 43^2–47^1.*

ROLANT-THOMAS, John David, b. 14
May 33, s. of Major E. C. Thomas. B,
46^3–51^2. Exhibitioner of Magdalen, Ox-
ford, M.A. N/S. The Royal Welch Fusi-
liers, 52. 2nd Lt. Bar, Middle Temple.
International Publishing Corp. Ltd.

ROLES, Francis Crosbie, M.R.C.P., b.
17 Nov. 01, s. of F. C. Roles. Tu, 15^3–
20^2; Scholar. Lees Knowles Exhibitioner,
Trinity, Cambridge, M.A., B.Chir. St.
Bartholomew's Hospital (Shuter Scholar-
ship, Baly Research Scholarship).
M.R.C.P. Retired. Emeritus Consulting
Physician. N.H.S. Hospital Service.

ROLLS, Major Ralph Gerald. M, 16^1–
19^3.*

ROME, George Harold Stiles (see
Maclachlan of Maclachlan, G. S. R.).

RONALD, Keith Montagu, T.D., b. 30
June 02, elder s. of the late B. G. Ronald.
C, 16^3–21^2; Cap, 20. University College,
Oxford. ✕ Westminster Dragoons (T.A.),
R.A.C., 30–45. Major. T.D. London
Woolbroker, 24, until retired, 63. Son, 832.

ROONEY, Maurice Granville Brook, b.
23 Feb. 21, s. of the late T. J. Rooney.
SH, 34^3–37^2. ✕ R.A.F. Sgt. Observer.
Rhodes Univ., Grahamstown, S.A. University of South Africa, M.A., Hons. B.A.
Asst. Sec., Economics & Marketing,
Ministry of Agriculture, Salisbury, Rhodesia. *Rhodesiana Society; Salisbury Repertory Players.*

ROPER, David Harry, F.C.A., b. 20
July 32, s. of the late L. W. Roper, F.C.A.
K, 46^2–51^2. F.C.A., A.C.I.S., F.I.Arb.,
A.T.I.I., M.Inst.A.M., M.B.I.M. Partner,
Leyland & Co.; Director, Albatros Engin-
eering Ltd. & Associates; L.L. & H.
(Agencies) Ltd. & Associates, & others.
Senior Trustee, The Herbert H. Bowland
Charitable Settlement & others. Apptd.
Approved Auditor of H.M. Treasury, 68.
Chrmn., Southport Branch, Liverpool &
District Soc. of Chartered Accountants
Member, The Adolph C. Meyer Expedi-
tion to the Sierra Nevada (U.S.), 67.
*Athenæum, Liverpool; Doncaster Literary &
Social Society; Royal Economic Society.*

ROSE, Alan Heath. Tu, 19^2–22^1.*

ROSE, Edward Michael, C.M.G., b. 18
Oct. 13, s. of F. A. Rose. B, 27^3–32^1.
Exhibitioner of St. John's, Cambridge;
Scholar, 35. B.A. H.M. Foreign Service,
37. Served in Oslo, Algiers, Copenhagen,

Berlin (Deputy to British Commandant, 52–55), Bonn (Minister, 60–63), Congo (Kinshasa), Ambassador, 63–65, Dep. Sec. to Cabinet, 67. Dir. & Sec., East Africa & Mauritius Association since 69. C.M.G., 55.

ROSE, Eliot Joseph Benn, b. 7 June 09, s. of E. A. Rose, M, 22³–27²; Scholar. New College, Oxford. ✕ R.A.F., Wing Cdr. U.S.A. Legion of Merit. Publication, "Colour & Citizenship". Chrmn., Penguin Books Ltd. & Editorial Dir., Westminster Press. Literary Editor, "The Observer", 48–51. Dir., International Press Institute, Zürich, 51–62. Dir., Survey of Race Relations in Britain, 63–69. *Garrick, & Bath Clubs.*

ROSENBERG, Ernest Stephen. K, 43³–48³.*

ROSLING, Hugh Patrick, b. 13 Jan. 10, 2nd s. of the late Sir E. Rosling. Tu, 23³–28³. Trinity, Oxford, B.A. Chartered Accountant, 34. F.C.A. ✕ R.A. (T.A.), 39–45. Major. Company Director, Public Companies. Retired, 69. *City University Club.* Son, 791.

ROSS, David James MacBean. W, 40²–44¹.*

ROSS, Ian Dalrymple, b. 13 Oct. 19, s. of S. K. Ross. Sh, 33³–37². Trinity Hall, Cambridge, B.A. Edinburgh Univ., LL.B. ✕ Cameronians (Scottish Rifles), 39–45. Major. Dispatches. Writer to the Signet, 48. N.P. Vice-Consul for Greece. Solicitor. Partner in Thomson & Baxter, W.S. *New Club, Edinburgh; Special Forces Club, London.*

ROSS, Wallace Michael, B.Mus., F.R.C.O., b. 19 Sept. 20, s. of the late J. W. Ross. W, 33³–38²; Scholar; Music Cup, 38. Royal College of Music, M.A., B.Mus. Organ Scholar of Balliol, Oxford. ✕ R.A., 45–47. Sgt. Articled Pupil to Organist, Chichester Cathedral, 47–48. F.R.C.O., C.H.M. Diploma. Dir. of Music, Pocklington School, 48–50. Alderman Newton's Boys' School, Leicester, 51–54 & King's School, Gloucester (also Asst. Cathedral Organist), 54–58. Master of the Music, Derby Cathedral, and Music Master, Sturgess Boys' School, Derby since 58. Conductor, Derby Bach Choir, Derby Cathedral Orchestra & Derby Cathedral Brass Ensemble since 59. Founder/Sec., Derby Schools R.F.U., 59–69. Schools Liaison Officer, Derby R.F.C., 69–72. Pres., Derby Schools R.F.U. since 71. 3 Counties (Notts., Lincs., Derby) R.F.U. Qualified Coach, 60.

ROSS-HUME, Major Percy Gilbert, M.C. SF, 02³–06².*

ROSS STEWART, David Andrew (formerly Stewart, D. A. R.), b. 30 Nov. 30, s. of the late Major-General W. Ross Stewart. Sh, 44³–48³; Scholar. Exhibitioner of Clare, Cambridge, B.A. Alex. Cowan & Sons Ltd., Trainee & Manager, 52–65. Spicers (Stationery) Ltd., Gen. Man. & Dir., 65–68. John Bartholomew & Son Ltd., Man. Dir. since 68. *New Club, Edinburgh.* Board Member, Scottish Milk Marketing Board.

ROTHERHAM, Gerald Alexander. SH, 13²–17².*

ROTTENBURG, Paul Anthony. B, 33³–38³. Son, Francis Trevor. B, 69³–.*

ROUGHEAD, William Nicol, b. 19 Sept. 05, 3rd s. of the late W. Roughead, W.S. W, 19²–24¹; Levée; Head of House; XV, 21–23 (Capt.); XXII, 21; Bantam Boxing, 20. Oriel, Oxford, B.A.; Rugby Blue, 24–26. Scotland XV, 27–28. ✕ R.N., 39–45. Leading Hand. Literary Agent, now retired. *Wilton Fly-Fishers' Club.*

ROUGHTON, Cyril Henry Heude, b. 9 Apr. 17, s. of N. J. Roughton, C.S.I., C.I.E., I.C.S. K, 31³–35². Corpus Christi, Cambridge, M.A. School of Military Engineering. Regular Army, R.E., 38. ✕ Major. Dispatches. Retired, 49. C.Eng., F.I.C.E. Founder Partner, Roughton & Partners, Consulting Civil Engineers, London, Bristol, Maidstone, Kampala & Nairobi.

ROUSE, Andrew Murray. Sh & St, 43³–48².*

ROWE, Charles Havelock Graham, b. 4 May 26, eldest s. of the late R. H. G. Rowe (or C 04). SF, 39³–44². University College, Oxford (Naval Short Course). ✕ R.N., 45–48. Webber-Douglas Academy of Dramatic Art, 49–51. Member, British Equity since 51. Brother, R. M. M. Rowe.

ROWE, Nicholas Charles. M, 43³–47².*

ROWE, Reginald Marshman Mudie, b. 10 Jan. 31, 2nd s. of the late R. H. G. Rowe (or C 04). SF, 44³–49². N/S. R.A. 2nd Lt. Liverpool Univ. 1 year Law. Chartered Accountant. Financial Auditor, Alcan, Canada. Brother, C. H. G. Rowe.

ROWLANDS, John Edward, F.R.C.S. SH, 23¹–27².*

ROWLANDS, John Heywood Barlow, M.B., B.Chir. W, 31³–36².*

ROWLEY, Keith Stewart. T, 46³–49³.*

ROWSE, John Norman, b. 17 Oct. 17, s. of the late A. A. Rowse. K, 31¹–35³. F.C.I.S. ✕ Royal Marines, 39–46. Capt. Chrmn., F. H. Rowse Ltd., London. J.P., Middlesex.

ROYCE, Michael Elliott Applebee. Sh, 33³–36¹.*

RUAULT, John Anthony. St, 44³–48².*

RUNDELL, Major William Westcott Oram. Tu, 96²–98². Son, 1062.*

RUSHALL, Edgar Boswell. T, 30²–32³.*

RUSHALL, Richard Boswell, b. 14 Sept. 11, 2nd s. of the late R. B. Rushall, M.B.E. T, 25²–29³. St. John's, Cambridge, M.A. ✕ Burma Army (A.B.R.O.), attd. R.I.E. (Docks Operating & Port Operating), 41–46. Master Stevedore. Partner, Man. Dir., Rushall & Co. Ltd. (Burma), Ship Agents & Stevedores, 35–57. Company Dir. since 58. Cert. Ed., Southampton Univ., 67. Asst. Master, New Milton County Jr. School, New Milton, Hants., since 67. *Overseas Club.* Brother, E. B. Rushall.

RUSSELL, Major Leslie Dunstan, b. 19 May 07, 3rd s. of the late A. S. Russell. B, 21²–25¹. R.M.A., Woolwich. Gazetted to Royal Artillery, 27. ✕ 39–45. Major. Retired, 47. Farmer, retired.

RUSSELL, Michael, b. 30 May 33, 2nd s. of the late E. D. Russell (OR W 15). W, 46³–52²; Levée; Senior Scholar, 49; Head of School; Exhibitioner; XXII; Fives IV, 51–52 (Capt.). Cadet Officer. Scholar of Christ Church, Oxford. N/S. Royal Horse Guards, 57–58. Commission. Literary Agent. Publisher.

RUSSELL, Philip Henry, b. 12 Dec. 32, eldest s. of the late A. H. Russell (OR W 17). W, 46²–50³; XV, 50; Fives IV, 50. Nottingham Univ. LL.B. Solicitor. Partner in Danby Eptons & Griffith, Lincoln. *Law Society.* Brothers, 214 & 215.

RUSSELL, Patrick Morries Gordon, F.R.C.S., F.R.C.O.G., b. 4 Sept. 07, s. of the late Judge A. D. Russell. K, 21¹–

25¹. University College, London. University College Hospital, M.B., B.S.,F.R.C.S., F.R.C.O.G. ✕ R.A.M.C., 42–46. Lt.-Col. Consultant in Obstetrics & Gynaecology, Royal Devon & Exeter Hospital. Retired.

RUSSELL-ROBERTS, Lt.-Col. Denis Guy, b. 28 July 09, eldest s. of the late F. V. Russell-Roberts (OR W 88). B, 23³–26³; XV, 26. R.M.C., Sandhurst. Intermediate Term Scholarship. "Blue" for Rugby Football, 28–29 & Lawn Tennis, 29. Played Tennis for the Army, 30 & 34, & Rugby Football & Tennis for Hampshire, 30. Gazetted to King's Shropshire Light Infantry, 30. Transferred to 11 Sikh Regt., Indian Army, 39. ✕ D.A.A.G., 2nd Echelon, Malaya, 40. Major. P.O.W. in Singapore, 42–45. Retired, 47. Author of "Spotlight on Singapore". Retired Officer (Civil Servant) in Ministry of Defence at the School of Electronic Engineering, R.E.M.E., Arborfield.

RUSSELL-SMITH, Henry Francis, b. 1 Feb. 23, 2nd s. of the late W. Russell-Smith (OR SF 00). SF, 36³–41¹. ✕ R.N.V.R., 41–46. Lt. Rubber Planting in Malaysia, 47–67. Now Apple Growing. Brother, R. H. Russell-Smith.

RUSSELL-SMITH, Roy Sabine, M.R.C.S., L.R.C.P., b. 1 July 15, s. of the late H. E. Russell-Smith (OR SF 01). SF, 29¹–32³. St. John's, Cambridge, M.A. St John's, Cambridge, M.A. St. Bartholomew's Hospital Medical School, M.R.C.S., L.R.C.P. Physician & Surgeon. *Royal Southampton Y.C.* Son, 2539.

RUSSELL-SMITH, Rupert Hugh. SF, 43³–48².*

RUSTON, Ronald Sowerby, b. 6 Jan. 93, s. of the late A. A. Ruston. B, 06³–09³. ✕ 5th Bn. Suffolk Regt. 54th Divnl. Cyclist Corps. Capt. T.F. Reserve. Solicitor, 19. Partner in Rustons & Lloyd, Newmarket. Retired.

RUTHERFORD, Edwin Vickerman, b. 25 Nov. 96, s. of the late V. H. Rutherford. St, 10³–14³; XV, 13, 14 (Capt.); G. VIII, 12, 13; Boxing, Middleweight, 14. ✕ Northumberland Yeomanry, att. 21st Lancers. Lt. Trinity, Oxford. Solicitor, 25. Partner in Ralph, Bond, Veitch & Bilney of London. Retired. Now Farming. *Cavalry Club.*

RUTHERFORD, Ronald, b. 21 Mar. 28, 3rd s. of the late R. P. Rutherford. B, 41³–46². Trinity, Cambridge, M.A. N/S.

R.E. Lt. The Nuclear Power Group, Chief Engineer.

RUTHVEN-STUART, Capt. Alexander Whitewright (formerly Stuart, W.), b. 19 Jan. 83, younger s. of the late W. W. Stuart. M, 96³–00¹. Trinity, Cambridge. Political Private Secretary to the late Duke of Montrose, 06, & later Lord Chaplin & Sir A. Shirley Benn. ✕ 7th Bn. Gordon Highlanders (T.F.), R.F.C., R.A.S.C. Capt. Later Pilot in R.F.C. Worked for the Red Cross in Paris, 24. Pres. of *Anglo-Scottish Society in Paris* between 20–34. Big-game hunter (Yukon, 27). *New Club, Edinburgh; Highland Society.*

RUTLEDGE, John Atkinson, b. 4 Jan. 24, 2nd s. of the late R. W. Rutledge. W, 37³–42²; Exhibitioner; Levée; Head of House; King's Prize. Scholar of Magdalene, Cambridge, B.A., LL.B. ✕ 27th

Lancers, 44–45. Solicitor, 51. Senior Partner in Evershed & Tomkinson of Birmingham. Pres., Birmingham Law Society, 71; *Edgbaston G.C.; Birmingham Book Club* (Pres., 72).

RUTNAM, Michael Donald, b. 2 Aug. 26, s. of the late D. R. Rutnam, O.B.E., I.C.S. SH, 40²–44²; Scholar; XI, 43–44. Trinity Hall, Cambridge, B.A. Sundry executive appointments, wine trade; plantations in the East; now Merchant Banking (Lazard Bros. & Co. Ltd.).

RYCROFT, Richard Noel, M.C., M.R.C.S., L.R.C.P., b. 24 Dec. 15, s. of A. T. Rycroft, L.D.S., R.C.S. W, 29³–34². St. John's, Cambridge, B.A. Birmingham Univ., M.R.C.S., L.R.C.P. ✕ R.A.F. (Medical Service), 42–45. F/Lt. M.C. General Practitioner since 45.

S

SABEL, John Paul. SF, 33³–38¹.*

SADLER, James Derek. b. 9 May 25, s. of J. H. Sadler. W, 39²–43 2. ✕ R.A.F., 43–47. Chartered Accountant. F.C.A. In Practice. Son, Peter Brian. W, 68³–.

SAINSBURY, Alfred Vernon. M, 24³–28².*

ST. JOHN COX, Peter Robin. SF, 46³–48¹.*

SALE, Lt.-Col. Robert Edward Walker, M.C., b. 26 Nov. 13, s. of the late E. L. Sale, I.C.S. Tu, 27³–31³. R.M.C., Sandhurst. Gazetted to Welsh Guards, 33. ✕ British Somaliland, 39–40; N. Africa, 43; Italy & Austria, 44–45. Major. M.C. Retired, 58, as Lt.-Col. Now Farming.

SALLITT, Thomas Woodford. Tu, 22³–27².*

SALLITT, Brig. William Baines, O.B.E., b. 15 July 06, s. of the late W. W. Sallitt. Tu, 20³–24³; Levée; Head of House; XV, 24; XXII, 23. R.M.A., Woolwich; passed out first; XV, 25; King's Medal. Gazetted to R.E., 26. Emmanuel, Cambridge, B.A. Resigned from Army and joined Ford Motor Co., 34. Mechanical Engineer, Copper Assoc., 37–39. ✕ Rejoined R.E., 39–45. Brig. O.B.E. With English Electric Co., 45–48. Man. Dir., Spooner Food Machinery Engineering Co. Ltd., 48–56.

Dir., Superheater Co. Ltd., 56–68. Retired. F.I.Mech.E., M.B.I.M., C.Eng. Brother, T. W. Sallitt. Son, 139.

SALMON, Christopher Robin Lawson, b. 21 Dec. 26, 4th s. of the late J. Salmon. K, 42²–44². King's, Cambridge (for 1 year). N/S. R.A.F., 46–48. Cpl. With J. Lyons & Co. Ltd. since 48. Now Director.

SALT, Col. David Frederick, b. 8 Oct. 16, 2nd s. of the late Rev. F. J. Salt (OR SH 86). SH, 30²–34¹. R.M.C., Sandhurst. Gazetted to Royal Berkshire Regt., 37. ✕ India & Germany. Major. Retired as Colonel. Now boat builder, designer and boat hirer, Norfolk Broads. *Army & Navy Club.* Brother, J. S. Salt.

SALT, Col. John Stevenson, b. 27 Jan. 14, eldest s. of the late Rev. F. J. Salt (OR SH 86). SH, 27²–32². Army Officer, Southern Rhodesia Staff Corps. (subsequently Fed. of Rhodesia & Nyasaland). ✕ Rhodesian African Rifles, 40–43. No. 3 Commando, 43–46. Capt. Commd. The Rhodesian African Rifles, 58–60. Dispatches (Malaya). Commd. Rhodesian L.I., 61–62. Bulawayo Area, 63, as Col. Retired, 63. Now P.R.O. for a sugar & citrus growing company in Lowveld of Rhodesia, named Hippo Valley Estates. *Bulawayo Club.* Brother, D. F. Salt.

SALWAY, Cdr. Stuart, R.N., b. 3 May 27, s. of L. S. Salway. T, 40³–44³. R.N.

Special entry cadet, 45. Lieut, 49. Now Commander, R.N.

SAMPSON, The Rev. Jeremy John Egerton, b. 1 Dec. 23, 2nd s. of the late S. J. M. Sampson (OR SF 97). SF, 37^3–39^2. King's College, Newcastle-upon-Tyne, Durham Univ., B.Sc. Wells Theological College. Ordained Deacon, 48; Priest, 49. Vicar of Killingworth, Dio. of Newcastle.

SAMPSON, John Anthony. W, 37^3–42^1. Sons, John Stephen, W, 67^3–72^2 and Thomas Robert, W, 70^3.*

SAMPSON, Lt.-Cdr. John Michael, R.N. K, 44^3–48^2.*

SAMPSON, Nicolas Stewart. SF, 39^3–42^2.*

SAMPSON, Cdr. Thomas Stephen, R.N., b. 30 June 18, eldest s. of the late T. H. Sampson. W, 32^3–36^1. R.N. Special entry, 36. ✕ At sea. Lt., 40. Lt.-Cdr., 48. j.s.s.c. Commander, H.M. Destroyer *Ulster*, 51–52. Nato Defence College. Commander, R.N. Seaman specialist. Retired, 65. Farmer since 65. *R. Ocean Racing Club.* Brother, J. A. Sampson. Son, Thomas Bradbury. W, 72^1–.

SAMUEL, Adrian Christopher Ian, C.M.G., C.V.O., b. 20 Aug. 15, s. of the late G. C. Samuel. M, 30^3–34^2. Leaving Exhibition. Kitchener Scholar. History Exhibitioner of St. John's, Oxford, B.A. H.M. Diplomatic Service, 38–63. ✕ R.A.F. Coastal Command, 40–44. Pilot. F/Lt. Dir., British Agrochemicals Assoc. C.M.G., C.V.O. *Garrick Club.* Sons, 1531 & Adrian Charles, K, 72^3–.

SAMUEL, The Hon. Dan Judah, b. 25 Mar. 25, 2nd s. of E. Samuel, 2nd Viscount Samuel. SH, 39^2–43^2. ✕ Yorkshire Hussars, 43–47. G.H.Q., Cairo. Major. Balliol, Oxford, M.A. U.S. Govt. grant & fellowship at School of Advanced International Studies, Washington, D.C. With the Royal Dutch Shell Group since 52. Gen. Man., Shell Co. of Thailand, 62–66. Pres., Belgian Shell, 68–69. Now Marketing Coordinator, Oil, Shell International Petroleum Co., London. Trustee (appointed by H.M.G.), Asian Inst. of Technology, Bangkok, 66–68. Order Royal Crown of Thailand, 66. Officer of the Order of the Crown, Belgium, 68.

SAMUELSON, Charles Frederick, b. 25 Aug. 23, s. of F. Samuelson. Tu, 37^2–41^2. Cadet Pair, 40. Christ's, Cambridge, M.A. ✕ R.E.M.E., 43–47. India. Lt. M.I.Mech.E., C.Eng. Steam Turbine Design with B.T.H. at Rugby & Larne, N.I. Gas Turbine design at A.E.I., Manchester and G.E.C., Whetstone, Leics. Now Engineering Man., G.E.C. Gas Turbine Ltd., Whetstone.

SAMUELSON, Geoffrey Martin, b. 30 Nov. 05, s. of B. M. Samuelson. C, 19^3–23^3. Joined Reckitt & Sons Ltd., Hull. ✕ R.A. Capt. Recalled to business, 40. Dir. of Reckitt & Colman Ltd. from 40. Vice-Chrmn. Retired. Chrmn. of Reckitt & Colman (Overseas) Ltd. from 46. Retired. Consultant as Vice-Chrmn., Fenner (Holdings) Ltd. and Dir. of other companies. *Oriental Club.* Son, 190.

SANDEMAN, Major Gerald, b. 27 Dec. 94, s. of the late E. Sandeman. K, 08^3–13^2. Gazetted to the R.A., 14. ✕ 90th, 93rd & 92nd Bdes., R.F.A., U Bty., R.H.A., 16th Bde., R.H.A., 24th Bde., R.F.A. A/Major. Dispatches. Lt. Capt., 27. Retired as Major, 36. ✕ Recalled from Reserve. Employee of the Eastern Bank Ltd., 37–59.

SANDERS, Douglas Francis. M, 03^3–08^2.*

SANDERSON, The Hon. Murray Lee, b. 12 Jan. 31, 2nd s. of the late Rt. Hon. Lord Sanderson, M.C. (OR B 08). SH, 44^3–49^1. Trinity, Oxford. King's, Cambridge. District Officer, Kenya, 56–63. In private business, Zambia since 63. Chrmn., Zambian Industrial & Commercial Assoc., 71–73. *Bath Club.*

SANDFORD, Hugh Nicholas Folliott, b. 25 June 23, s. of the late F. H. B. Sandford (OR SH 03). SH, 37^2–41^3; XV, 41. Magdalen, Oxford, B.A. ✕ K.O.S.B. (with K.A.R. mostly), 42–46. Lt. F.R.I.C.S. Partner in Messrs. Smith-Wooley & Co., Chartered Surveyors, of Newark.

SANDFORD, Victor Henry, b. 15 May 96, s. of the late H. B. Sandford. SH, 10^1–13^3. ✕ Oxfordshire Yeomanry (T), 2nd Life Guards. Lt. Yorkshire Dragoons (T) T.D. Magdalen, Oxford, M.A. Solicitor, 22. Partner in Rodgers & Co. of Sheffield. Diocesan Registrar, Dio. of Sheffield since 25.

SANDOVER, Raymond Ladais, D.S.O., T.D., b. 28 Mar. 10, 2nd s. of the late W. L. Sandover. W, 24^1–28^3; Cap, 27; H. XI, 28. Chartered Accountant, 35. Dir., Harris Scaife & Sandover Ltd., Perth, W. Australia, 35–39. ✕ 2nd Australian Imperial Force, N. Africa, Greece, Crete. S.W.P.A. C.O., 2/11 Bn., 41–43. Commd., 6 Aust. Infantry Bde., 43–45. D.S.O., E.D. Dispatches thrice. Brig. Returned to U.K., 46. Hon. Citizen of Rethymno, Crete, 48. Dir., William Sandover & Co. Ltd. Member, Council, London Chamber of Commerce. Vice-Chrmn., Fairbridge Soc. Son, William Geoffrey. W, 68^3–.

SARGANT, Sir (Henry) Edmund, Kt., b. 24 May 06, s. of the late Rt. Hon. Lord Justice Sargant (OR SF 69). SF, 19^3–24^2. Cadet Officer. Trinity, Cambridge, M.A. Solicitor, 30. ✕ R.A.F.V.R., 40–45. Wing-Cdr. Partner in Radcliffes & Co., London, 30–71 (Senior Partner, 51–71). President of the Council of the Law Society, 68–69. Chrmn., Disciplinary Cttee. of Architects Registration Council, 64–66. Master, Merchant Taylors Co., 54–55. Knight Bachelor, 69. *Army & Navy Club, United Oxford & Cambridge Univ. Club.* Son, 322.

SARGANT-FLORENCE, Prof. Philip, Ph.D. SH, 04^2–09^2.*

SARGENT, Prof. John Richard, b. 22 Mar. 25, s. of the late Sir J. P. Sargent. M, 38^3–43^2; Scholar; Levée; Head of House; Head of School; Exhibitioner. ✕ R.N.V.R. H.M.S. *Holderness* & H.M.S. *Loch Fyne.* Scholar of Christ Church, Oxford, B.A. George Webb Medley Senior Scholarship for Research in Pol. Econ. Lecturer at Christ Church, 49–51. Fellow & Lecturer in Economics, Worcester, Oxford, 51–62. Economic Consultant, H.M. Treasury, 63–65. Prof. of Economics, Warwick Univ., Coventry since 65. *Reform Club, Council, Royal Economic Soc.*

SARRA, Edward David, b. 25 Dec. 22, younger s. of Dr. W. H. Sarra, M.R.C.S., L.R.C.P. SF, 36^3–41^1; XXII. ✕ R.A.F. Sgt. Pilot. Lincoln, Oxford, M.A. Chrmn., Universities Assurance Services Ltd. of London. *Lansdowne Club.* Son, Nicholas John. SF, 70^2–71^3.

SATCHELL, Harold Leslie, M.B.E., b. 3 Apr. 96, s. of the late J. G. Satchell. T, 09^3–14^2; Benn Scholar; G. VIII, 12–13 (represented Rugby in P.S. Comptn. at Aldershot). ✕ 12th Bn. Royal Warwickshire Regt. Flight Commander, R.F.C. Capt. Dispatches, 14–19. Joined B.T.H.

(later A.E.I. & now G.E.C.) in 20. Dir. & Man. of Rugby works & finally Dir. of manufacture. F.I.D., F.I.W.M., M.B.E. (Civil).

SATTERTHWAITE, Major Charles William Edward, b. 22 July 17, elder s. of the late R. E. Satterthwaite (OR SH 02). SH, 31^1–35^2; XXII. R.M.C., Sandhurst. Gazetted to Somerset L.I., 37. ✕ Middle East, Italy & N.W. Europe. Major. Wounded. p.s.c. Retired, 69. Now employed as Retired Officer at H.Q. Light Div., Winchester. *Light Infantry Club.* Brother, R. G. Satterthwaite.

SATTERTHWAITE, Lt.-Col. Richard George, O.B.E. SH, 33^2–38^2.*

SATTERTHWAITE, Thomas Christopher Vyvyan. SF, 20^2–22^1.*

SAUER, Hans Nikolas (now Fitzgerald, N. M.).

SAUL, John Wingate. SF, 93^3–96^2.*

SAUNDERS, Arnold Norman Westbury, b. 22 Dec. 00, elder s. of A. F. Saunders. SF, 14^3–19^2; Scholar; Levée; Head of House; XXII, 18; Exhibitioner. Scholar of New College, Oxford, M.A. Asst. Master, Bradfield College, 24–37 and of Rugby School, 37–65. Retired. Brother, P. F. Saunders. Sons, P. H. & M. I. C. Saunders.

SAUNDERS, Martyn Isham Creswell, b. 11 June 33, 2nd s. of A. N. W. Saunders (OR SF 14). SF, 46^3–51^2; Scholar; Levée; Head of House. New College, Oxford. Chrysler U.K. O.E.M. Sales Manager. Brother, P. H. Saunders. Son, Keith Philip. T, 72^3–.

SAUNDERS, Philip Frederick, b. 22 Feb. 02, younger s. of A. F. Saunders. SF, 15^3–20^2; Scholar; Head of School; XI, 19–20 (Capt.); Cadet Officer. Scholar of Brasenose, Oxford, M.A. Asst. Master, Uppingham School, 29. Now retired. Brother, A. N. W. Saunders. Son, 700.

SAUNDERS, Philip Hector, b. 19 May 28, eldest s. of A. N. W. Saunders (OR SF 14). T, 41^3–46^3; Levée; Head of House. Peterhouse, Cambridge, B.A. A.R.I.B.A. Worked for various architects in London, 52–62, then Courtaulds Technical Services. Since 67 employed by Industrial Development Consultants at Stratford-upon-Avon. Brother, M. I. C. Saunders. Son, Francis William, Sh, 72^3–.

SAW, Kenneth Hughes. T, 23^2-28^2.*

SAWDON, George Ernest, M.B., B.Ch. Tu, 03^2-06^1.*

SAWERS, Colin Simon Hawkesley, b. 2 Nov. 22, younger s. of the late Lt.-Col. J. Sawers (OR SH 92). M, 36^3-41^2. ✕ R.N.V.R.(F.A.A.). Lt. (A.). Observer, 42–46. King's College, London Univ., B.Sc. Aero-engine Development Engineer with Armstrong Siddeley, Bristol Siddeley & Rolls-Royce Ltd. since 49. Brother, J. M. Sawers.

SAWERS, Major-Gen. James Maxwell, M.B.E., b. 14 May 20, elder s. of the late Lt.-Col. J. Sawers (OR SH 92). M, 34^1–38^1. R.M.A., Woolwich. Gazetted to Royal Signals, 39. ✕ Major (T/Lt.-Col.). West Africa, 41–43. Burma, 43–45. Dispatches twice. Korea, 52–53. M.B.E. Malaya, 53–55. p.s.c. i.d.c., 70. Now Signal Officer-in-Chief in rank of Major-General. M.B.I.M. *Army & Navy Club.* Brother, C. S. H. Sawers. Sons, 2153 & Nigel Charles, M, 68^2-71^2.

SAYER, Lt.-Col. Harold Bouchier, O.B.E. C, 08^3-13^2.*

SAYLES, Alan, b. 8 Mar. 33, s. of L. Sayles. T, 46^3-51^3; Levée; Head of House. Brasenose, Oxford, M.A. Solicitor. Sec., Brentwood Housing Trust, 67–70. Member, Congregational Council, 67–72. Solicitor, Hilliard & Ward, Chelmsford. *Wig & Pen Club.*

SCANLON, Peter, b. 14 May 24, s. of the late H. Scanlon. W, 37^3-42^1; Crick Winner; Capt. of Fives. Corpus Christi, Oxford. Half Blue for Fives. School of Oriental & African Studies, London. ✕ Intell. Corps., India, Burma, Malaya & Java. Capt. H.M. Overseas Civil Service, Sarawak, 49–64. H.M. Diplomatic Service since 64. *Lansdowne.*

SCHAW MILLER, Robert Grant, W.S., b. 10 Nov. 25, s. of A. G. Schaw Miller. Sh, 39^3-43^3. ✕ R.A., 44–47. Capt. Peterhouse, Cambridge, B.A. Edinburgh Univ., LL.B. Writer to the Signet. Governor, John Watson's School. *H.C.E.G. New Club, Edin.*

SCHLEE, Charles Alexander. Tu, 43^3-47^3.*

SCHLEE, David Nicholas Rowland, b. 17 July 31, 4th s. of the late R. Schlee. Tu, 44^3-48^2. University College, Oxford, B.A.

Sales Conference Organiser, Kanzell Associates Ltd. of London. Brothers, R. A., P. J. R. & C. A. Schlee.

SCHLEE, Philip John Ringland, b. 23 Mar. 24, 2nd s. of the late R. Schlee. C, 37^3-41^2; XV, 40. ✕ 1st Special Air Service Regt. Lt. P.O.W. L.S.E. Dir., Sea Containers Inc. Resident Partner, Astaire & Co., Far East, Hong Kong. *Junior Carlton Club.* Brothers, R. A., C. A. & D. N. R. Schlee.

SCHLEE, Robert Anthony, b. 12 Jan. 20, eldest s. of the late R. Schlee. C, 33^3-38^1; Scholar. University College, Oxford. ✕ R.A., 40–46. Capt. F.C.A. Lloyd's Underwriter. *City University Club.* Brothers, P. J. R., C. A. & D. N. R. Schlee. Son, Clive Edward Benedict. C, 72^3-.

SCHURHOFF, Gerhart Walter, b. 4 Feb. 04, 2nd s. of the late G. Schurhoff. St, 17^3-22^2. Queen's, Oxford & Heidelberg Univ. Retired.

SCHUSTER, Major Aubrey William, M.B.E., b. 9 Feb. 06, s. of the late Dr. E. H. J. Schuster, O.B.E., D.Sc. K, 19^3-24^2; Cadet Officer, 23. Trinity,Cambridge, M.A. ✕ R.A.S.C., 39–45. Major. Brigade Major. M.B.E. Member, London Stock Exchange. Past Master, Wor. Com. of Upholders. Commander of the Royal Order of St. Olav of Norway. *City of London Club, Moor Park G.C.*

SCHUSTER, Leonard Francis, b. 22 June 89, s. of the late Sir A. Schuster, F.R.S. K, 03^3-07^1. Trinity, Cambridge. Gazetted to the Reserve of Officers, Yeomanry, 12.✕ 3rd London Yeomanry, 150th Siege Bty., R.G.A., 46th Bde., R.G.A. Capt. Wounded. Dispatches. Retired.

SCHWARZSCHILD, Robert Boris (see Shields, R. B.).

SCOTT, Alexander, b. 17 June 04, elder s. of the late T. Scott. St, 18^3-20^1. Dir., James Scott & Sons, Langholm Ltd., The Langholm Dyeing & Finishing Co. Son, 2085.

SCOTT, David Miller, b. 13 Mar. 11, s. of H. C. Scott, K.C. SH, 24^3-28^3.Organ Scholar of Gonville & Caius, Cambridge, M.A. Solicitor, 36. Bar, Middle Temple, 47. Western Circuit. Retired, 70. ✕ R.A., 41–45. I.t.-Col. T.A., 47–50. *United Oxford & Cambridge Univ. Club.* Holder of Yachtmaster's Certificate (Coaster).

SCOTT, Edward Cumin, b. 22 Feb. 87, 4th s. of the late C. J. Scott (OR SF 60). SF, 01²–04². ✕ Royal Marine Artillery. Pte. Active Ceylon Tea Planter.

SCOTT, The Rev. Edward Geoffrey Spencer, b. 9 July 21, eldest s. of the late E. S. Scott (OR St 84). St, 35³–40²; Scholar; Levée; Cap, 39; King's Medal; Exhibitioner. ✕ R. Fusiliers (City of London Regt.), 41–45. Lt. Wounded. Scholar of King's, Cambridge, B.A. Chichester Theological College. Ordained, 49. Curate, St. Michael's, Howe Bridge, 49–50 and St. Peter's, Burnley, 50–53. Priest in charge, St. Peter's, Colombo and Chaplain to the Bishop of Colombo, 53–57. Vicar of Darton, Yorkshire, 58–63. Vicar of Woodhouse, Huddersfield, 63–70. Vicar of Honley, Huddersfield since 70. Brothers, J. S. & M. S. Scott.

SCOTT, Edward John. St & K, 38²–42².*

SCOTT, Ian Colin Guillum. SF, 20³–23².*

SCOTT, Ian Douglas. SF, 19³–22².*

SCOTT, John Sewell, b. 16 July 23, 2nd s. of the late E. S. Scott (or St 84). St, 37¹–41². Middlesex Hosp. Medical School, M.B., B.S. South Carolina Medical College, Charleston & State Hosp. Columbia, S.C. Asst. in Neurology, Bowman Gray School of Medicine, Winston-Salem, N.C. Diplomate, American Board of Neurology, Neurologist & Electro-Encephalographer at Orlando, Florida, U.S.A. B.M.A,, A.M.A., American Academy of Neurology. American E.E.G. Soc.

SCOTT, Lawrence Prestwich, b. 10 June 09, eldest s. of the late J. R. Scott. W, 23²–28². Trinity, Cambridge. Toynbee Hall. ✕ R.A.F., 41–44. Dir. of various companies.

SCOTT, Michael George. M, 21²–25¹.*

SCOTT, Martin Spencer, b. 7 July 26, 3rd s. of the late E. S. Scott (OR St 84). M, 40³–45¹; Levée; XV, 44; Leaving Exhibition. ✕ Royal Marines. Scholar of King's, Cambridge, M.A. 6th Form History Master, Clifton College, 50–62. Head of History Dept. and 2nd Master of Winchester College since 62. *Athenæum*. Author, "Medieval Europe". Brothers, E. G. S. & J. S. Scott.

SCOTT, Ralph Easdale, M.B., B.Chir., b. 9 Nov. 31, s. of the late F. C. Scott, M.R.C.V.S. C, 45³–50²; Scholar; Levée; Head of House. Scholar of King's, Cambridge, M.A., M.B., B.Chir. St. Thomas's Hospital,   D.Obst.R.C.O.G.   N/S. R.A.M.C. Capt. In general medical practice in Bury St. Edmunds. Clinical Asst. to E.N.T. Dept., West Suffolk General Hospital. B.M.A. *R. Harwich Y.C.*

SCOTT, Robert Prestwich, b. 25 Oct. 30, 2nd s. of C. R. Scott. SH, 44³–49³; Stovin Scholar. Organ Scholar of Pembroke, Cambridge, B.A. Royal College of Music. A.R.C.O. Schoolmaster.

SCOTT, Thomas Barrett, b. 15 July 22, s. of Dr. G. C. Scott. B, 36²–41². Clare, Cambridge, M.A., M.B., B.Chir. Middlesex   Hospital,   M.R.C.S.,   L.R.C.P., F.R.C.P.(C) Canada. Dermatologist, Toronto East General Hospital. Assoc. Physician (Dermatology), Univ. of Toronto.

SCOTT, William Astley Hesketh, b. 8 Feb. 01, elder s. of W. H. Scott. K, 15²–19¹. Gazetted to 8th Bn. Worcestershire Regt. (T.F.), 22. Solicitor, 24. Partner in Scott & Holyoake, Bromsgrove. Clerk to the Commissioners of Taxes and to Justices, Bromsgrove, Alcester and Redditch. Now retired.

SCOTT-BROWN, George Graham, b. 25 Oct. 29, s. of W. G. Scott-Brown, C.V.O., M.D., F.R.C.S. M, 43³–48¹; Cap. Corpus Christi, Cambridge, M.A., M.B., B.Chir.   St.   Bartholomew's   Hospital, F.R.C.P. Physician, Leprologist in Nepal. Leader of International Nepal Fellowship.

SCOTT-DAVIDSON, Walter William, M.B.E., b. 16 Nov. 90, s. of the late J. S. Davidson. W, 04³–07². Trinity, Cambridge, B.A. ✕ Enlisted in A.S.C., 14 and in retreat from Mons. Commission, R.F.C., 16. Dispatches. Short service commission R.A.F., 19. Worked in experimental and research unit and later for commercial manufacturing company. Now retired. County Councillor. Ex-Chrmn., T.A.A. & ex-County Commissioner, Scouts. M.B.E., D.L.

SCOTT-MONCRIEFF, Col. Robert, b. 24 May 09, s. of the late K. A. Scott-Moncreiff, M.I.E.E. SF, 22³–27². R.M.A., Woolwich. Served in Army in India, Egypt, Greece, Germany, Palestine, Britain & Cyprus. Higher Standard Urdu. p.s.c. Staff appointments in British Military Mission to Egypt, British Forces,

Greece, Control Commission, Germany, Middle East, Egypt & Cyprus. Retired as Lt.-Col., 55. Now fruit farming. *Camping Club of G.B.*

SCOTT-OWEN, William Seymour. M, 33^2–37^2.*

SCRIMGEOUR, James Cameron, b. 17 Apr. 25, s. of G. C. Scrimgeour, D.S.O., O.B.E., M.C. M, 39^1–43^1. ✕ 2nd R. Lancers, Indian Armd. Corps, 43–47. Lieut. Gonville & Caius, Cambridge, B.A., LL.B. Solicitor. Dir. of Studies, Wolsey Hall, Oxford. *Indian Cavalry Officers Assoc.*

SEARLE, Trevor Netley, b. 18 Sept. 32, s. of W. N. Searle. K, 46^2–50^1; S. VIII, 48–49. University College, London. Tea Buyer. The Bell Tea Company Ltd. of N.Z.

SEDDON, Richard Goulburn, b. 29 Dec. 18, s. of the late T. R. Seddon. Tu, 32^3–37^1. Fitzwilliam, Cambridge, M.A. Student of the Inst. of Actuaries, 37–39. ✕ The Devonshire Regt. & R.A., 39–46. Major. D.A.A.G., H.Q. Allied Land Forces, S.E. Africa. Shell U.K. Head of Remuneration since 67. Council, Anthroposophical Soc. in G.B.

SEEBOHM, Derrick, b. 14 Jan. 07, eldest s. of the late H. E. Seebohm (OR C 80). C, 20^3–25^2; R. VIII, 25; S. VIII, 25. Trinity, Cambridge, B.A. F.I.B. Local Dir. of Barclays Bank. Dir., Luton Water Company. With Min. of Economic Warfare during the War. American Medal of Freedom.

SEEDS, Robert. K, 27^3–29^1.*

SEEWER, Marcus Vinicius. T, 35^2–37^2.*

SELBY SMITH, Richard, b. 13 June 14, s. of the late S. Smith. St, 27^3–33^2; Scholar; Levée; Head of House; Head of School; Jex-Blake Exhibition; XXII, Cap. Classical Demyship of Magdalen, Oxford, M.A. Harvard Univ. Graduate School of Education, M.A. ✕ R.N.V.R. Lt.-Cdr. Dep. Chief Education Officer, Warwickshire C.C., 51–53. Principal, Scotch College, Melbourne, 53–64. Foundation Prof. of Education and Dean, Faculty of Education, Monash Univ., Melbourne, 64–72. Latrobe Univ. Council, 64–71. Monash Univ. Council, 70–72. Principal, Tasmanian College of Advanced Education, 70–72. Prof. of Education, Univ. of Tas-

mania since 73. Author of two books and numerous articles in professional journals. *Naval Club, London, The Melbourne Club.*

SELLMAN, Roger, F.C.A., b. 8 Nov. 23, s. of the late E. Sellman, M.B.E. C, 37^2–41^2. ✕ 2nd County of London Yeomanry (Westminster Dragoons). R.A.C. Lt. New College, Oxford, M.A. F.C.A. Man. Dir., Hewell Spring Co. Ltd., Redditch, Worcs. Son, Nigel Roger. C, 69^3–.

SELWYN, Brian Cecil. K, 30^2–34^2.*

SELWYN, Edwyn Charles Jasper, T.D., b. 22 Feb. 25, 3rd s. of the Very Rev. E. G. Selwyn, D.D. SH, 38^3–43^1. ✕ 358th Medium Regt., R.A. (Suffolk Yeomanry) T.A. India, 43–47. Lt. Corpus Christi, Cambridge, B.A. Solicitor, 52. Asst. Sol. with firms in Bury St. Edmunds & Shrewsbury, 52–57. Partner, Jeffreys & Powell of Brecon since 57. Commd. Local T.A. Bty., 61–64. T.D. *Brecon Rotary.* Son, Nicholas Alexander. SH, 70^1–.

SEMPLE, John Edward, M.D., F.R.C.S. K, 17^3–21^2.*

SEQUEIRA, Cecil (formerly Cartlidge, C.). SH, 12^3–15^2.*

SEVERS, John Vaux. Tu, 31^2–33^3.*

SEYMER, Nigel Victor Evelyn. SH, 39^3–43^3.*

SHACKEL, Edward Meredyth, M.B., B.Chir., b. 17 Mar. 01, 2nd s. of Dr. G. A. Shackel. SF, 14^3–19^1. Trinity, Cambridge, M.A., M.B., B.Chir. St. Thomas's Hospital, M.R.C.S., L.R.C.P. General Practitioner from 26–72 at Mayfield, Sussex. Now retired. Brother, G. M. Shackel. Son, 859.

SHACKEL, Major George Meredyth, M.C. M, 07^3–12^2.*

SHACKLEFORD, Arthur Neville. W, 95^1–97^3.*

SHAIRP, Brian Edward, M.R.C.S., L.R.C.P., b. 14 Jan. 22, s. of the late A. Shairp. SF, 35^2–40^2. Clare, Cambridge, M.A., M.B., B.Chir. St. Bartholomew's Hospital, M.R.C.S., L.R.C.P. In general medical practice. Son, David Brian. SF, 73^2–.

SHAND, Bruce Middleton Hope, M.C., D.L., b. 22 Jan. 17, s. of P. M. Shand. M, 30^3–34^3. R.M.C., Sandhurst. Gazetted to

12th Royal Lancers, 37. ⚔ Served France, 40 & Libya, 41–42. Major, 42. Wounded. P.O.W., 42. M.C. and Bar. Retired, 47. Wine Merchant. Chrmn. & Man. Dir., Ellis Son & Vidler Ltd., Hastings & London. D.L., Sussex, 62. Queen's Bodyguard, Yeoman of the Guard, 71. *White's and Cavalry Clubs.*

SHANN, George Nevill, b. 26 June 18, s. of the late Dr. E. W. Shann, B.Sc., Ph.D. T, 31^2–37^2; Levée; Head of House; King's Medal; Leaving Exhibition. Scholar of Gonville & Caius, Cambridge, M.A. Cert. Ed., Dip. Ed. ⚔ R. Northumberland Fusiliers & K.A.R., 39–45. Capt. Education Officer, Tanganyika, 45–59 (Senior, 59–62). Teaching Posts, Sussex, 62–65. Asst. Education Officer, Staffordshire C.C. since 65. Silver Acorn, Boy Scouts, 62. Anglican Lay Reader since 52.

SHARLAND, David John. Sh, 36^1–38^1. Son, 3019.*

SHARMAN, John Michael, b. 29 Apr. 32, s. of A. B. Sharman. Tu, 45^3–50^2; Scholar. N/S. R. Signals, 50–52. Trinity Hall, Cambridge. Bar, Middle Temple, 57. Now Solicitor. *Moortown G.C., Leeds Gilbert & Sullivan Soc.*

SHARP, Christopher Chaldecott, b. 9 Dec. 26, 2nd s. of the late E. G. Sharp (OR SF 06). SF, 40^1–44^3. ⚔ Scots Guards & R.A.S.C., 44–48. Royal Agricultural College, Cirencester. M.R.A.C. Farming since 50.

SHARP, David Harold, b. 2 May 23, s. of the late H. S. Sharp. Tu, 37^2–41^2. Christ's, Cambridge, M.A. ⚔ R.A.F., 41–46. F/Lt. F.R.I.C.S. Chartered Surveyor.

SHARP, Stephen Hugh, b. 18 Jan. 22, s. of the late Ven. J. H. Sharp (OR Tu 01). Tu, 35^3–39^3. ⚔ London Irish Rifles, 40–46. Major. Dispatches. Member of London Stock Exchange. Dir., Hoare & Co. Govett Ltd. *R.A.C.* Sons, John Timothy. Tu, 69^1–. Nicholas Hugh. Tu, 71^1–.

SHARWOOD, Albert Cyril, b. 7 Mar. 99, eldest s. of the late A. J. Sharwood. C, 13^1–17^1; XXII, 14. ⚔ R.N.A.S., H.M.A.S. *Sydney.* R.A.F. Capt. Dispatches. Queen's, Oxford. F.C.A. Director of Public Companies. Retired. *M.C.C., Bath Club.*

SHAW, Alan Heaton, b. 7 Sept. 10, 2nd s. of the late F. Shaw (OR St 95). St, 24^3–29^2; XV, 28. Oriel, Oxford, B.A. ⚔ R.A., 40–45. Capt. Dispatches. Shell International Petroleum Co., 38–54.

SHAW, John Francis St. George, b. 23 Apr. 03, 2nd s. of Canon R. V. G. Shaw. SF, 17^1–20^2. University College, London, B.Sc. F.I.C.E., F.I.Mech.E., F.I.E.E. ⚔ R.E., 40–45. Lt.-Col. Chrmn., Assoc. of Consulting Engineers, 67–68. Consulting Engineer, now retired. Previously Senior Partner of Preece, Cardew & Rider, formerly of London but now of Brighton. *St. Stephen's Club.* Sons, 109, 355 & 1008.

SHAW, John Michael, M.C., Q.C., b. 14 Nov. 14, 2nd s. of the late M. J. Shaw. SH, 28^2–32^2; S. VIII, 32. Worcester, Oxford, B.A. Bar, Gray's Inn, 37. S.E. Circuit. ⚔ Royal Fusiliers, 39–45. Major. M.C. Wounded. In practice at Bar, 46–49. Q.C. Regional Chrmn. of Industrial Tribunals, 70. *R.A.C.* Son, 1100.

SHAW, Richard Brinkley, b. 29 July 20, younger s. of the late M. Shaw, Mus.Doc. (Cantuar.), O.B.E. C, 34^3–39^2; Music Scholar; Levée; Head of House. Choral Scholar of King's, Cambridge, M.A. Royal Academy of Music under Lennox Berkeley. Gold Medal, R.A.M. Composer, Conductor. Headmaster. *Middlesex C.C.C.* Son, Martin Edmund. K, 69^3–. Nephew, Robert John Martin. B, 69^3–.

SHEARER, James Francis, C.B.E., b. 11 Apr. 13, 2nd s. of the late J. D. Shearer. B, 26^3–30^3. A.C.A., 37. ⚔ H.A.C., 39–40. R. Signals, 40–45. Lt.-Col. O.B.E. F.C.A. Partner, Cooper Bros. & Co., Chartered Accountants of London. C.B.E.(Civil). *Travellers Club, United Services & Aero Club.* Sons, 2032 & 2304.

SHEASBY, Arthur Geoffrey, b. 10 Feb. 04, s. of the late A. W. Sheasby. T, 17^3–21^2. F.C.A. Assoc. Institute of Taxation, 42. Retired.

SHEASBY, Herbert Basil, O.B.E., J.P., F.C.A., b. 1 Aug. 05, eldest s. of the late H. J. Sheasby. T, 19^3–22^1. F.C.A., F.S.A.A. Partner, Sheasby, Ellam & Co. of London. O.B.E., J.P. *Royal Commonwealth Soc.* Brother, J. D. Sheasby.

SHEASBY, John Derek, b. 18 July 08, 2nd s. of the late H. J. Sheasby. T, 22^2–26^3. M.I.C.E., F.I.Mun.E., C.Eng., A.M.T.P.I. Dep. Engineer & Surveyor, Littlehampton U.D.C., 34–39. Dep. Borough Engineer & Surveyor, Chelmsford, 39–46. Borough Surveyor & Water Engineer, Devizes, 46–52. Civil Engineer to Air Ministry, Min. of Public Buildings & Works and Dept. of the Environment since 52. Brother, H. B. Sheasby.

SHEBBEARE, John Digby, b. 9 Mar. 19, 2nd s. of Rev. C. J. Shebbeare, D.D. M, 32^3–36^3. R.M.C., Sandhurst. Gazetted to Indian Army, 39. ✕ Poona Horse (17th Q.V.O. Cavalry), 40–47. Capt. A/Lt.-Col. Retired, 48. Political Officer, South Arabia, 65–67. Sultanate Sec. in Internal Affairs, Muscat and Oman, 68–71. *Cavalry Club.*

SHELDON, Alan Peter, M.B., B.Chir., D.P.M., b. 14 Mar. 33, s. of the late Dr. L. Sheldon. C, 46^3–51^1; Scholar; Levée. Queens', Cambridge, M.A., M.B., B.Chir. Westminster Medical School, D.P.M., S.M.(Harvard), M.R.C.(Psych.). Various medical appointments, Westminster Hosp., Maudlsey Hosp., Massachusetts General Hosp., Harvard Medical School. Lecturer in Psychiatry. Assoc. Prof. of Business Admin., Harvard Business School since 71. W.H.O. Travelling Fellowship, Editorial Board, Science, Medicine & Fellowship. Author of several books relating to medical health. U.S. Citizen.

SHELLABEAR, George David. B, 17^3–21^3.*

SHELLEY, John Bernard, b. 2 June 26, s. of the late K. E. Shelley, Q.C. (OR W 08). W, 40^2–44^2. ✕ Intell. Corps, 44–47. Sgt. Merton, Oxford, B.A. Bar, Middle Temple, 51. F.C.I.S. With Save & Prosper Group Ltd. *Gresham, Hurlingham.*

SHEPPARD, Edward Duncan. SH, 22^3–27^1.*

SHERRING, Ian Brodie. SF, 23^2–27^2.*

SHEWELL, Major John Michael Henry, b. 26 Jan. 31, s. of Brig. H. A. L. Shewell, O.B.E. M, 44^3–48^1. Seale Hayne Agricultural College, Devon. C.D.A. Army, 53. Commissioned in Army Catering Corps, 54. Major.

SHIELD, Ian Noel Ridley, b. 24 Dec. 14, s. of the late N. R. Shield. W, 28^3–33^2; XI, 33. Oriel, Oxford, B.A. ✕ R.A., 39–45. Pilot in Air O.P. Capt. M.B.E. Solicitor, 47. Commercial Dir. of Engelmann & Buckham Ltd. *East India Sports & Public Schools Club. M.C.C.*

SHIELDS, Robert Boris . (formerly Schwarzschild, R. B.), b. 20 Oct. 21, s. of J. A. Schwarzschild. K, 37^3–39^2. A.C.A. To Canada, 52. Partner, Hayos, Kenton, Kingsland, Shields & Co., Chartered Accountants, Ontario, Canada.

SHIELL, William George. W, 04^3–08^2.*

SHIFFNER, Sir Henry David, Bt. M, 43^3–47^1.*

SHILLCOCK, Thomas Derek, b. 4 Mar. 12, s. of T. P. Shillcock. T, 26^1–30^1. ✕ R. Signals, 40–46. Capt. T.A. since war. Major. Electrical Industry on commercial side, training with Birmingham wholesaler. Joined Tube Investment Co. Simplex Electric Co. Ltd., 37–70. Radiation Creda Catering Equipment Ltd. as specialist in this type of equipment, 70–71.

SHILLINGTON, Commodore Courtenay Alexander Rives, R.N.V.R. (retired), b. 18 Mar. 02, eldest s. of the late T. C. Shillington. C, 15^3–19^1. Past Pres., Irish Linen Guild. Past Chrmn., N. Ireland Joint Electricity Cttee. Served in R.N.V.R., 24–52. Retired as Commodore. Hon. A.D.C. to successive Governers of N. Ireland from 27. Dir., Broadway Damask Co., 30–58. Now Chrmn., Transport Development Cttee. N. Ireland Chamber of Commerce & Industry. C.B., C.V.O., V.R.D., D.L. Comdr., Order of St. John. Pres., *Ulster Automobile Club. Ulster Club, Naval Military & Royal Aero Club, R. Ulster Y.C.* Brother, M. A. Shillington.

SHILLINGTON, Maurice Averell, b. 15 June 05, 2nd s. of the late T. C. Shillington. C, 19^2–22^2. Worcester, Oxford, B.A. Colonial Service .Supt. of Education, Northern Province, Nigeria, 28–36. B.B.C. as announcer in Belfast, 36; in London, 41–45. Retired, 65 after being Senior Announcer, Belfast. *Royal Co. Down G.C.* Brother, C. A. R. Shillington.

SHILLITOE, Arthur John, M.B., M.R.C.P., b. 14 May 19, s. of the late F. C. Shillitoe. T, 33^3–37^2. Guy's Hospital. Golding Bird prize in Bacteriology, 40–41. M.B., B.S., M.R.C.P. Consultant Pathologist, Leeds Regional Hosp. Board. F.R.S.M. Author of medical articles.

SHILLITOE, Gordon Francis, b. 15 Feb. 22, s. of the late F. S. Shillitoe. T, 35^3–39^2. Farmer. Chrmn. of Brackley Branch of N.F.U., 52. Syresham Parish Council, 52–61. Chrmn., 55–61. Retired.

SHIRRES, Alleyn Leslie Maynard. C, 09¹–13².*

SHORE, Thomas Leonard Hall, b. 9 Sept. 09, s. of Dr. L. E. Shore, O.B.E. W, 23¹–27³. St. John's, Cambridge, M.A., M.B., B.Chir. London Hosp. Med. School, M.R.C.S., L.R.C.P. ✕ R.A.M.C., 42–46. Major. Consultant Physician, West Somerset Hosp. Group. *West Somerset Medical Club, West Country Physician Club.*

SHORTO, Edward Herbert Charles, b. 11 Mar. 06, s. of the late Rev. D. E. Shorto (A). B, 19³–23². Engineering (Locomotive) apprenticeship & pupilship at Crewe Loco. Works. Improver in Motive Power Depot. F.I.Mech.E., Ch.Eng. Various supervisory appmts. in Locomotive Running Dept. of L.M.S.Rly./B.R., ending as Regional Fuel Supplies Officer, B.R. (Midland Region). Retired.

SHOUBERSKY, André (see Khilkoff-Choubersky, A.).

SIDEBOTTOM, David Nowell. M, 29³–33³. Son, 2743.*

SIDGWICK, Robert Benson. M, 32³–36³. Sons, 2582, 2583 & 2999.*

SILBERSTEIN, George (see Sutton, George Christopher).

SILLEM, Arthur Lammin. K, 35³–39².*

SILVER, Prof. Ian Adair, M.R.C.V.S., b. 28 Dec. 27, s. of the late G. J. Silver. M, 41³–45². Corpus Christi, Cambridge, M.A. Agricultural Research Council Post-Graduate Scholar to Royal Veterinary College, London Univ. M.R.C.V.S. Fellow of Churchill College, Cambridge. Tutor for Advanced Students & Dir. of Studies, Churchill College. Dir. of Studies, Selwyn College and St. Catharine's. Now Prof. of Comparative Pathology, Bristol Univ. Anatomical & Pathological Socs.

SIMCOX, William Martin, b. 28 June 89, younger s. of the late J. W. Simcox. SH, 02³–06³. Pembroke, Cambridge, B.A. Solicitor in Birmingham, 14–63. Retired.

SIMMONDS, Burnham Clifford. T, 09³–15¹.*

SIMMONDS, Preb. William Alfred, T.D., b. 15 Mar. 90, eldest s. of the late W. T. Simmonds. T, 03²–09². Keble, Oxford, M.A. Ordained, 13. Curate of

Bakewell, 13 and of St. Peter's, Eaton Square, London, 17. Vicar of St. Matthew's, Hammersmith, 24. Vicar of St. Peter's, Eaton Square. Rural Dean of Westminster (retired). Preb. of St. Paul's. T.D. Brother, B. C. Simmonds.

SIMMONS, Philip Lander. W, 42³–45².*

SIMONS, George Antony. C & Tu, 37²–42¹.*

SIMPSON, Brian Henry, b. 22 Mar. 21, 2nd s. of S. Simpson, C.M.G. T, 34³–39³. Dip. in Public Admin. A.C.I.S. ✕ Royal Marines, 39–45. Capt. S. Rhodesian Public Service. Principal Private Sec. to the Prime Minister of S. Rhodesia, 60–63. Resigned 65 & returned to U.K. Presently Company Accountant. Lt.-Col., Royal Rhodesia Regt. (T.F.). *Royal Overseas League.* Brothers, D. W. & G. S. Simpson.

SIMPSON, Christopher Robert, b. 7 Dec. 29, 2nd s. of Lt.-Col. M. R. Simpson, O.B.E., T.D., D.L. K, 43³–47³; Cap, 47. Magdalene, Cambridge, M.A. Solicitor, 55. Partner in Herbert Simpson, Son & Bennett of Leicester. Executive Cttee. of East Midlands Sports Council. Chrmn. of British Gliding Assoc., 72. Dep. Man., British Gliding Team, U.S.A., 70 & Yugoslavia, 72. *The Alpine Club, Leicestershire Club.* Brothers, J. R. Simpson & 349.

SIMPSON, David William, b. 9 Nov. 17, eldest s. of S. Simpson, C.M.G. T, 31²–36². Exeter, Oxford, B.A. ✕ Burma Frontier Service, 39 as Admin. Officer, Shan States. Served in Chin Hills, Burma, 42–45. Capt. Administrator, Hsipaw State, Shan States. After Burma's independence, Admin. posts in Sarawak & N. Rhodesia. English Language Consultant in various countries since 62. *Royal Over-Seas League.* Brothers, B. H. & G. S. Simpson.

SIMPSON, Derrick Paul, b. 19 June 19, s. of the late J. M. Simpson. T, 32³–38². ✕ R.A., 40–46. M.C.I.I. Insurance Officer, 58–69. Now Insurance Broker with Oakley Vaughan & Co. of Birmingham. Jt. Council of Christian Service Centre, Coventry Cathedral. Knight of St. Columba. Son, Hugh Adrian. T, 68³–71².

SIMPSON, Edward Osmond Thornhill, T.D., b. 11 Oct. 05, s. of the late E. T. B. Simpson. M, 19²–24¹. Magdalen, Oxford, B.A. ✕ Queen's Own Yorkshire Dragoons, 26–45. Major. T.D. 1st Cl. Mining Cert. G.B. & British Columbia.

Past Pres., Mining Assoc. of B.C. Gen. Man. & Vice-Pres., Mining Collieries Resources Ltd., Vancouver. Now retired. *Vancouver Club.* Fellow, *Royal Commonwealth Soc.*

SIMPSON, The Rev. Francis Haldane, b. 6 Sept. 06, 2nd s. of The Rev. Canon A. H. Simpson. T, 20³–25². Exhibitioner of Corpus Christi, Cambridge, B.A. Cuddesden College, 28. Ordained, 30. Miss. Dio., Shantung, 32–45. Canon of Romsey, Dio. Winchester from 64. Retired, 71.

SIMPSON, Geoffrey. SH, 16¹–19³.*

SIMPSON, Gordon Russell, D.S.O., T.D., b. 2 Jan. 17, 2nd s. of A. R. Simpson. SF, 30³–34²; Cadet Pair; S. VIII, 34. ✕ 2nd Lothian & Border Horse, 39–46. Wounded. D.S.O. & Bar. Stockbroker since 35. Partner in Bell Cowan & Co. (now Bell Lawrie Robertson & Co.). Pres., Council of Assoc. Stock Exchanges since 71. Dep. Chrmn., British Investment Trust. Dir., General Accident Fire & Life Assrce. Corp. Ltd. Queen's Bodyguard for Scotland (R.C.A.). *New Club, Edinburgh, Puffins.* Sons, 2233 & 2540.

SIMPSON, Geoffrey Samuel. T, 38²–40².*

SIMPSON, Sir (John) Cyril (Finucane), Bt., b. 10 Feb. 99, 3rd s. of the late Sir F. R. Simpson, Bt., C.B. (OR K 79). B, 12³–16²; XI, 15–16; Rackets Pair, 15–16. ✕ R.N.A.S. R.A.F. Lt. Wounded. Queen's, Oxford. Rackets Blue, 20–22. Amateur Doubles Champion (with R. C. O. Williams of Eton), 23–24. Amateur Singles Champion, 26–28. Stockbroker, retired. *White's, Buck's, Northern Counties, Vincent's.*

SIMPSON, John Rowton, T.D., D.L., b. 19 Sept. 26, eldest s. of Lt.-Col. M. R. Simpson, O.B.E., T.D., D.L. St & K, 40²–44²; Levée; R. VIII, 43–44 (Capt.). Magdalene, Cambridge, M.A., LL.B. ✕ Gordon Highlanders (seconded to Sierra Leone Regt., R.W.A.A.F.). Capt. Solicitor, 52. In private practice. T.D. Lt.-Col. R.E. D.L., Leics., 72. Brothers, C. R. Simpson & 349.

SIMPSON, John William. M, 19²–23¹.*

SIMPSON, Patrick Weir Ackroyd. M, 32³–36¹.*

SIMPSON, Patrick William, b. 14 Mar. 22, 3rd s. of the late A. R. Simpson, W.S. SF, 35³–40². ✕ Enlisted in R. Scots, 41.

Commissioned R.A., 42. Ayrshire Yeomanry (Field Regt.) Iraq. M.E.F. Italy. Capt. C.A., 50. Partner, Chiene & Tait, C.A., Edinburgh since 52. General Commissioner of Income Tax. *New Club, Edinburgh, The Cockburn Assoc.* Brother, R. J. B. Simpson. Son, 2934.

SIMPSON, Robert John Blantyre, M.B.E., T.D., b. 28 Aug. 14, eldest s. of the late A. R. Simpson, W.S. SF, 28¹–32². Magdalen, Oxford, M.A. Edinburgh Univ., LL.B. Writer to the Signet, 38. ✕ The Royal Scots (T.A.) T.D. & Clasp. Belgian Croix Militaire 1st Cl. Lt.-Col. M.B.E., 54. *New Club, Edinburgh, The Royal Scots.* Brother, P. W. Simpson. Son, 1301.

SIMS, Alan, b. 28 Apr. 01, elder s. of C. Sims, R.A. SF, 15³–19³; Scholar; Cap, 18. Scholar of Hertford, Oxford. Schoolmaster, retired. Author of three books. ✕ Asst. County A.R.P. Officer for Berkshire, 39–45.

SINCLAIR, Ian Henry Nash-Webber. SH, 46³–51².*

SINCLAIR, John Christopher Ormiston, b. 6 Dec. 28, s. of N. T. Sinclair (A). SH & C, 42³–46². Merchant Navy, 47. Marr Downie & Co. Ltd., Glasgow, Manufacturing Stationers, 48. Spicers Ltd., Paper & Board Makers, 49–58. Wolvercote Paper Mill, Oxford, Asst. Controller, 58–62. Western Board Mills Ltd., Treforest, Glam. since 62 (Dir., 65).

SINCLAIR, Capt. Sir Kenneth Duncan Lecky, D.L., R.N.R., b. 13 June 89, 3rd s. of the late Rt. Hon. T. Sinclair, P.C. SF, 02³–07¹. Trinity, Cambridge. Bacon Curer, Man. Dir. With Belfast Harbour, member for 36 years. Chrmn. for 18 years. Pres., Ulster Curers Assoc. for many years. Sundry interests in L'pool. Retired. D.L., 33. Knight Bachelor, 55. Hon. Capt. R.N.R. *Ulster Club, Belfast.* Son, T. R. L. Sinclair.

SINCLAIR, Thomas Roland Lecky, b. 27 Mar. 15, s. of Capt. Sir K. D. L. Sinclair, D.L., R.N.R. (OR SF 02). Tu, 28³–33². Trinity, Cambridge. Food Technologist. Exec. Vice-Pres., Kingans, Indianapolis, Indiana. Owner, Eldon Farm & Dir., Virginia Angus Assoc., U.S.A. Retired. Chrmn., J. & T. Sinclair & Co. Ltd., Montserrat (Investment Co.). *Ulster Club.*

SINCLAIR, William Richardson. SF, 97³–01².*

SING, Richard Millington (see Synge, R. M.).

SINGLE, Herbert Stanley, b. 6 Mar. 93, eldest s. of the late S. Single. Tu, 07¹–11². Exhibitioner of Lincoln, Oxford, M.A. ✕ 2nd & 8th Bns. East Surrey Regt. Lt. Wounded. Indian Forest Service since 21.

SISSONS, Richard Chamberlin, b. 1 Mar. 06, 2nd s. of the late H. H. Sissons. St, 19²–23². Pembroke, Cambridge, M.A. ✕ R.A.F. Coastal Command, 42–46. F./Offr. Late Man. Dir. & Chrmn., Sissons Brothers & Co. Ltd., Hull. Past Pres., National Paint Fed. Retired. Son, 2711.

SITWELL, Edward Anthony Wilmot, b. 14 Mar. 14, s. of the late A. T. Sitwell, B.Sc. (OR C 92). C, 28¹–31². In business and played tennis for Gloucestershire before war. ✕ S. African Field Artillery, 40–43. R.A., 43–46. Lt. Served in Kenya, Somaliland, Abyssinia, Eritrea, Egypt & Italy. Trade & Technical Journalist. Now retired.

SKEGGS, Peter Lyndon (see Lyndon-Skeggs, P.).

SKEY, Charles Henry Alan. K, 45²–49².*

SKINNER, Edmund Horsfall. SH, 32²–37¹.*

SKINNER, John Hershell, b. 21 Mar. 10, eldest s. of the late J. H. Skinner. K, 23³–27². A.M.B.I.M. Lilley & Skinner Ltd. (Footwear Distributors), 27–62. ✕ 86th (H.A.C.) H.A.A. Regt., R.A., 39–42 & R.E.M.E., 43–45. Lt. *Devonshire Club, Denham G.C.* Wor. Co. of Cordwainers. H.A.C. Brothers, R. B. & M. O. Skinner.

SKINNER, Michael Owen, b. 15 Apr. 19, 3rd s. of the late J. H. Skinner. K, 32³–36³; XV, 36. ✕ R.A., H.A.A., 39–46. Major. Dir., British Shoe Corp. Footwear Ltd. Man. Dir., Saxone, Lilley & Skinner. Liveryman, Wor. Co. of Cordwainers. *Goodwood & Thurlestone G.C.* Brothers, J. H. & R. B. Skinner. Sons, 1284 & 2445.

SKINNER, Ralph Becher. SH, 23¹–27³.*

SKINNER, Robert Banks, b. 18 Feb. 12, 2nd s. of the late J. H. Skinner. K, 25³–29³; XV, 28–29. ✕ R.A. Major. Chrmn., London Provision Exchange, 54–55. Treasurer, Inst. of Food Distributors since 66 and Pre-Retirement Assoc. since 69.

Chrmn., Carless Capel & Leonard Ltd. Dir., Morris & David Jones Ltd. *Devonshire Club, Moor Park G.C.* (Chrmn.). Brothers, J. H. & M. O. Skinner. Sons, 488 & 1193.

SKINNER, Russel Thomas Francis. SH, 22²–26³.*

SKYRME, Sir William Thomas Charles, K.C.V.O., C.B., C.B.E., T.D., J.P., b. 20 Mar. 13, s. of C. G. Skyrme. K, 26³–31²; S. VIII, 28–31; Cadet Officer, 30–31. New College, Oxford, M.A. Shooting Blue, 32–34 (Capt.). Univ. of Paris and Dresden. Bar, Inner Temple, 35. Practised at the Bar (Western Circuit), 38–39 ✕ R.A., 39–44. Wounded twice. Lt.-Col. Sec. to Lord Chancellor, 44–48. Sec. of Commissions, House of Lords since 48. C.B., C.B.E., 53. T.D., J.P., K.C.V.O., 74. F.R.G.S. Pres. Commonwealth Magistrates Assoc. since 70. *Garrick Club.*

SLATER, Ian George, b. 2 Sept. 14, s. of the late R. A. Slater. T, 28³–32². Major. Foundationer. ✕ R.E.M.E., 40–46. Capt. Chartered Electrical Engineer, M.I.E.E. Son, 2648.

SLATER, John Michael Whittenbury. Sh, 43¹–46².*

SLATER, Col. Owen, C.I.E., M.C., b. 19 June 90, s. of the late E. M. Slater. SH, 04³–08³. R.M.A., Woolwich. Gazetted to R.E., 10. ✕ R.E. Staff Capt. M.C. Dispatches thrice. Served in India, Mesopotamia, Transcaspia and East Prussia, 14–20. In survey of India, 21. Retired, 47. C.I.E. *United Service & Royal Aero Club.*

SLEIGHT, Rowland Derek Lambert, b. 9 May 08, s. of the late Major R. Sleight (OR St 91). St, 22²–26³; XV, 25–26; Cadet Officer. Member of the Chartered Soc. of Physiotherapy ✕ R.A.F.V.R., 41–46. Private Practice, Physiotherapy.

SLOAN, George Christopher. Sh, 42²–46².*

SMALLBONE, Derek John Kimpton. M, 36¹–40².*

SMALLWOOD, James Lloyd. SF, 18³–22².*

SMART, Arthur David Gerald, A.R.I.C.S., b. 19 Mar. 25, s. of Dr. A. H. J. Smart (OR SF 08). SF, 39¹–43². King's, Cambridge, M.A. Central Polytechnic, London (Dip. T.P.). F.R.T.P.I.

⚔ Rifle Brigade, 43–47. Capt. A.R.I.C.S. Various appointments in County Councils in London, Midlands & North. County Planning Officer, Hampshire C.C. since 63. On several Govt. Cttees. concerned with Town Planning from 64.

SMART, Arthur Herbert John, M.B., b. 18 Oct. 94, s. of the late Dr. W. H. Smart. SF, 08³–12¹. Gonville & Caius, Cambridge, M.B., B.Ch., B.A. St. Thomas's Hospital, M.R.C.S., L.R.C.P. ⚔ British Red Cross. R.N.V.R. Surg.-S/Lt. Wounded. Surg.-Lt., R.N., 19–20. Medical Practitioner, now retired. Son, A. D. G. Smart.

SMART, Raymond, b. 12 Aug. 22, s. of the late A. J. Smart. K, 36¹–40². King's, Cambridge. St. Mary's Hospital. Joined Allen & Hanbury Ltd., 52. Marketing Dir., 61–65. Man. Dir., 65–70. Dep. Chrmn. since 70. Commercial Dir., Glaxo Holdings Ltd. since 68. Royal Soc. of Medicine. Underwriting Member of Lloyd's.

SMEATON, Frederick Forbes. T, 32³–36³.*

SMELLIE, Lt.-Col. Alastair James Donaldson. W, 34¹–38².*

SMELLIE, Ian Maclure, b. 25 Nov. 30, eldest s. of the late Prof. J. M. Smellie, M.D., F.R.C.P. SF, 44³–49²; R. VIII, 49. King's, Cambridge, M.A. N/S. R.A. 2nd Lt. The Boots Company Ltd. Home & Garden Buyer. Hon. Sec. *Notts. R.F.C.*

SMELLIE, James Rintoul, D.S.C., b. 10 Apr. 00, eldest s. of the late W. Smellie. SF, 14¹–18². King's, Cambridge, M.A. In the petroleum business, mostly in London. Retired from Gulf Oil (G.B.) Ltd., 63. Rear-Commodore of *Royal Ocean Racing Club*, 38. Vice-Commodore, 45–46. ⚔ R.N.V.R., 39–45. Lt.-Cdr. D.S.C. & Bar. Son, 1150.

SMITH, Alfred Clough, b. 2 Feb. 25, 2nd s. of the late H. G. Smith. M, 38³–43¹. R.A.F. F/Lt. New College, Oxford (War Course). R.A.F.V.R. since 48. Textile Engineer and Manufacturer. J.P. (Keighley Bor.). Chrmn., Keighley Cons. Assoc. since 67.

SMITH, Alan Malcolm, F.R.C.S., b. 8 Dec. 28, s. of C. M. Smith, O.B.E., M.D. W, 42³–47²; Scholar; Levée; Exhibitioner. Trinity, Oxford, M.A., B.M., B.Ch. University College Hospital,

London, M.R.C.P.(Ed)., F.R.C.S.(Ed)., M.R.C.O.G. Consultant Obstetrician & Gynaecologist, Wolverhampton Group of Hospitals. F.R.S.M.

SMITH, Anthony David. B, 40³–44².*

SMITH, Eric Edward, b. 22 Nov. 22, s. of the late C. F. T. Smith. C, 36³–41¹; R. VIII, 40–41. ⚔ 13/18th R. Hussars. Capt. Wounded twice. N.W. Europe. Stockbroker. Partner in J. & A. Scrimgeour since 59. *Hurlingham, M.C.C.* Son, David Eric, C, 72³–.

SMITH, Francis Armitage, O.B.E., b. 11 Oct. 01, youngest s. of the late Joseph Smith. SH, 15¹–19². St. John's, Oxford, B.A. Solicitor, 25 (Prizeman). ⚔ R.A.F. Wing-Cdr. O.B.E. Partner in Moon, Beaven & Hewlett of London. Retired, 70. *Oriental Club.* Brother, J. R. A. Smith.

SMITH, Francis John Gorrill, b. 11 July 11, s. of Col. J. W. Smith, R.A.M.C., T.D., D.L. K, 24³–30¹; Scholar; Levée; Cadet Officer. Scholar of Oriel, Oxford, M.A. Full-time worker, Oxford Group, Moral Rearmament since 34, especially post-war in Britain, Germany & Switzerland. ⚔ 41–46. Capt. R.A.

SMITH, Col. Francis Longden, M.B.E., M.C., T.D., D.L., J.P., b. 23 Oct. 92, younger s. of the late A. Smith, O.B.E. M, 06³–11¹. ⚔ 6th Bn. West Riding (Duke of Wellington's) Regt. Major. Wounded. M.C. In T.A. till 31. Bt. Col. T.D. Textile Machine Maker, 11–68. Retired. M.B.E., D.L., J.P.

SMITH, Gordon Philip Hugh, b. 4 July 11, 2nd s. of the late James Smith, F.R.C.S. C, 25²–28². F.C.A. ⚔ R.A. (Field), 39–45. Major. Chartered Accountant in practice. H.A.C. & Leicestershire Yeomanry.

SMITH, Col. Ian Frederick Cory, b. 7 Jan. 02, eldest s. of the late Col. F. J. Smith, C.B., V.D., D.L., J.P. SH, 15³–20². R.M.C., Sandhurst. Gazetted as 2nd Lt. to 12th R. Lancers, 21. Lt., 23. ⚔ Lt.-Col., 43. Dispatches thrice. Retired as Hon. Col., 50.

SMITH, James Huth, M.C., M.B., B.Ch., b. 3 Apr. 05, eldest s. of the late James Smith. C, 19¹–23²; Cap, 22. Jesus, Cambridge, B.A., M.B., B.Ch. St. Thomas's Hospital, M.R.C.S., L.R.C.P. Retired from General Practice.

SMITH, John Bernard, b. 25 May 29, s. of B. Smith. B, 42^3–47^1. Man. Dir., Bernard Smith (Hopwas) Ltd. Horticulture.

SMITH, John Lister, M.B., Ch.B., b. 8 July 26, s. of the late John Smith. T & K, 40^2–45^1; R. VIII, 45. ✕ R.N.V.R., 45–48. A.B. Edinburgh Univ., M.B. Ch.B. General Practitioner. Fellow of the *Royal Commonwealth Soc.* B.M.A.

SMITH, John Neville, b. 18 July 04, youngest s. of the late J. H. Smith. B, 18^3–22^2; Cap. XXII. Jesus, Cambridge, B.A. Retired after 35 years with family business of Woolcombers and Worsted spinners in Bradford, followed by 5 years with P.O.S.B. in London.

SMITH, John Timothy Arthur, B.E.M., b. 29 Aug. 26, 2nd s. of the late L. A. Smith. C & Tu, 40^2–44^2. ✕ R.A., 44–47. Lt. B.E.M. University College, Oxford, M.A. Solicitor. Partner in Lee Crowder & Co. of Birmingham. Retired. Pres., Birmingham Law Soc., 73. Local Dir., Legal & General Life Assurance Soc. Ltd. *Birmingham Union Club & Chamber of Commerce Clubs.*

SMITH, Joseph Eric. K, 22^2–26^1.*

SMITH, Joseph Reginald Armitage, b. 9 Oct. 97, 2nd s. of the late Joseph Smith. SH, 11^3–16^2; Head of House; R. VIII, 16; Cadet Officer. ✕ 366th Bty., R.F.A. Lt. St. John's, Oxford, M.A. London Univ. Dip.Ed. Diplômes de Français at Grenoble, Dijon & Poitiers. Asst. Master, Dulwich College, 22–28. Rugby School, 28–62 (Housemaster, Bradley, 45–59). *Army & Navy Club.* Brother, F. A. Smith.

SMITH, Oscar Graham. St, 30^2–34^2.*

SMITH, Peter Fox, b. 26 Feb. 22, 2nd s. of R. H. Smith, J.P. Tu, 35^3–40^1. ✕ R.A.F., 40–46. Pilot. F/Lt. Textile Machinery Maker. Man. Dir. Son, David Peter Hattersley, Tu, 67^3–71^2.

SMITH, Philip Sascha, T.D., b. 16 Jan. 14, 2nd s. of T. Smith. C, 27^3–32^2; Scholar; Exhibitioner; XI, 30. XV, 31; Scholar of Corpus Christi, Oxford, B.A. Man. Dir., Kado Ltd., 47–72. Dep. Chrmn. since 72. Chrmn., Teesside Marriage Guidance Council since 59. J.P., 60. Now Chrmn., Teesside Probation Cttee. ✕ Intell. Corps. Major. Son, 833.

SMITH, Raymond Walter, b. 22 July 96, 2nd s. of the late J. J. Smith. T, 11^2–13^3. ✕ R.A.F. 2nd Lt. Engineer, Hong Kong Water Works. Now retired.

SMITH, Wing-Cdr. Robert Higson, O.B.E. Sh, 31^3–35^2.*

SMITH, Major Robert James Tull, T.D., b. 6 Apr. 13, s. of P. J. Smith. M, 26^3–30^3; Levée. London Univ., LL.B. Gazetted to 7th Bn. Sherwood Foresters (T.A.), 31. Capt. Solicitor, 35. ✕ Major. Dispatches. T.D. p.s.c. Staff Capt. D.A.A.G. G.S.O.3. Major. D.A.Q.M.G. Since 35 partner in Clifton, Woodward & Smith (now Clifton, Smith & Tutin) of Nottingham. Mem. Council of the Law Society, 54–72. Pres., Nottinghamshire Law Soc., 61. *Nottingham & Notts. United Services Club.*

SMITH, Ronald Longden. M, 38^3–42^3.*

SMITHELLS, Richard Worthington, M.B., B.S., b. 12 July 24, younger s. of C. J. Smithells. B, 39^1–43^3. St. Thomas's Hospital Medical School, M.B., B.S., F.R.C.P.(Lon.), F.R.C.P.(Ed.). Prof. of Paediatrics & Child Health, Univ. of Leeds.

SMYTH, Anthony John. T & C, 42^1–46^2.*

SMYTH, Ian Coulter, b. 7 Apr. 27, 3rd s. of W. B. Smyth. C & Tu, 40^3–45^2. Trinity College, Dublin, B.A. Univ. "Pink" for Lawn Tennis. Solicitor to National Film Finance Corp. Brothers, R. & W. D. Smyth.

SMYTH, Robert. C, 35^2–39^2.*

SMYTH, William Daniel, b. 28 Dec. 24, 2nd s. of W. B. Smyth. C & Tu, 39^1–43^2. Jt. Man. Dir. with brother, Robert, of family Feed Milling Co. (Robert Smyth & Sons Ltd., Strabane). Chrmn., Londonderry Gaslight Co. Ltd. Mem., Electricity Board for N. Ireland. Jt. Master, Strabane & Donegal Hounds since 67. Conductor, Strabane Choral Soc. since 55. D.L. (County Tyrone), 70. Brothers, R. & I. C. Smyth. m. Rosemary, d. of A. Blair-White (OR Tu 06).

SMYTH, William Roland Beatty. M, 07^2–10^3.*

SMYTHE, Group-Capt. Howard Alexander, D.S.O., D.F.C., A.F.C. St, 23^2–27^3.*

SMYTHIES, Bertram Evelyn, b. 11 July 12, elder s. of E. A. Smythies, C.I.E. SH, 26¹-30²; Scholar; Holder of Selous Natural History Exhibition. Christ's, Cambridge; Balliol, Oxford, B.A. Burma Forest Service, 34-48. ✕ C.A.S.(B). Major. Dispatches. Colonial Forest Service in Sarawak & Brunei, 49-64. Author of "The Birds of Burma" & "The Birds of Borneo". Retired, 64. F.L.S., F.R.G.S. *Special Forces Club, R. Brunei Y.C.* Brother, J. R. Smythies.

SMYTHIES, John Raymond, M.D., F.R.C.S., b. 30 Nov. 22, 2nd s. of E. A. Smythies, C.I.E. SH, 36³-40¹. Exhibitioner & Prizeman of Christ's, Cambridge, M.A., M.B., B.Chir. University College Hospital, M.R.C.P., F.R.C.Psych. ✕ R.N.V.R., 46-48. Surg.-Lt. F.R.C.S., 48. D.P.M.(Lon.), 52. Ireland Prof. of Psychiatry & Prof. of Biochemistry, Univ. of Alabama. Lately, Reader in Psychiatry, Univ. of Edinburgh. Senior Registrar, Maudsley Hospital. Nuffield Fellow in Medicine. Pres., International Soc. for Psychoneuroendocrinology. Consultant W.H.O. R. Soc. of Medicine. *Athenæum.* Brother, B. E. Smythies. Sons, 2910 & Christopher John Evelyn, SH, 70³-.

SNELL, David John Hammersley. K, 44³-49¹.*

SNOWDEN, Arthur John, b. 27 July 31, 2nd s. of the late A. O. Snowden (OR SF 99). SF, 45²-49²; XI, 47; XXII, 48-49. Worcester, Oxford. The Buffs (T.A.) Lieut. Schoolmaster till 64. Master Printer since 64. Brother, H. T. H. Snowden.

SNOWDEN, Hubert Thomas Harcourt, b. 23 May 14, elder s. of the late A. O. Snowden (OR SF 99). SF, 28¹-32²; XI, 32; H. XI, 32. Worcester, Oxford, M.A. ✕ Coldstream Guards, 41-46. Capt. Served in Middle East & Italy. Headmaster of Hildersham House, Broadstairs, 46-71. Hon. Sec., O.R. Soc. & Address Sec., 72. Regional Dir., I.S.I.S. (London & S.E.) since 73. *M.C.C., Vincent's, Army & Navy Club, R. & A. G.C.* Brother, A. J. Snowden.

SOKOLOW, Stephen Edward. K, 38¹-40².*

SOLLY, Jocelyn Norbury, M.C., b. 13 Nov. 97, 2nd s. of the late E. Solly, M.B., F.R.C.S. (OR M 73). M, 12²-15³. ✕ Cheshire Yeomanry, 16-17. 1st Bn. Scots Guards, 17-19. Lt. M.C. With Reade & Co. Silk Spinners, Congleton, 19-28.

Electrical & Radio Engineer on own account from 28. ✕ R.A., 40-45. Capt. Now retired, but for last 20 years in Voluntary Hospital Management.

SOLOMON, Andrew Bernard. M, 35¹-39¹.*

SOLOMON, Patrick James Baker. B, 29²-34¹.*

SOLOMON, William Balfour Saul, b. 12 May 13, elder s. of The Hon. Mr. Justice S. Solomon. B, 27¹-30³. Cape Town Univ., B.A. Sworn Translator in three languages (self-employed). *Durban Country Club, Johannesburg Country Club.* Brother, P. J. B. Solomon.

SOMERS, Col. Thomas Vivian, O.B.E., b. 7 Apr. 09, 2nd s. of S. S. Somers, O.B.E. B, 22³-27². R.M.A., Woolwich. Gazetted to R.A., 29. ✕ 39-45. France, Belgium, Western Desert & N.W. Europe. T/Lt.-Col., 43. O.B.E., 45. p.s.c. j.s.s.c. Retired as Col., 56. Olympic Games, Helsinki, 52 (Yacht Racing). Dir., Walter Somers Ltd., 56-62. Farmer. *Army & Navy Club, R.Y.S.* Son, 1954.

SOMERVELL, Ronald Arthur, b. 21 Feb. 00, elder s. of the late Sir Arthur Somervell, M.A., Mus.Doc. SH, 13³-18². ✕ Guards Cadet Bn. 2nd Lt. Coldstream Guards, 18. Exhibitioner of Trinity, Cambridge, B.A. Dir., Somervell Bros. Ltd., 36-59. Chrmn., K Shoes Ltd., 59-65. Retired, 65. ✕ R.A.F. (Intell.), 41-45. F/Lt. High Sheriff, Westmorland, 58-59. Kt. of St. Gregory (Papal Dec.), 71. *Brooks's.*

SOMERVELL, Theodore Howard, C.B.E., F.R.C.S., b. 16 Apr. 90, elder s. of the late W. H. Somervell. C, 04³-09²; Leaving Exhibition. Scholar of Gonville & Caius, Cambridge, B.A. Scholar of University College Hospital, M.R.C.S., L.R.C.P. ✕ 34 Casualty Clearing Station, B.E.F., 15-19. Military Hospital, Leeds, 19-20. Capt. Dispatches. On Everest Expeditions, 22-24. London Mission Hospital, Neyyoor, South India, as Med. Supt., 23-49. Christian Med. Coll., Vellore, 49-61, as Prof. of Surgery. Retired, 61. Hon. Freeman of Kendal, 56. Kaisar-i-Hind Gold Medal, 40. O.B.E., 55. *Alpine Club.* Hon. Mem., *Italian Alpine Club.*

SOUTHALL, James Rae. C & Tu, 39³-42².*

SOUTHAM, John Armitage, F.R.C.S., b. 27 Aug. 29, s. of the late A. H. Southam, M.A., M.D. (OR C 02). B, 43²-46³. Manchester Univ. Medical School, M.B., Ch.B., F.R.C.S., F.R.C.S.(Ed.). Consultant Surgeon, Epsom & West Park Group of Hospitals. *R.A.C.*

SOUTHAN, Robert Joseph, b. 13 July 28, s. of T. Southan. T, 42²-47¹. St. Edmund Hall, Oxford, M.A. University College, London, LL.M. Bar, Inner Temple, 53. Barrister. *R. Corinthian Y.C., Hurlingham.*

SPAFFORD, George Christopher Howsin, b. 1 Sept. 21, s. of the late C. H. Spafford. St, 35²-39². ✕ Instructor S.T.C. (Cert. B), 39-45. R.A. T/Capt. Brasenose, Oxford, M.A., B.C.L. Bar, Middle Temple, 48. Northern Circuit.

SPARKS, John Peel, M.D., M.R.C.P., b. 28 Feb. 15, s. of the late Dr. J. P. Sparks, M.D., J.P. W, 28³-33¹; Cap. Gym. VIII; Fives IV. For career, see Part III under Assistant Masters. Medical Officer, Rugby School.

SPEED, Sir Robert (William Arney), C.B., Q.C., b. 18 July 05, s. of the late Sir E. A. Speed, M.A., LL.D. (OR B 82). B, 19³-24²; XI, 24; H. XI, 24; Levée; Head of House. Trinity, Cambridge, B.A. Bar, Inner Temple, 28. Treasury, Solicitor's Dept., 34. Principal Asst. Solicitor, 45. C.B., 46. Solicitor to the Board of Trade, 48-60. Kt., 54. Counsel to the Speaker since 60. Bencher, Inner Temple, 61. Q.C., 62. *United Oxford & Cambridge Univ. Club.* Son, 102.

SPEIRS, Robert Robson, b. 15 Mar. 25, s. of the late Col. G. C. T. Speirs, M.C., D.L. Tu, 38³-43¹; Cap. Emmanuel, Cambridge for 1 year. ✕ R.N., 43-46. P.O. Radar Mechanic. Chrmn., Speirs Ltd. (Building Contractors), Glasgow. Son, Andrew Charles. Tu, 67³-71³.

SPENCER, Christopher Maurice, b. 8 Dec. 23, 2nd s. of the late M. C. Spencer. SH, 37³-42¹; Cap, 41. ✕ R.N. (F.A.A.), 42-46. Lieut.(A), R.N.V.R. F.C.A. Chief Accountant, Legal & General Assurance Soc. Ltd. *City Livery Club.* Brother, M. D. Spencer.

SPENCER, Jack Crosland, b. 12 June 94, s. of the late F. Spencer. W, 08²-13². Trinity, Oxford. ✕ 3rd Bn. Wiltshire Regt., 14. B.E.F. France. 2nd Bn., 15. Gen. Staff, War Office, 16. Invalided, 17.

Lieut. A.M.I.Loco.E. Man. Dir., George Spencer Moulton & Co. Ltd., 36-60 (Chrmn., 46-56) (Pres. since 60). Retired. Member, Uckfield R.D.C. since 64. *United Services, Carlton & Argentine Clubs.* Son, 2001.

SPENCER, Michael Desbois, b. 9 Nov. 19, eldest s. of the late M. C. Spencer. SH, 33²-38¹. St. John's, Oxford. Exec. Dir., Canadian Firm Development Corp., Montreal. ✕ Canadian Army. Brother, C. M. Spencer.

SPENS, Lt.-Col. Hugh Stuart, M.B.E., M.C., T.D., b. 30 Nov. 16, 2nd s. of the late Col. H. B. Spens, C.B.E. (OR SH 98). SH, 30²-35². Trinity, Cambridge, B.A. Gazetted to Argyll & Sutherland Highlanders, 39. ✕ M.B.E., M.C. Dispatches thrice. Wounded, 43. Major. p.s.c. j.s.s.c. Commanded 1st Bn. Argyll & Sutherland Highlanders. Retired, 62. T.D. Dir., Robert Fleming & Co. Ltd., Merchant Bankers. Brother, T. P. D. Spens. Son, 2494.

SPENS, Paul George, b. 13 Oct. 17, eldest s. of the late Sir W. Spens, C.B.E. (OR SH 96). SH, 31³-36²; Scholar; Levée; Exhibitioner. Scholar of Corpus Christi, Cambridge, B.A. Fellow, 45. Univ. Demonstrator in Engineering, 46-49. Dir. of Studies in Engineering & Domestic Bursar, Corpus Christi. Brother, S. N. Spens.

SPENS, Stephen Nicholas. SH, 37³-39³.*

SPENS, Thomas Patrick, O.B.E., M.C., b. 10 July 94, 4th & youngest s. of the late J. A. Spens, LL.D. SH, 08³-13²; R. VIII, 13; Head of House. Trinity, Cambridge, M.A. ✕ 5th Bn. Cameronians. Wounded. M.C. Staff Lt. Intell. Corps. Aberdeen Garrison & Tay Defences. Dispatches. Solicitor. W.S., 21. Partner, Maclay Murray & Spens of Glasgow, 22-71. Chancellor, Dio. of Glasgow & Galloway from 33; Dio. of St. Andrews from 38; Dio. of Aberdeen, 72. ✕ 39-45. Staff. H.Q. Scottish Command & H.Q. Land Forces, Norway. O.B.E.(Mil.), 42; Bronze Star, U.S.A., 45; Freedom Cross Norway, 45. Hon. LL.D. Glasgow, Univ. Royal Faculty of Procurators in Glasgow of which Dean, 62-65. *Western Club, Glasgow; New Club, Edinburgh.* Son, 21.

SPENS, Major Thomas Patrick Douglas, M.B.E., b. 15 Feb. 14, eldest s. of the late Col. H. B. Spens, C.B.E. (OR SH 98).

SH, 27^3–31^1. R.M.C., Sandhurst-Scholar. Gazetted to 1st Bn. Argyll & Sutherland Highlanders, 32. ✕ 39–45. Major. M.B.E. Wounded. Member of H.M. Bodyguard for Scotland. J.P., Co. Durham. British Steel Corp. *Army & Navy Club.* Brother. H. S. Spens.

SPENS, The Rt. Hon. The Lord (William George Michael), M.B.E., b. 18 Sept. 14, eldest s. of the late The Rt. Hon. The Lord Spens (OR SH 99). SH, 27^3–32^2; XI, 31. New College, Oxford, M.A. Gazetted to R.A., 38. ✕ Indian Mountain Artillery, 38–43. G.S.O.3 & G.S.O.2 on Staff of Military Adviser-in-Chief, Indian States Forces, 43–44. G.S.O.2, Control Commission for Germany, 45–48. Major. Control Commission for Germany, 48–55. Retired from Army, 48. M.B.E. Bar, Inner Temple, 46. Chartered Accountant, 60. Partner in Fuller, Jenks Beecroft & Co. of London. Dir., Fed. of British Carpet Manufacturers. Succeeded father as 2nd Baron, Nov. 73. *Carlton Club, M.C.C., Royal Commonwealth Soc.* Sons, 1248 & 1506.

SPICER, Lancelot Dykes, D.S.O., M.C., b. 22 Mar. 93, youngest s. of the late Rt. Hon. Sir A. Spicer, Bt. Tu, 07^1–12^2; Head of House; Cadet Officer. Trinity, Cambridge, B.A. With Spicer Ltd., Wholesale Paper Merchants (Chrmn., 50–59). ✕ 9th Bn. Yorkshire L.I. Bde. Major. 64th Infantry Bde. Capt. Wounded. M.C. (Bar), D.S.O. Dispatches. *Oxford & Cambridge Univ. Club.*

SPITTLE, Lewin Trevor, b. 6 July 16, eldest s. of the late J. T. Spittle (OR Tu 01). Tu, 30^2–35^2; S. VIII, 33–35 (Capt.). Clare, Cambridge. Solicitor, 49. ✕ 17/21st Lancers, 40–46. Lt.-Col. Wounded. N. Africa, 42. Partner, Messrs. Longbourne, Stevens & Powell of London, 49–64. Retired through ill-health. *Cavalry Club.* Brother, S. D. T. Spittle. Son, 2897.

SPITTLE, Stanley Denys Trevor, b. 4 June 20, 2nd s. of the late J. T. Spittle (OR Tu, 01). Tu, 34^2–38^3. Pembroke, Cambridge. Edward S. Prior Prize, 47. M.A., A.R.I.B.A. ✕ R.E., 41–46. Royal Commission on Historical Monuments (Editor at Cambridge Office). Fellow, Soc. of Antiquaries. Brother, L. T. Spittle.

SPORBORG, Henry Nathan, C. M. G., b. 17 Sept. 05, eldest s. of the late H. N. Sporborg. St, 19^2–24^1. Emmanuel, Cambridge, M.A. Solicitor, 30. Partner in Slaughter & May, 35–39. ✕ Min.

of Economic Warfare, 39–40. Special Ops. Exec., 40–46 (Vice-Chief, 43–46). Lt.-Col. C.M.G. Chevalier Légion d'Honneur; Croix de Guerre; Order of St. Olaf of Norway; also American & Danish Decs. Dir., Hambros Ltd. Chrmn. and/or Dir. of numerous Public & Private Comps. Chrmn., Board of Governors of St. Mary's Hospital. Dir., P.L.A. Commissioner to Earl Fitzwilliam. *Boodle's, Carlton. Puckeridge & Thurlow Hunt Cttee.* (Chrmn.). Son, 877.

SPOTTISWOODE, Anthony Derek, b. 19 July 25, 2nd s. of the late D. Spottiswoode. St & K, 39^1–43^2; Levée; Head of House; Holder of Bigside Bags, 43; R. VIII, 42–43 (Capt.); Crick Winner, 43. ✕ R.N.V.R., 44–46. S/Lt. Pembroke, Cambridge, B.A. Half Blue, Running, 44. Solicitor, 50. Partner in Herbert Smith & Co. of London. Brother, H. D. Spottiswoode.

SPOTTISWOODE, Hugh David, F.C.A., b. 8 June 20, elder s. of the late D. Spottiswoode. St, 34^1–38^2; R. VIII, 38. Pembroke, Cambridge, M.A. ✕ Hampshire Regt., 40–42. R. Indian A.S.C., 42–46. Served in Burma. Major. Dispatches. F.C.A. Since 50 with Joseph Lucas Organisation. Dir., Joseph Lucas Export Ltd., 59–70. Sec., Joseph Lucas (Industries) Ltd. and Dir., Lucas Subsidiaries since 70. *Ladbrook Park G.C.* Brother, A. D. Spottiswoode. Son, 2713.

SPRAWSON, Eric, D.F.C. B, 24^3–28^3.*

SPROTT, Ernest Philip Mawdsley. St, 27^1–31^1.*

SPURGIN, John Alistair Wingrove. Tu, 36^3–41^2. Son, William David John. Tu, 73^3–.*

SPURGIN, Peter Readman, b. 14 Feb. 25, 2nd s. of the late Major E. W. Spurgin, M.C. Tu, 38^3–43^2. ✕ Coldstream Guards, 43–47. N.W. Europe. M.E.L.F. Lt. Pembroke, Cambridge, M.A. Asst. Master, Wellesley House, Broadstairs, 50–51. Strathallan School, Perth, 52–73 (Housemaster, Riley House, 58–60; Freeland House, 60–73). Master i/c Hockey, 60–73. Appointed a Selector of Scottish Schoolboys XI, 66. *New Club, Edinburgh.* Brother, J. A. W. Spurgin.

SPURRELL, David James Francis, b. 15 May 29, youngest s. of the late Major W. J. Spurrell, D.S.O., M.C. Sh, 42^3–47^2. Farmer. Dress shop owner since 69; extending to menswear, 71. 6 shops in Norfolk. Brother, P. M. N. Spurrell.

SPURRELL, Peter Morris Newnham, b. 11 Dec. 23, 2nd s. of the late Major W. J. Spurrell, D.S.O., M.C. Sh, 37^3–42^2. Gonville & Caius, Cambridge. Farming & Gardening. Brother, D. J. F. Spurrell.

SPURRIER, Henry John Marston, b. 7 Sept 13, s. of J. M. Spurrier. C, 27^2–31^3. Christ Church, Oxford. ✕ 1st Derbyshire Imperial Yeomanry, 39–45. Capt. Dispatches. Dir., Hilton Gravel Ltd., 47–66. Farmer & Chrmn., Marston-on-Dove Estates Ltd. Sons, 834 & 1126.

SQUIRE, Gordon Peter James, b. 30 Oct. 28, s. of P. J. A. Squire. W, 42^3–46^3; Cap, 45; S. VIII, 46. Selwyn, Cambridge, M.A. Man. Dir., Henry Squire & Sons Ltd., Lock Manufacturers. *Royal Anglesey Y.C., R. St. George Y.C., Dun Laoghaire.*

STABB, His Honour William Walter, Q.C., b. 6 Oct. 13, 2nd s. of the late Sir N. J. Stabb, O.B.E. St, 27^2–31^2. University College, Oxford. M.A. Bar, Inner Temple, 36. ✕ R.A.F.V.R., 40–46, Equipment Branch. Chrmn., Beds. Quarter Sessions, 61–69. Q.C., 68. Bencher, Inner Temple, 64. Official Referee of the Supreme Court, 69. Circuit Judge.

STAFFORD, Owen Sydney. M, 32^3–37^1. Sons, James Alexander Bethune. M, 69^1–; & Nigel John. M, 72^2–.*

STAFFORD, Thomas Bethune, b. 28 Apr. 16, s. of the late T. C. Stafford. M, 29^3–34^2; XXII. Brasenose, Oxford, B.A. Chartered Accountant, 40. ✕ R.A.S.C. & Gloucestershire Regt. Blackburns Robson Coates, C.A.'s, 46–51. The Amalgamated Press (later Fleetway Publications), 51–66. International Publishing Corp. Ltd. since 66. *East India, Sports & Public Schools, M.C.C., Hampstead C.C.*

STAIB, Christian Fredrik Edward. SF, 33^2–37^2.*

STAIG, David. SH, 41^3–46^1.*

STAIR, Alastair Arthur. K, 27^1–30^2.*

STALLARD, Frederick Richard. C, 46^3–50^2.*

STALLARD, George Robin. Tu, 41^3–46^2.*

STALLARD, Godfrey Bradby, b. 15 Sept. 89, 3rd s. of the late G. Stallard (former Housemaster, Tudor). Tu, 03^3–07^3; Head of House. R.M.A., Woolwich.

Gazetted to R.A., 09. Retired, 13. ✕ I.A.R.O. att. 25th Punjabis. Lt. Rubber Planter in F.M.S. Now retired. Son, G. R. Stallard.

STANDRING, Major Denis Arthur Tennant, b. 14 May 97, 2nd s. of the late W. Standring (OR SH 80). K, 11^3–15^3; Cap, 15; XI, 15. R.M.A., Woolwich. ✕ 75th Bty., R.F.A., 17–19. Lt. Served in Salonica, Palestine & Egypt. Brasenose, Oxford. Reserve of Officers, R.A. Assistant Schoolmaster, Summerfields, St. Leonards-on-Sea, 24–62. Retired. ✕ Movement Control Officer, Southampton, Liverpool & War Office, 39–45. Major. *O.U. Authentics & Band of Brothers C.C., R.A.C.* Brother, H. W. Standring.

STANDRING, Henry Woolf, O.B.E., b. 21 Sept. 01, 3rd s. of the late W. Standring (OR SH 80). K, 15^3–20^3; XI, 18–20. Brasenose, Oxford, M.A. F.R.I.C.S., F.A.I. Land Agent & Surveyor. Senior Partner, Godfrey Payton & Co., Warwick, Coventry, Market Harborough & Salisbury. O.B.E. Brother, D. A. T. Standring.

STANFORD, Christopher John Neil, b. 12 June 22, eldest s. of the late Lt.-Col. J. K. Stanford, O.B.E., M.C. (OR SH 05). SH, 36^1–40^2. ✕ 17/21st Lancers, 40–46. Lt. P.O.W. N. Africa, Italy & Germany, 43–45. Exporter of bloodstock & livestock. Chrmn., Neil Stanford Ltd. Son, David Neil. SH, 71^1–.

STANFORD, John Rodney, b. 10 Oct. 30, eldest s. of the late Ven. L. J. Stanford, M.A. T, 44^3–49^2; Tancred Scholar; Squire Scholarship. Gazetted to the R. Warwickshire Regt. (Emergency Commission), 50. Merton, Oxford, M.A. Pupil to the Resident Land Agent at Old Warden, Beds., 54–56. Unilever Ltd., 56–60. Asst. to the Editor of "The Field", 60–68. With the Central Council for Agricultural & Horticultural Co-operation, 69–73. Farmer. Brother, J. G. Stanford.

STANFORD, Julian George, b. 15 Jan. 33, 2nd s. of the late Ven. L. J. Stanford, M.A. T, 45^3–51^2; Levée; Head of House; R. VIII, 51; Crick Winner, 51; Cadet Officer. N/S. Sherwood Foresters, 52. 2nd Lt. Worcester, Oxford, M.A. F.C.I.S., A.I.B. Asst. Dir., Morgan Grenfell & Co. Ltd. Brother, J. R. Stanford.

STANFORD, Lt.-Col. William, R.A., b. 16 Dec. 30, 2nd s. of the late Brig. H. M. Stanford, C.B.E., M.C. SH, 44^2–48^3. R.M.A., Sandhurst. Gazetted to R.A., 51 as 2nd Lt. p.s.c. j.s.s.c. Senior Officers' War Course, Greenwich, 71. Regimental & Staff service in Germany, East Africa, Malta, Cyrprus, U.K., Middle East, Far East & Ulster. Lt., 53; Capt., 56; Major, 61; Lt.-Col., 71. C.O., 19th Field Regt., R.A. since 71. *Army & Navy Club.*

STANILAND, Geoffrey Meaburn, b. 14 Aug. 01, elder s. of the late G. Staniland (OR M 95). M, 15^3–18^3; G. VIII, 18. Motor Engineer. ✗ R.A.F., 41–45. F/Lt. Retired. *East India, Sports & Public Schools Club.*

STANILAND, Meaburn Francis, M.C. M, 27^3–32^1.*

STANILAND, Robert William, b. 12 Aug. 10, 2nd (twin) s. of the late Capt. M. Staniland (OR M 92). M, 24^2–28^2; R. VIII, 27–28. Trinity, Cambridge, B.A. Farmer, retired. Brother, M. F. Staniland. Son, Meaburn Charles. SF, 69^1–.

STANNING, John Duncan. M,29^3–33^2.*

STAPLEDON, Richard, b. 10 May 01, s. of the late J. N. Stapledon. Tu, 15^3–19^2; XI, 18–19; Cap, 18. Queen's, Oxford; Athletics Half Blue, 20; Blue, 21–23. Joined Alfred Holt & Co., Shipowners, L'pool. In Singapore, 28. Prep. School Headmaster, 46–68. Retired. *Vincent's, Oxford.*

STARLING, John Francis, b. 22 Apr. 24, younger s. of the late F. H. Starling. W, 38^1–42^2. ✗ R.N.V.R., 42–46. S/Lt.(E). Employed in the family Electrical & Mechanical Engineering and Contracting Company since 46 (now Man. Dir.). Various sailing clubs. Son, Peter Anthony. W, 73^1–.

STATHERS, Douglas Nicholson. Tu, 33^3–35^1.*

STEEL, Anthony Bedford, O.B.E., Litt.D., LL.D., b. 24 Feb. oo, elder s. of the late Major E. B. Steel (OR C 86). C, 13^3–18^2; Scholar; Head of House; Cap, 17–18; Major & Minor Exhibitioner. ✗ 2nd Lt. R.A.S.C., M.T. Germany, 18–19. Scholar of New College, Oxford, B.A. Fellow of Christ's, Cambridge, 24; M.A. (Cantab), 25; Litt.D., 55. Dir. of Studies in History, Christ's (Steward, 37–39; Tutor, 45–49). Senior Proctor, Cambridge Univ., 37–38. M.O.I., Temp. Principal, 38–40. British Council, 40–45. O.B.E., 45. Principal, University Coll., Cardiff, 49–66. Retired. C.St.J., 53. Asst. Dir.-Gen.

(Overseas) St. John Amb. Assoc., 52–54. Vice-Chancellor, Univ. of Wales, 56–58 & 59–61. Hon. LL.D. Wales, 67. F.R.H.S. Various Publications. *United Service & Royal Aero Club, Cardiff & County.* Son, D. A. B. Steel.

STEEL, David Anthony Bedford, B.C.L., b. 15 June 28, s. of Dr. A. B. Steel, O.B.E. (OR C 13). Tu & C, 43^3–46^3. New College, Oxford, M.A. B.C.L. (McGill); M.B.A. (Toronto). Barrister & Solicitor, Province of Ontario, Canada. Partner, Borden, Elliot, Kelley & Palmer, of Toronto. *National Club, Toronto.* Son, Antony Wynne Bedford. C, 71^2–.

STEEL, David Edward Charles, D.S.O., M.C., b. 29 Nov. 16, 2nd s. of the late G. A. Steel, C.B. (OR W 97) & Grandson of C. G. Steel (OR W, 67) (former Housemaster of Stanley). W, 30^3–35^2; Exhibitioner; Head of House; XV, 34; XI, 33–35 (Capt.). University College, Oxford, B.A. ✗ Inns of Court Regt., 38–39. 9th Queen's Royal Lancers, 40–46. Major. D.S.O., M.C. Dispatches thrice. T.D. Solicitor, 47. Joined British Petroleum Co. Ltd. as Legal Asst., 50; Man. Dir., 65; Dep. Chrmn., 72. Chrmn., War Memorial Trustees & Governor of Rugby School. Pres. O.R. Soc., 68–69. *Cavalry Club, Links,* N.Y. Son, Michael Price. W, 73^3–.

STEEL, Col. Richard Greville Acton, T.D., b. 6 Mar. 04, younger s. of the late Col. R. A. Steel, C.M.G., C.I.E. (OR M 87). SH, 17^3–22^2; Exhibitioner; Cap, 21; XXII, 21. Hertford, Oxford, B.A. F.C.A. Commissioned, 52. H.A.A. Regt., R.A. (T.A.), 38. ✗ R.A., 39–45. Asst. A.A. Offr. U.S. 1st Army, 44–45. Commd. 490(M) H.A.A. Regt., R.A. (T.A.), 48–52. Lt.-Col. T.D. U.S. Bronze Star. Col., retired, 60. Guaranty Trust Co. of N.Y. (later Morgan Guaranty Trust Co. of N.Y.), 28–62 (Asst. Vice-Pres.). *United Oxford & Cambridge Club.*

STEEL, Wilfred Sayer, b. 27 June oo, eldest s. of the late S. A. Steel. SF, 14^2–18^3; Levée; Cap, 18; Cadet Officer. ✗ R.A.F., 41–45. F/Lt. Steel Manufacturer. Now retired. *Carlton. R.A.C.*

STEELE, John Robert, b. 11 Mar. 29, s. of F. W. Steele, B.Sc. T, 43^3–46^2. Agricultural Engineering. Gen. Man., E. Ward (Fuels) Ltd., Wellingborough (Fuel Oil Distributor for Shell-Mex & B.P. Ltd.). *Wellingborough G.C. Rushden & Dist. Caledonian Soc.*

STEELE-BODGER, Michael Roland. Tu, 39²–43³.*

STEELL, John Walter Graham, M.R.C.S., L.R.C.P. SH, 02¹–05².*

STEPHEN, Alexander Moncrieff Mitchell, b. 5 Mar. 27, 2nd. s. of Sir A. M. Stephen. Sh, 40³–45². R.N., 45–48. P.O. Trinity Hall, Cambridge, B.A. Shipbuilder to 68. Now Engineer. Dir., Alexander Stephen & Sons, Scottish Widows Fund & Clydesdale Investment Col. Ltd. Served Royal Yachting Assoc. Council. *Western Club, Glasgow; Royal Northern Y.C.* Brother, J. F. Stephen.

STEPHEN, James Frederick, V.R.D., b. 17 Dec. 23, eldest s. of Sir A. M. Stephen. Sh, 37³–42²; Scholar; Levée. Scholar of Trinity Hall, Cambridge, B.A. C.Eng. ✕ R.N. S/Lt.(E), 44–46. V.R.D. Dir., Alexander Stephen & Sons Ltd. of Glasgow. Engineers & Ship Repairers. *Caledonian Club, London.* Brother, A. M. M. Stephen. Son, 2407.

STEPHENS, Bruce Fitzstephen. C, 19¹–20².*

STEPHENSON, John Stansfield. Tu, 45³–50³.*

STEPHENSON, Michael Champness. St & W, 41³–45².*

STERN, James Bertram. C, 19³–23¹.*

STEVENS, John Reginald Cloete. SH, 16³–20².*

STEWARD, Major Charles Anthony. W, 33¹–37².*

STEWART, David Andrew Ross (see Ross Stewart, D. A.).

STEWART, Lt.-Col. Douglas Norman, D.S.O., M.C., b. 24 June 13, s. of the late Gen. I. Stewart. SF, 27¹–31²; Cap. R.M.A., Sandhurst. Gazetted to Royal Scots Greys, 33. ✕ 39–45. D.S.O., M.C. & Bar. Lt.-Col. Member of the winning English Horse Jumping Team, Olympic Games, 52. Retired, 54. *Cavalry Club.*

STEWART, Lorn Alastair. Sh, 32²–35².*

STEWART, Patrick Findlater, M.C., b. 20 Mar. 18, s. of the late Sir T. Stewart, K.C.S.I., K.C.I.E. B, 31³–36²; Scholar; Levée; Head of House; King's Medal; Paddison Art Prize; Prize Poem; Leaving

Exhibitioner. Scholar of Christ Church, Oxford, B.A. ✕ 11th Hussars, 40–43. Capt. M.C., American Silver Star. Invalided with severe wounds. Miscellaneous journalism. Author of "History of 12th Royal Lancers, 1715–1945", 44–48. Co-founder & Sec., National Assoc. for the Paralysed, 48–56. Min. of Defence, 56–72. Retired. Vice-Pres., Queen Elizabeth's Foundation for the Disabled. Son, William Mungo Alexander, B, 71³–.

STEWART, Ronald Compton. B, 17¹–20³.*

STEWART ROSS, William Graeme, L.D.S., R.C.S. Sh, 46¹–49¹.*

STIRLING, Gwynne Arthur Chetham. K, 24³–28³. Son, 1739.*

STIRLING, James, T.D., D.L., b. 8 Sept. 30, s. of the late A. Stirling. B, 44²–49²; XV, 48; Fencing III, 49; Athletics Cup, 47–49. N/S. Argyll & Sutherland Highlanders, 50. 2nd Lt. ✕ Korea, 50. Wounded. Trinity, Cambridge, B.A. F.R.I.C.S. Partner in Kenneth Rydey & Partners, Chartered Surveyors, Edinburgh. Lt.-Col. Commanding 7th & 3rd Bns. Argyll & Sutherland Highlanders. T.A. T.D. D.L., Stirlingshire. *New Club, Edinburgh.*

STOBART-VALLARO, René Paul (formerly Stobart, R. P.). B, 16³–20¹.*

STOCKS, The Hon. John Rendel, b. 23 Mar. 18, s. of the Late J. L. Stocks (OR B 96). C, 31³–35². Liverpool Univ., B.Eng. ✕ R.N., 40–46. Lt.(E). Shell International Petroleum Co. Ltd. since 46. Son, Jonathan Edward Rendel, C, 67²–70³.

STODART, Derek Hunter, b. 30 Apr. 15, s. of A. B. Stodart. SH, 28³–34¹; Scholar; Cap R. VIII. Scholar of Magdalene, Cambridge, M.A. ✕ 5th Canadian Armd. Div. Staff Capt. Chartered Accountant, 46. Canadian Trans-Lux Corp. Ltd.

STOKES, Dom. Godfrey Julian Fenwick, O.S.B., b. 3 July 04, s. of the late W. H. Stokes. SH, 18²–23². Sidney Sussex, Cambridge, B.A. Westcott House. Ordained Deacon, 30; Priest, 31. Asst. Curate, St. John Baptist, Staveley, 30–34 & 40–42. Cambridge Mission to Delhi, 34–39. Monk at Nashdom Abbey, Burnham, Bucks. since 42.

STOKES, The Rev. Henry Hudleston, b. 21 Apr. 98, 3rd s. of the late J. W. Stokes.

SF, 12^1-16^2; S. VIII, 15. ✗ 3rd Bn. London Regt. 2nd Lt. Wounded. Bishop's College, Cheshunt. Ordained, 29. Curate of St. Mary's, Walton on the Hill, Dio. L'pool, 29–34; of St. Peter's, Fort Colombo, 34–35. Priest in charge of St. Luke's, Ratnapura, Ceylon, 35–37. Rector of Rochford, Dio. Worcester, 37–46; of Felton with Preston Wynne, 46–48; of Culmington, 48–57; of Ovington with Itchenstoke & Abbotstone, 57–60; of West Winch, Dio. Norwich, 60–68. Retired, 68.

STOKES, Richard Adrian Durham. K, 39^2-43^2.*

STOKES, Thomas Gabriel. SH, 09^1-12^2.*

STONE, Charles Graham. M, 99^3-05^2.*

STONE, James William Markham, M.B., B.Chir., b. 18 Oct. 23, eldest s. of the late G. W. Stone. St & K, 37^2-42^2. Gonville & Caius, Cambridge, M.A., M.B., B.Chir. St. Thomas's Hospital, M.R.C.S., L.R.C.P. Late Major, R.A.M.C. Fellow Royal Philatelic Soc., London.

STONE, Richard Frederick, Q.C., b. 11 Mar. 28, s. of Sir L. Stone, O.B.E. Sh, 43^3-46^1. Trinity Hall, Cambridge, M.A. N/S. Worcestershire Regt., 47–48. 2nd Lt. Bar, Gray's Inn, 52. Q.C., 68. Member, Panel of Lloyd's Arbitrators in Salvage Cases. *Hayling Island Sailing Club.*

STONE, Weland Dinnis, D.M., M.R.C.P., b. 21 May 32, s. of W. G. Stone. Sh, 46^1-50^2; Stovin Exhibitioner. Exhibitioner of Balliol, Oxford, M.A., D.M. St. Thomas's Hospital Medical School, M.R.C.P. Consultant Physician & Gastroenterologist, York. British Soc. of Gastroenterology.

STOOP, Michael, M.C. St, 36^3-40^3.*

STOOP, Robert Geoffrey. K, 29^3-30^3.*

STOREY, David Ian, M.B., B.Chir., b. 4 Nov. 25, s. of the late M. H. Storey. K, 38^3-42^2. King's, Cambridge, M.A., M.B., B.Chir. St. Thomas's Hospital, D.P.M. Consultant Psychiatrist. Psychiatric Medical Director, Ascot, Berks.

STOREY, Llewelyn Robert Owen, Ph.D. SH, 41^2-45^2.*

STORY, Philip John, b. 14 June 01, youngest s. of R. Story. C, 15^3-19^3; Cap,

19. Oriel, Oxford, M.A. Chrmn. & Man. Dir. of Sharp Perrin & Co. Ltd., Wholesale Textile Warehousemen. Retired.

STOTT, Major Arthur Boyce. Tu, 04^2-07^2.*

STOTT, The Rev. John Robert Walmsley, b. 27 Apr. 21, s. of the late Major Gen. A. W. Stott, K.B.E. (OR K 99). K, 35^1-40^2; Levée; Head of School; Exhibitioner. Scholar of Trinity, Cambridge, M.A. Ridley Hall. Ordained, 45. Rector of All Souls, Langham Place, London since 50. Hon. Chaplain to the Queen since 59. Chrmn., Church of England Evangelical Council. Pres., Scripture Union, 72–73. Inter-Varsity Fellowship, 72–73. Evangelical Alliance, 73–74. Hon. D.D., Trinity Evangelical Div. School, Deerfield, Illinois, U.S.A.

STOW, John George Raymond. K, 46^3-51^2.*

STRACHAN, Douglas Frederick, b. 26 July 33, 2nd s. of The Hon. Lord Strachan. B, 46^3-51^2. N/S. The Royal Scots, 51–53. 2nd Lt. Corpus Christi, Oxford, M.A. Brewer with A. Guinness, Son & Co. (Dublin) Ltd., 56–67. Man. Dir., Cantrell & Cochrane Group Ltd., Dublin, 67–72. Dir., Showerings Vine Products & Whiteways Ltd., Shepton Mallet since 72. *Hurlingham.* Brother, T. W. Strachan. Son, Mark Douglas Ashley. B, 72^2-.

STRACHAN, Michael Francis, M.B.E., b. 23 Oct. 19, 2nd s. of Capt. F. W. Strachan. K, 33^2-37^3; Scholar; Cadet Officer; Levée. Exhibitioner of Corpus Christi, Cambridge, M.A. ✗ 39–46. Bde. Major, 26. Armd. Bde., 44–45. Lt.-Col. M.B.E. Wm. Thomson & Co., Managers of the Ben Line, 46. Chrmn., The Ben Line Steamers Ltd. since 70. Mem. of the Soc. for Nautical Research and of the Queen's Bodyguard for Scotland. Trustee of the National Galleries of Scotland since 72. Publications: "The Life and Adventures of Thomas Coryate", "The East India Company", "Journals of Capt. William Keeling & Master Thomas Bonner". Sons, 2467 & 2827.

STRACHAN, Timothy Warren. B, 40^3-45^2.*

STRACHEY, John Ralph Severs. Tu, 19^3-22^2.*

STRACHEY, Richard Philip Farquhar. Tu, 17^1-21^3.*

STRADLING THOMAS, John, b. 10 June 25, s. of T. R. Thomas. C & W, 39^2–42^2. London Univ. N/S. in agriculture during War. Member, Council N.F.U., 63–70. Member of Parliament (C) for Monmouth since 70.

STRAHAN, Alexander John, b. 30 Aug. 18, s. of Dr. S. S. Strahan. C, 32^3–37^3; Scholar; XV; XXII; Leaving Exhibition. Exhibitioner of Hertford, Oxford, M.A. Licence-ès-Lettres (Lille), 61. ✕ 39–46. R.A. Wounded, 42. Middle East. Dispatches. Assistant L'Anglais, Nice, 48–49. Asst. Master, Sedbergh School, 49–59. Headmaster, Sudbury Grammar School, 60–72 and Sudbury Upper School (Mixed Comprehensive) since 72.

STRANGE, Frederick Griffiths St. Clair, F.R.C.S., b. 22 July 11, elder s. of the late C. F. Strange, M.R.C.S., L.R.C.P. SH, 25^3–29^2; Cap, H. XI, 29. The London Hospital Medical College. London Univ. XV. United Hospitals H. XI. L.R.C.P., F.R.C.S. Consultant Orthopaedic Surgeon, Kent & Canterbury Hospital & Royal Sea Bathing Hospital. Hon. Civilian Consultant in Orthopaedics to the Army at the Royal Herbert Hosp. Hon. Orthopaedic Surgeon to Kent C.C.C. Fellow & Past Pres. & Hon. Sec., Section of Orthopaedics, Royal Soc. of Medicine. Vice-Pres., B.O.A., 71–72. Nuffield Travelling Fellow. Robert Jones Gold Medal, B.O.A., 43. Late Hunterian Prof., R.C.S., 47. Author: "The Hip" and many contributions to orthopaedic literature. *Kent & Canterbury Club.*

STRANGE, Thomas Laurence Cresswell, b. 23 Jan. 09, elder s. of the late Rev. C. Strange. B, 22^3–27^1. Ribble Motor Services Ltd., Preston, 27. ✕ R.A.S.C., 39–45. Capt. Dispatches. Traffic Man., Western Welsh Omnibus Co. Ltd. Gen. Man., Rhondda Transport & Devon General. Retired, 72. F.C.I.T. *Royal Over-Seas League, Lancs. C.C.C.*

STRAUSS, The Rt. Hon. George Russell, P.C., M.P., b. 18 July 01, 2nd s. of A. Strauss. SF, 15^3–19^1. M.P. (Lab.) for Vauxhall Div. of Lambeth since 50. P.P.S. to Min. of Transport. Lord Privy Seal & later Min. of Aircraft Production, 42–45. Minister of Supply, 47–51. P.C., 47.

STRAUSS, Henry George (see The Rt. Hon. Lord Conesford).

STREATFEILD, The Hon. Sir Geoffrey (Hugh Benbow), M.C., b. 28 July 97, 2nd s. of the late Major H. S. Streatfeild. K, 11^1–14^2; G. VIII, 14. ✕ 14–18. 4th Bn. Durham L.I. No. 9 & No. 16 Squadron, R.F.C. & R.A.F. Capt. M.C. Wounded. Bar, Inner Temple, 21. Practised N.E. Circuit. K.C., 38. Recorder of Rotherham, 32; Huddersfield, 34; Kingston-upon-Hull, 43. Bencher, 45. Judge of the High Court of Justice (K.B.D.), 47. ✕ 39–45. Asst. Judge Advocate General. Retired, 66. Dep. Chrmn., Somerset Quarter Sessions, 66. Knight Bachelor, 47. Hon. D.C.L. Durham Univ., 57.

STREET, Hugh George Henry Lee. T, 28^3–30^1.*

STRINGER, Colin Selwyn, b. 22 May 11, elder s. of the late H. S. Stringer (OR K 93). SH, 25^1–29^2.

STRONG, Edward Cortis, b. 29 Feb. 08, 2nd s. of the late E. Strong. W, 22^1–25^2. ✕ R.N.V.R., 40–45. Lt.-Cdr. Retired Merchant & Company Director.

STRONG, Peter. SF, 45^3–49^2.*

STRONG, Thomas. SF, 14^3–18^1. Son, 110.*

STROTHER-SMITH, Norman Charles, b. 14 Sept. 17, s. of the late F. F. Strother-Smith, I.M.S. SF, 31^2–35^3. R.M.A., Woolwich. Peterhouse, Cambridge, M.A. C.Eng., M.I.E.E., M.I.Fire.E. ✕ R.A. 39–41. R.E.M.E., 41–46. Major. R.E.M.E. (Reserve). Metropolitan Vickers Ltd., Personnel Admin., 46–52. Dir., Fire Protection Assoc. since 52. O.B.E., E.R.D. *Knole Park G.C.* Son, 2069.

STROVER, Major Michael Christopher. SH, 36^3–41^2.*

STUART, Burleigh Edward St. Lawrence. SH, 34^1–38^2.*

STUART, Jonathan Balfour, b. 10 Jan. 33, s. of M. M. Stuart, C.I.E., O.B.E. St, 46^3–51^2. N/S. R.E.M.E., 51–53. 2nd Lt. St. John's, Cambridge, M.A. G.M.I. Mech.E. The General Electric Co. Ltd. Chrmn., *Burton Manor Squash Club.* Platoon Cdr., 118 Army Recovery Coy., R.E.M.E.(V). T.D.

STUART, Lt.-Col. John William Brownlow, M.B.E., M.C., b. 30 May 17, elder s. of the late Brig.-General B. F. B. Stuart, C.B., C.M.G. SH, 30^3–35^2. R.M.C.,

Sandhurst. Commissioned as 2nd Lt. in The Worcestershire Regt., 37. ✕ Palestine, 38–39. M.C. Sudan & Eritrea, 39–41. Western Desert, 41–42. Italy, 44–46. Egypt, 50–52. Kenya, 56–57. West Indies, 58–60. With N.A.T.O. in Turkey, 62–64 and at S.H.A.P.E., 64–67. Retired as Lt.-Col. with Hon. Rank of Col., 72. Staff Coll., Haifa, 43. j.s.s.c., 55–56. Commanded 1st Bn. The Worcestershire Regt., 59–61. Instructor at R.M.A., Sandhurst, 47–50. M.B.E., 44. Dispatches twice.

STUART-WILLIAMS, John Anthony, b. 17 Dec. 04, eldest s. of the late Sir S. C. Stuart-Williams. C, 18³–21³. Apprenticed, J. I. Thornycroft & Co. Ltd., 22–25. City & Guilds Engineering College, 25–28. C.Eng., M.I.Mech.E. General Engineering in India, 29–39. Asst. Adviser on Engineering Supplies, India, 39–42. Dir. of Engineering, D.G.M.P., India, 42–45. Various appointments, India & Middle East, 46–54 & in U.K., 54–71. Retired. Efficiency Medal (Vol. Cavalry). Bihar Light Horse (India) Polo Team, 39. *Oriental Club, Bengal Club, Calcutta.*

STUART, Whitewright (see Ruthven-Stuart, A. W.).

STUBBS, John Alfred, b. 29 Aug. 31, elder s. of A. Stubbs. W, 45¹–50²; Scholar; Peppin Cup; Head of School Music. Jesus, Oxford, M.A. Barrister at Law. Member Instit. of Packaging. A.M.B.I.M. N/S. R.N., 54–56. R.N.R., Lt., 56–64. Purchasing Dept., Thomas Hedley & Co., 58–61. Pers. Asst. to Dir., Henry Simon Ltd., 61–63. Gen. Man., New Cheshire Salt Works Ltd. since 63. Dir., Fodens Ltd. since 73. *Naval Club.*

STURDEE, Brig. Peter Wadham Doveton, b. 27 June 08, s. of the late Major P. G. Sturdee. SH, 22²–26¹. R.M.C., Sandhurst. Association Football "Blue". Commissioned 2nd Lt. R. Tank Corps, 28. ✕ Middle East & Italy, 39–45. Lt.-Col., 50. Retired, 56, with hon. rank of Brigadier. Dispatches.

STURGES, Michael. T, 42²–45².*

STURGIS, Gerald Clare, b. 4 Sept. 92, s. of the late M. C. Sturgis. SH, 06³–10³. Indian Police, 12–38. ✕ Calcutta Light Horse. Trooper. ✕ R.A.F.V.R., 40–45.

STURROCK, Anthony Michael. SF, 35¹–39².*

STUTFIELD, Hugh Geoffrey, b. 20 Feb. 01, s. of the late H. E. M. Stutfield (OR W 72). SF, 15¹–19¹; Scholar; XXII, 18; R. VIII, 18–19 (Capt.). Slade School of Fine Art. Sorbonne. Finalist, Prix de Rome Painting Scholarship, 23 & 27.

SULLIVAN, Prof. Donovan Michael, Ph.D., b. 29 Oct. 16, 3rd s. of the late E. A. Sullivan. Sh, 30³–34². Corpus Christi, Cambridge, M.A. London Univ., B.A. Harvard Univ., Ph.D. Lecturer in Art History & Curator, Art Museum, Singapore Univ., 54–60. Lecturer in Asian Art, London Univ., 60–66. Visiting Prof. of Oriental Art, Michigan Univ. since 64. Prof. of Oriental Art, Stanford, California since 66. Slade Prof. of Fine Art, Oxford, 73–74. Author of seven books on Chinese Art and numerous articles. Litt.D. (Cantab.), 66. *Athenæum.* Brother, M. Sullivan.

SULLIVAN, Matthew (formerly Barry Seaghan), b. 7 June 15, 2nd s. of the late A. E. Sullivan. W, 29³–34². New College, Oxford. Hanseatic Scholar, Hamburg Univ. ✕ R.A.F.V.R., 40–46. Navigator & later Intell. Sqn. Ldr. Farmer trainee, 47. Schoolmastering & Publishing, 49–52. European Service of the B.B.C. since 52. Author of "Fibre" (novel), "Adam Unbound" (3 plays). *International P.E.N. Club.* Brother, D. M. Sullivan.

SUMMERSKILL, James Rodney, F.C.A., b. 14 Dec. 28, s. of J. C. Summerskill. B, 43²–47²; Cadet Officer. N/S. R.A. 2nd Lt., 48. Liverpool Univ., B.Comm., F.C.A. Partner, Dolby Summerskill & Co., Chartered Accountants of Liverpool. Dir., St. Helens Armoury Ltd. Son, James Roger. B, 70¹–.

SUMNER, Robert Arnold Crothers, b. 30 June 16, 2nd s. of the late B. Sumner. M, 30²–33³. College of Aeronautical Engineering, Chelsea. ✕ R.A.F., 40–46. Engineer Officer. Man. Dir., Engineering Company. Now retired.

SURTEES, Conyers Alfred, b. 13 June 07, 4th s. of the late H. P. Surtees (OR St 84). St, 21²–25². Balliol, Oxford, B.A. Winter Williams Scholarship. Solicitor, 34. ✕ Ox. & Bucks. L.I., 40–45. British Army Staff in Washington, 44–45. Lt.-Col. U.S. Legion of Merit. Partner, Norton, Rose, Botterell & Roche, of London. *Bath Club, City Univ. Club.* Sons, 446, 447 & 2164.

SUTER, Ian Roy. Sh, 38³–43².*

SUTRO, John Richard, b. 23 Apr. 03, 3rd s. of L. Sutro. M, 16^3–21^2; Scholar. Scholar of Trinity, Oxford, B.A. Barrister at Law. Film Producer, now retired. *Garrick & Beefsteak Clubs*. Vice-Pres., *Anglo-Texan Soc*.

SUTTON, George Christopher, M.B., M.R.C.P. (formerly Silberstein, George), b. 4 Feb. 34, s. of J. M. Silberstein. T, 46^3–52^3; Levée; Head of House. Corpus Christi, Cambridge, M.A., M.D. Warwickshire County Major Scholar. University College Hospital. M.R.C.P. Consultant Physician, Hillingdon Hospital, Uxbridge. Senior Lecturer, Cardio-Thoracic Inst., London.

SUTTON, James. Sh, 43^2–47^2.*

SWANN, Henry Huddart. M, 19^3–23^1.*

SWANN, John Edward Frederick, b. 26 May 09, eldest s. of the late F. W. Swann. B, 22^3–27^2; Scholar; Levée; Head of House. Scholar of Clare, Cambridge, B.A. Mem. Instit. of Office Management & of British Computer Soc. ⚔ R.A.F. Coastal Command. Flt.-Sgt. Retired as Principal Systems Analyst, S.E. Gas Board.

SWANN, The Rev. Canon Sidney Ernest, b. 24 June 90, eldest s. of the late Rev. S. Swann. K, 04^3–08^3; Holder of Bigside Bags, 08; R. VIII, 07–08. Trinity Hall, Cambridge, M.A. Rowing Blue, 11–14 (Pres., 14). Ridley Hall. Ordained, 14.⚔ Chaplain to the Forces, 14–19. Coached Cambridge crews, 20–22, 24 & 46. Chaplain of Trinity Hall, 20–24. Archdeacon of Nairobi, 26 & of Egypt, 28–33. Vicar of St. Mary Redcliffe, Bristol, 37–51. Hon. Canon of Bristol Cathedral, 38. Canon Emeritus since 51. Vicar of Timberscombe, Minehead, 51–59. Chaplain to the Queen, 52–65 (& to King George VI, 41–52). In Leander Crew which won the Eights Gold Medal at Olympic Games, 12 & Silver Medal, 20.

SWANNELL, Major David William Ashburnham, M.B.E., b. 18 Apr. 18, elder s. of the late W. A. Swannell. Tu, 32^1–36^2. R.M.C., Sandhurst. Gazetted to Durham L.I., 38. ⚔ D.L.I. Capt. Major, 51. Retired, 56. Jockey Club Official (Handicapper), 56. Clerk of the Course: Thirsk, Beverley. M.B.E., 53. *United Service & Royal Aero Club*. Son, 2619.

SWANSTON, Mungo. K, 35^3–39^2. Sons, 2055, 2381, 2672 & David Mungo. K, 67^3–71^2.*

SWEATMAN, Eric Allen. C, 19^3–24^2.*

SWEET, John Cyril Leslie, b. 14 Feb. 25, s. of G. H. L. Sweet. St & W, 38^3–42^2. ⚔ 3rd Carabiniers, R.A.C. & City of London Yeomanry (T.A.). Capt. Solicitor, 50. Partner, Iliffes of Chesham, Bucks. & London. *Law Soc., Anglo-Portuguese Soc*.

SWETE, Gerald Frank. M, 27^3–30^2.*

SWINDELLS, Major Alan Cawley, M.C., b. 11 Sept. 90, 3rd s. of the late F. E. Swindells. B, 04^3–08^2. Cotton Spinner. Gazetted to 2nd West Lancashire Bde., R.F.A.(T.F.), 13. ⚔ 276th Bde., R.F.A. Service in France, 15–18. Major. M.C. (Bar). Resigned, 22. Fine Spinners & Doublers, 08–60. Son, P. C. Swindells. Grandson, 2758.

SWINDELLS, Lt.-Col. George Michael Geoffrey, b. 15 Jan. 30, eldest s. of the late G. M. Swindells (OR B 13). B, 43^3–48^2; Levée; Head of House. Regular Army. 5th Royal Inniskilling Dragoon Guards, 49–69. Commd. 9th/12th Royal Lancers, 69–72. Now on Directing Staff, Staff College, Camberley. Lt.-Col. *Cavalry Club*.

SWINDELLS, John Cawley, b. 15 Sept. 24, 2nd s. of the late F. H. Swindells. B, 38^2–42^3; Cap. ⚔ R. Armd. Corps. (Recce.), 43–47. Capt. Chartered Accountant. Partner, Harper-Smith Bennett & Co. J.P. Local R.D.C. Councillor. Son, Stephen Cawley, B, 70^2–.

SWINDELLS, Peter Cawley, b. 4 Feb. 21, eldest s. of Major A. C. Swindells, M.C. (OR B 04). B, 35^1–39^1. Cotton Spinner. Company Dir. ⚔ East Lancashire Regt. Major. Son, 2758.

SWINGLER, Humphrey Charles. W, 26^3–30^2.*

SWINHOE, Thomas Rodway. St & W, 39^2–43^1. Sons, Paul Rodway. St, 67^2–71^3. & Richard Thomas. St, 70^3–.*

SWORD, Major William James David, b. 7 Nov. 22, s. of the late W. Sword. B, 36^3–41^2; Athletics Cup, 41. Edinburgh Univ. Joined Royal Scots, 41. R.M.C., Sandhurst, 42. ⚔ Commissioned Argyll & Sutherland Highlanders, 42. Served N. Africa, Europe & Palestine. Wounded twice. Dispatches twice. Demobilised, 46. Major. Bahrain Petroleum Co. Ltd., 47. 25 years with Caltex & Texaco. Dir. *Caledonian Club, London*.

SYDENHAM, Brig. Philip St. Barbe, C.B.E. M, 11^3–16^2. Son, R. H. St. B. Sydenham.*

SYDENHAM, Robert Humphrey St. Barbe, b. 19 Oct. 29, s. of Brig. P. St. B. Sydenham, C.B.E. (OR M 11). M, 43^2–48^1; XV, 47; S. VIII. St. Catharine's, Cambridge, B.A. Dir., J. H. Little, Engineering Ltd. of London. *Royal Ocean Racing Club.*

SYKES, Arthur Frank Seton, b. 4 July 03, eldest s. of the late Brig.-Gen. Sir P. Sykes, K.C.I.E., C.B., C.M.G. (OR SF 82). SF, 17^1–21^3. Agricultural College. Agric. Adviser to the Queen at Windsor, 52–72. Mem., Royal Commission on East Africa, 52. Alderman of Wilts., 61. Vice-Pres., Royal Agricultural Soc. of England, 70. C.V.O., D.L. *Farmers' Club, R. Soc. of Arts.* Brothers, E. M. & G. R. L. Sykes. Son, T. S. Sykes. Grandson, Jonathan Seton. SF, 73^1–.

SYKES, Edward Molesworth, F.C.A., b. 10 Jan. 10, 3rd s. of the late Brig.-Gen. Sir P. Sykes, K.C.I.E., C.B., C.M.G. (OR SF 82). SF, 23^3–27^2. St. John's, Oxford, B.A. Lawn Tennis Blue, 31. F.C.A. ✕ Intell. Corps., 40–45. Brothers, A. F. S. & G. R. L. Sykes.

SYKES, Geoffrey Richard Lawrence, b. 10 Aug. 13, 4th s. of the late Brig.-Gen. Sir P. Sykes, K.C.I.E., C.B., C.M.G. (OR SF 82). SF, 27^1–29^2. Harper Adams Agric. College. Nuffield Farm Scholarship in U.S. Appointed Mem. of Official Mission to U.S., 46, to study U.S. & Canadian Poultry Industries. Self-employed in farming. Introducer to U.K. of broiler chicken industry, and the concept of Agribusiness. Author: "Poultry, a Modern Agribusiness". *Farmers' Club.* Nuffield Farm Scholar Assoc. Brothers, A. F. S. & E. M. Sykes.

SYKES, Humphrey Hugh, b. 8 Dec. 07, 2nd s. of the late Major H. R. Sykes. SF, 21^2–26^2; Cap, XXII; H. XI, 26. R.M.C., Sandhurst. Gazetted to King's Shropshire L.I., 28. 9th Lancers, 30. Lt., 32. ✕ France (2nd Armd. Bde. H.Q.), 40. Major, 41. Staff College, 41–42. British Army Staff, Washington, 42–44. Retired, 46. Landowner in Dumfriesshire. *Pratt's, R. & A. G.C., Prestwick G.C.*

SYKES, Peter Henry, b. 9 Jan 11, s. of the late Brig.-Gen. C. A. Sykes, C.M.G., D.S.O. Tu, 24^3–27^3. ✕ Indian Army, 40–45. p.s.c. (Quetta). Small-scale farmer. *Oriental Club, M.C.C.*

SYKES, Lt.-Col. Peter Thomas Wellesley, O.B.E., D.L. SF, 17^3–21^1.*

SYKES, Tristram Seton, b. 4 Feb. 31, s. of A. F. S. Sykes (OR S 17). SF, 44^3–49^2; Levée; Head of House. Oxford Univ., M.A. Farmer & Agric. Marketing Consultant. Chrmn., Wilts. County N.F.U., 72–73. Chrmn. or Vice-Chrmn. of two Agric. Marketing Cos. T.D. Son, Jonathan Seton, SF, 73^1–.

SYMES, Edward Wymond Cory, b. 10 Jan. 05, elder s. of the late W. C. Symes. SH, 18^2–22^1. City & Guilds Inst., London, Civil Engineering. B.Sc.(Eng.). With Dorman Long & Co. Ltd., 24–34. Own business, 35–39. ✕ R.E., 39–45. Major. With Neuchatel Asphalte Co. Ltd. (Dir. of Sub. Co.) from 46. Retired. *Junior Carlton.*

SYMINGTON, Kenneth Michael, b. 5 July 30, elder s. of the late K. W. Symington, T.D. (OR St 19). SF, 43^3–48^2; XV, 47; S. VIII, 46–48 (Capt.). King's, Cambridge, M.A. N/S. R.A. in Malaya. Family business, Symington's Soups. Chrmn. & Man. Dir., 63, till Co. sold to J. Lyons in 69. Brother, 111. Sons, Toby William. K, 71^3– & John Michael, K, 73^1.

SYMINGTON, Neil Colquhoun, b. 18 July 31, s. of D. A. C. Symington. W, 45^3–47^3. Cape Town Univ. Sidney Sussex, Cambridge, M.A. Entirely with African Explosives & Chemical Industries (A.E. & C.I.) initially at Somerset West factory, then at Modderfontein & finally Head Office in Johannesburg. In various positions. Now in marketing of Plastic raw materials. *Kelvin Grove Club, Cape Town.* Plastic Inst. of Southern Africa.

SYMONDS, Charles Charters. SF, 35^3–38^3.*

SYMONDS, Sir Charles (Putnam), K.B.E., C.B., M.D., F.R.C.P., b. 11 Apr. 90, eldest s. of the late Sir Charters Symonds, K.B.E., C.B., M.R.C.S., L.R.C.P. St, 04^1–08^2; Scholar. Scholar of New College, Oxford, M.A. ✕ Dispatch Rider, R.E. 101 Field Ambulance, R.A.M.C. Capt. Wounded twice. Médaille Militaire. Entrance Scholar of Guy's Hospital, D.M.(Oxon.), F.R.C.P. (Lon. & Ed.). Hon. Consultant, Emeritus, Guy's Hospital. Hon. Consultant, National Hospital, Queen Square. ✕ R.A.F., 39–45. Air Vice-Marshal. K.B.E., 46. C.B., 44. Hon. Fellow, R. Soc. of Medicine. *R.A.F. Club.* Brother, J. C. Symonds. Sons, R. C., J. R. C., C. C. & W. J. C. Symonds.

SYMONDS, John Charters, b. 26 Aug. 91, 2nd s. of the late Sir Charters Symonds, K.B.E., C.B., M.R.C.S., L.R.C.P. St, 05²–09²; Cap, 08; XI, 08–09. A.M.Inst. C.E., A.M.I.A.E., A.M.I.Mech.E. ✕ Motor Transport, A.S.C. Major. Dispatches. Engineer. Chrmn. & Man. Dir. Property Co. *M.C.C.* Brother, Sir Charles Symonds.

SYMONDS, John Richard Charters. SF, 32³–36².*

SYMONDS, Ronald Charters, b. 25 June 16, eldest s. of Sir Charles Symonds, K.B.E., C.B., M.D. (OR St 04). C, 29³–34². New College, Oxford, M.A. Official of the British Council from 38. ✕ Intell. Corps, 39–46. Major. U.S. Bronze Star. Brothers, J. R. C., C. C. & W. J. C. Symonds.

SYMONDS, William James Charters. K, 36³–39³.*

SYMONDSON, Stanley Lister, b. 9 Mar. 99, 2nd s. of the late H. W. Symondson.

M, 13¹–16³. ✕ Nos. 79 & 23 Squadrons, R.F.C., 17–19. Lt. Member of Lloyd's, 20. ✕ R.A.F., 39–45. Wing-Cdr. Underwriter, retired.

SYNGE, Patrick Millington, b. 17 Sept. 10, s. of the late E. M. Synge. Tu, 24¹–28²; Junior Athletics Cup, 26. Corpus Christi, Cambridge, M.A. Dir., Lindsay Drummond, Publishers, 37–58. Editor, The Royal Horticultural Soc.'s Journal & Pubs., 45–70. ✕ Intell. Corps, 39–45. Major. Mem., Oxford Univ. Exploration Club Sarawak Exped., 31–32, & British Museum E. African Exped., 34–35. Author of numerous books on Horticulture. F.R.G.S. Veitch Memorial Medal and Victoria Medal of Honour of R. Horticultural Soc. *Travellers'.* Son, 2722.

SYNGE, Richard Millington, M.C. (formerly Sing, R. M.), b. 10 Aug. 89, younger s. of the late A. M. Sing. B, 03³–07². Christ Church, Oxford. ✕ 4th West Lancashire Bde., R.F.A. Staff Capt. M.C. Dispatches. Stockbroker, Liverpool Stock Exchange. Cttee. Mem., 18 years. Chrmn., 52–60. Retired.

T

TABBUSH, Cecil Wilfred. M, 04²–08³.*

TAGGART, Redmond Thibeaudeau, b. 1 Oct. 03, s. of the late W. D. R. Taggart. C, 17³–22²; XV, 21; Cadet Officer. Balliol, Oxford, B.A. Architect & Civil Engineering Consultant. M.I.C.E., L.R.I.B.A. ✕ R.N.V.R. Comdr. V.R.D. *Ulster Club, Belfast.* Son, 1820.

TAIT, Alan Richard, b. 6 Aug. 26, 5th s. of the late W. A. Tait (OR K 95). C & Tu, 40²–44². Queens', Cambridge. Naval Short Course, 44, 45. After working for B.A.T. Co. Ltd. in England, Denmark, Singapore and Indonesia, 47–49, settled as 4th generation in family business as partner in Tait & Co. of Oporto since 50. *Cryptics, Anglo-Portuguese Society.* Brothers, W. L. E., C. G., G. C. & B. W. Tait.

TAIT, Brian Walter, b. 7 June 22, 4th s. of the late W. A. Tait (OR K 95). C, 36²–41²; H. XI, 40–41. Queens', Cambridge, M.A. Hockey Blue, 43. Civil Engineer with Ministry of Fuel & Power from 44. Opencast Coal Production, and with various Ministries from 52 run by the N.C.B. *Oporto Lawn Tennis & Cricket Club.* Brothers, W. L. E., C. G., G. C. & A. R.

Tait. Sons, William Andrew, C, 68³–72², and Charles Edward, C, 73³–.

TAIT, Claud Gilbert, b. 19 Mar. 15, 2nd s. of the late W. A. Tait (OR K 95). C, 29¹–33². Worcester, Oxford, B.A. (Hons., Portuguese). ✕ Intelligence Corps, 40–47. Capt. Farming & Mining, 47–57. British Council Teacher of English to the Portuguese Armed Forces, 57–59. Own business, 59–70. Translator & Interpreter since 70. *Lisbon Sports Club.* Brothers, W. L. E., G. C., B. W. & A. R. Tait.

TAIT, Geoffrey Colin, b. 8 July 17, 3rd s. of the late W. A. Tait (OR K 95). C, 31²–35². Queen's, Cambridge, M.A. Farming in Portugal until 64, and now Director of various companies. *Naval & Military Club, Royal British Club, Lisbon.* Brothers, W. L. E., C. G., B. W. & A. R. Tait.

TAIT, Hubert Edwin. T, 20²–23¹.*

TAIT, William Liot Elles, b. 19 Nov. 10, eldest s. of the late W. A. Tait (OR K 95). C, 24²–28³. Worcester, Oxford, B.A. Worked in Portugal, 33–39. ✕ R. Scots, 39–46 (P.O.W. in Germany, 40–45). Intelligence Corps, 46. Demobilised, 47.

Recalled, 50–51 for Korea. Since 52 lived in England in various occupations, now semi-retired. *R.A.C., Japan Society of London.* Brothers, C. G., G. C., B. W. & A. R. Tait.

TALBOT KELLY, Richard Giles, F.R.S.A., M.S.I.A., b. 26 Oct. 29, s. of the late R. B. Talbot Kelly, M.B.E., M.C. (OR K 11). Sh, 43^2–48^2; Levée; Head of House; Cap, 47; Sw. VIII, 46–48 (Capt., 47, 48); Cadet Officer, 47–48. The Patent Glazing Scholarship to the Architectural Assoc. Inc. St. Martin's School of Art & Design. Private Practice since 50. Organising Consultant, Dept. of Education, Republic of Ireland, 61–63. Head of Dept. of Design, Coventry College of Art & Design, 65–68. F.R.S.A. Member of Society of Industrial Artists & Designers, Society of Typographical Designers, Institute of Creative Advertising & Design, and the Council of Design, Republic of Ireland.

TALLON, Claude Reginald, b. 6 Jan. 10, younger s. of J. Tallon. T, 23^3–28^2; R. VIII, 27–28; Crick Winner, 27. Chartered Accountant, 33. ✕ R.A. & R.A.O.C. Major. Graduated at U.S. General Staff & Command School, Fort Leavenworth, Kansas, 44. Senior Partner, Sharp, Parsons, Tallon & Co. of London. *Gresham Club.* Brother, E. M. Tallon. Sons, 1071 & 2200.

TALLON, Ernest Maurice. T, 22^1–24^3. Son, 1195.*

TANNER, Ralph Esmond Selby, b. 24 Aug. 21, 2nd s. of the late A. R. Tanner. B, 35^3–39^2. ✕ R. Berks. Regt., 40–42. Pte. Dispatches. K.O.Y.L.I., 42–45. Capt. Asst. Resident, Burma Frontier Force, 45–48. District Officer, Colonial Administration Service, Tanganyika, 48–61. Interpretership in Kiswahili, 51. Diploma in Social Anthropology, Oxford, 55 and B.Sc., 59. Principal Asst. Sec., Ministry of Education, Tanganyika, 61. Chrmn., East Institute of Social Research, Makerere Univ. College, Uganda, 63–67. Lecturer in Comparative Religion, Heythrop Coll. (Univ. of London) since 67. D.Phil. (Stockholm), 70. Author of "Transition in African Belief", & "Homicide in Uganda".

TATHAM, Allen Ralph, J.P., b. 4 Aug. 92, elder s. of the late G. A. R. Tatham. SH, 06^3–11^2; Cap, 11. University College, Oxford, M.A. Asst. Master, Rugby School, 17–52. Housemaster, Stanley House, 29–42 (requisitioned by Government). Dir. of Rugby & Warwick Building Society since 50. J.P. & Commissioner of Taxes, 48–67.

TATHAM, Cecil Francis. Tu, 02^1–06^1.*

TATHAM, William. M, 34^3–37^2.*

TATLOW, David Mark, T.D., b. 7 Feb. 29, eldest s. of E. M. Tatlow. Tu, 42^3–47^2; Cap. Man. Dir. of a number of subsidiary companies of J. H. Sankey & Sons Ltd., Builders Merchants. Lt.-Col. R.A.(V). T.D. Son, Peter Mark, Tu, 69^3–.

TATLOW, William Frederick Tissington, M.D., F.R.C.P.(C), b. 17 Sept. 15, s. of the late R. E. T. Tatlow. W, 29^2–33^2. St. Bartholomew's Hospital, M.D., B.S., M.R.C.P., L.M.C.C.(Canada), F.R.C.P. (Canada). ✕ R.A.M.C., 40–46. Capt. Chief Neurology Service, Queen Mary Veterans' Hospital, Montreal General Hospital. Asst. Professor (Neurology) & Lecturer (Dental Faculty), McGill Univ. Now Neurologist, Lakeshore General Hospital, Asst. Physician (Neurology) and Head of Dept. of Electroencephalography, Montreal General Hospital.

TAYLOR, Alexander Giles Cameron, M.R.C.S., L.R.C.P., b. 24 July 98, elder s. of Brig.-General A. W. Taylor. M, 12^2–16^3. ✕ A.S.C. Lt. St. Thomas's Hospital, M.R.C.S., L.R.C.P., F.F.R. Radiotherapist, Wessex Regional Board, 32–63. Retired, 63. Now Farmer. *Royal Cruising Club.* Brother, G. J. C. Taylor.

TAYLOR, Bernard Alfred. T, 19^3–22^3.*

TAYLOR, Christopher Barnard Grimwood, b. 12 June 24, 2nd s. of the late S. Grimwood Taylor (OR St 92). St & W, 38^3–42^2. Corpus Christi, Cambridge, M.A. Commissariat à l'Energie Atomique, Paris, 49. AB Atomenergi, Stockholm, Sweden, 50–54. Dept. of Atomic Energy, Bombay, India (Head of Isotope Div.), 54–61. The Radiochemical Centre, Amersham, Bucks. (Man. of Isotope Production Unit at Harwell), since 61. Brother, J. R. S. Grimwood-Taylor. Sons, 3024 & William Sancroft Grimwood, St, 71^2–.

TAYLOR, Godfrey John Cameron. M, 16^1–20^2.*

TAYLOR, John Timothy Cheetham, b. 3 Aug. 31, s. of G. G. C. Taylor. SH, 45^3–49^3. Corpus Christi, Oxford, B.A. Played Tennis v. Cambridge. Solicitor. Partner in Jaques & Co. (Solicitors).

TAYLOR, Kenneth Ford, b. 12 July 09, s. of J. Taylor. B, 23^1–27^2. ✕ R.N.V.R. Lt. My brother-in-law and I are sole Direc tors of Atkin & Taylor Ltd., Stockinette Manufacturers, Bolton.

TAYLOR, Lt.-Col. Philip Seth, M.C., b. 24 Oct. 16, 2nd s. of J. D. Taylor. Sh, 30^2–34^2. Corpus Christi, Cambridge, B.A. ✕ Gazetted 2nd Lt. 17/21 Lancers, 39. M.C. Wounded twice. p.s.c., 48. Retired as Lt.-Col., 60. Confederation of British Industry since 61. Asst. Dir. since 66. *Cavalry Club.* Son, 2323.

TAYLOR, Ralph Kipling. K, 17^1–21^1.*

TAYLOR, Sydney Endfield, D.S.C. K, 10^3–15^2.*

TAYLOR-YOUNG, Harold Strang, F.R.C.S., b. 3 Mar. 02, 2nd s. of the late H. C. Taylor-Young. Tu, 16^1–21^2; XXII, 21; Cadet Officer; Racket Pair, 21 (Capt.). Trinity, Cambridge, B.A., B.Ch. St. Thomas's Hospital, M.R.C.S., L.R.C.P., M.B., F.R.C.S., Surgeon, 31–58. Senior Surgeon, Salisbury General Hospital. Surgeon in Chief, St. John's Ambulance Brigade. Whole-time Volunteer at H.Q., 59–66. Now active for the National Trust (Chrmn. Local Centre). Assoc. of Surgeons of G.B. & Ireland. Knight of Grace of Order of St. John. *M.C.C., Lansdowne Club.*

TEACHER, Col. Norman Brian Cecil, M.C., b. 8 June 15, 3rd s. of the late D. McD. Teacher. Tu, 29^1–33^2; XV, 31; H. XI. R.M.A., Woolwich. Gazetted to Royal Artillery, 35. ✕ M.C. Wounded in France, 40. Major. Instructor, Staff College, Camberley. Retired, 62 as Colonel. Regional Dir. for Scotland, Economic League Ltd. since 62. *Western Club, Glasgow, United Hunts Club.*

TEAGE, The Rev. Alan Dixon. St, 30^3–35^2.*

TEAL, Michael Brierley, M.B., B.Chir., b. 5 Aug. 29, s. of the late H. S. Teal. M, 42^3–47^2; Scholar; Exhibitioner. Scholar of Trinity, Cambridge, B.A., M.B., B.Chir. St. Mary's Hospital, London. General Medical Practitioner, Drs. Stallard, Teal, Pimblett & Edwards. *Royal Ocean Racing Club.*

TEMPLE, The Rt. Rev. Frederick Stephen (Bishop of Malmesbury), b. 29 Nov. 16, s. of the late F. C. Temple, C.I.E., C.B.E. (OR SH 92). SH, 30^3–35^2. Balliol, Oxford, M.A. Westcott House and Trinity Hall, Cambridge, B.A. ✕ British Red Cross, Friends Ambulance Unit. Croix de Guerre.

Médaille Coloniale. Ordained, 47. Curate of Arnold, 47–49; Newark, 49–51. Rector of St. Agnes, Manchester, 51–53. Dean of Hong Kong, 53–59. Senior Chaplain to Archbishop of Canterbury, 59–61. Vicar of Portsea, 61–69. Archdeacon of Swindon, 70. Bishop of Malmesbury, 73. Son, Stephen William Guy, SH, 68^3–72^3.

TEMPLETON, Ian Malcolm, D.Phil., F.Inst.P., b. 31 July 29, s. of W. Templeton. T, 42^3–47^2; Major Foundationer; Exhibitioner. Exhibitioner of University College, Oxford, M.A., D.Phil. Fellow, Institute of Physics. Fellow, Royal Society of Canada. Research Physicist. Joint Head, Metal Physics Group, Physics Div., National Research Council of Canada. *Oxford Society.*

TETLOW, Alfred John. M, 43^3–48^1.*

THAVENOT, Alexander Henry Moncaster. SH, 29^1–34^1.*

THEW, Henry Whitworth. K, 23^3–28^3.*

THIMBLEBY, Peter, A.R.I.B.A., b. 12 Sept. 27, s. of A. W. Thimbleby. T, 41^2–45^1; Paddison Art Prize. Leicester School of Architecture, F.R.I.B.A., A.I.A.A. & S. Architect in Private Practice in Rugby. Alderman, Rugby Corporation, 70. Son, Harold William, T, 68^3–.

THOMAS, Alan Hugh, b. 3 Apr. 30, 2nd s. of L. Thomas. T, 43^3–48^2; Major Foundationer. Birmingham Univ., B.Sc. Warwickshire C.C. Major Award. N/S. R.E.M.E., 49. 2nd Lt. Joined B.T.H. as Graduate Apprentice, 52. M.I.E.E. Principal Scientific Officer, Ministry of Technology, 67 & Civil Aviation Authority, 72.

THOMAS, Alan Roderick. St, 23^3–28^3.*

THOMAS, Alan Wallace, b. 27 Oct. 15, eldest s. of the late H. E. R. Thomas. T, 29^3–33^2. Banking, later Agricultural Engineer.

THOMAS, The Rev. Christopher Leonard Howell, M.B.E., b. 8 Dec. 07, 2nd s. of the late G. A. Thomas, C.I.E., I.C.S. M, 21^3–26^2; Levée; Head of House. Emmanuel, Cambridge, M.A. Asst. Master, Bishop's Stortford Coll., 29–36. Housemaster, Doon School, Dehra Dun, U.P., India, 36–41. ✕ 41–46. 3/9th Gurkhas. Major. M.B.E. Dispatches twice. Ordained, 47. Vicar, Marske-by-Sea, 50–56; Wadsley Bridge, Sheffield, 56–61; Attercliffe, Sheffield, 61–69. Retired, 69.

Executive, Hemel Hempstead Constituency Labour Party. Watford Samaritans.

THOMAS, Edward Wynne (see Wynne-Thomas, E. W.).

THOMAS, James Haigh. St, 27^1–31^1.*

THOMAS, Michael David Howell. M, 46^3–51^1.*

THOMAS, Nicholas Donald, b. 20 Mar. 30, 2nd s. of the late D. W. Thomas. SF, 43^3–48^2. N/S. D.C.L.I., 48–50. 2nd Lt. Corpus Christi, Oxford, M.A. Cert.Ed. London Univ. Diploma in Educational Studies, Nottingham Univ. Head of Dept. of Business Studies, Percival Whitley Coll. of Further Education, Halifax, Yorks.

THOMAS, Nigel Eric Lynam, b. 18 Feb. 33, elder s. of T. L. Thomas, F.R.G.S.(A). St, 46^3–51^2; Cap. N/S. R.A., 51–53. 2nd Lt. St. John's, Cambridge. Fellow of Incorporated Society of Valuers & Auctioneers. B.B.C. Brother, 580.

THOMAS, Thomas Roe. B, 26^2–30^2.*

THOMAS-DAVIES, Joseph. W, 18^2–23^1. Son, 48.*

THOMLINSON, Raymond Hugh, M.B., B.Ch. W, 36^2–40^2.*

THOMPSON, Alan Prescott, b. 25 Nov. 01, eldest s. of the late W. G. Thompson. SH, 15^2–20^2; XV, 19; XI, 19–20. Harper Adams Agricultural Coll., Newport, Salop. Agricultural Journalist. Retired. Author of "The Complete Poultryman".

THOMPSON, Arthur Frederick Bennett, b. 26 Feb. 09, eldest s. of the late B. Thompson (OR C 92). C, 23^1–27^1. Trinity Coll., Dublin, B.A., LL.B. Solicitor (Irish Free State), 32. Partner, Messrs. Bennett Thompson & Edwards of Dublin. Retired from active practice, 72. *Royal Irish Y.C.*

THOMPSON, Charles Edward. B, 16^3–20^2.*

THOMPSON, Christopher Ryland, b. 17 Nov. 25, 2nd s. of G. Thompson. St & W, 39^3–43^3; Levée; Head of House. Scholar of University College, Oxford, M.A. ✕ K.R.R.C., 44–47. Lt. Foreign Office, 50–52. Thereafter teaching in Greece (3 yrs.), England (5 yrs.), Scotland (12 yrs.). Now at Harris Academy, Dundee.

THOMPSON, Clive Duncan, C.B.E. B, 05^2–10^2.*

THOMPSON, David Morgan, b. 9 July 29, s. of J. A. J. Thompson (OR SH 14). SH, 43^3–47^3; Scholar; Exhibitioner; S. VIII, 46–47. Scholar of Corpus Christi, Oxford. Art Critic; Theatre, Film and Opera Director. Art Critic of "The Times", 56–63. Dir., "Stage Sixty" Theatre Co., 64–65. Dir., Institute of Contemporary Arts, London, 70–72.

THOMPSON, Lt.-Cdr. Geoffrey William Marshall, R.N., b. 16 Apr. 29, 2nd s. of the late C. M. Thompson, M.B., Ch.B. K, 43^1–46^2. Naval air crew, Observer. Royal Navy. Lt.-Cdr. Joint Warfare Establishment, Old Sarum, Salisbury.

THOMPSON, George Eric Sadler, b. 26 Oct. 12, s. of the late G. Thompson (OR Tu 95). Tu, 26^3–31^2; XV, 30–31; R. VIII, 30–31; H. XI, 30–31. Builders' Merchant. ✕ R.A.O.C., 40–46. Major. Dispatches.

THOMPSON, Henry Reynolds, M.B., B.Ch., F.R.C.S., b. 14 Feb. 08, eldest s. of the late H. T. Thompson. K, 21^3–26^1; XV, 25; H. XI, 26; Boxing Featherweight, 23; Light Heavyweight, 25. Christ's, Cambridge, M.A., M.B., B.Ch. London Hospital, M.R.C.S., L.R.C.P., F.R.C.S. ✕ Lt.-Col. R.A.M.C. Dispatches. Consultant Surgeon to the Army. Senior Surgeon, St. Marks Hospital, London. President, Medical Society of London, 66. Master of the Worshipful Society of Apothecaries, 68 and of Barbers, 59. Fellow & Councillor, Hunterian Society. Sons, 1135, 1446 and 1740.

THOMPSON, Hubert William Eccles. B, 45^2–49^3. Son, Robin Mark Eccles. B, 72^3–.*

THOMPSON, John Archibald Julius, b. 12 Mar. 00, s. of J. T. Thompson. SH, 14^1–17^3. ✕ R.A.F. Cadet, 18–19. F.R.I.C.S. Taylor Bros., Manchester, 20–30. Survey Dept., Colonial Service, Tanganyika, 29–49. ✕ East African Engineers, 39–45. Retired. Son, D. M. Thompson.

THOMPSON, John de Forrest. B, 12^3–17^3. Son, 463.*

THOMPSON, John Hill Graham, M.B., B.Ch. Tu, 13^3–17^1.*

THOMPSON, Michael Andrew, b. 3 Jan. 30, s. of J. B. Thompson. B, 43^3–48^2. F.C.A. Chief Accountant, Cascade (U.K.) Ltd.

THOMSON, Cyril Howard, b. 9 Aug. 98, 4th s. of W. Thomson. Tu, 13^1–17^1; Cap, 16. ✕ 108 Bde, R.F.A., 17–18. 2nd Lt. Wounded. Dir. of D. C. Thomson & Co. Ltd., Printers & Publishers (family business), Dundee. Now retired. J.P. for County of Angus. *Edinburgh & Angus Club, R. & A. G.C., Carnoustie G.C., Senior Golfers Society.*

THOMSON, Lt.-Col. David, D.S.O., M.C. SH, 05^3–10^2.*

THOMSON, David Paget, b. 19 Mar. 31, 2nd s. of Sir George Thomson, F.R.S. SH, 44^3–49^3. History and Lees-Knowles Exhibitioner. Grenoble Univ. Scholar of Trinity, Cambridge, M.A., M.I.B. Lazard Bros. & Co. Ltd. from 56 (a Man. Dir. from 65). Seconded to H.M. Diplomatic Service, 71–73 as Counsellor (Economic) at Bonn. Lt.-Cdr. R.N.R., R.D. A Manager and Vice-President, The Royal Institution Editorial Board, The Round Table. *Pitt Club, Athenæum.*

THOMSON, Kenneth Derek Bousfield, O.B.E., M.B., B.S., D.P.H., b. 16 Aug. 25, s. of Dr. C. de B. Thomson. SF, 39^2–43^2. Middlesex Hospital, M.B., B.S.,M.R.C.S., L.R.C.P. D.T.M. of H.(London), 55. D.P.H.(Glasgow), 67. Temp. Medical Officer, Colonial Medical Service, Nigeria since 51. Senior Medical Officer (Admin.), N. Nigeria, 60. Principal Rural Health Officer, N. Nigeria, 65. Consultant, Sleeping Sickness Service, Nigerian Institute for Trypanosomiasis Research, 67–73. Retired from Nigerian Public Service, 73. O.B.E., 66.

THOMSON, William Bennett, b. 30 May 33, s. of N. B. Thomson. St, 46^3–51^2; S. VIII, 50–51. N/S. Scots Guards, 52. 2nd Lt. Regular Army to 60, retiring as T/Major. Army Ski Team, 58–59. National "B" Team. M.E.L.F. Shooting Champion, 54. Army 100, 55. Served in Cyprus, Egypt and Germany. Various Commercial Appointments. Started own Gallery in London (Albany Gallery), 65. Specialists in English Watercolour Drawings of 18th & 19th Centuries. Society of London Art Dealers.

THORN, Anthony Peter, b. 26 June 20, eldest s. of the late W. S. Thorn. SH, 34^2–39^1; S. VIII. Exeter, Oxford. ✕ Irish Guards, 39–46. N. Africa, Sicily, Italy & S. France. Capt. Elastic Fabric Manufacturer. *M.C.C., Bath Club.*

THORN, Sackville Alexander, b. 24 Feb. 97, s. of the late P. A. N. Thorn. St, 10^3–13^2; Scholar. ✕ 7th Bn. West Yorkshire Regt. Lt. Wounded. Schoolmaster. Retired. Son, 2104.

THORNE, Robin Horton John, C.M.G., O.B.E., b. 13 July 17, s. of the late Sir J. Thorne. C, 31^3–36^1; Scholar. Scholar of Exeter, Oxford, M.A. Farnell Studentship to Greece, 38. ✕ Devonshire Regt., 39–46 (Seconded to K.A.R., 40–45). Capt. Colonial Administration Service, Tanganyika, 46–58. South Arabia, 58–67. (Permanent Sec. to Chief Minister (Aden), 63–65, & Asst. High Commissioner, 65–67.) Now Asst. Sec., Committee of Vice-Chancellors & Principals of U.K. Universities. O.B.E., 63; C.M.G., 66. *Royal Commonwealth Society.*

THORNELOE, Christopher Derek. K, 42^3–47^3.*

THORNELOE, Peter Bernard Lulham. St & K, 41^1–44^3.*

THORNELY, Gervase Michael Cobham, b. 21 Oct. 18, elder s. of Major J. E. B. Thornely, O.B.E. Tu, 32^3–37^2; Tom Hughes Prize; S. VIII, 34–37 (Capt.). Organ Scholar of Trinity Hall, Cambridge, M.A. Asst. Master at Sedbergh School, 40–54. Headmaster since 54. *East India, Sports and Public Schools.* F.R.S.A. Son, Richard Michael Gervase, Tu, 69^3–.

THORNLEY, David Kerr. SF, 31^3–36^1.*

THORNTON, Edward Charles Bexley, M.B.E., b. 22 July 01, s. of F. B. Thornton. M, 15^3–18^2. Faraday House Electrical Engineering College, London. Chartered Electrical Engineer. F.I.E.E. Asst. Engineer, Callenders Cable & Construction Co. Ltd., 23–25. Messrs. Merz & McLellan, 25–30. Various Grades on Electric Traction Staff, & Electric Traction Superintendent of Great Indian Peninsular Railway, Bombay, 30–48. Asst. Electrification Engineer, British Railways, 49–56. Now retired. M.B.E. *Royal Bombay Yacht Club.*

THORNTON, The Rev. Canon Reese Fairfield, b. 22 Sept. 92, 2nd s. of the late G. Q. Thornton. Tu, 06^3–10^1; Cap, 09. Western Theological Seminary, Chicago, Illinois. Degree of S.T.B. Ordained in Protestant Episcopal Church, 17. One-time Archdeacon of Camaguey, Cuba. Now Canon, Christchurch Cathedral, Indianapolis, Ind. Missionary Episcopal

Church, Cuba. Rector, St. John's Church Lafayette, Ind. Chaplain to Episcopal Church, Purdue Univ., Lafayette, Ind. Retired, 60.

THORP, Andrew Fenwick. Tu, 04³–08².*

THORPE, Donal Winton, T.D. St, 13³–18¹.*

THRESHER, Philip Brian, b. 22 June 25, elder s. of the late H. B. Thresher, M.A. C & Tu, 39²–43³; King George VI Gold Medal, 43. Leaving Exhibition to New College, Oxford, B.A. Hudson's Bay Scholar at McGill Univ., Montreal, M.A. ✕ Rifle Bde., 43–47. Capt. Business Economist. Undertook special Study on behalf of International Union for the Conservation of Nature to establish possibilities of wildlife utilisation in E. African Countries, 63–64. Planning Adviser for Tanzanian Parks, 64–72. Now Resource Economist on U.N.D.P/F.A.O. Wildlife Management Project in Kenya.

THURSBY, Edward Nevill. M, 22³–26¹.*

THURSFIELD, Rupert Macnaghten Cecil. SH, 12³–17¹. Sons, 661 & 1188.*

THWAITES, Col. Peter Trevenen, b. 30 July 26, 2nd s. of Lt.-Col. N. G. Thwaites, C.B.E., M.V.O., M.C. SH, 40³–43³. Commissioned Grenadier Guards, 44. p.s.c. j.s.s.c. Brigade Major, 1st Federal Infantry Brigade, Malaya, 59–61. G.S.O.2, Ministry of Defence, 65–67. C.O., Muscat Regt., 67–70. A.Q.M.G., H.Q. London District, 71. Present employment, Commander, British Army Staff, Singapore. Sultan's Bravery Medal. Distinguished Service Medal (Oman). *Guards Club.*

TILDEN, Philip Armstrong.K,02²–03².*

TILLARD, Brig. John Arthur Stuart, O.B.E., M.C., J.P., b. 24 Nov. 89, 4th s. of the late P. E. Tillard. C, 03³–08². R.M.A., Woolwich. Gazetted to the R.E., 09. ✕ 23rd Signal Corps. R.E. Major. M.C. Croce di Guerra. O.B.E. Dispatches five times. Transferred to R. Signals, 20. Major, 25; Col., 36; Brig., 42. Retired, 46 as Brigadier. J.P., East Sussex, 49.

TILLEY, Edward Graham, b. 31 May 00, s. of the late A. E. Tilley. C, 14³–17². A.C.A. Partner in Singleton Fabian & Co. Now retired. *M.C.C.* Son, 171.

TILNEY, Charles Edward, C.M.G., b. 13 Apr. 09, 2nd s. of the late Lt.-Col. N. E. Tilney, C.B.E., D.S.O. K, 22³–27²; Scholar; Exhibitioner. Scholar of Oriel, Oxford, M.A. Ceylon Civil Service, 32–48. Administrative Service, Tanganyika, 48–60. Financial Sec., Tanganyika, 53–60. C.M.G., 56. *United Oxford & Cambridge University Club.* Son, John Martin, K, 67³–.

TINDALL, Wing.-Cdr. John Austin. K, 16³–21².*

TINKER, Brig. Edward Hayden, b. 7 Mar. 09, 2nd s. of the late H. Tinker. St, 22³–27³. Worcester, Oxford, B.A. Commissioned 2nd Lt. 13th/18th Royal Hussars (Q.M.O.), 30. ✕ Served in Palestine Egypt, Italy and Netherlands. Comdr. of the Order of Orange Nassau. Lt.-Col., Comdg. 13th/18th Royal Hussars, 50. Comdr. Land Forces, Persian Gulf, 58. Retired, 60, as Brigadier. Farmed in Hawke's Bay, New Zealand since 60. *Cavalry Club, Royal Central Asian Soc.*

TINKER, Henry James Cossart, M.C. M, 33³–38¹.*

TIPPETTS, Rutherford Berriman, b. 8 Feb. 13, s. of the late P. W. B. Tippetts. B, 26³–30³. Trinity, Oxford, M.A. Imperial Defence College. Civil Service, 36. Principal Private Sec. to President of B.O.T. & Minister of Supply, 42–45. Under-Sec., Dept. of Trade & Industry. Retired, 73. *Junior Carlton Club.* Son, 2366.

TIRRELL, David Johnson. St, 45³–46².*

TIZARD, Prof. John Peter Mills, F.R.C.P., D.C.H., b. 1 Apr. 16, eldest s. of the late Sir H. T. Tizard, G.C.B., A.F.C., F.R.S. SF, 29³–34¹. Oriel, Oxford, M.A., B.M., B.Ch. Middlesex Hospital Medical School, F.R.C.P. Nuffield Medical Travelling Fellowship. ✕ R.A.M.C., 42–46 (T/Major). Asst. Dir., Paediatric Unit, St. Mary's Hospital Medical School, 49–54. Reader & later Professor, Institute of Child Health and Royal Postgraduate Medical School, London, 54–72. Professor of Paediatrics, University of Oxford since 72. Fellow, Jesus, Oxford. Member British Paediatric Assoc. Association of British Neurologists. Neonatal Society. European Society for Pediatric Research (President 70/71). *Athenæum.* Brother, R. H. Tizard.

TIZARD, Richard Henry, b. 25 June 17, 2nd s. of the late Sir H. T. Tizard,

G.C.B., A.F.C., F.R.S. SF, 30^3–34^2. Bristol Univ. Oriel, Oxford, B.A. F.I.E.E. Hon. Fellow, British Computer Society. Senior Tutor, Churchill College, Cambridge. *Athenæum, Oxford & Cambridge Sailing Society.* Brother, J. P. M. Tizard.

TODD, David Cargill, T.D., b. 21 Nov. 08, 2nd s. of the late G. Todd. C, 22^3–26^2. Oriel, Oxford, B.A. Bar, Inner Temple, 30. Practised Northern Circuit, 30–39. ✕ R. Scots Fusiliers (T.A.). Major. Wounded. Colonel Commandant, Ayrshire Army Cadet Force, 46. T.D. Local Government, Ayr County Council, 45–51. Now a Farmer. *Western Club, Glasgow, H.C.E.G. Muirfield, Prestwick G.C.* Brother, G. C. Todd. Sons, 2441 & 2666.

TODD, George Cargill, b. 1 Oct. 07, eldest s. of the late G. Todd. C, 21^3–25^3; XI, 25. Wadham, Oxford, B.A. Farmer. Brother, D. C. Todd. Sons, G. R. C. Todd & 541.

TODD, George Ellerman. b. 24 Aug. 31, 2nd s. of J. S. E. Todd. SH, 45^3–49^2. N/S. Commission, 1st King's Dragoon Guards, 50–52. 2nd Lt. S.R. R.A.C., 52. F.C.A. Partner, Rowe, Swann & Co., Stockbrokers. *Rye G.C.* Liveryman of the Fishmongers Company.

TODD, George Richard Cargill, b. 6 June 33, elder s. of G. C. Todd (or C 21). C, 46^3–51^2. Queens', Cambridge, M.A. Mechanical Engineer, Shell Refining & Marketing Co. Ltd., 56–57. Engineer/ Technologist, Shell Chemicals U.K. Ltd., 57–72. *Prestwick G.C.*

TODHUNTER, Brig. Edward Joseph, T.D., D.L., J.P., b. 4 Oct. 00, eldest s. of B. E. Todhunter, O.B.E. Tu, 14^3–18^2. ✕ R.A.F. Cadet. University College, London. Civil Engineer. Gazetted to 104 Bde., R.F.A. (T.A.), 22. Essex Yeomanry, Lt.-Col., 38. ✕ Served in Palestine, Western Desert, Italy and India, 39–45. P.O.W., 41–43. T.D. Colonel, 45; Brigader, 47. O.B.E. J.P., Essex, 46. Essex County Councillor, 52. D.L., Essex, 53.

TOLLINGTON, Richard Bartram Boyd, C.B.E., b. 28 Aug. 03, s. of the late Rev. Canon R. B. Tollington, D.D., D.Litt. SH, 16^3–21^2. Balliol, Oxford, B.A. Entered Levant Consular Service, 26. Trinity Hall, Cambridge, Arabic, Persian and Turkish Course, 26–28. Served in Persia, Holland, Morocco, Bulgaria, Boston & Washington (U.S.A.), London, Oporto, Leopoldville, Belgian Congo (now Kinshasa, Zaire), and Ambassador to Nepal, 55–57, and to Republic of Honduras, 60–63, when retired. O.B.E., 48; C.B.E., 55. *R.A.C., Himalayan Club, Oporto Cricket & Lawn Tennis Club, Anglo-Portuguese Society.*

TOLSON, Roger Martin Ward, b. 1 May 29, s. of the late R. W. Tolson. K, 42^3–47^2; Cap; Cadet Officer, 46. Clare, Cambridge, B.A. A.T.I. In Woollen Trade. Patons & Baldwins Ltd. for 7 years as Trainee. Mill Man. & Export Sales, 13 years. Leigh & Sillavan Group Ltd., Metal & Mineral Merchants. Sons, James Ward, K, 69^3–, & Andrew Ward, SH, 73^1–.

TOMALINSON, Christopher William Sterling. SH, 41^1–45^1.*

TOMALINSON, Peter Winslow. K, 32^3–37^1.*

TOMPSON, Frederic Philip, b. 4 July 21, s. of F. J. Tompson. K, 35^3–40^2. Emmanuel, Cambridge, M.A. Ordained, 45. Asst. Curate, Sevenoaks Parish Church, 45–48. Travelling Sec., Scripture Union, 48–71. Sec., The Great St. Helen's Trust since 71. *Royal Commonwealth Society.*

TOOTH, Guy. M, 14^1–18^2.*

TOOTH, Geoffrey Cuthbert, M.D. SH, 22^2–25^3.*

TOPHAM, Alexander Mark Romer, b. 30 Apr. 07, s. of the late A. F. Topham, K.C.C. 21^2–26^1; Levée; Head of House; Cap, 24. Trinity Hall, Cambridge, B.A. Barrister. Private Sec. to the Lord Privy Seal, 42. Now retired.

TOPHAM, John Patrick Wakelyn. SH, 28^1–30^1.*

TOPLAS, George Matthew, b. 19 Dec. 21, s. of G. W. Toplas. K, 35^3–40^3; Levée; XV, 39–40 (Capt.); XI, 40; H. XI, 39–40. Scholar of Corpus Christi, Cambridge, B.A. ✕ R.N.V.R., 41–47. Lt. (Sp.). Joined H.M. Foreign Service, 49. 3rd Sec., H.M. Mission, Tokyo, 49 and 2nd Sec., 50. 2nd Sec., H.M. Foreign Office, London, 51. Joined Messrs. Addis of Hertford, 72. Founded "Top Enterprises" (Representative Import/Export), 73. Son, David Hugh Sheridan, K, 69^3–.

TOSSWILL, Timothy Dymond, b. 9 July 14, eldest s. of M. J. Tosswill. B, 28^2–32^2. Exhibitioner of Exeter, Oxford, M.A. ✕ The Devonshire Regt., 39–46.

Major. Dispatches. Published 5 Text-books, and made about 100 broadcasts for the B.B.C. Asst. Master, Royal Masonic School, 35–39 and Rugby School, 47–71. Visiting Lecturer, Univ. of California at Berkeley, 65–66. Associate Professor, Whitman Coll., Washington, U.S.A., 70–73. Son, 2356.

TOWERS, Basil Clifford. K, 43³–48¹.*

TOWNSEND, Bruce Arnold, b. 29 July 29, s. of the late J. Townsend. T, 43²–47³. University College, London, C.Eng., F.I.Chem.E., B.Sc. With Courtaulds Ltd. since 54. Man. Dir., Ashton Bros. & Co. Ltd. Chrmn., Accrington Brick & Tile Co. Ltd. Chrmn., Talbot Weaving Co.

TOWNSHEND, Lt.-Cdr. John Howard, R.N., b. 29 June 26, eldest s. of the late G. M. Townshend (OR W 96). W, 40²–43³. ✕ Joined R.N. as Special Entry Cadet, 44. Lt. Now Lt.-Cdr., Royal Navy. Brother, R. C. Townshend. Sons, John Richard, W, 69³–, & David William, W, 71²–.

TOWNSHEND, Richard Chambrè. W, 43¹–47².*

TOYNBEE, Theodore Philip. SF, 30¹–34².*

TRAILL, Ian Baikie. Tu, 16³–20¹.*

TREMLETT, Walter Guy. B, 45³–49³.*

TREMLETT, William D'Arcy. B, 18²–22³. Son, 26.*

TREMLETT-JOHNSTONE, Edward (formerly E. T. Johnstone), b. 19 Nov. 21, s. of the late C. B. Johnstone. M, 35³–40¹. ✕ K.R.R.C. Capt. P.O.W. Farmer.

TRETHEWY, Robert Bidewell. T, 34¹–38³.*

TREVITHICK, Cdr. Richard Beverley, R.N., b. 4 Nov. 28, elder s. of the late R. G. Trevithick, M.A., B.L., LL.B. T, 41³–45³. R.N. Cadetship, 46. ✕ Korea, 50. Lt.(S), 50. Cdr., R.N. Staff of C.-in-C., Naval Home Command, Portsmouth. At Ministry of Defence since 73. *Emsworth Sailing Club, Nuffield Officers Club.*

TRITTON, Julian Seymour, F.I.C.E., F.I.Mech.E., M.Cons.E., b. 31 Oct. 89, elder s. of the late Sir S. Tritton, K.B.E. SH, 03³–07²; Gym VIII, 06, 07; represented School at Aldershot in the Gym

Pair in 07. Kings College, London. ✕ R.E. War Office & in Afghanistan Campaign. ✕ Technical Adviser to India Supply Mission in Washington. Pres., Inst. of Locomotive Engineers, 47 & 51. Chrmn., Assoc. of Consulting Engineers, 53–54 and President, 55–56. International Federation of Consulting Engineers (F.I.D.I.C.), 55–63. Fellow & Silver Medallist, Royal Society of Arts. C.Eng., F.I.C.E., F.I.Mech.E., M.Cons.E. Retired. *Athenæum, R.A.C.*

TROLLOPE, Charles Jarvis Napier, b. 9 Feb. 33, s. of the late Brig. H. C. N. Trollope, C.B.E., D.S.O. (OR St 09). St, 46³–47². Went to Abbotsholme School. Sandhurst, 53–54. Suffolk Regt., after amalgamation 1 Anglian Regt., 54–64. Fruit Grower since 64. *West Mersea Y.C.*

TROLLOPE, Edward Harvey, F.R.I.C.S., F.A.I., b. 3 Mar. 12, eldest s. of A. H. Trollope. SH, 25³–30²; H. XI, 30. College of Estate Management. Partner, George Trollope & Sons, Chartered Surveyors (Senior Partner latterly), 35–65. ✕ 1st British Survey Regt., R.A., 40–46. Capt. F.R.I.C.S., 47. P.R.O., Trollope & Colls Ltd., Contractors, 67–70. Consultant, Hammersons Property Co., 70–72. Southwark Cathedral Council, 72. Former Dir. of Greencoats Allied London Properties & other Public Property Cos. Now retired. *The East India, Sports & Public Schools Club.* Son, 1101.

TRUMPER, Col. Francis John, O.B.E., T.D., b. 11 Aug. 04, s. of J. A. Trumper. SF, 18³–22². Practised as Chartered Surveyor & Land Agent, 24–39. ✕ Dorsetshire Regt., T.A., 39–45. Colonel. Dep. Dir. of Quartering, War Office. O.B.E., T.D. Senior Partner in Cluttons. Retired, 69. Chartered Surveyor. Sometime Council member. Chartered Land Agent. President of C.L.A. Society, 49–51. *Bath Club, R. & A. G.C., Rye G.C., Senior Golfing Society.* Son, 1011.

TRUSCOTT, Sir Denis (Henry), G.B.E., T.D., J.P., b. 9 July 08, s. of the late H. D. Truscott. M, 22³–25². Magdalene, Cambridge. London School of Printing. Master Printer. President of Brown Knight & Truscott Ltd. Sheriff of the City of London, 51–52. Kt., 53. Lord Mayor of London, 57–58. G.B.E., 58. Senior Alderman, City of London. Former Master of The Vintners Company; Stationers & Newspaper Makers; Musicians; & the Guild of Freemen of the City of London. President of Institute of Printing, 61–63.

Board of Governors, St. Bartholomew's Hospital, 49–69. Board of Governors, Royal Hospital & Home for Incurables, Putney since 38. Council of Royal Holloway College, Egham, 47–69. Executive Cttee. of A.A. since 52. Executive Cttee., Royal Academy of Music, 53–67. Commissioned, T.A., 38. ✕ A.A. Command, 39–45. T.D. *United Oxford & Cambridge University Club, City Livery Club, R.A.C.*

TRUSCOTT, Sir Eric Homewood Stanham, Bt. M, 12^2–15^1.*

TUCK, Major Harry Brian Ritson. SF, 44^1–48^1.*

TUCKER, Major Victor Murray, R.E., b. 5 June 23, s. of H. Tucker. M, 37^3–41^2. Birmingham University (Army Wartime Course). ✕ R.E., 41. Regular Commission. 2nd Lt., R.E., 42. 8th Army, 43; Sicily, 43; France, Belgium, Holland & Germany, 44–45; Palestine, 46–47. W.O., 48–49. Long Army Transportation Course, 50–52; Hong Kong, 55–57. Voluntary retirement (Major, R.E.), 61. Joined Midland Bank in 62. Currently their Legal Dept. Librarian. *Officers Pension Society.*

TUCKETT, Cedric Ivor, M.B.E., M.Ch., F.R.C.S., b. 12 Dec. 01, s. of the late I. L. Tuckett, M.D. SF, 15^3–20^2; Cap, 20. Trinity, Cambridge, M.A., M.Chir. Scholar of St. Thomas's Hospital, M.R.C.S., L.R.C.P., F.R.C.S. Cheselden Surgery Medal, 26. Medical Officer, Tonbridge School. Consulting Surgeon, Kent & Sussex Hospital. Homoeopathic Hospital, Tunbridge Wells, & Tonbridge Cottage Hospital. Retired, 66. ✕ R.A.M.C., 42–46. Lt.-Col. M.B.E. Son, 1465.

TUDOR JONES, Geoffrey Cecil. Tu, 34^3–37^3.*

TUDOR PRICE, David William (formerly Price, D. W. T.), b. 29 Jan. 31, eldest s. of T. H. Price. St, 44^3–49^2; XV, 47–48; R. VIII, 47–48; H. XI, 49; Junior Athletics Cup, 47. N/S. Welsh Guards, 50. Magdalene, Cambridge. Barrister at Law. Junior Treasury Counsel at the Central Criminal Court. *Moor Park G.C., Bar Golfing Society.* Son, Simon Howell, St, 72^2–.

TULLOCH, William Alexander, M.C., T.D., b. 20 Sept. 10, elder s. of the late Major J. T. Tulloch, M.C. SF, 24^3–29^2. Clare, Cambridge, B.A. C.A. Partner, Arthur Young McClelland Moores & Co. Dir., Scottish United Investors Ltd.

James Finlay & Co. Ltd. ✕ Ayrshire (E.C.O.) Yeomanry. P.O.W. May, 43; Escaped, 43; Wounded, 44. M.C., T.D. Major. *Prestwick G.C., H.C.E.G. Muirfield, Western Club, Glasgow.* Sons, 1151, 1388, 2472 & 2473.

TUPPEN, Bernard Roy, M.I.E.E., b. 22 June 11, 2nd s. of the late E. B. Tuppen. T, 25^1–29^3; Foundationer. Rugby College of Technology & Arts. London Univ. External Degree. B.Sc. Apprentice, 30–34 & from 35 Electrical Engineer with B.T.H. Co. Ltd., Rugby. M.I.E.E., C.Eng. Now with Marconi Radar Systems Ltd., Leicester.

TURCAN, Henry Hutchison, T.D., b. 2 Mar. 07, 2nd s. of the late J. W. Turcan. SH, 20^3–26^1; XV, 23–25 (Capt.); H. XI, 26; Levée. Trinity, Oxford, M.A. Rugby Football Blue, 28. ✕ Fife & Forfar Yeomanry, 39–45. Major. T.D. Dispatches. Dir., Robert Hutchison & Co. Ltd. of Kirkcaldy, Fife. *R. & A. G.C.* (Capt., 59–60), *H.C.E.G. Muirfield.* Brother, P. W. Turcan. Sons, 1102, 1371 & 2012.

TURCAN, Patrick Watson. SH, 26^3–31^1.*

TURNBULL, David Alexander. Sh, 44^3–48^3.*

TURNBULL, Cdr. Derwent Greville, b. 4 Jan. 22, s. of Professor H. W. Turnbull, F.R.S. SH, 35^3–40^2; Scholar; Levée. Scholar of St. John's, Cambridge, M.A., M.Sc. ✕ Royal Navy, 42–68. Instructor Commander. Now Lecturer in Mechanical Engineering, Dundee Univ. *Naval & Military, R. & A. G.C.*

TURNBULL, Robertson. M, 07^3–10^1.*

TURNER, Charles Walter, M.C. B, 06^3–10^2.*

TURNER, Hugh James. C, 18^3–21^2.*

TURNER, Marcus Walford. M, 10^3–13^2.*

TURNER, Maurice Charles Champion. St, 24^1–27^3.*

TURNER, Peter Ernest, V.R.D., b. 26 Apr. 16, 5th s. of the late G. L. Turner. Tu, 30^2–34^2. ✕ R.N., 39–46. Lt. R.N.R. Lt.-Cdr. V.R.D. Herbage & Cereal Seeds, Man. for North Devon Farmers Ltd. Fellow, National Institute Agricultural Botany, Cambridge.

TURNER, Raymond Clifford (see Clifford Turner, R.).

TURNER, Major Richard. SF, 20^3–25^2.*

TURNEY, Fleckney Harry Reeve. T, 20^2–23^2.*

TWALLIN, Hugh Belton. K, 23^3–28^2.*

TWALLIN, John Charles Hickman, b. 16 July 04, eldest s. of the late C. G. Twallin, C.B.E. K, 18^3–22^3; Cap, 22. Choral Exhibitioner of Emmanuel, Cambridge, M.A. Entered Buck & Hickman Ltd. of London E., 33; Dir., 37; Asst. Man. Dir., 52. Retired. Master of the Ironmongers Company, 64–65 & 65–66. *United Oxford & Cambridge University Club.* Brothers, H. B. & T. R. Twallin. Son, J. R. C. Twallin.

TWALLIN, John Randall Charles, b. 2b Jan. 33, s. of J. C. H. Twallin (OR K 18). K, 46^3–51^2; Sw. VIII, 52. N/S. R.N.V.R. Midshipman (Sp.). Emmanuel, Cambridge, M.A. Company Dir., Thos. P. Headland (London South) Ltd. C.A. Clemson & Sons Ltd. *London Rowing Club, Wildernesse Club, British Sportsmans Club.*

TWALLIN, Theodore Roe, b. 30 Sept. 11, 3rd s. of the late C. G. Twallin, C.B.E. K, 25^3–30^1. Emmanuel, Cambridge, B.A. Joined Buck & Hickman Ltd., 33; Dir., 46; Joint Man. Dir., 64. Resigned, 71. ✕ T.A. Artists Rifles. Commissioned, 39. K.O.Y.L.I., 46. Capt. Territorial Efficiency Medal. Now retired. Master of the Ironmongers Company, 71. *British Sportsmans Club.* Brothers, J. C. H. & H. B. Twallin. Son, 2382.

TWEEDY, Major Ivan Marshall. M, 07^2–11^2.*

TWISS, Richard Quintin. M, 34^3–38^2.*

TWIST, Derek Norman, b. 26 May 05, younger s. of the late C. F. Twist. C, 18^3–23^2; Levée; Head of House; Cadet Officer. Gonville & Caius, Cambridge, B.A. With Asiatic Petroleum Co. in London & Malaya, 27–31. In the Film Production Industry from 31. ✕ R.A.F., 40–45. Wing-Cdr. Dispatches. Retired. *E.S.U.*

TYLDESLEY JONES, Basil Humphrey. SH, 29^2–33^3.*

TYLER, John Robertson, b. 18 Dec. 20, s. of the late R. C. Tyler. K, 34^3–38^2. ✕ R.E. & R. Leicestershire Regt. Attd. K.A.R. Capt. F.C.A. Man. Dir., John Tyler & Sons Ltd.

TYSON, Alan Walker, b. 27 Oct. 26, eldest s. of H. A. M. Tyson. Sh, 40^3–45^1; Scholar; Levée; Classical Exhibitioner. N/S. R.N.V.R., 45–47. Demy of Magdalen, Oxford. M.A. De Paravicini Scholarship, 49. Fellowship by Examination, All Souls College, 52. Assoc. Member, British Psycho-Analytical Society, 57. M.B., B.S., London, 65. Visiting Lecturer in Psychiatry, Montefiore Hospital & Albert Einstein College of Medicine, New York, 67–68. Visiting Professor of Music, Columbia Univ., New York, 69. Member of the Royal College of Psychiatrists, 71. Elected Senior Research Fellow at All Souls Coll., 71. Doctor & Psychoanalyst; Musicologist. Brothers, J. B. Tyson & 283.

TYSON, John Baird, M.C., b. 7 Apr. 28, 2nd s. of H. A. M. Tyson. Sh, 41^3–46^3; Levée; Head of House. Magdalen, Oxford, M.A. For Career, see Part III, under Assistant Masters of Rugby School. Brothers, A. W. Tyson & 283.

U

UGLOW, Wing-Cdr. Michael John, R.A.F., M.R.C.S., L.R.C.P., b. 23 Jan. 30, s. of the late J. C. Uglow. T, 43^3–47^2. St. Thomas's Hospital, M.R.C.S., L.R.C.P., D.P.H. Medical Branch of the R.A.F., Wing Cdr.

UNDERHILL, Graham Collingwood, b. 18 Jan. 30, s. of the late B. C. S. Underhill, F.R.I.B.A. B, 43^3–47^3; Athletics Cup, 46. Emmanuel, Cambridge, B.A. In teaching profession. Asst. Master at King Edward's School, Birmingham since 65.

UNDERWOOD, Frederick Lewis, O.B.E. SF, 11^2–15^1.*

UPCOTT, John Philip. B, 26^3–30^2.*

URQUHART, Hector Maconochie, F.R.C.S., b. 27 Mar. 17, elder s. of G. H. Urquhart. C, 31^1–35^1. Edinburgh Univ.,

M.B., Ch.B., D.L.O., F.R.C.S.(Edin.). Consultant E.N.T. Surgeon, Northern Regional Hospital Board, Scotland. ✕ R.A.F., 40–46. Sqn. Ldr. Dispatches. Royal Society of Medicine. Son, 2828.

URWICK, Alan Bedford. SF, 43^3–47^2.*

URWICK, William Gilbert Desmond Harold, M.R.C.S., L.R.C.P. B, 11^3–14^3.*

USMAR, Gordon Graham. St, 29^1–32^2.*

USMAR, John Alan, b. 2 June 25, s. of N. A. Usmar. St & K, 39^2–43^2; Leaving Exhibition. ✕ R.H.A., 43–47. Sgt. Trinity, Cambridge, B.A. Farming. At present, Director of Community Council of Devon. National Trust; Devon Trust; British School at Athens.

V

VALENTINE, Anthony Seymour, M.B., B.Chir., D.Obst.R.C.O.G., b. 4 Feb. 28, s. of the late L. Valentine. K, 42^1–46^2. St. John's, Cambridge, B.A., M.B., B.Chir. Guy's Hospital. Certification, College of Family Physicians of Canada. Medical Officer, H.M. Overseas Civil Service, Sierra Leone, 56–60. General Practice, Beeston, Nottingham, 60–69. Family Physician, Winnipeg since 69. Lecturer in Family Practice, St. Boniface General Hospital, Manitoba Univ. Royal College of General Practitioners of the Canadian Medical Association.

VALENTINE, Roy Lindley. W, 19^2–23^2.*

VAN GRUISEN, Michael Henry, b. 29 Apr. 22, s. of the late H. Van Gruisen (OR M 07). M, 35^3–40^2; Levée; S. VIII, 39; Exhibitioner. ✕ 5th R. Tank Regt., H.Q. 4th Armd. Bde. Army Air Liaison Group, Middle East. R. Tank Regt. (T.A.) since 47. Lt.-Col. T.A.V.R., T.D. Pembroke, Cambridge, M.A. Director, Scottish & Newcastle Breweries Ltd. *Special Forces Club.*

VANSITTART, Arnold Mark. SH, 40^3–45^2.*

VARLEY, Gilbert Alec. SF, 30^2–34^1.*

VARLEY, John Francis, M.B., B.Chir., b. 7 Sept. 03, eldest s. of the late G. Varley. SF, 17^3–22^1; Scholar; R. VIII, 21–22. Christ's Cambridge, B.A., M.B., B.Chir. Half Blue, Cross Country, 23–24; Athletics, 24. St. Bartholomew's Hospital, M.R.C.S., M.R.C.P. Hon. Physician, Southlands Hospital, Shoreham-by-Sea. ✕ R.A.M.C. Major. Retired. Brother, G. A. Varley. Nephew, 2234.

VAUDREY, John Randle, M.B.E., b. 10 June 16, eldest s. of the late R. H. N. Vaudrey. SF, 29^3–34^1. F.C.A. ✕ 2nd

Bn. Royal Warwickshire Regt., 40–42. D.A.A.G. & A.A.G., 30 Corps, 43–46. M.B.E. Lt.-Col. Director, Reed Engineering & Development Services Ltd. Brother, O. C. Vaudrey. Sons, 1302 & 2235.

VAUDREY, Oliver Claude, b. 4 Feb. 23, 2nd s. of the late R. H. N. Vaudrey. SF, 36^3–40^2. Royal Indian Navy, 41–48 (compulsorily retired on transfer of power in India). ✕ R.I.N. Lieut. Various positions in Industry, 48–54. Factory Manager, Pims Popcorn Ltd., 54–58. Man. Dir., 58–70. Now farming. *R.N. Sailing Association, West Mersea Y.C.* Brother, J. R. Vaudrey. Sons, Claude William, SF, 68^3–, & Joseph Henry, SF, 70^3–.

VAUGHAN, Major David Wyamar, C.B.E., LL.D., b. 15 July 06, younger s. of the late Dr. W. W. Vaughan, M.V.O. (OR SH 79). SH, 20^1–24^2. Entered Barclays Bank Ltd., Lombard St., 30; Local Director, Shrewsbury, 34; Cardiff, 39–72; Windsor since 72; Director of Bank since 54. ✕ Welsh Guards, 39–45. Major. Chrmn., Finance Cttee. Church in Wales since 55. Hon. Treas., Univ. College of S. Wales & Mon., 52–57, and Welsh National School of Medicine, 62–67. J.P. Glamorgan, 56–66. High Sheriff, Glamorgan, 63. Trustee, Historic Churches Preservation Trust since 68. Churches Main Cttee. since 68. C.B.E., Hon.LL.D., Wales. *Boodle's.* Brother, H. J. Vaughan. Sons, E. J. W. & P. W. D. Vaughan. Grandson, David John Wyamar, St, 71^2–.

VAUGHAN, Edwin John Wyamar, b. 14 Mar. 30, elder s. of Major D. W. Vaughan, C.B.E. (OR SH 20). SH, 43^3–48^2; Levée; Head of House; Leaving Exhibition. Scholar of New College, Oxford, B.A. N/S. Welsh Guards. 2nd Lt. Furniture & Clock Expert, Messrs. Sotheby & Co. Brother, P. D. W. Vaughan.

VAUGHAN, Halford John. SH, 15^1–20^2.*

VAUGHAN, Peter David Wyamar, T.D., b. 29 May 31, 2nd s. of Major D. W. Vaughan, C.B.E. (OR SH 20). St, 45^1–49^2; Cap. Director of a Firebrick Company. M.B.E., T.D. *Northern Counties Club.* Brother, E. J. W. Vaughan. Son, David John Wyamar, St, 71^2–.

VAWDREY, Daniel Llewelyn, b. 16 Dec. 91, eldest s. of the late Rev. D. Vawdrey. St, 05^3–10^2; Scholar. Scholar of Trinity, Oxford. ✕ 2nd Worcestershire Regt., 14–19. Capt. Assistant Master, Fettes College, Edinburgh, 20–52. Second Master, Acting Headmaster, 50–51. King's School, Worcester (part time), 52–64. Retired, 64. T.D. Special Constabulary Medal (Edinburgh), 46. *The Church House, Worcester.*

VEALE, Derek Tankard, b. 28 Dec. 08, 2nd s. of Dr. H. Veale. Tu, 22^3–27^1. Scholar of Christ's, Cambridge, M.A. F.C.A., 42. Retired. *Spanish Club.*

VEASEY, Colin John. T, 22^3–24^3.*

VEASEY, David Jeremy. SF, 46^2–50^2.*

VELLACOTT, David Norman Strain, b. 23. Oct. 30, 2nd s. of J. M. Vellacott. B, 44^2–49^2; Levée; Head of House; Cadet Officer. St. John's, Cambridge, M.A. Univ. Basketball Team. F.R.I.C.S. Sub-Agent under Strutt & Parker on Orsett Estate, Essex. Resident Agent to Orsett Estate Company. Now Estates Bursar, Winchester College. Brother, J. P. M. Vellacott.

VELLACOTT, John Patrick Millner. B, 42^3–47^1. Son, Jonathan James. B, 72^3–.*

VENNER, Major John Boldrewood, M.C., b. 17 Feb. 30, elder s. of the late J. F. Venner, C.M.G. (OR W 15). W, 43^3–47^2. ✕ 8th K.R.I. Hussars, Korea, 50–51. M.C. Lt., 7th Queen's Own Hussars, 52. Lt.-Col. commanding The Queen's Own Hussars. *Cavalry Club.* Son, Rolf Franklyn, W, 71^1–.

VERDEN-ANDERSON, William John, b. 28 Mar. 32, eldest s. of E. W. Verden Anderson. St, 45^3–50^1. Director, Smith Anderson & Co. Ltd., Papermakers, Leslie, Fife. Brother, 448.

VEREKER, John Stanley Herbert Medlicott. K, 41^2–45^1.*

VERSCHOYLE, Michael John Stuart. B, 38^3–43^1.*

VERSCHOYLE, Major Terence Trevor Hamilton, M.C., b. 9 Sept. 94, s. of the late S. Verschoyle. B, 08^3–12^2; Scholar; Minor Exhibitioner. Imperial College of Science (Royal College of Science), 12–14 and 19–20, Ph.D., D.Sc. ✕ 5th Bn. Royal Inniskilling Fusiliers. Capt. Wounded twice. M.C. Order of Crown of Italy. Dispatches twice. Resigned, 19. Research Chemist with Brunner Mond & Co., 20–26. Farmer, 26–37. ✕ Recalled to Colours, 39–45. British Council, 45–51. Retired, 51. Member of Salisbury Diocesan Board of Finance since 53. *Gallipoli Assoc., Royal Philatelic Soc., Anglo-Turkish Soc.*

VERTUE, Charles Brooke, F.C.A., b. 4 Apr. 33, s. of the late H. B. Vertue. B, 46^3–50^3. F.C.A. Stockbroker. Partner in Beardsley & Co. *Rye G.C.*

VICKERS, Martin, A.M.I.E.E. St & K, 38^3–42^2. Son, 2589B.*

VICKERY, Michael Ralph Lawton. C, 36^3–41^2.*

VINES, Howard William Copland, M.D., b. 10 Mar. 93, younger s. of Prof. S. H. Vines, D.Sc., F.R.S. Tu, 07^3–11^2. Christ's, Cambridge, M.A., M.D. Univ. Trial VIII, 13. St. Bartholomew's Hospital, M.R.C.S., L.R.C.P. Fellow, Christ's College. Pathologist, Charing Cross Hospital, 28 & Lecturer in Pathology; Prof. Pathol., Ch. X Med. School (London Univ.); Dean, Ch. X Med. School; Member, Ch. X. Hosp. Council and Board of Governors, N.W. Metro. Reg. Board; Sector Pathologist, E.M.S., 39–44; West Cornwall H.M.C. Retired. Son, R. C. B. Vines.

VINES, Richard Copland Brindley. Sh, 42^3–44^2.*

VINEY, Laurence Walter Merriam, b. 17 Apr. 19, 2nd s. of Col. O. V. Viney. K, 32^3–37^2; H. XI, 37. E.S.U. Exchange Scholarship to Phillips Academy, Andover, Mass., U.S.A., 37–38. Master Printer with Hazell Watson & Viney Ltd., London & Aylesbury, 38. ✕ Ox. & Bucks. L.I. (T.A.), 38–45. Glider Pilot, Regt. Army Air Corps., 42–43. Sales Director, Hazell Watson & Viney Ltd. *Garrick Club.* Sons, 1686 & 2479.

VINGOE, Michael, b. 9 May 25, s. of C. F. Vingoe. T, 40^3–41^3. ✕ R.A.F., 42–46. Fighter Pilot. R.N.V.R. (F.A.A.), 46. Career in publishing since 46. Dir. of

George Newnes Ltd. since 69. Advert. Controller, I.P.C. Magazines Ltd., London. Cttee., Code of Advertising Practice and Retail Standards Trade Council. *Frinton G.C.*

VOELCKER, Oswald John, C.B.E., b. 25 Apr. 05, 4th s. of A. F. Voelcker, M.D., F.R.C.P. B, 18^3–23^2. Queens', Cambridge, M.A. Colonial Agric. Scholar, Oxford Univ. & Imperial College of Tropical Agric. Associate, Dept. Agric., Nigeria, 28–44. Dir., West African Cacao Research Inst., 44–49 and Agric., Malaya, 50–55.

W

WADDILOVE, Douglas Edwin, M.B.E., LL.B. Sh, 32^1–36^3. Son, 3020.*

WADDINGTON, David. B, 45^3–48^3.*

WADDY, The Rev. Canon Richard Patteson Stacy, b. 31 May 04, eldest s. of the late P. S. Waddy. T, 19^3–22^1. Balliol, Oxford, M.A. Cuddesdon College, Oxford. Ordained, Deacon, 27; Priest, 28. Curate of St. Peter's, Leicester, 27–30; India, 30–47 (Senior Presidency Chaplain, Bombay Cathedral, 42–47); Rector & Rural Dean, Ampthill, Beds., 47–52; Warden, College of the Ascension, Selly Oak & Hon. Canon of Birmingham, 52–59; Rector of Morley, Derbyshire & Hon. Canon of Derby, 59–67; Chaplain, Queen Anne's School, Caversham, 67–72; Chaplain, Community of All Hallows, Ditchingham, Norfolk from 72.

WADHAM, Malcolm Hugh. C, 19^1–23^2.*

WADHAM, Rohan Nicholas, D.F.C., b. 4 Dec. 23, 2nd s. of the late N. W. Wadham (OR SF 07). SF, 37^3–42^2; Levée; Head of House; XV, 41; XI, 41, 42; Tom Hughes Prize. ✕ R.N.V.R., 42–46. Lt. D.F.C. Trinity, Oxford, B.A. Clerk of the House of Lords, 49–50. "Daily Telegraph", 50–51. Stockbroker with Rowe & Pitman since 51.

WADSWORTH, Arthur Mayow, b. 19 Feb. 15, s. of the late T. Wadsworth. T, 29^1–33^2. Birmingham Univ., M.B., Ch.B., M.R.C.S., L.R.C.P.(Lon.), 38. ✕ R.A.M.C., 39–45. Major. Dispatches. J.P. *Alpine Club, Climbers' Club.*

WAINWRIGHT, The Rev. Ronald Charles, b. 21 Oct. 89, younger s. of the

Retired, H.M. Overseas Service. C.B.E., 49. *The Farmers' Club.*

VOGT, Johan Herman Lie, b. 20 June 04, s. of the late J. Vogt. W, 18^1–22^2; Cap, 21; Cadet Officer. Studied abroad three years. Shipbroker. F.I.C.S. ✕ Norwegian Campaign with Independant Coy. No. 1, att. to British Embassy, Madrid & British Consulate General, Tangiers. British Rep., Civil Affairs, French Morocco. Knight 1st Class of Order of St. Olaf. *Old Hall, Exchange & Palatine, Liverpool.* Son, 795.

late H. G. Wainwright. SF, 03^3–08^2; Cap, 07; Cadet Officer. Trinity, Cambridge, M.A. Ordained, 13. ✕ Chaplain, att. 61st Div. Dispatches. Vicar of St. Marks, Washwood Heath, 26. Retired.

WAITE, Clifford Geoffrey. K, 40^3–43^2.*

WAITE, Ian Clapham, b. 2 Sept. 30, 2nd s. of C. Waite. K, 44^3–48^3; Cap. N/S. 17/21 Lancers, 49–51. 2nd Lt. Magdalene, Cambridge, M.A. City of London Yeomanry (Sharpshooters) T.A. from 51. Solicitor. *Oriental Club, Farmers' Club.* Brother, C. G. Waite.

WAKEFIELD, Humphrey. Sh, 39^3–43^1.*

WALDING, Anthony Thomas Randall. SH, 43^3–48^3.*

WALDRON, Arthur Trengrouse, b. 13 May 05, 3rd s. of W. G. Waldron. Tu, 19^2–22^3; Cap, 22. Sheep farming in Patagonia (Chile & Argentine). *Naval & Military Club.*

WALFORD, David de Guise, T.D., b. 10 Aug. 17, 3rd s. of the late A. A. B. Walford, F.C.A., J.P. M, 31^2–36^2; XI, 35, 36; H. XI, 36; Cadet Officer. Joined 5th Bn. D.L.I. (T.A.), 36. ✕ R.A. T/Major. T.D. Self-employed Chartered Accountant (in partnership). English Hockey International. F.I.H. Umpire. Brothers, E. W. & M. M. Walford. Son, 2730.

WALFORD, Edward Wynn, b. 28 May 10, eldest s. of the late A. A. B. Walford, F.C.A., J.P. M, 24^2–28^3; Cap, 27; XXII; H. XI, 28. F.C.A. Partner in firm of Chartered Accountants. Brothers, M. M. & D. de G. Walford.

WALFORD, Michael Moore, b. 27 Nov. 15, 2nd s. of the late A. A. B. Walford, F C A., J.P. M, 29^1–34^2; XV, 31–33; XI, 31–34 (Capt.); H. XI, 32–34. Trinity, Oxford, M.A.; Cricket Blue, 35–38; Rugby Football Blue, 35–37; Hockey, 35–36 & 38. ✕ R. Signals, 40–45. Major. Master, Sherborne School since 38. Now 2nd Master. Brothers, E. W. & D. de G. Walford.

WALKER, Clement Willoughby, M.B., B.Chir. W, 17^2–22^2. Son, 510.*

WALKER, David Dixon, b. 9 Sept. 05, 3rd s. of the late T. S. Walker. K, 19^2–23^2. Pembroke, Cambridge, M.A. F.I.E.E. Electrical Instrument Manufacturer. Man. Dir., Evershed & Vignoles Ltd., 40–64. Director, Thomas Walker & Son Ltd. since 41 (Chrmn. & Man. Dir., 64). Member, Council and one-time Chrmn., British Electrical & Mechanical Assoc. *Royal Dart Y.C.* Brother, S. T. Walker. Son, 1811.

WALKER, Derek Nicholas, b. 25 Oct. 24, s. of F. S. Walker, M.C. W, 38^3–42^2. Peterhouse, Cambridge. ✕ R.N.V.R., 43–46. Lt. F.C.A., C.A. (Alberta, Canada). Brown, Fleming & Murray, Chartered Accountants, London, 47–53. Clarkson, Gordon & Co., C.A., Toronto & Calgary, Canada, 53–55. With Canadian Export Gas & Oil Ltd., Calgary since 55 (now Sec. Treasurer).

WALKER, George Gordon, M.B., B.Ch., b. 24 Jan. 24, eldest s. of the late R. L. Walker. Tu, 37^3–42^1; H. XI, 42. Trinity Hall, Cambridge, B.A., M.B., B.Chir. Middlesex Hospital. In General Medical Practice. *Royal Norfolk & Suffolk Y.C., Aldeburgh Music Soc.* Sons, 3033, Ian Randel, Tu, 67^3–72^2 & Michael Lawrence, Tu, 69^3–.

WALKER, George Michael Henderson, b. 17 May 28, s. of the late Col. A. D. Walker (OR SF 11). SF & C, 41^3–46^2; Levée; Head of House; XV, 45; H. XI, 45, 46 (Capt.); Exhibitioner. Trinity Hall, Cambridge, B.A., F.C.A. Dir. & Sec. of Initial Services Ltd.

WALKER, Brig. Harry Charles, M.B.E., M.C. Tu, 34^3–39^1.*

WALKER, Hugh Michael, b. 26 Jan. 25, eldest s. of the late H. C. Walker (OR SF 92). SF, 38^3–43^2. Hertford, Oxford, M.A. ✕ R.N., 44–46. S/Lt. Dip. Cam., M.Inst. M., M.B.I.M. Man. Dir., Hugh Walker

(Training & Development) Ltd. *Naval Club.* Member of Hertford Society Cttee.

WALKER, John Brian, B.M., B.Ch., b. 16 Mar. 24, s. of Dr. W. B. Walker. W, 37^3–41^2; Exhibitioner (Biology). New College, Oxford, M.A., B.M., B.Ch. Radcliffe Infirmary. London Hospital. Ophthalmic House Surgeon, London Hospital. 5 years Short Service Commission, R.A.M.C. Capt. Ophthalmologist to E. Africa Command since 52. General Practitioner in S.E. London. *Royal Corinthian Y.C., Royal Ocean Racing Club.* Son, Michael Laurence, W, 69^3–.

WALKER, John Henry Chesshyre, b. 16 Mar. 05, s. of Rev. R. E. C. Walker. Tu, 18^3–23^2. Trinity, Cambridge, B.A. Schoolmaster at Monkton Combe School, 31–46, 51–65. At Felsted School, 46–50. Retired.

WALKER, John Mark, b. 8 Apr. 30, s. of H. M. Walker. M, 43^3–48^2. N/S. R.A.F. Pilot Officer. Leicester College of Technology. Company Director in textiles manufacture and in food. Farmer.

WALKER, Stansfeld Thomas, b. 10 Feb. 02, 2nd s. of T. S. Walker. K, 16^1–20^2; Cap, 19; XXII, 20; G. VIII, 18–20 (Capt., 19, 20). Pembroke, Cambridge, M.A. Architectural Assoc. Dip.AA. F.R.I.B.A. President, Birmingham & Five Counties Architectural Assoc., 56–57. Architect. Guardian, Birmingham Assay Office. Life Governor, Birmingham Univ. *Edgbaston G.C., Birmingham Conservative Club.* Brother, D. D. Walker.

WALKER, Thomas Charles, b. 21 Dec. 22, s. of the late C. E. Walker, A.C.A. M, 36^3–40^3. L.S.E. B. Comm. ✕ R. Signals, 41–46. Capt. A.C.A., 42. Partner in Turquands, Barton, Mayhew & Co., Jersey since 52. Sons, 2679 & 2882.

WALKER, Walter Basil Scarlett, b. 19 Dec. 15, s. of the late J. S. A. Walker (OR M 01). Tu, 29^3–34^2; Fives IV. Clare, Cambridge, M.A. ✕ R.N.V.R. Lt.-Cdr. (S). Chartered Accountant, Partner in Peat Marwick Mitchell & Co. Part-time member of U.K. Atomic Energy Authority. *Junior Carlton & R.A.C.* Son, 2135.

WALKER, William Sylvester Cecil. St, 14^3–18^3.*

WALLACE, Brian Adair, T.D., b. 25 July 13, s. of D. Wallace. K, 27^2–31^3. Westminster Dragoons, T.A., 34. ✕ 39–45.

Major. Dispatches. T.D. Bronze Lion of the Netherlands. Chrmn. & Man. Dir. of Rubber Latex Ltd. of Manchester. *Manchester Tennis & Racquets Club*. Son, 2992.

WALLACE, Cranstoun L'Estrange. W, 08³–12².*

WALLACE, William Ernest. SH, 01³–05³.*

WALLACE, William Harrold Stuart. C, 27¹–30².*

WALLACE-JONES, Dudley Richard, M.B., B.Chir., D.M.R.D., b. 19 July 23, eldest s. of the late Dr. H. Wallace-Jones. Sh, 37¹–40². Gonville & Caius, Cambridge, M.A., M.B., B.Chir. Liverpool Univ. N/S. Surg.-Lt. R.N.V.R., 47–49. D.M.R.D., 51. Consultant Radiologist, North Merseyside Hospital Group. Brothers, H. D. & G. M. Wallace-Jones.

WALLACE-JONES, George Maurice, b. 2 Feb. 28, 3rd s. of the late Dr. H. Wallace-Jones. Sh, 41³–45²; XV, 44; XXII, 45; H. XI, 44, 45. Gonville & Caius, Cambridge, B.A. F.I.C.E. Consulting Engineer & Contractor, England & South Africa. Now Director, Engineering Surveys. *R.A.C.* Brothers, D. R. & H. D. Wallace-Jones.

WALLACE-JONES, Henry Dennis, b. 14 Aug. 25, 2nd s. of the late Dr. H. Wallace-Jones. Sh, 39¹–43¹; XV, 42. Gonville & Caius, Cambridge, M.A. Solicitor. *R.A.C.*, *Poole Harbour Y.C.*, *Broadstone G.C.* Brothers, D. R. & G. M. Wallace-Jones.

WALLER, Richard Heron, b. 15 Mar. 18, s. of Sir M. L. Waller, K.C.B. SH, 31³–36²; R. VIII. University College, Oxford, B.A. ✕ Guides Cavalry, Indian Army, 39. Major. R.A.F., Fighter Command, 42. F/Lt. Wounded. London Univ. Teacher Diploma, 59. F.A.O. of U.N. Teacher in Africa, India & U.K. Now wildlife conservation in connection with World Wildlife Fund. Mainly in India & Nepal to conserve tiger & prey species. F.R.G.S.

WALMSLEY, Peter Robert Vincent. M, 39¹–43².*

WALMSLEY, Thomas Percy. M, 31¹–36¹.*

WALSHAM, Rear-Admiral Sir John (Scarlett Warren), Bt., C.B., O.B.E. K, 24³–28².*

WALTON, Anthony James, M.B., F.R.C.S., b. 11 Sept. 13, s. of the late Sir James Walton, K.C.V.O., M.S., F.R.C.S. Tu, 27¹–32². Corpus Christi, Cambridge, M.A., M.B., B.Ch. London Hospital, Elementary Prize in Clinical Surgery, L.R.C.P., F.R.C.S. ✕ R.N.V.R. Surgical Specialist. Hon. Asst. Surgeon, The London Hospital. Consultant Surgeon, Bethnal Green & St. Andrew's Hospital, Bow. Medical Soc. of London. Son, 1841.

WANSTALL, Humphrey John Boraston. T, 02³–07².*

WARBURG, David John, b. 22 Aug. 23, eldest s. of F. J. Warburg. B, 37²–42². Clare, Cambridge. Half Blues for Lawn Tennis, Squash, Rackets & Tennis. ✕ R.E.M.E., 42–47. Capt. Asst. Master, King's College School, Wimbledon. Outside "name" at Lloyds. Amateur Champion, Real Tennis, 59, 61 & 65. *Queen's, M.C.C., R.A.C.*

WARD, Frederick Godsalve, B.M., B.Ch., F.R.C.S., b. 30 Nov. 09, s. of the late V. G. Ward, M.D. SF, 23³–28². New College, Oxford, B.M., B.Ch. St. Bartholomew's Hospital, F.R.C.S.✕R.N.V.R., 39–45. Surg.-Lt.-Cdr. V.R.D. Senior Orthopaedic Surgeon, Ashford Hospital, Middlesex, 50–70. Now District Scout Commissioner, North Dorset. *Oriental Club.*

WARD, Thomas Wortley, b. 26 June 29, eldest s. of T. W. Ward. M, 43²–47²; Cap; XXII; H. XI, 47. Major Territorial Army, R.A.O.C. T.D. Man. Dir., Thomas Ward & Sons Ltd., Cutlery Manufacturers of Sheffield. *Ski Club of G.B., E.S.U.* Son, Thomas Duncan, M, 71³–.

WARD, Lt.-Cdr. William Denby, b. 7 Apr. 94, s. of the late W. P. Ward. SH, 08¹–11³. R.M.C., Sandhurst. ✕ South Lancashire Regt. Capt. N.W. Frontier Operations, India, 19. Retired with rank of Lt.-Col. *Army & Navy Club, M.C.C.* Son, 334.

WARDILL, James Campbell, M.B., B.Chir., F.R.C.S., b. 5 Aug. 25, 2nd s. of the late W. E. M. Wardill, F.R.C.S. W, 38³–43²; XV, 41–42; XI, 41–43; H. XI, 42–43. Peterhouse, Cambridge, B.A.,M.B., B.Chir. Middlesex Hospital Medical School. F.R.C.S.(Edin.), F.R.C.S.(C). Orthopaedic Surgeon. N/S. R.A.F.(Medical), 50–52. F/Lt. Brothers, W. R. & W. S. Wardill.

WARDILL, Walter Scott. W, 40³–45².*

WARDILL, William Russell, M.B., B.Chir., b. 27 Feb. 22, eldest s. of the late W. E. M. Wardill. W, 35³–40²; XV, 39; XXII, 40. Peterhouse, Cambridge, M.B., B.Chir. Middlesex Hospital Medical School, M.R.C.P. N/S. R.A.M.C., 47–49. General Medical Practitioner. Brothers, J. C. & W. S. Wardill.

WARDLAW, John Mackenzie Lake, b. 2 Feb. 02, eldest s. of the late G. L. Wardlaw (OR SH 79). SH, 16¹–19³; Cap, 19. Pembroke, Cambridge, B.A. Grazier on a Sheep Station, Australia. ✕ R. Australian Air Force, 40–45. Sqn. Ldr. Director of Personnel, I.R.O., Geneva. Director of Administration, U.N.E.S.C.O., Paris, 45–53. Retired.

WARDROP, Colin Glen. B, 38²–41³.*

WARNER, John William. K, 35¹–40².*

WARREN, Edward Peter. C, 24³–28³.*

WARREN, John Frederick, b. 16 June 13, s. of the late G. S. Warren. SH, 26³–31². Corpus Christi, Cambridge, B.A. Solicitor, 38. ✕ Royal Berkshire Regt. Major. Secretary, E. & T. The Law Society, London. *Aldeburgh G.C.* Son, 2331.

WARRINGTON, The Rt. Rev. The Bishop of (see Bickersteth, J. M.).

WASON, Cathcart Roland, b. 2 Apr. 07, s. of Rear-Admiral C. R. Wason, C.M.G., C.I.E., R.N. SH, 20³–26²; Scholar; Levée; Minor Exhibitioner. Scholar of Gonville & Caius, Cambridge. John Stewart of Rannoch Scholarship, 28. First Watson Studentship, 29. B.A., M.C.I.T. Prof. of Classical Archaeology, Toronto Univ., 31–32. Lecturer in Classical Archaeology, Edinburgh Univ., 32–38. Retired. *Queen's Club.*

WASON, Michael Sandys, b. 27 Sept. 29, 2nd s. of the late R. Wason (OR SH 84). SH, 43²–47³. Exhibitioner of Worcester, Oxford. Royal College of Art. Des. R.C.A., M.S.I.A. Designer & Manufacturer of Toys & Furniture. Soc. of Industrial Artists and Designers. Brother, R. Wason.

WASON, Rigby, b. 11 Nov. 25, elder s. of the late R. Wason (OR SH 84). SH, 39²–43³; Senior Entomology Prize, 43. ✕ R.A.F., 44–47. Sgt.-Pilot. Wadham,

Oxford, M.A. London Transport Executive, Traffic Manager. Brother, M. S. Wason.

WATERFIELD, Major John Everard, b. 10 May 11, eldest s. of the late N. E. Waterfield, O.B.E., F.R.C.S. C, 24³–29²; XI, 29. Corpus Christi, Oxford, B.A. ✕ R.A. (T.A.), 39–45. Major. T.D. Farmer in Kenya, 48–68. Bursar in U.K. since 68. *Cryptics, Butterflies.* Brother, R. E. Waterfield.

WATERFIELD, Robert Everard, b. 27 Aug. 14, 3rd s. of the late N. E. Waterfield, O.B.E., F.R.C.S. C, 28³–30³. Child Care Worker. ✕ R.A. & Intell. Corps, 40–41. Seconded to Foreign Office, 41–46. Berks. C.C., 50–56. C.M.S. Missionary in Persia, 57–73. Retired, 74. Author of "Christians in Persia". Brother, J. E. Waterfield.

WATERS, Howard Randall Brocas. Tu, 20³–23². Son, 1999.*

WATLING, John Martin Paul, b. 19 Nov. 27, s. of J. B. Watling. K, 41³–46²; Levée; Head of House; S. VIII, 46. Brasenose, Oxford, B.A. Half Blue (Shooting). F.C.A. Partner, Watling & Partners, Chartered Accountants. Dir. & Sec., Bristol Economic Building Soc. & Bristol Sinfonia Ltd.

WATLING, Stephen Richard, b. 20 Sept. 23, younger s. of Major H. R. Watling, C.B.E., J.P. St, 37²–41¹. ✕ R.A.F., 42–46. F/Officer. Wounded. Director of various companies. *St. James' Club, Savile Club.* Son, Henry Richard McLaren, St, 70²–.

WATSON, Basil Charlton. St, 32¹–34².*

WATSON, Douglas Alexander. B, 20²–23².*

WATSON, Herbert Barry. Tu, 26²–29².*

WATSON, Brig. Ian Darsie, C.B.E., b. 2 May 15, s. of the late D. Watson (OR B 03). B, 28³–33²; XXII. Trinity, Oxford, M.A. Farmer & Land Agent. F.L.A.S. ✕ Ox. and Bucks. L.I. Brigadier. C.B.E. Dispatches. T.D. *United Oxford & Cambridge Club.*

WATSON, Ian Edward, b. 13 Jan. 02, s. of E. A. Watson. Tu, 15³–18². Served with I.C.I. Ltd. in India (Calcutta, Karachi, Lahore & Madras) for 27 years. Final appointment, Staff Manager. ✕ Calcutta Light Horse. *East India, & Sports Club, Liphook G.C.*

WATSON, Lt.-Col. John Douglas, M.B.E., R.E., b. 1 May 22, s. of Lt.-Col. D. P. Watson. SH, 35^3–40^2; Cap, 39. ✕ R.E., 40–46. Temp. Commission, 41. M.B.E., 45. Corpus Christi, Cambridge, B.A. C.Eng., M.I.Mech.E., A.M.B.I.M. Gazetted Capt. to Regular Commission in R.E., 46. Lt.-Col. *Royal Ocean Racing Club.* Son, James Douglas, SH, 68^3–72^3.

WATSON, John Hugh Adam, C.M.G., b. 10 Aug. 14, eldest s. of J. C. Watson. St, 27^3–30^3; Cadet Officer. Scholar of King's, Cambridge, B.A. Joined Diplomatic Service, 37. Served at H.M. Legation, Bucharest, H.M. Embassies, Cairo, Moscow and Washington. Head of African Dept. F.O., 56–59. British Consul-General, Dakar, 59. H.M. Ambassador, Federation of Mali, 60–61. Senegal, Mauritania & Togo, 60–62. Cuba, 63–66. Under Secretary, F.O., 66–68. Gwilym Gibbon Fellow, Nuffield College, Oxford, 62–63. Diplomatic Adviser, British Leyland Motor Corp. since 68. Author of "The War of the Goldsmith's Daughter" and "Nature and Problems of Third World". *St. James' Club.* Brother, B. C. Watson.

WATSON, Leslie Dundas, b. 26 May 94, 2nd s. of the late T. W. Watson. K, 08^3–10^1. R.M.C., Sandhurst. Capt., King's Dragoon Guards. Retired.

WATSON, Reginald Paxton, b. 28 June 05, eldest s. of P. Watson. St, 19^3–23^2. Queen's, Oxford, B.A. Architect. Articled to Sir Giles Scott, 30–33. In private practice, 33–39 & 46–50. ✕ R.N.V.R., 39–45. Dispatches. Worked on the design for rebuilding the House of Commons, 45–46. Retired due to stroke.

WATSON, Richard Charles Challinor (The Rt. Rev. The Bishop of Burnley), b. 16 Feb. 23, s. of the late Col. F. W. Watson, C.B., M.C., D.L. (OR M 07). M, 36^3–41^1; Scholar. Scholar and Liddon Student of New College, Oxford, B.A. ✕ R.A. in India, 42–45. Capt. Westcott House, Cambridge. Ordained, 51. Curate of St. John's, Stratford, London E., 52–53. Tutor & Chaplain, Wycliffe Hall, Oxford, 54–57. Chaplain of Wadham and Chaplain of Oxford Pastorate, 57–61. Vicar of Hornchurch, 62–70. Examining Chaplain to Bp. of Rochester, 56–61 and Bp. of Chelmsford, 62–70. Asst. Rural Dean of Havering, 67–70. Bishop and Rector of Burnley since 70. Hon. Canon of Blackburn. *Lansdowne Club.* Son, David Charles Challinor, M, 70^2–.

WATSON, Terence Cecil Bewley. SF, 28^3–33^2.*

WATT, Alexander Peter Fordham, M, 28^3–33^2.*

WATT, Donald Cameron, b. 17 May 28, eldest s. of R. C. Watt (A). T & St, 40^2–46^2; Scholar; Levée; Head of House; Exhibitioner; R. VIII, 46; King's Medal, 46. Scholar of Oriel, Oxford, M.A. Foreign Office Research Dept., 51–54. Asst. Lecturer in Political History, L.S.E., 54–56. Lecturer in International History, L.S.E., 56–62; Senior Lecturer, 62–65. Editor, Survey of International Affairs, Royal Inst. of International Affairs, 62–71. Reader in International History, London Univ., 65–72. Prof. since 72. Member, Social Science Research Council Cttee. on Govt. & Information. Anglo-German Group of Historians. Author of many books. Broadcaster and Journalist. Sec., Assoc. of Contemporary Historians. Brothers, R. J. G. Watt & 133.

WATT, The Rev. Robert James Gordon, b. 24 Sept. 30, 2nd s. of R. C. Watt (A). T, 43^3–49^2. Corpus Christi, Cambridge, B.A. Edinburgh Univ., LL.B. Solicitor & W.S., 56. Glasgow Univ., 63–66. B.D. Minister of the Church of Scotland, 66. Working for the development of social concern in West Pilton, Edinburgh. Brothers, D. C. Watt and 133.

WATTS, Ronald Williams, M.D., B.Chir., b. 25 Apr. 13, s. of C. Watts. W, 26^3–31^1; Cap; H. XI, 31. Clare, Cambridge, B.A., M.B., B.Chir. St. Thomas's Hospital, M.R.C.S., L.R.C.P. ✕ R.N.V.R., 39–45. Surg.-Lt.-Cdr. Son, 1502.

WAUGH, Arthur Duncan. W, 36^3–41^2.*

WAUGH, Denis Frank, b. 14 May 17, s. of the late F. A. Waugh. SF, 30^3–35^3; Cap, 34; XXII; H. XI, 33–35 (Capt.). Clare, Cambridge, B.A. ✕ 11th R.H.A. (H.A.C.), 40–46. Lt. P.O.W., 42–45. Jt. Man. Dir., Tar Residuals Group of Companies. Regional Dir., Lloyds Bank (Southern). *M.C.C., United Oxford & Cambridge Club.* Son, Christopher Denis, SF, 69^3–.

WAUGH, Hamish Allen Grant. W, 34^3–39^1.*

WAYMAN, Edgar John Geoffrey, b. 7 May 26, s. of F. G. Wayman. M, 40^2–44^2; R. VIII, 44. Queen's Univ., Belfast (Short Course). ✕ R.E., 46. Airborne

Forces, 46–48. Wounded. Lt. Major, Parachute Regt. (T.A.). Export Dir., Rocol Ltd. to 69. Man. Dir., I.X.P. Ltd. since 69.

WAYMAN, Gerald Eric. Tu, 05¹–09¹.*

WEALE, Eric Cuthbert Sidney. St, 18²–22².*

WEBB, Douglas Arthur, b. 11 May 18, s. of the late W. H. Webb. T, 31³–37¹; R. VIII, 37; Crick Winner, 37. Export Office, 37–39. ✂ Green Howards, 39–44. R.A.S.C. 44–47. W.O.1(S.S.M.). Chief Clerk. Hotel work, S. Africa, 46–49. British Tourist Authority, London (Tourist Executive Officer) since 49.

WEBB, The Rev. Edward Oliver, b. 17 July 92, 5th s. of the late E. A. Webb. SH, 06³–10¹. Christ's, Cambridge, B.A. Six months in Hanover to learn German. ✂ 28th Bn. London Regt. 109th Machine Gun Corps. 2nd Lt. Became a Roman Catholic in 15 before leaving for France to take part in the 3rd Battle of Ypres and Cambrai. Benedictine Monk since 19. Ordained Priest, 25. Religious name, Bruno.

WEBB-WARE, Basil St. Martin Frank, b. 12 Sept. 08, s. of the late Lt.-Col. F. C. Webb-Ware. W, 22³–26². Trinity, Cambridge, B.A. F.I.E.E. Chief Transmission Project Engineer, Central Electricity Generating Board. Retired. *United Oxford & Cambridge University Club.*

WEBSTER, John Lawrence Harvey, C.M.G., b. 10 Mar. 13, s. of the late S. Webster. SH, 27¹–31². Balliol, Oxford, M.A., Dip.Ed. Colonial Admin. Service, Kenya, 35–64. On retirement from H.M.O.C.S. served with the British Council in Bangkok, Colombo, Hong Kong, Istanbul and London since 64. C.M.G., 63. *Leander, Nairobi (Kenya), Royal Commonwealth Soc.*

WEBSTER, William James, b. 31 Dec. 95, 3rd s. of the late Sir F. Webster. B, 09³–14³; XV, 13–14; XXII, 13. Trinity, Oxford. Of Francis Webster & Sons, Flax Spinners and Weavers, Arbroath.

WEEDY, Kenneth Charlton. Tu, 29³–33².*

WEEKS, Robert David, B.M., F.R.C.S. T, 40¹–45². Sons, Robert Loring, Sh, 70³– & Mark Loring, Sh, 73¹–.*

WEILER, Eric Herman, b. 26 Sept. 98, s. of the late M. Weiler. B, 12³–17¹. R.F.A. Cadet School, Brighton. ✂ R.F.A., 32nd Trench Mortar Bty. 2nd Lt. Royal College of Science, London Univ. A.R.C.S. Chemist, Ardath Tobacco Co. Salesman in various jobs. Now retired.

WELBOURN, Donald Burkewood, b. 11 Feb. 16, 3rd s. of the late B. Welbourn, A.K.C., Hon.M.Eng.(L'pool.). W, 29³–34²; Baines Leaving Exhibition. Scholar of Emmanuel, Cambridge, M.A. ✂ R.N.V.R., 42–46. Lt.-Cdr.(E). Univ. Lecturer in Engineering, Cambridge, 52–70. Fellow, Selwyn Coll., 55. Dir. in Industrial Co-operation & Head of Wolfson Industrial Unit, Cambridge Univ. since 70. Author, "Control Theory for Mechanical Engineers". Part author, "Dynamics of Machine Tools". *Overy Staithe Sailing Club.* Brothers, J. T. B., F. B. & R. B. Welbourn.

WELBOURN, The Rev. Frederick Burkewood, b. 14 Oct. 12, 2nd s. of the late B. Welbourn, A.K.C., Hon.M.Eng. (L'pool.). W, 26²–31²; Levée; Head of House; Jex-Blake & Science Exhibitions. Emmanuel, Cambridge, M.A. Westcott House. Ordained, 38. Chaplain variously of Caius, Trinity Hall & Trinity College, 38–43. Gen. Sec., S.C.M. in Schools, 43–46. Makerere College, Uganda, 46–64. Senior Lecturer in Religious Studies Bristol Univ. since 66. International African Institute. Brothers, J. T. B., D. B. & R. B. Welbourn.

WELBOURN, Joseph Thomas Burkewood, b. 30 Aug. 05, eldest s. of the late B. Welbourn, A.K.C., Hon.M.Eng. (L'pool.). B, 18³–23²; R. VIII, 23. Scholar of Birmingham Univ., B.Sc., F.I.Min.E., M.I.M.M. Past Vice-Pres., S. Wales Inst. of Engineers. Powell Duffryn Ltd., 28–46. N.C.B., 47–57. Dir., Powell Duffryn Technical Services Ltd., 57–70. Retired. *Pennard G.C.* Brothers, F. B., D. B. & R. B. Welbourn.

WELBOURN, Prof. Richard Burkewood, M.D., F.R.C.S., b. 1 May 19, 4th s. of the late B. Welbourn, A.K.C., Hon.M.Eng.(L'pool.). W, 32³–37²; Chemistry & Practical Chemistry Prizes, 37; Exhibitioner. Emmanuel, Cambridge, M.A., B.Chir., M.D. Liverpool Univ. Mayo Foundation, Rochester, Minn., U.S.A. ✂ R.A.M.C., 43–47. Capt. F.R.C.S., 48. Prof. of Surgical Science, Queen's Univ. of Belfast, and of Surgery, Univ. of London, 58–63. Dir., Dept. of Surgery, Royal Postgraduate Medical

School and Hammersmith Hosp. since 63. Hunterian Prof., Royal College of Surgeons, 58. James Berry Prize, R.C.S., 70. Part author, "Clinical Endocrinology for Surgeons", "Clinical Endocrinology for Physicians & Surgeons". Past Pres., Surgical Research Society. Member, Medical Research Council since 71. Chrmn., Soc. for Study of Medical Ethics. *Athenæum, Moynihan Chirurgical Club.* Brothers, J. T. B., F. B. & D. B. Welbourn.

WELCH, Charles Donald Graham, b. 15 Mar. 03, eldest s. of the late D. H. Welch. Tu, 17^1–19^3. Le Rosey, Rolle, Vaud, Switzerland. H.A.C.(T.F.). 2nd Lt., 25. Served in R.A.F. in India. General Duties, 26–31. ✂ 39–45. R.A.F. Fighter Command. Wing-Cdr. In Textile trade, 31–39 & 45–61. Retired. *R.A.F. Club.*

WELCH, James Johnson, b. 10 June 88, younger s. of the late W. G. Welch. W, 02^2–07^2; Minor Exhibitioner. Scholar of Trinity, Cambridge, M.A. Asst. Master, Eastbourne College, 14–15. ✂ R.G.A. att. Field Survey Bn., R.E. Lt. Asst. Master, Malvern College, 19. Dir. of Students in Mathematics, Fitzwilliam House, Cambridge from 24. Retired.

WELLBY, Major Montagu Richard, T.D. SF, 24^1–27^2.*

WELSH, John Sherrill, b. 30 Nov. 06, 4th s. of the late W. Welsh. SH, 20^2–24^3. Trinity Hall, Cambridge, M.A. With Shell-Mex & B.P., Aviation Dept., 30–40. M.Inst.Fuel. M.Inst.Eng.Inspec. ✂ R.A.F. Technical Engineer Branch, 40–46. Wing-Cdr. Petroleum Board, Black Oils Supervisor, 46–48. Man. Dir., Smith & Forrest Oils Ltd., Holt Town Oil Works.

WESLEY-SMITH, Arthur James. B, 39^3–43^1.*

WEST, John Frankland, M.B., B.Ch. C, 02^1–05^3.*

WEST, Richard. Tu, 29^3–34^2.*

WEST, Roger Rolleston Fick. D.S.O. K, 04^3–08^2.*

WESTACOTT, John Bentley. W, 44^3–48^3.*

WESTBURY, David George Arthur, M.B., B.S., b. 12 Sept. 23, s. of A. L. Westbury. T, 37^1–42^2; Major Foundationer; Levée. Guy's Hospital, London Univ., M.B., B.S., M.R.C.Psych., D.P.M.

✂ Red Cross att. R.A.M.C., 45. R.A.M.C., 48–50. Capt. Consultant Forensic Psychiatrist to the Home Office, to Newcastle Regional Hosp. Board and to the Dept. of Psychological Medicine, Univ. of Newcastle upon Tyne. British Academy of Forensic Sciences.

WESTCOTT, Anthony John, b. 8 July 32, eldest s. of F. C. Westcott. C, 46^3–50^3; XV, 49–50; S. VIII, 49–50. Pembroke, Cambridge. General Manager, Davis Graphics Ltda, Santiago, Chile. Pres., Chilean Hereford Breeders Assoc. Brother, 542.

WEST RUSSELL, His Hon. Judge, David Sturrock, b. 17 July 21, s. of Sir A. West Russell. Tu, 35^1–40^1. ✂ Q.O. Cameron Highlanders, 41–42. Parachute Regt., 42–46. Major. Dispatches. Pembroke, Cambridge, B.A. Bar, Middle Temple, 53. Member, The Dent Cttee. on Legal Aid in Criminal Proceedings, 64–65. Dep. Chrmn., Inner London Quarter Sessions, 66–71. Circuit Judge from 72. *Athenæum.*

WETHERILL, Peter Hindley. K, 33^2–38^2. Sons, 2525 & 2926.*

WHALLEY, The Rev. Edward Ryder Watson. SH, 44^3–49^3.*

WHALLEY, Guy Ainsworth, b. 26 May 33, 2nd s. of the late P. G. R. Whalley. SH, 46^3–51^2; Cadet Officer. N/S. Rifle Brigade, 51–52. 2nd Lt. Royal Fusiliers, 52. ✂ Korea, 52–53. Gonville & Caius, Cambridge, B.A. Solicitor, 59. Asst. Solicitor with Freshfields, 59. Partner, 64. Non-Executive Dir., Higgs & Hill Ltd., 72. *Bath Club, M.C.C.* Brother, E. R. W. Whalley.

WHARTON, Clifford Goslett, b. 29 Jan. 11, eldest s. of F. M. Wharton. St, 23^3–29^2; Levée; Lees Knowles Exhibition; Cadet Officer. Trinity, Cambridge, B.A. Partner, Laurence Prust & Co., Stockbrokers. Brother, T. R. B. Wharton.

WHARTON, Trevor Raymond Blundell, b. 9 Aug. 18, 2nd s. of F. M. Wharton. St, 32^1–37^1; Levée; Cap; Capt. of Tennis. ✂ 14/20 King's Hussars. Stockbroker. Brother, C. G. Wharton. Son, 2088.

WHATMORE, Michael. SH, 42^3–45^3.*

WHEATCROFT, Lt.-Col. Antony John, b. 3. Mar. 20, eldest s. of the late C. J.

Wheatcroft (OR SH 98). SH, 33³–38².
R.M.A., Woolwich. Gazetted to R.E., 39.
Royal Military College of Science, B.Sc.
(Eng.). R.E., 39–70. ✕ India, Persia,
Iraq, Egypt & Italy. Retired as Lt.-Col.
French Interpreter. A.M.B.I.M. Career
Adviser with the Univ. of London since
70. Sons, 1971 & Robert Antony Hopton,
SH, 70¹–.

WHEATCROFT, Eric Oscar. T, 26²–
29².*

**WHEATCROFT, Prof. George Shorrock
Ashcombe,** b. 29 Oct. 05, s. of the late
H. A. Wheatcroft. SH, 19³–23². New Col-
lege, Oxford, B.A. Solicitor, 29. John
Macknell Prize. J.P., County of London.
Partner in Corbin, Greener & Cook of
London, 30–51. ✕ R.A.S.C., 42–45. Lt.-
Col. Dispatches twice. Master of the
Supreme Court (Chancery Division), 51–
59. Prof. of English Law at London Univ.
(L.S.E.), 59–68. Dir. of various Com-
panies from 68. Chrmn. of Assoc. Business
Programmes Ltd. & G.S.A. & M. Wheat-
croft Advisory Services Ltd. Vice-Chrmn.
of Hambro Life Assurance Ltd. Editor of
"British Tax Review", 56–70 (now Con-
sultant). Ed. of "British Tax Encyclo-
paedia", 62–71 (now Consultant). Author of
numerous books on Taxation. Adviser to
H.M. Customs & Excise on V.A.T., 70–72.
Son, 57.

WHEATLEY, Sir George Andrew,
C.B.E., B.C.L., b. 24 Aug. 08, s. of the
late R. A. Wheatley (OR B 88). B, 22²–
26². Exeter, Oxford, M.A., B.C.L. Solicitor, 32. Asst. Solicitor to the County
Council of Pembrokeshire, 32, E. Suffolk,
34 and N. Riding of Yorkshire, 36. Dep.
Clerk of Peace & Dep. Clerk, Cumberland
C.C., 39 (Clerk, 42). Clerk of Peace and
Clerk of Hampshire, 46–67. D.L., Hants.,
67–70. Member, Home Office Advisory
Cttee. on Publicity & Recruitment for
Civil Defence and Allied Services; Member, Local Govt. Advisory Panel, Dept.
of Technical Co-operation; Hon. Sec.,
Society of Clerks of the Peace of Counties
and of the Clerks of County Councils,
61–67; Member, Royal Commission on
Assizes & Quarter Sessions, 66. Kt., 67.
Member, Local Govt. Boundary Commission for England, 71. Sons, 768, 1072
& 2201.

WHEATLEY PRICE, Michael (formerly
Price, M. W.), b. 28 Apr. 28, elder s. of
T. Wheatley-Price, M.A. B, 41³–45²;
Arnold Exhibitioner. Sheffield Univ.
(Univ. 1st Chess Team). N/S. Green
Howards & R.A.S.C., 47–49. 2nd Lt.

Balliol, Oxford & St. Benet's Hall, M.A.,
B.M., B.Ch. Vienna Univ. & Westminster
Hospital. Doctor since 58. Dept. of Dermatology, Royal Infirmary, Cardiff. *Ski Club
of G.B.*

WHEELER, Mark, b. 9 June 03, eldest
s. of the late G. R. Wheeler. SH, 17²–21².
Trinity Hall, Cambridge, M.A. Schoolmaster, Amesbury Prep. School, Hind-
head. ✕ Royal Sussex Regt., 39–45. Capt.
Joint Headmaster, Cheam School, Newbury, 47–59. Retired.

WHEELER, Michael Mortimer, Q.C.,
b. 8 Jan. 15, s. of Sir Mortimer Wheeler.
SF, 29¹–33²; Scholar; Levée. Law Scholar
of Christ Church, Oxford. Bar, Gray's
Inn & Lincoln's Inn, 38. ✕ R.A., 39–45.
Lt.-Col. Dispatches. Q.C., 61. Bencher,
Lincoln's Inn, 67. *Garrick Club, M.C.C.*

WHEELER, Peter James Freeman,
O.B.E. SH, 42²–46³. Son, Anthony James,
SH, 70³–.*

**WHEELWRIGHT, John Michael
Hoyle.** W, 18²–22². Sons, 1093 & 2002.*

WHELON, Charles Eric. C, 00¹–03².*

WHEWELL, Thomas Michael. SF,
37²–41¹.*

WHINNEY, Douglas Harold, b. 28 Aug.
02, 3rd s. of the late Sir A. F. Whinney,
K.B.E. C, 16³–19². Trinity, Oxford, B.A.
Chartered Accountant. 4th Ox. & Bucks.
L.I.(T.). Lt., 26. A.C.A., 30. F.C.A., 36.
Partner in Whinney, Smith & Whinney. ✕
Capt., 4th Bn. Ox. & Bucks. L.I. (T.A.).
P.O.W. (Germany), 40–45. T.D. Now
retired.

WHINYATES, Guy. SH, 98³–02¹.*

WHISHAW, Richard Harold, M.C. C,
31¹–35².*

WHITBY, Thomas Addison, b. 10 July
18, s. of the late H. B. Whitby. St, 32²–
36². Oriel, Oxford, B.A. ✕ R.A., 39–46.
Major. India & Pakistan, 47–56. Now Executive with International Computers Ltd.

WHITE, Edward John, b. 8 Oct. 86, 2nd
s. of the late G. White. C, 02³–05²;
Scholar. Scholar of Corpus Christi, Cambridge, B.A. Leeds Univ. Retired.

WHITE, Henry George Roland, b. 17
Apr. 07, elder s. of the late Major H. H. R.
White, D.S.O., O.B.E. (OR SH 93). SH,
21¹–24¹. Faraday House, London (Hon-

ours Roll). Engaged since 43 with firms round Chicago on radar & other scientific projects. Brother, J. M. White.

WHITE, Howard Charles, B.Sc., M.B., D.P.M., b. 20 Mar. 27, 2nd s. of B. C. White. T, 40³–45²; R. VIII, 45; Exhibitioner. Birmingham Univ. Univ. Open Scholarship (Nat. Sc.), 47–48. B.Sc., M.B., Ch.B., F.R.C.P.E., M.R.C.Psych. Foundations Fund Research Fellow, Boston Univ., 62–63. Consultant Psychiatrist, United Birmingham Hosps. and All Saints Hosp., Birmingham. Clinical Lecturer in Psychiatry, Birmingham Univ.

WHITE, James Douglas Campbell, b. 29 Mar. 32, s. of G. C. White. B, 45³–50²; Levée; Head of House. N/S. R.A.F., 51–52. Pilot Officer. Trinity, Cambridge. 7 years' mining experience in West Africa. Now Airline Transport Pilot employed by Transmeridian Air Cargo Ltd. *Ski Club of G.B.*

WHITE, Col. John Maxwell, O.B.E., b. 12 July 09, 2nd s. of the late Major H. H. R. White, D.S.O., O.B.E. (OR SH 93). SH, 23¹–27³. R.M.C., Sandhurst. Gazetted to King's Royal Rifle Corps, 29. Capt., 38. ✕ K.R.R.C., 39–45. T/Lt.-Col., 44. O.B.E. Lt.-Col., 51. Commdr. of Military Govt. for Cologne, 45–48. p.s.c. O.C., Queen Victoria's Rifles (K.R.R.C.), T.A., 50–53. Dir., Public Relations, Middle East Land Forces, 53–56. Now retired. *Army & Navy Club.* Brother, H. G. R. White.

WHITE, Kenneth George Walter, b. 29 June 27, s. of G. F. White, B.Sc., A.R.I.C. T, 41²–45³; Minor Foundationer. Birmingham Univ., L.D.S.(Birm.), L.D.S., R.C.S.Eng., 52. Warwickshire Executive Council. N/S. R.A.D.C. Capt., 52–54. Private practice in Rugby. British Dental Assoc. Rugby Medical Soc.

WHITE, Oliver Martin, b. 18 Jan. 02, s. of J. M. White. Tu, 16²–20². New College, Oxford, B.A. C.Eng., F.I.E.E., F.I.Mech. E., M.I.C.E. Manager of Leicestershire and Warwickshire Electric Power Co., 32–45. Balfour Beatty & Co. Ltd., 45–67. Dir. in charge of Electrical, Mechanical Engineering. Now retired. *25 Club, Hon. Civic Soc., Georgian Group.*

WHITE, Lt.-Col. Peter Francis, O.B.E., b. 22 Apr. 99, s. of the late E. F. White. C, 13¹–17²; Cap, 16; G. VIII & Pair, 16–17. R.M.A., Woolwich. ✕ R.E. 2nd Lt. Lt., 19. Jesus, Cambridge, B.A. ✕ R.E., 39–45. England & N.W. Europe. Lt.-Col. O.B.E. Retired, 50. *Farmers' Club.* Fellow,

The Genealogical Soc. F.R.G.S. *Arctic Club* (Pres., 70–71). Sons, 771 & 1377.

WHITE, Robert Harold, b. 11 May 23, s. of the late H. J. White (OR B 05). B, 36³–41³; XV, 41; S. VIII, 40–41. ✕ R.E., 42. Capt. R.E. (T.A.), 49. Mohair Spinner. Retired, 71. *Union Club, Bradford, Downhill Only Club.* Son, Thomas Harold, B, 70¹–.

WHITE, Rolf Bryan, b. 21 Mar. 32, eldest s. of J. White. C, 45³–49³; XV, 49; Sw. VIII, 48–49; Public Schools Exploring Soc., 48. N/S. 14/20 K. Hussars, 50–52. Lt. Midland Counties Dairy Ltd. from Milkman to Dir., 53–62. Unigate Ltd., Marketing Dir., 62–72. Midland Counties Ice Cream Co. Ltd., Man. Dir. since 72. Council Mem., Ice Cream Fed. Brother, 317.

WHITEHEAD, Charles Parkin, b. 10 Jan. 04, eldest s. of W. H. Whitehead. M, 18¹–22¹. Oriel, Oxford, M.A. Solicitor, 28. Clerk to the Justices, Bearsted, 51–69 and Mallind, 55–69. Coroner for Borough of Maidstone, 37–62. ✕ Scots Guards, 40–45. Capt. Under Sheriff for Kent, 57–69. Retired, 69. *Garrick, Kent County Club.* Son, 642.

WHITEHORN, John Roland Malcolm, C.M.G., b. 19 May 24, s. of A. D. Whitehorn. SF, 37³–42²; Leaving Exhibition. Exhibitioner of Trinity, Cambridge, B.A. ✕ R.A.F.V.R., 43–46. Pilot. F/Officer. With Federation of British Industries since 47. Deputy Director-General, F.B.I. since 66. C.M.G., 74. *Reform, M.C.C.*

WHITEHOUSE, Martin Henry Leigh, b. 13 Mar. 21, eldest s. of W.H. Whitehouse. B, 35¹–39². Peterhouse, Cambridge, M.A. ✕ R.A.F.V.R., 41–46. Sqn. Ldr. Dispatches. London Univ., B.Sc., C.Eng., M.I.Mech.E., M.I.E.E. Edmundsons Electricity Corp., 46–48. British Mechanical Engineering Fed., 49–68. Sec. since 68. R.A.F. Reserves. Author & Broadcaster.

WHITELOCK, Miles Edmund, b. 10 July 18, s. of the late A. R. Whitelock, M.A., LL.B. (OR B 82). B, 32³–37²; XI, 36–37. Trinity, Cambridge, B.A. Silver Plate Manufacturer. ✕ 1st Bn. Parachute Regt. Major. Wounded. Man. Dir., Hawker Marris Ltd. of Birmingham. *M.C.C., United University Club.* Son, 2034.

WHITEMAN, John William Inge. SH, 14²–18². Son, 524.*

WHITLEY, John Nigel. Tu, 16³–20³.*

WHITLEY, Peter Norman, b. 22 Oct. 23, s. of the late Sir N. H. P. Whitley, M.C. K, 37^3–41^3; Levée; Head of House; Cadet Officer. ✗ Commissioned Grenadier Guards, 42. Served France & Germany, 44–45 & Palestine, 46. Capt. Wounded. Dispatches. Joined Distillers Company Ltd., 47. Dir., Wm. Sanderson & Son Ltd., 55. Man. Dir., White Horse Distillers Ltd., 68. Jt. Master, Southdown Foxhounds, 72.

WHITSON, Harold Alexander, C.B.E., b. 20 Sept. 16, elder s. of R. A. Whitson, M.I.C.E. M, 30^1–35^1; Levée; Head of House; XV, 34. Trinity, Cambridge, B.A. Civil Engineering Contractor. ✗ R.E. Major, att. Q.V.O. Madras Sappers & Miners. Chrmn., Melville, Dundas, Whitson Ltd. Pres., Glasgow Chamber of Commerce, 65–68. Member, East Kilbride Development Corp. since 66. C.B.E. *Devonshire Club, R.S.A.C.* Son, 2064.

WHITTAKER, Augustus Reginald. T, 40^3–44^2.*

WHITTALL, David Edwin Barnett. SH, 40^3–45^2.*

WHITTALL, Edward, b. 5 July 02, 6th s. of F. E. Whittall. SH, 16^2–20^2; XV, 17–19; XI, 17–20. Shipping Agent. London Stock Exchange. Imperial Forces 5 years. Major. Canada (Accountant), now retired.

WHITTALL, Geoffrey William, M.B., B.Ch., b. 16 Jan. 06, 4th s. of the late W. J. H. Whittall. Tu, 20^1–24^2; Cap, 23; Head of House. Gonville & Caius, Cambridge, B.A., M.B., B.Ch. St. Thomas's Hospital, M.R.C.S., L.R.C.P. ✗ R.A.M.C. Capt. General Practice, 35–55. Senior Medical Officer, Dept. of Health & Social Security, 55–70. Retired. Brothers, H. M. & J. W. Whittall.

WHITTALL, Hugh Mackinley, D.S.O., b. 11 Nov. 96, eldest s. of the late W. J. H. Whittall. Tu, 10^3–13^2. ✗ Royal Marines, General List. Intell. Corps. Capt. D.S.O. Dispatches. Served in Gallipoli, Palestine & Turkey. Languages: French, Turkish & Greek. ✗ Served in Syria, Eritrea & Dodecanese. Merchant. Dir. of Companies. Retired. *Mowa Deniz Klubu, Istanbul.* Brothers, G. W. & J. W. Whittall.

WHITTALL, James William. Tu, 25^2–29^2.*

WHITTALL, Michael Charlton, O.B.E. SH, 39^3–44^1.*

WHITTLE, Francis David, b. 5 May 31, elder s. of Air-Commodore Sir Frank Whittle, K.B.E., C.B., F.R.S. R.A.F. (retired). T, 44^3–49^2. Middlesex Hospital, M.B., B.S. N/S. R.A.F., 57–59. Pilot Officer. H.N.D.(Engineering), 66.

WHITWORTH, Barrington Allen, D.F.C., b. 9 Apr. 22, eldest s. of the late E. E. A. Whitworth, M.C., M.A.(A). Tu, 35^3–40^2. Magdalene, Cambridge, B.A. Rowing Blue, 42. Farmer. ✗ R.A.F. F/Lt. D.F.C. Brother, L. E. Whitworth.

WHITWORTH, Lorimer Eric, b. 29 Jan. 28, 2nd s. of the late E. E. A. Whitworth, M.C., M.A.(A). Sh, 41^2–45^2. N/S. Queen's R. Lancers, 45–47. 2nd Lt. Trinity, Cambridge (Army Short Course). Fertiliser Manufacturer with Fisons Ltd. Now Genstar Ltd., Montreal. Brother, B. A. Whitworth.

WHITWORTH, Robert William, Ph.D., b. 5 Oct. 32, elder s. of the late Dr. A. B. Whitworth. T, 46^1–51^2; Scholar; Leaving Exhibition. Scholar of Queen's, Cambridge, M.A., Ph.D., M.Inst.P. Senior Lecturer in Physics, Birmingham Univ.

WICKHAM, Joseph Raymond Shakespear. B, 11^2–14^2.*

WIGGINS, Henry John. T, 19^2–21^1. Son, 1716.*

WIGLEY, Frank Stanley Gardiner. B, 27^1–30^2. Son, 1875.*

WIGLEY, Jack Gardiner, F.R.C.S., b. 31 Aug. 02, 2nd s. of the late H. P. Wigley. B, 16^2–20^2. Trinity, Cambridge, M.A., B.Ch. St. Thomas's Hospital, L.R.C.P., F.R.C.S. Consultant Obstetrician & Gynaecologist, Chester Group of Hospitals. Retired, 67. Fellow, Royal Soc. of Medicine. *Union Club, Malta.* Brother, F. S. G. Wigley. Son, 1644.

WILBERFORCE, John. K, 26^3–30^1.*

WILCOCK, Frederick Carrington. C, 11^3–16^2.*

WILCOX, Major Francis, M.C., b. 22 Feb. 21, 2nd s. of F. J. Wilcox. SH, 34^3–39^2. Pembroke, Cambridge. Gazetted to the Royal Scots, 41. Capt. ✗ Attd. Indian Army, 42–47. Italy. M.C., 44. Assoc. M.B.I.M. Brother, M. Wilcox.

WILCOX, Lt.-Col. Michael, b. 31 July 16, eldest s. of F. J. Wilcox. SH, 30¹–35³. Scholar of R.M.C., Sandhurst. ✕ Gazetted to Indian Army, 36. 1st Bn. Frontier Force Rifles till 47. R.A.S.C., 47–65. p.s.c. R.A.O.C., 65–71. Lt.-Col., retired. employed with Min. of Defence. Member, Institute of Food Technologists. *R.A.C., Caravan Club.* Brother, F. Wilcox. Son, 2952.

WILD, Peter Dickinson, b. 1 June 18, youngest s. of the late F. D. Wild. SF, 32²–36²; XXII, 36. St. John's, Cambridge, M.A. ✕ The Green Howards, 39–46. Wounded. Major. In industry (light engineering). M.B.I.M. Social work (Probation Service). C.C.E.T.S.W. Sons, 2072 & 2542.

WILDER, John Herbert Wyndham, O.B.E., b. 29 Mar. 21, s. of R. J. Wilder. Tu, 34³–39³; Levée; Head of House; Cadet Officer. Exhibitioner of Trinity Hall, Cambridge, B.A. ✕ R.E.M.E., 42–47. Major. Man. Dir., John Wilder (Engineering) Ltd. Fellow, Royal Agricultural Socs. Fellow & Past Pres., Institute of Agricultural Engineers. 1st Vice-Pres., Agricultural Engineers Assoc. O.B.E. *Leander, Farmers' Club.* Son, Timothy Gibson, Tu, 68²–.

WILES, Philip, F.R.C.S. SF, 13²–15¹.*

WILFORD, Michael Thomas. SF, 44³–48².*

WILKIN, Col. Hugh, O.B.E., M.C., b. 20 Aug. 97, eldest s. of R. H. Wilkin, M.R.C.S., L.R.C.P. Tu, 11²–12². King Edward IV Grammar School until 14. ✕ 5th Bn. Bedfordshire Regt. 1st Bn. Royal West Kent Regt., Staff Captain. G.H.Q., Egypt. Capt. Wounded twice. M.C. Dispatches. M.B.E., 23. Staff Officer to Local Forces and Adj., Barbados Volunteers, 24. Retired, 35. Man. Dir., Gardiner Austin & Co., Barbados, 35–39. Lloyd's Agent there. R.A.R.O., 35. Bt. Major, 37. Major & 2nd i/c Barbados Volunteer Force. Lt.-Col., 38. Garrison Commdr., Barbados, 39. O.B.E., 43. Garrison Commdr., Trinidad S.G.A. Col., 43. Retired, 45. *Army & Navy Club, Old Comrades Assoc.*

WILKINSON, Cecil Spenser. Tu, 99²–02².*

WILKINSON, John. T, 45³–49³.*

WILKINSON, John Michael Rhodes. SF, 43³–47².*

WILKINSON, Michael Arthur, b, 18 Sept. 30, Nephew & Ward of C. B. Cook. SF, 44³–48². N/S. R.A.O.C. 2nd Lt. F.C.I.S. Dir., Powell Duffryn Ltd. Son, Richard James, SF, 70³–.

WILKINSON, Sir Peter Allix, K.C.M.G., D.S.O., O.B.E., b. 15 Apr. 14, s. of the late Capt. O. C. Wilkinson. SF, 27³–31³. Corpus Christi, Cambridge, B.A. ✕ Royal Fusiliers, 35–47. Active service in Poland, 39. Polish Cross of Valour. France, 40. Dispatches. Crete, 41; Italy, 43; Yugoslavia, 43. Retired, 47. Czech Order of the White Lion, 45. H.M. Diplomatic Service. Served in Vienna, Washington, Bonn and as Under Secretary at the Cabinet Office, 63. Chief Civilian Instructor, Imperial Defence College. Ambassador, Saigon, 66. Dep. Under Sec. of State, F.O., 68. Ambassador, Vienna, 70. Retired, 72. D.S.O. & O.B.E. (Civil), 44. C.M.G., 60. K.C.M.G., 70. *White's, Army & Navy.*

WILLANS, Kyrle William. B, 97³–01².*

WILLARD, Colin Gerald Robert, F.R.I.C.S., b. 3 Feb. 06, 4th s. of the late T. W. Willard. T, 19²–24¹; R. VIII, 23–24; Crick Winner, 24. F.R.I.C.S. Quantity Surveyor in practice in Nottingham, 46–51; in Nairobi, 51–60. ✕ R.E., 39–45. Lt.-Col. Dispatches. Now Q.S. Min. of Works, Kenya Govt., Nairobi. *Nairobi Club, Royal Soc. of St. George.* Brothers, J. D. & R. A. Willard. Son, 925.

WILLARD, James Donald, b. 2 Apr. 97, eldest s. of the late T. W. Willard. T, 10³–15²; R. VIII, 14–15; Crick Winner, 15; 2nd Athletic Cup, 14. R.M.C., Sandhurst. ✕ South Staffordshire Regt. Machine Gun Corps. 13th Tank Bn. Capt. Wounded. Dispatches. R.A.R.O., 19. College of Estate Management. F.R.I.C.S. Member of the Institute of Registered Architects. ✕ Recalled to the Colours, 39–45. Architect and Surveyor in Private Practice, 19–67. Retired. Brothers, C. G. R. & R. A. Willard.

WILLARD, Rupert Allen. T, 24²–25¹.*

WILLEY, Maurice William, b. 12 May 24, eldest s. of Prof. B. Willey, F.B.A., Litt.D. W, 39¹–42²; R. VIII, 42. Choral Scholar of King's, Cambridge, M.A. ✕ The Queen's Royal Regt. & Durham L.I. Capt. Sec., Group Sports & Social Clubs, Personal Services Div., P. & O. Steam Navigation Co. *Company of Veteran Motorists.* Brother, P. J. B. Willey.

WILLEY, Peter James Basil, b. 7 June 30, 2nd s. of Prof. B. Willey, F.B.A., Litt.D. W, 43³–48³; Fives IV, 48. Exhibitioner of Pembroke, Cambridge, M.A. N/S. R.A., 49–50. 2nd Lt. A.D.C. to O.C. Plymouth as A/Capt. Tonbridge School, 53–67 (Senior English Master, 60–67). Dir. of Studies & Housemaster, Oakham Sch., 67–68. Senior English Master, City of Leicester G.S., 68–69. Senior English Master & Housemaster, Millfield Sch. since 69. Sec., Leicester City & Leicestershire Branch, N.A.TE., 68. Cellist, Leicester Symphony Orch., Tunbridge Wells Symphony Orch., 54–69. Brother, M. W. Willey.

WILLIAMS, Alexander Butler, b. 8 Apr. 24, s. of the late F. J. Williams. Sh, 37³–42². Trinity Hall, Cambridge. War Short Course. ✕ Rifle Brigade in B.L.A. India & Palestine, 44–46. Capt., 46. Regular Commission in Royal Ulster Rifles, 47. Korea, 50–51. School of Slavonic and Eastern European Studies, 51–53. Interpretership in Bulgarian. Min. of Defence since 56. *Army & Navy Club, West Mersea Y.C.*

WILLIAMS, Lt.-Col. David Geoffrey. SH, 07³–12¹.*

WILLIAMS, David Owen, M.B.E., b. 4 June 07, s. of W. J. Williams, LL.D. M, 20³–25²; Scholar; Exhibitioner. Postmaster of Merton, Oxford, B.A. Brewer, A. Guinness Son & Co. Ltd., 29. ✕ R.A.F.V.R., 40–44. F/Lt. M.B.E. Seconded to N.A.A.F.I. O. i/c beer supplies, N.W. Europe, 44–45. Sqn. Ldr. Order of Leopold II (Officer). Head Brewer, A. Guinness Son & Co. Ltd., Dublin, 56. Asst. Man. Dir., 60. Dir., 69. Now retired. Son, 196.

WILLIAMS, Edward Vaughan. B, 22²–26¹.*

WILLIAMS, John Michael, b. 24 Aug. 27, 2nd s. of the late N. T. Williams. SF, 40³–45²; XV, 43–44 (Capt.); XI, 44–45; H. XI, 45; Cadet Officer; Tom Hughes Prize. N/S., 45–48. Clare, Cambridge, B.A. Rugby Football Blue, 49. England XV, 50. Solicitor, 53. Man. Dir., Fluid Power Div., International Compressed Air Corp. Ltd. *M.C.C., Bath.* Rugby Internationals. A.M.P. International. Brother, N. J. D. Williams. Son, 3008.

WILLIAMS, Major John Montague, M.B.E. B, 91³–94³.*

WILLIAMS, Maurice John Nelson, b. 4 Oct. 06, elder s. of Rev. P. W. Williams. St, 20³–25²; XV, 24; XXII, 23; H. XI. Bank of England, 26–41. ✕ Pioneer Corps, 41–46. Capt. Master at Prep. Schs. Now part-time Rosehill Sch., Tunbridge Wells. *M.C.C., 40 Club. Bluemantles C.C.* (Hon. Fixture Sec.).

WILLIAMS, Sir Michael (Sanigear), K.C.M.G., b. 17 Aug. 11, s. of the late Rev. F. F. S. Williams. SH, 25²–29¹. Trinity, Cambridge, B.A. Exhibition, 31. Entered Foreign Office, 35. Served at H.M. Embassies in Spain & Rome. Rio de Janeiro, 50–52; Bonn, 56–60; Guatemala, 62–63 and the Holy See, 65–70. Retired, 70. K.C.M.G., 68.

WILLIAMS, Michael Spencer Ainslie, b. 4 Mar. 05, 3rd & youngest s. of the late F. Williams. Tu, 18³–22³. Paris; Heidelberg; Leipzig. University College, Oxford, B.A. Bookseller, 30–40. R. Signals, 41. Pte. Farming, 43–68.

WILLIAMS, Nicholas James Donald, b. 21 Oct. 25, elder s. of the late N. T. Williams. SF, 38³–43³; Scholar; Levée; Head of School; Exhibitioner; XI, 42–43; XV, 42–43; Cadet Officer. Scholar of Clare, Cambridge. ✕ Royal Marines (42 Commando), 44–47. Capt. Solicitor, 50. Partner, Nicholas Williams & Co., London, 50–61. Senior Partner, Surridge & Beecheno, Karachi, 55–61. Joined The Burmah Oil Co. Ltd., London as Company's legal adviser, 61; Dir., 65; Man. Dir. & Chief Executive since 69. Chrmn. of Castrol Ltd. and of Anglo-Ecuadorian Oilfields Ltd. *Oriental Club, M.C.C., Royal Ocean Racing Club.* Brother, J. M. Williams. Son, 2130.

WILLIAMS, Patrick Howard, b. 25 Aug. 30, younger s. of H. M. Williams, J.P. Sh, 44³–49¹. N/S. R.A.S.C. Lt. Exeter, Oxford, M.A. Insurance Broker. A.C.I.B. Dir. of Insurance Broking Company. T.D. *East India, Sports & Public Schools Club.*

WILLIAMS, Rashleigh Henry, b. 2 June 97, 5th s. of the late Lt.-Col. M. S. Williams. Tu, 11³–15³. ✕ 4th Bn. Royal Fusiliers. Lt. Severely wounded at Arras, 3.5.17. In hospital from age of 19 to 24. Then spent 11 years at Sarasota, Florida, U.S.A. and on return joined Gresham Life Assurance Soc. for 24 years until 58. Retired.

WILLIAMS, Robin Walton, D.F.C. SH, 29¹–31². Son, Anthony Robin Walton. SH, 67²–71³.*

WILLIAMS, Roland William. Tu, 38²–41³.*

WILLIAMS, Thomas Meurig, b. 6 May 10, s. of the late M. T. Williams. C, 23³–28²; Cap. Oriel, Oxford, B.A. Theodore Williams Physiology Scholarship. B.M., B.Ch., F.R.C.S.(Eng.). Surgeon, Indian Medical Service (retired). Consultant Surgeon, Bury St. Edmunds.

WILLIAMSON, Hugh Everard, b. 22 Mar. 16, elder s. of the late G. E. Williamson (OR SH oo). SH, 29³–34². Trinity, Cambridge, B.A. Industrial Consultant. ✕ R.A.O.C. & R.E.M.E. Capt. P.O.W. in Far East.

WILLIAMSON, James Bruce, b. 16 Dec. 92, s. of the late J. M. Williamson, M.D. W, 07³–11². Trinity, Cambridge, M.A. Middlesex Hospital, L.M.S.S.A., F.R.A.S., F.R.Met.Soc. General Medical Practice in Ventnor. Long Service Medal as Auxiliary in H.M. Coastguards. Now retired. Late M.O. R.A.F. Ventnor. *Royal Meteorological Soc., Guild of Church Bellringers, Antiquarian Horological Soc.*

WILLIAMSON, James Leslie Dowkar, M.C. B, 08³–11³.*

WILLIAMSON, Mark Herbert, b. 8 June 28, 2nd s. of the late H. S. Williamson. B & C, 43³–46²; Sw. VIII, 46. N/S. Ox. & Bucks. L.I., 50–52. 2nd Lt. Christ Church, Oxford, M.A., D.Phil. Demonstrator, Dept. Zoology, Oxford, 52–58. S.S.D., S.M.B.A. Oceanographic Lab., Edinburgh, 58–62. Lecturer, Dept. Zoology, Edinburgh, 63–65. Prof., Dept. Biology, York since 65. Visiting Prof. Univ. of California, 70–71. Brother, P. K. Williamson.

WILLIAMSON, Paul Kenyon, b. 10 May 25, elder s. of the late H. S. Williamson. B, 38³–43²; Scholar; Levée; Head of House; Leaving Exhibitions in Science & Maths.; Ronald Prize for Music (Oboe). Scholar of Trinity, Cambridge, M.A. Senior Scholarship, 45. Imperial College, London. D.I.C. Chemical Engineer. M.I.Chem.E. Employed by Courtaulds Group since 46. At present working for British Cellophane Ltd. Brother, M. H. Williamson. Sons, Michael Paul, B, 70³– & Peter John, B, 72¹–.

WILLIS, George Bertram. SF, 02²–05¹.*

WILLIS, Timothy Robert Crum. M, 41³–45².*

WILLIS-DIXON, John Reginald, b. 15 Feb. 07, 2nd s. of the late A. Willis-Dixon (A. W. Dixon, OR St 84). St, 21¹–24¹. ✕ R.A.F., 42–46. India, Burma & Malaya. F/Officer. Dir., Midland Area, Kelsey Industries Ltd. Retired. Brother, N. Willis-Dixon.

WILLIS-DIXON, Norman. St, 20¹–23¹.*

WILLS, Adam Peter, D.F.C. St, 37¹–40².*

WILLS, Arthur Francis. St, 17²–21¹.*

WILLS, Erik Raymond Björkman, b. 24 Apr. 31, s. of L. N. Wills (OR St 21). St, 45²–49²; Cap, 48. N/S. The Queen's Royal Regt. New College, Oxford, B.A. Golf Blue. Engineering Industry. Electronics & Aircraft. Now, Asst. Gen. Man., Plessey Radar, Addlestone, Surrey. *Oxford & Cambridge Golfing Soc.* Capt. O.R.G.S. 74.

WILLS, John Graham. St, 29³–34². Son, 2089.*

WILLS, Leslie Norman, b. 24 Nov. 07, 3rd s. of the late A. S. Wills. St, 21³–26¹. New College, Oxford, M.A., B.C.L. Solicitor, 33. Retired. Brothers, J. G. & P. D. Wills. Son, E. R. B. Wills.

WILLS, Philip Desmond. St, 23¹–26¹.*

WILMOT, Major Gordon Darwin, b. 30 Mar. 18, 2nd s. of the late Capt. S. D. Wilmot, R.A. (OR St oo). St, 31³–35²; R. VIII, 34. R.M.A., Sandhurst. Commissioned into Royal Scots Fusiliers, 38. ✕ Wounded. 40 Glider Bn., 1st Airborne Div., 43–45. Retired as Major, 59. Social Services Dept., West Sussex C.C. *Lowland Brigade Club.* Brother, M. S. Wilmot. Son, Patrick Gordon, St, 67³–72².

WILMOT, Major Martyn Sacheverel, b. 2 Sept. 14, eldest s. of the late Capt. S. D. Wilmot, R.A. (OR St oo). St, 28²–31³. R.M.A., Woolwich. Gazetted to Royal Artillery, 35. ✕ Crete. P.O.W., escaped Mar. 45. Major. Retired. Brother, G. D. Wilmot. Sons, 2414 & 2617.

WILMOT-SITWELL, Guy Sacheverell. C, 21²–24³.*

WILSHERE, Herbert David, D.Sc. SF, 40²–44².*

WILSON, Charles Derek, b. 11 July 10, elder s. of the late B. Wilson (OR SH 93). SH, 24³–28²; Exhibitioner. Balmer Lawrie & Co. Ltd., Calcutta, 31–62 (Chrmn.). 5/6 Rajputana Rifles. Burma. Brigade Major, Peshawar. Chrmn., Indian Tea Assoc., Calcutta, 57–58. Vice-Chrmn., Indian Tea Board. Now Man. Dir., J. T. Davenport Ltd. Dir., British Indian Tea Co. Ltd. *Royal Calcutta G.C., Tollygunge Club, Calcutta, Rye G.C.*

WILSON, Christopher John, T.D., b. 4 Nov. 04, 2nd s. of the late Rev. R. A. Wilson (OR SH 82). SF, 18²–23²; Cap, 22. With the Bank of England from 24. H.A.C. (T.A.), 24–45. ✕ H.A.C. & Staff, 39–45. Major. T.D. Hon. Treasurer of O.R. Soc. Son, 2302.

WILSON, Ernest Ian, b. 20 Dec. 32, 2nd s. of the late F. M. Wilson. K, 46³–51¹; Cap, 50; R. VIII, 51; Fives, IV. N/S. R.N.V.R. S/Lt.(S). Joined Ernest Wilson & Son, Drapers, 53. Company Dir. of Drapery Business. *Moortown G.C.* Son, Paul Richard, K, 73¹–.

WILSON, Hugh Radcliffe. M, 96²–00¹.*

WILSON, John Francis, b. 29 Dec. 05, s. of the late Major-General F. A. Wilson, C.M.G., D.S.O. (OR SF 87). SF, 19²–23². R.M.A., Woolwich. Commissioned in Royal Artillery, 25. Lt., 27. ✕ Placed on half pay July 42 and subsequently awarded war disability pension. Major. Retired.

WILSON, John Laurence. St, 12³–17¹.*

WILSON, Lawrence Patrick Roy, b. 10 Oct. 16, 3rd s. of Sir R. Wilson. St, 30³–35¹. Oriel, Oxford, B.A. Heath Harrison Open Univ. Travelling Scholarship in German, 33. ✕ Royal Marines, 39–45. Capt. & Adj., 11th Searchlight Regt., R.M. P.O.W. Crete. Political Div., Control Commission for Germany. Liaison Officer in Berlin for B.B.C. German Service. Conservative Central Office, Speakers Dept. Since 50, literary translator from German & French. Author. Warden, Hostel for ex-offender male alcoholics, Newcastle upon Tyne, 70–71. Brother, M. T. Wilson.

WILSON, Major Michael Thomond, b. 7 Feb. 11, eldest s. of Sir R. Wilson. St, 24³–29². Oriel, Oxford, B.A. ✕ R.A., 39–45. M.B.E., Major. F.I.B. Dir. &

Chief Gen. Man., Lloyds Bank Ltd. Chrmn., Export Guarantees Advisory Council. Brother, L. P. R. Wilson. Sons, 210 & 581.

WILSON, Paul Alexander. K, 17³–22².*

WILSON, Rowland Holt. C, 46¹–49².*

WILSON, Richard Kirby, b. 9 Nov. 31, 2nd s. of F. K. Wilson. C, 46³–50¹; XI, 49. Brasenose, Oxford, B.A. Record retailer, The Left Bank, Exeter.

WILSON, Stuart Henry Moreau, b. 30 Mar. 02, s. of the late A. B. B. Wilson. M, 16³–19². Trinity, Oxford, B.A. Solicitor, 26. Senior Partner, Dawson & Co. of London. *Bath Club.*

WILSON, Cdr. William Eames, R.N., b. 26 Jan. 00, younger s. of the late W. N. Wilson (former Housemaster of Cotton) SF, 14¹–18²; Levée; XV, 16–17. R.N. College, Keyham. R.N., 18. Lt., 22. Comdg. H.M.S. *Cricket, Electra,* & *Esk,* 31–37. Commander, 37. ✕ Comdg. H.M.S. *Juno,* 39–40. Retired, 46. Now self-employed in picture restoration & glass engraving. *United Service Club &* *Royal Aero Club.* Brother, J. L. Wilson.

WILSON JOHNSTON, Ian Campbell. SF, 17³–22¹.*

WIMBLE, John William Bowring. b. 17 May 29, s. of L. B. Wimble (OR Tu 14). M, 42³–47¹. Engineer with General Electric Co. Then with C. T. Bowring & Co. Ltd. Now Dir., Fenchurch Insurance Holdings Ltd. & Jessel Securities Ltd. *Bath Club.* Son, Andrew Bowring, M, 71²–.

WIMBLE, Leslie Bowring, b. 26 Sept. 00, elder s. of the late Sir J. B. Wimble, K.B.E. Tu, 14³–19²; XV, 18; XI, 18–19; Cadet Officer. New College, Oxford, B.A. Dir., C. T. Bowring & Co. (Insurance) Ltd. & English & American Insurance Co. Ltd. ✕ R.E. (M.C.S.). Capt. Company Director (retired). Underwriting Member of Lloyd's. *Vincent's, Bath Clubs.* Son, J. W. B. Wimble. Grandson, Andrew Bowring, M, 71²–.

WIMBUSH, Henry Laurence. Tu, 96³–99².*

WINCH, Thomas Beverley Charles, b. 30 Apr. 30, 2nd s. of the late Dr. W. Winch. SH, 43³–48¹. N/S. R.A.F., 49. Pilot Officer. St. John's, Cambridge, M.A.

F.R.S.A., 69. Fine Arts Valuer. *Furniture History Soc.*

WINDER, Arthur Smallwood. SF, 18³–23².*

WING, Antony John, D.M., M.R.C.P., b. 2 May 33, eldest s. of the late H. J. T. Wing. SF, 46³–52¹; Levée; Head of House; XV, 49–51 (Capt.); XXII. Lincoln, Oxford, M.A., D.M. (Old Members Exhibition). St. Thomas's Hospital, M.R.C.P. ex Sqn.-Ldr. R.A.F. Physician, St. Thomas's Hospital. Royal Soc. of Medicine. B.M.A. Soc. Apothecaries. Brother, 564.

WINGATE, Robert Bruce (see Bruce, R. H. W.).

WINGATE-SAUL, Anthony Sylvester, b. 30 Apr. 12, 3rd s. of the late Sir E. Wingate-Saul, K.C. (OR SF 88). SF, 25³–30². Trinity, Oxford, B.A. Sugar refiner. ⋊ R.A. (T.A.), 39–45. Lt.-Col. G.S.O.1, Staff College, 44. Dir., Tate & Lyle Ltd. Brother, B. S. Wingate-Saul. Son, 701.

WINGATE-SAUL, His Honour Judge Bazil Sylvester, b. 15 June 06, 2nd s. of the late Sir E. Wingate-Saul, K.C. (OR SF 88). SF, 20³–24²; H. XI, 23. St. John's, Oxford, B.A. Bar, Inner Temple, 28. ⋊ R. Berkshire Regt., 40–45. Major. Junior Counsel, Min. of Agriculture & Fisheries, Forestry Commission, Commissioners of Crown Lands, 49–59. Recorder of Oldham, 50–59. County Court Judge, 59–71. Master of the Bench of Inner Temple, 58. Circuit Judge, 71. Brother, A. S. Wingate-Saul.

WINSKELL, Ian Malcolm. W, 42²–46².*

WINSKELL, Robert Dane Halsbury, T.D., b. 22 June 19, elder s. of R. Winskell. W, 33¹–36². Solicitor, 47. ⋊ R.A. Major (at age of 22). Dispatches. T.D. Now Senior Partner, firm of Solicitors and Chrmn. of a Building Society. *R. & A. G.C., Northumberland Club.* County Golfer at age of 18. Brother, I. M. Winskell. Son, 2751.

WINTER, George Delap, b. 22 June 22, 3rd s. of W. de L. Winter. K, 36²–40³. Nottingham Univ. School of Architecture. ⋊ R.A., 42–46. Capt. Agricultural Planner and Administrator with Birds Eye Foods Ltd. Brothers, J. K. & W. M. Winter.

WINTER, John Kift, b. 4 Aug. 11, eldest s. of W. de L. Winter. K, 25³–30²; Lees Knowles Exhibition; XV, 29. Trinity, Cambridge, M.A. Capt., Univ. Sailing Team, 33–34. With Universal Grinding Wheel Co. Ltd., Stafford (now Chrmn.). Dir. of Universal Grinding Ltd. (parent co. of above), 57–72. *R. Thames Y.C., Royal Yachting Assoc.* (Council Member, 45–57). Brothers, W. M. & G. D. Winter.

WINTER, Lt.-Col. Patrick Antony, M.B.E., younger s. of the late E. P. Winter. T, 38³–43². ⋊ Scots Guards, 43–52. Commissioned, 44. Seconded to Parachute Regt., 48–49 and to Special Air Services, 50–53. Transferred to Royal Ulster Rifles, 52. Commd. 1st Bn. York & Lancaster Regt., 66–69. Transferred to Royal Irish Rangers, 69. Present Appt., G.S.O.1, H.Q. West Midland District, Shrewsbury. p.s.c. Dispatches twice. M.B.E., 62.

WINTER, William Michael, M.R.C.S., L.R.C.P. K, 27³–32².*

WISE, Anthony Forster, b. 2 July 86, s. of the late The Hon. B. R. Wise, K.C. (OR T 70). B, 01¹–05². Queen's, Oxford, B.A. In shipping business in India. ⋊ Calcutta Light Horse. I.A.R.O. Staff Capt. Army H.Q. Capt. Retired, 22. ⋊ Home Guard. Served as General Commissioner of Taxes, Kensington Div. *Oxford & Cambridge Univ. Club.*

WISHART, David Fraser. Sh, 45²–49³. Brother, 712.*

WISHART, Ernest Edward. St, 16¹–20².*

WOLLEY DOD, Anthony Kirk, b. 21 Dec. 18, s. of the late J. C. Wolley Dod (OR SH 05). SH, 32³–37²; Scholar; XV, 36. ⋊ R.A.F., 39–45. F/Offr. Solicitor, 47. With Batesons of Liverpool to 62. Actively Farming since 62. J.P. Cheshire, 65. Chester & N. Wales Law Soc. N.F.U., C.L.A.

WOLLEY DOD, Hova Charles Kirk, b. 27 June 31, s. of the late C. F. Wolley Dod (OR Tu 06). K, 44³–50¹; Scholar; Levée; Head of House. Scholar of Corpus Christi, Oxford, M.A. Solicitor. Partner in Taylor & Humbert of London. The Law Society.

WOOD, David Overend, b. 16 July 25, elder s. of J. O. Wood. B, 39³–43²; XXII; Bigside Bags; H. XI. Bursary to Clare, Cambridge, B.A. N/S. S/Lt.(E), R.N.,

45–47. E. S. & A. Robinson (Holdings), Ltd., 47–66. Dickinson Robinson Group Ltd. Executive Dir. Div. Chief Executive since 66. *Lucifer Golfing Society.*

WOOD, Edward Guy, M.C. M, 09¹–10².*

WOOD, Frank Russell. Tu, 15³–19².*

WOOD, Gerald Montague, b. 11 Oct. 28, younger s. of the late M. W. Wood. Tu, 43²–46¹. Univ. of Toronto, B.A.Sc., M.Comm. Professional Engineer. P.Eng. Canadian SKF Co., Production Manager. McCullock of Canada, Asst. Works Manager. Now Pres, Peterson Steels (Canada) Ltd. *Granite Club.*

WOOD, John Craig Mure, T.D. b. 18 Mar. 19, 2nd s. of D. M. Wood. Sh, 32³–36³. ✕ Lanarkshire Yeomanry. Major. T.D. Director of various Paper & Printing Companies. *Garrick Club.* Son, Michael Mure, Sh, 67²–71³.

WOOD, John Michael, b. 11 Apr. 12, eldest s. of the late Lt.-Col. W. M. R. Wood, C.I.E. M, 26¹–30¹. Merchant Banking, 30–38. Publishing, 38–39. Joined T.A., 38. ✕ Grenadier Guards, 39–45. Capt. Royal Opera House, Covent Garden, 46–66 (P.R.O., 46–58). Gen. Man., Royal Ballet, 58–66. Dir. of Royal Ballet School since 66. *Brooks's.*

WOOD, Roger Henry, b. 10 Feb. 07, eldest s. of the late H. C. Wood (OR M 94). M, 21¹–25¹. Trinity, Cambridge, M.A. With the Calico Printers Assoc. Ltd., Manchester, 28–39. ✕ R.A.O.C. Middle East. Colonel. Dir. of Fothergill & Harvey, 47–66. Member of British National Export Council for Europe, 64–70. Retired. *Army & Navy Club, St. James's Club, Manchester.* Son, 2065.

WOOD, Timothy Campbell, B.M., B.Ch., b. 3 Oct. 28, s. of the late Dr. G. E. M. Wood. Tu, 42²–47²; S. VIII, 46–47 (Capt.). Hertford, Oxford, M.A., B.M., B.Ch. N/S R.A. 2nd Lt. University College Hospital, D.Obst.R.C.O.G. General Practitioner, Watford. Med. Officer, Merchant Taylors School.

WOODALL, John Corbet, b. 8 Nov. 83, 5th s. of the late Sir C. Woodall. M, 98¹–01². Trinity, Cambridge, B.A. A.M.Inst. Automobile Engineers. Engineering in Birmingham from 05. Pte. in "The Rangers" 12th London T.A., 13. ✕ Commissioned Surrey Yeomanry, 14–18. Lt.

Dispatches. Now retired after a number of jobs in the Motor Industry. Past Captain, *O.R.G.S.* Sons, J. D. C. & M. C. Woodall. Grandson, 1876.

WOODALL, John David Corbet, T.D., b. 18 May 12, eldest s. of J. C. Woodall (OR M 98). K, 26¹–30²; Cap, 29. Trinity, Cambridge, B.A. Regent Street Polytechnic, C.Eng., F.Inst.Gas.E., M.Inst.F., M.Inst.M. Gas Light & Coke Co., 33–36. S.E. Gas Corp., 36–39 & 45–49. Commissioned "The Rangers" K.R.R.C. (T.A.), 35. ✕ K.R.R.C., 39–45. T/Lt.-Col. T.D. S.E. Gas Board, 49–71. Retired. Councillor, Godstone R.D.C. Governor, Oxted School. *R. Thames Y.C., Rye G.C., Croydon Bowling Club.* Brother, M. C. Woodall. Son, 1876.

WOODALL, John Michael, b. 23 May 32, s. of L. A. Woodall. W, 46¹–50². O. & H.N.C. in Mechanical Engineering, G.M.I.Mech.E. N/S R. Signals, 50–52. Mechanical Engineer with Joseph Lucas Ltd., Birmingham since 53.

WOODALL, Michael Corbet, M.C., b. 22 Jan. 24, 3rd s. of J. C. Woodall (OR M 98). M, 37³–42²; Cap; Cadet Officer, 42. Trinity, Cambridge. ✕ Coldstream Guards, 43–47. Capt. M.C. Wounded. Career in shipping. Gen. Man. for Canada, Furness, Withy & Co. Ltd., Montreal. Canadian Citizen. *Guards Club.* Brother, J. D. C. Woodall.

WOODD-WALKER, Geoffrey Basil, F.R.C.S., b. 9 June 00, s. of the late B. Woodd-Walker, M.D. St, 14³–18². King's, Cambridge, M.A., M.B., B.Chir. St. Mary's Hospital Medical School, F.R.C.S. (Eng.). Consultant Surgeon, West London Hospital. Vice-Dean. Retired. *Athenæum.* Medical Soc., London. Assoc. of Surgeons. Sons, 41 & 439.

WOODHOUSE, Frank, T.D., b. 6 May 91, younger s. of the late Sir P. Woodhouse, K.B.E., D.L., J.P. K, 05³–07³. Gazetted to 9th Bn. Manchester Regt. (T.F.), 09. ✕ Egypt, Gallipoli and France. Capt. T.D. Partner in Woodhouse Hambly & Co., Cotton Manufacturers, of Manchester. Now retired.

WOODHOUSE, Geoffrey Clayton, J.P., b. 16 Nov. 97, eldest s. of the late A. E. C. Woodhouse. W, 11³–15². ✕ 6th Bn. Dorsetshire Regt. Lt. Wounded. Farmer. Retired, 61. J.P., Somerset County to 70. Chrmn., Bridgwater County Bench, 36–70. Brothers, L. C. & M. C. Woodhouse.

WOODHOUSE, Lionel Clayton, b. 3 May 03, 3rd s. of the late A. E. C. Woodhouse. W, 16³–21²; XI, 20–21. St. John's, Cambridge, M.A. M.I.E.E., M.I.Ch.E. Engineering with Argentine Railways, later Consulting Engineer. Retired. Brothers, G. C. & M. C. Woodhouse. Son, 151.

WOODHOUSE, Michael Clayton, M.B., B.Ch., D.Phys.Med. W, 24¹–28².*

WOODLEY, Francis Richard. Tu, 96³–99².*

WOODS, Arthur Harold. St, 15²–19².*

WOODS, Robert Carr, b. 25 Nov. 30, 2nd s. of the late P. C. Woods. SF, 44²–49². N/S. 3rd Regt., R.H.A., B.A.O.R., 50. 2nd Lt. Trinity Hall, Cambridge. Insurance Broker. Man. Dir., Woods & Maslen Ltd. Member of Lloyd's. *City of London Club.*

WOOLLAN, The Rev. John Ernest Minors, b. 25 July 16, s. of the late E. B. Woollan. C, 30²–35¹; Cadet Officer. Queen's, Oxford, M.A., Dip. Ed. Lincoln Theological College. ✕ R.N., 40–46. Lt. Watchkeeping Officer's Certificate. Warden of Kingham Hill School, 46–53. Ordained, Deacon, 55; Priest, 56. Rector of Waddington, 58–65. Vicar of Helston since 65. Chaplain of the *Rugby Clubs.* Sons, 2444 & 2765.

WOOLLEY, John Michael, b. 22 Jan. 28, eldest s. of H. D. Woolley. SF, 41³–46². Exhibitioner of Peterhouse, Cambridge, M.A. Cambridge Univ. Press, 62–72. European Sales Office. *Anglo-Hellenic League, Anglo-Albanian Assoc.*

WOOLLEY, Philip Michael, b. 30 Sept. 26, eldest s. of the late Col. E. J. Woolley, M.C. Tu, 40³–44². Commissioned in Coldstream Guards, 44–48. Lt. R.A.R.O., 49. Dir., Collingham Communications Ltd. and Henry Sherwood Productions Ltd. Council, People's Dispensary for Sick Animals. Publicity Cttee., D.G.A.A. *Boodle's, Guards Club, R.Y.S.*

WOOTTEN, Major-Gen. Richard Montague, C.B., M.C., b. 19 June 89, elder s. of the late M. W. Wootten, J.P. (OR C 65). SH, 02³–07³. R.M.C., Sandhurst. Gazetted to Inniskilling Dragoons, 09. ✕ Staff Capt., 6th Cavalry Bde. D.A.A. & Q.M.G., 3rd Cavalry Div. Major. M.C. Queen's Bays, 21. Staff College, 21–22. G.S.O.3, M.I.Dept., War Office, 23. D.A.A.G., 25.

Instructor, Staff College, 28–31. Commd. The Queen's Bays, 32–36. Dir. Gen. T.A., 38–39. Palestine & Egypt, 36–39. ✕ 5 Corps H.Q., Narvik. C.B. Commander Legion of Merit, U.S.A. Retired, 45. *M.C.C.* R. Institute of International Affairs.

WORDSWORTH, Christopher William Vaughan. W, 28³–33¹.*

WORMALD, Frank Douglas, b. 30 Aug. 99, s. of the late G. F. Wormald. K, 13²–16³. ✕ Cheshire Yeomanry. L/Cpl. Insurance Surveyor with Wm. Heap & Son Ltd. of Manchester, 19. Farmer, retired.

WORTHINGTON, Edgar Barton, C.B.E., Ph.D., b. 13 Jan. 05, s. of E. Worthington. M, 18²–22³; Cap, 22; Sw. VI. Gonville & Caius, Cambridge, M.A., Ph.D. Frank Smart Research Student, 27–29. Naturalist. Leader, expeditions to African Lakes, 27–32. Scientist to African Survey, 34–37. Dir., Freshwater Biological Assoc., 37–46. Scientific Sec., Colonial Research Cttee., 46–50. Development Adviser, Uganda, 46. Sec.-Gen., Science Council for Africa, 50–56. Chief Scientist, Nature Conservancy, 57–64. Scientific Dir., International Biological Programme since 64. F.L.S., F.R.G.S., F.Z.S., S.C.G.B., C.B.E., 65. Author of many publications. *Athenæum, Farmers'.*

WREFORD-BROWN, Louis Carless, b. 9 Jan. 20, elder s. of the late R. L. Wreford-Brown. SF, 33³–37³; XV, 36–37. Trinity, Oxford, B.A. ✕ Somerset L.I. & Intell. Corps, 40–46. Major. Civil Servant (Foreign Office), 47–51. Senior Lecturer in History and Contemporary Affairs (later Dep. Head of Dept.), B.R.N.C., Dartmouth since 60. R. Institute of International Affairs. Inst. of Strategic Studies. Sons, 1836 & 2588.

WRIGHT, Charles Gordon. B, 26³–30².*

WRIGHT, Charles Herbert, M.A., F.R.S.A., b. 16 Apr. 04, s. of the late Sir Herbert Wright. C, 18¹–22¹; Cap, 20–21. Gonville & Caius, Cambridge, M.A. ✕ Ox. & Bucks. L.I. and Staff, 39–45. Capt. Dir. and Chrmn. of Public and Private Companies since 27; in particular Eastern Plantations Corp. Retired. Author (countryside subjects). Sons, 2579, 2834 & Christopher Philip Comstive, C, 67³–.

WRIGHT, Derek Rowland, b. 8 Sept. 30, s. of R. Wright. T, 44²–49²; Parry Leaving Exhibition; XI, 47–49 (Capt.);

H. XI, 48–49. Trinity Hall, Cambridge. Stone & Webster Canada Ltd., Toronto.

WRIGHT, Gordon Herbert, M.D., b. 4 Jan. 18, elder s. of H. A. Wright. Sh, 33^3–36^2; Scholar; Baines Leaving Exhibition. Birmingham Univ. Minor Scholar of King's, Cambridge, M.A., M.D., B.Chir. London Hospital Medical College, M.R.C.S., L.R.C.P. House Physician, Hertford County Hosp., 42. ✕ R.A.M.C., 42–46. Major. Departmental Demonstrator in Anatomy, Cambridge, 46–47. Univ. Demonstrator, 47–51. Univ. Lecturer since 51. Assoc. in Anatomy, Univ. of Pennsylvania, 52–53 (Sabbatical Year). Fellow & Tutor, Clare, Cambridge since 58.

WRIGHT, Geoffrey Michael, b. 13 July 26, s. of W. A. Wright. SF, 40^2–44^2; Capt. of Lawn Tennis. ✕ 2nd Regt., R.H.A., 44–48. Lt. Man. Dir. of Private Brewery.

WRIGHT, Geoffrey North, M.B.E., T.D., b. 3 May 15, 3rd s. of the late C. N. Wright. B, 29^1–32^2. F.C.A. ✕ R.A., 39–46. Lt.-Col. M.B.E., T.D. Dispatches. Sec., Flower & Sons Ltd. of Stratford upon Avon, 47–54. Dir., Tarmac Ltd. of Wolverhampton since 54. Dir., West Midlands Gas Board, 64–72 and South Staffs. Waterworks Co. since 67. General Commissioner of Taxes. F.I.D. *Les Ambassadeurs.* Brother, C. G. Wright.

WRIGHT, George William Barrington. SF, 02^3–07^1.*

WRIGHT, James Francis. St, 16^3–19^3.*

WRIGHT, Kenneth Gordon, b. 3 Dec. 16, s. of W. T. M. Wright, C.I.E. Sh, 30^2–34^3. Exhibitioner of Exeter, Oxford. ✕ Middlesex Regt. & No. 4 Commando. Croix de Guerre (Bronze Star). Major. Dispatches. Wounded. Underwriting member of Lloyd's. Man. Dir., Independent Security Consultants Ltd. (De La Rue), 61–65. Independent Security Consultant to Industry since 65. Author of "The Shopkeeper's Security Manual" & "Cost Effective Security". *M.C.C., Bath Club.* Past Capt. *O.R.G.S.*

WRIGHT, Michael, b. 25 Mar. 28, s. of J. F. Wright. Tu, 43^3–46^1; XV, 45. R.M.A., Sandhurst. Regular Army in R.A. Major. Now farming. *Cavalry Club.*

WRIGHT, Lt.-Col. Robert Francis, b. 27 Aug. 99, eldest s. of the late R. T.

Wright. St, 13^3–17^2; XV, 16; XI, 16–17. R.M.A., Woolwich. Commissioned into Royal Artillery, 19. Served in China & Gibraltar, 27–32. ✕ In Western Desert, 41–43. Lt.-Col. Wounded. Retired, 44. *Royal Over-Seas League.*

WRIGHT, Robin Franklin Pringle. SH, 44^2–48^2.*

WRIGHT, Robert Thomas. Sh, 44^1–47^3.*

WRIGHT, Roger Bruce, M.B., B.Chir., F.F.A.R.C.S., b. 28 Oct. 16, s. of the late G. H. Wright. Sh, 30^2–35^2. Nat. Sc. Exhibition to Gonville & Caius, Cambridge, M.A., M.B., B.Chir. St. Thomas's Hospital, M.R.C.S., L.R.C.P., D.A.(Eng.). F.F.A.R.C.S.(Eng.). ✕ R.A.M.C. (Anaesthetic Specialist), 40–46. Major. India & Burma. Consultant Anaesthetist, St. Thomas's Hospital. Council, Medical Protection Soc., Royal Soc. of Medicine. *Rye G.C.* Sons, 2290 & Michael James Robert, Sh, 69^3–.

WRIGHTSON, Alfred Nigel. St, 17^3–19^2.*

WRIGLEY, Frederick Richardson Gordon. Tu, 21^2–24^3.*

WRIGLEY, Ronald. W, 96^3–02^2.*

WYE, Francis Thomas Eric, b. 11 Feb. 25, s. of the late Major F. P. Wye, M.C. M, 38^3–43^1. ✕ R.A., 43–45. Scholar of Trinity Hall, Cambridge, B.A. Joined a shipping firm in Edinburgh. Son, 2533.

WYLIE, Francis Richard, b. 3 Nov. 06, eldest s. of Sir F. Wylie. C 20^3–25^2; XV, 24; H. XI, 24–25. Oriel, Oxford, M.A. Schoolmaster, Dragon School, Oxford, 28–29, 33–47 & 49–56. Ridge School, Johannesburg, 29–33 & 49. Master i/c Junior School, Cranbrook, Sydney, 48. Warden of Royal Alexandra and Albert School, Reigate, 56–65. Abberley Hall since 65. *Vincent's, Wanderers' Club, Johannesburg.*

WYNNE-EDWARDS, Evan Cameron, b. 21 May 02, 3rd s. of the late H. C. Wynne-Edwards. SH, 15^3–20^2. Emmanuel, Cambridge, B.A., M.B., B.Chir. St. Thomas's Hospital, F.R.C.S.(Edin.). Thoracic Surgeon, Norwich area. Retired.

WYNNE-EDWARDS, Prof. Vero Copner, C.B.E., b. 4 July 06, 3rd s. of the late Rev. Canon J. R. Wynne-Edwards. SH,

20^1–24^2; G. VIII, 22. New College, Oxford, M.A., D.Sc. Senior Scholar, 27–29. F.R.S. (Canada, Edinburgh & London). Asst. Associate Prof. of Zoology, McGill Univ., Montreal, 30–46. Regius Prof. of Natural History, Aberdeen Univ. since 46. Chrmn., Natural Environment Research Council, 68–71. Vice-Principal, Aberdeen Univ. since 72. C.B.E., 73. *New Club, Edinburgh, United Service, London.*

WYNNE-THOMAS, Edward Wynne (formerly Thomas, E. W.), b. 31 Dec. oo, eldest s. of H. Wynne-Thomas, M.R.C.S., L.R.C.P. St, 14^3–19^2. Emmanuel, Cambridge, M.A. St. Bartholomew's Hospital Medical School. With Hodder & Stoughton Ltd., Publishers. Retired, 6o. Fellow, Royal Philharmonic Soc. *United Oxford & Cambridge Univ. Club.*

WYNN-HAMEL, Geoffrey Fergus, O.B.E., (formerly Hamel, G. F. W.), b. 17 July o1, s. of the late F. E. Hamel. C, 16^1–18^2. University College School, London. Manchester School of Technology. Loco. Supt., Nigerian Railways, 24–26. Traction Supt., Buenos Aires & Pacific Rly., 26–31. Lubrication Engineer, Texas Oil Co., Brazil, 31–40. ✕ R.A.S.C., 40–45. Capt. C.Eng., F.I.Mech.E. Technical Writer & Editor. Consultant, Railway Engineering. O.B.E., 46.

Y

YATES, James Donald, b. 24 Dec. 22, 2nd s. of W. Yates. C, 36^3–41^1; XV, 40; H. XI, 40–41 (Capt.). Christ Church, Oxford, M.A. Hockey Blue. ✕ 1st The Royal Dragoons. Capt. Agriculture, Farm Management. Self-employed. *Farmers' Club, Norfolk Club.* Son, Robert Edward Charles, C, 70^1–.

YATES, John Henry Samuel. B, 01^3–04^2.*

YEO, Brig. Colin John Russell, C.B.E., M.C., J.P., b. 16 May 15, elder s. of F. R. Yeo. K, 28^3–33^2; Cap. R.M.A., Woolwich. In R.M.A. 1st Team for Rugby Football, Boxing, and Golf. Gazetted to Royal Artillery, 35. ✕ 39–45. Major. M.C. Brigadier, retired. C.B.E., J.P. *Army and Navy Club.*

YEOMAN, Harold John Newton. K, 42^3–46^2.*

YOUNG, Frederick John Lenane, b. 8 June 24, s. of the late F. W. Young, M.B.E. (OR T 93). T, 37^3–42^2. Minor Foundationer. St. Andrews Univ., M.A. William Blair Memorial Prize in Political Economy. Commonwealth Travel Fellowship of Goldsmith's Company for Economic Research in Canada, 5o. Queen's Univ., Canada, M.A. (Postgraduate). ✕ R. Scots & R. Warwickshire Rgt. att. 10th Gurkha Rifles, 43–47. Capt. Polymor Corp., Canada, 52–54. St. Andrews Coll., Canada, 54–56. Queen's Univ., Canada, 56–63. Dir., Industrial Relations Centre of Victoria, Univ. of Wellington, N.Z. since 63. Associate Professor. Economic Society of Australia and New Zealand. N.Z. Association of Economists.

YOUNG, Lt.-Col. Gavin David, b. 24 Sept. 97, s. of the late G. J. Young. St, 11^3–14^3; Sw. VI. R.M.C., Sandhurst. ✕ Inniskilling Dragoons. Lt. Welsh Guards, 2o; Capt., 28; Major, 32. Retired, 39. ✕ Lt.-Col. T.A., 39. Retired. *Guards, R.O.R.C., M.C.C.* Son, G. D. Young, jnr.

YOUNG, Gavin David (jnr.), b. 24 Apr. 28, s. of Lt.-Col. G. D. Young (OR St 11). SH, 42^1–45^2. N/S. Welsh Guards, 46–48. Lt. Served in Palestine and Jordan. R.M.C., Sandhurst. Trinity, Oxford, B.A. Joined Ralli Bros. Ltd. in 5o. Posted to Basrah, Iraq in 51. Now Foreign Correspondent of "The Observer". *Guards' Club.*

YOUNG, Ian Strang, M.B., Ch.B., F.R.C.S., b. 9 Mar. 20, elder s. of Dr. G. Young, M.C., M.B., F.R.C.S.G. M, 33^3–37^2. Glasgow Univ. Gardiner Bursary in Physics and Chemistry, 38. M.B., Ch.B. ✕ R.A.F. (Medical Branch), 43–46. F/Lt. F.R.C.S.(Edin.), 47. Consultant Otolaryngologist, United Norwich Hospital. Fellow, Royal Society of Medicine. *Royal Harwich Yacht Club.* Sons, 2681 and John Strang Walker, M, 68^3–.

YOUNG, Ian William, B.M., B.Ch., F.R.C.S., b. 25 Feb. 29, s. of G. S. Young. T, 42^2–47^2; Major Foundationer; Senior Scholarship, 45; Levée; Head of House; Cadet Officer. Postmaster of Merton, Oxford, M.A., B.M., B.Ch. University College Hospital, London, F.R.C.S. Consultant in Accident and Orthopaedic Surgery at Princess Margaret Hospital,

Swindon, Wilts. Son, John Richard, Tu, 70³-.

YOUNG, Patrick Templeton, b. 5 July 25, younger s. of Sir Arthur S. L. Young, Bt. B, 39¹–44²; Levée; Head of House. ✕ R. Armd. Corps. Capt. Architectural Assoc. A.A. Dipl., A.R.I.B.A. Architect, Partner Douglas Marriott, Worby & Robinson of London. *Royal Northern Yacht Club.*

YOUNG, Peter Scott, b. 19 Sept. 12, s. of the late J. J. B. Young. SF, 24²–29²; XXII. Pembroke, Cambridge, B.A.; Lawn Tennis Blue. Sudan Political Service, 36–44. ✕ Sudan Defence Force, 42–43. Civil Service, Board of Trade, 44–54. Chief Executive, Dollar Exports Council, 54–59. Locana Corp. (London), 59–62. Man., Lloyds & Bolsa International Bank Ltd. since 62.

YUILLE, Archibald Buchanan, D.F.C., b. 6 Nov. 96, eldest s. of the late H. B. Yuille. B, 10³–14². ✕ 8th Bn. East Lancashire Regt., 14–18. R.F.C. R.A.F. Capt. Wounded. D.F.C. Partner in George White & Co., Tea and Rubber Brokers. Later Chrmn. of George White Sanderson (Tea Brokers) Ltd. Retired. ✕ R.A.F.V.R., 39–45. ✕ Group Capt. Son, T. B. Yuille.

YUILLE, Thomas Buchanan, b. 1 Dec. 30, s. of Group Capt. A. B. Yuille, D.F.C. (OR B 10). B, 44²–48²; R. VIII, 48. N/S. Army Pay Corps, 49. 2nd Lt. Tea Broker.

YUILLE-SMITH, Charles Robert, b. 18 June 04, s. of the late F. Yuille-Smith. T, 18³–21³. R.C.M. Wesley Exhibition, 26 & 27. Second Cobbett Prize, 27. A.R.C.M., 28. Musician, retired.

Z

ZIEGLER, Frank Henry, b. 6 July 07, 2nd s. of the late G. F. Ziegler. K, 21²–25³. Pembroke, Oxford, B.A. ✕ R.A.F. (Intelligence). F/Lt. Dispatches. Freelance Journalism, Author and Translator. *R.A.C., Alpine Ski Club, Ski Club of Great Britain.* Brother, H. C. Ziegler.

ZIEGLER, Harold Colin, b. 12 June 10, 3rd s. of the late G. F. Ziegler. K, 24²–27³. Christ Church, Oxford; Univ. Ski Team, 29–31. Insurance Broker from 35. Member of Lloyd's from 36. R.A. (T.A.), 38. ✕ R.A. (H.A.A.), 39–46. Capt. *Boodle's.* Brother, F. H. Ziegler.

ZIMAN, Herbert David, b. 21 Mar. 02, s. of D. Ziman. B, 15³–20²; Scholar; Major & Minor Exhibitioner. Scholar of University College, Oxford, M.A. Journalist, "Liverpool Daily Post", 25–27. Freelance, 27–33. "Daily Telegraph" from 34,

retiring in 68 as Literary Editor. ✕ Artists Rifles, Middlesex Regt. & Intelligence Corps, 39–44. Capt. and G.S.O.3. War Correspondent of "Daily Telegraph" with 1st Canadian, 2nd British and 1st U.S. Armies, 44–45. Territorial Efficiency Medal. Now free-lance Journalist, mostly reviewing books. *Reform Club, PEN, Anglo-Belgian Union* (Council), *Friends of National Libraries* (Committee, formerly Hon. Sec.).

ZIMMERMAN, Philip Russell, b. 9 Jan. 21, s. of the late T. J. Zimmerman. M, 34³–39¹; Levée. Scholar of Trinity, Oxford. Columbia Univ. B.A. ✕ U.S.A.A.F. Member, *Phi Beta Kappa.* Publisher. *Oxford and Cambridge Combined Universities Club.* Son, 2682.

ZOCHONIS, John Basil. M, 43³–48².*

PART II

Post 1947

PERCY HUGH BEVERLEY LYON
(O.R.)
Elected Headmaster in 1931

ENTRANCES IN JANUARY 1947

1 **ALSTON, Robin Carfrae,** b. 29 Jan. 33, younger s. of W. L. Alston (OR SH 14). SH, 47¹–51¹. Brit. Columbia, B.A.; Toronto, M.A.; Oxford, M.A.; London, Ph.D. Teaching Fellow, University College, Toronto, 56–58; Lecturer in English, Univ. of New Brunswick, 58–60; Lecturer in English, Leeds Univ. from 64. Author of many publications on the English Language.

2 **CORBOULD-WARREN, Richard,** b. 19 June 33, elder s. of W. Corbould-Warren. SH, 45¹–51². Lincoln Agricultural College, N.Z. Univ., Christchurch, Diploma of Agriculture. Brother, 603.

3 **WALDING, Richard Michael Waldron,** b. 16 Aug. 33, younger s. of the late T. W. Walding (OR T 08). SH, 47¹–51³; Cap, 50; XV, 51; Cadet Officer. Director, Anderson & Coltman, Mincing Lane.

4 **MATHEWS, James Weir,** b. 22 May 33, s. of P. Mathews. T, 47¹–50³.

5 **MORGAN, David John,** b. 31 May 33, s. of F. K. Morgan. T, 47¹–52². Lincoln, Oxford, M.A. Head of Physics Dept., Oakham School, Rutland.

6 **WHITE, Colin David,** b. 12 July 33 younger s. of F. A. White. T, 47¹–51². Indentures with Rootes Motors Ltd. O.N.C. in Production Engineering. Member of the Institute of Purchasing & Supply. Production Buyer with Chrysler United Kingdom Ltd. *Rugby Hockey Club, Daventry Golf Club.*

7 **WARDROP, David Nicol,** b. 11 July 33, elder s. of the late D. Wardrop, F.R.C.S. (OR T 18). T, 47¹–47².

8 **LAW, Andrew Bonar,** b. 27 July 33, younger s. of the Rt. Hon. Lord Coleraine, P.C. B, 47¹–51². Trinity College, Dublin, Scholarship. Brit. Market Research Bureau, 58–60; International Trade Information, 60–61; Windett, Burrows & Bonar Law Ltd., Research Dir., 61.

9 **FARRIS, Roger Edward,** b. 22 June 33, elder s. of L. S. E. Farris. K, 47¹–51². Trinity Hall, Cambridge, B.A. Tinsley Wire Industries Ltd., Sheffield, Management Trainee, spells in Works, Sales and Computer; Cost Accountant of Sheffield Factory, 67; Group Corporate Planning Manager, 70. Brother, 838.

10 **SMITH, Robert S.,** b. 16 June 33, s. of R. Smith. SF, 47¹–50³.

11 **ALFORD, Jonathan Robert,** b. 10 July 33, s. of the late J. B. Alford (OR C 19). Sh, 47¹–51²; Head of House; Levée; Cap, 1950. Jesus, Cambridge, B.A. Army Officer, Royal Engineers commanding 25 Engineer Regiment. Lt.-Col. p.s.c. *R.O.R.C.*

12 **KENDALL-JACKSON, Geoffrey,** b. 14 Jan. 32, younger s. of J. Kendall-Jackson. Sh, 47¹–50². Sec., Craigside Hydro Ltd., 56; Sec. & Man., 62.

13 **CRUICKSHANK, Martin Melvin,** b. 17 Sept. 33, s. of M. M. Cruickshank, Brig. I.M.S. (Retired), C.I.E., K.St.J., B.Sc., M.D., Ch.M., F.R.C.S.(Edin.), F.I.C.S., F.A.C.S., F.R.S.(Edin.), F.R.S.M., D.O.M.S. St, 47¹–51². Cambridge. Commission in Gordon Highlanders, 52; served Malaya, 52–53 (Dispatches); Cyprus, 55–56; Germany, 60–61; Congo, 62 (Company Commander); Nigeria, 62–64 (Brigade Major; Chief Instructor, Nigeria Mil. College); retired, 67. Landed Proprietor. F.R.G.S., F.S.A.(Scot.). *Naval and Military,* O. St. J. (Scottish Council of Order of St. John since 70).

14 **HURST, Charles Henry Frederick,** b. 25 May 33, elder s. of the late C. W. Hurst. St, 47¹–50³. Steelcraft Industries, Cairns Qld. Brother, 754.

15 **FRANCIS, Francis (jnr.),** b. 2 July 33, elder s. of F. Francis (OR SH 20). Tu, 47¹–51²; Cap, 49; XI, 49–50; Cap, 51. Trinity Hall, Cambridge, M.A., LL.B.; Harvard, LL.M. Barrister, Gray's Inn. *M.C.C., Travellers' Club, Paris.*

16 **COX, Richard Hugh,** b. 19 May 33, 4th s. of G. H. Cox. W, 47¹–51³. Brother, J. E. Cox.

17 **DAVIES, David Alban**, b. 4 June 33, s. of the late Surg.-Cdr. J. Davies, M.D., M.R.C.P. W, 47¹–51².

18 **LEES-JONES, William Richard**, b. 18 June 33, elder s. of R. W. T. Lees-Jones. W, 47¹–51²; XV, 49, 50; XXII, 50, 51. Clare, Cambridge, B.A. Managing Director, J. W. Lees & Co. (Brewers) Ltd. T.D. Brother, 457.

ENTRANCES IN MAY 1947

19 **BAILEY, Kenneth Nicolas Patrick**, b. 15 Sep. 33, younger s. of K. V. Bailey, M.C., M.D., M.R.C.P., F.R.C.O.G. SH, 47²–52². Died, Dec. 57.

20 **BUCHANAN, Nigel Walter**, b. 22 July 33, 3rd. s. of the late Col. E. P. Buchanan, O.B.E., M.C., D.L. (OR SF 07). SH, 47²–52¹. Trinity, Oxford, B.A.; Glasgow Univ., LL.B. Writer to the Signet. Partner in J. & F. Anderson, W.S. of Edinburgh. *New Club (Edin.).*

21 **SPENS, John Alexander**, b. 7 June 33, s. of T. P. Spens, O.B.E., M.C. (OR SH 08). SH, 47²–51². Corpus Christi, Cambridge, B.A.; Glasgow Univ., LL.B. Solicitor, Partner, Maclay Murray & Spens, Glasgow. Member, Queen's Body Guard for Scotland (Royal Company of Archers), R.D. *Western Club, Glasgow.*

22 **DIXON, Michael**, b. 2 July 33, s. of A. Dixon. SH, 47²–52². M.A. Cantab. Research Scientist.

23 **SMITH, Howard John**, b. 10 July 33, younger s. of N. B. Smith. T, 47²–52².

24 **GREENFIELD, Richard Hilary**, b. 17 Nov. 33, s. of Sir H. Greenfield, C.S.I., C.I.E. B, 47²–52². Pembroke, Oxford. N/S. Welch Regt. (Commission), seconded to Malay Regt., later served in 4th Bn. Welch Regt. (T.A.). Trained in journalism on "Walsall Observer". Staff reporter on "Birmingham Mail". Journalist, "Sunday Telegraph" since 64. *East India, Sports & Public Schools Club, London Press Club.*

25 **JOHNSTON, Gordon Gleadell**, b. 29 July 33, 3rd s. of the late F. B. Johnston. B, 47²–51². Died, 18 Sept. 72. Brothers, F. J. & I. B. M. Johnston.

26 **TREMLETT, John D'Arcy**, b. 9 May 33, younger s. of W. D'A. Tremlett (OR B 18). B, 47²–50¹. Member, Institute of Quarrying, Institute of Plant Engineers, Institute of Road Transport Engineers; Assoc. Member, British Institute of Management. Director, Public Company engaged in quarrying and brick-making industry

27 **BLANDFORD, Robert Laurence Roy**, b 17 Oct. 33, s. of the late Lt.-Col. N. L. Blandford, R.E. (OR C 18). C, 47²–50². Computer Systems Analyst.

28 **LEYNS, Eric**, b. 12 Nov. 33, s. of E. J. T. Leyns. C, 47²–50². Partner, Simon & Coates, Stockbrokers.

29 **TEGNER, Ian Nicol**, b. 11 July 33, son of the late S. S. Tegner, O.B.E. C, 47²–51³; Levée; Head of House. C.A. (Scotland & Ontario). Formerly Partner, Barton Mayhew & Co., C.A. Now Finance Director, The Bowater Corporation Ltd.

30 **BROWN, William Hays Harold**, b. 2 July 33, s. of the late Sir S. H. Brown (OR K 17). K, 47²–51². Solicitor, 60. With Linklater & Paines, then with Allen Allen & Hemsley in Sydney, N.S.W., 66. *Junior Carlton Club.*

31 **CASSELS, Michael Kennedy**, b. 10 May 33, eldest s. of A. K. Cassels (OR K 20). K, 47²–51¹; Cap, 50. P.A., R.I.C.S. Land Agent (resident) to Sir Denys Lowson, Bt., Trustees of Dunsinnan Estate and others. J.P. *Royal Perth Golfing Society and Country Club.* Brothers, 347, 773 and 1527.

32 **CHARLESWORTH, Thomas**, b. 27 Oct. 33, younger s. of J. Charlesworth, LL.D. K, 47²–52¹. Hertford, Oxford, M.A. Member of the Institute of Management Consultants. Courtaulds Ltd., 58–65. P.A. Management Consultants Ltd. since 65. Currently Senior Consultant.

33 **HALEY, David Jeremy**, b. 3 Aug. 33, younger s. of Sir W. Haley, K.C.M.G. K, 47²–51². Marketing Manager, British Oxygen Co. Ltd., London. Brother, Donald J. Haley.

34 **TUBBS, Ian Gordon**, b. 14 Nov. 33, s. of L. G. Tubbs. K, 47²–51³; Cap. Managing Director, Aluminium Stockholding Company.

35 **FORBES-ROBERTSON, Kenneth Hugh**, b. 12 Sept. 33, s. of the late Col. J. Forbes-Robertson, V.C., D.S.O., M.C., D.L. SF, 47²–49³. Dartmouth, 49; Midshipman, 51; Lt., 56; Lt.-Cdr., 64. *United Services Club.*

36 **RAMSDEN, Jonathan Hesketh,** b. 17 Aug. 33, s. of the late H. A. Ramsden (OR SF 12). SF, 47^2–51^2. Company Director.

37 **COCHRANE, Antony Varian Dundonald,** b. 14 Nov. 33, s. of H. V. Cochrane. Sh, 47^2–51^2. Trinity, Oxford. Kleinwort Benson Ltd., 56–61, Export Finance Group, now London American Finance Corporation Ltd.; presently Director of Euro Dollar Credits Ltd., one of the Group subsidiaries.

38 **CRAWLEY, John Maurice,** b. 27 Sept. 33, eldest s. of C. W. Crawley. Sh, 47^2–52^1; Scholar; Levée; Head of House; Leaving Exhibition. Scholarship to New College, Oxford, M.A.; Merton College, Oxford, Harmsworth Scholar, 59. Home Civil Service. Currently Assistant Secretary, Secretaries Office, Inland Revenue since 59. Brothers, 433 and 1084.

39 **KING, Thomas Jeremy,** b. 13 June 33, s. of J. H. King. Sh, 47^2–51^2; Cap, 50; XI, 50, 51; Captain of Fives. Emmanuel, Cambridge, B.A. Joined E. S. & A. Robinson Ltd., as trainee, 56. Various positions held till Divisional General Manager. Left on adoption as Conservative candidate for Bridgwater. Elected bye-election, March 70 and General Election, June 70. P.P.S. to C. Chataway, Minister for Industrial Development.

40 **RADCLIFFE, John Robert Hugh,** b. 9 Dec. 33, s. of H. C. Radcliffe. Sh, 47^2–51^2.

41 **WOODD-WALKER, Robert Basil,** b. 20 Sept. 33, elder s. of G. B. Woodd-Walker, M.B., F.R.C.S. (OR St 14). Sh, 47^2–52^1. Clare, Cambridge, M.B., B.Chir., M.A. St. Mary's Hospital Medical School, Paddington, D.C.H., M.R.C.P. Consultant Paediatrician at Essex County Hospital, Colchester and St. John's Hospital, Chelmsford. Brother, 439.

42 **INGLIS, John Nigel D'Oyly,** b. 22 Nov. 33, s. of Lt.-Col. E. J. D'O. Inglis (OR St 13). St, 47^2–50^3.

43 **JAMESON, John Valentine McCulloch,** b. 5 Oct. 33, younger s. of Col. A. McC. Jameson, J.P., D.L. St, 47^2–51^3. N/S. 2nd Lt. 4/7 Royal Dragoon Guards, 52–54. College of Estate Management, B.Sc., F.R.I.C.S. Shell Petroleum Co., 54–59; Richard Costain (Canada) Ltd., 59–64; Partner, G. M. Thomson & Co., Chartered Surveyors since 64.

44 **HETHERINGTON, Ian Maxwell,** b. 27 June 33, younger s. of W. M. Hetherington, M.B., Ch.B. Tu, 47^2–51^2. Commissioned R.A., 54. Arthur Guinness, Son & Co. Ltd., 60. Brother, T. C. Hetherington.

45 **NELSON, Robert Haigh,** b. 13 Oct. 33, eldest s. of R. R. Nelson. Tu, 47^2–51^2; R. VIII, 51. F.C.A. Price Waterhouse & Co., Newcastle upon Tyne. Brothers, 367 and 727.

46 **SLADE, Stephen John,** b. 17 Sept. 33, s. of J. N. Slade. Tu, 47^2–51^2. Univ. of Denver College of Law, B.S.L. Assistant Sec., Los Angeles Airways Inc., 62, Corporate Sec., 64–67; Manager Civic Affairs, Trans World Airlines Inc., Los Angeles, 68, Director Civic Affairs, N.Y. since 69. U.S. Army Signal Corps, 59–60. *Salem Golf Club (N.Y.), E.S.U.*

47 **BROWN, Gourley Robert Lindsay,** b. 31 Oct. 33, elder s. of the late A. L. Brown, M.C., C.A. W, 47^2–51^3. C.A. (Scotland). Partner of Arthur Young McClelland Moores & Co. *R.A.C., H.C.E.G., New Club (Edin.).* Brother, 1328.

48 **THOMAS-DAVIES, John Anthony,** b. 21 Mar. 34, elder s. of J. Thomas-Davies (OR W 18). W, 47^2–51^1. Oriel, Oxford, M.A. Dip.Ed. Schoolmaster at Ottershaw School, Chertsey, Surrey.

49 **WHITTER, David Charles,** b. 18 Sept. 33, s. of C. L. Whitter. W, 47^2–51^3. New College, Oxford, M.A.; King's, Cambridge, Cert. Ed. Public Relations Officer, Imperial Chemical Industries Ltd. *Folio Society.*

ENTRANCES IN SEPTEMBER 1947

50 **BOWEN, Basil John,** b. 18 Sept. 33, s. of Capt. B. H. Bowen, R.N. (Retired). SH, 47^3–52^2; Tennis VI, 51, 52. Hertford, Oxford, B.A. Solicitor. Partner in Herbert and Gowers & Co. of Oxford.

51 **BOWERING, John Anthony,** b. 7 Feb. 34, son of J. Bowering. SH, 47^3–52^1. Sidney Sussex, Cambridge, B.A.; Wycliffe Hall, Theological College, Oxford. Curate of Hornchurch, Diocese of Chelmsford, 59–62; Succentor, 62 and Precentor of Chelmsford Cathedral, 63–64; Vicar of Brampton Bieslow, Diocese of Sheffield, 64–69; Vicar of Norton Lees, Sheffield, 70.

52 **DRAKE, Nicholas James,** b. 8 Dec. 33, younger s. of A. G. Drake. SH, 47^3-52^2; Cap, 51. Jesus, Oxford, B.A. Market Research Executive, 57–59; Burton and Bowles, 60; Unilever, 61; Research Bureau Ltd., 62; Market Information Services Ltd.

53 **FONTES, Anthony Richard,** b. 3 Sept. 34, elder s. of A. C. Fontes. SH, 47^3-52^2. F.C.A. Partner in Messrs. Warmsley Henshall & Co. of Chester. Brother, 801.

54 **KITTERMASTER, Julian Radcliffe,** b. 11 Nov. 33, s. of M. R. Kittermaster (OR SH 19). SH, 47^3-52^2. Trinity Hall, Cambridge, M.A., F.R.I.C.S. Chartered Surveyor and Land Agent. Branch partner in Messrs. Strutt & Parker, Salisbury, Wilts. Since 1968.

55 **MONTGOMERY, Anthony Alan,** b. 16 Aug. 33, younger s. of Prof. G. A. Montgomery, LL.B., Q.C. SH, 47^3-51^2. Trinity Hall, Cambridge, B.A. Edinburgh Theological College. Deacon, 58; Priest, 59. Curate, St. John's, Dumfries, 58–63; Rector, St. Paul's, Airdrie, 63–68; Chaplain, Gordonstoun School, Morayshire.

56 **MASSON, Kenneth Ely Brooke,** b. 15 Jan. 34, elder s. of A. Masson. SH, 47^3-51^3. F.C.A. In professional practice. *Walton Heath Golf Club.* Brother, 518.

57 **WHEATCROFT, Timothy Martin,** b. 25 Jan. 34, younger s. of Prof. G. S. A. Wheatcroft (OR SH 19). SH, 47^3-52^3.

58 **WILSON, Mervyn Raynold Alwyn,** b. 4 Nov. 33, elder s. of the Rev. E. R. Wilson. SH, 47^3-51^1; Stovin Scholarship. Exhibition to Queen's, Cambridge; Ripon Hall, Oxford. Ordained, 59. Rector of Bermondsey since 69. Brother, 1640.

59 **ADCOCK, Colin Stuart,** b. 12 July 33, s. of E. N. Adcock. T, 47^3-47^3.

60 **CARRICK, Michael Evan,** b. 27 Mar. 34, elder s. of G. A. Carrick. T, 47^3-52^2; Minor Foundationer; R. VIII, 52. Durham Univ., B.Sc. Applied Science (Naval Architecture and Marine Engineering), Liverpool Univ. Cert. Ed. Assoc. Member, Royal Institute of Naval Architects. Work in shipbuilding commerce. At present Schoolmaster in Physics at King's Norton Grammar School for Boys, Birmingham. *R.Y.A., Bala Sailing Club.*

61 **EVANS, Philip Donald,** b. 4 June 34, eldest s. of D. W. Evans. T, 47^3-52^2; R. VIII, 52. Oriel, Oxford, M.A.; Half Blues Cross Country and Athletics; Capt., O.U. Cross Country, 56. F.C.I.I. Provincial Insurance Co. Ltd., in Kenya and Tanzania, now Administrative and Overseas Manager, English & American Insurance Co. Ltd. (subsidiary of C. T. Bowring & Co. Ltd.). Brother, 389.

62 **FOX, John McLean,** b. 4 Jan. 34, elder s. of the late K. McL. Fox. T, 47^3-52^2. Queens', Cambridge, M.A., C.Eng., M.I.Mech.E., M.I.M.C. Senior Management Consultant with P.A. Management Consultants Ltd. Brother, 812.

63 **HOGG, Peter Francis,** b. 15 May 34, s. of F. G. Hogg. T, 47^3-52^2. Birmingham Univ., LL.B. Solicitor with Hertfordshire County Council (Legal Dept.).

64 **JOHNSON, Ralph Hudson,** b. Dec. 33, s. of S. R. E. Johnson. T, 47^3-52^2; Foundationer. St. Catherine's, Cambridge, Lord Kitchener Scholar & Drapers Co. Scholar, 52, B.A., M.B., B.Chir. Univ. College Hospital Med. Sch., House Surgeon, 58; House Physician, 59. Senior House Officer, Radcliffe Infirmary, Oxford, 59–60. Polio Research Fund Research Fellow, Radcliffe Infirmary, 61. Senior Member, Worcester, Oxford, D.Phil., 65. M.D.(Cantab.), 66. Senior Lecturer, Glasgow University. Consultant, Glasgow Teaching Hospitals.

65 **LUKER, Brian Gordon,** b. 26 Aug. 35, elder s. of P. H. Luker. T, 47^3-53^2; Foundationer. Exhibition to Sidney Sussex, Cambridge, M.A. Economics Group Manager, Planning Dept., I.C.I. Mond Division, Runcorn, Cheshire. Society of Business Economists.

66 **McKENZIE, Grahame Donald,** b. 12 Nov. 34, s. of the late D. A. McKenzie. T, 47^3-52^3. Chartered Accountant, 61. Assistant Accountant, W. J. Tatem Ltd., 61. Sec./Chief Accountant, H. Parrott & Co. (London) Ltd., 62.

67 **MATTHEWS, John Jenkin,** b. 24 Dec. 34, s. of A. E. Matthews. T, 47^3-53^2; Scholar; Levée; Head of House; Leaving Exhibition. Scholarship to Queens', Cambridge, M.A., C.Eng., M.I.E.E. With A.E.I. Ltd., 56–64. Foundation Member, Lecturer and now Senior Lecturer, Dept. of Engineering Science, Univ. of Exeter since 64.

68 **OLDHAM, Richard Thomas,** b. 25 Aug. 33, s. of T. J. F. Oldham. T, 47^3–52^2. Manchester Univ., B.Sc. Associate of the Textile Institute. Marketing Representative, Textile Fibre Sales.

69 **WILSON, John Michael,** b. 8 June 34, s. of J. E. Wilson. T, 47^3–53^2. Oriel, Oxford, M.A., F.B.C.S. Company Secretary, United Glass Ltd.

70 **CLEVERLY, John Grover,** b. 18 Dec. 33, s. of G. C. Cleverly (OR B 10). B, 47^3–52^2; Levée; Head of House. Magdalene, Cambridge, F.R.I.C.S. Partner, B. L. Wells & Sons, Surveyors, Beverley, E. Yorks.

71 **DIXON, Timothy Graham,** b. 21 Apr. 34, s. of the late W. G. Dixon, B.Sc. B, 47^3–51^3. Solicitor, 57. Barrister, Solicitor & Attorney in Western Australia, 58. Senior Partner with Dixon Elgar & Griffith, Solicitors of Fordingbridge, Hants. Member of British Ornithologists Union. Past Chairman of Fordingbridge Chamber of Trade.

72 **JOHNSON, Graham Belton,** b. 31 July 29, s. of the late G. B. Johnson. B, 47^3–48^2. Univ. of Oklahoma, U.S.A. Killed in motor accident, 28 Dec. 51.

73 **LEACOCK, Christopher Gordon,** b. 26 May 34, s. of D. G. Leacock (OR B 21). B, 47^3–52^2.

74 **LOCKWOOD, John Trevor,** b. 28 Mar. 34, s. of J. F. Lockwood. B, 47^3–53^2; Levée; Head of House; XXII, 53. Magdalene, Cambridge, M.A. Leeds University Dental Hospital, B.Ch.D., L.D.S. Dental Surgeon.

75 **MILLIGAN, James George,** b. 10 May 34, s. of the Rt. Hon. Lord Milligan. B, 47^3–52^1; Cap, 50/1; R. VIII, 52. Univ. College, Oxford, B.A.; Edinburgh Univ., LL.B. Faculty of Advocates, 59; Standing Junior Counsel to Scottish Home and Health Dept., and Dept. of Health and Social Security in Scotland; Advocate-Depute, 71; Q.C., 72. *New Club, Edinburgh; H.C.E.G., Muirfield.* Brother-in-Law, 2086.

76 **STIRLING-WYLLIE, David Rodger,** b. 12 Apr. 34, s. of the late Col. K. R. Stirling-Wyllie (OR B 12). B, 47^3–52^2.

77 **WILKIE, Alasdair David,** b. 22 Mar. 34, elder s. of J. Wilkie, M.B., C.H.B., D.P.H. B, 47^3–51^2; Scholar;

Lees Knowles Leaving Exhibition; Sw. VIII (Capt.), 51. Exhibition to Trinity, Cambridge, M.A. N/S. R.A.F., 55–57. F.F.A. and F.I.A. Employed by Scottish Widows Fund, 51–52 and 57–61; Swiss Reinsurance Co., Zürich, 61–62; Standard Life Assur. Co., Edinburgh since 62. Brother, 923.

78 **EYRE, John Alasdair Geddes,** b. 30 Oct. 33, elder s. of F. A. Eyre. C, 47^3–51^2. Leeds University, City & Guilds Diploma in Leather Manufacture. Silvester Litton Ltd. (Tanners), 54–57; Director, James G. Brown Ltd. (Leather Merchants), 57–71. Self-employed, Nursery and Garden Shop since 71. Brother, 677.

79 **FEATHER, Michael Godfrey,** b. 5 June 33, s. of Professor N. Feather, F.R.S. C, 47^3–51^3; H. XI, 51; XXII. N/S. R.A.F., 52–54. Edin. Univ., B.L.; Cambridge Univ., B.A., LL.B. Barrister, Legal Adviser, Federation of Civil Engineering Contractors, 60–63; Hawker Siddeley Aviation, 63–65. Now Secretary, Society of Motor Manufacturers and Traders. *R.A.C.*

80 **FIELD, Roger John James,** b. 4 Oct. 33, s. of J. W. Field. C, 47^3–52^2; Sw. VIII, 50, 51, Capt., 52. Varied experience in industry, mainly management, until 65, then medical student at St. Bartholomew's Hospital, London. Now Medical Student and Company Director.

81 **FROOMBERG, Derek Leon,** b. 16 Sept. 34, 2nd s. of A. Froomberg. C, 47^3–51^3. B.I.M., Company Director. *B.S.A.C.* (Hampstead Branch). Brothers, J. S. Froomberg and 538.

82 **RUSSELL, William Michael,** b. 18 Apr. 34, s. of W. R. Russell, M.D., F.R.C.P. C, 47^3–52^2; R. VIII, 50–52. Holder of Bigside Bags, 52. Trinity, Oxford, B.A. St. Thomas's Hospital, 56–59, B.M., B.Ch., D.C.H.

83 **TURRALL, William Guy Bolton,** b. 27 July 33, s. of Major R. G. Turrall, D.S.O., M.C. C, 47^3–51^3; Scholar; Scholarship to Trinity Hall, Cambridge, B.A.; Ridley Hall, Camb. Instructor at Outward Bound Mountain School. Worked in factories in East End of London and in Warrington with a view to Missionary work in these fields. Died 8 July 63.

84 **BAINBRIDGE, Michael Norman,** b. 23 Feb. 34, s. of the late J. E. M. Bainbridge (OR K 20). K, 47^3–52^2. University

of Grenoble, France, A.I.C.S. P. & O. Group, 7 years India and Pakistan. Now Asst. Manager, Insurance and Claims, P. & O. General Cargo Division.

85 **BUNTING, Martin Brian,** b. 28 Feb. 34, s. of T. B. Bunting. K, 47³–52¹. Chartered Accountant, Asst. Managing Director, Courage Ltd.

86 **CURRIE, Giles Edward,** b. 21 Sept. 34, s. of J. E. L. C. Currie. K, 47³–52²; Scholar; Cap, 51. Magdalen, Oxford, B.A. Partner, E. B. Savory Mills & Co., Stockbrokers since 66. Conservative Candidate, 64 & 66. Chairman, Blackheath Cator Estate Ltd. *Junior Carlton Club.*

87 **DAVIDSON, John Gerald Walker,** b. 9 June 33, eldest s. of Brig. T. W. Davidson, M.B. K, 47³–51²; XI, 51. Graduate of Staff College and American Joint Forces Staff College. Dispatches, 55. Promoted Lt.-Col., 73. *M.C.C.* Brother, 251.

88 **HEDDERWICK, Ronald Nelson,** b. 24 June 34, younger s. of C. Hedderwick. K, 47³–52¹; Levée; R. VIII. N/S. R.N., 52–54. S/Lt. R.N.V.R., 57. Aluminium Merchant Business, 54–62. Agricultural work, 62. Brother, P. D. N. Hedderwick.

89 **LUSHINGTON, Colin John,** b. 11 Feb. 34, 3rd s. of P. J. Lushington. K, 47³–51²; S. VIII, 50–51. Fellow, Visible Record & Mini Computer Society; Qualified Member Swimming Teachers Assoc. Computer Software Manager, British Olivetti Ltd. Life Member, *Royal Life Saving Society and National Rifle Association.*

90 **MILWARD, Ian Newton,** b. 9 May 34, s. of Sir A. H. Milward, C.B.E. (OR K 18). K, 47³–52². Shipping Manager, Shipping Industrial Holdings, London. R.N.V.R.

91 **MURDOCH, Robert Alan,** b. 11 Apr. 34, younger s. of W. R. F. Murdoch. K, 47³–49².

92 **NEWBOULT, James Michael Scott,** b. 2 Dec. 33, s. of the late H. O. Newboult. K, 47³–52²; H. XI; Cap; Junior Racket pair. Merton, Oxford, M.A. A.C.A. Corporate Finance. Industrial & Commercial Finance Corporation Ltd.

93 **PASTEUR, Thomas Hugh,** b. 1 May 34, younger s. of H. W. Pasteur. K,

47³–52³; Levée; XV, 51–52 (Capt.). King's, Cambridge, B.A., M.I.M.C. Shaw Savill Line. P.E. Consulting Group.

94 **BLAIKLEY, Bruce John,** b. 10 Oct. 33, elder s. of J. B. Blaikley, F.R.C.S., F.R.C.O.G. M, 47³–52¹. Clare, Cambridge, M.A. M.I.C.E., 63. Consulting Civil Engineer with Sir Alexander Gibb & Partners, 57–64. Now Senior Engineer with G. Mansell & Partners. Brother, 417.

95 **CHAPMAN, John Michael Dobson,** b. 9 Feb. 34, elder s. of W. D. Chapman. M, 47³–51³; XV, 50–51; XI, 51; H. XI, 50–51. N/S., 52–54. Commissioned. Mercantile Asst. Andrew Gale & Co. Ltd., Calcutta, 54–59. Director, Fred Fearnley Ltd. (Motors), Manchester, 56.

96 **DONALD, Colin Dunlop,** b. 24 July 34, s. of the late C. D. Donald (OR M 93). M, 47³–53¹; Scholar. Minor Scholarship to Gonville & Caius, Cambridge, B.A.; Glasgow University, LL.B. N/S., 53–55. 2nd Lt. The Cameronians (Scottish Rifles); Territorial Service with 6/7th Bn., 55–65, retiring as Captain. Solicitor, McGregor Donald & Co., Solicitors, Glasgow, 58; Partner, 66. *Western Club, Glasgow.*

97 **GORDON, Alastair Strathearn,** b. 28 Nov. 34, s. of E. F. S. Gordon, M.D. M, 47³–52³; Scholar; Jex-Blake Classical Exhibition; Scholar, New College, Oxford, B.A. Principal, Department of the Environment. Hon. Sec., Greenwich Society.

98 **HINTON, David Anthony,** b. 27 May 34, 2nd s. of W. K. Hinton, J.P. M, 47³–52². St. John's, Cambridge, B.A.

99 **MICKLEM, Henry Spedding,** b. 11 Oct. 33, younger s. of the late Rev. E. R. Micklem (OR St 06). M, 47³–52²; Scholar; Levée; Head of House; Leaving Exhibition. Classical Scholarship to Oriel, Oxford, M.A., D.Phil. Scientific Staff of the Medical Research Council, 57–66. Lecturer (Senior from 72) in Zoology, Univ. of Edinburgh from 66. Author of "Tissue Grafting and Radiation" and of numerous research papers in scientific journals.

100 **RALSTON, David Bird,** b. 25 Dec. 29, elder s. of J. M. Ralston of New Jersey, U.S.A. M, 47³–48².

101 **RAWSON, David Robert,** b. 20 Feb. 34, s. of S. H. Rawson. M, 47³–52².

102 **SPEED, John Arney,** b. 30 Mar. 34, s. of Sir R. W. A. Speed, C.B., Q.C. (OR B 19). M, 47³–52². Trinity, Cambridge, B.A. Bar, Inner Temple, 58. In Chambers, 2 Harcourt Buildings, Temple. *Brooks's Club.*

103 **STUART, Duncan,** b. 1 July 34, s. of I. C. Stuart. M, 47³–53¹; Levée; Head of School; Head of House; XV, 51, 52, Capt., 53. Classical Scholarship to Brasenose, Oxford, B.A. N/S. Ox. & Bucks. Light Infantry, 2nd Lt. Joined H.M. Diplomatic Service, 59. Office of Political Adviser, Berlin, 60–61; 2nd Sec., Embassy, Helsinki, 64–66; 1st Sec., Dar-es-Salaam, 66–69; Embassy, Helsinki from 70. General Service Medal, Cyprus. *Oxford & Cambridge United Universities Club, Vincent's Club.*

104 **FLETCHER, Christopher Michael,** b. 1 Mar. 34, younger s. of W. W. Fletcher. SF, 47³–51³. Constantine Technical College, Middlesbrough. Works Chemist, Dorman Long & Co., Tar Distillation Works, Port Clarence, 53–54. Now Conservation Asst. (Antiquities), Dorman Museum, Middlesbrough. *Tees-side Music Society.*

105 **HESS, John Peter,** b. 17 May 34, son of the late N. Hess (OR SF 11). SF, 47³–52². Trinity, Cambridge, M.A. Company Director.

106 **MUIR, Andrew Gray,** b. 14 Feb. 34, eldest s. of W. E. G. Muir, W.S. SF, 47³–52¹. Magdalen, Oxford, B.A.; Edinburgh Univ., LL.B. Writer to the Signet. Solicitor. V.R.D. *New, Edinburgh.*

107 **OAKLEY, Nigel Wingate,** b. 6 Dec. 33, s. of W. G. Oakley, M.D., F.R.C.P. SF, 47³–52²; S. VIII, 50, 51, 52. Captain, 51, 52; Senior Scholarship; Leaving Exhibition. Major Scholarship to King's, Cambridge, M.A., M.B., B.Chir. University College Hospital Medical School, M.R.C.P. Physician. Senior Lecturer in Human Metabolism, St. Mary's Hospital Medical School, London. Represented Gt. Britain in small-bore rifle shooting, 55–60. Gold medal (prone position), World Rifle Championship, Moscow, 58.

108A **PORTER, Charles Antony,** b. 22 Mar. 34, younger s. of A. E. Porter, C.S.I., C.I.E. SF, 47³–52²; Scholar; Levée; Head of House; XV, 51; Capt. of Boxing, 51, 52. Scholar of Corpus Christi, Oxford, B.A. Schoolmaster, Institute Aufdem

Rosenberg St. Gallen, 57–58. Sutton Valence School, 59.

108B **PRIOR, Robert Stephen,** b. 16 June 33, s. of late R. M. Prior. SF, 47³–51²; Phillip's Prize, 51. R.M.A., Sandhurst. Self-employed. Late Royal Artillery.

109 **SHAW, Edward Nicholas,** b. 5 Apr. 34, eldest s. of J. F. St. G. Shaw (OR SF 17). SF, 47³–52². Trinity Hall, Cambridge. With Preece Cardew & Rider, Consulting Engineers. Brothers, 355 and 1008.

110 **STRONG, Michael Timothy,** b. 6 Jan. 34, younger s. of T. Strong (OR SF 14). SF, 47³–51³. Brother, P. Strong.

111 **SYMINGTON, Peter Howard,** b. 13 Jan. 34, younger s. of the late Col. K. W. Symington, T.D., D.L. (OR St 19). SF, 47³–52²; H. XI, 52. Trinity Hall, Cambridge, M.A. W. Symington & Co. Ltd., 58; Co. Sec., 61. Brother, K. M. Symington.

112 **ALDERSON, Jeffrey Gerald,** b. 7 June 34, youngest s. of the late G. G. Alderson, F.R.C.S. Sh, 47³–52². Gonville & Caius, Cambridge, M.A., A.R.I.C.S. Assistant with firm of Land Agents, Peckover Burrill & Owen, N. Wales, 57–58. Resident Sub-Agent on an Estate in Oxfordshire, 58–65. Member of the Executive Staff of Voluntary Service overseas since Dec. 65. *Alpine Ski Club.*

113 **BARTRAM, Robin Murray,** b. 11 Dec. 33, younger s. of Lt.-Col. R. A. Bartram, M.C., T.D. Sh, 47³–50³. Brother, G. C. Bartram.

114 **BERTHOUD, Roger Charles Tilston,** b. 15 Sept. 34, younger s. of Sir E. A. Berthoud, K.C.M.G. Sh, 47³–52²; Fives IV, 51, 52. N/S. R.A. Germany and Korea, 52–54. Trinity Hall, Cambridge, B.A. "Evening Standard" (diarist, feature writer and editor of "Londoner's Diary"), 59–67. "The Times" since 67 (founding editor of "Times Diary", correspondent in Bonn, chief correspondent Brussels). Brother, M. S. Berthoud.

115 **BRADSHAW, Haydon Leigh,** b. 9 Feb. 34, eldest s. of H. D. Bradshaw (OR W 23). Sh, 47³–51³. School of Economic Science. N/S. Rifle Brigade. Tea trade. Now tea and coffee specialist to the Nestlé Co. Ltd. Liveryman of Grocers Co. *Cobden Club.* Brothers, 499 and 1197.

116 **BRODBELT, Thomas Edward,** b. 1 Oct. 33, elder s. of the late T. W. B. Brodbelt. Sh, 47³–52². Fellow, Chartered Insurance Institute. Royal Insurance Co. Ltd., Liverpool. Brother, 861.

117 **HARRIS, Christopher Armitage,** b. 22 Aug. 33, eldest s. of M. W. A. Harris. Sh, 47³–51³. Royal Artillery, 52–62. Retired as Captain. One-year Agricultural Course, 62–63. Obtained N.C.A. Farmer. Brothers, 567 and 1762.

118 **LAYBOURNE, Alan James Burnett,** b. 4 June 34, s. of Rear-Admiral A. W. Laybourne, C.B., C.B.E. Sh, 47³–52¹. Qualified Submarine Commanding Officer. Commander, Royal Navy. Commanding Officer H.M.S. *Sovereign* (nuclear fleet submarine). *M.C.C., Friends of Durham Cathedral.*

119 **MORTON, Robert,** b. 15 Dec. 33, s. of R. Morton. Sh, 47³–52²; Levée; Head of House. Clare, Cambridge, B.A. Army, Short Service Commission 17th/21st Lancers, 53–59. Since then farming in Co. Wexford, Eire. *Cavalry Club, Kildare St. Club, Dublin.*

120 **PARKER, Rodney Kevan Hassard,** b. 12 Jan. 34, s. of L. Parker. Sh, 47³–52². Bristol Univ., M.B., Ch.B., D.R.C.O.G. General Practitioner, Bushey, Herts. Secretary, Watford Vocational Training Scheme for General Practice. *Moor Park Golf Club.*

121 **ROBERTS, Gilbert Howland Rookehurst,** b. 31 May 34, s. of Col. Sir T. L. H. Roberts, Bt., C.B.E., D.L. Sh, 47³–52², Sw. VIII, 52. Gonville & Caius, Cambridge, B.A., C.Eng., M.I.Mech.E. Manager, Advanced Products. Allied Ironfounders, Falkirk, Scotland, 8 yrs. Computer & Aero Space Inds., California, 6 yrs. Presently with Information Magnetics, 5743 Thornwood Drive, Goleta, Cal. 93017.

122 **YEARSLEY, Geoffrey Bradburn,** b. 26 July 34, s. of J. B. Yearsley. Sh, 47³–52². Articled, Peat Marwick Mitchell & Co., A.C.A., 58. Partner, Turquands, Barton Mayhew & Co., C.A. *St. James's Club, Manchester.*

123 **EAGAR, Michael Antony,** b. 20 Mar. 34, s. of the late Col. F. M. Eagar. St, 47³–52³; Scholar; XV, 52; XI, 50–52; H. XI, 51–52. Scholarship to Worcester, Oxford, B.A. Asst. Master, Eton Coll., 60–64. Ionian Bank (Investment Dept.),

64–67. Shrewsbury School since 67. Careers Master and Head of Economics, Shrewsbury School. *Vincent's Club.*

124 **GOODWIN, Richard Berry,** b. 13 Sept. 34, s. of L. F. H. Goodwin. St, 47³–52². Production Supervisor, British Home Entertainment Ltd. *Lansdowne Club.*

125 **HODGE, Michael Robert,** b. 24 Apr. 34, s. of Professor Sir W. V. D. Hodge, F.R.S. St, 47³–52². Pembroke, Cambridge, M.A.; Ridley Hall, Cambridge. Deacon, 59; Priest, 60. Vicar, Old St. George, Stalybridge, Cheshire, 62–67. Vicar, Cobham, Kent from 67. Proctor in Convocation of Canterbury, and Member of General Synod for Dio. of Rochester from 70.

126 **IONIDES, Christopher Luke,** b. 6 Nov. 33, s. of M. G. Ionides. St, 47³–51². Christ Church, Oxford. Advertising.

127 **KENT, James Michael,** b. 3 Mar. 34, s. of Sir H. S. Kent, G.C.B. (OR St 17). St, 47³–52². King's College, London, B.Sc. Royal Dutch Shell, 58; Petroleum Engineer with Compania Shell de Venezuela Ltd.; Chemical Engineer with Monsanto Chemicals Ltd., at Ruabon.

128 **LINDSAY, Henry Pooler Patrick,** b. 1 Nov. 33, elder s. of Brig. P. L. Lindsay. St, 47³–52². Queens', Cambridge, B.A. Picture Restorer. Appointed to lead British team working on flood-damaged pictures in Florence. Brother, 443.

129 **OWEN, Geoffrey David,** b. 16 Apr. 34, younger s. of the late L. G. Owen. St, 47³–52²; Scholar; Levée; Head of House; XV, 51. H. XI, 50, 51, 52; Tennis VI, 48–52, Capt. Scholarship to Balliol, Oxford, B.A.; Hockey Blue, 55, 56; Tennis Blue, 53–56. Assistant Editor, "The Financial Times".

130 **REID, Simon Eric Morton,** b. 6 Oct. 33, 2nd s. of Major N. Reid (OR St 19). St, 47³–51². Member, Institute of Purchasing and Supply. Purchasing staff of Unilever Ltd., London; temporarily attached to Unilever South Africa (Pty.) Ltd., Durban. *M.C.C., Point Yacht Club, Durban.*

131 **SELLORS, Patrick John Holmes,** b. 11 Feb. 34, s. of Sir T. H. Sellors, M.D., M.Chir., F.R.C.S. St, 47³–52². Oriel, Oxford, M.A., B.M., B.Ch. Middlesex Hospital, F.R.C.S.(Eng.). Consultant

Ophthalmic Surgeon to St. George's Hospital, London, Croydon Eye Unit. Royal Society of Medicine.

132 STRACHAN, Richard Alexander, b. 22 Mar. 34, younger s. of J. H. Strachan, M.C. St, 47^3–52^2. New College, Oxford, M.A. Partner of D. E. & J. Levy, Commercial Estate Agents, London, S.W.1. *Turf Club.*

133 WATT, John Robertson, b. 7 Sept, 34, youngest s. of R. C. Watt (A). St. 47^3–52^2. Balliol, Oxford, B.A.; Harvard Univ., M.A.; Columbia Univ., Ph.D. Member of American Historical Association, Association of Asian Studies. Asst. Professor, Massachusetts Institute of Technology, 67–68. Fellow in History, Johnston College, Univ. of Redlands since 68. Author, "The District Magistrate in Late Imperial China".

134 WILLS, Charles Julian, b. 20 Nov. 34, younger s. of the late C. H. A. Wills (OR St 13). St, 47^3–51^3. Dir. & Chairman of Cooper Wills Associates Ltd., Cooper Wills & Vantage Associates Ltd., Brusewitz & Wills Ltd.

135 BALFOUR, David, b. 30 Jan. 34, elder s. of J. S. Balfour. Tu, 47^3–51^3; Scholar; State Scholarship. Exhibition to Gonville & Caius, Cambridge, M.A., M.I.E.R.E. Decca Radar (Engineer). Now Manager, Filter Division, Vernitron, Thornhill, Southampton.

136 CHAPLIN, Malcolm Hilbery, b. 17 Jan. 34, s. of Sir G. F. Chaplin, C.B.E., J.P. Tu, 47^3–52^2; Levée; Head of House; XV, 49–51; XXII, 52; Athletics Cup; Junior, 49; Senior, 52; record for ¼ mile and equalled record 220 yds.; Cadet Officer, 51. Trinity Hall, Cambridge, M.A.; Athletics Blue, 56 & 57. F.R.I.C.S. Surveyor, Jones, Lang, Wootton, 57–61. Partner, Hilbery Chaplin & Co., Chartered Surveyors, Romford, Essex since 61. *Hawks Club, Cambridge, United Oxford & Cambridge University Club.*

137 LLOYD, Richard Hey, b. 25 June 33, s. of the late C. Y. Lloyd. Tu, 47^3–51^3; Music Scholar. Organ Scholar of Jesus, Cambridge, M.A., B.Mus., F.R.C.O., A.R.C.M. Asst. Organist of Salisbury Cathedral, 57–66. Organist & Master of the Choristers at Hereford Cathedral since 66.

138 McCLAY, Robert David, b. 2 July 33, younger s. of R. McClay. Tu,

47^3–49^3. Sons, Carey King, Tu, 71^1– and Robert Brian, Tu, 73^2–.

139 SALLITT, Timothy William Baines, b. 21 Mar. 34, eldest s. of Brig. W. B. Sallitt, O.B.E. (OR Tu 20). Tu, 47^3–51^2. Bradford, Johannesburgh & Borough Technical Colleges, F.I.W.M. Director, Hawker Siddeley Electric Ltd.; Managing Director, Brush Transformers. *East India, & Sports & Public Schools.*

140 YATES, Stephen Richard Barry, b. 30 Apr. 34, s. of the late J. C. Yates. Tu, 47^3–52^2.

141 CARRUTHERS, John Lawson, b. 21 Jan. 34, s. of H. W. Carruthers. W, 47^3–52^1; Cap, 50. R.M.A., Sandhurst; Staff College, Camberley. A.I.B., A.M.B.I.M., A.D.C. to Governor of Singapore, 58–59. Served in 2nd K.E.O. Gurkha Rifles from 54–70 and retired as Major. Now in Barclays Bank International Ltd. *Naval and Military Club, Piccadilly.*

142 COBB, David Gerald, b. 26 Apr. 34, elder s. of Cdr. J. Cobb, R.N. (retired). W, 47^3–52^2. Journalist (Aberdeen, London, Calgary & Toronto), now Canadian Broadcasting Corporation. Brother, 915.

143 DELACAVE, Jacques Theodore Louis, b. 27 Aug. 33, s. of P. Delacave. W, 47^3–51^2. Trinity, Cambridge, B.A.; Freiburg Univ.; Columbia Univ., N.Y. Bank de Bruxelles, Brussels, 59. Deputy Economic Adviser, 61.

144 EAVES, Elliott Weir, b. 8 Jan. 30, elder s. of E. W. Eaves of N.Y. W, 47^3–48^2.

145 EWING, John Frederick, b. 10 May 34, s. of B. G. Ewing. W, 47^3–52^2.

146 GREANY, John Martin, b. 31 Jan. 34, 2nd s. of H. W. Greany, C.B.E. (OR W 14). W, 47^3–48^1. Left for health reasons. Went to Harrow, 48^2–52^2. R.M.A., Sandhurst. Joined Wilts. Regiment, 55. Staff College, Camberley, 65. p.s.c. A.C.I.S. Army Officer. Brother, 1661.

147 HAMILTON, Andrew John Gailey, b. 2 Feb. 34, s. of R. A. G. Hamilton, M.D. W, 47^3–52^1. Corpus Christi, Cambridge, B.A. Solicitor, admitted 61. *Richmond Hockey Club, The Grannies Cricket Club.*

148 HASLAM, James Raymond, b. 24 Mar. 34, eldest s. of J. Haslam, M.B., Ch.B., F.R.C.S.W, 47^3–52^2. S.VIII, 50–52. College of Technology, Dundee, C.Eng., M.I.Mech.E. Director, J. J. Haslam Ltd. and Haslams (S.M.W.) Ltd., Bolton. Brother, 455.

149 HASLAM, The Rev. Robert John Alexander, b. 31 Aug. 34, elder s. of Rev. J. A. G. Haslam, M.C., D.F.C. (OR W 10). W, 47^3–52^3; Levée; Head of House. Corpus Christi, Cambridge, B.A. College of the Resurrection, Mirfield. Ordained, 60. Brother, 733.

150 STEPHENSON, Patrick Tinsley, b. 10 Mar. 34, younger s. of S. Stephenson. W, 47^3–52^2; XXII, 51, 52. Clare, Cambridge, M.A. Director George Harker & Co. Ltd. *M.C.C.*

151 WOODHOUSE, Robin Clayton, b. 29 Apr. 34, eldest s. of L. C. Woodhouse (OR W 16). W, 47^3–52^2; XXII, 52; H. XI, 52. St. John's, Cambridge, M.A., M.I.C.E. Civil Engineer. Presently with Sir Alexander Gibb & Partners, working in hydroelectric schemes in Patagonia, Argentine.

ENTRANCES IN JANUARY 1948

152 ADDIS, William Stewart, b. 22 Mar. 34, 2nd s. of H. E. Sir William Addis, K.B.E., C.M.G. (OR SH 16). SH, 48^1–52^1. Accountant, Hong Kong and Shanghai Banking Corporation (Jakarta). Brothers, 1367 and 1663.

153 JEFFREY, John William, b. 30 May 34, s. of W. G. Jeffrey, C.A. SH, 48^1–52^2; Levée; Head of House; Tennis VI, 52. Exhibition to Clare, Cambridge. Solicitor. Partner with Shacklocks & Ashton Hill, Solicitors, Nottingham.

154 LLOYD-DAVIES, Reginald Wyndham, b. 24 June 34, s. of Dr. A. W. Lloyd-Davies. SH, 48^1–52^2. Univ. of London. St. Thomas's Medical School, M.B., F.R.C.S., M.S. Consultant Surgeon to St. Thomas's Hospital, Department of Urology. Adviser to the Dean at St. Thomas's Hospital Medical School for the Pre-Registration Year. Fellow of the Royal Society of Medicine. Member of the British Association of Urological Surgeons. *Junior Carlton Club.*

155 NEILL, John Whitley, b. 15 May 34, s. of Lt.-Col. F. H. Neill (OR SH 12). SH, 48^1–52^2; H. XI, 52; Tennis Team,

51, 52. F.C.A. N/S. 2nd Lt. R.A. 20th Field Regt., 58–60. Director, Greenall Whitley & Co. Ltd., Warrington, 60–70. Since 70 own property company. Non-Executive Director since 62 of Mackie & Co. Ltd., Warrington. Guardian newspaper series. *Bowden Hockey Club, Mere Golf Club.* England and Great Britain Hockey International, 58–68. Three Olympics—Rome, Tokyo, Mexico. Capt. at Mexico. Most caps for G.B., 56.

156 CLARKE, John Neil, b. 7 Aug. 34, s. of G. P. Clarke. T, 48^1–52^2. King's Coll., London University, LL.B., F.C.A. Partner, Rowley Pemberton Roberts & Co., Chartered Accountants, 60–69. Director, Charter Consolidated Ltd., and other companies, 69.

157 DEZELSKI, Desmond Ernest, b. 4 July 34, s. of E. S. Dezelski. T, 48^1–52^3; Minor Foundationer. Associate of the Institute of Quality Surveyors, 60. Surveyor Manager, J. Jerrard & Sons Ltd., 63.

158 THOMAS,   David   Hendry Gwynne, b. 28 Jan. 35, eldest s. of R. G. Thomas. T, 48^1–51^2.

159 REDFEARN, Auberon, b. 10 Aug. 34, s. of Mrs. Elsie Redfearn and 2nd son of the late A. H. Redfearn. B, 48^1–52^2; Leaving Exhibition; State Scholar; W. Riding C.C. Scholarship. Trinity Hall, Cambridge, M.A. Scientific Officer (Blood Transfusion Service, Leeds), 62–70. Trinity Hall, 70–72. College Foundation Scholarship, B.A.(Med.Sc.), St. Bartholomew's Hospital Medical College from 72. Medical Student.

160 FENWICK, Peter Trevor, b. 26 Jan. 35, 2nd s. of J. F. T. Fenwick, J.P. C, 48^1–52^2. Regular Army, 14th/20th Kings Hussars, 52–59. Retired with rank of Capt. Director of Fenwick Ltd., Managing Director of Fenwick of Bond St., Ltd. since 59. *Cavalry Club, Northern Counties Club.* Brothers, J. J. Fenwick and 537.

161 PURSSELL, David John Lyon, b. 30 June 34, elder s. of the late F. J. Purssell. C, 48^1–52^3. Shell Petroleum Co. Ltd., 55–59; Shell Co. of Malta Ltd., 59; Kenya Shell Ltd., 59–64; Shell Co. of Hong Kong Ltd., 64–68; Shell Philippines Inc., 68–71; Shell International Petroleum Co. Ltd. since 71. Brother, 1669.

162 **ANDREWS, John Ryton,** b. 3 Sept. 34, s. of the late J. L. Andrews (OR C 07). K, 48^1–53^2; Levee; Head of House; Cadet Officer, 53. N/S. 2nd Lt. Devon Regiment, 54–55. Peterhouse, Cambridge, M.A. King's Coll., London Univ. (P.G.C.E.). Teaching, 59–69. Professional Numismatist and at present in University Library, Exeter Univ.

163 **BROWN, Peter Michael,** b. 11 July 34, elder s. of the late M. G. H. Brown (OR K 21). K, 48^1–52^2. F.C.A., M.I.P.M., M.M.R.S. Chairman, Synergy Holdings, New Opportunity Press, Bevan Group. *Junior Carlton Club.* Brother, 468A.

164 **CUNLIFFE, Jerome James,** b. 2 Aug. 34, s. of J. W. Cunliffe, L.D.S. M, 48^1–52^2. Liverpool Univ., Bachelor of Dental Surgery. Self-employed.

165 **DOHERTY, Christopher George,** b. 21 Aug. 34, younger s. of W. D. Doherty, M.Ch., F.R.C.S. M, 48^1–52^1; XV, 51. Lt. Royal Artillery, 54. Eaton International Inc., Zug, Switzerland; Resident in Johannesburg since 63 as Manager, Southern Africa Territories. *Bryanston Country Club, Transvaal, R.S.A.* Brother, H. D. Doherty.

166 **MORTON, John Richard,** b. 8 Aug. 34, elder s. of H. J. Morton. M, 48^1–52^3. London County Scholarship and Entrance Exhibition to Jesus, Cambridge, M.A. Agricultural Research Council Research Studentship. Appointed Hon. Genetic Adviser to Advisory Committee for T. Wall & Sons Ltd., Pig Progeny Testing Station, 62. Ph.D., 63. Snr. Asst. in Research in Animal Genetics at Dept. of Applied Biology, Cambridge, 65 and Teaching of Animal Genetics since 66. Many publications on the subject. Extended N/S. Commission in 7th Q.O. Hussars, 53–55. Served in Germany and Hong Kong.

167 **OLIVER, Francis Geoffrey,** b. 1 Apr. 34, elder s. of Admiral Sir G. N. Oliver, G.B.E., K.C.B., D.S.O. (OR SF 11). SF, 48^1–48^2. To Gordonstoun School. Farming.

168 **SMITH, John Anton** (changed name by deed poll to J. Anton-Smith), b. 30 June 34, s. of R. W. Smith (OR T 11). SF, 48^1–52^2. Gonville & Caius, Cambridge, B.A. (Dip. Agric.); Bristol, Cert. Ed.; Imperial Coll., Trinidad, D.T.A.; Reading, 62–63. Agronomist with Zambian Govt., 59–71. Attempting to be a writer on horticultural subjects, 71. Building up a nursery business.

169 **STAVELEY, Nicholas Tom,** b. 21 Mar. 34, younger s. of T. Staveley, T.D. SF, 48^1–52^2. Advertising Agent, J. Walter Thompson & Co. Ltd., London.

170 **WHINNEY, Frederick John Golden,** b. 14 July 34, elder s. of the late E. F. G. Whinney (OR C 12). SF, 48^1–52^3. N/S. R.N.V.R., 53–54. S/Lt. Resigned as Lt., 60. Chartered Accountant, admitted 60. Partner in Whinney Murray & Co., Chartered Accountants, since 64. *M.C.C., City of London Club.*

171 **TILLEY, Wendon Marshall Graham,** b. 27 May 34, s. of E. G. Tilley (OR C 14). Sh, 48^1–51^3. Accountant, British Caledonian Airways. *M.C.C.*

172 **COGHLAN, Terence Granville,** b. 10 May 34, s. of G. B. Coghlan (OR Tu 21). Tu, 48^1–52^3; Leveé; XV, 51, 52; Cadet Officer, 52. Borneo Company Ltd. (Shipping), in Far East, 54–57. Seafield School, 57. Joint Headmaster, 60. Financial Adviser. *East India, Sports & Public Schools Club.* Son, Anthony James, Tu, 71^2–.

173 **LOVELL, Charles Nelson,** b. 14 July 34, 2nd s. of Lt.-Col. H. O. Lovell (OR Tu 16), 48^1–52^2. Oriel, Oxford, B.A.; Wycliffe Hall, Oxford. Ordained, 59 at Lichfield. Vicar of Esh and Hamsteels, Langley Park, Nr. Durham since 67.

174 **HUNT, Capt. Robert Alastair,** R.A., b. 15 July 34, elder s. of R. T. Hunt. W, 48^1–52^2; Scholar; XV, 51; XI, 50, 51; H. XI, 50–52 (Capt.). N/S. R.A. Commission. Regular Commission, R.A., 55. Capt., 61. Brother, 371.

175 **MACKIE, Richard Geraty,** b. 22 July 34, 2nd s. of the late J. H. M. Mackie (OR W 07). W, 48^1–52^2. Nottingham Univ., B.A. Advertising and Marketing. Current employment, Beecham Foods. Brother, 653.

176 **BEATTIE, Michael Holden,** b. 10 Nov. 34, eldest s. of Capt. S. H. Beattie, V.C., R.N. (OR SH 22). SH, 48^2–51^3. Brother, 2005.

177 FAWCETT, Thomas, b. 31 Oct. 34, elder s. of R. J. Fawcett, F.C.A. (OR SH 20). SH, 48^2–53^2. St. John, Cambridge; Balliol, Oxford. Research & Development Officer, J. Glixten & Sons Ltd., Market Harborough. Brother, 515.

178 PETTIT, Donald Richard, b. 20 Aug. 34, 3rd s. of C. S. Pettit (OR SH 17). SH, 48^2–52^2; XV, 51; Sw. VIII, 50, 51, 52. Harper Adams, Agricultural Coll., Shropshire. Director & Plantation Manager, Parnol (Nigeria) Ltd., part of Plantation Group, Unilever Ltd. *Liphook Golf Club.*

179 COCKE, John, b. 4 Nov. 34, s. of K. J. R. Cocke. T, 48^2–53^2. Clare, Cambridge, B.A. Director of Market Research & Public Relations. *R.A.F. Club.*

180 HEWITT, Timothy, b. 28 May 35, s. of W. Hewitt. T, 48^2–53^2. Oxford, M.A., A.C.A. Partner in Miles Watson, Gow, and Ford, Chartered Accountants, Bournemouth.

181 HOLLOMBY, Barry, b. 27 Jan. 33, younger s. of C. Hollomby. T, 48^2–52^1. John Holt & Co., Liverpool. Asst. Agent, Nigeria, 57. Manager, 61.

182 LUNT, Peter Cowley Winstanley, b. 24 May 35, younger s. of J. W. Lunt. T, 48^2–52^2. F.C.A. Secretary, Halmatic Ltd.

183 WHITWORTH, Arthur John, b. 19 Apr. 35, younger s. of Dr. A. B. Whitworth. T, 48^2–54^2; Levée; Head of House; Hodson Memorial Prize. St. Catherine's, Cambridge, M.A. M.B., B.Chir. The London Hospital, Whitechapel. D.R.C.O.G. General Medical Practitioner.

184 HOGBEN, Jeremy Geoffrey Harwood, b. 21 Oct. 34, younger s. of S. J. Hogben, C.B.E. B, 48^2–53^2. Cambridge, M.A.; Kingston (Dip.Arch.), A.R.I.B.A. Partner in Hubbard Ford & Partners, Architects, London. *M.C.C., Brooks's Club.*

185 HOOPER, Arthur John Stanbury, b. 8 Sept. 34, s. of J. S. Hooper. B, 48^2–52^3; Senior Scholarship, 51; State Scholarship, 51; Cap, 52. Scholarship to Clare, Cambridge, B.A. Distillers Co. Ltd., 60. Production Manager, Dagenham Factory, 62.

186 MITCALFE, Alan Hugh, b. 27 July 34, younger s. of the late W. S. Mitcalfe, M.C. B, 48^2–52^2. Brasenose, Oxford, B.A. Solicitor. Marketing Director with The Glenlivet Distillers Ltd., in charge of European Sales. *Cavalry Club.*

187 RAINE, George Edward Thompson, b. 1 Aug. 34, s. of R. T. Raine, M.C., M.A., M.B., B.Chir. B, 48^2–52^2. Emmanuel, Cambridge, M.A., M.B., B.Chir. St. Thomas's Hospital Medical School, F.R.C.S. Capt., R.A.M.C. (Short Service Commission), 60–63. Subsequently Orthopaedic Surgery. Fellow, Royal Society of Medicine. Assoc., British Orthopaedic Association.

188 FERGUSSON, Malcolm Lyon, b. 24 Dec. 34, youngest s. of I. V. L. Fergusson. C, 48^2–53^2. Pembroke, Cambridge, M.A., M.B., B.Chir. St. Thomas's Hospital, London, D.Obst.R.C.O.G. General Practice.

189 FLOREY, Charles du Vé, b. 11 Sept. 34, s. of Sir H. W. Florey, M.D., Ph.D., F.R.S. C, 48^2–53^1; Levée; Head of House. Gonville & Caius, Cambridge, B.A., M.B., B.Ch.; Yale Univ., M.R.C. Epidemiological Research Unit, Mona, Kingston, W.I.

190 SAMUELSON, Martin, b. 15 Aug. 34, s. of G. M. Samuelson (OR C 19). C, 48^2–52^2. St. John's, Cambridge, M.A. Spooner Dryer Eng. Co. Ltd., Ilkley, Yorks.

191 WYLIE, James Colin, b. 2 Sept. 34, s. of the late J. Wylie. C, 48^2–52^2; Cap, 51. Managing Director of Reckitt & Colman (Rhodesia) (Pvt) Ltd. *Royal Salisbury Golf Club, Parkview Golf Club, Johannesburg.*

192 JOHNS, Michael Philip, b. 29 Nov. 34, s. of Cdr. P. L. Johns, R.N. K, 48^2–53^1.

193 MORLEY, Marcus John Owen, b. 19 Aug. 34, s. of C. O. Morley. K, 48^2–53^2. Managing Director, Postans Ltd., Birmingham.

194 BATTY, Michael George, b. 14 Sept. 34, younger s. of W. H. Batty. M, 48^2–52^2; Cap, 51. N/S. 14th/20th King's Hussars. Partner in Thompson Lloyd & Ewart, Tea Brokers. *Oriental Club.*

195 BRYANT, Peter William, b. 18 July 34, s. of the late C. S. D. Bryant,

M, 48^2–52^2; S.VIII, 50, 52. Clare, Cambridge, M.A., M.I.Mech.E., C.Eng. Graduate Apprenticeship, C. A. Parsons & Co. Ltd. Production Engineer, Production Manager, Operations Manager, Baker Perkins Ltd.

196 **WILLIAMS, David Richard,** b. 29 Nov. 34, s. of D. O. Williams, M.B.E. (OR M 20). M, 48^2–53^2.

197 **BOYD, Nicholas Robert Hawker,** b. 9 Oct. 34, elder s. of R. H. Boyd, F.R.C.S. SF, 48^2–53^2. Brother, 639.

198 **HARDMAN, James Adrian William Innes,** b. 9 Sept. 34, eldest s. of Air Chief Marshal Sir J. D. I. Hardman, G.B.E., K.C.B., D.F.C. SF, 48^2–52^2; Cap, 51. N/S. 13th/18th Hussars. Marine Underwriter at Lloyd's. *Cavalry Club.*

199 **McKERRON, Colin Gordon,** b. 8 Sept. 34, s. of Sir P. A. B. McKerron, K.B.E., C.M.G. SF, 48^2–52^2. Charing Cross Hospital Medical School (Univ. of London), M.B., B.S., F.R.C.P. Sen. Lecturer in Medicine & Honorary Consultant Physician, King's College Hospital, London, S.E.5. Royal Society of Medicine.

200 **MEDLICOTT, John Alexander Sadler,** b. 23 July 34, s. of S. J. E. Medlicott. SF, 48^2–52.

201 **BARRON, Julian Nigel Fraser,** b. 9 Aug. 34, younger s. of the late Col. J. Barron, M.C. (OR Tu 12). Sh, 48^2–52^1. Special entry to Dartmouth. Specialised in Aircraft Direction & Navigation. Served in Korea Campaign. Lt. R.N. Died 11 Oct. 61 in a diving accident at H.M. Dockyard, Rosyth.

202 **DEAN, John Trevor,** b. 24 Apr. 35, s. of H. W. Dean. Sh, 48^2–53^2. Gonville & Caius, Cambridge, M.A. Messrs. H. W. Dean & Son, 61.

203 **DENIS-SMITH, Derek,** b. 14 Mar. 35, s. of C. D. Denis-Smith. Sh, 48^2–53^2. Gonville & Caius, M.A., M.B., B.Chir. Guy's Hospital, D.Obst. R.C.O.G. Medical Practitioner.

204 **GILCHRIST, Alastair Ogilvie,** b. 8 July 34, 2nd s. of A. Gilchrist, M.B., B.Ch. Sh, 48^2–52^3; Levée; Head of House; Basil Johnston Cup, 52. Scholarship to Trinity Hall, Cambridge, M.A. Churchill College, Ph.D. British Railways Research Department. Joined Dynamics Section, 64. Latterly responsible for Research & Development aspects of "Advanced Passenger Train". *Derby Music Club* (Committee).

205 **MILNER, Nigel Andrew,** b. 30 Nov. 34, s. of S. M. Milner, M.B., F.R.C.S. (OR T 15). Sh, 48^2–53^2. University of Liverpool, B.V.Sc., M.R.C.V.S. Biological Research, Pharmaceutical Industry. Member of British Veterinary Assoc.

206 **REEVES, Michael Clive,** b. 1 Aug. 34, s. of Lt.-Col. G. C. Reeves. Sh, 48^2–52^2. 1 yr. at Royal Military College of Canada. N/S. Instrument Fitter R.A.F., then Commerce. Currently self-employed Company Director.

207 **ABBOTT, Jonathan Hart Colleer,** b. 1 Sept. 34, elder s. of H. H. Abbott. St, 48^2–52^2. St John's, Cambridge, M.A. A.M.I.P.A. (Television). Trainee, J. Walter Thompson Co. Ltd.; Producer, John Hobson & Partners; Senior Producer, Ogilvy and Mather; Associate Creative Director, Pritchard Wood & Partners; Partner, Rupert Chetwynd & Partners. *The Game Conservancy.*

208 **LAWLEY, Richard Henry,** b. 27 Oct. 34, s. of T. H. Lawley. St, 48^2–52^3; Cap, 52. Magdalen, Oxford. Managing Director, Westbrook Fabrics Ltd., 61.

209 **MACKENZIE, Alexander Ian,** b. 25 Oct. 34, elder s. of Lt.-Col. A. U. MacKenzie, M.B.E., R.A.O.C. St, 48^2–52^2. R.M.A., Sandhurst. Royal Military College of Science, Shrivenham. Staff College, Camberley, p.s.c. Instructor in Germany. Commissioned Royal Artillery, 55. Technical Officer, R.R.E., Malvern, 63–65. Deputy Assistant Adjutant General, Malta, 69–71. Second in Command, 12 Lt. A.D. Regiment, R.A. since 71. Captain.

210 **WILSON, Michael John Francis Thomond,** b. 9 Sept. 34, elder s. of M. T. Wilson, M.B.E. (OR St 24). St, 48^2–52^3. Oriel, Oxford. Solicitor (admitted 61). Brother, 581.

211 **LEGGE, Martin Joseph,** b. 9 Oct. 34, s. of J. E. Legge. Tu, 48^2–53^1; Levée; Head of House; Cap, 52. Director, Central Arcade, Wolverhampton, Ltd.; J. Legge & Co. Ltd.

212 **ROBERTS, John Richard Lloyd,** b. 18 Jan. 35, s. of R. S. Roberts, F.R.C.V.S., F.C.Path. Tu, 48^2–53^2. Peterhouse, Cambridge, M.B., B.Chir. West-

minster Hospital, M.R.C.S., L.R.C.P. General Practitioner. Clinical Assistant, Brompton & Westminster Hospitals. Senior Examiner, Scottish Widows Fund. Adviser on Windward Islands to Save the Children Fund. *Hurlingham, St. Lucia Yacht Club.*

213 WALL, Edward Llewellyn Vernon, b. 30 Nov. 34, s. of E. Wall, M.C., F.I.C.E. Tu, 48^2–53^2. S. VIII, 51–52, Capt., 53; Cadet Officer, 52–53. Royal Military Academy, Sandhurst. Fitzwilliam House, Cambridge, M.A. p.s.c. (Shrivenham & Camberley). Army Officer. Commissioned, R.E., Feb. 55. Specially employed, Federation of Malaysia, 61–64. Officer Commanding 25 Field Squadron, R.E., 69–71. Promoted to Major, 67. Awarded Malaysian "Ahli Maugku Negara", 64. Son, Anthony Ernest James, Tu, 73^1–.

214 RUSSELL, Arthur Christie, b. 8 Dec. 34, 3rd (twin) s. of A. H. Russell, M.R.C.S., L.R.C.P. (OR W 17). W, 48^2–53^2. Brothers, P. H. Russell & 215.

215 RUSSELL, Nicholas Christie, b. 8 Dec. 34, 2nd (twin) s. of A. H. Russell, M.R.C.S., L.R.C.P. (OR W 17). W, 48^2–52^2. Brothers, P. H. Russell & 214.

216 WRIGHT, Talbot Alexander Kemp, b. 16 July 34, s. of A. A. K. Wright. W, 48^2–52^3. S. VIII, Capt., 52. Pembroke, Cambridge, B.A.; Half Blue, Match Rifle Shooting. Member of British Institute of Managers. Paper Industry: British Paper and Board Industry Research Assoc., 56–67. R. & W. Watson Ltd., Production Manager and Technical Director, 67–71. Managing Director, Brittains-Arborfield Ltd., from 71. Managing Director, Brittains (Paper) Ltd., Jan. 72. *Climbers Club, North London Rifle Club.*

SIR ARTHUR (FREDERIC BROWNLOW) FFORDE (O.R.) Elected Headmaster in September 1948

ENTRANCES IN SEPTEMBER 1948

217 BOND, Peter Robert Michael, b. 26 Apr. 35, elder s. of Cdr. M. M. Bond. SH, 48^3–53^2. Qualified as Solicitor, 59.

218 COOPER, Patrick Ernest, b. 27 Mar. 35, younger s. of the late S. R. Cooper, M.C. (OR SH 09). SH, 48^3–53^1. N/S. West Yorkshire Regt. 2nd Lt. (1 yr. in

Malaya). Chartered Accountant. 10 yrs., Cooper Brothers & Co., Chartered Accountants. Chairman, Clive Holdings Ltd., and Clive Discount Co. Ltd. *Royal Ashdown Forest Golf Club.*

219 FINBURGH, Samuel Philip (name changed to Phillips, Philip King), b. 14 Sept. 35, s. of N. Finburgh. SH, 48^3–49^3. Joined Snell & Co., Tobacconists, 53; Dir., 55; Man. Dir., 59; Chairman, 61. Chairman & Man. Dir., The Southerner Co. Ltd., & Saglere Ltd., 63.

220 GESSLER, Henry, b. 7 Sept. 34, s. of H. Gessler. SH, 48^3–52^3; Scholar; S. VIII, 51, 52. New Coll., Oxford, M.A. Venezuela, 58–60. Asst. Export Manager, Jaguar Cars, 61–63. Man. Director, Pedoka Ltd., Importers of Electronic Components.

221 HOLLAND, Henry Christopher, b. 21 July 34, younger s. of the late Maj.-Gen. J. C. F. Holland, C.B., D.F.C. (OR SH 11). SH, 48^3–53^1; Scholar; Levée; Head of House; Scholar of Gonville & Caius, Cambridge, B.A. Qualified as Solicitor, 61.

222 HUTCHINGS, Graham John Balfour, b. 4 Oct. 34, s. of G. B. Hutchings, C.M.G. SH, 48^3–52^1. Qualified as Solicitor, 57. Partner in Lovell White & King, 61.

223 McNEIL, Ian Reddie, b. 24 Apr. 35, s. of Capt. J. R. McNeil. SH, 48^3–53^2. Queens', Cambridge, 1st Class (Engineering). English Electric Co., 58–60; Marconi Instruments, 60–62; Production Engineering Ltd., Management Consultants, 63. *R.A.C.*

224 MAILER, Colin McGregor, b. 17 Mar. 35, s. of R. Mailer, M.D., M.S., F.R.C.S. SH, 48^3–53^2; Levée; Head of House; R. VIII, 53. Edin. Univ. Medical School, Moorfields Eye Hospital, M.B., Ch.B.(Ed.), M.R.C.P.(Glas.), F.R.C.S. (C.), D.O., R.C.P. & S., E.C.F.M.G., L.M.C.C. General Medical Council Principal List. Ophthalmologist in practice at London, Ontario (Canada). Courtesy Specialist staff, Victoria and St. Joseph Hospitals, London, Ontario. Fellow, Royal Society of Medicine. Fellow, American Academy of Ophthalmology & Otolaryngology.

225 MOULSON, David, b. 14 Feb. 35, s. of N. Moulson, M.D. SH, 48^3–52^2. Admitted Solicitor, 57.

226 **RAISMAN, Jeremy Philip,** b. 6 Mar. 35, younger s. of Sir J. Raisman, G.C.M.G., G.C.I.E., K.C.S.I. SH, 48³–53². Solicitor, 59. Partner, Jacques & Co., London.

227 **REYNELL, Nicholas,** b. 8 Jan. 35, younger s. of Cdr. R. Reynell, R.N. SH, 48³–51². R.M.A., Sandhurst. Commissioned into the Royal Norfolk Regt., 55. Transferred to the Royal Army Ordnance Corps., 65. Regular Officer, Army.

228 **DAVIS, Alan,** b. 5 Oct. 34, s. of C. Davis. T, 48³–53². Birmingham Univ., B.Sc. Principal Lecturer, Newland Park College of Education.

229 **GILES, Gordon Francis Arthur,** b. 1 Apr. 35, s. of A. H. Giles. T, 48³–51³. International Correspondence Schools, Advertising. M.A.A., M.I.A.M.A. Publicity Manager.

230 **KNIGHT, Peter Charles,** b. 21 Feb. 35, s. of C. A. Knight. T, 48³–52³; S. VIII, 51, 52. School of Accountancy. Associate of Institute of Cost & Management Accountants; Associate of Institute of Chartered Secretaries and Administrators. Management Accountant, G.E.C. Turbine Generators Ltd. of Rugby. F.R.H.S.

231 **MOORE, John Michael,** b. 12 Dec. 35, elder s. of R. Moore. T, 48³–54²; Major Foundationer; Jex-Blake Leaving Exhibition. Scholarship to Clare, Cambridge. G.C.W.Warr Research Scholar, 57, Ph.D., M.A. Asst. Master, Winchester Coll., 60–64. Asst. Master, Radley Coll. since 64. Head of Classics Dept. from 66. Junior Fellow, Center for Hellenic Studies, Washington, D.C., U.S.A., 70–71. Sundry Publications.

232 **STANFORD, Adrian Timothy James,** b. 19 July 35, youngest s. of The Ven. Archdeacon L. J. Stanford. T, 48³–53²; Tancred Scholarship; State Scholar. Merton, Oxford, B.A. Samuel Montagu & Co., Merchant Bankers. Brothers, J. R. & J. G. Stanford.

233 **BARRACLOUGH, David Bruce George,** b. 29 Jan. 35, s. of F. Barraclough, C.B.E. B, 48³–53². Queen's, Oxford, M.A. Operating Officer, British Rail, Doncaster Division, Eastern Region, B.R.

234 **BELLWOOD, David Power** (formerly Franklin, D. P.), b. 31 Jan. 35, elder s. of H. J. Franklin, A.R.I.B.A. B, 48³–52².

235 **BULMER, James Esmond,** M.P., b. 19 May 35, eldest s. of the late E. C. Bulmer. B, 48³–53³; Cap, 53; Cadet Officer, 53. King's, Cambridge, B.A.; Sorbonne, Paris. Director, H. P. Bulmer Ltd. Conservative M.P., Kidderminster, 74. *Boodle's.* Brother, 529.

236 **HARRIS, Simon John Minshaw,** b. 24 Aug. 35, elder s. of the late H. J. M. Harris. B, 48³–52²; Music Scholar. Guildhall School of Music, London; Merton Coll., Oxford, M.A., B.Mus., Hon. A.R.A.M. Junior Research Fellow, Merton College, 57–59. Lecturer in Musical Composition, Univ. of Sydney (N.S.W.), 59–63. Appointed to professorial staff, Royal Academy of Music, 63. Composers' Guild. Brother, 533.

237 **HART, George Philip Parkins,** b. 18 Feb. 35, 2nd s. of Sir W. O. Hart, C.M.G., J.P. (OR B 17). B, 48³–53². New College, Oxford, B.A. Solicitor, 61. Group Secretary, The Bath & Portland Group Limited. Brother, 1265.

238 **HOPE-SIMPSON, Anthony Robert,** b. 11 Apr. 35, 3rd s. of J. W. Hope-Simpson, M.D., M.R.C.P., M.M.S.A., J.P. B, 48³–54¹; Scholar; Levée; Head of House; Stubbs Cup for Music. Classical Scholar of Balliol, Oxford.

239 **MARSHALL, Nigel Bernard Dickenson,** b. 9 Apr. 35, s. of N. D. Marshall. B, 48³–53². Queens', Cambridge, LL.B., M.A. Solicitor. Partner in Underwood & Co. of London and Miller & Co. of Cambridge. *Oriental, Pitt Club.*

240 **TYLER, Richard Henry Coultas,** b. 7 Dec. 34, s. of Col. H. W. H. Tyler, M.C., T.D., D.L. B, 48³–53². Queens', Cambridge, B.A. Managing Director, John Tyler & Sons Ltd.

241 **WILLIAMSON, Charles James Francis Lloyd,** b. 4 Apr. 35, elder s. of the late J. C. F. L. Williamson, M.D., F.R.C.S. (OR B 18). B, 48³–53². Emmanuel, Cambridge, B.A., M.B., B.Chir. St. Bartholomew's Hospital, London, M.R.C.S., L.R.C.P., D.A., D.Obst.R.C.O.G. General Practitioner, Horley, Surrey.

242 **BLUNT, Christopher Graham,** b. 7 July 35, eldest s. of A. G. Blunt, V.R.D. (OR C 23). C, 48³–53². Queensland Univ.,

B.Ag.Sc.; Post Graduate Honours in Agrostology. Investigating Animal Production from irrigated tropical pastures with Commonwealth Scientific and Industrial Research Organisation. Australian Institute of Agricultural Science. Brothers, 1123 and 1374.

243 BOURNE, Henry Graham Stanley, b. 13 Feb. 35, elder s. of H. R. Bourne (OR C 19). C, 48^3–53^2. N/S. Royal Navy. S/Lt. A.C.A. Partner, Laurence Prust & Co., Stockbrokers. Liveryman, Grocers Company. *Royal St. Georges G.C., The Bath Club.* Brother, 1877.

244 DAY, James Trelawny, b. 19 Apr. 35, s. of the late Lt.-Cdr. H. T. Day. C, 48^3–53^2. Trinity Hall, Cambridge, M.A., G.I.Mech.E. Computer Executive, International Computers Ltd., Stevenage. Lt., Royal Naval Reserve (Retired). *Haileybury Squash Rackets Club.*

245 FANSHAWE, Hew George, b. 12 June 35, s. of Major-General G. D. Fanshawe, C.B., D.S.O., O.B.E. C, 48^3–53^3; Levée; Head of House; State Scholarship; School Leaving Exhibition to Trinity, Cambridge, M.I.C.E. Civil Engineer, Binnie & Partners, Consulting Engineers, London. *Emsworth Sailing Club, Royal H.K. Yacht Club.*

246 MARSTON, Richard Hilton Harvey, b. 14 Feb. 35, s. of Dr. W. H. Marston, O.B.E., T.D. C, 48^3–53^2.

247 STEIN, Richard Jonathan Beaver, b. 9 Dec. 34, younger s. of L. J. Stein. C, 48^3–52^3; State Scholarship. Pembroke, Cambridge, M.A., G.I.Mech.E., F.C.A., 1st & 2nd Certificate of Merit, Institute Prize, Whinney Prize (twice), Knox Scholarship, Plender Prize. Manager, Corporate Finance, Samuel Montagu & Co. Ltd. (Merchant Bankers), 62–68. With the Reckitt & Colman Group from 68. Now Group Treasurer.

248 BLACKWELL, Charles Anthony Walter, b. 27 Nov. 34, s. of the late T. A. W. Blackwell (OR K 25). K, 48^3–53^2; R. VIII, 52, 53. N/S. R.N., 53–55. Magdalene, Cambridge.

249 BROWN, Anthony Harold, b. 30 Jan. 35, elder s. of P. B. H. Brown (OR K 16). K, 48^3–53^2; Leaving Exhibition. Trinity, Cambridge, B.A.(Mech.Sc.), M.I.Mech.E. Managing Director, Star Refrigeration Ltd. Brother, 640.

250 CARTER, Roger Michael George, b. 27 Mar. 35, s. of W. R. Carter, F.C.A. K, 48^3–54^1; Levée; Head of House; Head of School, 54; R. VIII; Leaving Exhibition, 53^2. Minor Scholarship to Jesus, Cambridge, A.C.A. Chartered Accountant in practice.

251 DAVIDSON, William Stanley Walker, b. 3 Jan. 35, 2nd s. of Brig. T. W. Davidson. K, 48^3–53^2. Brother, 87.

252 GIVEN, John Anthony, b. 26 Feb. 35, s. of Rear Admiral J. G. C. Given, C.B., C.B.E., R.N. K, 48^3–53^1. Royal Navy, 53–58. Resigned as Lt., R.N. Joined Mather & Crowther Ltd. (Advertising Agency), 58. Now a Director of Mathers & Bensons Advertising Ltd. *Naval Club, Rye G.C.*

253 HENDERSON, David Beveridge, b. 10 Apr. 35, 5th s. of T. B. Henderson. K, 48^3–50^2. Brothers, T. B. & M. Henderson.

254 PREECE, Michael John Stewart, b. 29 Dec. 34, elder s. of Col. J. Preece, O.B.E., T.D. K, 48^3–53^2; Cap, 52; XI, 51, 52, 53. H. XI, 52, 53. Emmanuel, Cambridge, M.A. Partner in firm of Solicitors. *Cavalry Club.* Brother, 776.

255 BOURNE, Christopher John, b. 2 Apr. 35, eldest s. of J. Bourne (OR M 18). M, 48^3–53^2. S. VIII, 53. Corpus Christi, Cambridge, M.A. Member of Council, St. George's Hospital Medical School. Member of the Board of Governors, St. George's Hospital. Vice-President, Oxford Street Association. Chairman and Managing Director, Bourne & Hollingsworth Ltd. *Junior Carlton, Walton Heath G.C.* Brother, 1447.

256 BRAITHWAITE, Antony Robin, b. 9 Sept. 34, s. of N. Braithwaite, M.B., B.S. M, 48^3–53^1; Scholar.

257 DYDE, John Anthony, b. 30 May 35, elder s. of J. H. Dyde. M, 48^3–53^2. H. XI, 51, 52; Capt., 53. Corpus Christi, Cambridge; Hockey Blue, 56. Guy's Hospital, M.B., B.Chir., M.R.C.S., L.R.C.P., F.R.C.S. Consultant Cardiac Surgeon, Birmingham Regional Cardio-Thoracic Unit, Walsgrave Hospital, Coventry. *Hawks Club.* Brother, 1896.

258 EDDISON, David William, b. 5 May 35, s. of A. G. Eddison, M.B., B.Chir. (OR M 16). M, 48^3–53^2. Pembroke, Cambridge, M.A., F.C.A. Now Financial

Director, W. & R. Balston Ltd., Maidstone, Kent. Formerly Guest Keen & Nettlefolds Ltd. (Head Office). Liveryman, Grocers Company. *East India, Sports & Public Schools Club.*

259 **FORSTER, Brian Cameron,** b. 17 July 35, 2nd s. of Wing-Cdr. A. D. Forster, D.F.C. M, 48^3–53^2.

260 **HUGHES, John Medwyn,** b. 14 Mar. 35, s. of Dr. T. Hughes. M, 48^3–53^2.

261 **KELLY, Timothy Arthur Grenfell,** b. 8 Feb. 35, s. of the late Lt.-Col. H. A. Kelly, J.P. M, 48^3–52^3. N/S. Commission. K.O.S.B. Private Schoolmaster, Seafield School, Bexhill; Manchester Business School. Post Experience Course, 69. Management trainee, B.O.A.C. Now Manager, India, Srilanka, Bangladesh. *Royal & Ancient G.C., Royal Commonwealth Society.*

262 **LEWIS, John Jessel,** b. 18 Feb. 35, s. of L. Lewis. M, 48^3–53^2. St. John's, Cambridge, M.A. Managing Director of group of family controlled furnishing and property companies. Councillor, Newcastle City Council (Retired). On Committee of *Newcastle on Tyne Aero Club.*

263 **MacINNES, Keith Gordon,** b. 17 July 35, eldest s. of K. L. MacInnes, C.B.E., J.P., D.L. (OR M 19). M, 48^3–53^2; Scholar; Leaving Exhibition. Scholarship to Trinity, Cambridge, M.A. H.M. Diplomatic Service. *United Oxford and Cambridge University Club.* Brothers, 745 and 1797.

264 **NAYLOR, Colin Frank,** b. 6 July 35, 2nd s. of the late F. A. Naylor. M, 48^3–52^3. Commerce. Company Director. T.D. Brother, 554.

265 **PAUL, Robert Cameron,** b. 7 July 35, s. of the late F. W. Paul, M.B., Ch.B. M, 48^3–53^2; Levée; Head of House; State Scholarship; Leaving Exhibition. Open Scholarship to Corpus Christi, Cambridge, B.A. Foundation Scholarship, 56–58. M.I.Chem.E. N/S. Royal Engineers in B.A.O.R., 2nd Lt., 53–55. I.C.I. Mond Division since 59. Present, Works Manager, Castner Kellner Works, Runcorn. *Sandiway Golf Club.*

266 **ROBINSON, John Edward,** b. 4 May 35, youngest s. of L. B. Robinson. M, 48^3–52^2.

267 **ROSE, David Michael,** b. 27 Aug. 34, s. of H. Rose. M, 48^3–52^2. University College, London, LL.B. Solicitor, Commissioner for Oaths. Partner in Randall Rose & Co. (Solicitors), London, W.1, and Randall Rose & Fulton (Solicitors), of Amersham, Bucks. The Law Society. *R.A.C.* Son, Nicholas Peter, M, 71^3.

268 **SHAW, George David Cecil,** b. 8 Apr. 35, elder s. of G. R. Shaw. M, 48^3–53^2; XI, 52. Sheffield Univ., LL.B. Solicitor. In private practice. *The Sheffield Club.* Brother, 783.

269 **ALLAN, John Lewis Forsyth,** b. 20 Aug. 34, s. of Lt.-Col. A. J. W. Allan. SF, 48^3–52^2.

270 **BECK, Martyn Ronald,** b. 27 Feb. 35, younger s. of R. G. Beck. SF, 48^3–53^2; Cap, 52; XXII, 52. Middlesex Hospital Medical School, London University, M.B., B.S., D.Obst. R.C.O.G. Brother, A. M. I. Beck.

271 **BURR, John Shepard,** b. 15 Dec. 31, eldest s. of J. R. Burr of N.Y. SF, 48^3–49^2.

272 **HILL, William Lumsden,** b. 28 June 35, elder s. of R. F. Hill. SF, 48^3–53^2; S. VIII, 51, 52, 53. Christ's, Cambridge, M.A., A.I.Mech.E. Mechanical Engineering, Building and Civil Engineering. Self-employed. *Brands Hatch M.R.C.*

273 **KENMORE, Stephen Marcel,** b. 16 Feb. 35, s. of W. Kenmore. SF, 48^3–52^3; Scholar. Exhibition to Clare, Cambridge, B.A. Company Director, Carl Zeiss Jena Ltd. *Cavalry Club.*

274 **ODDY, William Roland,** b. 21 Nov. 34, elder s. of A. W. Oddy. SF, 48^3–52^2; XXII, 51. Vice-President, Ballantyne Sweaters Ltd. Brother, 588.

275 **SLATTER, Arthur Guy Malins,** b. 31 July 35, s. of A. M. Slatter. SF, 48^3–52^2. Christ Church, Oxford, B.A. Studio Manager, External Services, B.B.C., 59.

276 **SUMMERSCALE, Peter Wayne,** b. 22 Apr. 35, elder s. of Sir J. P. Summerscale, K.B.E. SF, 48^3–52^3; Queen's Medal; Dewar Travelling Scholarship. Open Exhibition to New College, Oxford, B.A. Senior Branch of H.M. Foreign Office, 60. 3rd Sec., H.M. Political Residency, Bahrain, 62.

277 **SWANWICK, Richard Graham,** b. 14 May 35, elder s. of G. R. Swanwick, M.B.E. SF, 48³–54¹; Levée; Rackets Pair, 53, Capt.

278 **THRELFALL, Jonathan,** b. 13 Dec. 34, s. of H. W. Threlfall. SF, 48³–53²; Leaving Exhibition. Trinity Hall, Cambridge, B.A. Management Consultancy. Regional Director, P.A. Management Consultants Ltd.

279 **TRENTHAM, David George,** b. 23 Feb. 35, elder s. of Capt. D. P. Trentham, R.N. SF, 48³–53²; Stovin Scholar; Levée; Head of House; XI, 52, 53; H. XI, 53; Tennis VI, 50; Leaving Exhibition. Worcester, Oxford, B.A. Asst. Master, Uppingham School, 58–62; Rugby School, 62–67; seconded to Noble High School, Masulipatam, S. India, 65–66; Asst. Master, Monkton Combe School since 69 (Second Master, 70). Brother, 2071.

280 **COLVILLE, The Hon. Charles Anthony,** b. 5 Aug. 35, 2nd son of the late Rt. Hon. The Viscount Colville of Culross. Sh, 48³–53¹; Scholar; Levée; Head of House; Head of School Music. Magdalen, Oxford, B.A. H.M. Overseas Civil Service (Kenya), 58–63; British Council, 64–65; Solicitor, 69. Brothers, The Rt. Hon. The Viscount Colville of Culross and 863.

281 **ROSS, William Muirhead,** b. 30 Apr. 35, s. of J. M. Ross, F.F.A., F.R.S.E. Sh, 48³–52². C.A. (Scotland). Accountant, B.P. Chemicals International Ltd., Grangemouth.

282 **STEPHEN, David,** b. 6 Mar. 35, s. of the late J. G. Stephen, M.C. Sh, 48³–53²; Tennis VI, 53. N/S. S/Lt.(S) R.N.V.R., 53–55. O.N.C. Naval Architecture; Diploma in Personnel Management, Strathclyde Univ. Assoc. Member of Inst. Engineers & Shipbuilders in Scotland, Institute of Personnel Management and British Institute of Management. Alex Stephen & Sons Ltd, 55–58; Senior Personnel Officer, Upper Clyde Shipbuilders Ltd., 55–70; Director, Topstaff Employment Ltd. since 70; Director, Clydesdide Homes Ltd. since 72. *Western Club, Royal Northern Yacht Club.* Vice-Chairman, Glasgow area, *Union of Youth Clubs.*

283 **TYSON, Donald Alexander,** b. 3 Aug. 35, 3rd s. of H. A. M. Tyson. Sh, 48³–53³. Magdalen, Oxford, M.A. Asst. Master, The King's School, Grantham,

60–61; King's Coll., Taunton, 61–67; Lancing Coll., Sussex, since 68.

284 **BAGNALL, Charles Henry,** b. 9 Oct. 34, elder s. of C. F. R. Bagnall, C.B.E. (OR C 18). St, 48³–52³, Cap.

285 **BODDINGTON, Richard Michael Herbert,** b. 24 Dec. 34, elder s. of E. S. H. C. Boddington. St, 48³–53²; Levée; Head of House; XI, 51, 52, Capt., 53; R. VIII, 51, 52, 53; Holder of Bigside Bags, 53. Magdalen, Oxford for 1 yr. Schoolmaster. Housemaster, Wellesley House School, Broadstairs. *Junior Carlton, M.C.C.* Brother, 870.

286 **DAWSON, Richard George,** b. 6 Mar. 35, s. of Col. W. C. P. Dawson, M.B.E. (OR St, 10). St, 48³–53².

287 **PARTRIDGE, Christopher John,** b. 15 Nov. 34, s. of S. H. Partridge. St, 48³–52³. Solicitor in private practice as partner. *Leicestershire Club, Constitutional Club, Leicester.*

288 **STALLWORTHY, Jon Howie,** b. 18 Jan. 35, s. of J. A. Stallworthy, F.R.C.S. St, 48³–53²; R. VIII, 52. Magdalen, Oxford, B.A., B.Litt. Editor, Oxford Univ. Press, 59–71. Visiting Fellow, All Souls Coll., 71–72. Editor, Clarendon Press, Oxford since 72. *Vincent's Club, Oxford.*

289 **TETLOW, Timothy George,** b. 11 Mar. 35, s. of G. Tetlow. St, 48³–53². Guy's Hospital Dental & Medical Schools, B.D.S., F.D.S., R.C.S.Eng., D.D.O., R.C.P.S.(Glas.), L.R.C.P., M.R.C.S. Orthodontist practising in Hamilton, Bermuda. Captain, London University Golf Team, 60–61.

290 **PROCTOR-BEAUCHAMP, Christopher Radstock,** b. 30 Jan. 35, elder s. of Sir I. C. Proctor-Beauchamp, Bt., M.B., B.Chir. Tu, 48³–53².

291 **BRUMWELL, John Coltman Heron,** b. 17 Nov. 34, s. of J. Brumwell, M.B., F.R.C.S. Tu, 48³–53². Leaving Exhibition to Peterhouse, Cambridge, M.A. Fellow of Institute of Actuaries. The Prudential Assurance Co. since 56. Currently Senior Principal Investment Analyst.

292 **COOTE, Nicholas Howard Neill,** b. 12 Mar. 35, s. of A. B. Coote. Tu, 48³–53³; Scholar; Head of House; Levée; Head of School; State Scholar. Open Scholar of Worcester, Oxford. Ordained

Priest (R.C.). Left Priesthood, reading Philosophy & Theology at Oxford, 71.

293 O'DWYER, Julius Gillespie, b. 4 July 34, s. of R. G. O'Dwyer (OR Tu 14). Tu, 48³–53¹. Moore McCormack Lines Inc., (B.A.) 60–64. Farming, Argentine. *English Club, Buenos Aires.*

294 PHILLIPS, John Michael, b. 18 Dec. 34, s. of the late A. D. Phillips (OR Tu 12). Tu, 48³–53². Courtauld Institute of Art, London Univ., B.A. Television Director. B.B.C. Producer.

295 ROBY, Christopher John Martin, b. 22 May 35, s. of the late W. W. Roby. Tu, 48³–53². John Roby Ltd., Brass Founders, 55.

296 STEPHENSON, Mark Stansfield, b. 23 Oct. 35, younger s. of Major N. D. Stephenson. Tu, 48³–53³; Levée; State Scholar. Peterhouse, Cambridge. Scholar, 58–59, B.A. Asst. Master, Winchester College, 59. Brother, J. S. Stephenson.

297 ALLTON, Christopher Paul Westoby, b. 30 Apr. 35, s. of D. Allton. W, 48³–53². Qualified as Chartered Accountant. Joined family Wholesale Grocery Company, 60, Burton Allton & Johnson Ltd., of Mansfield.

298 DEANE, Leon David, b. 15 June 35, s. of E. A. Deane. W, 48³–52³; XV, 52. Entrepreneur. *Conservative Club, Dunbar G.C.*

299 de SALIS, Henry John Aldworth Fane, b. 8 Nov. 35, younger s. of J. P. F. de Salis. W, 48³–54². Magdalene, Cambridge, B.A.(Eng.). Bristol Siddeley Engine Co. 1st Class Merit Award in the International Air Rally at Jersey, 61. Third in Tiger Trophy Race and 4th in the King's Cup Air Race, 62. While a member of a formation giving flying displays and during the final fly past, a faster and heavier machine came into the prohibited area and crashed into his aircraft from behind, killing him instantly on 25 Aug. 62.

300 GRAY, Randolph Alan, b. 4 Apr. 35, elder s. of R. V. C. Gray. W, 48³–53²; H. XI, 53; Capt. of Boxing & Fencing, 53. Selwyn, Cambridge, B.A. Associate of Chartered Auctioneers & Estate Agents Institute, 60. A.R.I.C.S., 61.

301 HALL, William Brian, b. 26 June 35, s. of Major B. Hall. W, 48³–53¹.

302 JOHNSON, Nigel Margrave, b. 6 July 35, younger s. of H. A. Johnson, F.R.I.B.A. W, 48³–52³; Scholar; Leaving Exhibition. Scholarship to Corpus Christi, Cambridge, M.A. Asst. Principal, General Post Office, Nov. 59; Principal, Dec. 64; Asst. Secretary, Apr. 69; Ministry of Posts & Telecommunications, Oct. 69.

303 MACPHERSON, Ewen Charles Fitzroy, b. 7 June 35, s. of Lt.-Col. E. A. F. MacPherson, M.C. Waiting House, 48³.

ENTRANCES IN JANUARY 1949

304 BURNETT, Anthony Robin, b. 7 May 35, elder s. of C. W. Burnett. SH, 49¹–53². University College, Oxford and Cuddesdon Theological Coll., M.A. Asst. Priest, St. Paul's, Rondebosch, Cape, 60–62; Good Shepherd, Maitland, Cape, 62–64; Rector, All Saints, Hopefield, Cape, 65–72; Priest-in-Charge, St. John's, Bellville South, Cape since 72. Brother, 631.

305 DAVENPORT, Peter Lindsay, b. 22 Aug. 35, s. of B. H. Davenport (OR SF 17). SH, 49¹–53². Director in Textiles. *British Deer Society.*

306 LEAKE, John Burnell, b. 3 Jan. 35, younger s. of S. H. Leake, O.B.E. SH, 49¹–53². Lincoln, Oxford, M.A. College of Resurrection, Misfield. Ordained, Durham Diocese, 59. Asst. Priest, Billingham-on-Tees, 59–63; W.S.P.G. Missionary, 63–72; Warden of Chilena Lay Training Centre, 69–72; Secretary of Department of Mission & Unity, British Council of Churches since 72.

307 BURNS, Ivan Alfred, b. 18 Jan. 35, s. of the late C. I. Burns. T, 49¹–52¹.

308 GREGORY, Andrew Philip, b. 4 July, 35, s. of A. D. Gregory. T, 49¹–54².

309 SEAR, Lionel Roger, b. 6 Feb. 35, elder s. of H. L. Sear. T, 49¹–51².

310 WALLIS, Graham Blair, b. 1 Apr. 36, elder s. of A. S. Wallis, B.Sc. T, 49¹–53²; Scholar; Two Leaving Exhibitions. Major Scholarship to Trinity, Cambridge, 52. M.A., Ph.D. Massachusetts Institute of Technology, S.M. Member, American Society of Mechanical Engineers. Professor, Dartmouth Coll., Hanover, N.H. 03755, U.S.A. Brother, 1112.

311 BARCLAY, James David Innes, b. 6 July 35, s. of J. I. M. Barclay (OR B 18). B, 49¹–49².

312 **MARSHALL, Charles Jonathan,** b. 21 May 35, elder s. of Col. V. J. C. Marshall, T.D. (OR B 18). B, 49^1–53^1; Sw. VIII, 52. Royal Naval Engineering College. M.I.Mech.E. Royal Navy, 53–67. Retired as Lt.-Cdr. Now with British Hovercraft Corporation. *Naval Club.* Brother, 671.

313 **MORRIS, John Risk,** b. 28 May 35, s. of the late C. F. Morris, O.B.E. (OR B 05). B, 49^1–53^2; Sw. VIII. Chartered Accountant, 59. *Lansdowne Club.*

314 **TURNER, George Nevill,** b. 15 July 35, younger s. of Col. B. G. Turner. B, 49^1–53^2; H. XI, 53; Cadet Officer. Queens', Cambridge, B.A. Texaco Trinidad Inc. (Operations), 58–61. I.C.I. Dyestuffs Div. Sales, London, 61.

315 **LAUNDER, Ewan Quayle,** b. 13 Sept. 35, s. of F. S. Launder. C, 49^1–53^2.

316 **MOODY, Graham Earnst Butler,** b. 2 July 35, s. of A. J. B. Moody. C, 49^1–53^2. Accountancy, 53–55. N/S. 14/20 Hussars, 55–57. Wine Trade, 57–59. Stock Exchange, 59.

317 **WHITE, Richard Olof,** b. 21 Feb. 35, 2nd s. of J. White. C, 49^1–52^3.

318 **BARKER-BENNETT, Charles Robert,** b. 19 June, 35, s. of A. C. Barker-Bennett (OR K 20). K, 49^1–53^2; Sw. VIII, 53. General Accident Fire & Life Assur. Corp. Ltd., Perth, Scotland. *Rye G.C., The Bombay Gymkhana.*

319 **HOBDAY, John Charles Bardell,** b. 7 July 35, younger s. of S. H. Hobday. K, 49^1–50^3.

320 **McCAY, Colin Ramsay,** b. 2 Aug. 35, elder s. of C. A. R. McCay, F.R.C.S., D.P.H. K, 49^1–53^2; XV, 52; XXII, 52; H. XI, 53. Trinity, Oxford. W. D. & H. O. Wills. Brother, 841.

321 **COCHRANE, William Grant,** b. 11 Aug. 35, s. of the late W. A. Cochrane, M.D., Chir.B., F.R.C.S. SF, 49^1–53^2. C.A. (Scotland). Appointed Manager of The Edinburgh Investment Trust Ltd., 70. *New Club, Edinburgh, Royal Forth Yacht Club.*

322 **SARGANT, James Edmund,** b. 24 Aug. 35, s. of Sir H. E. Sargant (OR SF 19). SF, 49^1–53^2. Trinity, Cambridge, B.A. Resident Stage Manager, Arts Theatre, Cambridge, 58; Stage Manager, Sadlers Wells Opera, 58–61; Design & Graphics Administrator, A.B.C. Television Ltd., 61–64; Production and Promotions Controller, Madame Tussauds Ltd., London, 66–71; Production Controller, Royal Shakespeare Co. from 71. *Hurlingham Club.*

323 **COLE, Martin Davey,** b. 27 Sept. 35, younger s. of K. D. Cole (OR St 19). St, 49^1–53^2. 1st Degree French (Etranger), Grenoble Univ. C.A., M.I.M.C. Qualified as Accountant with Thomson McLintock & Co. (London). Employed as Consultant in Computer & Computer Programming Methods with McLintock Mann & Whinney Murray.

324 **GODFREY, Ingram Timothy Gray,** b. 29 June 35, younger s. of Major E. A. Godfrey. Tu, 49^1–52^3. Folland Aircraft Ltd., 55; Information & Press Officer, 58; Asst. Press Officer, Westland Aircraft Ltd., 59; P.R. Executive, J. Walter Thompson Ltd., 60. Director, Patric Baker Ltd. P.R. Consultants, 63.

325 **HODSON, Peter,** b. 24 July 35, 3rd s. of J. Hodson, LL.B. Tu, 49^1–53^2. Commissioned Royal Air Force. Manager, Tube Investments Ltd., India, Singapore, Hong Kong. Currently Company Director, Special Vehicle Engineering. Part-time Lecturer on overseas marketing to e.g. Chambers of Commerce & Companies. *Leamington Tennis Court Club.*

326 **MARSTON, John James Shepherd,** b. 19 Feb. 35, elder s. of J. W. Marston. Tu, 49^1–53^2. Coll. of Technology, Manchester Univ., B.Sc.; Univ. XV, 55 & 56. A.M.I.C.E. Building Contractor. Director of W. J. Marston & Son Ltd., Marston Properties, Hotel Imperial (Hythe) Ltd., Stade Court Hotel Ltd. Chairman, *Shirley Wanderers R.F.C.* Vice-Chairman, *Putney & Fulham Sea Cadets Royal Harwich Yacht Club.*

327 **NELSON, Edward Montague,** b. 26 Mar. 35, s. of the late G. M. B. Nelson (OR Tu 14). Tu, 49^1–52^2. With Davis Gelatine Co., Australia, 58.

328 **GOODBODY, Keith Woodcock,** b. 4 Apr. 35, s. of M. V. W. Goodbody. W, 49^1–52^3.

329 **KING, John Orford,** b. 16 Feb. 35, s. of J. A. King, C.A. W, 49^1–52^3. Glasgow Univ. Mann Judd Golden & Co., 54–57. Institute of Chartered Accountants of Scotland. Accountant, E. S. & A. Robinson (Holdings) Ltd., 61. Chief

Accountant, Strachan & Henshaw Ltd., Ashton Vale Rd., Bristol.

330 LOH, James Hsiao-Kwung, b. 9 July 35, s. of M. E. I. Lung Loh, B.S. W, 49^1–54^2. Southampton Univ.

331 MURCHISON, Alexander Kenneth Rambaut, b. 25 July 35, elder s. of the late R. C. Murchison (OR W 13). W, 49^1–51^3. Apprentice to John Laing & Son Ltd., Management Consultant. Brother, 473. Son, Charles Roy, W, 73^1–.

ENTRANCES IN MAY 1949

332 CATTY, Robert Hugh Craig, b. 11 Dec. 35, younger s. of Col. T. C. Catty, C.M.G., D.S.O. SH, 49^2–53^2. St. Thomas's Hospital, London, M.B., B.S. M.R.C.S.(Eng.), L.R.C.P., D.Obst. R.C.O.G., M.R.C.G.P. General Medical Practitioner in Durham. *Antarctic Club.*

333 GUINNESS, John Ralph Sidney, b. 23 Dec. 35, younger s. of E. D. Guinness, C.B.E., R.D. (OR SH 07). SH, 49^2–54^2; Head of House; Levée; Queen's Medal; Tom Hughes Prize; Leaving Exhibition for History. N/S. R.A.F., 54–56. Trinity Hall, Cambridge, M.A. Joined Foreign Office, 62. Seconded to the United Nations Secretariat as Special Assistant to the Under Secretary for Economic & Social Affairs, 64–66. Foreign & Commonwealth Office, 67–69. First Secretary (Economic), British High Commission, Ottawa, 69–72. Seconded to the Cabinet Office as a member of Lord Rothschild's Central Policy Review Staff, 72. *St. James's Club, United Oxford and Cambridge Club.*

334 WARD, Robert William, b. 17 Oct. 35, s. of Lt.-Col. W. D. Ward (OR SH 08). SH, 49^2–53^2; XI, 52, 53; H. XI, 53. R.M.A., Sandhurst. Army Officer. Commissioned into Queen's Bays, 55. Present rank, Lt.-Col. Present regiment, 1st the Queen's Dragoon Guards. M.B.E. *M.C.C., Cavalry Club.*

335 COLLINS, Kenneth William, b. 9 Nov. 35, s. of W. A. Collins. T, 49^2–54^2.

336 COWLIN, John Barrington, b. 30 Sept. 35, younger s. of F. J. Cowlin, O.B.E., M.I.Mech.E., M.I.Mar.E., R.E. C.Eng. T, 49^2–54^2. Mid-Warwicks Coll. of Further Education, B.Sc.Eng.; Univ. of Wales, Swansea Coll.; Leamington Coll. of Further Education, B.Sc. (Metal-

lurgy), M.I.Prod.E., C.Eng., M.I.M.C. E.E.C. (Atomic Power); U.K.A.E.A. (Atomic Power); Radio Corp. of America, N.Y., U.S.A. (Transistor Production); Ship & Boat Building (General Manager, Blue Line Group); P.A. International Management Consultants Ltd., Consultant in East Europe. *Sloughden (Aldeburgh) Yacht Club.*

337 JAEGER, Jean François, b. 15 May 36, s. of Dr. C. Jaeger. T, 49^2–54^2; Minor Foundationer; R. VIII, 54; State Scholarship; Leaving Exhibition. Exhibition to Corpus Christi, Cambridge. Caldwell Scholarship. M.A. London University, Imperial Coll., Ph.D., D.I.C. (Elect. Eng.), C.Eng., M.I.Mech.E. English Electric Co. Ltd., Atomic Power Dept., 61–64. Sulzer Bros. Ltd., Winterthus, Nuclear Dept., Reactor and Heat Exchanger Development, 65–71. Sales: Combined plants, Nuclear components from 71. British Nuclear Energy Society.

338 WILLIAMS, Trefor Richard, b. 11 June 35, eldest s. of W. Williams. T, 49^2–54^2; State Scholar. Queen's, Cambridge, B.A. Foundation Scholar, 58. Research Fellowship in Department of Parasitology. Liverpool School of Tropical Medicine, 59.

339 AGNEW, Alexander James Blair, b. 6 Oct. 35, s. of J. P. Agnew, D.L., O.St.J., LL.D., C.A. B, 49^2–54^1; Cadet Officer. H.M. Forces, Royal Scots Fusiliers, Royal Highland Fusiliers, 54–65. Captain. Member of Scottish Stock Exchange, 68. *Western Club, Glasgow.*

340 HAWORTH, Timothy, b. 15 May 35, s. of the late P. K. Haworth (OR B 09). B, 49^2–53^2. Trinity, Oxford. Farmer & Chairman of T. Haworth (Insurance Brokers Ltd.). *City University Club, Farmers' Club.*

341 PATTEN, David Basil Charles, b. 30 June 35, elder s. of the late A. J. H. Patten, M.C. B, 49^2–53^2. Commissioned R.N., 53–55; R.N.V.R., 55–62. With Lyon Lohr & Sly Ltd., Lloyd's Brokers, 55–62. Marine Insurance Brokers, Rhodesia. *M.C.C.*

342 RILEY, Victor William, b. 21 July 35, s. of V. Riley. B, 49^2–52^3. Bromsgrove Coll. of Further Education; Birmingham Coll. of Commerce; London Business School. R.S.A. Advanced Accountancy. National Certificates of Commerce. G.K.N., 53–72. Apprenticeship

Production/Sales Management. Appointed Divisional Sales Director, 72. *R.A.C.* Worshipful Company of Coach Makers & Coach Harness-Makers.

343 BARTON, Jack Elson, b. 16 Aug. 35, younger s. of C. Barton. C, 49^2–52^2. F.C.A. Accountant, Barton Transport Ltd.; Director, Barton Transport Ltd., Carl Barton Ltd., Hall Bros., South Shields Ltd.

344 COWGILL, Christopher Roger, b. 27 July 35, younger s. of J. H. Cowgill. C, 49^2–53^2; Scholar. Millfield School, 53–54. Scholarship to Balliol, Oxford, M.A. Joined Unilever, 57. Congo, 62. Accountancy in England, 64–65. Casablanca, 70. Financial Director, The United Africa Co. of Tanzania Ltd., Dar-es-Salaam, 70. Brother, T. J. Cowgill.

345 SPENCE, Robert Walter Rudolf, b. 13 Sept. 35, s. of R. F. Spence. C, 49^2–53^2. Senior Scholarship. City and Guilds Coll., London Univ., B.Sc., A.C.G.I., M.I.C.E. Civil Engineer. Now with Cementation Piling & Foundations Ltd., Rickmansworth, Herts.

346 BENNETT, John Henry, b. 31 July 35, elder s. of S. R. J. Bennett. K, 49^2–53^2. Director, F. W. Kerridge Ltd., Alton, Hants.

347 CASSELS, David Kennedy, b. 3 Aug. 35, 2nd s. of A. K. Cassels (OR K 20). K, 49^2–53^2; Capt., Waterpolo, 53. Birmingham Coll. of Technology and Sundridge Park Management Centre, Kent. Courses on Work Study, Production Organisation & Management. Superintendent, Liebig's, Paraguay, 64; Factory Manager, Liebig's, Argentina, 67; Factory Manager, Frigorifico La Gloria, Colombia, 71; Factory Manager, Pampa S.A., Paraguay, 73. Brothers, 31, 513, 773 & 1527.

348 FARMER, Peter Stansfield, b. 12 June 35, elder s. of D. Farmer. K, 49^2–53^2; Sw. VIII, 51–53. With family business of Wholesalers in Ladies Knitwear, 54–69. Now running own business of manufacturing Ladies Knitwear. *Leicestershire G.C.*

349 SIMPSON, Anthony Maurice Herbert, b. 28 Oct. 35, 3rd s. of Lt.-Col. M. R. Simpson, O.B.E., T.D., D.L. K, 49^2–53^3. Magdalene, Cambridge, M.A., LL.B. Barrister on Midland circuit. Conservative Prospective Parliamentary Candi-

date for West Leicester since 72. T.D. Major, 23rd Special Air Service Regt. (V.). *Leicestershire Club, Special Forces Club.*

350 BISHOP, John Robert Anthony, b. 23 Aug. 35, s. of the late J. H. Bishop. M, 49^2–53^2. Sorbonne, Paris. I.N.S.E.A.D. Fontainebleau. F.C.A. Partner in Rawlinson & Hunter. *Bath Club.*

351 BROWN, Andrew James Mac-Myn, b. 13 July 35, elder s. of J. D. Brown, O.B.E. (OR Tu 13). M, 49^2–53^3; S. VIII, 53. Trinity Hall, Cambridge. Royal Agricultural Coll., Cirencester. N/S. Commission in 15th/19th The King's Royal Hussars. Overseas Civil Service, Administration, Northern Rhodesia. Agriculture. Brother, 1029.

352 CHAPMAN, Sydney Brookes, b. 17 Oct. 35, younger s. of the late W. D. Chapman. M, 49^2–52^3. Manchester Univ., Dip. Arch., Dip.T.P., A.R.I.B.A., M.R.T.P.I. Architect, Surveyor, Town Planning Consultant & Lecturer. M.P. for Birmingham, Handsworth since 70. Associate Partner, McDonald, Hamilton & Montefiore, London, S.W.1. Planning Consultant, House Builders Federation.

353 COULTON, Peter Trevena, b. 13 Oct. 35, s. of F. T. Coulton. M, 49^2–54^2. Jesus, Cambridge. "The Daily Telegraph", Manchester. *East India, Sports & Public School Club, Leander Club.*

354 HOLBECHE, Michael John, b. 5 June 35, younger s. of R. H. Holbeche. M, 49^2–52^1.

355 SHAW, Timothy Robert, b. 13 Aug. 35, 2nd s. of J. F. St. G. Shaw (OR SF 17). M, 49^2–53^3. Lincoln, Oxford, B.A., F.C.A. Financial Director, Costains (W. Africa). *R.A.C.* Brothers, 109 & 1008.

356 DANIEL, Owen Richard, b. 22 July 35, s. of the late M. C. C. Daniel (OR SF 18). SF, 49^2–53^3; Scholar; Head of House; Levée; Cap, 51; XV, 52. Dewar Travelling Scholarship.

357 GARRETT, David Richard, b. 18 Dec. 35, s. of Cdr. C. R. Garrett, R.N. (Retired). SF, 49^2–53^3; Tennis VI, 53. Chartered Accountant.

358 KENNEDY, William Michael Clifford, b. 29 Oct. 35, elder s. of C. D. Kennedy, M.B., Ch.B., F.R.C.S.E., F.R.C.O.G. SF, 49^2–54^1; Cap, 52; XV, 53; H. XI, 54. Merton, Oxford, B.A., C.A.

With Joseph Sebag & Co. Stockbrokers, London, 63. *Highland Brigade Club.* Brother, 857.

359 OSBORNE, Christopher Edgar John, b. 14 Dec. 35, s. of W. E. Osborne. SF, 49^2–54^2; Head of House; Levée; XV, 51–53. N/S. R.E.M.E., 55–56. 2nd Lt. Pembroke, Cambridge, M.A. Diploma of Communication Advertising & Marketing. Fellow Institute of Practitioners in Advertising. Member, Institute of Marketing. Member, Marketing (Council Member). Market Research Asst., Cunningham & Walsh Inc. (U.S.A.), 59–60; Marketing Executive, Warner-Lambert International Inc., U.S.A., 60–61; Marketing Services/ International Manager, Osborne-Peacock Ltd., 62–65 and Managing Director, 66–68; Chairman & Group Chief Executive, The Osborne Group Ltd. since 68. *Royal Thames Yacht Club.*

360 WESTON, Nigel David, b. 10 Aug. 35, eldest s. of W. G. Weston, C.M.G. SF, 49^2–53^2. Proprietor, Independent Building & Industrial Services, and I.B. International Homes (Building Contractors & Export Houses). Brothers, 1303 & 1677.

361 EVERS, Robert Patrick Guy, b. 24 Nov. 35, s. of R. E. G. Evers. Sh, 49^2–53^2. Under Manager's Certificate, North Staffordshire Tech. Coll. Licentiate of the Institute of Ceramics. 15 yrs. Refractory Brick manufacture, culminating as a Director. Redundant, 71. Now Manufacturers' Agent. Worshipful Company of Upholders. Worcestershire Association.

362 MACKIE, Ian David Gordon, b. 21 Aug. 35, s. of E. G. Mackie, M.B., Ch.B., F.R.F.P. & S. Sh, 49^2–53^3. Queens', Cambridge, B.A.; Melbourne Univ., M.Eng.Sc., C.Eng., M.I.C.E.

363 MAGNUS, George Colin, b. 2 Oct. 35, s. of J. A. Magnus, M.D., F.R.C.S., D.O.M.S. Sh, 49^2–54^1; Fives IV, 52–54. Kings, Cambridge, M.A., M.I.M.C. Company Director. Managing Director, I.C.C. Ltd., London, W.1. *Lansdowne Club.*

364 SPENCE, Ralph Everard, b. 8 Sept. 35, elder s. of T. E. Spence. St, 49^2–54^2. Balliol, Oxford.

365 HOLLOWAY, Brian David, b. 20 Oct. 35, s. of B. S. Holloway. Tu, 49^2–53^2.

366 LATIMER, John Geoffrey, b. 8 Nov. 35, elder s. of J. Latimer. Tu, 49^2–53^3; XXII, 52. N/S. 54–56. 2nd Lt., R.A. Inchcape Group, Calcutta, 56–66. Currently Credit Factoring Ltd., Feltham, Middx.

367 NELSON, Anthony George, b. 5 June 35, 2nd s. of R. R. Nelson. Tu, 49^2–52^2. Brothers, 45 & 727.

368 OAKLEY, Patrick Edward Villiers, b. 17 Aug. 35, s. of E. C. Oakley, O.B.E., M.C., F.C.A. Tu, 49^2–54^2. LL.B. London, 60. Solicitor, 61. Member of Law Society's Interviewing Panel. Died 19 June 73.

369 RODOCANACHI, Paul Stephen, b. 29 June 35, younger s. of A. J. Rodocanachi (OR Tu 14). Tu, 49^2–53^2. Stockbroker, Merrill Lynch, Pierce, Fenner & Smith Inc., New York City, U.S.A. *Junior Carlton.*

370 DAUNCEY, Hugh Robin, b. 13 Nov. 35, s. of H. F. Dauncey. W, 49^2–53^2. Joined Henry Gardner & Co. Ltd., Metal & Commodity Merchants, 56. Nominee Rep. of the Company on the London Commodity Exchange, 60.

371 HUNT, Nigel Mitchell, b. 19 Dec. 35, younger s. of R. T. Hunt. W, 49^2–53^2; XI, 53. Farming. Brother, 174.

372 PARKER, Hamish Bernard, b. 28 June 35, younger s. of J. S. Parker. W, 49^2–53^2. General Manager, Stoneguard (Seaguard) Ltd., London, N.W.1. Specialists in restoration of buildings and stone cleaning.

373 RAWDON-SMITH, Henry Stewart, b. 18 Nov. 35, younger s. of the late G. F. Rawdon-Smith, T.D., M.D., F.F.A.R.C.S. (OR W 96). W, 49^2–53^2. Middlesex Hospital Medical School, M.B., B.S.(Lond.), D.Obst.R.C.O.G. General Medical Practitioner.

ENTRANCES IN SEPTEMBER 1949

374 AITKEN, James Mark, b. 27 Jan. 36, elder s. of the late J. Aitken. SH, 49^3–54^2; H. XI, 54; Tennis VI, 54. Civil Service Interpretership in Russian. Managing Director of Cyprus Associated Company of the British-American Tobacco Co.

375 AROYO, Dorian David, b. 16 Sept. 35, elder s. of M. N. Aroyo of Malta.

SH, 49^3–54^2; Paddison Art Prize; Piano Prize. Corpus Christi, Cambridge. Brother, 1064.

376 **BACH, John Theodore**, b. 18 Feb. 36, s. of F. J. Bach, D.M. SH, 49^3–54^2. New College, Oxford, M.A. Solicitor. Partner, Stephenson Harwood & Tatham, London, E.C.2.

377 **BEDINGFIELD, Christopher Ohl Macredie**, b. 2 June 35, s. of N. M. Bedingfield. SH, 49^3–50^3. Univ. Coll., Oxford, M.A. Barrister, Gray's Inn. Recorder, Wales and Chester circuit. T.D. *Reform, Army and Navy*.

378 **GLUCKSTEIN, John Michael Howard**, b. 17 Jan. 36, s. of L. Gluckstein. SH, 49^3–53^3; Cadet Pair. Gonville & Caius, Cambridge, B.A. Director of J. Lyons & Co. Ltd., European Co-ordinator. London Business School Association.

379 **HALFORD, John Michael Finch**, b. 17 Nov. 35, s. of C. F. Halford. SH, 49^3–53^2. St. Catherine's, Cambridge, B.A. Hyde Farm Stud, Broughton, Hampshire. Farmer, Aberfeldy, Perthshire.

380 **HALL, John Maynard**, b. 20 Mar. 36, elder s. of the late J. P. Hall (OR SH 11). SH, 49^3–53^3. Admitted Solicitor, 60. Brother, 516.

381 **HODDER, Edwin James, jnr.**, b. 19 Oct. 31, elder s. of E. J. Hodder of Mass., U.S.A. SH, 49^3–50^2.

382 **JOHNSON, Oliver**, b. 1 Jan. 37, younger s. of S. Johnson. SH, 49^3–55^2; XXII; H. XI. Queens', Cambridge, B.A.; Hockey Blue, 60, 61. Surveyor & Valuer. *Hawks Club*.

383 **MASON, Henry Peter**, b. 17 July 36, s. of A. Mason. SH, 49^3–54^2. St. Catharine's, Cambridge.

384 **RUTHERFORD, David Colin**, b. 2 Mar. 36, s. of the late C. C. Rutherford. SH, 49^3–54^1; Levée; Head of House. Magdalen, Oxford, B.A. Courtaulds Ltd. *Leander*.

385 **WALKER, Robert Henry Lees**, b. 31 May 36, s. of H. G. Walker, M.B.E., M.I.C.E. SH, 49^3–54^3. Clare, Cambridge, B.A., C.Eng., M.I.Mech.E. Apprenticeship with Rolls-Royce Ltd. Current position, Project Cost Engineer for new projects with Rolls-Royce (1971) Ltd.

386 **BENNETT, William David John**, b. 17 Sept. 36, s. of J. D. Bennett. T, 49^3–54^2; XXII, 54. Sorbonne, Paris.

387 **CANSDALE, Michael John**, b. 8 May 36, eldest s. of J. H. Cansdale. T, 49^3–54^3. St. Edmund Hall, Oxford, M.A. Solicitor. Managing Director, Inter-City Direct Mail Ltd.

388 **CHAMPION, John Anson**, b. 22 Dec. 35, s. of L. G. Champion, B.D., D.Th. T, 49^3–53^2. Finance Manager, The Plessey Co. Ltd., Ilford, Essex.

389 **EVANS, Roger Wentworth**, b. 7 May 36, 2nd s. of D. W. Evans. T, 49^3–54^2. Brother, 61.

390 **GRAY, David Francis**, b. 18 May 36, elder s. of J. M. Gray. T, 49^3–54^2; XV, 53; H. XI, 54. Trinity, Oxford, M.A. Solicitor. Partner in firm of Lovell, White & King, London, E.C.4. *Ski Club of Gt. Britain, Princes Water Ski Club, Mid-Surrey Hockey Club*.

391 **HALL, Kenneth Julian**, b. 30 July 36, elder s. of E. S. Hall. T, 49^3–53^2. A.C.A. N/S. R.N., 59–61. S/Lt. With Messrs. A. E. Limehouse & Co., Rugby, 62. Brother, 814.

392 **MOURANT, John Nicholas Boyd**, b. 28 Dec. 36, s. of J. P. B. Mourant. T, 49^3–55^2; Minor Scholarship; Cap, 53; XV, 54. Keble, Oxford, B.Sc. Farmer, Home Farm, Swinford, Rugby.

393 **STRETTON, Antony Oliver Ward**, s. of A. T. Stretton. T, 49^3–54^2; S. VIII, 52, Capt., 54; State Scholarship. Exhibition to St. Catherine's, Cambridge, M.A., Ph.D. Stringer Fellow of King's, Cambridge, 64–70. Instructor in Biochemistry. M.I.T., 60–61. Scientific Staff, M.R.C., Laboratory of Molecular Biology, Cambridge, 61–71. Research Associate in Neurobiology, Harvard Medical School, 66–67. Associate Professor of Zoology & Molecular Biology, Univ. of Wisconsin since 71.

394 **WAIN, Andrew John Douglas**, b. 17 Mar. 36, elder s. of C. A. Wain. T, 49^3–53^2. Birmingham Univ. Brother, 1423.

395 **BLANCHARD, Jeremy Rendall**, b. 21 Mar. 36, s. of H. H. Blanchard. B, 49^3–53^3; R. VIII, 53. A.R.I.C.S. Partner of Messrs. Humbert, Flint, Rawlence & Squarey (Chartered Surveyors & Estate Agents).

396 BOWYER, David Wortley, b. 21 May 36, s. of G. Bowyer, C.A. B, 49^3–54^2; R. VIII, 53, 54. Whitbread & Co., 56–58; Advertising Manager in Belgium, 60–63; Commercial & Sales Manager in France, 64. *Hurlingham Club, M.C.C.*

397 BROWN, Philip John Trevett, b. 18 May 36, s. of H. J. Brown, LL.B. B, 49^3–54^2. N/S. R.A., 54–56. Actuarial Trainee, Prudential, 56–58. Shell, Overseas in Trinidad & Nigeria, 58–61. International Computers Ltd. (I.C.L.) since 61. 4 yrs. in Australia. Currently Sales Support Manager, Bristol.

398 HARRISON, Michael James Harwood, b. 28 Mar. 36, s. of Col. Sir James J. H. Harrison, Bt., T.D., M.P. B, 49^3–53^3. Aviation Insurance Broker with Robert Bradford Hobbs Saville & Co. Underwriting Member of Lloyd's. Mercers Company. *Aldeburgh Yacht Club, Royal Yacht Assoc., Sail Training Assoc.* (Council).

399 LINDSAY, Courtenay Traice John, b. 8 Jan. 36, elder s. of Major-General C. T. D. Lindsay, C.B. (OR B 24). B, 49^3–53^3; XXII; State Scholarship. Exhibition to Trinity Hall, Cambridge, B.A. Director, Wogan-Intersceptre Ltd. Brother, 825.

400 NASH-WILLIAMS, The Rev. Piers le Sor Victor, b. 21 Dec. 35, younger s. of the late V. E. Nash-Williams, D.Litt. B, 49^3–54^1; Senior Scholarship, 52. Minor Scholarship to Trinity Hall, Cambridge, B.A. Cuddesdon Theological College, Oxford. Ordained Deacon, 61; Priest, 62. Asst. Curate, St. Mary Magdalene, Milton, Hants., 61–64; Asst. Chaplain and Asst. Conduct., Eton College, 64–66; Classics Teacher, Hurst Court School, Hastings, 66–68; Asst. Curate, St. Peter, Maidenhead, 69–72; Vicar of St. George, Wash Common, Newbury since 72. S.P.C.K.

401 OGILVIE, Angus David, b. 15 Mar. 36, 3rd s. of the late D. D. Ogilvie (OR B 01). B, 49^3–54^2; Levée; Head of House; H. XI, 54. Edinburgh College of Agriculture. Scottish Diploma in Agriculture. Farmer, Owner-occupier. *Royal & Ancient G.C.* Brothers, D. F. and G. H. Ogilvie.

402 ROBINSON, Christopher John, b. 20 Apr. 36, s. of the late Rev. J. Robinson. B, 49^3–54^2; Music Scholar. Organ Scholar, Christ Church, Oxford. Birmingham Univ. Education Dept., M.A., B.Mus., F.R.C.O. Music Master, Oundle School, 59–62; Asst. Organist, Worcester Cathedral, 62–63, Organist since 63. Conductor of City of Birmingham Choir since 64; Principal Conductor of Worcester Three Choirs Festival in 66, 69 and 72.

403 SHARP, Sheridan Christopher Robin, b. 25 Apr. 36, s. of the late R. Sharp. B, 49^3–54^2. Radio News Editor, United Press, Montreal, 56–58; Reuters, London, 59–60; Australian Broadcasting Commission, 61–71, as staff correspondent in Europe, 63–68, and Washington correspondent, 69–71.

404 AINLEY, Martin Alfred, b. 5 Apr. 36, s. of A. J. Ainley. C, 49^3–54^2. Corpus Christi, Oxford.

405 DUNLOP, Colin Victor Craufurd, b. 28 Feb. 36, s. of Major H. C. Dunlop, M.B.E. (OR Tu 27). C, 49^3–52^3. Professional Yachtsman. Served in rank of Lt. in Ghurkas (Malay campaign). At present Naval Architect, Fiji. *R.O.R.C.*

406 EDDOWES, Hugh, b. 26 Feb. 36, younger s. of A. B. Eddowes, M.B., B. Chir. (OR C 14). C, 49^3–54^2; Levée; Head of House. St. John's, Cambridge, M.A. Birmingham Univ., M.Sc., M.I. Mech.E. Previously with Davy & United Engineering Co. Ltd., now a senior Design Engineer with the A.P.V. Co. Ltd. *Seaview Yacht Club.*

407 HARBORD, Martin Jonathan, b. 10 Sept. 36, s. of J. G. Harbord (OR St 16). C, 49^3–53^3; Scholar. State Scholarship to Trinity Hall, Cambridge, B.A. Marconi's, Elliott-Automation, G.E.C. Now as Engineer with I.B.M. (U.K.) Ltd., designing equipment for testing computer peripherals.

408 HOLT-WILSON, Alexander Daniel, b. 30 Apr. 36, younger s. of Cdr. D. S. Holt-Wilson, D.S.O., R.N. C, 49^3–55^2; Levée; Head of House. Pembroke, Cambridge. St. Bartholmew's Hospital, London, M.B., B.Chir. Senior Registrar, Moorfield's Eye Hospital, London.

409 LANCASTER, Jeremy, b. 24 Feb. 36, elder s. of N. G. Lancaster, M.B.E. C, 49^3–54^2. Sw. VIII, 54. Christ Church, Oxford, B.A. Brother, 680.

410 ARCULUS, Robin Gilman, b. 7 Mar. 36, s. of the late F. M. Arculus. K, 49^3–54^2; Draper Prize for English Literature; Capt. of Fencing. Worcester,

Oxford, M.A., A.C.A. Management Consultant with P.E. Consulting Group Ltd., London, S.W.1. *Cavalry Club, United & Cecil Club.*

411 ATTENBOROUGH, Philip John, b. 3 June 36, elder s. of R. J. Attenborough, C.B.E. (OR K 22). K, 49^3–54^2. Trinity, Oxford. Publisher (Director of Matthew Hodder Ltd., and various subsidiary companies). *Rye G.C., Wine Society.*

412 DUTHY-JAMES Christopher Donald, b. 3 Nov. 35, s. of G. Duthy-James. K, 49^3–54^2. Clare, Cambridge. Deceased.

413 MONTAGUE, Andrew Michael, b. 6 Oct. 35, s. of the late E. A. Montague, O.B.E. (OR K 13). K, 49^3–54^2; Levée; Head of House; R. VIII, 52, 53, 54; Winner of the Crick, 54; Holder of Bigside Bags, 54. Magdalen, Oxford, B.A. Dexion Ltd., 59–70. Director of small private company, Patterson Manufacturing Co. Ltd., 70.

414 SEDDON, John Alfred, b. 10 Mar. 36, s. of the late A. Seddon. K, 49^3–53^3.

415 ARMITAGE, Anthony Michael, b. 23 Apr. 36, s. of P. M. Armitage (OR M 20). M, 49^3–54^2.

416 BIRTS, John Donald Watkins, b. 23 Feb. 36, s. of the late I. W. Birts. M, 49^3–54^2; XI, 53–54. Magdalene, Cambridge, B.A. Director, Bain Stutter & Partners Ltd. *Hawks Club, Bath Club.*

417 BLAIKLEY, Ian Faraday, b. 28 Mar. 36, younger s. of J. B. Blaikley, F.R.C.S., F.R.C.O.G. M, 49^3–54^2. Clare, Cambridge, M.I.C.E. Civil Engineer, John Laing & Son Ltd. Brother, 94.

418 DRYSDALE, John Duncan, b. 28 Apr. 36, s. of D. Drysdale. M, 49^3–54^2; Levée; Head of House; Cap, 53; XXII; H. XI, 54. Brasenose, Oxford, B.A. N/S. 2nd Lt. Scots Guards, 54–56. Qualified C.A. with Messrs. Thomson McLintock & Co., Chartered Accountants, Glasgow. United Nations, F.A.O., Rome, 63–64; J. Sebag & Co., Stockbrokers, London, 64–66; Robert Fleming & Co. Ltd., Merchant Bankers, London, since 66. *Vincent's, United Oxford & Cambridge, M.C.C.*

419 JONES, Stuart Bristow, b. 7 Nov. 35, s. of the late A. Jones. M, 49^3–53^2. F.C.A., 73. N/S. R.N., 54–55. Articled Hibberd Bull, Gow Ford & Co., Bournemouth, 56–61. Price, Waterhouse & Co.,

62–64. A.C.A. Joined Philip Hill Higginson Erlangers, now Hill Samuel & Co., 64. Went to South Africa for Company, 66. Alternate Director, The Hill Samuel Group (S.A.), 70. Manager, Issues and Mergers Dept. *Rand Club, Johannesburg Country Club.*

420 MARSHALL, David Alexander Cadman, b. 29 Dec. 35, younger s. of Dr. G. G. Marshall, M.B., Ch.B., D.P.H., D.A. M, 49^3–54^2; Cap, 52; XI, 52, 53, Capt., 54; H. XI, 54. Brasenose, Oxford. Brother, J. C. Marshall.

421 PARKYN, Roger Francis, b. 18 Dec. 35, s. of R. Parkyn. M, 49^3–54^2; XV, 53. Corpus Christi, Cambridge.

422 PRESTON, Simon Huson, b. 22 Apr. 36, s. of Sir K. H. Preston (OR M 15). M, 49^3–53^3; Levée; Head of House; XV, 53. Trinity, Oxford, M.A. Mass. Institute of Technology, U.S.A. M.Sc. Marketing Director. *Royal Yacht Squadron.* Son, Giles Kenneth Huson, M, 73^2–.

423 ROSE, Edward McQueen, b. 2 Sept. 36, s. of H. R. Rose, 49^3–55^2; XV, 52, 53, 54; XI, 52, 53, 54, Capt., 55. Sidney Sussex, Cambridge,M. A. Farmer, Director of Companies in rubber manufacture, motor engineers, merchanting of insulants. *Hawks, M.C.C., R. Ashdown Forest G.C.*

424 WILKINSON, Jeremy Squire, b. 4 June 36, elder s. of P. S. Wilkinson. M, 49^3–54^2. Selwyn, Cambridge, M.A., LL.B. Solicitor, 62. Partner, Addleshaw Sons & Latham of Manchester. *St. James's Club, Manchester.* Brother, 1001.

425 BOOTH, James Morley, b. 14 Aug. 35, elder s. of the late W. R. Booth. SF, 49^3–53^2. Royal (Dick) School of Veterinary Studies, Edin. Univ., Bachelor of Vet. Med. & Surg., M.R.C.V.S. Veterinary Surgeon in private practice. Presently Head of Veterinary Research Unit of M.M.B.

426 GALLOWAY, Malcolm MacLellan b. 26 June 36, s. of J. W. Galloway. SF, 49^3–54^2. Cirencester Agricultural Coll. Farmer. *Lansdowne Club.*

427 HALL, Christopher Sandford, b. 9 Mar. 36, s. of Brig. G. S. Hall, T.D., LL.B. SF, 49^3–54^2. Trinity, Cambridge, B.A. Solicitor. Partner in Cripps Harries Hall & Co., Tunbridge Wells. T.D. *Cavalry Club.*

428 **HAWORTH, Timothy Goodier,** b. 9 May 36, s. of S. A. Haworth (OR M 17). SF, 49³–54². Grenoble Univ. Trinity, Cambridge, F.C.A. Arthur Young & Co., 59–68. Commonwealth Development Corp., 68–72. *Bath Club.*

429 **HENDERSON, Bruce Trevor,** b. 11 Nov. 35, younger s. of Col. C. R. Henderson, I.M.S. (Retired). SF, 49³–53². Gonville & Caius, Cambridge. Wiggins Teape Paper Mills Ltd., 58–63. Asst. Development Man., Star Paper Mills Ltd., Blackburn, 63.

430 **PORTER, Richard Henry Downham,** b. 8 Apr. 36, s. of R. Porter. SF, 49³–53². Royal Agricultural College, Cirencester. Agricultural Office, Victorian Dept. of Agriculture, Warragul, Australia.

431 **WEBSTER, James Bruce Lindsay,** b. 10 Oct. 35, s. of the late F. L. Webster. SF, 49³–54²; XV, 53; XI, 54; H. XI, 53, Capt., 54. Cambridge. St. Thomas's Hospital, London, 60–64. M.B., B.Chir. Medical Practitioner, Hayling Island. *Hawks Club, Cambridge.*

432 **BARRATT, Brian Julian,** b. 29 Aug. 35, elder s. of Capt. G. A. Barratt, R.N. (Retired). Sh, 49³–53². Computer Programming, Friden Inc., N.Y., U.S.A. N/S. R.N. 12½ yrs. Banking, Barclays Bank International Ltd.; 3 yrs. Investment Banking, Slater Walker & Withers Ltd. Now Horticulture, Hillier & Sons. Brother, 1466.

433 **CRAWLEY, Thomas Henry Raymond,** b. 17 May 36, 2nd s. of C. W. Crawley. Sh, 49³–54². Trinity, Cambridge, M.A. Solicitor. Partner, E. F. Turner & Sons, London, W.C.1. Brothers, 38 and 1084.

434 **CURRIE, Gilbert Allan Adam,** b. 1 Dec. 35, s. of the late Major A. P. Currie, M.C. Sh, 49³–54²; Levée; XI, 52, 53, 54; XV, 52, 53, Capt.; H. XI, 53, 54; Fives IV, 52. Merton, Oxford, M.A. Barrister. Legal Adviser, Tunnel Cement Ltd.

435 **HOLLOWAY, Anthony Paul,** b. 29 June 36, s. of A. G. Holloway. Sh, 49³–53². A.C.A., 59. The Metal Box Co. Ltd., 60. Branch Factory Accountant, 63.

436 **MACKERRACHER, Ronald Julian,** b. 26 Jan. 36, s. of the late G. Mackerracher, M.B., Ch.B. Sh, 49³–53². Contracts Officer, Rolls-Royce Ltd., Aero Engine Div., Derby.

437 **MOORES, Nigel Farrand,** b. 25 Jan. 36. Sh, 49³–53³.

438 **WILLIAMS, David Malcolm Younger,** b. 16 Dec. 35, s. of N. A. Williams. Sh, 49³–53³; Levée; Head of House; State Scholarship. Classical Exhibition to Gonville & Caius, Cambridge, B.A., A.M.I.Ex. Sales of Capital Goods to countries in the Soviet Bloc.

439 **WOODD-WALKER, Christopher Peter,** b. 13 Apr. 36, younger s. of G. B. Woodd-Walker, M.B., F.R.C.S. (OR St 14). Sh, 49³–54³. Clare, Cambridge, B.A. Midland Silicones Ltd., 60–63. I.C.I. Plastics Division since 63. Brother, 41.

440 **FOLKES, Paul,** b. 27 Mar. 36, younger s. of Lt.-Col. P. L. Folkes. St, 49³–53¹.

441 **HART, John Thornton,** b. 30 Sept. 36, s. of C. E. Hart. St, 49³–54²; Scholar; Evers Leaving Exhibition. Classical Scholar to St. John's, Oxford, M.A. Asst. Master, Stonyhurst College, 60–63; Asst. Master, Malvern College, 63 and Senior Classics Master since 67.

442 **KENT, John Richard Edward,** b. 11 Nov. 35, s. of L. H. Kent (OR St 16). St, 49³–54²; Levée; XI, 54. N/S. Middlesex Regt., 55–56. 2nd Lt. Brasenose, Oxford, B.A., M.I.C.E. Joined Sir Alexander Gibb & Partners, London, Consulting Engineers, 59; Seconded to associated firm of Gibb Petermüller and Partners, Architects and Consulting Engineers, Athens, 69; Associate in said firm, 72. *Oxford and Cambridge Golfing Society.*

443 **LINDSAY, Richard James,** b. 31 Oct. 35, younger s. of Brig. P. L. Lindsay. St, 49³–54². Queens', Cambridge, M.A. The Marconi Co. Ltd. Brother, 128.

444 **MARRIOTT, Martyn Charles,** b. 7 Mar. 36, s. of C. Marriott. St, 49³–54²; Cap. N/S. Welsh Guards, 55–57. Worked with De Beers Group, 57–68. Independent Consultant to the diamond industry; in particular Diamond Consultant to the Government of Botswana from 69. *Rye Golf Club.*

445 **SHAW, Christopher William,** b. 16 Apr. 36, elder s. of Group Capt. G. Shaw, D.F.C., D.L. St, 49³–54². Mass. Institute of Technology; Degree in Mathematics; Advanced Degree in Metallurgy. Co-Founder, Chrmn., Man. Dir. of Micro-Metalsmiths Ltd.; Co-Founder, Chrmn.

of Spectra-Tek U.K. Ltd.; Co-Founder, Man. Dir. of Die Mould Castings Ltd. F.R.S.A., A.F.S. Brother, 755.

446 SURTEES, Anthony Conyers, b. 2 Sept. 35, younger (twin) s. of C. A. Surtees (OR St 21). St, 49^3–53^3; Fives IV, 52, 53; Tennis VI, 52, 53. Balliol, Oxford, B.A. Solicitor, Messrs. Norton Rose Botterell & Roche, London, 60. Brothers, 447 & 2164.

447 SURTEES, Christopher Conyers, b. 2 Sept. 35, elder (twin) s. of C. A. Surtees (OR St 21). St, 49^3–53^3. Balliol, Oxford, M.A. Member of Stock Exchange, London. Brothers, 446 & 2164.

448 VERDEN-ANDERSON, Eric David Herdman, b. 3 Jan. 36, younger s. of E. W. V. Anderson. St, 49^3–53^3. Director of Smith, Anderson & Co. Ltd., Fettykil Paper Mills, Leslie, Fife. Manufacturers of paper, paper bags and other forms of packaging including plastics. Brother, W. J. Verden-Anderson.

449A BLACKFORD, John Andrew, b. 2 Sept. 35, s. of G. A. R. Blackford. Tu, 49^3–54^2. Petty Officer, C.C.F. Naval Section. N/S. Royal Navy, 54–56. A.C.I.I., A.C.I.S. Lloyd's, London, 56–62. Baloise Insurance, Basle, 62–65. Hitti A.G., Schaan, Liechtenstein, 65. Thoeny Textil, Schaan, Liechtenstein since 65. General Service Medal with Cyprus Bar. *British Club* in Liechtenstein (Founder Member).

449B BUCHANAN, Julian Buchanan (formerly Brooker), b. 1 Aug. 36, s. of P. A. Brooker. Tu, 49^3–54^2; S. VIII, 53, Capt. Wye College, Ashford, B.Sc. (Agric.). Lecturer in Animal Husbandry, Jamaica School of Agriculture, 58. Farm Manager, 59–63. Tenant Farmer, 64. Died 2 Aug. 70.

450 COOPER, Roger William Graham, 1 June 36, elder s. of H. T. Cooper. Tu, 49^3–53^2. Solicitor in private practice. Brother, 2092.

451 FRANCIS, Peter, b. 21 Apr. 36, younger s. of F. Francis (OR SH 20). Tu, 49^3–53^3; XV, 51, 52, Capt., 53; XI, 53; H. XI, 53. Royal Naval College, Dartmouth. Underwriting Member of Lloyd's. Director, Howson-Dutton Group of Companies. *Naval & Military, M.C.C.* Brother, 15.

452 HOBSON, David Hugh, b. 11 Aug. 35, s. of the late Capt. A. L. Hobson, R.N. Tu, 49^3–51^3; S. VIII, 51. Chartered Engineer. M.I.Mech.E. Served in R.N., 52–66. Employed as Engineer in Industry.

453 COCKS, David John, b. 19 Sept. 35, elder s. of W. H. G. Cocks, C.B.E. W, 49^3–53^2. Exhibition to New College, Oxford, B.A. Bigelow Teaching Fellow, Univ. of Chicago, 58–59. Bar, 61. Brother, 1046.

454 COX, Peter Goodhall, b. 14 Apr. 36, eldest s. of E. G. Cox. W, 49^3–54^2. Company Director.

455 HASLAM, William Joseph Lionel, b. 30 Jan. 36, 2nd son of J. Haslam, F.R.C.S. W, 49^3–50^2. Bolton Coll. of Tech. Engineering Diploma. Engineering, Director, Haslams (S.M.W.) Ltd., & J. J. Haslam Ltd. *Markland Hill Lawn Tennis Club.* Brother, 148.

456 HIRST, John David, b. 26 May 36, eldest s. of J. R. Hirst. W, 49^3–54^2. Exeter, Oxford, B.A. Middle East Correspondent of "The Guardian", 63. Brothers, 706 & 707.

457 LEES-JONES, Christopher Peter, b. 4 Mar. 36, younger s. of R. W. T. Lees-Jones. W, 49^3–54^2. Associate of Chartered Auctioneers & Estate Agents Institute, 58. J. W. Lee & Co., 60. Director, 61. *Pullin Schools Club.* Brother, 18.

458 RICHARDSON, Timothy Hubert Paul, b. 25 Mar. 36, younger s. of the late C. W. N. Richardson (OR W 15). W, 49^3–54^3; Head of House; Levée; Head of School; Cap. XXII; H. XI, 53, 54; Tom Hughes Leaving Exhibition. Trinity Hall, Cambridge, B.A. Chartered Patent Agent. Partner, J. A. Kemp & Co., Chartered Patent Agents, London, W.C.1.

459 SAVAGE, Miguel Babatunde Richard, b. 3 Nov. 35, s. of R. G. A. Savage, O.B.E., F.R.C.S. W, 49^3–54^2; Cap., 53; H. XI, 54. Trinity Hall, Cambridge.

ENTRANCES IN JANUARY 1950

460 COOTE, James, b. 3 Nov. 36, s. of Sir C. R. Coote, D.S.O. (OR SF 07). SH, 50^1–54^3. Sports Correspondent, "The Daily Telegraph". *Naval & Military Club.*

461 **LACHELIN, Thomas Pierre Hilbury**, b. 23 July 36, s. of P. J. A. Lachelin. SH, 50¹–54². Magdalene, Cambridge, B.A. N/S. Commissioned Rifle Brigade, 4th (Uganda) Batt., K.A.R., 54–56. A.C.A 62. *Lansdowne Club.*

462 **PILLAI, Raghaven (Roger) Sushill**, b. 6 Apr. 36, elder s. of Sir R. Pillai, K.C.I.E., C.B.E., LL.B. SH, 50¹–54². Brother, 764.

463 **THOMPSON, John Cockburn de Forest**, b. 8 June 36, s. of J. de F. Thompson (OR B 12). SH, 50¹–52²; Levée; Head of House; Head of School; Leaving Exhibition. Dewar Travelling Scholarship, 55 (West Africa, S. Africa). University College, Oxford, B.A. Father's business—Scaioni's Studio, Commercial Photography. F.R.G.S. *M.C.C.*

464 **DRAPER, David Warwick**, b. 23 Feb. 36, s. of A. Draper. T, 50¹–54². Imperial College, London Univ., B.Sc., A.C.G.I. Graduate Apprenticeship, B.T.H. Co. Ltd., Rugby. Chartered Engineer. M.I.E.E. Chief Engineer, Industrial Applications, G.E.C., Elliott Ellectrical Projects Ltd., Boughton Road, Rugby. *Draycote Water Sailing Club.*

465 **GEBBELS, David Edward**, b. 14 June 36, youngest s. of the late H. T. J. Gebbels. T, 50¹–54².

466 **HERBERT, Clair Geoffrey Thomas**, b. 14 Aug. 36, eldest s. of R. G. Herbert. T, 50¹–55¹; R. VIII, 54, 55; Dewar Travelling Scholarship; Winner of the Crick; Minor Foundationer. Tyndale Hall Theological College, Bristol. Ordained. Deacon, 64; Priest, 65. Asst. Curate, St. Saviour's, Nottingham, 64–67; Asst. Curate, St. Matthew's, Harwell with All Saint's, Chilton, Berks., 67–70. At present Vicar of St. Mary's, Bucklebury with Marlston, Berks. since April 70. Fellowship of Evangelical Churchmen.

467 **McCONNELL, Brian James**, b. 8 June 36, s. of J. L. McConnell. B, 50¹–54². Gonville & Caius, Cambridge, M.A. Associated Lead Manufacturers Ltd. since 59.

468A **BROWN, Nigel Sime**, b. 27 Aug. 36, younger s. of the late M. G. H. Brown (OR K 21). K, 50¹–54³; S. VIII, 53. Trinity, Cambridge. Brother, 163.

468B **MILLAR, Luke**, b. 9 Jan. 37, younger s. of the late G. A. Millar, M.C. (OR K 09). K, 50¹–54³.

469 **POOLE, Anthony Arthur Croker**, b. 30 June 36, s. of Lt.-Col. A. E. C. Poole (OR C 14). SF, 50¹–54². Emmanuel, Cambridge.

470 **BOOT, Benjamin Edward**, b. 10 Aug. 36, elder s. of B. E. Boot. Sh, 50¹–53³. Christ's, Cambridge. Farming. Brother, 787.

471 **HIRST, John Robert Antony**, b. 12 July 36, elder s. of R. T. Hirst. Sh, 50¹–54². Queens', Oxford, M.A. Sales Director, C. & J. Hirst & Sons Ltd. (Fancy Woollen Cloth Manufacturers). Brother, 909.

472 **EVANS, Edward James John**, b. 23 Aug. 36, s. of J. G. Evans. Tu, 50¹–54¹; XV.

473 **MURCHISON, Roderick Charles Patrick**, b. 7 July 36, younger s. of the late R. C. Murchison (OR W 13). Tu, 50¹–54²; Levée; Head of House; XV, 52, 53, Capt., 54. N/S. R.N.V.R., 54–56. Bowater Packaging Ltd., 57–60. P.R.O., Galitzine & Partners, 61–63. Hodgkinson Partners, 63. P.R.O., Courage (Eastern) Ltd., London. Brother, 331.

474 **SHARP, Andrew Tabuteau**, b. 16 June 36, younger s. of Capt. A. D. Sharp, R.N.V.R. Tu, 50¹–54³. N/S. R.N. Midshipman (S), 55–57. Lt. R.N.R. Self-employed running Companies engaged in Finance & Property Development. Wildfowl Trust.

475 **WELDON, Leonard Anthony**, b. 28 June 36, elder s. of L. E. Weldon. Tu, 50¹–54³. Chrmn., Weldon & Wilkinson Ltd., Nottingham, Dyers & Finishers of Textiles. Dir., Anthony Mordern & Sons Ltd., and Mortensen Water Purification Ltd. *Carlton Club, Nottinghamshire Club, Nottingham.*

ENTRANCES IN MAY 1950

476 **CHARVET, Richard Christopher Larkins**, b. 12 Dec. 36, s. of P. E. Charvet. SH, 50²–54³. Director of Killick Martin & Co., Ltd., & Killick Martin Travel & Co. Ltd. Member of the Court of Common Council of the City of London. R.D. *City Livery Club.*

477 **FAGAN, Brian Murray**, b. 1 Aug. 36, elder s. of B. W. Fagan, C.B.E., M.C. (OR SH 06). SH, 50²–54². Pembroke, Cambridge, M.A., Ph.D. Keeper of Pre-

history, Livingstone Museum, Zambia, 59–65. Director, Bantu Studies Project, British Institute for History and Archaeology in East Africa, 65–66. Visiting Associate Professor, Univ. of Illinois, 66–67. Professor of Anthropology, Univ. of California, Santa Barbara since 67. Associate Dean, College of Letters and Science, U.C.S.B. since 72. F.R.G.S., Royal Anthropological Institute. Guggenheim Fellow, 72–73. Brother, 657.

478 ROBERTS, Michael Collingwood, b. 19 Oct. 36, elder s. of C. C. Roberts (OR SH 14). SH, 50^2–55^2. University of Surrey, B.Sc., M.I.Chem.E., M.I.M.C. Reckitt & Colman Ltd., 62–64. Shell Petroleum Ltd., 64–67. P.A. Management Consultants Ltd. from 67. Brother, 1067.

479 STANFORD, James Keith Edward, b. 12 Apr. 37, younger s. of the late Lt.-Col. J. K. Stanford, O.B.E., M.C. (OR SH 05). SH, 50^2–54^3. R.M.A., Sandhurst. Served 17th/21st Lancers, 56–63. Retired as Capt. Employed by I.B.M. (U.K.) London, 66–72. Since 72 joined Paterson Zochonis, W. African Traders, Manchester. *Cavalry, St. James's, Manchester.*

480 EDWARDS, John Herbert, b. 22 Aug. 36, s. of H. Edwards. T, 50^2–53^1.

481 FRANKLIN, David Hamilton, b. 3 Aug. 37, s. of S. H. Franklin. T, 50^2–56^2; Benn Scholarship; Levée; Head of House; Head of School. Leaving Exhibition, Royal College of Vet. Studies, Edinburgh Univ., B.Sc., M.B., Ch.B. Dept. of Medicine, Edinburgh Royal Infirmary.

482 BOLTON, Alexander John Osborne, b. 25 Nov. 36, s. of A. R. C. Bolton. B, 50^2–54^3. Rep., Kearney Sayers & Co. Pty. Ltd., Sydney, N.S.W.

483 FLEMMING, Nicholas Coit, b. 10 Nov. 36, elder s. of Sir G. N. Flemming, K.C.B. (OR SH 11). B, 50^2–54^2. Pembroke, Cambridge, B.A., Ph.D. Chief Consultant, Commercial Oceanology Study Group, 65–67. National Institute of Oceanology since 67, now Principal Scientific Officer. Society for Underwater Technology; Underwater Association. Author of "Cities in the Sea", New English Library. Brother, 1095.

484 SOUTHWARD, David Conner, b. 24 Aug. 36, eldest s. of R. Southward, M.B., Ch.B., M.R.C.P. B, 50^2–54^2.

Trinity Hall, Cambridge, M.A. Man. Dir., Lecson Audio Ltd., Bio Science Supplies Ltd. Brothers, 1121 & 2033.

485 JOHNSON, Robert Michael Ward, b. 21 Sept. 36, elder s. of P. C. Johnson (OR C 24). C, 50^2–55^1. Christ Church, Oxford, B.A. Presently temporarily employed packaging in a cotton mill. Brother, 679.

486 PUNSHON, Richard Guy, b. 7 Oct. 36, s. of G. Punshon, M.B., B.S., F.R.C.S.E. C, 50^2–54^2. Trinity Hall, Cambridge, M.A. N/S. Commissioned in 4th/7th Royal Dragoon Guards, 55–56. Member of Lloyd's, 65. With Tennant Budd & Roderic Pratt Ltd. (Lloyd's Brokers) rising to Associate Director, 59–72. Now General Manager of the Appin Group of Companies (Buildings and Property Developers).

487 MARCH, Joseph Maclea, b. 27 July 36, elder s. of G. F. March, C.M.G., M.C. (OR K 07). K, 50^2–54^2. Personal Asst. to Man. Dir., Wholesale Tobacco, 61. Brother, 690.

488 SKINNER, Jeremy John Banks, b. 15 Nov. 36, eldest s. of R. B. Skinner (OR K 25). K, 50^2–55^1; Levée; Head of House; XV, 53, 54. Clare, Cambridge, B.A. Solicitor. Partner, Linklater & Paines. Brother, 1193.

489 APPLEBY, Simon Arundel, b. 9 Mar. 37, s. of the late D. F. Appleby, C.B.E. (OR M 18). M, 50^2–55^2; Sw. VIII, 53–54, Capt., 55. Christ Church, Oxford, B.A. Executive (Industrial Relations & Personnel), R.H.M. Flour Mills Ltd.

490 MILNER, David Selby, b. 10 Mar. 37, s. of Col. A. S. Milner, O.B.E. M, 50^2–55^2; Sir Walter Preston Scholarship. St. John's, Cambridge, M.A., M.I.C.E. Computers Manager.

491 ROBERTS, Sir William James Derby, Bt., b. 10 Aug. 36, eldest s. of the late Sir J. D. Roberts, Bt., O.B.E. (OR M 18). M, 50^2–54^2; Sw. VIII, 53. R.A.C., Cirencester. Farmer. Brothers, 696 & 931.

492 ROBSON, Christopher William, b. 13 Aug. 36, s. of L. Robson. M, 50^2–55^2; S. VIII, 54, 55. Solicitor, Senior Partner, Punch Robson Goundry & McCallum of Middlesbrough, Teeside.

493 SCOTT GRAHAM, Peter James, b. 24 Oct. 36, s. of G. Scott Graham. M,

50^2–54^2. St. John's, Cambridge. Chartered Accountant, I.C.I. Ltd., London.

494 WATKINS, Hubert John, b. 25 Sept. 36, eldest s. of Lt.-Col. H. B. Watkins, O.B.E., M.C., D.C.M., D.L. M, 50^2–54^3; XV, 52, 53, Capt., 54. Hertford, Oxford, B.A. The Radnorshire Co. Ltd., 59. Director, 62. High Sheriff of Radnorshire, 73.

495 BAYLEY, Michael John, b. 9 Nov. 36, eldest s. of Cdr. J. M. Bayley, D.S.C., R.N. (OR SF 20). SF, 50^2–54^3. Corpus Christi, Cambridge, B.A. Lincoln Theological College. Deacon, 62; Priest, 63. Curate, Church of the Epiphany, Gipton, Leeds, 62–66. Diploma in Social Studies, Sheffield Univ., 66–67. Since 67 Research worker in Dept. of Sociological Studies with the care of the mentally handicapped; part-time tutor in Social Administration and honorary assistant curate in the parish of St. Mark's, Broomhill, Sheffield. Ph.D. Sheffield Univ., 72. Author of "Mental Handicap and Community Care".

496 CHIENE, John, b. 27 Jan. 37, s. of J. Chiene, O.B.E. SF, 50^2–55^1. Queens', Cambridge, M.A. Member, Council, Society of Investment Analysts. Managing Partner, Wood, Mackenzie & Co. (Stockbrokers). *New Club (Edin.), Cavalry Club.*

497 TURNER, The Hon. James Andrew, b. 23 July 36, eldest s. of the Rt. Hon. Lord Netherthorpe, LL.D., B.Sc. SF, 50^2–55^1; Levée; Head of House; XV, 53, 54, Capt., 55; XXII, 54. Pembroke, Cambridge. Chartered Accountant. Vice-Chrmn., Dalgety Ltd. Dir., Lazard Bros. & Co. Ltd., Babcock & Wilcox Ltd., The Commercial Bank of Australia Ltd. Member of the Covent Garden Market Authority. Brothers, 1152 & 2397.

498 BIRTLES, John Fiddian, b. 13 Aug. 36, younger s. of R. A. Birtles, M.B.E. Sh, 50^2–53^3. Royal Agricultural College, A.R.I.C.S., A.I.Ag.S. Principal, Land Agent, Multiple Accounting Services Ltd. Brother, A. F. Birtles.

499 BRADSHAW, Richard George, b. 27 Aug. 36, 2nd s. of H. D. Bradshaw (OR W 23). Sh, 50^2–54^2. 1st Green Jackets, 54–59. Commissioned, 55. Tea Taster, J. Lyons & Co., 57–59. Nairobi, 59–60. Tea Broker, Wilson Smithets & Co., 60. Partner, 63. *International Sportsmens', Jesters & Green Jackets Clubs.*

500 EDWARDS, Christopher Hugh Charlton, b. 8 Sept. 36, eldest s. of W. C. Edwards. Sh, 50^2–54^2; Sw. VIII, 51–53, Capt., 54. F.C.A. Director, Mantle Steels Ltd., a private Company. Brothers, 788 & 1911.

501 ROBERTSON, James Douglas, s. of H. D. Robertson, M.R.C.S., L.R.C.P. Sh, 50^2–53^2. C.Eng., M.I.C.E., M.Inst.-H.E. Civil Engineer.

502 CRAWFORD, Gavin Fleming, b. 14 Sept. 36, s. of the late Rev. W. Crawford, B.D. St, 50^2–54^2. Pembroke, Cambridge, B.A., Dip. Ag. Scottish Agricultural Industries (Technical Rep.), 60–64. Shell International Chemicals Ltd., Agricultural Chemicals Marketing since 64. With Shell in São Paulo, Brazil since 72. *Caledonian Club, London.*

503 DYKES, John Bryan, b. 15 Sept. 36, s. of J. E. H. Dykes. Tu, 50^2–55^1; XV, 54.

504 O'SULLIVAN, Daniel Stewart, b. 23 Aug. 36, younger s. of Judge D. N. O'Sullivan. Tu, 50^2–54^2. Gonville & Caius, Cambridge.

505 WINDRED, Richard Graham, b. 16 July 36, s. of the late G. L. Windred. Tu, 50^2–55^1; Levée; Head of House; State Scholarship. King's, Cambridge, B.A. Trainee, Joseph Rank Ltd., 60. P.A. Group Scientific Adviser, Rank Hovis McDougall Ltd., 62.

506 CROFT, Maurice Bootheway, b. 4 July 36, s. of M. J. Croft. W, 50^2–53^2.

507 HASLAM, Timothy Paul, b. 22 Sept. 36, s. of C. S. Haslam, T.D. W, 50^2–53^2. N/S., 54–56. Buyer, E. S. & A. Robinson, 57. *R.A.C.*

508 RANDALL, Peter Lionel Michael b. 7 Oct. 36, s. of R. F. Randall. W, 50^2–54^2.

509 STIRRUP, David Michael, b. 17 July 36, elder s. of T. C. Stirrup, M.C. W, 50^2–53^3; XV, 53; Sw. VIII, 53. Vice-Pres. and Gen. Man., Alexander Craig Ltd., Toronto, Canada. Brother, 1662.

510 WALKER, Peter Elton, b. 31 July 36, s. of C. W. Walker, M.B., B.Chir. (OR W 17). W, 50^2–54^2. St. John's, Cambridge, M.A., M.B., B.Chir. St. Thomas's Hospital, M.R.C.P., D.C.H. Paediatrician, Farnham H.M.C. Group Hospitals and N.-W. Surrey H.M.C. Group Hospitals.

511 WILSHERE, Jonathan Edward Owen, b. 24 June 36, younger s. of the late H. O. Wilshere, M.B.E. W, 50^2–54^3. F.C.I.I., A.C.I.S., F.B.S.C., L.H.G. Underwriter, Commercial Union Assurance Co. Ltd., 55–62. Asst. Man., Leics. Trade Protection Soc., 62–65. Asst. Man., Bradford Building Society at Leicester, 66–69. Proprietor, Chamberlain Music and Books, Leicester since 70. Proprietor, Leicester Research Services (Genealogical Researchers and Publishers of Historical Booklets) since 68. Lecturer in History, Leicester Adult Education Centre since 70. Patron, Leicester Philharmonic Society and Leicester Bach Choir. Member, Leicester Chamber Music Club. Article on Leicestershire for "The Guardian" newspaper, 71. Armorial Bearings granted by College of Arms, 67.

ENTRANCES IN SEPTEMBER 1950

512 BARLOW, Paul Charles Hainsworth, b. 7 May 37, younger s. of A. N. Barlow (OR SH 11). SH, 50^3–54^2. Brother, P. N. Barlow.

513 CASTELLO, Simon James, b. 16 Apr. 37, s. of E. J. Castello. SH, 50^3–54^1. Articled Clerk to Accountant, 54–56. N/S. 56–58. Joined Daniel Castello & Sons, 58 (now Castello Parsons & Co.). Member of the Stock Exchange. *M.C.C.*

514 CRAMB, Ewen Cameron, b. 21 May 37, s. of D. R. Cramb, M.D., F.R.C.S.E. SH, 50^3–55^2. Corpus Christi, Cambridge.

515 FAWCETT, John Patrick, b. 15 Mar. 37, younger s. of R. J. Fawcett, F.C.A. (OR SH 20). SH, 50^3–55^2; Cap., 54; H. XI, 53; Tennis VI, 54, 55; Senior Athletics Cup, 54. Cambridge Univ., B.A. Architectural Association School. R.I.B.A. Architect. Brother, 177.

516 HALL, Philip Brian, b. 12 Apr. 37, younger s. of the late J. P. Hall (OR SH 11). SH, 50^3–51^3. Brother, 380.

517 MALCOLM, Timothy David, b. 15 Nov. 36, elder s. of V. N. Malcolm. SH, 50^3–54^2; Tennis VI, 54. Director, Court Line Ltd., London, W.1. *Brooks's Club.*

518 MASSON, Jeremy David, b. 3 Nov. 36, younger s. of A. A. Nassim. SH, 50^3–55^1. Brother, 56.

519 PERCIVAL, Alfred James MacGregor, b. 10 Mar. 37, s. of the late Lt.-Gen. A. E. Percival, C.B., D.S.O., O.B.E., M.C., D.L. (OR SH 01). SH, 50^3–55^1. R.M.A., Sandhurst. Commissioned into the Cheshire Regiment, 56. Dispatches (Malaya), 59. Promoted Major, 69. p.s.c., 70. Brigade Major, 12 Mechanised Bde., B.A.O.R. *United Service & Royal Aero Club, M.C.C.*

520 RICHARDS, Andrew John Marston, b. 26 Feb. 37, s. of O. L. Richards. SH, 50^3–54^2; Sw. VIII, 54.

521 ROBERTS, Christopher William, b. 4 Nov. 37, s. of F. Roberts, M.B.E. SH, 50^3–55^2. Magdalen, Oxford, M.A. Lecturer in Classics, Pembroke, Oxford, 59–60. Entered Home Civil Service, 60. Private Secretary to the Prime Minister since 70. *United Oxford & Cambridge University Club.*

522 TILDESLEY, James Matthew George, b. 14 Jan. 37, s. of J. M. Tildesley. SH, 50^3–55^3; XXII, 54; H. XI, 55; Rackets Pair, 54, Capt., 55. Public Schools Singles Rackets Champion, 55. Queen's, Oxford. Managing Director of Precision Screw & M/S Co. Ltd., Universal Fasteners Ltd., In-X Fastener Corporation, U.S.A., Prefa G.M.B.H. England Squash. Amateur Double Rackets Champion. *Jesters Club, Escorts.*

523 WATSON, Christopher John Hamilton, b. 9 Apr. 37, elder s. of J. P. Watson, W.S., LL.B. SH, 50^3–55^1; Scholar. Scholar of Corpus Christi, Oxford, M.A., D.Phil. Fellow, Merton, Oxford. Research Physicist with U.K. Atomic Energy Authority, Cudham Laboratory. Brother, 808.

524 WHITEMAN, Peter John MacIver, b. 21 Nov. 36, s. of J. W. I. Whiteman (OR SH 14). SH, 50^3–55^1. Hertford, Oxford, M.A. Solicitor. T.D. *United Oxford & Cambridge University Club.*

525 BASTIN, Clive David, b. 13 Mar. 37, s. of L. H. Bastin. T, 50^3–54^2. F.C.A. Partner in Spicer & Pegler, Chartered Accountants, London, E.C.3 (formerly articled to them). *Marine Club.*

526 WATTS, Gordon, b. 21 Jan. 37, s. of E. H. Watts. T, 50^3–54^3; Minor Foundationer; Levée; Head of House. Warwickshire County Scholarship. Oriel, Oxford, B.A. Freelance T.V. Producer/Writer/Director.

527 **WORSTER, John,** b. 23 Apr. 37, s. of E. C. Worster. T, 50^3–55^2; Scholar; Levée; Head of House; State Scholarship; School Leaving Exhibition. Open Scholarship to Trinity Hall, Cambridge, M.A. Sheffield University, Ph.D., A.F.I.M.A., M.B.C.S. Scientific Officer, Air Ministry, 59–62. Senior Scientist, G.E.C./A.E.I., 66–70. Lecturer, Loughborough University since 70.

528 **BLUMER, Rodney Milnes,** b. 26 July 36, younger s. of the late C. E. M. Blumer, F.R.S.E. B, 50^3–55^2; Levée; Head of House. Christ Church, Oxford, B.A. Publishing (finally Editorial Manager, Rupert Hart-Davis Ltd.), 62–70. Currently Writer and Critic; professional name, "Rodney Milnes". Contributor to "The Spectator", "Opera Magazine", "Times Ed. Supp.", "Harpers", "Queen", "Time Out", etc. *Savile Club.*

529 **BULMER, David Edward,** b. 13 May 37, 2nd s. of the late E. C. Bulmer. B, 50^3–55^2. Dir., H. P. Bulmer Ltd. Brother, 235.

530 **CATTERALL, Gerald Charles,** b. 6 Apr. 37, 3rd s. of J. Catterall. B, 50^3–55^1. Brothers, R. A. and J. Catterall and 971.

531 **DEREHAM, Simon William Britten,** b. 19 Sept. 36, eldest s. of the late W. D. Dereham (OR B 18). B, 50^3–54^3. R.M.A., Sandhurst. Marketing Manager. Brothers, 767 & 1264.

532 **DOW, Peter Anthony,** b. 7 Oct. 33, 2nd s. of D. Dow. B, 50^3–51^2; Cap, 51; Sw. VIII, 52. University of Michigan, U.S.A., 51–55. Director of Advertising, Chrysler Corporation, U.S.A. *Country Club of Detroit.*

533 **HARRIS, Julian James Minshaw,** b. 19 Nov. 37, younger s. of H. J. M. Harris. B, 50^3–54^2; Scholar. Christ Church, Oxford, B.A. Market Research with A. C. Nielson Ltd., 59–61. Dir., Test Marketing Services & Export Marketing, 62. Brother, 236.

534 **MACDONALD, William Flint St. Andrew,** b. 3 Nov. 36, elder s. of D. B. Macdonald. B, 50^3–52^2. Glasgow University. Man. Dir., Donald Macdonald Ltd., Dunbartonshire. *Western Club, Glasgow.*

535 **SHAW, George Davidson Geoffrey,** b. 20 Dec. 36, s. of G. M. Shaw, B.Sc., F.G.S. B, 50^3–55^2; VI, Cap, 54; XXII, 54; H. XI, 54, Capt., 55.

536 **BROOKS, Arthur David Bentley,** b. 15 Dec. 36, s. of G. Brooks, T.D., J.P. (OR C 17). C, 50^3–54^3. R.M.A., Sandhurst. Major, The Queen's Royal Irish Hussars. Farmer. *Army & Navy Club.*

537 **FENWICK, Christopher Mark,** b. 24 Aug. 37. C, 50^3–55^1. Brother, J. J. Fenwick & 160.

538 **FROOMBERG, Richard Harry,** b. 30 Nov. 37, youngest s. of A. Froomberg. C, 50^3–55^2. Director of London and County Investments Ltd., Bankers. Brothers, J. S. Froomberg and 81.

539 **MACLAREN, Antony John Shaw,** b. 23 Mar. 37, s. of A. S. MacLaren (OR C 16). C, 50^3–55^2. B.A.(Cantab.). Solicitor.

540 **MARSHALL, Richard John,** b. 2 Feb. 37, s. of R. M. Marshall, B.M., B.Ch. (OR C 20). C, 50^3–51^2. Killed in motor accident, 51.

541 **TODD, David Charles Cargill,** b. 3 June 37, younger s. of G. C. Todd (OR C 21). C, 50^3–55^3. Royal Agricultural College, Cirencester. Certificate of Agriculture. Farming.

542 **WESTCOTT, Michael Grenville,** b. 1 Mar. 37, younger s. of F. C. Westcott. C, 50^3–55^2; Sw. VIII, 55. Pembroke, Cambridge, M.A. Harvard Business School, M.B.A. Executive Vice-President, Davisco, S.A.C., Santiago, Chile. *Leander Club, Harvard Club of New York City.* Brother, A. J. Westcott.

543 **BUCKLEY, Martin Christopher Burton,** b. 5 Oct. 36, s. of Hon. C. B. Buckley, M.B., B.Ch. K, 50^3–54^3; Scholar. Trinity, Oxford, B.A. Bar, Lincoln's Inn, 61. Sir Thomas More Bursary. Cholmeley Scholarship. *United University Club.*

544 **GARRATT, Frederick Paul,** b. 15 May 37, 2nd s. of A. L. Garratt, J.P. K, 50^3–55^2; S. VIII, 53, 54, Capt., 55. Peterhouse, Cambridge, B.A. N/S R.A., 55–57. Rediffusion (Merseyside) Ltd., 61. Manager, West Birmingham Branch, 63. *Junior Army & Navy Club.* Brother, D. J. Garratt.

545 **HILBERY, Anthony David Rowland,** b. 1 May 37, s. of G. P. M. Hilbery, T.D. (OR SH 23). K, 50^3–55^2. Royal Veterinary College. University of London. Bachelor Vet. Med., M.R.C.V.S. Partner,

Bowditch Grime Guthrie & Hilbery, The Veterinary Hospital, Windsor.

546 HUTTON, William Noël, b. 8 Mar. 37, elder s. of Sir Noël K. Hutton, K.C.B. K, 50³–55². Clare, Cambridge, M.B., B.Chir., M.A. Middlesex Hospital, London, W.1, M.R.C.P. Consultant Physician to Wharfedale Group of Hospitals. Research, Nuclear Medicine, Leeds General Infirmary. B.M.A., B.R.S.C.C. Brother, 1404.

547 JARVIS, Franklin Huddleston, b. 30 Nov. 36, s. of F. A. Jarvis. K, 50³–55²; Scholar.

548 LEES, David John, b. 19 Sept. 37, s. of M. Lees, M.B., B.S. K, 50³–54³. University of London, Kings College, LL.B. Solicitor. Sir George Fowler Prizeman. Partner in private practice in Torquay. *Royal Ocean Racing Club.*

549 NIL.

550 NEAME, Colin Roger Beale, b. 11 Dec. 36, eldest s. of L. B. Neame. K, 50³–55²; Levée; Head of House; XI, 54, 55; Rackets Pair, 55; Fives IV, 53. Birmingham University, Diploma in Malting & Brewing. Production Director, Shepherd Neame Ltd., Faversham Brewery. *M.C.C., Ski Club of Gt. Britain.* Brothers, 1783 & 1933.

551 REEVE, Peter Richard Grant, b. 24 Sept. 36, s. of A. R. Reeve. K, 50³–55².

552 SHAWCROSS, Francis Wilfred, b. 3 Nov. 36, s. of C. W. Shawcross, LL.B. K, 50³–55²; S. VIII, 53, 54; Paddison Art Prize. St. John, Cambridge, M.A. (Prehistoric Archaeology). Appt. Lecturer in Prehistory, University of Auckland, N.Z., 61. Senior Lecturer in Prehistory, Australian National University, 73.

553 BRADSHAW, John Robin Whittington, b. 29 Mar. 37, s. of Lt.-Col. J. R. L. Bradshaw. M, 50³–55²; Levée; Head of House; H. XI, 55. Worcester, Oxford, B.A. Articled Accountant.

554 NAYLOR, Procter, b. 17 May 37, youngest s. of the late F. A. Naylor. M, 50³–55². Advertising Agent. Associate Dir., Charles Hobson & Grey. Brothers, J. M. P. Naylor & 264.

555 RACKOWE, Miles David Adam Bulkyn, b. 22 Aug. 36, 2nd s. of S. S. A. B. Rackowe. M, 50³–54². Pembroke, Cambridge, M.A., C.Eng., M.I.E.E. 8 yrs. Coutant Electronics Ltd. Finally as Technical Dir. Now Man. Dir. & Chrmn., Powertron Ltd. Brother, 1434.

556 TANBURN, Nicholas Paul, b. 16 Nov. 36, younger s. of H. S. Tanburn. M, 50³–54³; Waddington Exhibition. Christ Church, Oxford.

557 WASS, Michael Hall, b. 17 May 37, 2nd s. of S. H. Wass, M.S., F.R.C.S. M, 50³–55². Christ's, Cambridge, M.A., A.C.A. Deceased. Brothers, P. H. Wass, 2126 & 2315.

558 ANDERSON, David Paley, b. 19 Oct. 36, 4th s. of L. R. D. Anderson, M.C. (OR SF 00). SF, 50³–55²; XV, 54; XXII, 54, 55. State Scholarship, St. John's, Cambridge, M.A., M.I.C.E., M.I.W.E. N/S. 2nd Lt. R.A., Malaya, 55–57. Asst. Engineer, Messrs. Binnie & Partners, London, 60–67. Senior Asst. Engineer, Nairobi City Council, Kenya, 67–70. With Sir Alexander Gibb & Partners since 70. Nairobi, 70. Senior Resident Engineer, Mauritius, 71.

559 BRADLEY-MOORE, Patrick Ralph, b. 23 May 37, s. of R. Bradley-Moore (OR SF 13). SF, 50³–55²; Cap, 53; XXII, 54; H. XI, 55. Corpus Christi, Oxford, M.A., B.M., B.Ch. St. Thomas's Hospital, Scholar, M.R.C.P., D.M.R.D. Formerly expert on Nuclear Medicine, International Atomic Energy Agency in Vietnam. Now Scientist, Brookhaven. Nat. Lab., Upton, L.I. *Vincent's Club, Harveian Soc.*

560 ELLIOT, Alan Christopher, b. 9 Mar. 37, eldest s. of I. F. L. Elliot (OR M 07). SF, 50³–55²; Cap, 53, 54. Christ Church, Oxford, M.A. Chrmn., Blick National Systems Ltd. *Bath, Buck's, Portland.*

561 KITWOOD, Thomas Marris, b. 16 Feb. 37, s. of P. Kitwood (OR SF 20). SF, 50³–55²; Scholar; Levée; Head of House; State Scholarship to King's, Cambridge, B.A. Wycliffe Hall, Oxford. Bradford University, Psychology & Sociology of Education. Master at Sherborne School, Dorset, 60–68. Master and Chaplain at Busoga College, Uganda, 68–72. Publications: "What is Human?", "A Guide to Advanced Level Qualitative Analysis".

562 LANE, Jeremy Peter, b. 4 June 37, elder s. of the late P. Lane (OR SF 25). SF, 50^3-55^2. Brother, 1007.

563 LEACH, Michael Ernest Humphrey, b. 9 May 37, s. of the late E. H. Leach, B.Sc. SF, 50^3-55^2. Exhibition, Merton, Oxford, M.A. Chief Development Engineer, Borg Warners Ltd., Letchworth, Herts. Holder of British & U.S. Patents for Transmission Control Mechanism for 4-speed Transmission. *Round Table, Letchworth.*

564 WING, Graham Robert, b. 12 May 37, younger s. of the late H. J. T. Wing. SF, 50^3-55^2. Glasgow University, B.Sc., C.Eng., M.I.E.E. Electrical Engineer for Mott, Hay & Anderson, Engineering Consultants, Croydon.

565 ABBOTT, Anthony Thomas Dixon, b. 22 Sept. 36, younger s. of T. D. Abbott. Sh, 50^3-54^2. Brother, J. R. Abbott.

566 CORRY, Martin, b. 29 May 37, elder s. of D. C. Corry, M.D., F.R.C.S. Sh, 50^3-55^2. Queen's, Oxford. Brother, 938.

567 HARRIS, Jolyon Heaton, b. 9 Oct. 36, 2nd s. of M. W. A. Harris. Sh, 50^3-55^1; Scholar; Levée; Head of House; Tennis VI, 53, Capt., 54; Fives IV, 55. State Scholarship. N/S. R.A., 2nd Lt., 55-57. Clare, Cambridge, M.A. Tennis Blue, 60. F.R.I.C.S. With Messrs. Ireland, Chartered Surveyors, Estate Agents & Auctioneers, Norwich since 60. Partner, 63. *Hawks Club, Norfolk Club.* Brothers, 117 & 1762.

568 JARMAN, Colin James Cumming, b. 3 Mar. 37, younger s. of R. Jarman, D.S.C., M.R.C.S., L.R.C.P. Sh, 50^3-54^1.

569 JOHNSON, Nicolas Patrick, b. 5 Apr. 37, s. of W. E. P. Johnson, A.F.C. Sh, 50^3-55^2. New College, Oxford. Perugia Univ., Italy. Shell International Petroleum Ltd., 58-61. Smee's Advertising Ltd., 61-63. Martech Consultants Ltd., 63.

570 MILLER, Alastair Robert John Dunlop, b. 5 Mar. 37, elder s. of J. B. Miller. Sh, 50^3-54^2. University of Edinburgh. Purdue University (U.S.A.). B.Sc., M.Ag., N.D.A. Chrmn., Elba Growers Ltd. (Agricultural Co-operative). Self-employed. Farming. *Gullane G.C.*

571 PRATT, Mark Alistair Johnstone, b. 10 July 36, elder s. of S. J. Pratt. Sh, 50^3-55^1; H. XI, 55; Fives IV, 54, Capt., 55. Clare, Cambridge. Monsanto Chemicals Ltd., Mitsubishi Monsanto Chemical Co., Tokyo.

572 FLETCHER, Giles Timothy Forster, b. 7 Mar. 37, s. of the late W. F. Fletcher. St, 50^3-55^2. Trinity, Cambridge, B.A., Post Grad. courses in Naval Weapon Engineering, 60. Post Grad. courses in Nuclear Engineering, 65. R.N. Staff Course, 73. M.L.E.E. Royal Navy. Present employment from 73, Senior Engineer Officer of H.M.S. *Courageous* (nuclear-powered submarine). Lt.-Cdr. Fellow of the Royal Society of Arts.

573 HOBSON, Nicholas John, b. 7 Apr. 37, eldest s. of J. W. Hobson (OR St 22). St, 50^3-55^2; Levée; Head of House. King's, Cambridge. Advertising Consultant. Man. Dir., Network Advertising Consultants. *Ashridge G.C.* Brothers, 939 & 2557.

574 JEANS, Michael Anthony, b. 21 Sept. 36, elder s. of the late Sir J. Jeans, O.M., D.Sc., LL.D., F.R.S. St, 50^3-54^3. Pembroke, Cambridge, B.A., M.I.M.E. With Louis Newmark Ltd., Croydon.

575 McCARTNEY, Timothy Andrew, b. 1 Jan. 37, s. of A. E. McCartney. St, 50^3-55^2; Paddison Art Prize, 55. Institute of Bankers Examination, Part I. Accountant with the Chartered Bank. Appointments in Calcutta, Bombay, Singapore, Hong Kong, Hamburg and Bahrain from 73. *The Oriental Club, London.*

576 MacLEOD, Ewan Douglas, b. 13 Nov. 36, younger s. of the late D. H. MacLeod, M.S., F.R.C.P., F.R.C.S., F.R.C.O.G. St, 50^3-55^2. Anderson Webb Scholarship in Architecture to Trinity, Cambridge, M.A., Dip. Arch. (Hammersmith), A.R.I.B.A. Working as Principal in Architectural practice on private sector flats & houses both in London and country. *Georgian Group.*

577 McNEIL, Ian David, b. 31 Dec. 36, elder s. of K. G. McNeil, C.B.E., J.P. St, 50^3-55^2; Broker at Lloyd's, 57-66. Underwriting Box at Lloyd's, 66-68. Underwriting Agent at Lloyd's, 68. Dir., Harris & Graham Ltd., 72. Member of Worshipful Company of Musicians. Dir. of New Opera Co. *City Livery Club.*

578 MARSHALL, John Dent, b. 3 May, 37, s. of the late R. M. Marshall, M.B., F.R.C.S., J.P. St, 50^3–54^2; R. VIII, 54. F.C.A. Dir. & Gen. Man., Tarmac Roadstone Holdings Ltd., West German Region, Nürnberg.

579 MAYO, Peter William Francis, b. 22 Sept. 36, s. of F. C. Mayo, M.R.C.S., L.R.C.P., T.D., D.L. (OR St 19). St, 50^3–55^1; Levée; Head of House; Head of School; XV, 54; XI, 54; R. VIII, 53, 54; Open Athletics Cup, 53, 54. Minor Scholarship to Pembroke, Cambridge. Killed in climbing accident in Switzerland on or about 7 Aug. 59.

580 THOMAS, Michael Gavin Lynam, b. 14 Aug. 36, younger s. of T. L. Thomas, F.R.G.S. (A). St, 50^3–55^2; XV, 54; Tennis VI, 53–54, Capt., 55. N/S. Army, 55–57. Trinity, Oxford, M.A. Bank of England, 61–68. Dir., Avoncroft Museum of Buildings, Bromsgrove, Worcs. since 68.

581 WILSON, Patrick Simon, b. 29 Mar. 37, younger s. of M. T. Wilson, M.B.E. (OR St 24). St, 50^3–55^2. Brother, 210.

582 BLACK, William Sebastian, b. 1 Apr. 37, s. of G. W. Black, F.R.C.S., L.R.C.P. Tu, 50^3–55^3; Levée; XI, 55; H. XI, 55. County Scholarship.

583 COGHLAN, Michael Lake, b. 17 June 37, elder s. of K. L. Coghlan (OR Tu 25). Tu, 50^3–55^3; Scholar; Levée. Hampshire County Major Award, Pembroke, Cambridge, B.A. Commissioned in 4th/7th Royal Dragoon Guards, 60–63. Sales and Sales Management in data-processing industry, 63–71. R. P. Martin & Co. Ltd., as a Money Broker since 72. *St. James's Club, Manchester.* Brother, 880.

584 DRUMMOND, David Scott, b. 17 May 37, s. of the late D. Drummond. Tu, 50^3–55^2. Exeter, Oxford, B.A., B.Sc. I.C.I. Ltd., Mond Div., Runcorn, Ches.

585 HARCOURT, Giles Sidford, b. 14 Sept. 36, s. of Rev. Canon M. Harcourt, B.D., B.A., S.T.D. Tu, 50^3–55^2; Cap, 54; XI, 55. Inns of Court (Gray's Inn). Teaching in U.S.A., Sweden and U.K., 56–68. Hospital Research Adviser (N.Y., 64). Westcott House, Cambridge. Ordained, 71. Asst. Curate, Theatre Chaplain, Asst. Polytechnic Chaplain and Asst. Hospital Chaplain, centred on Bishopwearmouth Parish Church, Sunderland, Co. Durham. Illustrator of "Portraits of Destiny" (Sheed & Ward), U.S.A., 66. *The Lansdowne Club, Actors' Church Union.*

586 LEESON, Ian Arthur, b. 13 Mar. 37, s. of A. C. Leeson (OR Tu 26). Tu, 50^3–55^2. University Coll., Oxford, M.A., A.C.A. Partner in Whinney Murray & Co., Chartered Accountants. *Woking G.C.*

587 MACPHERSON, Robert Norman, b. 22 June 37, elder s. of N. C. Macpherson. Tu, 50^3–55^2. Edinburgh Univ., M.A., LL.B. Writer to the Signet. Solicitor in private practice. *R.N.V.R. Club, Scotland.*

588 ODDY, Michael Arthur, b. 8 Mar. 37, younger s. of A. W. Oddy. Tu, 50^3–55^2; XI, 54, 55; H. XI, 55. Textiles, Man. Dir., Ballantyne of Peebles, 65–70. Man. Dir., Midland Hosiery Mills Ltd. since 71. British Amateur Squash Champion, 60–61, 61–62; Amateur Champion Australia, 59; New Zealand, 59; South Africa, 62. Brother, 274.

589 PATTISSON, Peter Richard Merriman, b. 19 Mar. 37, younger s. of R. D. M. Pattisson (OR Tu 22). Tu, 50^3–55^2; Levée; Head of House; Holder of Bigside Bags, 55. Major Scholarship to Pembroke, Cambridge, M.A. St. George's Hospital, London, M.B., B.Chir. Bible Training Institute, Glasgow, Dip.Th. (Lond.). Medical Missionary with Overseas Missionary Fellowship. Present post, i/c Children's Dept., National Tuberculosis Hospital, Masan, Korea.

590 REID, David Alexander Graeme, b. 10 Mar. 37, s. of J. D. G. Reid. Tu, 50^3–55^2. N/S. Commission in Royal Dragoons, 55–57. Royal Agricultural College, Cirencester, F.R.I.C.S., M.R.A.C. 2 yrs. Assistant in Surveyor's office, Dumfries, 61–63. Sole Partner in own Land Agency business, Cupar, Fife since 63.

591 SELKIRK, Andrew Robert Logan, b. 18 Apr. 37, eldest s. of W. L. Selkirk. Tu, 50^3–55^2. Hon. Sec. of N.H.S. New Coll., Oxford, B.A., A.C.A. Left accountancy to launch archaeological magazine, "Current Archaeology", now editor and writer. The Prehistoric Society, The Society for Medieval Archaeology. Brothers, 943 & 1629.

592 TENNENT, Thomas Gavin, b. 5 Apr. 37, s. of T. Tennent. Tu, 50^3–55^2. Oxford Univ., M.A.; Cambridge Univ., Diploma in Criminology. Middlesex Hospital, London Univ., 66–68. D.M.D.P.M.,

M.R.C.Psych. Dir., Special Hospital Research Unit, 69–72. Presently Medical Dir., St. Brendan's Hospital, Bermuda. Fellow of Royal Society of Medicine. *Bath Club.*

593 DAY, Jeremy Robert, b. 19 Dec. 36, 3rd s. of F. C. Day. W, 50^3–55^2. Jesus, Cambridge.

594 LAWSON DICK, Charles Henry, b. 29 Oct. 36, elder s. of the late I. Lawson Dick, M.D., Ch.M., F.R.C.S.E. W, 50^3–54^2. Balliol, Oxford, B.A. Company trainee and manager with the Metal Box Co. Ltd., in Liverpool, London, Malaysia, Kenya and now Leicester from 60. Brother, 1549.

595 MacRAE, Alastair Christopher Donald Summerhayes, b. 3 May 37, s. of the late A. M. MacRae, M.B., Ch.B. W, 50^3–55^3; Levée; Head of House; State Scholar; Leaving Scholarship; Dewar Scholarship; Queen Victoria Memorial Prize. N/S. R.N., 56–58 (Commissioned). Lincoln, Oxford, B.A. Harvard Univ., Mass., U.S.A. Commonwealth Relations Office, 62, later Foreign and Commonwealth Office. Now, First Secretary, Head of Chancery, British Embassy, Brussels. F.R.G.S.

596 MEAKIN, John David, b. 19 June 36, eldest s. of C. A. Meakin (OR W 16). W, 50^3–54^2; Scholar. New College, Oxford, B.A., A.C.A., 64. Brother, 1232.

597 MORLEY, Bryan Arthur, b. 20 Mar. 37, twin s. of G. W. R. Morley, O.B.E. W, 50^3–55^2. Solicitor. Leasco World Trade Co. Ltd., London. Brother, 598.

598 MORLEY, Philip Edward, b. 20 Mar. 27, twin s. of G. W. R. Morley, O.B.E. W, 50^3–55^2; Capt. of Fencing. Production Management Trainee, 57–59. Bowater Corp. Ltd., 60–64. Asst. Export Man., Spirax Sarco Ltd., Cheltenham, 64. *Naval & Military Club.* Brother, 597.

599 WEIR, John Fergus, b. 13 May 37, 2nd son of T. K. Weir, LL.B. W, 50^3–55^2; Scholar; Queen's Medal, 55. Exhibition to Balliol, Oxford. Died 14 Oct. 59.

600 WILLIAMS, John Bruce Alexander, b. 8 May 37, elder s. of A. T. Williams, C.M.G., M.B.E. W, 50^3–55^2; Levée; Head of House; Leaving Exhibition. Northern Rhodesia Government Scholarship, 55. Gonville & Caius, Cambridge, B.A. Joined B.O.A.C., 60. Currently District Manager, Switzerland. Brother, 1337.

ENTRANCES IN JANUARY 1951

601 ANSTEY, Simon John, b. 25 May 37, s. of J. Anstey, C.B.E. SH, 51^1–55^2. Trinity, Oxford. Investment Banker.

602 BOWRING, Clive John, b. 1 Sept. 37, s. of G. E. Bowring (OR SH 24). SH, 51^1–55^2. Dir., C. T. Bowring & Co. (Insurance) Ltd.; Dir., The Bowring Steamship Co. Ltd. *Royal Ocean Racing Club, Hurlingham.*

603 CORBOULD-WARREN, Anthony, b. 4 Sept. 37, younger s. of W. Corbould-Warren. SH, 51^1–54^3. New Zealand College. Fruit Farming. Brother, 2.

604 GREEN, Anthony Edward Maurice, b. 25 Aug. 37, elder s. of J. M. S. Green, O.B.E., T.D. (OR SH 19). SH, 51^1–53^2; Cap. R.M.A., Sandhurst, 55–57. Commissioned into 13th/18th Royal Hussars (Q.M.O.) in 58. Served in Europe & Far East until 63. Company Director. Brother, 1851.

605 MAXWELL, Arthur Patrick, b. 8 Oct. 37, elder s. of Col. A. T. Maxwell, T.D. (OR SH 18). SH, 51^1–55^3; Cap, 54; Sw. VIII, 54, 55; Capt. Fencing, 55. Brother, 1699.

606 TAYLOR, Thomas Francis Frederick, b. 9 Aug. 37, 2nd s. of the late D. B. Taylor, O.B.E. (OR B 17). SH, 51^1–55^2. N/S. R.N., 55–57. University College, Oxford, M.A. Solicitor. Partner in Denton Hall & Burgin, Gray's Inn, London.

607 INGRAM, Hugh Albert Pugh, b. 29 Apr. 37, elder s. of A. W. K. Ingram. T, 51^1–56^2; Levée. Emmanuel, Cambridge, B.A. Hatfield College, Durham, 60–63. Ph.D. Demonstrator in Botany, University College of N. Wales, Bangor, 63–64. Staff Tutor in Natural Science, Dept. of Extra-Mural Studies, University of Bristol, 64–65. Lecturer in Botany (Ecology), University of Dundee since 65. Member of Council of Scottish Wildlife Trust since 69. Brother, 2020.

608 WILLIAMS, Roger Galsworthy, b. 3 Mar. 37, s. of the late A. L. Williams. T, 51^1–55^3; Foundationer; Levée. Pembroke, Cambridge, M.A. A.C.A., 66. Chief Financial Accountant, Capseals Ltd. from 73.

609 LEE-LANDER, Paul Edward Michael, b. 23 Mar. 37, younger s. of F. Lee-Lander, O.B.E., M.D., F.R.C.P. B, 51¹–54². Film & Television Casting Director.

610 STABLER, Robert John, b. 12 June 37, younger s. of F. E. Stabler, M.D., F.R.C.S., F.R.C.O.G. B, 51¹–55². Balliol, Oxford, B.A., B.M., B.Ch. Royal Victoria Infirmary (Newcastle Medical School), 60–63. D.M.R.D., F.F.R. Consultant Radiologist, Gateshead Hospital Group & Honorary Consultant Radiologist to Royal Victoria Infirmary, Newcastle upon Tyne.

611 BAINES, Anthony John, b. 28 Sept. 37, s. of the late N. Baines, M.C.C, 51¹–56²; XXII. Sorbonne Univ., Paris. Commercial Union Assurance Group, 59.

612 CHESTERS-THOMPSON, Stephen, b. 4 July 37, s. of S. Chesters-Thompson. C, 51¹–55². Downing, Cambridge, M.A., F.R.I.C.S. Fellow Chartered Auctioneers and Estate Agents Institute. Partner, S. Chesters-Thompson & Son of Manchester, also at Bramhall, Cheshire and Heaton Moore, Stockport. *Old Rectory Club, Manchester, Bramhall G.C.*

613 PONTÉ, Alan Joseph, b. 19 Aug. 37, elder s. of Capt. L. Ponté. C, 51¹–55³; Cap. Jesus, Cambridge. General Manager, U.K. & Eastern European Div., Lloyds & Bolsa International Bank Ltd. *Cavalry.*

614 SEELEY, Louis Christopher Robin, b. 28 Aug. 37, s. of Major L. L. Seeley, M.B.E. C, 51¹–55³; Levée; Head of House; XV, 55. Jesus, Cambridge. 1st Secretary, Foreign and Commonwealth Office.

615 CLEMENTSON, John Stewart, b. 2 May 37, s. of T. W. Clementson. K, 51¹–55².

616 KILLICK, Ian Simon, b. 1 June 37, s. of G. C. Killick. K, 51¹–55³; Levée.

617 LARBY, Charles Julian Burton, b. 6 Aug. 37, eldest s. of N. B. Larby. K, 51¹–56¹; Levée. Downing, Cambridge, M.A., LL.B. Barrister, England. Advocate, Kenya. Legal profession. Partner in law firm in Nairobi, Kenya. *East India, Sports & Public Schools Club, Muthaiga Country Club.* Brother, 1281.

618 MILWARD, Timothy Michael, b. 24 Mar. 37, s. of F. J. Milward, M.Ch.,

F.R.C.S. (OR K 16). K, 51¹–55². N/S. R.N.V.R., 55–57, Midshipman. Clare, Cambridge, M.B., B.Ch. St. Thomas's Hospital, F.R.C.S. Now Senior Registrar in Plastic Surgery at Queen Mary's Hospital, Roehampton, London.

619 BULL, Peter Anthony, b. 8 July 37, s. of W. E. A. Bull. Sh, 51¹–55².

620 BIRD, Richard Ashton, b. 23 Sept. 37, 3rd s. of W. E. Bird. St, 51¹–56². University of Sheffield, M.B., Ch.B. Medical Practitioner, Gainsborough, Lincs.

621 BUTLER, John George, b. 16 May 37, s. of G. Butler. St, 51¹–55². Farmer.

622 LITTLEFIELD, Gordon Morgan, b. 14 May 37, s. of Capt. G. A. Littlefield, U.S. Navy. St, 51¹–51³. U.S. Navy Academy.

623 SHERRARD, Anthony Clifton, b. 19 Oct. 37, s. of G. W. E. Sherrard. St, 51¹–55³; Levée; Head of House; Cap, 54.

624 WILD, Michael John Tylden, b. 26 June 37, eldest s. of R. S. Wild (OR SF 23). St, 51¹–55²; XXII, 55. Completed N/S., 56–58. Joined A. E. Wild & Co. Ltd., 58. Died 12 Jan. 63.

625 SMITH, William Donald Nial, b. 15 July 37, s. of Professor A. G. Smith. Tu, 51¹–56². Edinburgh University, M.A., LL.B., W.S. Solicitor. Partner in legal firm in Edinburgh. *Caledonian Club, Edinburgh.*

626 CARTLIDGE, Piers Julian, b. 13 Feb. 38, s. of J. W. Cartlidge. W, 51¹–56³. Ecole Supérieure de Commerce, Neuchâtel, Switzerland, 56–60. Holder of Procuration in The Foreign Syndicate Department of Credit Suisse, Zürich.

627 DAWSON, William Bruce, b. 30 July 37, s. of G. B. Dawson. W, 51¹–55². Chartered Accountant. Accountant to Tagarts Division of P. D. Timber Ltd. Member of the Powell Duffryn Group.

628 FRANCIS, David Harvey, b. 6 May 37, s. of J. H. Francis, M.B., D.C.L. (OR SF 12). W, 51¹–55²; XXII, 54–55; Fives IV, 55. London University. Dentistry. B.D.S., L.D.S., D.Orth.R.C.S. General Practice. *United Services Club, Nottingham, Notts. G.C.*

629 **FRASER-MACKENZIE, Colin Lionel Angus,** b. 9 July 37, s. of the late Lt.-Col. R. A. L. Fraser-MacKenzie. W, 51^1–55^2. Royal Agricultural College, Cirencester. Capt., Argyll & Sutherland Highlanders. W. D. & H. O. Wills, Bristol. *Junior Carlton Club.*

630 **KIRKWOOD, The Hon. James Stuart,** b. 19 June 37, younger s. of the late Rt. Hon. Lord Kirkwood. W, 51^1–56^2; Levée; Sw. VIII, 54–56, Capt., 56. Trinity Hall, Cambridge, M.A. Partner of Strutt & Parker. A.R.I.C.S., Q.A.L.A.S., 64. *Caledonian Club.* Brother, The Rt. Hon. Lord Kirkwood.

ENTRANCES IN MAY 1951

631 **BURNETT, Timothy Michael,** b. 10 Sept. 37, younger s. of C. W. Burnett. SH, 51^2–55^3; Levée; Head of House. Oriel, Oxford, M.A. Middlesex Hospital Medical School, London, M.B., B.S. Asst. teacher, St. Augustine's Secondary School, Penhalonga, Rhodesia, 59–64. House Physician in Paediatrics at Kettering General Hospital, Northants., 72. Brother, 304.

632 **GEDDES, Euan Michael Ross,** b. 3 Sept. 37, s. of The Rt. Hon. Lord Geddes, K.B.E., D.L. (OR SH 21). SH, 51^2–55^3. Gonville & Caius, Cambridge. Harvard Business School (P.M.D.). Lt.-Cdr. R.N.R. (Retired). Development Manager, P. & O. Shipping Division, P. & O. S.N.C.O. *Royal Lymington Yacht Club.*

633 **GORMAN, Max Edward Wemyss** b. 19 June 37, elder s. of Sqn. Ldr. E. Gorman. T, 51^2–55^3.

634 **MITCHELL, John Colin,** b. 6 Feb. 38, s. of J. J. Mitchell. T, 51^2–56^2. Nottingham University, B.Sc. Application Engineer, A.E.I. Ltd., Manchester. Now Divisional Technical Director, Advance Electronics Ltd., Bishop Stortford, Herts.

635 **PEACH, Michael Edwin,** b. 7 May 37, s. of the late S. M. Peach, M.Sc. T, 51^2–55^3; Levée; Baines Exhibition. Exhibition to Jesus, Cambridge, M.A., Ph.D. N.A.T.O. Research Fellow, Technische Hochschule, Graz, Austria, 62–63. Research Fellow, University of Göttingen, Germany, 63–65. Asst. Professor, Dalhousie University, Halifax, Canada, 65–66. Lecturer, Loughborough Univ. of

Technology, 66–67. Acadia University, Wolfville, Nova Scotia, Canada, Asst. Professor of Chemistry, 67–71, Associate Professor of Chemistry since 71. Fellow, The Chemical Society (London). Member, Chemical Institute of Canada.

636 **BOOTH, Timothy George,** b. 20 July 37, s. of G. N. Booth. B, 51^2–55^2. Manchester University, M.I.C.E., C.Eng. Roads Engineer in the North-West Road Construction Unit.

637 **STENHOUSE, Edward Hamilton,** b. 21 Oct. 37, s. of the late Lt.-Col. E. E. Stenhouse, D.S.O. (OR B 16). B, 51^2–55^3; Cap, 55. R.M.A., Sandhurst. Gazetted to King's Dragoon Guards, 57; served in Malaya, 58. Then with the Queen's Dragoon Guards in Germany, 59–64. School of Tank Technology, 65. N. Ireland, 66 and Aden and Sharjah, 66, 67 as Squadron 2nd in Command; England, U.S. as Trials Officer, 68. R.M.C., Shrivenham, 70. Staff College, Camberley, 71. Sqn. Ldr. of Q.D.G., 71–72. Staff Officer, R.A.C. Centre, 73–74. Major.

638 **ANDERSON, Lt.-Cdr. Nigel David,** R.N., b. 3 Sept. 37, s. of D. M. Anderson, M.D., F.R.C.P. K, 51^2–55^3. Clare, Cambridge, B.A. Entered R.N. in Electrical Branch, 56, Lt., 61. Submarine Service, 63. Lt.-Cdr., Admiralty Reactor Test Establishment, Dounreay, Caithness.

639 **BOYD, Edward Charles Reynolds,** b. 5 Oct. 37, younger s. of R. H. Boyd, F.R.C.S. K, 51^1–56^1. Brother, 197.

640 **BROWN, Charles Harold,** b. 22 July 37, younger s. of P. B. H. Brown, O.B.E. (OR Tu 13). K, 51^2–55^3; Scholar; Levée; Head of House. Minor Scholar of Trinity, Cambridge, B.A. Harland Engineering Co. Ltd., Alloa, 61. Inst. Mech. Eng., 64. Brother, 249.

641 **KORN, Henry Ernest Thomas,** b. 22 Oct. 37, s. of the late H. A. Korn, M.D. K, 51^2–56^2. University of London, M.B., B.S. The Middlesex Hospital Medical School, M.R.C.P. Medicine, specialising in Haematology.

642 **WHITEHEAD, Francis Edward Paxton,** b. 17 Oct. 37, younger s. of C. P. Whitehead (OR M 18). M, 51^2–55^2. Webber Douglas Drama School, London. Actor/Manager, Artistic Director, Show Festival, Niagara-on-the-Lake, Ontario, Canada. Artistic Director & Manager, Playhouse, Vancouver, B.C., Canada.

643 **BRANDT, Nigel Jeremy**, b. 14 July 37, elder s. of H. A. Brandt (OR SF 15). SF, 51^2–55^2; XV, 54. Florence Univ. N/S. R.N. With William Brandt's Sons & Co. (Insurance) Ltd. *International Sportsmen's Club.* Brother, 1054.

644 **McCLEAN, William John**, b. 19 Oct. 37, s. of J. N. McClean (OR SF 22). SF, 51^2–56^2. Trinity, Cambridge, B.A. (Estate Management). Q.A.R.I.C.S., 64. Chartered Surveyor with G. M. V. Winn & Co., of Stamford Bridge, York.

645 **PUGH, Timothy William**, b. 6 Oct. 37, elder s. of W. I. Pugh. SF, 51^2–56^2; Cap, 55. University College, Oxford. Publishing, Oxford University Press. Now in America.

646 **SKAILES, John Anthony Derrick**, b. 19 Jan. 38, s. of the late G. A. D. Skailes. Sh, 51^2–56^1. A.C.A. Member of the London Stock Exchange, with Vivian Gray & Co.

647 **COLSTON, Colin Charles**, b. 2 Oct. 37, younger s. of E. L. Colston. St, 51^2–55^2. English-Speaking Union Exchange Scholarship. The Gunnery, Washington, Connecticut, U.S.A. Trinity Hall, Cambridge, M.A. Barrister. Practised on Midland Circuit since 62. *Northampton & County Club.*

648 **EDWARDS, Charles Marcus**, b. 10 Aug. 37, s. of J. B. Edwards. St, 51^2–55^1; Senior Scholarship. Open Scholarship to Brasenose, Oxford, B.A. Bar, Middle Temple, 62. H.M. Diplomatic Service, Spain, S. Africa, Laos & Whitehall, 60–65. In practice as Barrister since 65. F.R.G.S. *Beefsteak Club.*

649 **LANG, Ronald Fulton Stewart**, b. 28 Aug. 37, elder s. of J. F. Lang, D.S.C. St, 51^2–55^3. S. VIII, 54, 55, Capt., 55. Insurance Broker, 59. Underwriting Member of Lloyd's, 61. *Western Club, Glasgow.* Brother, 1088.

650 **HAMILTON, Alexander**, b. 29 Jan. 38, s. of Mrs. M. P. H. Hamilton. Tu, 51^2–55^2. North Western Univ., Chicago, U.S.A.

651 **RAINEY, George Vladimir**, b. 10 Oct. 37, eldest s. of F. T. Rainey. Tu, 51^2–55^3. Trinity, Cambridge, B.A. (Resident French Society). Dipl. I.N.S.E.A.D., Fontainebleau. Marketing, Publishing. Currently, Syndication, "Daily Telegraph". *Royal Corinthian Yacht Club.*

652 **GILBERT, Jonathan Sinclair**, b. 29 Sept. 37, 2nd s. of B. H. Gilbert. W, 51^2–55^2. N/S. 14/20 King's Hussars, 2nd. Lt. Member of Lloyd's and Dir. of Bland Welch & Co. Ltd., Lloyd's Brokers, part of Montagu Trust Group. *M.C.C., Addington G.C., O.R.G.S. Committee.* Brother, 1660.

653 **MACKIE, Patrick**, b. 2 Nov. 37, youngest s. of the late J. H. M. Mackie (OR W 07). W, 51^2–56^2; Levée; Head of House; H. XI, 56, XXII. Trinity Hall, Cambridge, M.A. Schoolmaster at a Preparatory School. Brother, 175.

ENTRANCES IN SEPTEMBER 1951

654 **ABBOTT, Roderick Evelyn**, b. 16 Apr. 38, eldest s. of S. E. Abbott, O.B.E. (OR SH 24). SH, 51^3–56^2; Levée; Head of House. Exhibition to Merton, Oxford, B.A. N/S., 56–58. Asst. Principal, later Principal, Board of Trade, 62–71. Foreign & Commonwealth Office, at present on special leave with European Communities Commission. *Royal Commonwealth Society.* Brothers, 945 & 2004.

655 **CHARLESON, Alasdair**, b. 31 Mar 38, s. of C. Charleson. SH, 51^3–52^3. R.M.A., Sandhurst.

656 **CLARKE, John Stephen Astley**, b. 3 May 38, 2nd s. of C. A. Clarke, M.D., F.R.C.P. SH, 51^3–55^3; Scholar; Levée; XV, 55; Dewar Travelling Scholarship; Leaving Exhibition. Scholarship to Corpus Christi, Oxford, B.A. T.V. Producer, Granada T.V., London. Brother, 1548.

657 **FAGAN, Donald Patrick**, b. 30 May 38, younger s. of B. W. Fagan, C.B.E., M.C. (OR SH 06). SH, 51^3–56^2; XV, 55; XXII, 55; XI, 56; H. XI, 56. Rackets Pair, 56, Capt. Shell Mex & B.P. Ltd., P.R.O. for Scotland. Brother, 477.

658 **HIGGINBOTHAM, Denis Ronald**, b. 8 Apr. 38, s. of the late W. R. Higginbotham (OR SH 11). SH, 51^3–56^2. Strathclyde Univ., Dip. in Pers. Management. Graduate Member of the Institute of Personnel Management. Army Officer, Major. Officer Commanding 522 Company Royal Pioneer Corps, Central Ammunition Depot, Kineton, Warwickshire.

659 **JEBB, David William Hope**, b. 29 Aug. 38, s. of W. H. H. Jebb, M.D. SH, 51^3–56^2.

660 WHYTE, The Rev. Henry Lewis, b. 3 Apr. 38, s. of L. G. Whyte. SH, 51^3–56^2. N/S. R.N., 57–58. Solicitor with Messrs. Hunters of Lincolns Inn, 63–65. Full-time youth work, 65–67. London College of Divinity (C. of E. Theological College), 67–70. A.L.C.D. Ordained Deacon, 70; Priest, 71. Asst. Curate, St. Mary's, Southgate, Crawley, Sussex since 70. The Law Society. *Copthorne G.C.*

661 THURSFIELD, John Richard, b. 2 Oct. 37, elder s. of R. M. C. Thursfield (OR SH 12). SH, 51^3–54^3. With Union Discount Co., London. Brother, 1188.

662 COURTS, Graham Edward, b. 5 June 38, s. of E. W. Courts, B.Sc. T, 51^3–57^2; Levée. Edinburgh Univ., B.Com. Courtaulds Ltd., Coventry. Asst. Unit Accountant, 64.

663 ELLIS, Brian Alexander, b. 11 Oct. 37, younger s. of Mrs. V. E. S. Mitchell. T, 51^3–51^3.

664 MAIN, Brian Joseph, b. 30 Jan. 38, s. of L. W. Main. T, 51^3–56^1; Levée; Cap, 54. Exhibition to Queens', Cambridge, B.A., M.B., B.Chir. Guy's Hospital Medical School, F.R.C.S. Orthopaedic Surgeon. At present Senior Registrar, Royal National Orthopaedic Hospital, London. British Orthopaedic Association. Sir Herbert Seddon Medal, 72.

665 PRICE, David Stewart, b. 9 Oct. 37, elder s. of S. Price. T, 51^3–56^2. Oriel, Oxford, M.A., A.C.A. Chief Accountant, Hall-Thermotank Ltd. of London. *Surbiton Hockey Club.*

666 STOTT, John Richard Rollin, b. 4 Oct. 38, s. of the late Rev. R. Stott, B.D. T, 51^3–56^3; Scholar; Levée. Gonville & Caius, Cambridge. The Middlesex Hospital, London. Imperial College of Science & Technology, London. M.A., M.B., B.Chir., M.R.C.P., D.C.H., D.I.C. Medical Practitioner. Currently Senior Registrar in the Department of Clinical Measurement, Westminster Hospital, London.

667 WILSON, Thomas Roger, b. 15 Apr. 38, s. of T. Wilson. T, 51^3–57^1; Major Foundationer; Levée. Liverpool University, M.A., Ph.D. Scientific Research Staff, Medical Research Council, 60–62. Research Fellow, Liverpool Univ. Medical School, 62–65. Lecturer in Psychopharmacology, Manchester Univ.

Medical School since 65, Hon. Lecturer in Psychology, Liverpool Univ. since 65. Fellow of Royal Society of Medicine. Member of the Royal College of Psychiatrists, Royal Psychological Society, British Pharmacological Society & Institute of Biology.

668 DALGLIESH, Robert Nicholas, b. 19 Feb. 38, s. of S. S. W. Dalgliesh (OR B 21). B, 51^3–56^2; Levée; Head of House; Cap, 54; XXII, 56. Jesus, Cambridge, B.A. Dir., R. S. Dalgliesh Ltd., Man. Dir., Watergate Shipping Co. Ltd. *Royal Thames Yacht Club.*

669 HOLE, Roderick Carr, b. 24 Apr. 38, s. of C. S. F. Hole (OR B 20). B, 51^3–56^2. Trinity Hall, Cambridge, A.C.A. Harmood Banner & Co., London, Chartered Accountants, 61–69. Peat Marwick Mitchell & Co., Frankfurt, 70–71. Security, Pacific National Bank, Frankfurt since 72.

670 JACKSON, Rowland Frederick Hart, b. 27 Apr. 38, s. of F. B. H. Jackson (OR B 21). B, 51^3–56^2; Levée. Trinity Hall, Cambridge.

671 MARSHALL, Christopher David, b. 14 Feb. 38, younger s. of Col. V. J. C. Marshall, T.D. (OR B 18). B, 51^3–54^2. Strasburg University. N/S. R.E., Malaya. Partner in Latin American Corporation S.A., Lima, Peru. *R.N.V.R. Club.* Brother, 312.

672 O'HANLON, John Christopher, b. 10 Feb. 38, eldest s. of G. O'Hanlon, M.C., T.D. (OR B 99). B, 51^3–56^2.

673 ROBERTS, Jeremy Christian, b. 6 Apr. 38, eldest s. of A. C. Roberts. B, 51^3–55^3; Scholar; Levée. Exhibition to Trinity Hall, Cambridge, B.A. Sorbonne Univ., Paris. F.C.A. Partner, Arthur Anderson & Co., London. Brothers, 1119 & 2365.

674 SWINDELLS, Christopher Humphrey, b. 23 Apr. 38, younger s. of the late G. M. Swindells (OR B 13). B, 51^3–54^1. H.M.S. *Worcester*, 54–56. Advertisement Manager.

675 BULMER, John Frederick, b. 28 Feb. 38, elder s. of B. Bulmer. C, 51^3–53^3. Brother, 981.

676 EVERS, Frank Michael, b. 2 Aug. 37, s. of F. A. Evers (OR C 23). C, 51^3–55^2. Birmingham University, LL.B. Solicitor.

677 EYRE, David Allen Geddes, b. 9 Apr. 38, younger s. of F. A. Eyre. C, 51³–56²; Levée. Trinity Hall, Cambridge. Lecturer in Painting, The Rochdale College of Art. Brother, 78.

678 HARVEY, David Ernest, b. 21 Oct. 37, elder s. of J. L. Harvey. C, 51³–55¹; Cap, 34. Harvard University. Graduate School of Business Administration. Chrmn., Black & Decker Professional Engineering Society, 67–68. Phelps-Dodge International Corp. Vice-President Manufacturing. Holder of various U.S. Patents. *Royal Liverpool G.C., Racquet Club, New York.* Brother, 1729.

679 JOHNSON, Edward Reynolds, b. 22 May 38, younger s. of P. C. Johnson (OR C 24). C, 51³–56¹; Scholar; Levée. Exhibition to Corpus Christi, Oxford, M.A. Articled Clerk with Herbert Smith & Co. of London, Solicitors, 61–66. Solicitor, 64. Due to ill-health worked as Asst. Solicitor with Lovell, White and King for only three months. Attending Middlesex Hospital. *Oxford University Occasionals Hockey Club.* Brother, 485.

680 LANCASTER, Richard, b. 25 Mar. 38, 2nd s. of N. G. Lancaster, M.B.E. C, 51³–56³; XI, 55, 56; Capt. of Boxing, 56. Sidney Sussex, Cambridge, B.A., B.Chir., M.B., M.R.C.P., Ph.D.(London). Lecturer in Clinical Pharmacology, Middlesex Hospital Medical School. Royal Society of Medicine. Brother, 409.

681 MITFORD, Timothy Bruce, b. 29 Aug. 37, eldest s. of T. B. Mitford, F.S.A. D.Litt. C, 51³–56¹; Scholar; Levée; Head of House. Scholarship to Corpus Christi, Oxford, M.A., D.Phil. Lt.-Cdr. R.N. (Signals Specialist). *Roman and Hellenic Societies.* Brothers, 1976 & R. E. B. C, 68³–.

682 MOORCROFT, William John Scarlin, b. 29 Mar. 38, younger s. of the the late W. Moorcroft. C, 51³–56²; H. XI. St. Edmund Hall, Oxford. Trustee, North Staffordshire Trustee Savings Bank. Pottery Manufacturer, W. Moorcroft Ltd.

683 PLESNER, Regnar Christian, b. 10 Mar. 34, younger s. of J. S. Plesner. C, 51³–52².

684 PLOWRIGHT, Robert Christopher, b. 13 Jan. 38, elder s. of R. J. O. Plowright. C, 51³–56². Magdalene, Cambridge.

685 CHANNON, Richard Francis, b. 18 Apr. 38, elder s. of J. B. Channon (A). K, 51³–56¹; Scholar; Levée. Britannia R.N. College, Dartmouth. Lt.-Cdr., R.N., 68. Qualified submarine Commanding Officer. Younger Brother of Trinity House. Fishery Protection Squadron; H.M.Y. *Britannia*; H.M. Submarines at home and in Far East, 61–70 (H.M.S. *Olympus*, in command, 68–70), H.M.S. *Falmouth*. About to take up appointment as Staff Officer Operations to Commodore, Clyde, at Faslane. *R.U.S.I., Society for Nautical Research.*

686 CROFTS, John Frederic, b. 2 Jan. 38, elder s. of the late F. B. Crofts. K, 51³–56². East Warwickshire College Further Education. M.Inst.M. N/S. Lt., 56–58. S. Smith & Sons, including service in Australia, Exec., 58–65. G.K.N. Marketing Exec., 65–68. Group Marketing Manager, Automotive Products Group, Leamington Spa since 68. *Naval & Military.* Brother, 1129.

687 GRUNDY, George William, b. 10 May 38, s. of E. Grundy. K, 51³–56². Sidney Sussex, Cambridge. Project Manager, 1900 Programming Ltd., Manchester.

688 HOWORTH, Anthony John Rupert, b. 10 Feb. 38, eldest s. of J. H. E. Howorth (OR K 23). K, 51³–56³. New College, Oxford, B.A., A.I.B. Joined Barclays Bank International Ltd., Trustee Dept., London, 62. Barbados, 64–72. Haberdashers Company, *Royal Commonwealth Society.*

689 LUCAS, Peter David, b. 3 Feb. 38, s. of D. W. Lucas (OR K 19). K, 51³–56². Kings, Cambridge.

690 MARCH, Richard Ogdin, b. 28 Dec. 37, younger s. of G. F. March, C.M.G., M.C. (OR K 07). K, 51³–55². Medway College of Technology. Harper Adams Agricultural College. N.D.A., Dip.Ag., H.A.C. Farming. Brother, 487.

691 MAY, Nigel William Morrison, b. 1 Apr. 38, s. of the late Rt. Hon. W. M. May, P.C., F.C.A., M.P. K, 51³–56²; Scholar; Levée; Head of House. Balliol, Oxford, M.A. C.A. (Ireland). 1st place in Final Exams. In practice as C.A. since 62. formed own firm 64, now partner Thomson McLintock & Co.

692 PASSEY, Michael Leighton Struth, b. 22 Dec. 37, 3rd s. of Professor R. D. Passey, M.C., M.D., B.S., D.P.H.

K, 51^3–55^3; Scholar; Levée; Leaving Exhibition. Trinity, Cambridge, M.A. Solicitor, 63. Legal Practice, 60–67. University Lecturer in Law at Leeds Univ., since 67.

693 TURNER, Adrian Stuart, b. 10 Dec. 37, s. of J. Turner. K, 51^3–56^2; Levée. Gonville & Caius, Cambridge, M.A., LL.B. Diploma in Private International Law. Partner in firm of Solicitors.

694 DRURY, Martin Dru, b. 22 Apr. 38, elder s. of W. N. D. Drury (OR M 22). M, 51^3–56^1; Levée; Head of House. Institut de Touraine, France. 2nd Lt., 3rd The King's Own Hussars, 57. Capt., Army Emergency Reserve, 67. Freeman & Goldsmith of the City of London, 60. Assoc. Dir., Mallett & Son (Antiques) Ltd., London. *Cavalry*. Brother, 1348.

695 PAUL, William Michael Kelso, b. 9 Apr. 38, s. of W. K. Paul, T.D. (OR M 23). M, 51^3–55^3. A.I.C. College of Management, Ealing. Cranfield Technical College, Management Services Faculty. Member of Institute of Data Processors. Senior Internal Consultant, Barrow Hepburn Leather Ltd. *Junior Carlton*.

696 ROBERTS, Andrew Denby, b. 21 May 38, 2nd s. of the late Sir J. D. Roberts, Bt. (OR M 18). M, 51^3–56^2. Christ Church, Oxford. Brothers, 491 & 931.

697 EVERS, David Bruce, b. 12 Jan. 38, eldest s. of C. R. Evers (OR SF 21). SF, 51^3–56^3; Levée; Head of House; Cap, 55. Trinity, Oxford, M.A. Asst. Master and Housemaster, Dragon School, Oxford. *Vincent's (Oxford)*. Brothers, 837, 1599 & 2226.

698 GRANT, Robin William, b. 14 May 38, elder s. of the late Rt. Hon. Lord Grant, Q.C. SF, 51^3–56^2; Levée; H. XI, 55, 56; Leaving Exhibition. Oriel, Oxford, B.A. C.A.(Scotland). Baring Bros. & Co. Ltd., 66–71. Director, Williams Glyn & Co. since 72. *Muirfield G.C.* Brother, 1004.

699 LATHAM, David Russell, b. 9 Nov. 37, younger s. of the late R. Latham, C.B.E., M.C. SF, 51^3–56^2. Director, James Latham Ltd. Brother, I. R. A. Latham.

700 SAUNDERS, Philip William Westbury, b. 4 Jan. 38, s. of P. F. Saunders (OR SF 15). SF, 51^3–56^1; Levée; Head of School; Head of House. Exhibition to Balliol, Oxford.

701 WINGATE-SAUL, Michael Anthony, b. 8 Feb. 38, elder s. of A. S. Wingate-Saul (OR SF 25). SF, 51^3–56^2; Levée; Head of House. King's, Cambridge, B.A. Employed as Asst. Solicitor by Crossman Block & Keith of Gray's Inn, 65–66. Joined Letcher & Son, Ringwood, Hants., 67. Partner, 68.

702 BASS, Nigel Moss, b. 5 Feb. 38, s. of the late E. W. Bass. Sh, 51^3–56^2. Hertford, Oxford.

703 FLEMING, Leslie Drummond, b. 22 Feb. 38, elder s. of J. P. Fleming, M.B., Ch.B. Sh, 51^3–55^3. Was employed on the commercial side of a Scottish steel company until it was requisitioned by British Steel Corp. Now partner in very small garden machinery company.

704 FOX, James Ingham Staley, b. 8 May 38, 2nd s. of H. S. Fox. Sh, 51^3–56^1. Northampton Gen. Man., Johnston Brothers (Dyers) Ltd. Brother, 1802.

705 HALL, David Francis Elsmie, b. 15 May 38, s. of Lt.-Col. G. E. Hall. Sh, 51^3–56^2. Edinburgh Univ.

706 HIRST, Robert James, b. 14 May 38, 3rd s. of J. R. Hirst. Sh, 51^3–56^2; R. VIII, 55, 56. Brothers, 456 & 707.

707 HIRST, Raymond Walter, b. 14 May 38, 2nd s. of J. R. Hirst. Sh, 51^3–56^2; R. VIII, 55, 56. International Sales, Plastics Industry. R.A.F.V.R.(T) Officer. *Yorkshire Gliding Club*. Brothers, 456 & 706.

708 JAMESON, James Neil St. Clair, b. 31 Jan. 38, s. of A. St. C. Jameson, W.S. Sh, 51^3–56^2. Edinburgh Univ., B.L. Writer to the Signet. Partner, Boyd Jameson & Young, W.S., Leith, Edinburgh. *Royal Forth Yacht Club*.

709 PATTULLO, David Bruce, b. 2 Jan. 38, s. of the late C. A. Pattullo, M.C. W.S. Sh, 51^3–56^2; Levée; H. XI, 56. Hertford, Oxford, B.A., A.I.B.S. Investment Manager, Bank of Scotland from 71. General Manager, Bank of Scotland Finance Co. Ltd. from 73. N/S., 2nd Lt., Royal Scots.

710 SCOTT, David Thurburn, b. 20 July 37, eldest s. of A. T. Scott, M.Sc. Sh, 51^3–52^2.

711 SLATER, Alan Humphrey, b. 27 Sept. 37, s. of A. R. O. Slater, F.C.A.

Sh, 51³–56¹; Scholar; Levée; Head of House; State Scholar. Minor Scholarship to Queens', Cambridge.

712 WISHART, George Brian Hood, b. 3 May 38, younger s. of D. F. Wishart. Sh, 51³–56². Clare, Cambridge, B.A. Director, D. F. Wishart & Co. Ltd., Edinburgh.

713 BRIGHT, Peter Edward, b. 21 Mar. 38, s. of T. B. Bright. St, 51³–56³; Levée; Head of House; Leaving Exhibition. Major Scholarship to Trinity, Cambridge, M.A., C.Eng., M.I.Mech.E. Shell International Petroleum Co. Ltd., Shell Centre, London.

714 COLTMAN, Arthur Leycester Scott, b. 24 May 38, s. of A. C. Coltman. St, 51³–56²; Levée. Exhibition to Magdalene, Cambridge, B.A. Diploma in Business Studies, Manchester Business School, 69. Member of H.M. Diplomatic Service since 61. Foreign Office, 61–62. 3rd Secretary, Copenhagen, 63–64. Cairo, 64–66. 2nd Secretary, Madrid, 66–69; 1st Secretary, 69. Foreign & Commonwealth Office, 70.

715 HUGHES, James Alexander, b. 17 July 37, s. of Brig. F. E. C. Hughes. St, 51³–55²; Scholar. Scholarship to Balliol, Oxford.

716 KEELE, Christopher Keith, b. 27 Aug. 38, younger s. of the late K. S. Keele. St, 51³–56². West Ham & University Colleges. Lincoln Univ., B.Sc., Cert.Ed. Teaching in England & Zambia. At present Lecturer in Mathematics & Physics, Kingston College of F.E., Surrey.

717 NEWELL, Michael Knipe, b. 14 Dec. 37, elder s. of R. Newell. St, 51³–56². Christ Church, Oxford. Dir. & Vice-Chrmn., Wolsey Hall, Oxford. *Army & Navy.* Brother, 1360.

718 PRINGLE, David Herbert John Mackay, b. 15 July 37, s. of J. M. Pringle, Q.C. St, 51³–56²; Music Scholar; Kenneth Stubbs Cup, 55. Merton, Oxford, M.A. Associate of the Institute of Actuaries. Instructor Lt., Royal Australian Navy.

719 WINTERTON, Nicholas Raymond, b. 31 Mar. 38, s. of N. H. Winterton. St, 51³–56³; Cap, 56. Sales & Gen. Man., Stevens & Hodgson Ltd., Birmingham since 60. Chrmn., Midland Branch of the Contractors Mech. Plant

Engineers, 67. Warwickshire County Councillor. Chrmn. of various public bodies at Atherstone & Political Club of Atherstone & Newcastle under Lyme. Conservative M.P. for Macclesfield, 71.

720 WRIGHT, Richard Paul, b. 12 Apr. 38, s. of Mrs. M. I. Wright. St, 51³–56².

721 BRICKHILL, David, b. 14 Mar. 38, eldest s. of H. Brickhill. Tu, 51³–56². Trinity, Cambridge. Manchester University. Company Director.

722 COLBOURNE, John Robert, b. 9 Nov. 37, s. of the late J. H. Colbourne. Tu, 51³–55³; Scholar; Head of School; Head of House; Major Scholarship; State Scholar; XV, 55; Tennis VI, 55. Scholarship to King's, Cambridge.

723 CRAWHALL, John Michael, b. 21 Feb. 38, s. of Major W. N. C. Crawhall. Tu, 51³–56²; XI, 56.

724 HEATH, Samuel Bonython, b. 11 Feb. 38, s. of D. W. Heath (OR M 19). Tu, 51³–55³; XV, 54, 55. Commissioned in R.A.F., 56, reaching rank of Flying Officer. Joined Samuel Heath & Sons Ltd., 56. Director, 61. Apptd. Joint Man. Dir., 63. Chrmn. & Man. Dir., 70. *Eccentric Club, London.*

725 LEGGE, David Brian, b. 14 Feb. 38, younger s. of W. H. Legge. Tu, 51³–56². Loughborough College of Technology. Diploma in Production Engineering. Grad.I.Prod.E. Works Director, J. Legge & Co. Ltd., Lock Manufacturers. *Wolverhampton Lawn Tennis & Squash.*

726 MAITLAND, Timothy David, b. 22 Feb. 38, s. of A. Maitland. Tu, 51³–56³. Exhibition to King's, Cambridge, M.A. Smiths Industries, Aviation Division, working on development of automatic landing, 62–66. G.E.C., working on computer-based automation systems for industry, 66–72. B.A.C. in Commercial Aircraft Div. since 73.

727 NELSON, Ian Alexander, b 14 Mar. 38, 3rd s. of R. R. Nelson. Tu, 51³–56². Selwyn, Cambridge. Brothers, 45 & 367.

728 STEEL, Anthony David, b. 1 May 38, elder s. of Sir J. Steel, C.B.E. Tu, 51³–56²; Levée; Head of House; Leaving Exhibition. Queen's, Oxford, M.A. Export Sales Director, Coles Cranes Ltd. *The Junior Carlton.* Brother, 1630.

729 **VAISEY, Nicholas Harry,** b. 14 Feb. 38, elder s. of A. W. Vaisey, M.B., B.Chir., J.P. Tu, 51³–56². Chartered Accountant, 64.

730 **BALDWIN, Christopher James,** b. 19 Nov. 37, elder s. of Major C. L. Baldwin, M.C. (OR W 11). W, 51³–55²; S. VIII, 55. Flying in the R.A.F. since 56. Currently employed flying as a VC10 Capt. Sqn. Ldr. *Naval and Military Club.* Brother, 1522.

731 **COOK, Harry Markham,** b. 14 Feb. 38, eldest s. of H. M. Cook. W, 51³–55². Harper Adams Agricultural College. Died as result of a shooting accident 4 Sept. 61. Brother, 889.

732 **GREGG, Richard Norman,** b. 27 Oct. 37, s. of H. N. Gregg, G.M., M.B., Ch.B., J.P. W, 51³–55³. Corpus Christi, Cambridge. Member, British Computer Society and British Institute of Management. N/S. R.A.F. commission & "wings". Management Consultant. Corporate Planner.

733 **HASLAM, William Malcolm Patrick,** b. 15 July 38, younger s. of Rev. J. A. G. Haslam, M.C., D.F.C. (OR W 10). W, 51³–56¹. Corpus Christi, Cambridge, M.A. Courtauld Institute of Art, London. M.A. Dealer in Victorian and Edwardian works of art. Writer. Brother, 149.

734 **PATTISSON, Simon Gilbert Noël,** b. 19 Mar. 38, s. of H. C. Pattisson (OR W 19). W, 51³–56²; Levée; XV, 54, Capt., 55; XXII, 54; Fives IV. N/S. Commission Rifle Brigade, 57–58. Worcester, Oxford, B.A. Solicitor, 65. Asst. Solicitor with Allen & Overy of London, 65–68 & with Withy King & Lee of Bath, 68–70. Bath University School of Education, Dip. Ed. Teaching, Chippenham Boys High School, 71. *Wiltshire Bee Keeping Association.*

ENTRANCES IN JANUARY 1952

735 **GOYDER, Daniel George,** b. 26 Aug. 38, eldest s. of G. A. Goyder. SH, 52¹–56²; Scholar; Levée. Open Exhibition in Classics to Trinity, Cambridge, M.A., LL.B. Senior Scholarship, 58. Solicitor, 62. Harkness Fellowship to U.S.A., 62–64 to study Anti-trust Law at Harvard Law School, 62–63 and University of California, 63–64. LL.M. Solicitor, Allen & Overy, London, 64–67. Partner at Birketts, Solicitors, Ipswich since 67. Asst.

to second edition of A. D. Neale's "Anti-Trust Laws of the U.S.A.". *Ipswich & Suffolk Club.* Brothers, 2007 & 2945.

736 **HAZELL, Charles Jonathan Stewart,** b. 27 July 38, s. of the late R. R. H. Hazell (OR SH 16). SH, 52¹–56²; S. VIII, 54, 55, 56, Capt., 56. *Cavalry Club.*

737 **PELLY, Raymond Blake,** b. 25 June 38, elder s. of Air Chief Marshal Sir Claude B. R. Pelly, K.C.B., C.B.E., M.C. (OR SH 16). SH, 52¹–56²; Sw. VIII, 55, 56. Hons. Theology, Worcester, Oxford. Docteur en Théologie, Univ. of Geneva. Clerk in Holy Orders (C. of E.). Trained: Bishop's Hostel, Lincoln, 61–63. Curate, All Saints, Gosforth, Newcastle upon Tyne, 63–65. Curate, St. Margaret's, King's Lynn, 69–71. Vice-Principal, Westcott House, Cambridge since 71. Brother, 1099.

738 **HILL, Christopher Meredith,** b. 22 May 38, eldest s. of R. C. Hill, M.B., B.S., D.C.P. T, 52¹–55¹. The Polytechnic, London University, B.Sc. Lecturer in Sociology, Hatfield College of Technology, Herts. Brother, 1106.

739 **EVANS, Michael George Corry,** b. 11 June 38, eldest s. of T. G. C. Evans. B, 52¹–55³. Royal Agricultural College. Land Agent. The Nature Conservancy, London. Brother, 920.

740 **FOSTER, Euan Woodroffe,** b. 16 June 38, s. of the Hon. Sir Peter H. B. W. Foster, M.B.E., T.D. (OR B 26). B, 52¹–56²; H. XI; Cadet Officer. F.R.I.C.S. *Cavalry Club.*

741 **JOHNSON, Ernest James, jnr.,** b. 8 Aug. 38, elder s. of E. J. Johnson, J.P. (OR C 26). C, 52¹–56². With H. & R. Johnson, Australia. Brother, 985.

742 **MENELL, Joseph Robert,** b. 26 Feb. 38, younger s. of S. G. Menell. C, 52¹–55¹. Brother, C. S. Menell.

743 **SAVILLE-SNEATH, Robert Christopher,** b. 2 July 38, s. of R. A. Saville-Sneath. K, 52¹–56².

744 **HOPE, James Arthur David,** b. 27 June 38, eldest s. of Lt.-Col. A. H. C. Hope, B.L., O.B.E., T.D. (OR M 11). M, 52¹–56³; Levée; Head of House. Minor Scholarship in Classics, St. John's, Cambridge, B.A. Edinburgh Univ., LL.B. Advocate (Scottish Bar), 65. Joint editor of "Gloag & Henderson, Introduction to the

Law of Scotland" (7th edition); "Armour on Valuation for Rating" (4th edition). *New Club, Edinburgh*. Brother, 2152.

745 MACINNES, Colin David, b. 13 Nov. 38, 2nd s. of K. L. MacInnes, C.B.E., J.P., D.L. (OR M 19). M, 52^1–56^2; Cap, 55. N/S. Commissioned in 3rd Hussars, 56–58. Trinity, Cambridge, M.A., T.D., F.C.I.S. Company Secretary, Slater, Walker Securities Ltd. of London. Brothers, 263 & 1797.

746 POTTS, Henry, b. 30 June 38, younger s. of H. Potts (OR M 14). M, 52^1–55^3. Solicitor. Partner, Potts & Co., Chester.

747 BANKS, William Lawrence, b. 7 June 38, elder s. of R. A. Banks, C.B.E., J.P. (OR K 16). SF, 52^1–56^2. Christ Church, Oxford, M.A. Robert Fleming & Co. Ltd., London, 61. Director, 70 to date. President, Robert Fleming Inc., New York, 68–73. *Turf Club*.

748 COLVILLE, Peter Robertson, b. 7 July 38, s. of J. R. Colville. SF, 52^1–57^2; Levée; Head of House; XV, 54, 55, 56, Capt., 56; XI, 55, 56, 57; H. XI, 55, 56, 57, Capt., 57; Lawn Tennis IV, 54. Christ's, Cambridge, B.A. Dip. Ed. Hockey Blue, 59, Capt., 60. Scottish Hockey International, 59–63 (Capt. 2 yrs.). G.B. Tour of India, 63–64. Schoolmaster at Uppingham School.

749 FORREST, Robert John, b. 29 June 38, elder s. of R. Forrest. M.B. Ch.B. SF, 52^1–55^1. Birmingham University. Inner Temple. Practising Barrister on the Oxford & Midland Circuit. Brother, 1489.

750 LIVINGSTONE, William Niel, b. 4 June 38, elder s. of J. L. Livingstone, M.D., F.R.C.P. Sh, 52^1–56^2; Levée; Head of House; XV, 54, 55; XI, 55, 56; H. XI, 54, 55, Capt., 56; Fives IV, 53–55. Worcester, Oxford, M.A. St. Thomas's Hospital, 60–63, B.M., B.Ch. General Practitioner in Oxford. *M.C.C., Vincent's Club*. Hockey for Scotland, 57–63, 23 Caps. Hockey for G.B., 59–63. Rome Olympics, 60. Brother, 1460.

751 MERE, Timothy David, b. 29 Mar. 38, s. of R. M. Mere. Sh, 52^1–56^2.

752 ROWLEY, Michael John, b. 24 July 38, elder s. of L. J. Rowley. Sh, 52^1–55^2. Queen's University, Kingston, Ontario. Asst. Accountant, Thorn Electronics, 64. A.C.A., 65. Chief Accountant,

Polstre Ltd., 66. Died 29 Mar. 69, as the result of a Rugger accident. Brother, 1614.

753 HANDFIELD-JONES, Michael Robert, b. 24 June 38, s. of R. M. Handfield-Jones, M.C., M.S., F.R.C.S. St, 52^1–56^2; XV, 54, 55; H. XI, 55. Sandhurst. Capt. of Football. Commissioned R.E., 58. Played for Hampshire, Combined Services. *Harlequins*. Served in Aden, 63–64. Killed in Aden, 1 June 64 on active service.

754 HURST, Timothy Stuart, b. 15 Aug. 38, younger s. of the late C. W. Hurst. St, 52^1–56^2. Marconi Co., 61. Engineer, Space Communications Div. Brother, 14.

755 SHAW, Jonathan Geoffrey, b. 25 June 38, younger s. of Group Capt. G. Shaw, D.F.C., D.L. St, 52^1–56^2. Pembroke, Cambridge, B.A. Solicitor, 65. Sales Director, Micro-Metalsmiths Ltd., Spectra-Tek U.K. Ltd., and Diemould Castings Ltd. *R.A.C., Junior Carlton, Ganton G.C.* Brother, 445.

756 STUART-MENTETH, Charles Henry (name changed to Menteith), b. 15 Apr. 38, elder s. of the late W. G. Stuart-Menteth (OR Tu 20). Tu, 52^1–56^2; Levée; Leaving Exhibition in History. Magdalen, Oxford, B.A., M.Sc. in Applied Entomology & Diploma of Imperial College, 66. Asst. Lecturer Grade B, Wigan Mining & Technical College, 62–65. Entomologist & Technical Rep. in Sudan for C.I.B.A. Agrochemicals Div., 66.

757 ARCHER, James William, b. 2 Sept. 38, eldest s. of J. R. Archer, LL.B. W, 52^1–56^2; Cap, 55. Emmanuel, Cambridge. Brothers, 1494 & 2170.

758 ESSLEMONT, William Alexander, b. 6 July 38, elder s. of A. S. Esslemont, M.B., Ch.B., D.R.C.O.G. W, 52^1–56^2. C.A.T., Birmingham. Now Aston University. O.N.C. Elec. Eng. Environmental Engineer, Sales Executive, Air Conditioning & Suspended Ceiling Contractors. Brother, 1229.

759 TRACY PHILLIPS, John Hywel, b. 2 Mar. 38, s. of G. Tracy Phillips. W, 52^1–56^2; Levée; XV, 55; Dewar Travelling Scholarship. Trinity Hall, Cambridge. Solicitor.

ENTRANCES IN MAY 1952

760 **BOOTH, Richard George William Pitt,** b. 12 Sept. 38, s. of Col. P. Booth. SH, 52^2–56^2; Tennis VI, 56. Merton, Oxford. Bookseller.

761 **CROFTS, Robert Frank,** b. 14 Oct. 38, younger s. of F. N. Crofts (OR SH 20). SH, 52^2–56^2.

762 **FORSTER, Jeremy Neil Ashley,** b. 14 Oct. 38, s. of N. G. Forster, T.D. SH, 52^2–52^2.

763 **OLIVER, Stephen John Lindsay,** b. 14 Nov. 38, 2nd s. of Capt. P. D. Oliver, C.B.E., R.N. (Retired). (OR SF 14). SH, 52^2–56^3. Oriel, Oxford, M.A. Practising Barrister. Middle Temple. Brother, 167.

764 **PILLAI, Raghaven (Raymond) Ajit,** b. 23 July 38, younger s. of Sir R. Pillai, K.C.I.E., C.B.E., LL.B. SH, 52^2–56^2. Trinity, Cambridge. Brother, 462.

765 **THOMPSON, George Peter Cary,** b. 17 Oct. 38, elder s. of J. M. Thompson. SH, 52^2–56^2. Exhibition to St. Catharine's, Cambridge, M.A. Programme Management Development, Harvard Business School. Thompson Reid Ltd., Director and Gen. Manager. *Strangford Lough Yacht Club.* Brother, 1411.

766 **CANSDALE, The Rev. George Graham,** b. 29 Aug. 38, 2nd s. of J. H. Cansdale. T, 52^2–57^1; Levée; Head of House. Merton, Oxford, M.A. Dip. Ed. Clifton Theological College. Ordination (C. of E.), 64. St. John's, Parkstone, Dorset, 64–67. With the Bible Churchmen's Missionary Society in the Anglican Church in Kenya since 68. At present as tutor in St. Paul's United Theological College, P.O. Limuru, Kenya. Brother, 387.

767 **DEREHAM, Orme Giles,** b. 20 Oct. 38, 2nd s. of the late W. D. Dereham (OR B 18). B, 52^2–56^2; Scholar; Levée; State Scholar; XV, 56; Sw. VIII, 55, 56. Trinity Hall, Cambridge, B.A. A.M.I.-Mech.E. Civil Engineering. Brothers, 531 & 1264.

768 **WHEATLEY, Robert Larke Andrew,** b. 14 Aug. 38, eldest s. of Sir G. A. Wheatley, C.B.E., B.C.L. (OR B 22). B, 52^2–56^2. McGill University, Montreal. Chartered Accountant (Quebec). Management Accountant, F. W. Woolworth & Co. Ltd., Swindon Distribution Centre. *Rifle Brigade Club.* Brothers, 1072 & 2201.

769 **HUGHES, Barrie Nigel,** b. 24 Nov. 38, s. of S. R. Hughes. C, 52^2–56^3.

770 **JACKSON, John Benjamin,** b. 12 July 38, s. of H. F. Jackson (OR C 22). C, 52^2–57^2; Levée; Head of House; Cap, 56; XXII, 57. Gen. Manager, Rea Bulk Handling of Birkenhead (Sub. of Ocean Transport & Trading Ltd.).

771 **WHITE, Samuel Driver,** b. 19 Sept. 38, elder s. of Lt.-Col. P. F. White, O.B.E. (OR C 13). C, 52^2–56^2; Cap, 55. Solicitor. Director of Worcestershire Building Preservation Trust. Liveryman of the Royal Society of Apothecaries. Governor of Abbey School, Malvern. M.C. *B.A.R.C.* Brother, 1377.

772 **WRIGHT, Charles Christopher,** b. 15 July 38, elder s. of C. G. Wright, L.D.S., R.C.S.Eng. C, 52^2–56^2; Levée; Head of House. New College, Oxford. Solicitor. Partner in the firm of Lee & Pembertons, London. *Harewood Downs G.C.* Brothers, 1945 & 2982.

773 **CASSELS, Patrick Kennedy,** b. 21 Aug. 38, 3rd s. of A. K. Cassels (OR K 20). K, 52^2–55^3. Sales Manager, Timber Merchant, and Company Director. *Royal Philatelic Society, London.* Brothers, 31, 347 & 1527.

774 **HANKEY, The Hon. Donald Robin Alers,** b. 12 June 38, elder s. of Rt. Hon. Lord Hankey, K.C.M.G., K.C.V.O. (OR K 19). K, 52^2–57^2. Brother, 2146.

775 **HANKEY, Ian Raymond Alers,** b. 23 Dec. 38, s. of R. B. A. Hankey. K, 52^2–57^1. A.C.A., Dip. I.N.S.E.A.D. With Arbuthnot Latham & Co. Ltd., London.

776 **PREECE, Arthur Patrick James,** b. 5 Sept. 38, younger s. of Col. J. Preece, O.B.E., T.D. K, 52^2–57^2; Levée; Head of House; XV, 56; XI, 56; H. XI, 57. Emmanuel, Cambridge, M.A., M.B., B.Chir. St. Thomas's Hospital, London, D.Obst. R.C.O.G. General practitioner in Group Practice in Fakenham, Norfolk. Brother, 254.

777 **ROWLEY, Christopher Owen Bergin,** b. 12 Aug. 38, s. of O. Rowley. K, 52^2–56^3; R. VIII; Holder of Bigside Bags; record holder for Crick. Clare, Cambridge, B.A. Asst. Controller, Current Affairs & Documentaries, Thames Television, London.

778 **COOPER, Antony Fox,** b. 2 Feb, 38, s. of F. R. Cooper. M, 52^2–56^2; Levée. Peterhouse, Cambridge. N/S. Commissioned R.A., 56–58. Worked on London Stock Exchange. Now Solicitor in private practice at Petersfield, Hampshire,

779 **HARRIES, Michael Albert Allen,** b. 29 Sept. 38, s. of C. W. P. Harries. M. 52^2–57^2; Levée; Sw. VIII, 55, 56, Capt., 57. St. John's, Cambridge, M.A. Private Pilot's Licence. Managing Director, Bobs Harries Ltd., Thika, Kenya, Agricultural, Horticultural & Engineering concern. National President, 71–72, Association of Round Tables in Eastern Africa.

780 **LUSTY, Timothy David,** b. 7 Oct. 38, s. of W. Lusty. M, 52^2–57^1. St. Peter's, Oxford, M.A., B.M., B.Ch. Doctor. Farmer. Vice-Chrmn., Medical Panel of Oxfam. Family Planning. Liveryman of Lorimers Company. B.M.A. Officer of The Order of Hipolito Onuanue (for relief work in Peru).

781 **MORISON, Colin Ronald,** b. 24 Aug. 38, 3rd s. of R. P. Morison, Q.C., LL.B. M, 52^2–56^3.

782 **ROBERTS, Anthony Fenwick Denby,** b. 1 July 38, elder s. of the late W. D. Roberts (OR M 23). M, 52^2–56^2; Levée; Head of House. University College, Oxford, B.A. Farmer & Landowner. Lloyd's Underwriter. Brother, 1747.

783 **SHAW, Ronald Charles Anthony,** b. 14 Nov. 38, younger s. of G. R. Shaw. M, 52^2–56^3. Magdalen, Oxford, B.A. Nuffield, Oxford. Lt. Royal Artillery. Solicitor with Messrs. Freshfields, London. *United Oxford & Cambridge Club.* Brother, 268.

784 **SINCLAIR, Mark Francis,** b. 15 Aug. 38, s. of J. F. Sinclair. SF, 52^2–56^3; Cap, 54; Tennis VI, 55, 56. Pembroke, Oxford, B.A. (P.P.E.). Sloan Fellow, London Graduate School of Business. Director, Inter-Action Advisory Service.

785 **YOUNG, David Malcolm,** b. 13 July 38, s. of D. J. Young. SF, 52^2–56^3. Clare, Cambridge, M.A. C.Eng., M.I.-Mech.E. Rolls-Royce (1971) Ltd., Glasgow. Production Control Management. *Clyde Cruising & Royal Northern Yacht Clubs.*

786 **BAVIN, Richard,** b. 14 Sept. 38, s. of Lt.-Col. L. N. Bavin. Sh, 52^2–56^1.

787 **BOOT, Henry Malcolm,** younger s. of B. E. Boot. Sh, 52^2–56^3. Shropshire Farm Institute. Cambridge University, B.A. Farmer. Brother, 470.

788 **EDWARDS, Humfrey Guy Offley,** b. 9 Oct. 38, 2nd s. of W. C. Edwards, F.C.A. Sh, 52^2–56^3; Levée. Clare, Cambridge. Died in motor accident in Bulgaria, 15 July 62. Brothers, 500 & 1911.

789 **WARREN, William John,** b. 24 Aug. 38, s. of W. M. Warren. Sh, 52^2–56^2. Imperial College, London.

790 **KEITH, Peter Robert Bruce,** b. 23 June 38, elder s. of Cdr. W. B. Keith. St, 52^2–54^2. Died in 57. Brother, 1224.

791 **ROSLING, David Patrick,** b. 6 June 38, younger s. of H. P. Rosling (OR Tu 23). Tu, 52^2–56^2. Solicitor.

792 **STRATTON, Ian George Chadwick,** b. 16 Oct. 38, s. of the late G. H. Stratton. Tu, 52^2–56^2. Manchester University, LL.B. Solicitor, Hawtin Ltd. Co-Author "Partnership", and Strattons and Blackshaw, "The Law Relating to Moneylenders". Councillor, Lytham St. Annes, 69–72.

793 **TURNER, Hugh David,** b. 14 Sept. 38, s. of H. G. Turner. Tu, 52^2–56^2. University of Western Australia (1st Class Hons.). Christ's, Cambridge (M.Litt.). University Lecturer in History. *United Oxford & Cambridge University Club.*

794 **HALLAM, John Birks,** b. 14 Sept. 38, s. of M. B. Hallam, M.B., Ch.B., M.R.C.O.G. W, 52^2–56^2. St. Thomas's Hospital Medical School, M.B., B.S., L.R.C.P., M.R.C.S. Medical Practitioner, Saxmundham, Suffolk.

795 **VOGT, Paul Johan,** b. 6 Dec. 38, s. of J. H. L. Vogt (OR W 18). W, 52^2–56^2. Shipbroker. Member, Baltic Exchange.

ENTRANCES IN SEPTEMBER 1952

796 **BOWRING, Michael Peter,** b. 9 May 39, s. of P. R. Bowring (OR SH 26). SH, 52^3–57^2; R. VIII, 56, 57. Lloyd's Insurance Broker with C. T. Bowring & Co. (Ins.) Ltd. *M.C.C. & Cricket Society.*

797 **BUTTERS, John Anthony Howard** b. 27 Jan. 39, s. of the late H. M. Butters, W.S. SH, 52^3–56^2; Queen's Medal in

History; Exhibition to St. John's, Cambridge, B.A. Edinburgh University, LL.B., W.S. Notary Public. *New Club, Edinburgh.*

798 **DEAN, Peter Henry,** b. 24 July 39, s. of the late A. W. Dean. SH, 52^3–57^2; Levée; Head of House. London University, LL.B. Solicitor. Company Secretary, The Rio Tinto-Zinc Corp. Ltd. *Hurlingham Club.*

799 **de PENNING, Robert Gelson,** b. 18 Dec. 38, younger s. of W. F. de Penning. SH, 52^3–57^2; Rackets Capt., 56–57; Tennis VI, 56–57. Southampton Univ., B.A. Patent Agent. Director of de Penning & de Penning.

800 **FLEMMING, Jonathan Haden,** b. 16 Feb. 39, elder s. of C. W. Flemming C.B.E., M.D., M.Ch., F.R.C.S. (OR SH 15). SH, 52^3–57^1; Scholar; Levée. Trinity, Oxford, B.A., M.I.C.E. Engineer with Binnie & Partners. Work in U.K., Middle East, Hong Kong. Brother, 1695.

801 **FONTES, Stephen Shaw,** b. 11 May 39, younger s. of A. C. Fontes. SH, 52^3–57^2. Sidney Sussex, Cambridge, B.A. Francis Shaw & Co., Manchester (Engineers) from 62. Brother, 53.

802 **GUINNESS, Geoffrey Neil,** b. 27 Dec. 38, elder s. of B. C. Guinness (OR SH 17). SH, 52^3–57^1; Scholar; Levée; Head of House; Head of School; R. VIII, 55, 56, 57; Holder of Bigside Bags, 57; S. VIII, 56. Major Scholarship to Trinity, Oxford, B.A., A.C.A. With Guinness Mahon & Co. Ltd., London. *City University Club, Little Ship Club.* Brother, 1044.

803 **HODDER-WILLIAMS, Mark,** b. 24 Mar. 39, elder s. of Lt.-Col. P. Hodder-Williams, O.B.E., T.D. (OR SH 23). SH, 52^3–57^2; XXII. Corpus Christi, Oxford, M.A. Managing Director, Hodder Publications Ltd. *Vincent's Club, Oxford; Wildernesse Club, Sevenoaks.* Brother, 1403.

804 **MACKINTOSH-WALKER, Charles James,** b. 17 May 39, s. of the late C. A. Mackintosh-Walker, M.B.E. (OR SH 08). SH, 52^3–57^2. Commissioned Queen's Own Cameron Highlanders, 59. Captain, 66 (Retired). Landed Proprietor. J.P. for Nairnshire.

805 **ORMEROD, Charles Rupert,** b. 31 May 39, s. of the late A. H. Ormerod (OR C 23). SH, 52^3–56^2; S. VIII, 54, 56. Police Officer.

806 **SMITH, John Robert Barbour** (now J. R. Barbour-Smith), b. 5 Jan. 39, elder s. of Lt.-Col. K. C. C. Smith, D.S.O. J.P. SH, 52^3–56^2; Sw. VIII, 56. Royal Agricultural College, Cirencester. Short Service Commission in R. Warwickshire Regiment. Seconded to 4 K.A.R., Uganda, 56–59. Stockbroker, Easton Goff & Co., Glasgow. Member, Scottish Stock Exchange. *Western Club, Glasgow.*

807 **TURNER, John Rosser,** b. 28 Jan. 39, elder s. of W. G. Turner. SH, 52^3–57^2; Music Scholar; Levée; Leaving Exhibition. Organ Scholarship to Jesus, Cambridge, M.A., Mus.B., F.R.C.O. Stewart-of-Rannoch Scholar in sacred music. Cambridge Univ., 59–61. Asst. Music Master, Cheltenham College, 61–65. Organist & Master of the Music, Glasgow Cathedral. Lecturer, Royal Scottish Academy of Music & Drama. Organist, University of Strathclyde since 65. Recital & Lecture tour in U.S.A., 72. Broadcasts for B.B.C. Radio 3 & 4.

808 **WATSON, Patrick Wimperis Grant,** b. 22 May 39, younger s. of J. P. Watson, LL.B., W.S. SH, 52^3–57^1; Scholar; Waddington Leaving Exhibition. Demyship at Magdalen, Oxford. N/S. R.E. 2nd Lt. Lincolnshire Theological College. Ridley Hall Theological College. Private Student, Glasgow University, 67–70. Research Asst. at National Library of Scotland, 66–67. Apprentice & Asst. with Messrs. Mackay, Murray & Spens, 67–71. Now Solicitor (Asst.) with Messrs. Lindsay, W.S., Edinburgh since 71. *Edinburgh Inter-University Club.* Brother, 523.

809 **CALDWELL, Hugh Archibald,** b. 30 Oct. 38, eldest s. of the late J. Caldwell, B.Sc. T, 52^3–57^2. Edinburgh University & English Electric Co., Rugby. Mech. Eng. B.Sc.(Eng.), M.I.Mech.E., C.Eng. Design & Development Engineer (Turbines), E.E. Co. Ltd., Rugby, 62–69. Design & Development Engineer (Marine Gearing), W. H. Allen Sons & Co. Ltd., Pershore, Worcs. from 69. *Royal Yachting Assoc.*

810 **COLES, Gerald Christopher,** b. 7 Apr. 39, s. of V. R. Coles. T, 52^3–57^2; Levée; R. VIII, 56, 57; Winner of Crick, 57. Fitzwilliam, Cambridge, M.A., Ph.D. Research Fellow in Copenhagen University, 64. Makerere University, Uganda, 65–69 and University of Cambridge, 69–72. At present Research Biologist, I.C.I. Ltd., Pharmaceutical Div.

811 DIMMICK, Alexander Mark, b. 17 Oct. 39, s. of R. G. A. Dimmick, B.Sc. T, 52³–58²; Levée; State Scholarship; Leaving Exhibition. Exhibition to St. John's, Cambridge, M.A., M.I.Chem.E., C.Eng. Chemical Engineering, Production Management, Chemicals Manufacture with I.C.I. Petrochemicals Div., Billingham, Teesside.

812 FOX, Henry McLean, b. 24 Sept. 38, younger s. of K. McL. Fox. T, 52³–57²; XV, 56; XI, 55–57. Sales with Truman Ltd. *M.C.C.*, *Free Foresters*. Brother, 62.

813 GRAY, Christopher John, b. 23 Sept. 38, younger s. of J. M. Gray, B.Sc. T, 52³–55². Trained in Hotel Management in U.K., France & Switzerland. Held Managerial Posts in the Bahamas, Australia & England. N/S., Army, 2 years (18 months in Far East). Brother, 390.

814 HALL, Christopher Basil, b. 4 Sept. 38, younger s. of E. S. Hall. T, 52³–57²; Minor Foundationer. Pembroke, Cambridge, M.A., M.B., B.Chir. St. Mary's Hospital, Paddington, M.R.C.S., L.R.C.P., D.C.H., D.A., D.Obst. R.C.O.G. Family doctor, Colchester. Brother, 391.

815 HOPKIRK, Robert James, b. 15 July 39, younger s. of the late K. R. Hopkirk. T, 52³–57³; Levée; Head of House; S. VIII, 55, Captain, 56, 57. Emmanuel, Cambridge, M.A. King's College, London, Ph.D., M.I.Mech.E., C.Eng. Perkins Engines Ltd., Peterborough, 62–65. Vickers Shipbuilding Group, Barrow-in-Furness, 68–70. Consultant, Electro-Watt Engineering Services Ltd., Zürich since 70.

816 MORFEY, Christopher Leonard, b. 1 Apr. 40, s. of D. S. Morfey, B.Sc. T, 52³–57³; Scholar; R. VIII, 57; S. VIII, 57. Scholarship to Queen's, Cambridge, B.A. Southampton University, M.Sc., Ph.D. Bristol-Siddeley Engines Ltd., 62–64. Lecturer, Institute of Sound & Vibration Research, University of Southampton, 64–66 and from 67. On leave at Bolt Beranck & Newman Inc., Cambridge, U.S.A., 66–67. Silver Medal of British Acoustical Society, 71.

817 PORTER, Vincent John, b. 22 May 39, s. of E. A. Porter. T, 52³–57³; Levée; Evers Exhibition. Queen's, Oxford, M.A. Principal Lecturer in Film, Polytechnic of Central London. Corporate Member, British Kinematograph Sound & T.V. Society. Member Society of Film & T.V. Arts.

818 PRESS, Christopher John, b. 14 Jan. 39, elder s. of F. J. Press, J.P. T, 52³–56². Architectural Assoc. School of Architecture, London. A.A. Diploma. A.R.I.B.A. Partner, Leonard Manassem and Partners, Chartered Architects, Freshford, Bath and London.

819 PRIDMORE, Charles Malcolm, b. 27 July 38, elder s. of C. A. Pridmore (OR T 26). T, 52³–56³. F/Lt., R.A.F. Killed 23 July 66. Brother, 1110.

820 STONE, Anthony John, b. 4 Nov. 38, s. of B. J. V. Stone. T, 52³–57²; Senior Scholar; Levée; Head of House; Leaving Exhibition. Emmanuel, Cambridge (Major Scholar, Senior Scholar, Bachelor Scholar), Ph.D., M.A. University Research & Teaching. At present Asst. Director of Research in Theoretical Chemistry, University of Cambridge. *C.U. Gliding Club.*

821 TREVITHICK, Lt.-Cdr. Paul, R.N., b. 20 Dec. 38, younger s. of the late R. G. Trevithick, LL.B., B.L., M.A. T, 52³–56³; S. VIII. R.N. Engineering College, B.Sc. Manchester University (U.M.I.S.T.) B.Sc.(Eng.). Lon. Ext. A.M.I.Mar.E. Lecturer at R.N. Engineering College. Lt.-Cdr. Brother, R. B. Trevithick.

822 ALLEN, Nicholas Justin, b. 8 July 39, eldest s. of D. F. Allen. B, 52³–57²; Scholar; Levée. New College, Oxford, B.A., B.Sc., B.M., B.Ch. Senior House Officer in Psychiatry, Royal Edinburgh Hospital, 67.

823 JONES, Thomas Richard, b. 16 May 39, elder s. of the late T. Jones, B.C.L. (OR B 21). B, 52³–57². Solicitor, 63. R.A.F. Legal Staff Officer. Sqn. Ldr.

824 LEISK, Alan John Innes, b. 16 May 39, elder s. of J. Leisk, O.B.E. B, 52³–57. Sheffield University, B.Met. Assoc. Fellow, Australian Inst. of Management. Currently Works Export Superintendent, Australian Iron & Steel Pty. (Branch of B.H.P. Co. Ltd.). Inst. of Metals (Australian). Brother, 1569.

825 LINDSAY, Michael William, b. 3 Dec. 38, younger s. of Major-General C. T. D. Lindsay, C.B. (OR B 24). B, 52³–56²; Scholar; Levée. Trinity Hall, Cambridge. Joined Shell, 59. Currently Industrial Chemicals Manager for Malaysia & Singapore. *Rye G.C.*, *Royal Selangor G.C.* Brother, 399.

826 **MUSGRAVE, Michael John,** b. 9 Apr. 39, s. of J. Musgrave (OR B 21). B, 52^3–57^2.

827 **CONNELL, Michael John,** b. 9 Jan. 39, s. of the late H. A. Connell, LL.B. (OR C 25). C, 52^3–56^3. Emmanuel, Cambridge, B.A., Dip. Agric. Farming in Queensland.

828 **DALRYMPLE, Douglas Hugh Murray,** b. 26 Apr. 40, 2nd s. of I. M. Dalrymple, F.R.S.A. (OR C 17). C, 52^3–58^2; Levée; Head of House; XV, 57; XI, 58; H. XI, 57, 58. Oriel, Oxford, B.A. Asst. Master, Dragon School, Oxford, 62–68 and from 71. Asst. Master Diocesan Boys' School, Hong Kong, 68–70. Asst. Master, Melbourne Grammar School, Victoria, 70. *M.C.C., Travellers'.* Brother, 1375.

829 **GREGORY, Robert Berry,** b. 19 Apr. 39, elder s. of R. H. Gregory. C, 52^3–57^1; Cap, 56. Brother, 1525.

830 **NICOLL, John Angus,** b. 19 Dec. 38, s. of W. A. C. Nicoll. C, 52^3–57^2; H. XI, 57. Christ's, Cambridge, B.A. Royal Agricultural College. Bar, 62. Qualified Land Agent & Chartered Surveyor, 66.

831 **OASTLER, Christopher Lewis,** b. 16 June 39, elder s. of E. G. Oastler, T.D., M.B., F.R.C.P., F.R.C.P.S. (OR C 17). C, 52^3–57^2; Scholar. University Coll., Oxford, 59–64. B.Litt., M.A. Solicitor. Treasury Solicitor's Dept. Brother, 1578.

832 **RONALD, Michael James Keith,** b. 6 Feb. 39, s. of K. M. Ronald, T.D. (OR C 16). C, 52^3–57^2. Associate, Institute of Chartered Secretaries & Administrators. 6 yrs. Woolbroker, 8 yrs. Sand & Gravel industry—Accountant. Now Stockbrokers' Accountant.

833 **SMITH, Nathaniel Grey,** b. 22 Apr. 39, s. of P. S. Smith, T.D., J.P. (OR C 27). C, 52^3–57^2. Corpus Christi, Oxford. Managing Director, Kado Limited of Stockton-on-Tees.

834 **SPURRIER, Nicholas John Marston,** b. 28 Aug. 39, elder s. of H. J. M. Spurrier (OR C 27). C, 52^3–57^2. Partner, John W. Cork & Co., Estate Agents, 67. Brother, 1126.

835 **AUSTIN, Simon Bramston,** b. 24 Dec. 38, 2nd s. of F. B. Austin, K, 52^3–57^1. Brother, 2600.

836 **ELEY, Peter David Richard,** b. 24 Mar. 39, s. of Col. D. M. Eley. K, 52^3–57^2.

837 **EVERS, Christopher Claude,** b. 14 Apr. 39, 2nd s. of C. R. Evers (OR SF 21). K, 52^3–58^1; Levée; Head of House; Head of School; XV, 56, 57; XXII, 56, 57; H. XI, 57, Capt., 58. Corpus Christi, Oxford, B.A. Member of I.A.P.S., 70. Sedbergh School, Montebello, Quebec, Canada, 58–59 & 63–64. At West Hill Park, Titchfield, Hants., since 64. Deputy Head since 70.

838 **FARRIS, Christopher Antony,** b. 11 Feb. 39, younger s. of L. S. E. Farris. K, 52^3–58^1; Levée; Capt. of Boxing, 57. Christ's, Cambridge, B.A., M.I.Mech.E. Davy & United Engineering Co., 63–66. Arthur Lee & Sons Ltd. since 66. Brother, 9.

839 **GADDUM, Anthony Henry,** b. 16 Feb. 39, elder s. of P. W. Gaddum (OR K 16). K, 52^3–57^2. N/S. Commissioned 13/18th Royal Hussars (Q.M.O.), 60. Grenoble Univ. followed by travels in Germany, Switzerland & France, studying European business methods. At present in business with H. T. Gaddum & Co. Ltd., Macclesfield. *Cavalry Club & St. James's Club, Manchester.* Hon. Secretary, Manchester Branch *O.R. Society.*

840 **KIDNER, John Michael,** b. 7 Dec. 38, s. of H. J. Kidner (OR K 21). K, 52^3–57^2; XV, 56; Cap, 55. N/S. Commission Royal Norfolk Regt. Data Processing Manager, Legal & General Assurance Society Ltd.

841 **McCAY, David Alexander,** b. 19 Sept. 38, younger s. of C. A. R. McCay, F.R.C.S., D.P.H. K, 52^3–57^2. Trinity, Oxford. Guy's Hospital, B.M., B.Ch., M.A., M.R.C.S., L.R.C.P. General Medical Practitioner. Brother, 320.

842 **MADDEN, Christopher John Frank,** b. 9 Apr. 39, elder s. of W. E. Madden (OR K 20). K, 52^3–58^2; Levée; R. VIII, 57, 58; Holder of Bigside Bags, 57; Cadet Officer C.C.F., 58. University College, Durham. President Durham University Boat Club, 62–63. B.Sc. N/S. Commissioned Scots Guards with Stick of Honour, Mons. O.T.S., 59–60. Shell International Chemical Co., London, 63–65. Pfizer Ltd., Sandwich, Kent, 65–69. The Wellcome Foundation Ltd., London since 69. Now Group Marketing Research Manager. *Third Guards Club.* Brother, 1077.

843 **ROBERTSON, Angus,** b. 7 Apr. 39, s. of A. Robertson, M.B., Ch.B. K, 52^3–57^2. St. Andrew's University. Managing Director, Glaxo (Thailand) Ltd., Bangkok. *Royal Birkdale G.C., Royal Bangkok Sports Club.*

844 **CANN, Herbert Anthony,** b. 10 Jan. 39, s. of S. Cann. M, 52^3–57^2. B.Sc. Associate of the Textile Institute. Managing Director, Terminal Display Systems Ltd.

845 **CARR, Graham Douglas Quintin,** b. 4 June 39, elder s. of A. Q. Carr (OR M 19). M, 52^3–57^2. Chartered Accountant. Uganda as a Company Secretary, 63. Private Accountancy practice in Uganda, 70. In Kenya since 72. Brother, 1219.

846 **CARR, Jonathan Dodgson,** b. 13 Apr. 39, eldest s. of the late S. D. Carr. M, 52^3–57^2; Levée; XXII, 57. Emmanuel, Cambridge, M.A. Member of the Stock Exchange, London. Partner, L. Messel & Co., Bow Group. Chrmn., Vauxhall Conservative Assoc., 67–68. Brothers, 1286 & 2216.

847 **FOLLAND, Michael Henry Dudley,** b. 22 July 39, elder s. of D. C. Folland. M, 52^3–57^2. Brother, 1287.

848 **JOHNSTON, William Bancroft,** b. 26 Feb. 39, s. of K. R. H. Johnston, Q.C. (OR M 19). M, 52^3–57^2; Levée; Head of House. Exhibition to New College, Oxford, M.A. Carnegie Institute of Technology, Pittsburgh, Pa., U.S.A., M.S. Shoemaker.

849 **SELLS, Christopher Cedric Lytton,** b. 7 Apr. 39, s. of Professor A. L. Sells, Dés L. M, 52^3–57^2. Sidney Sussex, Cambridge, B.A., Ph.D. Scientific Civil Service. Fellow, *British Chess Problem Society*.

850 **TANQUERAY, David Andrew,** b. 23 May 39, s. of the late D. Y. B. Tanqueray. M, 52^3–57^2; S. VIII, 57. Clare, Cambridge, M.A. Hawker Siddeley Dynamics Ltd., Stevenage, 63–66. University of California, Berkeley, Electrical Engineering & Computer Science, 66–69. Control Data Ltd. since 69. Harkness Fellowship, 66, for 2 yrs.

851 **AITKEN, Robert Ian,** b. 7 Apr. 39, s. of R. L. Aitken. SF, 52^3–57^2. Glasgow University, B.Sc. Director of Engineering Company. *R.A.C.*

852 **BAIN, Alan William Shenton,** b. 9 Feb. 39, eldest s. of A. T. S. Bain. SF, 52^3–57^1; Scholar; Levée. Minor Scholarship to Gonville & Caius, Cambridge, B.A. Diploma, Copenhagen University. Federal Civil Servant since 65. Held positions in Dept. of Industry, Dept. of Finance & Canadian International Development Agency. With Dept. of Finance, International Programs Division since 72. Brother, 2534.

853 **BRUN, Olaf Constantin,** b. 7 June 39, eldest s. of H. C. Brun. SF, 52^3–57^2; Levée; Cap, 56. Pembroke, Cambridge, M.A., Dip. Agriculture. Farmer & Country Landowner. Brothers, 1147 & 2225.

854 **CAVAGHAN, Richard Henry Davis,** b. 11 May 39, eldest s. of H. D. Cavaghan. SF, 52^3–57^2. Lausanne University, Switzerland. Non-employed. *Hurlingham Club.* Brother, 1903.

855 **EYRE, John George Richardby,** b. b. 15 Apr. 39, s. of the late R. R. Eyre (OR SH 20). SF, 52^3–56^2. Southampton Univ., B.Sc. Kansas Univ. Exchange Studentship. British Aircraft Corp., 62. Engineer Scientist Specialist, 65. Technical Committee, Aerospace Electrical Society, 66.

856 **JOHNSON, Hugh Eric Allen,** b. 10 Mar. 39, younger s. of the late G. F. Johnson, C.B.E. SF, 52^3–56^3. Travelling Scholarship & Keasby Bursary. King's, Cambridge, M.A. Editor, "Wine & Food", 63–64. Travel Editor of "The Sunday Times", 67. Editor, "Queen", 68–69. *Garrick, Royal College of Art.* Publications, "Wine", 66; "The World Atlas of Wine", 71; "The International Book of Trees", 73.

857 **KENNEDY, Donald Sinclair,** b. 23 Sept. 38, younger s. of C. D. Kennedy, M.B., Ch.B., F.R.C.S.E., F.R.C.O.G. SF, 52^3–56^3. Corpus Christi, Cambridge. Farmer. Brother, 358.

858 **LAWRENCE, Martin,** b. 4 Apr. 39, s. of the late R. P. Lawrence. SF, 52^3–57^1. Edinburgh University, B.Arch. Scottish Special Housing Assoc., 63–67. Law & Dunbar-Nasmith, 67. *Royal Northern Y.C.*

859 **SHACKEL, Geoffrey George,** b. 6 June 39, s. of E. M. Shackel, M.B., B.Chir. (OR SF 14). SF, 52^3–57^2. Trinity, Cambridge, M.A., M.B., B.Chir. St. Thomas's Hospital, London, D.Obst.R.C.O.G. Medical Practitioner.

860 **BLANDY, John Walker Ernest,** b. 20 Feb. 39, younger s. of P. G. Blandy (OR SH 18). Sh, 52^3–57^2.

861 **BRODBELT, Robert Henry Warbrick,** b. 21 Nov. 38, younger s. of the late T. W. B. Brodbelt. Sh, 52^3–57^2; Tennis VI, 57. Liverpool Univ., L.D.S. Hockey Blue, 62. Dental Surgeon to Alder Hey Children's Hospital, 63–65. Lecturer in Operative Dental Surgery of Liverpool Dental School, 65–67. Brother, 116.

862 **CAMPBELL, Ian Adams,** b. 12 Jan. 39, s. of G. Campbell, B.M., B.Ch. Sh, 52^3–56^2.

863 **COLVILLE, The Hon. Angus Richmond,** b. 29 Apr. 39, 3rd s. of the late Cdr. The Viscount Colville of Culross. Sh, 52^3–57^1; Levée. F.R.I.C.S. N/S. 2nd Lt. Grenadier Guards, 57–59. Partner with Michelmore, Hughes & Wilbraham, Chartered Surveyors, Tavistock since 67. Brothers, The Viscount Colville of Culross and 280 & 863.

864 **FARRIS, David John Matthew,** b. 1 May 39, s. of C. D. Farris, M.R.C.S., L.R.C.P., L.D.S. Sh, 52^3–57^2. St. John's, Cambridge, M.A., A.R.I.C.S. Chartered Surveyor with Carter Jonas of Bristol.

865 **FRENCH, Thomas Jeremy,** b. 3 Apr. 39, s. of R. French. Sh, 52^3–57^2; Levée; XV, 55–56; H. XI, 56; Junior & Senior Athletic Cups. Grenoble University, France. F.C.A. Deputy Chrmn. & Deputy Man. Dir., Thomas French & Sons Ltd., Manchester. *St. James's Club, Manchester.*

866 **GEE, Robin Mackworth,** b. 30 Dec. 38, elder s. of E. A. M. Gee. Sh, 52^3–57^2. Britannia Royal Naval College, Dartmouth. Lt., R.N. H.M.S. *Renown*, 57. Brother, 1471.

867 **HAMILTON-MILLER, Jeremy Marcus Tom,** b. 2 Sept. 38, s. of D. J. V. Hamilton-Miller. Sh, 52^3–56^2; Scholar. Clare, Cambridge, M.A. University College, London. Guy's Hospital Medical School, Ph.D. Oxford University Research Fellow, M.A. London University, 67–72. Lecturer in Medical Microbiology, Royal Free Hospital Medical School since 72. 35 papers published in scientific journals on Biochemistry & Microbiology. *Biochemical Society.*

868 **LUARD, John Christopher Eckford,** b. 27 Mar. 39, eldest s. of I. C. E. Luard. Sh, 52^3–57^1; XI, 56. McGill University, Montreal, B.A. Massey-Ferguson Export Co., 63. Rep., Latin America, 65. District Sales Manager, Central America, 66. *M.C.C. & Boodle's Club.* Brother, 2404.

869 **PARK, Nigel Lennox Crawford,** b. 26 Dec. 38, s. of A. C. Park. Sh, 52^3–57^2; Levée; Head of House; Leaving Exhibition; Minor Scholarship in Classics. Christ's, Cambridge, B.A. French Government Scholarship. Sorbonne, Research in Greek and Roman History. N.A.T.O. International Secretariat, Brussels, Executive Secretariat, Office of Secretary-General. *Caledonian Society of Belgium.*

870 **BODDINGTON, Henry Geoffrey Cyrus,** b. 23 May 39, younger s. of H. C. Boddington. St, 52^3–58^1; Scholar; Levée; Head of House; XXII, 57. Magdalen, Oxford, M.A. Schoolmaster. *Vincent's Club, Oxford,* The Drapers Company. Brother, 285.

871 **CHASE, John Terry,** b. 7 Nov. 34, 4th s. of C. T. Chase of Mass., U.S.A. St, 52^3–53^2; Tennis Team, 53. Reed College and Princeton Univ. Teaching for 5 yrs. Asst. Editor, Education Department, American Heritage Publishing Co. of N.Y.

872 **FAIRBAIRN, David Henry Lawrence,** b. 15 Apr. 39, eldest s. of H. A. Fairbairn. St, 52^3–57^2; Scholar; Levée. Died, December 67.

873 **GERMAN, Peter Drummond,** b. 25 Oct. 38, s. of J. German. St, 52^3–56^2.

874 **GIBB, Robert John Alexander,** b. 31 Mar. 39, s. of J. E. Gibb (OR St 21). St, 52^3–57^2.

875 **NOEL-PATON, The Hon. Frederick Ranald,** b. 7 Nov. 38, s. of The Rt. Hon. Lord Ferrier, D.L. St, 52^3–57^2; Levée; Head of House; Cap, 56; H. XI, 56; Sw. VIII, 55. Haverford College, Philadelphia, Pa., U.S.A. McGil University, Montreal, P.Q., Canada, B.A. Manager, Programme Design, British Caledonian Airways.

876 **ROBINSON, Simon John Yates,** b. 8 June 39, s. of E. Y. Robinson. St, 52^3–57^2; XI, 56, 57. Investigation Accountant with Law Society, London.

877 **SPORBORG, Christopher Henry,** b. 17 Apr. 39, s. of H. N. Sporborg,

C.M.G. (OR St 19). St, 52^3-57^2; Hurdles Cup, 57; Cadet Officer, 57. N/S. Officer in Coldstream Guards. Emmanuel, Cambridge, B.A. Merchant Banker. Director Hambros Bank Ltd., also of other companies both quoted and unquoted in England & Australia. *Boodle's.*

878 **SYMINGTON, Andrew Philip,** b. 4 Apr. 39, eldest s. of the late S. P. Symington, M.C., T.D. (OR St 23). Levée. Clare, Cambridge, B.A. N/S. Royal Marines, 57–59. 2nd Lt. Joined Tradax, England on leaving Cambridge, 62. Transferred to Tradax, Genève, S.A. in 67, International Grain Merchandising. *Swiss Alpine Club, Aero Club de la Suisse.* Brothers, 1996 & 2254.

879 **TRIMBLE, David William,** b. 14 May 39, s. of W. S. Trimble (High Sheriff of Cumberland, 71–72). St, 52^3-58^1; Levée; R. VIII, 55, 56; Tennis VI, 56, 57, Capt., 57; Capt. of Rackets & Squash, 57, 58. N/S. Officer, 2nd Bn. Scots Guards, 58–60. Selwyn, Cambridge, M.A. United States Securities & Exchange Commission Principals Exam, Grade A, 70. Member of Lloyd's. Merchant Banker, Antony Gibbs & Sons Ltd., 63–68. Their rep. in the Bahamas, 68–73. Director & Officer, Mercantile Group Companies in Bahamas & Director, Mercantile Bank & Trust Company (Kayman) Ltd., 69–73. Director, Jacob Cowen & Sons, Cotton Manufacturers, U.K. Director, North Star Securities Ltd., H.P. & Finance Co., U.K. Mostly self-employed from 73. Member of the *Magic Circle, Pitt Club.*

880 **COGHLAN, Anthony Grant Lake,** b. 5 Apr. 39, younger s. of K. L. Coghlan (OR Tu 25). Tu, 52^3-57^2; XV, 57; XI, 57. A.C.A. Financial Director, Chapman, Lowry & Puttick Ltd., C.L.P. Plumbing & Heating Ltd., Olco Ltd., W. Kingshott & Co. Ltd., Riley & Whishaw Ltd., Ashpark Brickyard Ltd. Director, Riley & Whishaw (Retail) Ltd., Ilushin Estates Ltd., Waterside Estates Ltd., Nigerian Joint Agency Ltd., Agricultural & General Investments Ltd. Brother, 583.

881 **COGHLAN, Timothy Boyle Lake,** b. 29 Mar. 39, s. of P. B. L. Coghlan (OR Tu 21). Tu, 52^3-57^2; Levée; Head of House; XV, 56; XI, 54, 55, Capt., 56–57; Rackets Pair, 56–57. Pembroke, Cambridge, B.A. Partner in firm of London Stockbrokers, Messrs. de Zoete & Bevan. Director of Companies. *City University Club, Gresham Club.*

882 **EASTON, Richard John,** b. 28 Apr. 39, s. of H. K. Easton, F.C.A. Tu, 52^3-57^2. A.C.A., 63. With Peat Marwick Mitchell & Co., Rhodesia, 64–66. Financial Accountant, Janus Booth Aluminium Ltd., 67.

883 **LAWSON, David,** b. 22 Apr. 39, s. of Major A. D. D. Lawson, M.B.E. (OR Tu 17). Tu, 52^3-57^2. Writer; Musician.

884 **MARTIN, David Russell Branwhite,** b. 21 Dec. 38, elder s. of P. G. C. Martin, V.R.D., M.Chir., F.R.C.S. Tu, 52^3-56^3; XV, 54, 55. Queens', Cambridge, B.A. Licentiate of the Institute of Building. Agent with National Building Contractor. *Royal Burnham Yacht Club.*

885 **REES, Peter Charles,** b. 26 Apr. 39, s. of Sir Stanley Rees, B.C.L. Tu, 52^3-57^3. Univ. of London, B.A. Oxford, Dip. Ed. Univ. of Melbourne, B.Ed. Asst. Master, Le Rosey, Switzerland; Asst. Master, Geelong Grammar, Victoria, Australia; Counsellor, Alice Springs, Australia. Presently Post Graduate student at James Cook University, North Queensland, Master of Education Course. Worked in Australia since 67.

886 **WILLIAMS, John Francis Glynne,** b. 13 May 39, s. of the late H. G. Williams. Tu, 52^3-57^2; Scholar; Levée. Corpus Christi, Oxford, M.A. Trinity Cambridge, LL.B. Solicitor, Clifford Turner & Co., London.

887 **BARNETT, Peter John Thorold,** b. 6 May 39, elder s. of G. W. T. Barnett. W, 52^3-57^2. St. Andrews Univ., B.Sc. Institute of Chartered Accountants, Institute of Cost and Management Accountants, Institute of Management Consultants of Quebec. Management Consultant with Cooper Bros. & Co., London, 65–68 and Price Waterhouse Associates, Montreal, 69–72. Chief Executive, Airborne Industries Ltd., Southend, 72. *Beaconsfield G.C.* Brother, 1631.

888 **BEDDINGTON, Hugh David,** b. 5 Mar. 39, s. of Col. K. L. Beddington, C.B.E. (OR W 15). W, 52^3-57^2. N/S. R.A., 57–59. Lt. Joined Imperial Tobacco Co. Ltd., 59. At present with W. D. & H. O. Wills (of Imperial Tobacco) in Bristol in cigarette production management.

889 **COOK, David Markham,** b. 22 Jan. 39, 2nd s. of H. M. Cook. W, 52^3-57^2. St. Mary's Hospital Medical School,

M.B., B.S., D.C.H., M.R.C.P. Senior Registrar Paediatrics to United Sheffield Hospitals. *Sheffield Hockey & Squash Clubs.* Brother, 731.

890 FAULKNER, Alistair Merrick Thomas, b. 4 Feb. 39, s. of I. J. Faulkner, B.Sc., Ph.D. (OR T 15). W, 52^3–57^2. Constantine Technical College, Middlesbrough. H.N.D. Business Studies. I.C.I., 57–68. Project Manager, Northern Computer Bureau, Leeds, 68–70. Data Processing & Systems Manager, W. P. Butterfield (Engineers) Ltd., Shipley, 70–73. *Albemarle Club.* Capt. Royal Artillery (T.A.).

891 HAWKINS, Anthony Charles Simson, b. 30 Dec. 38, elder s. of G. C. Hawkins (OR W 16). W, 52^3–57^2; Levée. 1 yr., Geneva Univ., Language Course. A.C.A., 64. Joined family business of Hawkins & Tipson Ltd. in 64, left 68 to go back into the profession. Partner in Messrs. H. S. Humphrey & Co., Chartered Accountants, Eastbourne from Nov. 69. *Addington G.C.* Hon. Treasurer, Eastbourne Conservative Association. Governor, St. Bede's Preparatory School, Eastbourne. Brother, 1230.

892 MACDONALD, Ian Alexander, b. 12 Jan. 39, s. of I. W. Macdonald, C.A. W, 52^3–57^2; Scholar, Levée; Head of School; Head of House. Clare, Cambridge, M.A., LL.B. Barrister, Lecturer, Author.

893 PASS, Frank Graham, b. 4 Feb. 39, s. of F. Pass. W, 52^3–57^2. Manchester Univ., B.Sc.(Mech. Eng.). H.M. Forces, Royal Engineers.

894 PURSAILL, Andrew John, b. 9 Dec. 38, elder s. of J. N. H. Pursaill. W, 52^3–57^2; Scholar. Balliol, Oxford. Nettleship Scholarship (Music), 57. B.A. Tootal Broadhurst Lee Co. Ltd., Management Trainee, 60–64. Bar, Inner Temple, 64. Sussex Univ. Cert. Ed., 65. Lecturer in Law, Hertfordshire College of Building, 66. Brother, 1499.

895 WILLIAMS, Charles John, b. 2 May 39, 2nd s. of Major W. C. B. Williams, M.C., J.P. W, 52^3–57^2. Tea Planter, Ceylon, 60–62. Economist, A.N.Z. Bank, Melbourne, 63–66, also Economist, A.N.Z. Bank, Sydney, 67–72. Executive Officer, Scottish Australian Co. Ltd., Sydney since 72. Council Member, Australian Institute of International Affairs.

896 FINN, Arthur Rex Colthup, b. 19 June 39, younger s. of T. P. Finn. SH, 53^1–56^2. Kent Farm Institute, 60. Farmer. *Kent & Canterbury Club.*

897 VICKERS, Hugh, b. 25 June 39, younger s. of Sir C. G. Vickers, V.C. SH, 53^1–57^1.

898 BARBER, William Kneale, b. 4 July 39, elder s. of W. L. Barber. T, 53^1–56^2. British India Steam Navigation Co. Ltd. Brother, 1412.

899 FRENCH, Nicholas John, b. 29 June 39, elder s. of Lt.-Col. H. J. S. French, O.B.E., B.C.L. (OR B 26). B, 53^1–57^2; Levée; Head of House. Christ Church, Oxford. Farming.

900 HALL, William George Valentine, b. 18 June 39, s. of the late H. V. Hall. B, 53^1–57^2. Wharton Graduate School of Finance & Commerce. Univ. of Pennsylvania, U.S.A., M.B.A. Director, Anthony White & Sturgeon Ltd. of London. *Cavalry Club.*

901 ATTWOOD, Peter Bedford, b. 2 May 39, s. of B. G. W. Attwood. C, 53^1–56^3.

902 FLEMING, Andrew Scott, b. 10 Sept. 39, s. of E. O. Fleming. C, 53^1–57^3; Levée. Wadham, Oxford.

903 FORREST, Ian Robert, b. 21 July 39, 2nd s. of G. V. Forrest. C, 53^1–57^2.

904 CALVERLEY, Joseph Frederick Brooke, b. 1 Apr. 39, s. of J. A. Calverley. K, 53^1–56^3. Art student at Central School of Art & Design, London. Honours Diploma in Art & Design (Graphic Design). Publicity Dept., Royal Automobile Club, London.

905 HORDERN, Hugh Calverley, b. 8 July 39, s. of Lt.-Col. A. C. Hordern. K, 53^1–57^2.

906 GROVE-WHITE, Ion Greer, b. 5 July 39, elder s. of R. J. Grove-White, M.D., F.R.C.P. (OR M 29). M, 53^1–58^2; Levée. St. John's, Cambridge, M.A., M.B., B.Chir. The London Hospital Medical College, F.F.A., R.C.S. Consultant Anaesthetist, Dundee Teaching Hospitals and Angus Hospitals. Brother, 2123.

907 IRVINE, Michael Fraser, b. 21 Oct. 39, elder s. of Rt. Hon. Sir A. J. Irvine, Q.C., M.P. SF, 53¹–58²; R. VIII, 58. Oriel, Oxford, B.A. Bar, Inner Temple, 64. Barrister-at-Law. *United Oxford and Cambridge University.* Brother, 1299.

908 WOODHOUSE, Jeremy Patrick (now Henry de Clifford Jeremy), b. 7 Aug. 39, s. of the late Wing-Cdr. H. de C. A. Woodhouse, D.F.C., A.F.C. (OR SF 29). SF, 53¹–57³; Levée; Head of House; Cadet Officer. Christ Church, Oxford. Schoolmaster, Marlborough College.

909 HIRST, James Brook, b. 10 July 39, younger s. of R. T. Hirst. Sh, 53¹–57³; Levée. Chartered Accountant. Works Accountant, U.M.L. Limited, Port Sunlight, Cheshire. Brother, 471.

910 SHORT, Anthony Denis, b. 21 June 39, elder s. of R. W. Short. St, 53¹–57²; Levée. Christ Church, Oxford, M.A. Documentary Film Director since 62. Director, Otranto Productions Ltd. Brother, 1958.

911 WEISS, Nigel Oscar, b. 16 Dec. 36, s. of O. Weiss. St, 53¹–54². Clare, Cambridge, M.A., Ph.D. Lecturer in Applied Mathematics & Theoretical Physics, Univ. of Cambridge. Fellow of Clare College.

912 ANDERSON, Antony Faithfull, b. 23 July 39, eldest s. of Brig. W. F. Anderson, C.B.E., M.C. (OR Tu 19). Tu, 53¹–57². Pre-University Apprenticeship, Metropolitan Vickers Ltd., Manchester, 57–58. University of St. Andrews, Queens College, Dundee, B.Sc., Ph.D., M.I.E.E. Chrmn., North Scotland Graduate & Student Section, I.E.E., 63–64. A.E.I., Rugby, 65–67. N.R.D.C. Research Fellow at Dundee Univ., 67–70. International Research and Development Co. Ltd., Newcastle upon Tyne from 70. Group Leader, Electrical Machine Design (Superconducting A.C. Machines) since 71. Publicity Officer, Friends of the Newcastle Museum of Science and Engineering. Part author of various publications. Brothers, 1167 & 1922.

913 BERGIN, David James (name changed to Lonsdale in 1966), b. 12 June 39, s. of T. E. P. Bergin. Tu, 53¹–56³. Farming with parents in S. Africa till 61.

914 CLEGG, John Fawcett, b. 24 May 39, s. of H. F. Clegg. Tu, 53¹–57²; XXII, 57. St. John's, Cambridge & Manchester Univ., B.A., M.B., B.Chir., F.R.C.S.

Registrar in Surgery, Hammersmith Hospital. Registrar in Surgery, Park Hospital, Davyhulme, 68.

915 COBB, Peter Michael, b. 25 Mar. 39, younger s. of Cdr. G. Cobb, R.N. (Retired). W, 53¹–57². N/S. 58–60. Cockburn Smithes & Co. Ltd., 60. Stewart & Son of Dundee Ltd., 67. John Harvey & Sons Ltd. from 69. *M.C.C., Army & Navy Club.* Brother, 142.

916 COLE, Brian Michael, b. 25 June 39, eldest s. of T. Cole. W, 53¹–57². Died 6 June 64. Brothers, 1331 & 1780.

917 KAULBACK, Jalik Arbit, b. 25 May 39, s. of Lt.-Col. R. J. A. Kaulback, D.S.O., F.R.G.S. (OR W 25). W, 53¹–57². Trinity, Dublin, M.A. Australian Bureau of Mineral Resources, 62–66. Ocean Mining A.G., South-East Asia, 67–69. Charter Consolidated Ltd., Europe, 69–71. Consultant Geologist & Company Director, 71. Managing Director, Geotext Group, 71. *Traveller's Club.*

ENTRANCES IN MAY 1953

918 ANDERSON, Ian Stuart, b. 22 Oct. 39, 2nd s. of J. S. Anderson. SH, 53²–57³; Cap, 57; Fives IV, 57. A.C.A. Formerly employed by Cooper Bros. & Co., and C. F. Anderson & Son Ltd. Now in practice as Chartered Accountant. *M.C.C.* Brother, 1503.

919 BEVAN, Richard John, b. 25 Aug. 39, elder s. of T. R. A. Bevan. SH, 53²–57³. Jesus, Cambridge, B.A.(Eng). Golf Blue, 61–63. British Petroleum in London & New Zealand, concerned with general commercial administration. Played golf for Wales, 64–67. Brother, 1692.

920 EVANS, Stephen Telford Eyre, b. 31 Aug. 39, 2nd s. of T. G. C. Evans. B, 53²–57¹. Cirencester Agricultural College. Brother, 739.

921 HARTLEY, James William Harrison, b. 7 Oct. 39, elder s. of H. W. Hartley. B, 53²–57²; Cap, 56. Grenoble Univ. Shaw Carpets Ltd., Managing Director. *Huddersfield R.U.F.C. and Huddersfield G.C.*

922 INGRAM, David Vernon, b. 13 Nov. 39, s. of H. V. Ingram, O.B.E., T.D., M.B., B.S., F.R.C.S., D.O.M.S., M.R.C.S., L.R.C.P. B, 53²–58²; Levée; Head of School; Head of House; Cadet

Officers, 58. St. John's, Cambridge. Middlesex Hospital Medical School, M.A., M.B., B.Chir., F.R.C.S., D.O., M.R.C.S., L.R.C.P. Consultant Ophthalmologist, Sussex Eye Hospital, Brighton. Royal Society of Medicine (Fellow). Member of Ophthalmological Society of U.K.

923 **WILKIE, John Douglas Ferguson,** b. 17 Sept. 39, younger s. of the late J. Wilkie, M.B., Ch.B., D.P.H. B, 53^2–57^3; Senior Scholarship; Levée; Leaving Exhibition. Major Scholarship to Trinity, Cambridge, M.A. Engineering Dept., Cambridge, Ph.D. Graduate training in Drayton Controls Ltd., and James Archdale Ltd., 61–63. Joined Elliott Process Automation (now G.E.C.-Elliott Process Automation Ltd), 67. Head of Control Engineering, Computer Systems Dept. Freeman of Llantrisant. Brother, 77.

924 **FLEW, Timothy John,** b. 18 Oct. 39, elder s. of the late J. D. S. Flew, M.D., F.R.C.O.G. C, 53^2–58^1; Levée. Trinity Hall, Cambridge. University Coll. Hospital Medical School, M.B., B.Chir., F.R.C.S. Surgeon. Senior Registrar, Guy's Hospital, London. Fellow of the Royal Society of Medicine. Brother, 2475.

925 **WILLARD, Rodney Thomas William,** b. 2 Oct. 39, s. of C. G. R. Willard (OR T 19). C, 53^2–57^1. The Bank of Adelaide, Adelaide, S. Australia. *Calcutta Rowing Club, South Adelaide Football Club.*

926 **ATTENBOROUGH,   Michael Francis,** b. 21 Oct. 39, younger s. of R. J. Attenborough, C.B.E. (OR K 22). K, 53^2–58^1; Scholar; Levée; XV, 57; XI, 55, 57. Trinity, Oxford, M.A. Capt., Golf, 61. Director, Matthew Hodder Ltd. Managing Director, Coronet Books. *R. & A., Oxford and Cambridge Golfing Society.* Member of the Walker Cup Team. Brother, 411.

927 **DUMBELL, Malcolm Ronald,** b. 15 Nov. 39, younger s. of A. F. Dumbell. K, 53^2–58^2. M.I.W.S.P., M.I.M.H. In industrial engineering and management consultancy. Now Management Services Manager, Fibreglass Ltd., St. Helens, Lancs. *The Hightown Club.*

928 **NEILSON, Maxwell Frederick,** b. 1 Dec. 39, s. of D. F. A. Neilson, F.R.C.S. (OR K 05). K, 53^2–57^1.

929 **CHOLMELEY, Robert Cecil,** b. 28 Oct. 39, elder s. of Brig. L. N. Chol-

meley. M, 53^2–58^2; Levée. History Scholarship to Worcester, Oxford, B.A. Unilever Ltd., 61–72. Managing Director, Enceret Ltd., Property Development & Finance since 72. *Littlestone G.C., Queen's.* Brother, 1448.

930 **REEVE, James,** b. 12 Dec. 39, s. of M. R. Reeve (OR M 23). M, 53^2–57^3; Levée. Magdalen, Oxford. Painter.

931 **ROBERTS, David Gordon Denby,** b. 5 Jan. 40, 3rd s. of the late Sir J. D. Roberts, Bt., O.B.E. (OR M 18). M, 53^2–58^1. Edinburgh Univ. Chrmn. & Man. Dir., Strathair. Brothers, 491 & 696.

932 **BLAIR, Robin Orr,** b. 1 Jan. 40, eldest s. of Sir A. C. Blair, K.C.V.O., M.A. LL.B., W.S. SF, 53^2–58^2. St. Andrews Univ., M.A. Edin. Univ., LL.B. Writer to the Signet. Partner, Dundas & Wilson, Davidson & Syme, W.S. Edin., 67. *New Club, Edinburgh, Honourable Company of Edinburgh Golfers.* Brothers, 1146, 1901 & 2224.

933 **BOOTH, Clifford August,** b. 20 July 39, s. of L. E. Booth. SF, 53^2–57^2.

934 **CRICHTON-MILLER, Hugh Angus,** b. 15 Aug. 39, younger s. of D. Crichton-Miller. SF, 53^2–58^2; Levée; Head of House; XXII, 58. Pembroke, Cambridge. Marketing Manager, Rank Audio Visual, Brentford.

935 **DAVIES, John James Wallace,** b. 4 Oct. 39, s. of J. I. Davies. SF, 53^2–56^2.

936 **LYONS, Graham Anthony,** b. 15 Nov. 39, eldest s. of B. Lyons, C.B.E., J.P., LL.D.(Hon.) Leeds. SF, 53^2–58^2. Director of Alexandre Ltd., 61–64. Barrister. *M.C.C.* Brothers, 1346 & 1517.

937 **YOUNG, Paul Frederick,** b. 9 Aug. 39, s. of F. C. Young. SF, 53^2–57^2. A.C.I.I. N/S. 59–61. Commissioned in Royal Hampshire Regt. Service in West Indies. Various positions with Commercial Union Assurance Co. in India, Hong Kong, Malaysia, Singapore, 63–72. At present Asst. Manager for Japan, British Insurance Group. Secretary of Foreign Non Life Insurance Association of Japan. *The American Club, Tokyo, The Yokohama Country & Athletic Club.*

938 **CORRY, Robert,** b. 23 Mar. 39, younger s. of D. C. Corry, M.D., F.R.C.S. Sh, 53^2–58^1. Lincoln, Oxford, B.A. (Agriculture). Tenant Farmer on 700 acres.

Royal Ocean Racing Club, R.A.C. Brother, 566.

939 HOBSON, Timothy Hayward, b. 24 Oct. 39, 2nd s. of J. W. Hobson (OR St 22). St, 53^2–57^2. Brothers, 573 & 2557.

940 JOHNSON-HILL, Brian Harborough, b. 3 June 39, eldest s. of K. C. Johnson-Hill, J.P. (OR T 19). St, 53^2–57^2. Brothers, 1358 & 1995.

941 WATKINS, Travers Springett St. Barbe Lonsdale, b. 1 Nov. 39, s. of the late Lt. G. C. I. St. B. S. S. Watkins, R.N. (OR St 24). St, 53^2–56^3. Killed in motor-cycle accident, 58.

942 McKENZIE, Ian James, b. 14 Aug. 39, s. of J. McKenzie, J.P. Tu, 53^2–57^1.

943 SELKIRK, Frank Duncan Logan, b. 28 Aug. 39, 2nd s. of W. L. Selkirk. Tu, 53^2–58^2. Joint Services School of Languages. King's College, London. G.K.N. Sankey Industrial Sales, 64–67. Export Manager since 67. Brothers, 591 & 1629.

944 CRAWSHAW, Timothy Simon Bruce, b. 5 Oct. 39, s. of D. A. L. Crawshaw, M.R.C.S., L.R.C.P. W, 53^2–58^2; R. VIII, 58. Birmingham Univ.

ENTRANCES IN SEPTEMBER 1953

945 ABBOTT, Geoffrey Richard Alexander, b. 14 Sept. 40, 2nd s. of S. E. Abbott, O.B.E. (OR SH 24). SH, 53^3–58^2; Leaving Scholarship. Balliol, Oxford. I.B.M., U.K. Ltd.; on assignment, I.B.M., W.T.H.Q., White Plains, New York, 71–73. Member British Computer Society. Brothers, 654 & 2004.

946 BOYD, Nicholas Simon, b. 23 July 40, s. of A. G. Boyd (OR SH 18). SH, 53^3–58^2. R.A.F. Flying Scholarship. Grenoble Univ., 58–59. R.N. College, Dartmouth, 60. 848 Commando Squadron F.A.A., 62. 845 Commando Squadron, H.M.S. *Albion,* Borneo Campaign, 63–64. R.N.A.S. *Culdrose,* Instructor, 707 Commando Headquarters Squadron, 65. B.E.A. Helicopters, 66. Captain, 67. Senior Captain, 72. Chrmn., V/Stol Technical Study Group, British Airline Pilots Association. Member of C.A.A. Helicopter Legislation Advisory Group and C.A.A. Rotorcraft Requirements Co-ordinating Committee. Merchant Taylors Guild, *R.N. Ski Club.*

947 COLINVAUX, Anthony John, b. 2 Jan. 40, s. of R. P. Colinvaux. SH, 53^3–58^1. Keble, Oxford.

948 DAVIDSON, Brian Sinclair, b. 8 Feb. 40, s. of G. L. D. Davidson. SH, 53^3–58^2. Trinity, Dublin.

949 FERGUSSON, Donald Stuart Bagnall, b. 9 Feb. 40, younger s. of Sir E. M. F. Fergusson. SH, 53^3–58^1; XV, 58. Magdalen, Oxford. A.C.A. Chartered Merchant Bankers Ltd., Singapore. *M.C.C.*

950 FORRESTER, Giles Charles Fielding, b. 18 Dec. 39, elder s. of Major B. T. C. Forrester (OR SH 24). SH, 53^3–58^2; Levée; XV, 56, Capt., 57; XXII, 57; R. VIII, 57. Grenoble Univ., France. Trinity, Oxford. Bar, Inner Temple, 66. Barrister. *United Oxford & Cambridge University Club.* Brother, 2006.

951 HINTON, John Frederick, b. 20 Mar. 40, s. of F. W. C. Hinton. SH, 53^3–58^2. City & Guilds College. Imperial College of Science & Technology. London Univ., B.Sc., A.C.G.I., M.I.Mech.E., C.Eng. Engineering Manager, Imperial Chemical Industry Ltd., Agricultural Division, Billingham. *Old Draconian Society.* Chrmn., Teesside Branch of *Old Centralians.*

952 HOARE, The Rev. Rupert William Noel, b. 3 Mar. 40, s. of J. Hoare (OR SH 18). SH, 53^3–58^1; Levée; R. VIII, 58. Trinity, Oxford, B.A. Kirchliche Hochschule, Berlin. Westcott House, Cambridge & Fitzwilliam House, B.A. Theology. Deacon, 64; Priest, 65. Canon Theologian of Coventry Cathedral, 70. Curate, Oldham Parish Church, 64–67. Lecturer, Queen's Coll., Birmingham, 68–72. Rector, Parish of the Resurrection, Manchester, 72.

953 HUNG, Alan Brian, b. 1 Mar. 40, elder s. of the late W. C. Hung, J.P. SH, 53^3–57^3; XV, 56–57; Sw. VIII, 56; Paddison Art Prize. Solicitor. Partner, Bird & Bird of London. *R.A.C.* Brother, 1937.

954 LOWE, Martin Ralph, b. 16 Jan. 40, s. of the late Major R. M. Lowe. SH, 53^3–57^2.

955 MUCKLOW, Gerald Kay, b. 18 Mar. 40, younger s. of Prof. G. F. Mucklow, D.Sc. (OR M 07). SH, 53^3–58^2; Levée; Head of House; H. XI, 58; State

Scholarship; English Electric Industrial Scholarship. Birmingham Univ., M.Sc., M.I.Mech.E. Computer Consultant, Sandox Pharmaceuticals Ltd., Basle, Switzerland.

956 ROBINSON, Anthony John, b. 8 Mar. 40, s. of P. D. Robinson. SH, 53^3–58^2. Downing, Cambridge, M.A., M.I.C.E., C.Eng., U.K., A.M.S.A.I.C.E., Pr. Eng., South Africa. Civil Engineer with Jeffares & Green, Consulting Civil Engineers. Supervision of Freeway Construction in Natal.

957 WOODS, John Christopher, b. 6 Nov. 40, s. of the late Sir J. H. E. Woods, G.C.B., M.V.O. SH, 53^3–58^3; Scholar; Levée; Head of House; LeavingExhibition; XXII, 58. Open Scholarship for Classics to Corpus Christi, Oxford. Grenoble Univ., Premier Degré d' Études Française. Corpus Christi, Oxford, M.A. Bristol Univ. Dept. of Education, Cert. Ed. Schoolmaster, Hollingbury Court School, Warninglid, Sussex, 65–67. St. Anselms School, Bakewell, Derbyshire, 67. High Trees School, Horley, Surrey since 69. *M.C.C., United University Club.*

958 BARKER, Kenneth Robin, b. 30 Dec. 39, s. of A. R. Barker. T, 53^3–58^2; State Scholarship; Leaving Exhibition. Queens', Cambridge, B.A. Senior Process Engineer with Shell Chemicals.

959 BISHOP, Roger Lewis, b. 3 Mar. 40, elder s. of J. S. Bishop. T, 53^3–57^2.

960 CALDWELL, Alan Douglas (forenames changed to Lloyd), b. 22 Feb. 40, 2nd s. of J. Caldwell, B.Sc. T, 53^3–58^2; Major Exhibition, 53. Univ. of Edinburgh, B.Sc. Ph.D. University Lecturer, 67–71 (Edinburgh, Chemical Engineering). At present, Company Director. Graduate member of Institution of Chemical Engineers. Brother, 809.

961 CARNEGY, Patrick Charles, b. 23 Sept. 40, elder s. of the late Rev. Canon P. C. A. Carnegy. T, 53^3–58^2. Trinity Hall, Cambridge, M.A. Editorial Staff, "The Times Educational Supplement", 64–69. "The Times Literary Supplement", 69. Editor for Science, Music and Religious Books. Opera Critic, 71. Music Critic for "The Times" at Bayreuth, 67–69. Author of "Faust as Musician: a Study of Thomas Mann's Novel 'Doktor Faustus'." Brother, 1251.

962 HARDWICK, Nigel John, b. 18 Apr. 40, elder s. of J. V. Hardwick. T, 53^3–58^2. Rugby College of Engineering Technology. Design Engineer. A.E.I. Ltd., Rugby, 63–68. Brother, 1416.

963 JONES, Gavin David, b. 6 Nov. 39, elder s. of A. Jones. T, 53^3–58^2; S. VIII, 56, 58.

964 LEINSTER, Colin Ronald, b. 19 Dec. 39, elder s. of R. S. Leinster. T, 53^3–57^2. Brother, 1418.

965 MILLS, Roger John, b. 28 Oct. 39, s. of W. R. L. Mills. T, 53^3–57^3. Open Exhibition to Oriel, Oxford, M.A. Member of the Stock Exchange. Partner at Murray & Co. (Stockbrokers) of Birmingham. Society of Investment Analysts. *St. Paul's Club, Birmingham.*

966 PAINE, The Rev. Andrew Liddell, b. 19 Feb. 40, elder s. of the Rev. E. L. Paine. T, 53^3–59^1; Levée; Head of House; Cadet Officer, 58; Dewar Travelling Scholarship, 58. Dartmouth College, N.H., U.S.A. Jesus, Cambridge, Ridley Hall, Cambridge. Lecturer, Luton Parish Church, 65. Vicar of Essington, Nr. Wolverhampton, 69. Brother, 1420.

967 RAYDEN, Alan George, b. 3 Sept. 39, s. of R. G. Rayden, B.Sc. T, 53^3–58^2; Levée; Head of House; XV, 57; XI, 58; H. XI, 58; Baines Leaving Exhibition. Exhibitioner of Queens', Cambridge, M.A., Dip. Ed. Asst. Chemistry Master, Oundle School, 62–72. Housemaster of Grafton House, 66–72. Now Head of Chemistry Dept., King's College, Kampala, Uganda.

968 SCOTT, William, b. 10 Aug. 40, s. of J. Scott, B.Sc. T, 53^3–58^2; Senior Scholarship, 57; Leaving Exhibition. Exhibition to Corpus Christi, Oxford, B.A., D.Phil. Lecturer in History, Univ. of Aberdeen.

969 SYDENHAM, Richard Wyndham, b. 3 Oct. 39, s. of H. V. Sydenham, L.D.S. T, 53^3–57^2. A.C.A., 65. With Cooper Brothers & Co., Birmingham.

970 BRONNERT, Michael Henry, b. 20 Dec. 39, s. of Lt.-Col. R. Bronnert. B, 53^3–57^3. Harvard Univ., M.A. Bankers Trust Co., N.Y., 64. Asst. Treasurer, 67. Banker, 1st Nat. Bank of Boston, Mass., U.S.A.

971 **CATTERALL, Anthony Howard,** b. 16 Mar. 40, 4th s. of J. Catterall. B, 53³-58². A.C.A., M.I.M.C. Management Consultant, PE Consulting Group Ltd.

972 **FAIRCLOUGH, Donald John,** b. 30 May 40, s. of W. D. Fairclough (OR B 20). B, 53³-58²; Levée; H. XI, 58. Paisley College of Technology. The Polytechnic, Regent St., London, B.Sc. London External, 62. Babcock & Wilcox Ltd., Student Apprentice, 58-63. Project Engineer, 63-65. Contract Engineer with Elsinore Shipbuilding Co. Ltd., Denmark, 65-67. Sales Project Engineer with Babcock & Wilcox (Ops.) Ltd., 67-70. Works Project Manager since 70. Institution of Mechanical Engineers.

973 **KER, Robert Francis,** b. 19 Feb. 40, s. of N. R. Ker, B.Litt. B, 53³-58³; R. VIII, 58; State Scholarship; Leaving Exhibition. Peterhouse, Cambridge, B.A. Merton, Oxford, B.Sc. and D.Phil. Courses, 63-64. Bristol Univ. Cert. Ed., 65. Physics Master, Sevenoaks School, 65-69. Physics Master, Cranbrook School, Sydney, 70.

974 **KNOX, James Duxbury,** b. 28 Dec. 39, eldest s. of A. M. Knox. B, 53³-58². M.A.(Edin.). Unilever Ltd.

975 **LEHMANN, Donald John,** b. 21 Mar. 40, s. of G. D. Lehmann, D.Phil., B.Sc., M.R.C.S., L.R.C.P. B, 53³-58³. Trinity, Cambridge.

976 **LUNT, Ian Miller,** b. 22 Jan. 40, s. of R. A. Lunt. B, 53³-58². Edinburgh Univ. Computer Programmer, Lloyds Bank Ltd.

977 **POWER, Peter Clinton,** b. 22 Apr. 40, 3rd s. of G. P. Power. B, 53³-57¹. McGill Univ., Montreal, Canada, B.Comm. Chrmn. & Man. Dir. of Power Industries Ltd., Pakseal Industries Ltd., Package Sealing (Export) Ltd., Power Packaging (Canada) Ltd., Harcraft Ltd., Hygiene Tissues Ltd. Man. Dir. of Industrial Drives Ltd. President of Gerrard Company Ltd., Canada. *Lansdowne Club*, *Temple G.C.*

978 **RICHARDSON, Antony Aylwin,** b. 17 Dec. 39, s. of L. A. Richardson, F.R.C.S. (OR B 15). B, 53³-57³. Lausanne Univ. I.B.M. (Australia) Pty Ltd., Sydney.

979 **WARNER, Richard Weston,** b. 14 Oct. 39, elder s. of J. W. Warner. B, 53³-58². McGill Univ., Montreal, B.Eng., M.A.I.Ch.E. I.C.I., 63-66. Humphreys & Glasgow Ltd., 66-73. Morgan Grenfell & Co. Ltd. since 73. *The Oriental Club.*

980 **WARREN, John Peter,** b. 15 Mar. 40, s. of the late J. H. Warren. B, 53³-57². F.R.I.C.S. Partner in firm of Chartered Surveyors. *Stratford on Avon G.C.*

981 **BULMER, Giles Morwick,** b. 1 May 40, 2nd s. of B. Bulmer. C, 53³-58². King's, Cambridge, M.A. Purchasing & Development Director, H. P. Bulmer Ltd. Brother, 675.

982 **FAULKNER, Charles Stearns,** b. 10 Apr. 36, 4th s. of J. M. Faulkner, M.D. C, 53³-54². Harvard Univ., B.A. Univ. of Rochester, N.Y. Medical School, M.D. Certified Anatomic Pathology by the College of American Pathologists. Senior Instructor & Fellow in Pathology, 66-67. Capt., Medical Corps, U.S. Army. Asst. Prof. of Pathology, Dartmouth Medical School, Hanover, N.H., U.S.A. since 69. International Academy of Pathology. American Association of Pathologists & Bacteriologists. American Association for the Advancement of Science.

983 **HUGHES, Arthur Nicholas,** b. 15 Dec. 39, s. of A. H. Hughes, Ph.D. C, 53³-58². Trinity Hall, Cambridge.

984 **ISMAIL, Abdul Raouf,** b. 21 Apr. 40, s. of M. H. Ismail. C, 53³-58². Jesus, Cambridge.

985 **JOHNSON, Christopher John,** b. 4 Mar. 40, younger s. of E. J. Johnson, J.P. (OR C 26). C, 53³-58². Divisional Production Executive, Josiah Wedgwood & Sons Ltd. Brother, 741.

986 **WISEMAN, David Stephen,** b. 29 Jan. 40, elder s. of the late E. W. Wiseman. C, 53³-58². University of Keele, B.A., Dip. Ed. Teaching at Harold Malley School, Solihull, 63-66. Fettes College, Edinburgh, 66-68. Boroughmuir School, Edinburgh, 68-72. Now taking Master of Education degree at Edin. Univ. Research in modern maths. Edin. Univ. Faculty of Social Science, Committee Member. Teaching maths in Saughton Prison, Edin. Brother, 1275.

987 **CHAPPLE, Jeremy Norman,** b. 4 Jan. 40, s. of L. N. Chapple. K, 53³-58²; Music Scholar. London Univ., B.Sc. Clare, Cambridge, Research. B.Sc., G.I. Med.E. Management Consultant with I.C.I. & Columbia Broadcasting Systems. Now Project Controller of the Open University.

988 HUGHES, Richard Lionel Cress-well, b. 15 Dec. 39, s. of C. J. C. Hughes (OR K 22). K, 53³–58³; Levée. Sidney Sussex, Cambridge.

989 LEWIS, Barry Ian, b. 14 Aug. 40, s. of R. I. Lewis. K, 53³–58³; Scholar; Levée; Head of House; State Scholarship; Leaving Exhibition. Trinity Hall, Cambridge, M.A., LL.B. Solicitor in private practice.

990 WAINWRIGHT, Richard Barry, b. 10 June 40, elder s. of D. Wainwright, M.B., F.R.C.S. K, 53³–58²; Scholar; Levée; Head of House; XV, 57; XXII, 58; H. XI, 57, 58; Senior Athletics Cup, 58. Classical Scholarship to Trinity Oxford, B.A. Middle Temple, Astbury Scholar. Barrister. Legal Adviser, The British Petroleum Co. Ltd. *Royal Corinthian Yacht Club.* Brother, 1532.

991 WOODHEAD, Roderick John, b. 16 Apr. 40, elder s. of J. A. A. L. Woodhead, M.Sc., M.B., Ch.B. K, 53³–58². Manchester Medical School, M.B., Ch.B. Registrar in E.N. & T. South Manchester Group. Brother, 2058.

992 CHANCE, Robert James, b. 25 May 40, s. of J. H. O. Chance, M.R.C.S. M, 53³–58². Birmingham Univ.

993 CHETWOOD, Christopher John, b. 6 May 40, s. of the late L. W. Chetwood. M, 53³–58³. Brasenose, Oxford, M.A., A.C.A. Shell Mex & B.P., 67–70. Samuel Montagu since 70. *Royal Yacht Squadron.*

994 CLARK, Christopher Keats Urling, b. 6 Mar. 40, s. of the late Lt. E. K. U. Clark, M.V.O., R.N. M, 53³–58¹; Levée. Clare, Cambridge, M.A. Industrial Management, Cranfield. M.B.A., M.I.C.E. Plant Manager, Sir Alfred McAlpine & Son Ltd.

995 HODSON-MACKENZIE, Ian Carew, b. 4 June 40, elder s. of K. J. Hodson-Mackenzie (OR M 22). M, 53³–58².

996 HOPE, Charles Louis, b. 9 May 40 elder s. of J. L. Hope, LL.B., T.D. (OR M 19). M, 53³–58³. Magdalene, Cambridge, B.A. B.B.C. Electronic Engineer, 62. Brother, 1452.

997 KENRICK, Martin John, b. 5 Feb. 40, eldest s. of W. E. Kenrick (OR M 22). M, 53³–58². Trinity, Dublin. Cranfield School of Management, D.A.E. Com-

missioner of Taxes for Birmingham North. Guardian of the Birmingham Assay Office, both since 72. Bremer Vulkan, Bremen, Germany, 63–64. Archibald Kenrick & Sons Ltd., makers of Shepherd Castors. Director since 64. Business Graduates Assoc. Brother, 2220.

998 LEWTHWAITE, David Rainald, b.26 Mar. 40, elder s. of Brig. R. G. Lewthwaite, M.C. (OR M 27). M, 53³–58³; Levée; Head of School; Head of House; XV, 57, 58; Tennis VI, 57–58; Dewar Travelling Scholarship. Trinity, Cambridge, B.A. Morgan Guaranty Trust Co. of Montreal, 63. Chrmn. & Jt. Man. Dir., Supertravel Ltd., 64. Student, London College of Divinity. *Lansdowne Club.*

999 MacINNES, Patrick, b. 29 Dec. 39, elder s. of R. G. MacInnes, D.F.C. (OR M 17). M, 53³–57².

1000 MANN, Keith Anthony, b. 5 Feb. 40, youngest s. of G. H. Mann, M.B., Ch.B. M, 53³–58²; XV, 56, 57; H. XI, 57, 58. Jesus, Oxford, B.A., B.M., B.Ch. St. George's Hospital, London, L.R.C.P. Resident Appointments, St. George's Hospital, Cheltenham General Hospital. Medical Officer, British Virgin Islands since 72.

1001 WILKINSON, Oliver Nicholas, b. 23 Sept. 39, younger s. of P. S. Wilkinson. M, 53³–58¹; Scholar; Levée; Head of House. Scholarship to Corpus Christi, Cambridge. La Sorbonne. Barrister-at-Law. Author "Old Glass", "The Atomic Structure of 18th Century Glass". Brother, 424.

1002 AVERY JONES, John Francis, b. 5 Apr. 40, s. of Sir F. Avery Jones, C.B.E., F.R.C.P. SF, 53³–59¹; Levée; Head of House. Trinity, Cambridge, M.A., LL.B. Solicitor, 66. F.T.I.I., 70. Member of the Council of the Institute of Taxation and the Committee of the International Fiscal Assoc. (British Branch). Partner in Bircham & Co., Solicitors. Asst. Editor, "British Tax Review". General Editor, "Encyclopedia of Value Added Tax".

1003 FRY, Courtney Stewart Cuerden, b. 17 Aug. 40, s. of Sir L. A. C. Fry, K.C.M.G. SF, 53³–58³. Cours de Civilisation Française, Sorbonne. McGill Univ. Berry Bros. Rudd & Harveys, Wine Merchants. Free-lance Photographer. *Lansdowne Club.*

1004 **GRANT, David Edmond,** b. 16 Nov. 39, younger s. of the late Rt. Hon. Lord Grant, Q.C. SF, 53³–58²; R. VIII, 57, 58. Open Scholarship to Hertford Oxford, B.A. Director, William Grant & Sons Ltd., Scotch Whisky Distillers. *United Services.* Brother, 698.

1005 **JOHNSON, Jonathan James Drummond,** b. 26 Mar. 40, s. of the late Lt.-Col. D. S. W. Johnson (OR SF 19). SF, 53³–58².

1006 **JONES, Christopher Prestige,** b. 21 Aug. 40, 2nd s. of W. P. Jones. SF, 53³–58²; Scholar; Levée; School Leaving Exhibition. Scholarship to Balliol, Oxford, B.A.

1007 **LANE, Timothy,** b. 4 Jan. 40, younger s. of the late P. Lane (OR SF 24). SF, 53³–55¹. Brother, 562.

1008 **SHAW, Martin Whitney,** b. 26 Mar. 40, 3rd s. of J. F. St. G. Shaw (OR SF 17). SF, 53³–58². Trinity Hall, Cambridge, M.A., M.B., B.Chir. St. Thomas's Hospital, London, D.A. General Practitioner, Chichester, Sussex. B.M.A. *Ski Club of Gt. Britain.* Brothers, 109 & 355.

1009 **SNOWDON, John Ambler,** b. 30 Apr. 40, s. of E. W. Snowdon. SF, 53³–58². Clare, Cambridge. St. Thomas's Hospital. Royal North Shore Hospital of Sydney, M.A., M.B., B.Chir., M.R.A.C.P. M.R.C.Psych., M.Phil. Physician, Maudsley Hospital, S.E.5. Australian College of Physicians. *Hurlingham.*

1010 **THOMSON, George Michael Mackinnon,** b. 29 Mar. 40, s. of G. R. Thomson. SF, 53³–57². Scots Sutherland School of Architecture. A.R.I.B.A., A.R.I.A.S. Started own architectural practice under title of G. M. Mackinnon Thomson, 73. Exhibited R.S.A. Exhibition, 70. *Royal Northern Club.*

1011 **TRUMPER, John Oliver,** b. 27 Oct. 39, s. of Col. F. J. Trumper, O.B.E., T.D. (OR SF 18). SF, 53³–58³; Levée; Head of House; XV, 57, 58; XI, 56–57, Capt., 58. F.R.I.C.S. Partner in Cluttons, Chartered Surveyors. *Bath Club.*

1012 **FERGUSSON, Douglas Argyll,** b. 16 Dec. 39, elder s. of J. D. Fergusson, M.D., F.R.C.S. Sh, 53³–58². St. Thomas's Hospital, London, M.B., B.S., M.R.C.S., L.R.C.P., D.Obst.R.C.O.G. General Practitioner at Bourne End, Bucks. *M.C.C.* Brother, 1305.

1013 **GRIERSON, John Alexander Curtis,** b. 11 Jan. 40, s. of A. F. Grierson, M.C. Sh, 53³–58². B.Sc. Agriculture. Farmer.

1014 **HUNTER BLAIR, Andrew,** b. 12 Dec. 39, s. of P. Hunter Blair. Sh, 53³–58²; Levée; Head of House. Belfast M.Sc. C.Eng., M.I.C.E., M.I.W.E. Project Leader, Resources Group, Water Research Association.

1015 **MORTON, Kenneth John,** b. 11 Feb. 40, eldest s. of K. V. F. Morton, C.I.E. Sh, 53³–58¹; Levée; Head of House; Queen's Medal, 57; Dewar Scholarship. University Coll., Oxford, B.A., A.C.A. With Innes & Meyers Division of Hill Samuel & Co., Merchant Bankers. Manager, 69. Brothers, 1307, 1992 & 2772.

1016 **OSWALD, William Forbes Mackenzie,** b. 22 Jan. 40, s. of Major-General M. St. J. Oswald, C.B., C.B.E., D.S.O., M.C. (OR C 25). Sh, 53³–58². Portsmouth College of Technology, B.A. Business Studies. British Petroleum Co. Ltd., 59–69. Advertising Manager, Wiggins Teape Ltd., 69. *H.A.C.*

1017 **PILLANS, Michael Digby,** b. 10 Dec. 39, elder s. of the late R. N. A. Pillans. Sh, 53³–58¹; Cap, 57; Capt. of Fives, 58. Christ Church, Oxford, B.A. Solicitor.

1018 **SNELL, Peter Dorman,** b. 22 Oct. 39, elder s. of W. Snell. Sh, 53³–57³; XI, 57. Shipping Manager for Booker McConnell. *Formby G.C.* Brother, 1835.

1019 **TEARE, The Rev. Robert John Hugh,** b. 2 Dec. 39, eldest s. of Professor R. D. Teare, M.D., F.R.C.P., F.R.C.Path. Sh, 53³–58²; Levée. Bristol Univ., B.Sc. Post Graduate Diploma Theology, Leeds, 69. President, Bristol Univ. Students Union, 62–63. Priest, 71. Senior Curate, St. Peter & St. Paul, Fareham. Diocese, Portsmouth. *British Schools' Exploring Society.* Brothers, 1355 & 1955.

1020 **YABLON, Gordon Anthony,** b. 16 Apr. 40, s. of R. C. Yablon, LL.B. Sh, 53³–58¹; Levée. Pembroke, Oxford, B.A. Solicitor. Partner in Jaques & Co., Gray's Inn, London. *Lansdowne Club.*

1021 **BOWDEN-SMITH, Edward Philip,** b. 10 May 40, s. of R. P. Bowden-Smith (OR St 13). St, 53³–58². Royal College of Music, A.R.C.M., G.R.S.M. Music Editor with pisci-horticultural inclinations.

1022 **BROOK, Charles Groves Darville**, b. 15 Jan. 40, 3rd s. of the late Air Vice-Marshal W. A. D. Brook, C.B., C.B.E. (OR St 15). St, 53^3–58^2; Scholar; Levée; Head of House. Magdalene, Cambridge. St. Thomas's Hospital Medical School, M.A., M.D., M.R.C.P., D.C.H. Lecturer in Child Health & Growth at the Institute of Child Health, University of London.

1023 **ELLIOTT, Russell Pearson**, b. 27 Mar. 40, s. of A. P. Elliott. St, 53^3–58^3; Levée. Lincoln, Oxford, M.A.

1024 **FOWLE, William Michael Thomas**, b. 8 Jan. 40, s. of the late W. T. Fowle (OR M 00). St, 53^3–58^3. Clare, Cambridge, M.A., A.C.A. With Peat, Marwick, Mitchell & Co., Chartered Accountants, London.

1025 **JACKSON, George Andrew David**, b. 22 May 40, s. of the late Lord W. F. Jackson. St, 53^3–58^2; XV, 57; XXII, 57. Reading Univ., B.Sc. Man. Dir. Man. of Ross Ltd. Farming.

1026 **METCALFE-GIBSON, Richard de St. Croix**, b. 22 Dec. 39, elder s. of A. E. Metcalfe-Gibson. St, 53^3–58^2. Chartered Surveyor. Asst. Surveyor, Bridgewater Estates Ltd., Worsley, Nr. Manchester. Brother, 1225.

1027 **PRICE, Harold Richard Tudor**, b. 18 Apr. 40, younger s. of T. H. Price. St, 53^3–58^3; Levée; Head of House; XV, 57, Capt., 58. Magdalene, Cambridge, B.A. President & Chief Executive, Cow and Gate (Canada) Ltd., the Canadian subsidiary of Unigate Ltd.

1028 **BAIRD, Peter**, b. 19 Oct. 39, elder s. of M. Baird. Tu, 53^3–57^3. King's, Cambridge. Birmingham Univ., M.A., A.A.P.S.W. Lecturer in Social Administration, Birmingham Univ.

1029 **BROWN, David Douglas Southern**, b. 1 Apr. 40, younger s. of J. D. Brown, O.B.E. (OR Tu 13). Tu, 53^3–58^2. A.I.C.S., N.C.A. Farming. Brother, 351.

1030 **CARTWRIGHT, Nigel John Frederick**, b. 12 Aug. 39, elder s. of W. E. Cartwright, D.L., J.P. (OR Tu 20). Tu, 53^3–58^2; Levée; Head of House. Christ Church, Oxford, M.A. Stockbroker. Brother, 1362.

1031 **HAMMETT, Richard John**, b. 2 Mar. 40, s. of R. N. Hammett. Tu, 53^3–58^2; Scholar; Levée; Shell Industrial Scholarship. Exhibition to Pembroke, Cambridge, M.A. Member, A.P.E.O. Manager, Manufacturing Engineering. G.S.W. Ltd., Fergus, Ontario, Canada. *C.U.A.C.*

1032 **HIDE, Walter James Berry**, b. 9 Nov. 39, s. of W. Hide. Tu, 53^3–57^2.

1033 **PROCOPÉ, Johan Fredrik**, b. 15 Jan. 41, elder s. of the late H. J. F. Procopé. Tu, 53^3–58^3; Scholar; Levée; Head of House. King's, Cambridge. Brother, 1627.

1034 **COLEMAN, Robert Hayling**, b. 3 Mar. 40, elder s. of the late F. H. Coleman, M.D., M.R.C.P. (OR W 22). W, 53^3–58^2. The London Hospital.

1035 **FORRESTER, Malcolm Alexander Hugh**, b. 31 Dec. 39, s. of A. F. C. Forrester (OR W 15). W, 53^3–58^2. General Steam Navigation Co., 60. Blyth Bros. & Co., Mauritius, 62. Training Officer, Atlas Express Ltd., Rutherglen, 65.

1036 **HALL, The Rev. Charles John**, b. 24 Jan. 40, elder s. of the late Col. J. V. Hall, O.B.E., T.D. (OR W 15). W, 53^3–57^3. Britannia Royal Naval College, Dartmouth. London College of Divinity, A.L.C.D. Anglican Clergyman. Curate, St. George's, Morden, Surrey. Brother, 1931.

1037 **LLOYD HART, Richard William**, b. 19 Dec. 39, s. of V. E. Lloyd Hart, M.R.C.P. W, 53^3–58^1; Scholar; Levée. Open Scholarship to Corpus Christi, Oxford, M.A. Miami Univ., Oxford, Ohio, U.S.A., 58–59. Solicitor, 66.

1038 **LOWDON, Lennox**, b. 11 May 40, s. of A. F. Lowdon. W, 53^3–57^3; Cap, Sw. VIII, 57. A.C.A. Stockbroker with Cohen de Smitt Greener Dreyfus, London. *Caledonian Club, London Scottish Football Club.*

1039 **SHORT, Rodney Arthur Maxwell**, b. 5 Dec. 39, 3rd s. of W. A. Short, O.B.E. W, 53^3–56^3.

1040 **STANSFIELD, William Holdcroft**, b. 11 July 40, elder s. of His Honour Judge J. W. Stansfield, LL.B. W, 53^3–58^2. Sidney Sussex, Cambridge, B.A. Solicitor. Partner, Robert Davies & Co., Solicitors, Warrington, Lancs. Brother, 2729.

1041 **WARD, Robert Sydney Guthrie,** b. 11 Apr. 40, s. of J. G. Ward, C.M.G. W, 53³–58²; S. VIII, 58. Pembroke, Cambridge.

1042 **WEBSTER, Martyn Hector Cochrane,** b. 24 Dec. 39, younger (twin) s. of G. G. M. Webster. W, 53³–57². Glasgow Univ., M.B., Ch.B., F.R.C.S. Registrar, Regional Plastic Surgery Unit, Canniesburn Hospital, Glasgow. House Officer, Glasgow Royal Infirmary. Brother, 1043.

1043 **WEBSTER, Robert Gordon Mac-Lennan,** b. 24 Dec. 39, elder (twin) s. of G. G. M. Webster. W, 53³–57³; Levée; Head of House; Cap, 57. St. John's, Cambridge, B.A. University College, London, M.A. ,A.R.I.B.A., 67. Brother, 1042.

ENTRANCES IN JANUARY 1954

1044 **GUINNESS, Lucian Francis,** b. 1 Aug. 40, younger s. of B. C. Guinness, C.B.E., R.D. (OR SH 17). SH, 54¹–59²; Levée; Head of House; State Scholarship, 58. King's, Cambridge. St. Thomas's Hospital, London, M.B., B.Chir., D.R.C.O.G. Missionary Doctor, Ngora Church of Uganda Hospital. Brother, 802.

1045 **SAXTON, Christopher Barry,** b. 26 Sept. 40, s. of M. J. F. Saxton. SH, 54¹–59¹. Conservatoire National de Musique, Grenoble. Exeter, Oxford, B.A. Travel Agent (Tours Director, Glenton Tours).

1046 **COCKS, Peter Greenfield,** b. 26 Apr. 40, younger s. of W. H. G. Cocks, C.B.E. B, 54¹–58². Brother, 453.

1047 **CONWAY, Hugh Robert Graham,** b. 27 June 40, elder s. of H. G. Conway. B, 54¹–58³; Levée. Gonville & Caius, Cambridge, B.A. Stewart & Lloyds, 62. Chartered Mechanical Engineer, 69. Capper Pass & Son Ltd., North Ferriby, Yorks. Brother, 1208.

1048 **KIRK, Robert John Peter,** b. 16 July 40, s. of G. P. Kirk (OR C 25). C, 54¹–58². City University, London, B.Sc. Distillers Co. Ltd., Montreal. Engineering Co., Canada. Instrument Engineer.

1049 **LEA, Michael Carrington,** b. 20 May 40, elder s. of W. E. Lea. C, 54¹–55².

1050 **MACANDREWS, Julian Edward,** b. 4 July 40, younger s. of J. J. Mac-Andrews, M.B., B.Ch. C, 54¹–58².

1051 **WALTON, Field Lawrence Joseph,** b. 17 Apr. 40, eldest s. of J. F. H. Walton, M.R.C.S., L.R.C.P. C, 54¹–58²; XV, 57. Loughborough University of Technology, B.Tech., M.Sc., M.I.E.E., A.M.B.I.M. C.Eng. Project Engineer, Brush Electrical Eng. Co. Ltd., Loughborough, 64. Project Manager, John Laing & Sons Ltd., London, 68. Corporate Planning Manager, Plessey & Co. Ltd., London, 70. Analyst, Cazenove & Co., London since 72.

1052 **CAMPBELL, John Henry Duncan,** b. 15 Aug. 40, elder s. of W. H. D. Campbell, F.C.A. M, 54¹–58³; Levée. St. Edmund Hall, Oxford, B.A. President, Oxford University Travel Club. President, John Methuen Dining Club. A.C.A. Certified Public Accountant, C.P.A. Partner, Angus Campbell & Co. and Josolyne Layton-Bennett & Co. of London. Brother, 1794.

1053 **HAMSON, Michael Sidney,** b. 24 June 40, s. of J. Hamson, J.P. M, 54¹–58¹. Cap, 57. St. Andrews Univ., Scotland, B.L., C.A.(Scotland). Director of Finance and Administration, Philip Morris Asia-Pacific Inc. *Royal Melbourne G.C.*

1054 **BRANDT, Timothy Allen,** b. 2 June 40, younger s. of H. A. Brandt (OR SF 15). SF, 54¹–58²; Cap, 57; H. XI, 58. Killed in aeroplane accident in S. Africa, 20 Apr. 68. Brother, 643.

1055 **BRYANT, Peter Stuart,** b. 10 May 38, s. of the late S. R. Bryant. Sh, 54¹–57². Swarthmore Coll., U.S.A. & Witwatersrand Univ., S. Africa, B.Comm. With Hill Samuel & Co. Ltd., London, 63–69. Johannesburg, 69–72. Lewis & Peat Ltd., London as Asst. Man., 72. Dir., Guinness Mahon & Co. Ltd. and Lewis & Peat Merchant Bank Ltd., Singapore and Lewis & Peat Eastern Holdings Ltd., 73. *Johannesburg Club, Rand Club.*

1056 **REID, David Campbell,** b. 15 Nov. 40, s. of J. C. Reid. Sh, 54¹–58². House Furnisher and Antique Dealer. *New Club, Edinburgh, Hon. Co. of Edin. Golfers.*

1057 **WASON, John Eugene Monier,** b. 1 May 40, elder s. of E. R. Wason. Sh, 54¹–58². Director, Hogg, Robinson & Gardner Mountain, Lusaka, Zambia.

1058 **HAMILTON, Julian Edward,** b. 29 Aug. 39, 2nd s. of the late R. B. Hamilton. St, 54¹–56³.

1059 **ROBINSON, Douglas Gerald Finlay,** b. 7 Apr. 40, younger s. of Rev. A. G. Robinson. St, 54¹–58². Royal Agricultural College, Cirencester. Professional & Technical Officer, Property Services Agency, Defence Land Service.

1060 **BRINSDEN, Peter Robert,** b. 2 Sept. 40 eldest s. of D. Brinsden. Tu, 54¹–59²; Levée; Head of House. London University, St. George's Hospital Medical School, M.B., B.S., M.R.C.S., L.R.C.P., D.Obst. R.C.O.G. Surgeon Lt.-Cdr., R.N. Specialist in Obstetrics & Gynaecology. Brothers, 1485 & Mark Shelly, Tu, 70¹–.

1061 **COPE, Peter John,** b. 3 July 40, elder s. of J. W. Cope, M.B., B.Chir., F.R.C.S. Tu, 54¹–58². Brother, 2618.

1062 **RUNDELL, George Fraser Westcott,** b. 17 Mar. 40, youngest s. of Major W. W. O. Rundell (OR Tu 96). Tu, 54¹–56².

1063 **DUMMETT, Thomas Ian Peter,** b. 14 Aug. 40, elder s. of G. A. Dummett (OR W 21). W, 54¹–58². Pembroke, Cambridge, B.A. Patents Dept., Allbright & Wilson, 62. Fellow of Chartered Institute of Patent Agents, 66. Senior Technical Asst. to Group Patent Agents, Fisons Ltd., Felixstowe, 67.

ENTRANCES IN MAY 1954

1064 **AROYO, Robert Isaac,** b. 26 Oct. 40, younger s. of M. N. Aroyo of Malta. SH, 54²–59¹. L.S.E. Brother, 375.

1065 **BROWN, Adam Roger,** b. 1 Nov. 40, elder s. of L. W. Brown, O.B.E., B.Sc. SH, 54²–59²; Levée; R. VIII, 57, 58; Holder of Bigside Bags, 59. Peterhouse, Cambridge. Hawker Siddeley Aviation Ltd. *Thames Hare & Hounds.* Brother, 1693.

1066 **HARDMAN, John,** b. 21 Dec. 40, s. of J. Hardman, F.R.C.S. SH, 54²–58².

1067 **ROBERTS, Peter John,** b. 31 Aug. 40, younger s. of C. C. Roberts (OR SH 14). SH, 54²–59¹; Levée; Head of House; State Scholarship. Exhibition to University College, Oxford, B.A. Butterfield & Swire, shipping in the Far East. Brother, 478.

1068 **GREENWAY, Ian Peter,** b. 27 July 40, s. of B. A. Greenway. B, 54²–58².

1069 **JACKSON, Martin Burton,** b. 21 Dec. 40, s. of R. C. Jackson. B, 54²–57². Man. Dir., Bradley House Investments Ltd., Property Development & Investments.

1070 **MOTT, Michael Duncan,** b. 8 Dec. 40, s. of F. J. Mott. B, 54²–58³. Exhibition in Modern Languages to Gonville & Caius, Cambridge, M.A. Bar, Inner Temple & Midland & Oxford Circuits, "called", 63. Practised in Chambers in Birmingham, 64–69. Resident Magistrate in Kenya, 69–71. Resumed practice in Birmingham, 72.

1071 **TALLON, David Seymour,** b. 7 Oct. 40, elder s. of C. R. Tallon (OR T 23). B, 54²–58²; XI, 58. Articled to Deloitte & Co. (Chartered Accountants), 58–63. A.C.A. Partner of Dearden Lord Annan Morrish, London. Brother, 2200.

1072 **WHEATLEY, John Edwin Stobo Andrew,** b. 4 Aug. 40, 2nd s. of G. A. Wheatley, C.B.E., B.C.L. (OR B 22). B, 54²–58². Univ. of Western Ontario, M.B.A., C.A.(Canadian), 63. Manager with Thorne Gunn & Co., Chartered Accountants, Cranbrook, B.C., Canada. Brothers, 768 & 2201.

1073 **ADAM, Thomas Robertson Holcroft,** b. 22 May 40, s. of T. Adam (OR C 28). C, 54²–57³. 1st Bn. Royal Irish Fusiliers. Short Service Commission, 58–62. Lloyd's Insurance, 62–64. Border T.V., 65. Yorkshire T.V., 69.

1074 **COLE, David John,** 8 Oct. 40 eldest s. of Col. J. R. Cole. C, 54²–59²; XI, 58, 59. Brothers, 2038, 2305 & 2515.

1075 **FIGGIS, Anthony St. John Howard,** b. 12 Oct. 40, s. of R. R. Figgis, C, 54²–59¹; Levée; Cap, 58; H. XI, 59. King's, Cambridge, B.A. Member of H.M. Diplomatic Service since 62 (3rd Secretary, Belgrade and Foreign Office, 62–68; 2nd Secretary, Bahrain, 68–70; 1st Secretary, Madrid, 71–).

1076 **GAMBLE, Peter Charles David,** b. 23 Sept. 40, s. of F. D. M. Gamble. C, 54²–59². City & Guilds, Imperial College, London, B.Sc. Aeronautics, 62. W. H. Allen & Sons & Co., 62. Diesel Development Engineer, Davy Ashmore Ltd., 64. Executive Assistant to Group Technical Director, 67.

1077 **MADDEN, Patrick William Hugh,** b. 5 Oct. 40, younger s. of W. E.

Madden (OR K 20). K, 54^2–59^3; Levée; Head of House; Tennis VI, 57, Capt., 58, 59; Dewar Travelling Scholarship. Imperial College, London, B.Sc., A.C.G.I., M.I.Mech.E. Dowty Group, Student Apprentice, 64–66. Man., Production Control, Dowty Seals Ltd., 66–69. General Man., Klöckner-Dowty, Germany, 69–71. Man., Dowty Seals Ltd., European Export since 71. *Tewkesbury Squash Racquets Club*. Brother, 842.

1078 SMITH, John Norman (now known as Phipson, John Norman), b. 29 Nov. 40, eldest s. of N. H. W. Smith, K, 54^2–58^3. Solicitor, 64. Major, H.A.C. Partner in Linklaters & Paines (London) since 70. *Junior Carlton Club*. Brother, 1672.

1079 APPLEBY, Richard Saxton, b. 7 Jan. 41, s. of E. S. Appleby, LL.B., T.D. (OR M 29). M, 54^2–59^2; Levée; Head of House; XV, 58; XI, 58, 59. Solicitor in general practice. *Northern R.F.C.* (Secretary).

1080 PRESTON, Kevin Wentworth, b. 30 Oct. 40, younger s. of the late B. W. Preston, M.B.E. (OR M 18). M, 54^2–58^3; XV, 58.

1081 BACON, John Sewell, b. 25 Sept. 40, younger s. of the late Sir R. S. Bacon, M.B.E. (OR SF 09). SF, 54^2–58^3. London Univ., B.Sc., A.M.I.C.E., M.I.Mech.E. Shell International Petroleum Company. At present Senior Engineer in a U.K. Oil Refinery.

1082 FAURE, Peter Christopher Henry, b. 6 Sept. 40, elder s. of the late P. H. Faure, M.B.E. (OR SF 22). SF, 54^2–58^3; XV, 57, 58; XI, 57, 58; H. XI, 58. Market Executive, Faure Fairclough Ltd., London.

1083 LONGRIGG, Michael Charles Fallowfield, b. 10 June 40, s. of E. F. Longrigg (OR SF 20). SF, 54^2–58^2; XXII, 58. Director, Private Company, Sydney, Australia.

1084 CRAWLEY, William Francis, b. 19 Sept. 40, youngest s. of C. W. Crawley. Sh, 54^2–59^1; Scholar; Levée. Classical Scholarship to Trinity, Cambridge. St. Antony's, Oxford, D.Phil. Teaching in Nigeria, 59–60. Teaching history at St. Stephen's Coll., Delhi University, India, 64–66. B.B.C. Eastern Service, writer & commentator on South Asian affairs, 70. Published article on Indian history & contemporary affairs. Brothers, 38 & 433.

1085 DAVENPORT, Michael Telford, b. 18 Sept. 40, s. of M. E. Davenport. Sh, 54^2–58^2; Cadet Pair; S. VIII, 56. A.C.A. Audit Manager with Kidsons, Chartered Accounts, Manchester. *Altrincham Rifle Club*.

1086 NICOLSON, James Gavin Kendall, b. 22 Sept. 40, s. of the late Wing-Cdr. J. B. Nicolson, V.C., D.F.C. Sh, 54^2–59^1. Oriel, Oxford. R.E. Atkinson (York) Ltd., Wine Merchants & Shippers, Director, 67. *The Yorkshire Club*.

1087 STRONACH-HARDY, Alexander, b. 9 Aug. 40, s. of A. C. Stronach-Hardy. Sh, 54^2–58^3; Sw. VIII, 57, 58. Solicitor. Partner in private practice. The Law Society.

1088 LANG, Ian Bruce, b. 27 June 40, younger s. of J. F. Lang, D.S.C. St, 54^2–58^3. Sidney Sussex, Cambridge, B.A. Conservative Parliamentary Candidate, Central Ayrshire, 1970 election. Adopted prospective candidate, Glasgow Pollock, 72. Trustee Savings Bank of Glasgow, 70. Dir., Rose, Thomson, Young & Co. (Glasgow) Ltd., Insurance Brokers, 66. O. St. J., 72. *Western Club, Glasgow, Prestwick G.C.* Brother, 649.

1089 CARTWRIGHT-TAYLOR, Timothy John, b. 29 Jan. 41, s. of the late Gen. Sir M. C. Cartwright-Taylor, R.M. (OR Tu 25). Tu, 54^2–58^3; Cap, 58.

1090 HEARN, John Richard Whitcombe, b. 18 Aug. 40, elder s. of Col. J. N. W. Hearn (OR Tu 27). Tu, 54^2–59^1. Selwyn, Cambridge, M.A. College Scholarship, 62. English Electric Co., Stafford, 63. Quickfit & Quartz Ltd., 66. Brookes & Gatehouse Inc., 67. Director & Gen. Man. At present Cooper Bros. & Co. *Army & Navy Club, Royal Lymington Yacht Club*. Brother, 1540.

1091 MANN, Anthony Howard, b. 11 Dec. 40, s. of A. H. Mann. Tu, 54^2–59^1; Levée; Head of House. Jesus, Cambridge, M.A., M.B., B.Chir. St. Bartholomew's Hospital, M.R.C.P., M.Phil. Senior Registrar, Psychiatry, National Hospital, Queen Sq., London.

1092 STUART - MENTETH, James Sleigh, b. 29 Oct. 40, younger s. of W. G. Stuart-Menteth (OR Tu 20). Tu, 54^2–58^2. Brother, 756.

1093 WHEELWRIGHT, Richard John, b. 15 July 40, elder s. of J. M. H.

Wheelwright (OR W 18). W, 54²–58³; Levée; Head of House; Leaving Exhibition. Magdalene, Cambridge, B.A. Bankers Trust Company, 62–68. Thames & Hudson, Publishers. Brother, 2002.

ENTRANCES IN SEPTEMBER 1954

1094 BRUNYATE, James Roger Fulton, b. 16 Dec. 40, s. of W. M. W. Brunyate, M.C. (OR SH 12). SH, 54³–58²; Scholar. Trinity, Cambridge, B.A. University of Glasgow, Asst. Lecturer, 63–66, & Lecturer, 66–68, in History of Fine Art. Staff Producer, Glyndebourne Festival Opera, 68–71. Director of Opera Production, Florida State University since 72.

1095 FLEMMING, John Stanton, b. 6 Feb. 41, younger s. of Sir G. N. Flemming, K.C.B. (OR SH 11). SH, 54³–59¹. Trinity, Oxford. Nuffield College, Oxford. Lecturer & Fellow (Economics), Oriel, Oxford, 63–65. Fellow, Nuffield College, Oxford since 65. Senior Tutor, 69–70. Joint Investment Bursar, 70. Asst. Gen. Editor, Oxford Economic Papers, 70. Brother, 483.

1096 HEAP, Christopher John, b. 8 Mar. 41, s. of the late J. E. Heap (OR C 24). SH, 54³–58². La Sorbonne University. Heidelberg University. Registered Representative, New York Stock Exchange, American Stock Exchange, N.Y., National Association of Security Dealers, N.Y. International Banking. Man., Syndicate Dept., Europe. Merrill Lynch, Pierce, Fenner and Smith Securities Underwriter Ltd., New York/Paris. *Public Schools and East India Clubs.*

1097 LEGGAT, Hugh Campbell, b. 7 June 41, eldest s. of the late D. C. Leggat. SH, 54³–58². National Certificate in Building, 64. Management Trainee, John Laing & Sons, 60–63. Site Agent, Hugh Leggat Ltd., 63–65. Wholetime voluntary work with Moral Re-armament, 65. *Western Club, Glasgow, Incorporation of Masons, Glasgow.*

1098 MALCOLM, John Cowie St. Albans, b. 10 Feb. 41, s. of J. E. Malcolm, B.Sc., M.B., Ch.B., F.R.C.S. SH, 54³–59². King's College, London.

1099 PELLY, David Claude Raymond, b. 5 July 41, younger s. of the late Air Marshal Sir C. B. R. Pelly, K.C.B., C.B.E., M.C. (OR SH 16). SH, 54³–59³. Journalist, "Bristol Evening Post", now

Asst. Ed., "Yachting World". *Aldeburgh Yacht Club* (Committee). Brother, 737.

1100 SHAW, Nicholas More, b. 29 July 41, elder s. of J. M. Shaw, M.C., Q.C. (OR SH 28). SH, 54³–58³.

1101 TROLLOPE, The Rev. David Harvey, b. 28 Apr. 41, elder s. of E. H. Trollope (OR SH 25). SH, 54³–59²; XV, 58; H. XI, 59. Battersea College of Advanced Technology, C.C.A.A., B.Sc. (Mech.Eng.). Project Engineer for Ingersoll-Rand in New York & London. London College of Divinity. Ordained Deacon, 68; Priest, 69. C. of E. Curate to St. James Church, Bermondsey, London. Now serving in Uganda with Church Missionary Society working Kampala Diocese in Industrial Training project. *Uganda Mountaineering Club.*

1102 TURCAN, Henry Watson, b. 22 Aug. 41, eldest s. of H. H. Turcan, T.D. (OR SH 20). SH, 54³–59². Trinity, Oxford, M.A. Barrister at Law. Brothers, 1371 & 2012.

1103 BARHAM, Robert Francis, b. 29 July 41, elder s. of Rev. W. A. B. Barham, B.D. T, 54³–57³. Killed by a motor car when bicycling home from school on 10 Dec. 57.

1104 BRADLEY, Peter James, b. 12 July 41, elder s. of J. Bradley. T, 54³–59³. Queens', Cambridge.

1105 FURBER, Richard Mark, b. 11 May 41, younger s. of T. R. Furber, B.V.Sc., M.R.C.V.S. T, 54³–59². Sidney Sussex, Cambridge, M.A. School of Veterinary Medicine, Cambridge, Vet. M.B., M.R.C.V.S. Veterinary Surgeon in private practice. British Veterinary Assoc.

1106 HILL, Jonathan Edward, b. 25 Mar. 41, 2nd s. of R. C. Hill. T, 54³–59¹; Levée; Winner of Crick, 58. Keble, Oxford, M.A., B.Phil.(Oxon.). Asst. Dep. of English, University College, Dublin, 65–67. Foreign Lektor, Dep. of English, University of Gothenburg, Sweden, 67–69. Asst. Professor, Dep. of English, St. Olaf College, Northfield, Minnesota, U.S.A., 69. Modern Language Assoc. of America. American Assoc. of University Professors. Brother, 738.

1107 LEAVER, David Graham, b. 10 Dec. 40, s. of F. J. Leaver. T, 54³–59¹; Levée. Queens', Cambridge, M.B., B.Chir., M.R.C.P. Senior Registrar, King's College Hospital.

1108 **LEWIS, Anthony Philip,** b. 15 Feb. 42, elder s. of P. Lewis, T.D.(A). T, 54³–59². King's, Cambridge, B.A. London University, Cert. Ed. Leeds University, M.A. English Language Officer in the British Council, at present on secondment to the East-Central State Ministry of Education, Nigeria, as Senior Lecturer at the Advanced Teacher Training College, Owerri, East-Central State, Nigeria.

1109 **MORTIMER, Christopher John,** b. 21 Apr. 41, s. of C. P. Mortimer (A). T, 54³–59². Scholarship to Jesus, Cambridge.

1110 **PRIDMORE, John David Maffey,** b. 30 Jan. 41, younger s. of C. A. Pridmore (OR T 26). T, 54³–58². Westhill College of Education, Diploma in Youth Work. Leader/Manager, All Souls Clubhouse. Warden/Manager, The Rugby Clubs. Brother, 819.

1111 **ROBERTS, Alan Madoc,** b. 24 Aug. 41, eldest s. of V. M. Roberts, B.Sc. T, 54³–59³; Levée; Head of House. Trinity, Cambridge, B.A. University of California, Los Angeles, U.S.A., Ph.D. Lecturer in Zoology at University of Bristol. Member, Society for Experimental Biology.

1112 **WALLIS, Roger Alan,** b. 8 Aug. 41, younger s. of A. S. Wallis, B.Sc. T, 54³–59²; Peppin Cup. Trinity, Cambridge, B.A. Diploma in Industrial Management. Post Graduate Research Asst., Stockholm School of Economics. Producer for Swedish Broadcasting Corporation. Cultural Worker at "Music Network" on anti-commercial, co-operative record company run by active musicians in Sweden. J.U.L. (Swedish decoration).

1113 **GARTON, Richard Ashton,** b. 4 Feb. 41, s. of J. S. Garton. B, 54³–59¹; Cap, 58; XXII, 58. Farmer.

1114 **HULL, Richard Adin,** b. 25 Nov. 40, s. of A. Hull, M.B.E. (OR B 22). B, 54³–58².

1115 **LEWIS, Anthony Meredith,** b. 15 Nov. 40, s. of G. V. L. Lewis. B, 54³–59²; Levée. St. Edmund Hall, Oxford, M.A. Solicitor. Junior Partner in Joynson-Hicks & Co. of London. *Hurlingham Club.*

1116 **NIMMO, Ian Atholl,** b. 22 Nov. 40, eldest s. of J. A. D. Nimmo (OR B 20). B, 54³–59²; Scholar; Levée; Head of House; Cadet Officer, 59. Major Scholar-

ship to Emmanuel, Cambridge, M.A. Edinburgh Univ., Ph.D. Lecturer in Bio-chemistry, Edinburgh Univ. *Fisheries Society of British Isles, Salmon & Trout Assoc., Edinburgh Sports Club.* Brothers, 1268, 1872 & 2364.

1117 **PINKERTON, John Macpherson,** b. 18 Apr. 41, s. of the late J. C. Pinkerton, M.C., C.B.E., J.P., B.L., P.P.R.I.C.S. B, 54³–59³. Magdalen, Oxford, B.A. Edinburgh Univ., LL.B. Advocate. Standing Junior Counsel, Scottish Countryside Commission. Clerk of Faculty of Advocates. Honorary Fellow in Faculty of Law, Edinburgh Univ. Voluntary service overseas, 60. *New Club, Edinburgh.*

1118 **RITCHIE, Hugh,** b. 15 July 41, elder s. of T. H. W. Ritchie, M.D., B.Ch. B, 54³–59². Pembroke, Cambridge, M.A. Senior Biologist, Beverley Grammar School, Beverley, Yorks. Brother, 1973.

1119 **ROBERTS, Julian Nesfield,** b. 25 Mar. 41, 2nd s. of A. C. Roberts. B, 54³–59¹. Trinity Hall, Cambridge, M.A. Qualified Solicitor. Partner, Devonshire & Co., Solicitors. Brothers, 673 & 2365.

1120 **SHILLADAY, Tony John,** b. 13 Jan. 41, eldest s. of J. A. Shilladay. B, 54³–59².

1121 **SOUTHWARD, Nigel Ralph,** b. 8 Feb. 41, 3rd s. of R. Southward, M.B., Ch.B., F.R.C.P. B, 54³–59²; Levée; Cap, 58; Sw. VIII, 56, 57, Capt., 58, 59. Trinity Hall, Cambridge, M.A., M.B., B.Chir. Dean Memorial Prize, 62. Middlesex Hospital, M.R.C.P. Medical Practitioner. Brothers, 484 & 2033.

1122 **WILLS, Nicholas Kenneth Spencer,** b. 18 May 41, younger s. of Sir J. S. Wills. B, 54³–59². Queens', Cambridge, M.A., A.C.A. Morgan Grenfell & Co., 67–70. British Electric Traction Co., 70. Man. Dir., Birmingham & District Investment Trust, Electrical & Industrial Investment Co., National Electric Construction Co. Dir. of Argus Press. *R.A.C.*

1123 **BLUNT, Michael Arthur,** b. 24 June 41, 2nd s. of A. G. Blunt, V.R.D. (OR C 23). C, 54³–59². A.C.A. With firm of Chartered Accountants in City of London. Liveryman of Grocers Coy. Brothers, 242 & 1374.

1124 **BOURDILLON, Peter John,** b. 10 July 41, s. of J. F. Bourdillon, B.M.,

B.Ch., F.R.C.S. C, 54³–59²; Levée; H. XI, 59. Middlesex Hospital Medical School (London Univ.), M.B., B.S., M.R.C.P. Senior Registrar in the Department of Clinical Cardiology, Hammersmith Hospital, London. Royal Society of Medicine.

1125 **MEYER, Peter John Harvey,** b. 29 May 41, younger s. of L. H. P. Meyer. C, 54³–59³; Levée; Head of School; Head of House; Cap, 57; Sw. VIII, 57, 58, 59; State Scholarship. Pembroke, Cambridge, M.A. 6 yrs. with Hill Samuel & Co. Ltd., Merchant Bankers, currently representative for France, based in Paris. *R.A.C.*

1126 **SPURRIER, Steven Hugh Walthall,** b. 5 Oct. 41, younger s. of H. J. M. Spurrier (OR C 27). C, 54³–59². L.S.E., B.Sc.Econ. In wine trade. *Boodle's, The Travellers', Paris.* Brother, 834.

1127 **WATT, Richard Anthony John,** b. 19 July 41, elder s. of A. Watt, M.D., Ch.B., D.P.M. C, 54²–59². L.S.E.

1128 **ASFAW, John,** b. 19 Apr. 41, elder s. of F. K. Asfaw. K, 54³–59²; XI, 59; H. XI, 59.

1129 **CROFTS, Robin Bruce,** b. 28 Dec. 40, younger s. of the late F. B. Crofts. K, 54³–58³; Cap, 58; XXII, 58. Short Course at University of Warwick for Institute of Bankers. A.I.B. Commenced Chartered Accountancy, 70. Passed Intermediate Exam., 71. Articled Clerk, Chartered Accountants. Brother, 686.

1130 **HALL, John James,** b. 7 Jan. 41, s. of R. A. Hall (OR K 27). K, 54³–59²; Scholar; Jex-Blake Exhibition, 58. Scholarship to Trinity, Cambridge, M.A., Ph.D. Graduate Asst., Cambridge University Library, 65–66 & Asst. Under-Librarian since 66.

1131 **HODSON-MACKENZIE, Anthony Murdoch,** b. 24 Mar. 41, s. of the late R. P. Hodson-Mackenzie (OR M 20). K, 54³–59¹.

1132 **IRWIN, Michael St. George,** b. 11 Oct. 40, elder s. of Major-Gen. B. St. G. Irwin (OR K 31). K, 54³–59²; Levée; Head of House; Cap, 57; Winner of Crick, 59. Trinity Hall, Cambridge, M.A. School of Military Survey; Hertford, Oxford, M.Sc. Surveyor, Royal Engineers. Instructor in Field Survey at School of Military Survey, Newbury. Brother, 2051.

1133 **LEON, Robert Kenneth,** b. 8 Apr. 41, s. of J. K. Leon. K, 54³–58³.

1134 **SUNDERLAND, Robert Frank,** b. 6 May 41, elder s. of E. M. Sunderland. K, 54³–59². Letchworth College of Technology. H.N.C. Applied Physics. A.G.O. Services Electronics Research Labs. (R.N.S.S.), 59–65; Physicist, Advanced Research & Development, I.C.L., Stevenage, 65–70; European Advanced Engineering, N.C.R., Borehamwood, 70–71; Cyclotron Div., Radiochemical Centre (U.K.A. E.A.), Amersham.

1135 **THOMPSON, David Theodore,** b. 1 May 41, eldest s. of H. R. Thompson, M.B., B.Ch., F.R.C.S. (OR K 21). K, 54³–59². Christ's, Cambridge, B.A. Middlesex Hospital Medical School, M.B., B.Chir., F.R.C.S. Brothers, 1446 & 1740.

1136 **ABRAHAMIAN, Ervand Vahan,** b. 7 Dec. 40, elder s. of V. M. Abrahamian. M, 54³–59². St. John's, Cambridge. Brother, 1741.

1137 **BAIN, Harry Mark Wellesley,** b. 12 Oct. 40, youngest s. of the late Capt. J. D. S. Bain, R.A. M, 54³–58². Grenoble Univ. Liverpool Univ., B.Arch., M.C.D., R.I.B.A. Chartered Architect with Edward Skipper & Associates, Norwich.

1138 **BRENCKMAN, Wayne de Witt, jnr.,** b. 31 Dec. 37, s. of W. de W. Brenckman. M, 54³–55². Scholarship to Yale University.

1139 **HOYSTED, Desmond Christopher Fitzgerald,** b. 25 Mar. 41, s. of Brig. D. St. J. Hoysted, C.B.E. (OR M 19) & Grandson of the late D. M. F. Hoysted (OR M 89). M, 54³–58³. R.M.A., Sandhurst. Commissioned into the Royal Irish Fusiliers (Princess Victoria's), 60. Served in Germany, Libya, Singapore, Malaysia, Thailand, including 18 mths. active service in North Borneo, 65–66. Adjutant, 1st Bn. Royal Irish Fusiliers, 67–68. Military Asst. to Vice-Chief of the General Staff, Ministry of Defence, 69. Resigned Commission as Captain, 70. Joined Samuel Montagu & Co. Ltd., Merchant Bankers. Manager, 71.

1140 **MACLEHOSE, Norman Timothy,** b. 17 Jan. 41, elder s. of N. D. MacLehose, D.S.O., T.D. (OR W 28). M, 54³–58². Died 6 Mar. 70. Brother, 1985.

1141 **MORRIS, Edward Samuel,** b. 10 Aug. 40, s. of Cdr. E. R. C. Morris, R.N. M, 54³–59¹. Peterhouse, Cambridge.

1142 **POULSOM, William John,** b. 14 Apr. 41, s. of E. D. Poulsom (OR M 16). M, 54³–59². St. Mary's Hospital Medical School, M.B., B.S., L.R.C.P., M.R.C.S., D.R.C.O.G., D.P.H.(Bristol). Dept. of Public Health, City & County of Bristol.

1143 **PRESHO, Andrew,** b. 3 May 41, s. of S. E. G. Presho. M, 54³–57¹. Computer Sales Executive.

1144 **VANHEGAN, Robert Ian,** b. 25 Feb. 41, elder s. of J. Vanhegan. M, 54³–59³; Levée; Head of House. Open Scholarship to Keble, Oxford. Oxford Univ. Medical School, M.A., D.Phil., B.M., B.Ch. Formerly Lecturer Physiology, Lady Margaret Hall, Oxford. Now Medical Practitioner. Brother, 1950.

1145 **WILSON, Stephen,** b. 21 May 41, elder s. of Lt.-Col. N. Wilson. M, 54³–59¹; Scholar. Minor Scholarship to Christ's, Cambridge, M.A., Ph.D. Lecturer in European History, Univ. of East Anglia, Norwich. A.S.T.M.S.

1146 **BLAIR, Michael Campbell,** b. 26 Aug. 41, 2nd s. of Sir A. C. Blair, K.C.V.O., LL.B., W.S. SF, 54³–59²; Scholar; Levée; Head of House. Minor Scholarship to Clare, Cambridge, LL.B., M.A. Yale University (Mellon Fellow), M.A. Bar, Middle Temple, 65. Entered Lord Chancellor's Office, 66. Private Secretary to the Lord Chancellor (and Deputy Serjeant-at-Arms, House of Lords), 68–71. Senior Legal Asst., Lord Chancellor's Office, 71. Brothers, 932, 1901 & 2224.

1147 **BRUN, Peter Edward Constantin,** b. 8 Aug. 41, 2nd s. of H. C. Brun. SF, 54³–59³; Levée; Head of House; XV, 59. Pembroke, Cambridge. Brothers, 853 & 2225.

1148 **CAMPBELL, Colin Murray Roy,** b. 26 Mar. 41, s. of the late I. W. R. Campbell (OR SF 15). SF, 54³–59²; Levée; S. VIII, 56, 57, 58, Capt., 59; Winner of Longstaff Trophy; State Scholarship. B.N.C., Oxford, M.A. Solicitor.

1149 **MITCHELL, Douglas Hugh,** b. 27 Mar. 41, elder s. of G. V. K. Mitchell (OR SF 28). SF, 54³–59¹. R.M.A., Sandhurst. Commissioned Argyll and Sutherland Highlanders, 61. Retired as Captain, 68. Joined Beaverbrook Newspapers as Manager, 68. *The Caledonian Club, Edinburgh.*

1150 **SMELLIE, James Donald Cameron,** b. 30 June 41, s. of J. R. Smellie, D.S.C. (OR SF 14). SF, 54³–58². Diploma in Management Studies. Licentiate Inst. Prod. Eng. Student Apprenticeship, Eng., Rover Co., 59–65. Project Engineer, Metal Box Co. H.Q., 65–70. Midland Region Industrial Eng., Metal Box Co., 70. *Treardder Bay S.C.*

1151 **TULLOCH, Iain William Patrick,** b. 12 Dec. 40, eldest s. of W. A. Tulloch, M.C., T.D. (OR SF 24). SF, 54³–58³. Broun University, Providence, Rhode Island. Chartered Accountant. Worked in India for James Finlay & Co. Ltd., 69–71. At present Group Management Accountant of Scotcros Ltd., Glasgow. *Prestwick G.C., Western Club, Glasgow.* Brothers, 1388, 2472 & 2473.

1152 **TURNER, The Hon. Edward Neil,** b. 27 Jan. 41, 2nd s. of the Rt. Hon. Lord Netherthorpe, LL.D., B.Sc. SF, 54³–58³; Cap, 57. The Royal Agricultural College. London Univ. Chartered Land Agent. Chartered Surveyor. Post Graduate Diploma in Business Administration. Man. Dir., Edward Turner & Co. Ltd., and others. Brothers, 497 & 2397.

1153 **BATE, The Rev. Lawrence Mark,** b. 14 Aug. 40, younger s. of Rev. R. A. H. Bate. Sh, 54³–59²; Scholar; Levée; Head of House; Head of School; S. VIII, 56–59, Capt., 58. University College, Oxford, B.A. College of the Resurrection, Mirfield, 65–67. Ordained Deacon, 67; Priest, 68. Asst. Curate, St. James, Benwell, 67–69; St. Peter, Monkseaton, 69–72. Team Vicar, i/c St. John in the Wilderness, Exmouth, 72–73.

1154 **BAYMAN, Nigel Edward,** b. 29 May 41, elder s. of E. G. G. Bayman. Sh, 54³–59²; Fives IV, 59. Dir., George E. Gray Holdings Ltd. Brother, 1654.

1155 **DOODSON, Michael George,** b. 31 Mar. 41, s. of N. Doodson. Sh, 54³–59¹.

1156 **FLEMING, Simon,** b. 16 May 41, elder s. of W. J. D. Fleming, M.B., B.Chir. Sh, 54³–59². Railway Employee. Brother, 1470.

1157 **MACKINTOSH, Alasdair James,** b. 29 Mar. 41, eldest s. of J. A. Mackintosh. Sh, 54³–59³; XV, 58, 59; XI, 58; H. XI, Capt., 59. Magdalene, Cambridge, C.A. (Scotland). Thomson McClintock & Co. (Lisbon Office). Brother, 1611.

1158 **MERTON, Roger Lewis Harold,** b. 3 Jan. 41, elder s. of D. D. Merton. Sh, 54³–58². Director of family companies engaged in world-wide manufacturing & distributing of Briar Smoking Pipes & Smoker's Requisites. *R.A.C. Country Club.* Brother, 1914.

1159 **TODD, Ian Alexander,** b. 24 Sept. 41, s. of A. H. T. Todd. Sh, 54³–58³. Birmingham Univ., B.A., Ph.D. Fellow, British Institute of Archaeology, Ankara, Turkey, 66–69. Asst. Professor at Brandeis University, Waltham, Mass., Teaching Archaeology. Numerous Archaeological Societies.

1160 **ASHE, Frederick William Michael,** b. 2 May 37, s. of Cdr. G. P. B. Ashe, R.N. (Retired). St, 54³–55².

1161 **CHADWICK, John Murray,** b. 20 June 41, s. of the late Capt. H. G. Chadwick (OR St 24). St, 54³–59²; Scholar; Levée; Head of House; State Scholarship; Stovin Exhibition, 58; Cadet Officer, 59. Magdalene, Cambridge.

1162 **CLEGG, David Marshall,** b. 18 Mar. 41, s. of J. L. Clegg, M.D., Ch.B., D.P.H., D.P.M. St, 54³–59³. University College of St. David, Lampeter, B.A. Bookseller with Messrs. B. H. Blackwell, Oxford. Previously Editorial Asst. of the supplement to the "Oxford English Dictionary".

1163 **HUSAIN, Shahid,** b. 30 Sept. 39, s. of M. A. Husain of Pakistan. St, 54³–58². Christ's, Cambridge.

1164 **MacCOLL, Alistair David,** b. 26 Apr. 41, s. of E. P. MacColl, M.C., T.D. (OR St 28). St, 54³–58³.

1165 **MATHIESON, George,** b. 15 Feb. 41, s. of G. Mathieson (OR St 22). St, 54³–59². St. Andrews Univ., B.Sc. M.I.C.E. Civil Engineer, Rendel Palmer & Tritton, Consulting Engineers. F.R.G.S.

1166 **RENDEL, Andrew Robert,** b. 18 Jan. 41, elder s. of Major A. M. Rendel, M.B.E. (OR C 24). St, 54³–59³; Levée; Head of House; XXII, 59; H. XI, 59. Corpus Christi, Oxford, M.A., A.C.I.S. Asst. Secretary, Abbey National Building Society.

1167 **ANDERSON, David Coussmaker,** b. 1 Dec. 40, 2nd s. of Brig. W. F. Anderson, C.B.E., M.C. (OR Tu 19). Tu, 54³–58³. St. Andrews Univ. Med-

ical School, M.B., Ch.B., M.R.C.P., M.R.C.P.E., M.Sc.(Lond.). Formerly Registrar, Medical Professional Unit, Dundee. Registrar and later Research Asst., Hammersmith Hospital and Royal Post Graduate Medical School. Now Lecturer in Medicine and Hon. Senior Registrar, St. Bartholomew's Hospital, London. Fellow, Royal Society of Medicine. Brothers, 912 & 1922.

1168 **BUNBURY, Charles Napier St. Pierre,** b. 13 Feb. 41, s. of Brig. F. R. St. P. Bunbury, C.B.E., D.S.O. (OR Tu 24). Tu, 54³–59²; XI, 59. R.M.A., Sandhurst. Commissioned with the Duke of Wellington's Regt. Major. Instructor, R.M.A. *Army & Navy.*

1169 **CARSLAKE, John William,** b. 31 May 41, eldest s. of J. Carslake (OR Tu 21). Tu, 54³–59². Chartered Surveyor. Land Agent. Brothers, 1997 and Richard Charles, Tu, 69³–.

1170 **KEELING, Hugh David,** b. 9 Mar. 41, elder s. of R. G. M. Keeling, O.B.E., M.B., B.Ch. Tu, 54³–58³. Diploma in Spanish Culture, University of Madrid, 59. Banker, Bank of Nova Scotia, Toronto, Ont., Canada. Brother, 1491.

1171 **LOCKHART, Ian Stuart,** b. 19 Nov. 40, s. of the Rev. D. S. M. Lockhart. Tu, 54³–59²; Levée. Clare, Cambridge, M.A. Solicitor. Partner in Peake & Co., Solicitors, of London. *United Oxford & Cambridge University Club.*

1172 **RIVERS, Thomas Max,** b. 22 May 41, s. of the late E. M. Rivers. Tu, 54³–57². Exhibition to King's, Cambridge, B.A. Publisher.

1173 **ALLISON, Wade William Magill,** b. 23 Apr. 41, elder s. of Lt.-Cdr. J. L. W. M. Allison, R.N. (Retired). W, 54³–59¹; Levée; Head of House. Science Exhibition to Trinity, Cambridge, B.A. Christ Church, Oxford, M.A., D.Phil. Fellow of the Royal Commission for the Exhibition of 1851, 66. Research Lecturer at Christ Church, Oxford, 66. Post-doctoral appointment at Argonne National Laboratory, Illinois, U.S.A., 68. Research Officer at Nuclear Physics Laboratory, Oxford, 70. Lecturer in Physics at Christ Church, Oxford, 72. American Physical Society. Brother, 1542.

1174 **ARMSTRONG, Richard Michael,** b. 11 July 41, s. of Lt.-Col. W. B. J. Armstrong, M.C., R.E. W, 54³–59²; XI,

59. Clare, Cambridge. A.C.A. Lamson Industries Ltd., Corporate Planner. *N. Hants G.C., Fleet.*

1175 **BODDINGTON, Robert Christopher Hance,** b. 4 May 41, s. of the late Lt. R. E. Boddington, R.N. W, 54^3–59^2; Scholar; Evers Exhibition. Queen's, Oxford, B.A. Solicitor, 66. Ziman & Co., Solicitors, London. Law Society.

1176 **CARMICHAEL, Charles Henry,** b. 9 Jan. 41, s. of the late Rev. H. R. Carmichael. W, 54^3–58^3; Sw. VIII, 57, 58. R.M.A., Sandhurst, Staff College p.s.c. Major, Royal Regiment of Fusiliers.

1177 **CARTER, Adam Charles,** b. 3 Aug. 41, s. of R. Carter. W, 54^3–59^2; Levée; XV, 58. R.M.A., Sandhurst. Army Officer, 1st Bn. The Light Infantry, 61–71. Contract Helicopter Pilot serving with the Sultan of Oman's Air Force.

1178 **DENHOLM, Paul,** b. 21 Feb. 41, elder s. of G. L. Denholm, D.F.C., D.L. W, 54^3–59^2.

1179 **GEMMILL, Richard William John,** b. 28 Dec. 40, s. of J. A. Gemmill (OR W 28). W, 54^3–59^2; XI, 57, 58; Fives IV, 58, 59.

1180 **KNOX JOHNSTON, John Anthony,** b. 26 June 41, s. of A. G. Knox Johnston, C.M.G. W, 54^3–59^2; XV, 58; XXII, 59; Capt. of Fives, 59.

1181 **LUMB, Christopher Theodore,** b. 30 Aug. 41, s. of the late T. A. Lumb (OR W 26). W, 54^3–59^2. Man. Dir., Formica G.M.B.H., West Germany.

1182 **MARRIOTT, Simon Hugh Cadman,** b. 7 Mar. 41, elder s. of Lt.-Col. I. A. Marriott, T.D. (OR W 25). W, 54^3–58^3. R.M.A., Sandhurst. Major, Royal Green Jackets. *Army & Navy Club.* Brother, 1231.

1183 **THORNELOE, Michael Hugh,** b. 9 Feb. 41, elder s. of E. E. Thorneloe, B.Sc. W, 54^3–59^2; Levée; Head of House. Peterhouse, Cambridge.

ENTRANCES IN JANUARY 1955

1184 **BLAND, Richard Leslie,** b. 1st Oct. 40, elder s. of F. L. Bland, M.A., Ch.B. SH, 55^1–59^3.

1185 **BRIERLEY, John Francis,** b. 30 July 41, younger s. of the late F. E. Brierley. SH, 55^1–59^3; Levée; Cap, 59.

Man. Dir., J.H.B. Contracting Services Ltd., Burnley.

1186 **CLARKE, Douglas Michael Were,** b. 20 Aug. 41, s. of Major R. B. W. Clarke, T.D. (OR SH 18). SH, 55^1–59^2. University College of Rhodesia & Nyasaland, Diploma in Public Administration. A.C.I.S. N. Rhodesia/Zambia, Civil Servant, 60–66. Roan Selection Trust Ltd., Ndola, Zambia since 66. Currently Head of Organisation Development.

1187 **HUEBNER, Michael Denis,** b. 3 Sept. 41, s. of D. W. Huebner, M.Sc., Ph.D. SH, 55^1–59^3; Scholar; Levée; Head of House; Queen's Medal. St. John's, Oxford, B.A. Bar, Gray's Inn, 65. Civil Service (Lord Chancellor's Office), 66. Served in the Law Officer's Dept., 68–70. Lord Chancellor's Office since 70.

1188 **THURSFIELD, Anthony Cecil,** b. 15 June 41, younger s. of R. M. C. Thursfield (OR SH 12). SH, 55^1–59^2; R. VIII, 59. Sidney Sussex, Cambridge. Brother, 661.

1189 **LEATHERS, The Hon. Christopher Graeme,** b. 31 Aug. 41, elder s. of The Viscount Leathers. B, 55^1–59^2; S. VIII, 57–59. Brother, 1816.

1190 **WRIGHT, Michael Pochin Marius,** b. 4 Aug. 41, s. of M. Wright. B, 55^1–59^2.

1191 **WALDEN, Clive Melvyn Laurence,** b. 13 Aug. 41, s. of Lt.-Col. A. Walden. C, 55^1–59^3. Sheffield Univ., B.A. Part-time Tutor in Economics at Sheffield Univ., 68–71. Man. Dir. of Waldo (Sheffield) Ltd., Upholstery Manufacturers.

1192 **BAXTER, David,** b. 11 July 41, s. of A. G. Baxter. K, 55^1–59^3.

1193 **SKINNER, Robert Patrick Banks,** b. 23 Nov. 41, 2nd s. of R. B. Skinner (OR K 25). K, 55^1–60^1; Levée; Cap, 59; Captain of Fives, 60; Tennis VI, 58. Clare, Cambridge, M.A. Cranfield Institute of Technology, M.B.A. J. Sainsbury, 63–69. Thomas Linnel & Sons Ltd., Northampton since 70. Member of Business Graduate Assoc. Brother, 488.

1194 **NOAR, Michael David,** b. 2 Sept. 41, s. of R. J. Noar. M, 55^1–60^1.

1195 **TALLON, James Garforth,** b. 11 June 41, s. of E. M. Tallon (OR T 22). M, 55^1–55^2.

1196 **ANDERSON, Michael Heath,** b. 31 Aug. 41, youngers. of Rev. J. E. Anderson (OR Tu 17). SF, 55^1–59^2; Music Scholar. University College, Oxford, B.A. Royal College of Music, F.R.C.O. Administrative Staff of Church Commissioners, London, 63–67. Asst. Director of Music, Sutton Valence School, Kent, 68–71. Head of Music, Swanley Comprehensive School, Kent, 72.

1197 **BRADSHAW, Nicholas Dorman Ronald,** b. 19 July 41, 3rd s. of H. D. Bradshaw (OR W 23). Sh, 55^1–59^2. I.N.S.E.A.D., Fountainebleau, France. A.C.A. Binder Hamlyn & Co., London, Chartered Accountants, 60–67. La Fiduciaire de France, Paris, Consultants, 68. Asst. Vice-President, Kidder Peabody & Co. Ltd., Investment Bankers, since 69. Brothers, 115 & 449.

1198 **MARTIN-HURST, Richard William,** b. 18 Aug. 41, s. of W. F. F. Martin-Hurst (OR B 17). Sh, 55^1–59^2. Student Apprenticeship at Joseph Lucas Ltd., Higher National Diploma in Mechanical Engineering. Joseph Lucas, 60–67. Ford Motor Co., Engineering, 67–70. Ford Advanced Vehicle Operations, 70–71. Chrmn. of Litterlift Ltd., 72.

1199 **HENDRY, Iain Stuart Morrice,** b. 21 Oct. 41, younger s. of A. M. Hendry, M.B., Ch.B., F.R.C.S. St, 55^1–59^2. Birmingham School of Architecture. Dip. Arch., A.R.I.B.A. Registered Architect, A.R.C.U.K. Self-employed in London. Presently employed by County Borough of Northampton.

1200 **REED, Peter James,** b. 31 July 41, 3rd s. of D. A. Reed. St, 55^1–59^3; Tennis VI, 57–59. University of Michigan, U.S.A. Senior Management Course, 71. Group Sales Director, Austin Reed Group Ltd. Westminster Junior Chamber of Commerce.

1201 **SUFFOLK, Timothy Charles,** b. 4 Oct. 41, s. of the late C. H. C. Suffolk. St, 55^1–60^1. St. Andrews University, B.Sc. Southampton University, Dept. of Education, Cert. Ed. The Metal Box Co., Ltd., 64–68. Asst. Master, Portsmouth Northern Grammar School for Boys, since 70.

1202 **COWEN, David Anthony,** b. 9 Aug. 41, elder s. of G. A. Cowen (OR Tu 20). Tu, 55^1–59^2. Stockbroker, Newcastle upon Tyne. Brother, 1487.

1203 **WORTHINGTON, Sidney,** b. 24 July 41, s. of the late C. L. Worthington (OR Tu 14). Tu, 55^1–59^3; Cap, 59; XXII, 58, 59. Clare, Cambridge, M.A. Guy's Hospital, London, M.B., B.Ch., D.C.M., D.R.C.O.G. General Medical Practitioner, Wonersh, Guildford.

1204 **HEASLETT, Alastair Michael Matheson Macrae,** b. 23 Sept. 41, s. of E. A. Heaslett (OR W 26). W, 55^1–58^1.

ENTRANCES IN MAY 1955

1205 **HUGHES, Peter,** b. 9 Nov. 41, younger s. of W. N. Hughes (A). SH, 55^2–60^1. Exhibition to St. John's, Oxford, M.A. Academic Diploma in History of Art, Courtauld Institute, London, 66. Asst. Keeper in Dept. of Art, National Museum of Wales, Cardiff, 66.

1206 **LEWIS, Bryan Timothy Brendan,** b. 30 Sept. 41, s. of His Honour Judge B. Lewis. SH, 55^2–60^1; R. VIII, 59, 60. University College, London, LL.B. Dir. and Chief Exec., Continental Pioneer Companies. *Reform Club.*

1207 **ZAMBRA, David Roger Montgomery,** b. 3 Oct. 41, s. of the late Lt.-Col. W. Zambra, M.B.E. (OR SH 25). SH, 55^2–60^1. Stationery Buyer, W. H. Smith & Son Ltd.

1208 **CONWAY, Michael John,** b. 4 Oct. 41, 2nd s. of H. G. Conway. B, 55^2–60^1. Brother, 1047.

1209 **COWAN, Gerald William Bryan,** b. 7 Dec. 41, elder s. of D. J. L. Cowan. B, 55^2–58^3. Welbeck College. R.M.A., Sandhurst; Royal Military College Science, Shrivenham. Marketing Motor Fuel, Shell-Mex & B.P. Ltd.

1210 **DAVIES, Michael Charles Anthony,** b. 5 Nov. 41, elder s. of Rear Admiral A. Davies, C.B. B, 55^2–60^1. R.N.C., Dartmouth. R.N. Engineering College, Plymouth, B.Sc.(Eng.). R.N. Weapons Electrical Officer in Submarines at the Clyde Submarine Base, Helensburgh, Dunbartonshire.

1211 **BOARDMAN, Peter Stafford,** b. 4 Aug. 41, s. of K. O. Boardman. C, 55^2–59^2.

1212 **COMPTON, Anthony Spencer,** b. 16 Oct. 41, s. of Sir E. G. Compton, K.C.B., K.B.E. (OR C 20). C, 55^2–59^3. New College, Oxford.

1213 **LAZARUS, John Henry,** b. 12 Nov. 41, s. of S. Lazarus, M.D., F.R.C.P. C, 55^2–59^3. Queens', Cambridge, M.A., M.B., B.Chir., M.R.C.P. University of Glasgow, M.B., Ch.B. Physician. Lecturer in Medicine, University Hospital of Wales, Cardiff.

1214 **POWELL-BRETT, Christopher Francis,** b. 7 Dec. 41, s. of Col. F. B. Powell-Brett, R.A. (OR C 30). C, 53^2–60^1; Levée. St. Thomas's Hospital, M.B., B.S., L.R.C.P., M.R.C.S., D.Obst. R.C.O.G. Qualified, 65. Various junior hospital appointments, 65–68. Private Medical Practitioner since 68. Medical Society, London. Liveryman of Worshipful Company of Apothecaries.

1215 **WILLIAMSON, Kenneth Noel Bamford,** b. 6 Jan. 42, s. of the late C. B. Williamson. C, 55^2–60^1. Oriel, Oxford.

1216 **HIBBERD, John William Dominic,** b. 3 Nov. 41, s. of C. J. L. Hibberd, C.V.O. K, 55^2–60^1; Levée; Head of House; Sproat Exhibition. King's, Cambridge, M.A. University of Bristol, Cert. Ed. University of Manchester, Dip. in Advanced Study of Ed. Asst. English Master, The Manchester Grammar School, 65–70. Woodrow Wilson Lecturer, Northwestern Univ., U.S.A., 70–71. Tutor, Univ. of Exeter (Candidate for Ph.D., 73). Council Member, Exeter Civic Society.

1217 **PICKFORD, Robert William Granville,** b. 26 Nov. 41, elder s. of R. E. Pickford, T.D., LL.B. K, 55^2–59^3. Sheffield Univ., LL.B. Solicitor & Notary. *Sheffield Club.* Brother, 2147.

1218 **PRICE, Timothy James Carlyle,** b. 3 Dec. 41, s. of J. A. Price, M.D., F.R.C.P. K, 55^2–59^3. Clare, Cambridge. The Middlesex Hospital, London. B.A. (Cantab.), 63; M.B., B.Chir., 66; D.M.R.D., 72. Senior Registrar in Radiology to the Leeds Regional Branch. *O.R.G.S.*

1219 **CARR, Colin Victor Edmund,** b. 8 Oct. 41, younger s. of A. Q. Carr, M.B.E. (OR M 19). M, 55^2–59^3; Levée; State Scholarship; Leaving Exhibition. Trinity, Cambridge, B.A. London University, Cert. Ed. Taught in India, 64–66. Taught in Primary Schools in London, 67–68. African Boys' Secondary School, Rhodesia, 68–70. Secondary Mod. School in Kent, 71. Presently training for R.C. Priesthood, Diocese of Westminster. Brother, 845.

1220 **GARFORTH - BLES, Major George William,** b. 7 Oct. 41, elder s. of Lt.-Col. G. D. Garforth-Bles (OR SF 23). SF, 55^2–59^3; Cap, 59; Sw. VIII, 58. R.M.A., Sandhurst and Downing College, Cambridge, M.A. The Black Watch (R.H.R.), Major.

1221 **HAMILTON, Robert George,** b. 9 June 41, elder s. of R. A. Hamilton. Sh, 55^2–59^2. Queen's University, Belfast.

1222 **LINDSAY, James Robertson,** b. 20 Aug. 41, s. of W. Lindsay. Sh, 55^2–59^2. Univ. Grenoble. Univ. Madrid. Joint Man. Dir., Intra Trade G.M.B.H., Wien, Austria. *Bath Club.*

1223 **MATHESON, Duncan,** b. 10 June 41, s. of Col. D. Matheson, M.B., Ch.B., late R.A.M.C. Sh, 55^2–60^2; Levée; Head of House, XI, 60. Trinity, Cambridge, Senior Scholar, M.A., LL.B. Duke of Edinburgh Entrance Scholarship, Inner Temple and Major Scholarship, 64. Barrister.

1224 **KEITH, Andrew David Bruce,** b. 30 Nov. 41, younger s. of Cdr. W. B. Keith. St, 55^2–60^2; XV, 59; XXII, 60; 2nd Rackets Pair. Mayo Travelling Scholar. Brother, 790.

1225 **METCALFE-GIBSON, Michael Theodore,** b. 10 June 41, younger s. of A. E. Metcalfe-Gibson. St, 55^2–59^2. A.I.B. With Barclays Bank Ltd., Durham City. Member of Hartlepool Round Table. Brother, 1026.

1226 **TRACY, Ralph Hugh Turgis,** b. 3 Nov. 41, elder s. of Rear Admiral H. G. H. Tracy, D.S.C., R.N. St, 55^2–60. Pembroke, Cambridge, M.A., M.I.Mech.E. Project Engineer, I.C.I., Pharmaceuticals Div., Aldersley Park. Brother, 1772.

1227 **CHEYNE, Mark Rider,** b. 15 Sept. 41, s. of the late Cdr. A. R. Cheyne, R.N. Tu, 55^2–59^2. A.C.A. Wood & Co., Chartered Accountants, 59–65. Joseph Sebag & Co., Stockbrokers, 65–72. Secretary to the partnership Stephenson Harwood & Tatham, Solicitors, 72. *M.C.C.*

1228 **INGLEBY, John Mungo,** b. 17 Oct. 41, elder s. of J. A. Ingleby, J.P. Tu, 55^2–59^3; Levée; Head of House; XV, 58; Capt., 59. Pembroke, Cambridge, M.A., A.C.A. Farming. *Royal Northern.* Brothers 1806 & 1960.

1229 **ESSLEMONT, Richard John,** b. 13 Nov. 41, younger s. of the late A. S. Esslemont, M.B., Ch.B., D.R.C.O.G. W, 55^2-59^3; XV, 59. University of Wales. Harper Adams Agricultural College, B.Sc., N.D.A., Cert. Ed. Currently Research Agriculturist, Dept. of Agriculture, Univ. of Reading. Brother, 758.

1230 **HAWKINS, Edward George,** b. 22 Sept. 41, younger s. of G. C. Hawkins (OR W 16). W, 55^2-59^3; XV, 59. Sales Director, Marlow Ropes Ltd. *Beckenham Cricket Club.* Brother, 891.

1231 **MARRIOTT, Hugh William,** b. 4 Mar. 42, younger s. of Lt.-Col. I. A. Marriott, T.D. (OR W 25). W, 55^2-58^3. Southampton Univ., B.A. Partner in Yacht Broking firm, Jackson Jackson & Marriott. *Royal Lymington Yacht Club.* Brother, 1182.

1232 **MEAKIN, Timothy Simon,** b. 21 Oct. 41, 3rd s. of C. A. Meakin (OR W 16). St, 55^2-59^3. University College, Oxford. Marketing Manager, Drug Houses of Australia Ltd., Brooklyn, Victoria. Brother, 596.

1233 **PILKINGTON, Hugh Austin Windle,** b. 18 Apr. 42, s. of R. W. Pilkington, Ph.D. (OR W 28). W, 55^2-60^1; Scholar; Levée; School Leaving Exhibition. Major Scholarship to King's, Cambridge; Christ Church, Oxford. Lecturer, Univ. of Nairobi, 72. Translations Consultant, United Bible Societies. University Lecturer.

ENTRANCES IN SEPTEMBER 1955

1234 **ARNOLD-FORSTER, Richard William,** b. 6 Jan. 42, s. of P. P. Arnold-Forster (OR SH 27). SH, 55^3-59^2; Scholarship. R.N.C., Dartmouth.

1235 **BARCLAY, Stephen John,** b. 12 Apr. 42, s. of C. H. Barclay. SH, 55^3-59^3.

1236 **BRADBY, David Henry,** b. 27 Feb. 42, eldest s. of E. L. Bradby (OR SH 20). SH, 55^3-60^2; Levée; Cap, 59; R. VIII, 59, 60. Trinity, Oxford, M.A. Bristol University, Cert. Ed. University Lecturer in French at Strathclyde Univ., 66–67; Glasgow Univ., 67–70. Ph.D. Univ. of Kent at Canterbury since 71. Publication, "Kean by Sartre and Dumas". Brothers, 1846 & 2625.

1237 **CHESSHYRE, Robert Coxhead,** b. 20 Sept. 41, s. of Brig. N. H. L. Chesshyre, R.E. (OR SH 23). SH, 55^3-59^3. Christ Church, Oxford, M.A. Journalist, "Morning Telegraph", Sheffield, 63–66; "Sunday Citizen", 66–67; The "Observer" since 67.

1238 **COOPER, Jonathan Allan,** b. 23 Dec. 41, s. of D. A. M. Cooper. SH, 55^3-60^2. Commodore, Sailing. Commercial Union Assurance Co., 60–61. R.M.A., Sandhurst, 61–63. Commissioned into Royal Engineers, 63. Capt. R.E., served in U.K., B.A.O.R., Malaya, Borneo, Hong Kong. p.s.c. *Royal Engineers Yacht Club.*

1239 **ELLIS-JONES, Patrick Jones Armine,** b. 21 Feb. 42, s. of D. G. Ellis-Jones (OR SH 25). SH, 55^3-60^3; Levée; Head of House; S. VIII, 59, 60. Trinity, Oxford, M.A. Chartered Patent Agent. J. A. Kemp & Co., Chartered Patent Agents, London. *The Cumberland Lawn Tennis Club.*

1240 **GOLLIN, David Edgar Francis,** b. 3 Feb. 42, elder s. of G. J. Gollin. SH, 55^3-60^2; Scholar; Levée; Head of House; Cap, 59; Tennis VI, 58–60; State Scholarship. Shell Mechanical Sciences Scholarship. Major Scholarship to King's, Cambridge, B.A., C.Eng., A.M.Inst.F. Royal Dutch/Shell Group in U.K., West Germany, Singapore, Hong Kong & currently Brunei. Brother, 2138.

1241 **HAZELL, Jonathan Walter Peter** b. 28 Mar. 42, s. of the late P. Hazell, M.C. (OR SH 25). SH, 55^3-59^3. Emmanuel, Cambridge. Middlesex Hospital Medical School, M.A., M.B., B.Chir. E.N.T. Surgery. Registrar, Royal Ear Hospital, University College, London.

1242 **HUNT, James Andrew,** b. 26 Mar. 42, s. of A. J. Hunt (A). SH, 55^3-60^2; Scholar; Levée; State Scholarship; Shell Scholarship. Exhibition, King's, Cambridge, M.A. London Institute of Education, P.G.C.E. Manchester Grammar School, Asst. Chemistry Teacher. Watford Grammar School, Head of Physical Science Dept. Publications: "Multiple Choice Tests for Advanced Chemistry Courses" (Co-Author with C. Dobson), "Applications of Synthetic Methods in Organic Chemistry".

1243 **JUNG, Nawab Mohomed Ziauddin Khan (Wali),** b. 26 Jan. 42, s. of Begum Hasan Yar Jung. SH, 55^3-60^3.

1244 **KARNEY, Andrew Lumsdaine,** b. 24 May 42, 2nd s. of the Rev. G. H. P. Karney (OR SH 23). SH, 55³–60². County University Exhibition. Trinity, Cambridge. M.I.E.E. Telecommunications System, Planning Engineer at the Gas Council, London. Brother, 1553.

1245 **MURDOCH, Ian Bowman,** b. 17 Jan. 42, elder s. of R. Murdoch, T.D., M.D., M.R.C.O.G. SH, 55³–59³; Cap, 59. Pembroke, Cambridge, B.A. C.A. Scotland, 67. Member of Institute of Management Consultants, 72. Management Consultant with McLintock Mann & Whinney Murray, London. *Hawks, Cambridge.*

1246 **OLDROYD, David Christopher Leslie,** b. 6 Mar. 42, s. of Lt.-Cdr. L. Oldroyd, R.D., R.N.R. SH, 55³–59². College of Estate Management, London. A.R.I.C.S., A.R.V.A. Member of the Farm Management Assoc. In private practice as Chartered Surveyor and Chartered Land Agent. Worshipful Company of Coopers. London Scottish Company, 51st Highland Volunteers, T.A.V.R. *Naval & Military Club.*

1247 **SEYMOUR, Richard Keith,** b. 14 Jan. 42, s. of the late J. W. Seymour. SH, 55³–60²; XV, 58, 59; S. VIII, 58, 59. Atkinson College, York Univ. Toronto, B.A. Now on M.B.A. Course. Smiths Industries, London, Plant Accounting, 60–67. Canada Wire & Cable Co. Ltd., Div. of Noranda Mines Ltd., Finance Dept. from 67. *Royal Over-seas League, York U. Alumni.*

1248 **SPENS, The Hon. Patrick Michael Rex,** b. 22 July 42, elder s. of The Rt. Hon. The Lord Spens, M.B.E. (OR SH 27). SH, 55³–60²; Cap, 59. Corpus Christi, Cambridge, B.A., A.C.A. Qualified as Chartered Accountant with Fuller, Jenks, Beecroft & Co. Joined Morgan Grenfell & Co. Ltd., 69. Dir., 73. Brother, 1506.

1249 **ARCHER, John Vincent Parker,** b. 25 Apr. 42, s. of J. W. Archer. T, 55³–60². Hertford, Oxford.

1250 **BOYDEN, John,** b. 17 Mar. 42, s. of G. J. Boyden, T, 55³–57³. B.A.(London). Diploma in Museum Studies, Manchester University. Curator, Rutland County Museum, Oakham to 73. Hove Museum of Art since 73. *Royal Over-Seas League, Japan Society of London.*

1251 **CARNEGY, Colin David,** b. 16 Aug. 42, younger s. of the late Rev. Canon P. C. A. Carnegy. T, 55³–60³. Jesus, Oxford, M.A. Solicitor, 68. Dawson & Co., Lincoln's Inn. Law Society. Brother, 961.

1252 **CRESSWELL, Gordon Drew,** b. 28 Feb. 42, elder s. of G. D. Cresswell, M.B., Ch.B. T, 55³–59². A.I.B. Barclay's Bank, Birmingham High Street Branch.

1253 **EDMUNDSON, John Wigram,** b. 13 Mar. 42, elder s. of D. Edmundson. T, 55³–60²; Dewar Travelling Scholarship. Keble, Oxford. Manchester University. Unilever, 64–66. British Council since 66. Brother, 1860.

1254 **FOOTTIT, Robert Edward,** b. 13 May 42, elder s. of E. H. Foottit. T, 55³–60². St. John's, Cambridge, M.A. Solicitor. Partner in Browetts of Coventry. Brother, 2187.

1255 **GIBSON, Philip James Musgrave,** b. 1 June 42, s. of J. M. Gibson. T, 55³–58².

1256 **GILBERT, Bruce Charles,** b. 22 Sept. 41, elder s. of the late R. C. Gilbert. T, 55³–60²; Levée; Head of House. Merton, Oxford, M.A., D.Phil. Gibbs Scholar, Harmsworth Senior Scholar. Lecturer in Chemistry, York Univ. since 66. Brother, 1558.

1257 **GRAHAM, James Terence,** b. 29 Jan. 42, s. of J. A. Graham. T, 55³–58³. A.C.A. Various appointments with Rolls-Royce Ltd., Coventry. Now Manager of Accounting at Burroughs Machines Ltd., Stroud. Warwickshire Society of Chartered Accountants.

1258 **JORDAN, Richard,** b. 30 Sept. 42, s. of N. W. Jordan. T, 55³–60². Birmingham, B.Sc., Dip. Ed., Oxon. Secondary School Teacher, G.U.S.O. Ghana, 63–64; Kenya, 65–70; Australia (as International Teaching Fellow), 70–72. Papua, New Guinea since 73.

1259 **PRING, John Morris,** b. 29 Sept. 41, s. of R. M. Pring. T, 55³–60¹. A.C.C.A. Industrial Accountancy. Currently Public Accountancy.

1260 **RUFF, Christopher Robert,** b. 11 May 43, s. of H. R. Ruff. T, 55³–61². Bristol Univ. 2½ yrs. in Accountancy, now Publisher's Representative.

1261 **ARTHUR, Anthony Clifford,** b. 31 Mar. 42, 3rd s. of J. C. Arthur, M.B., B.S. B, 55³–60². Brother, 1262.

1262 **ARTHUR, Christopher John,** b. 31 Mar. 42, 2nd s. of J. C. Arthur, M.B., B.S. B, 55³–60³. Jesus, Cambridge, B.A. Cert Ed., London. Member of Field Survey in Fezzan, 65. Site Supervisor, Istanbul Excavations (summer seasons, 66, 67). English Language teacher in Greece, 66–67. Teacher of History and Art at Woodcote House School, Surrey since 67. *Llanabba Memorial Assoc., Society for Libyan Studies.* Brother, 1261.

1263 **CRAIG, Colin John,** b. 5 Feb. 42, elder s. of J. W. Craig, M.D. B, 55³–60²; Levée; Head of House; R. VIII, 59; Holder of Bigside Bags; Winner of Crick, 60; Cadet Officer, 60, Corpus Christi, Oxford. Director, Investment Development & Technical Services Ltd. of London.

1264 **DEREHAM, David John,** b. 5 Aug. 42, 3rd s. of the late W. D. Dereham (OR B 18). B, 55³–60²; Levée. Trinity Hall, Cambridge, M.A., C.Eng., M.I.Mech.E., M.I.Prod.E., A.M.B.I.M., A.M.I.M.C., M.I.O.P. Urwick Orr & Partners Ltd., Management Consultants; Purnell & Sons Ltd., Printers; now Unigate Foods Ltd., Trowbridge, Wilts. *Pitt Club, Bath Preservation Trust.* Brothers, 531 & 767.

1265 **HART, Thomas Richard Ogden,** b. 27 Jan. 42, youngest s. of Sir W. O. Hart, C.M.G., J.P. (OR B 17). B, 55³–59³; Scholar. New College, Oxford, M.A. Articled Clerk, London, 63–67. A.C.A., 67. Audit Clerk, Kitwe, Zambia, 68–70. Company Accountant, Roberts Construction Co. (Zambia), Ltd. since 70.

1266 **McFARLANE, Stuart John Warren,** b. 19 June 42, s. of G. J. McFarlane, M.R.C.S., L.R.C.P. B, 55³–60³; Levée; Cap, 60; Tennis VI, 60. Durham Univ., B.A. Dip. Ed. School Teacher. Currently at Ackworth School, Pontefract, Yorks.

1267 **MILNER, Patrick Daniel Russell,** b. 14 Oct. 41, s. of A. Milner, M.B., Ch.B. B, 55³–60². Leeds Univ., LL.B. Solicitor, 66. Partner, J. H. Milner & Son, Solicitors, Leeds & London. *Leeds Lions Club.*

1268 **NIMMO, Duncan Bryce,** b. 14 Jan. 42, 2nd s. of J. A. D. Nimmo (OR B 20). B, 55³–60¹; Scholar; Levée; XV, 59. Minor Scholarship to Emmanuel, Cambridge, B.A. Heidelberg Univ., Ph.D. Candidate, Edinburgh Univ., 65. Lecturer in History, Lancaster Univ., 67–71. Now studying higher education, Lancaster Univ. Brothers, 1116, 1872 & 2364.

1269 **DAVENPORT, John Daubeny,** b. 18 Apr. 42, s. of Wing-Cdr. J. R. Davenport, R.A.F. (OR C 25). C, 55³–60². Leeds Univ., C.Eng., A.M.Inst.F., G.I.Mech.E. Lubricants Marketing, Industrial Markets Div., Shell-Mex & B.P. Institute of Fuels.

1270 **DIXON, David,** b. 3 Apr. 42, elder s. of J. F. Dixon. C, 55³–60¹; Scholar. Scholarship, University College, Oxford, B.A. Post-Graduate Study of Transport in Greece (Scholarship from Greek Ministry of Education). Joined British Railways, 64 as Management Trainee, now Area Manager, Kensington, Olympia, London. Brother, 2142.

1271 **DYER, Michael George Graham,** b. 4 Apr. 42, s. of P. B. R. G. Dyer, M.C. C, 55³–60².

1272 **JACKSON, Martin Peter,** b. 26 Feb. 42, s. of Major P. H. Jackson. C, 55³–59²; Sw. VIII, 58. R.M.A., Sandhurst.

1273 **LEE, John Richard,** b. 31 July 42, eldest s. of R. H. G. Lee. C, 55³–60²; Senior Scholar; Levée; Head of House; Leaving Exhibition; State Scholarship. Minor Scholarship to Clare, Cambridge, B.Sc. Operational Research Group, N.C.B., 63–66. I.C.T. (later I.C.L.) Software programming since 66. *Royal Ocean Racing Club, Cambridge Univ. Cruising Club.* Brothers, 1577 & 2309.

1274 **DEANE, Terence Horton Walker** (name changed by Deed Poll from Walker, T. H.), b. 29 Dec. 41, elder s. of B. H. Walker. C, 55³–60²; Capt. of Fencing. Trinity College, Dublin, B.A., M.B., B.Ch., B.A.O., M.R.C.S., L.R.C.P. (London). Various hospital appointments in Dublin. At present Medical Practitioner, South Kensington, London.

1275 **WISEMAN, Alan Edward,** b. 28 Jan. 42, younger s. of the late E. W. Wiseman. C, 55³–60². Brother, 986.

1276 **CALVERLEY, David Maxwell,** b. 17 Oct. 41, s. of the late C. M. Calverley (OR K 20). K, 55³–59². Chartered Accountant, Trafalgar House Investments Ltd.

1277 CUTHBERTSON, John Layton, b. 24 Feb. 42, s. of the late J. H. Cuthbertson. K, 55^3–60^2; Cap, 59; XI, 57, 58, Capt., 59, 60; H. XI, 59, Capt., 60; Rackets Pair, 58, 59, 60. Worcester, Oxford, B.A., A.I.B. Asst. District Man., Barclays Bank. *R.A.C.*

1278 FEHR, Richard John Frank, b. 13 June 42, elder s. of B. H. F. Fehr (OR K 26). K, 55^3–59^3. Director, Frank Fehr & Co. Ltd. of London. Brother, 1671.

1279 HEAGERTY, The Rev. Alistair John, b. 1 May 42, elder s. of the late W. B. Heagerty. K, 55^3–60^1; XV, 58, 59; H. XI, 60. Oriel, Oxford, M.A. London College of Divinity, B. D. Ordained (C. of E.), 68; Priest, 69. Chaplain to H. M. Forces (Army). Brother, 1888.

1280 IVES, Stephen, b. 29 May 42, s. of F. W. Ives, K, 55^3–60^2. R.A.F. Scholarship. R.A.F. Cranwell. Flying Officer, R.A.F.

1281 LARBY, Adrian Guy Burton, b. 7 Feb. 42, 3rd s. of N.B. Larby. K, 55^3–60^3; XV, 60; H. XI, 60. Cambridge Univ., M.A., LL.B. Director of Companies. Solicitor with Leo Abse & Cohen, Cardiff. *Cardiff & Country Club.* Brother, 617.

1282 MATHIESON, Ian Niall Muir, b. 5 Mar. 42, s. of M. Mathieson. K, 55^3–60^2; Cap, 58. Aston Univ., B.Sc. McMaster Univ., M.B.A., C.Eng., P.Eng., A.M.I.Mech.E., A.M.I.Prod.E. Gen. Man., Mackay Industries. *Mechanical Engineers & Production Engineers Clubs.*

1283 SIMONDS, Robert David, b. 5 Mar. 42, s. of Major R. A. Simonds. K, 55^3–60^2. Advertising Intermediate Exam. Training with J. Walter Thompson, Advertising Agency till 71. London Tourist Board Course. Now in own Travel Agency. *United Services & Royal Aero Club, West London Aero Club.*

1284 SKINNER, David Michael Benson, b. 1 Feb. 42, eldest s. of M. O. Skinner (OR K 32). K, 55^3–60^3; Levée; Head of House; XV, 58, 59, Capt., 60; H. XI, 59–60; Tennis VI, 58, 59, Capt., 60; Senior Athletics Cup, 59, 60. Christ's, Cambridge, M.A. Director, J. T. Davies & Sons Ltd., Wine Merchants. *Hawks Club.* Brother, 2445.

1285 WYLLIE, Stephen Brendan Warren, b. 21 Feb. 42, s. of B. W. Wyllie, M.B., B.Ch. K, 55^3–57^2.

1286 CARR, David Cameron, b. 6 Apr. 42, 2nd s. of the late S. D. Carr. M, 55^3–60^1. Farmer. Member of Game Conservancy. Brothers, 846 & 2216.

1287 FOLLAND, David Dudley, b. 8 Mar. 42, younger s. of D. C. Folland. M, 55^3–58^1. Brother, 847.

1288 FORREST, Robin John, b. 20 Sept. 41, s. of J. E. Forrest. M, 55^3–59^2.

1289 HEALEY, Harry David, b. 19 Nov. 41, younger s. of D. A. Healey. M, 55^3–60^2.

1290 PEDLEY, Timothy John, b. 23 Mar. 42, s. of R. R. Pedley. M, 55^3–60^2; Scholar; Levée; Head of House; Leaving Exhibition; State Scholarship. Major Scholarship to Trinity, Cambridge.

1291 PRESTON, Richard Jeremy, b. 24 Apr. 42, s. of F. R. W. Preston (OR M 27). M, 55^3–59^3. Geneva Univ. Sales & Marketing. Marketing Man., Sublistatic S.A., Geneva. *Royal Yacht Squadron, Royal Thames Yacht Club.*

1292 WILKINSON, David Max, b. 7 Apr. 42, s. of R. Wilkinson. M, 55^3–60^3; Levée; Head of School; Head of House; Cap, 60. Industrial Scholarship (A.E.I., Rugby). Trinity Hall, Cambridge, B.A., Dip. Ed. Journalist, Newcastle "Chronicle & Journal". At present Editor, "The Teacher Newspaper".

1293 BARR, Andrew Charles Hall, b. 21 May 42, elder s. of C. J. H. Barr (OR SF 22). SF, 55^3–56^2.

1294 CHURCHILL, Winthrop Hallowell, jnr., b. 9 June 37, elder s. of W. H. Churchill of Mass., U.S.A. SF, 55^3–56^3. Harvard Univ.

1295 CRAWFORD, George Michael Warren Brown, b. 11 Jan. 42, s. of Surgeon-Capt. T. G. B. Crawford, M.B., B.Ch., R.N. SF, 55^3–60^1. Bank of England, 60–63. Buckmaster & Moore (Stockbrokers), 63–65. I.B.M. (Australia) Ltd., 66–70. Data Processing Manager, Buckmaster & Moore since 70. Computer Systems Engineer. Hon. Sec. of Stock Exchange. Computers Managers Assoc.

1296 ELLIOT, Graeme Arthur, b. 28 Aug. 42, 2nd (twin) s. of I. F. L. Elliot (OR M 07). SF, 55^3–60^3; Levée; Head of House; XV, 58, 59, 60; XI, 59, 60. Magdalene, Cambridge, M.A., A.C.A. Treasurer,

Conzinc Riotinto of Australia Ltd., Melbourne. *Bath Club*. Brothers, 560 & 1297.

1297 ELLIOT, Ian Clinton, b. 28 Aug. 42, 3rd s. of I. F. L. Elliot (OR M 07). SF, 55³–60²; XV, 58, 59; Tennis VI, 60. N/S. Commissioned 1st Bn. Welsh Guards, 62–64. Member of London Stock Exchange. Partner, Walter Walker & Co., Stockbrokers. *Turf Club, Bath Club*. Brothers, 560 & 1296.

1298 GINGOLD, Nicholas John Dorson, b. 23 Nov. 41, s. of J. M. Gingold. SF, 55³–59³. Hertford, Oxford. Died, 66.

1299 IRVINE, Robert Peter James, b. 29 June 42, 2nd s. of The Rt. Hon. Sir A. Irvine, P.C., Q.C., M.P. SF, 55³–60¹. Schoolmaster at St. Philip's Preparatory School, Kensington, London. Reading English at Bedford College, Univ. of London since 71. Brother, 907.

1300 McMULLEN, Ian Peter, b. 18 May 42, elder s. of Lt.-Col. R. P. McMullen, D.S.O., M.B.E., T.D., J.P. (OR SF 27). SF, 55³–60¹. Clare, Cambridge, M.A. Solicitor. Dir., McMullen & Son Ltd. Brother, 1753.

1301 SIMPSON, Michael John Russell, b. 30 Oct. 41, s. of R. J. B. Simpson, M.B.E., T.D. (OR SF 28). SF, 55³–60¹; Levée; Head of House; Cap, 58; H. XI, 59. Magdalen, Oxford. Edinburgh Univ. Writer to the Signet. Partner in Messrs. Tods Murray & Jamieson, W.S., Edinburgh. *New Club, Edinburgh*.

1302 VAUDREY, Christopher John, b. 2 Jan. 42, eldest s. of J. R. Vaudrey, M.B.E. (OR SF 29). SF, 55³–60¹; Rackets Pair, 58, 59. Accountant. Brother, 2235.

1303 WESTON, William Andrew, b. 30 May 42, 2nd s. of W. G. Weston, C.M.G. SF, 55³–60²; R. VIII, 60. Trinity Hall, Cambridge, B.A. Executive Committee, Society of London Art Dealers; Fine Arts and Antiques Export Committee (Dept. of Trade & Industry); Chamber Syndicale de L'Estampe, Paris. Director, Folio Society and Folio Fine Art Ltd., 64–67. Man. Dir., William Weston Gallery Ltd., London since 68. *Travellers' Club*. Brothers, 360 & 1677.

1304 CARMICHAEL, Andrew John, b. 21 Mar. 42, s. of J. W. Carmichael. Sh, 55³–60²; S. VIII, 57–60, Capt., 60. Manchester Univ.

1305 FERGUSSON, Ian Lewis Campbell, b. 11 Apr. 42, younger s. of J. D. Fergusson, M.D., F.R.C.S. Sh, 55³–60¹; Levée; Head of House; H. XI, 60. Jesus, Cambridge, M.A., M.B., B.Chir. St. Thomas's Hospital, London. F.R.C.S. Edin., F.R.C.S. Eng. Resident Gynaecologist, Chelsea Hospital for Women. R.N.R. Brother, 1012.

1306 MACRAE, Hamish Ian, b. 22 Jan. 42, elder s. of Major I. D. K. Macrae. Sh, 55³–59³; XV, 59. Capt. Royal Scots Dragoon Guards (Regular Officer). Capt. of the Army Cresta Team. *The Cavalry Club*.

1307 MORTON, Alexander Hargreaves, b. 11 Apr. 42, 2nd s. of K. V. F. Morton, C.I.E. O.B.E. Sh, 55³–60¹. University College, Oxford, B.A. S.O.A.S., London Univ., Ph.D. Wolfson Fellow, British Institute of Persian Studies, Teheran, Iran, 64–66. Dep. Dir. since 70. Brothers, 1015, 1992 and 2772.

1308 ROBINSON, John Francis Edward, b. 14 Oct. 41, s. of Major J. F. Robinson. Sh, 55³–59²; XI, 59; H. XI, 59. R.M.A., Sandhurst. Commissioned R.T.R., 62. *Army and Navy Club*.

1309 CARDWELL, Edward Anthony Colin, b. 9 Apr. 42, eldest s. of T. G. Cardwell. St, 55³–60¹; Scholar; State Scholarship; Lees Knowles Exhibition. Trinity, Cambridge, M.A. Graduate I.E.E. Assoc. Electrical Industries, Rugby, 63–67. British Railways Board, Research Dept., Derby since 67. Lay Reader, Church of England, Derby Diocese, since 70.

1310 DAVIES, Hugh Llewelyn, b. 8 Nov. 41, 2nd s. of V. E. Davies, O.B.E. St, 55³–60²; Levée; Head of House. Mayo Travelling Scholarship.

1311 DAVIES, Peter Hugh Charles, b. 22 July 42, elder s. of the late L. E. C. Davies, M.B.E., M.B. (OR St 23). St 55³–59³. Courage (Western) Ltd., Bristol.

1312 DODDS, Peter George Ridley, b. 18 Apr. 42, s. of G. R. Dodds, M.B., B.S. St, 55³–60²; H. XI, 60; Rackets Junior Pair, 57. Durham Univ., B.A. A.C.A. Banking, Chase-Manhattan, New York.

1313 HOUDRET, Michael Peter Burgoyne, b. 27 Jan. 42, elder s. of the late P. C. G. B. Houdret (OR St 24). St, 55³–60². University College, Oxford, B.A. Export Marketeer. *Gresham*.

1314 MATHESON, James Duncan Ewing, b. 25 Nov. 41, elder s. of A. J. Matheson. St, 55^3–59^2. A.C.A. Member of the Stock Exchange, London. *Buck's Club.*

1315 ROBINSON, Michael Edward, b. 29 Aug. 42, 3rd s. of the late W. C. Robinson. St, 55^3–60^2; Scholar; XI, 60. Worcester, Oxford. A.C.A. Management Consultant with I.C.F.C., Numas Ltd.

1316 THOMPSON, Ian Henry Ronald, b. 10 Nov. 41, s. of the late Capt. H. A. Thompson. St, 55^3–60^2. St. Catherine's, Oxford. 1st Public Examination in Chemistry, Mechanics & Physics. Diploma in Social Anthropology. Mining, Asst. General Foreman, Torco Plant, Rokand Div., N.C.C.M. Ltd., Zambia. F.R.Z.S.

1317 TITLEY, Marcus Hugh, b. 13 Dec., 41, younger s. of the late U. A. Titley (OR St 20). St, 55^3–60^2; XXII, 59. A few months at Alliance Française in Paris and about one month in Madrid. In Stock Exchange, London, with W. Greenwell, 61–66. Norris Oakley Richardson & Glover, Investment Advisers, 66. *M.C.C., Hawks.*

1318 ARMSTRONG, James Andrew, b. 20 Apr. 42, s. of W/O T. A. Armstrong, R.A.F. Tu, 55^3–60^1. Peterhouse, Cambridge.

1319 BROOME, James Nicholas, b. 5 Jan. 42, elder s. of R. N. Broome, O.B.E., M.C. (OR Tu 23). Tu, 55^3–59^3; Leaving Scholarship. Oriel, Oxford. Brother, 2091.

1320 DENNY, William, b. 18 May 42, s. of W. Denny. Tu, 55^3–60^2.

1321 FALK, Stephen John, b. 6 July 42, younger s. of J. A. Falk, M.B., B.Ch. Tu, 55^3–60^3; Levée. King's, Cambridge, M.A. Employed at Sotheby & Co. since 64. Cataloguer of Indian & Persian Miniatures and Manuscripts.

1322 HOWELLS, David Allen Leonard, b. 13 Jan. 42, s. of L. H. Howells, M.D., F.R.C.P. Tu, 55^3–59^2.

1323 MARTIN, Peter Gordon, b. 28 Nov. 41, elder s. of the late A. J. Martin, O.B.E., M.R.C.S., L.R.C.P. (OR Tu 23). Tu, 55^3–59^2.

1324 MILLER, Patrick Robert, b. 5 Aug. 42, elder s. of C. C. Miller. Tu, 55^3–60^2. Brother, 1808.

1325 PHILLIPS, Peter, b. 29 Mar. 42, s. of the late Major-Gen. C. F. Phillips, C.B., C.B.E., D.S.O., R.M. Tu, 55^3–60^2.

1326 STOTT, Herbert Reginald Swiers, b. 2 Feb. 42, s. of H. R. Stott. Tu, 55^3–59^2.

1327 BLAIKIE, Piers MacLeod, b. 29 Jan. 42, s. of F. W. L. Blaikie. W, 55^3–60^3. Gonville & Caius, Cambridge, M.A., Ph.D. Lecturer at Dept. of Geography, Univ. of Reading, 67–72. Lecturer at School of Development Studies, Univ. of East Anglia, 72. Institute of British Geographers. Royal Geographical Society.

1328 BROWN, Guy Alan, b. 23 May 42, younger s. of A. L. Brown, M.C., C.A. W, 55^3–60^3. Christ Church, Oxford. Brother, 47.

1329 BROWN, Lorne Sinclair, b. 30 Jan. 42, s. of D. S. Brown, M.R.C.V.S. W, 55^3–59^1; Cap, 58. A.R.I.C.S. In private practice on own account within the border counties of Scotland. Member of *Buccleuch Hunt.*

1330 CHASE, James Frederic Alliston, b. 20 Mar. 42, elder s. of F. J. A. Chase, D.F.C. (A). W, 55^3–60^2. Exhibition to Trinity, Cambridge, Ph.D. Died 21 Nov. 72.

1331 COLE, Ronald Melvyn, b. 14 Jan. 42, 2nd s. of T. Cole. W, 55^3–59^3. Keele Univ., B.A. Self-employed, Music Industry. Brothers, 916 & 1780.

1332 DOULTON, John Hubert Farre, b. 2 Jan. 42, eldest s. of A. J. F. Doulton, O.B.E., T.D. W, 55^3–60^3. Exhibition to Keble, Oxford, B.A. Schoolmaster, Rugby, 65–66. Radley since 66. Brothers, 1626, 1635 & 2429.

1333 EVERS, Michael Richard, b. 28 Jan. 42, s. of the late W. R. Evers (OR SF 23). W, 55^3–60^2; Scholar; Levée; Head of School; Head of House; XI, 58, 59, 60; Jex Blake Exhibition. Major Scholarship to Trinity, Cambridge.

1334 INGLIS, Alastair Duncan Murray, b. 25 Jan. 42, elder s. of Brig. W. M. Inglis, C.B.E. (OR W 28). W, 55^3–60^2. S.D.T. College. H.N.C., Business Studies. Bridport-Gundry Ltd., Bridport, Dorset; Management Trainee; Product Development Manager, 60–66. John Holt & Co., (L'pool) Ltd. Various management positions with Nigerian subsidiaries, 67–72.

Automatic Business Machines Ltd., London, Admin. Mgr., 73. Fellow, *R.C.S.;* Member, *V.S.C.C.*

1335 McQUEEN, John, b. 20 May 42, s. of L. G. McQueen, M.B., Ch.B., F.R.C.S.W, 55^3–60^2. Trinity, Cambridge. St. Thomas's Hospital Medical School, M.A., M.B., B.Chir., F.R.C.S., M.R.C.O.G., D.C.H. Obstetrician & Gynaecologist. At present employed at Chelsea Hospital for Women as Resident Surgical Officer. Royal Society of Medicine.

1336 THOMAS-DAVIES, The Rev. Richard James, b. 20 Apr. 42 (name changed to Davies, R. J.), younger s. of J. Thomas-Davies (OR W 18). W, 55^3–60^1. Exhibition to Peterhouse, Cambridge, M.A., Dip. Ed. Ordained Deacon, 69; Priest, 70. Curate of St. James's Mission, Nyamandhlovu, Rhodesia, 69–72. Curate in Parish of Southwick, Sussex since 72.

1337 WILLIAMS, Robert George Alexander, b. 20 May 42, younger s. of A. T. Williams, C.M.G., M.B.E. W, 55^3–60^2; Scholar; Levée; Waddington Leaving Exhibition. Open Scholarship to Corpus Christi, Oxford. Nuffield, Oxford, D.Phil. Research Officer, Dept. of Regius. Prof. of Medicine, Oxford. Brother, 600.

ENTRANCES IN JANUARY 1956

1338 ASUMANG, Joseph Kwasi. SH, 56^1–56^2; H. XI, 56. Edinburgh Univ.

1339 DAWSON, Andrew Christopher, b. 6 Aug. 42, s. of the late Lt.-Cdr. C. H. Dawson, R.N. (OR SH 19). SH, 56^1–60^2. R.M.A., Sandhurst (Languages). Capt.

1340 HARTLEY, Myles Spencer Harrison, b. 17 Aug. 42, younger s. of H. W. Hartley. SH, 56^1–60^2. Solicitor, 66. Articled to Hepworth & Chadwick, Leeds, 62–66. Slaughter & May, London, 67. Shaw Carpets Ltd., Barnsley, 68 to date (Deputy Man. Dir.). *Alwoodly G.C., Yorkshire Fly Fishers.* Brother, 921.

1341 BARSTOW, Oliver George, b. 29 July 42, elder s. of Capt. G. B. Barstow, R.N. (Retired). B, 56^1–60^2; Sw. VIII, 59. A.C.A. Allan Charlesworth & Co., Chartered Accountants, 61–68. Samuel Montagu & Co. Ltd., Merchant Bankers since 68. Brothers, 1718 & 2358.

1342 BRUCE, Richard Stephen Witherinton, b. 14 Aug. 42, elder s. of R. R. F. Bruce, D.F.C., B.Mus. (OR B 29). B, 56^1–61^2. Middlesex Hospital Med. School, M.B., B.Ch., F.F.A.R.C.S. Senior Registrar (Anaesthetics), Royal Perth Hospital, W. Australia. Brother, 2275.

1343 ROWE, John Robert, b. 9 May 42, elder s. of K. W. Rowe. C, 56^1–60^2. Brighton College of Technology. P.W.D., Barbados, 64–66. John Laing & Son, 66–68. Cementation, 68–71. M.I.C.E., 69. Frankpile, P.O. Box 829, Bahrain since 71.

1344 BUTT, Michael Acton, b. 25 May 42, 4th s. of L. A. K. Butt. K, 56^1–61^1; Levée; Head of House; R. VIII & Winner of the Crick, 61. Magdalen, Oxford (History). European Institute of Business Administration, Fontainebleau, France. Dir., Bland Welch & Co. Ltd., Insurance Brokers at Lloyd's.

1345 JOHNSON, David Ramsay Downward, b. 22 July 42, s. of F. B. Johnson, T.D. K, 56^1–60^3; H. XI, 60. Pembroke, Oxford.

1346 LYONS, Robert Marshall, b. 24 Aug. 42, 2nd s. of B. Lyons. K, 56^1–60^3; Queen's Medal. Pembroke, Oxford, M.A. Man. Dir., United Drapery Stores Properties Ltd. *Highgate G.C.* Brothers, 936 & 1517.

1347 ASHCROFT, Peter Blair, b. 20 Oct. 42, s. of D. W. Ashcroft, M.B., Ch.B., F.R.C.S., D.L.O. M, 56^1–60^3; XV, 60; XXII, 59; Cadet Officer, 60. Guy's Hospital, M.R.C.S., L.R.C.P., M.B., B.S. House Surgeon, Guy's Hospital, 67. Junior Lecturer in Anatomy, London Hospital, 68. Surgical Registrar, Royal National Throat, Nose & Ear Hospital, London. Royal Society of Medicine. Freeman of Merchant Taylors' Company. *H.A.C.*

1348 DRURY, Neil Godfrey Dru, b. 7 Sept. 42, younger s. of W. N. D. Drury (OR M 22). M, 56^1–60^2. Diploma in German, Goethe Institut Bad Aibling, Bavaria, S. Germany. Diploma in Commerce, London School of Foreign Trade. Stock Exchange Certificate, City of London Polytechnic. Leaf Tobacco Merchant. Export Sales Asst., Burmah Castrol Co. Stockbroker, Myers & Co. *M.C.C., Royal Ashdown G.C.* Brother, 694.

1349 HODSON-MACKENZIE, Keith Peirson, b. 13 Oct. 42, younger s. of K. J. Hodson-Mackenzie (OR M 22). M, 56^1–60^2. Brother, 995.

1350 **DOWLING, Peter John Osmond,** b. 10 May 42, elder s. of G. R. V. Dowling. SF, 56¹–60¹; R. VIII, 59, 60. A.C.A. A.M.B.I.M. Lecturer in Law & Accounts, Rich Russell & Co., Andover, 66–70. Now Man. Dir., Hampshire Business Supplies Ltd., Winchester. *Royal Ocean Racing Club.*

1351 **NUTOR, P. N. K.** SF, 56¹–56².

1352 **LEECH, William Cooper,** b. 15 Oct. 42, s. of R. C. Leech. Sh, 56¹–60¹. Grenoble Univ. Associate Member of the British Institute of Management. Dir. & Gen. Man. of K.X. Accessories Ltd. Gen. Man. of The British Vacuum Flask Co. Ltd. *Scaling Dam Sailing Club.*

1353 **PHILLIPS, Barry Charles,** b. 25 Sept. 42, s. of E. R. Phillips. Sh, 56¹–59³.

1354 **STUBBS, Albert William Gilmour,** b. 28 Sept. 42, younger s. of A. Stubbs. Sh, 56¹–61¹. Jesus, Oxford, M.A. Stanford Univ., California, M.B.A. Financial Analyst, A.E.I. Ltd., 67. Personal Assistant to Chief Executive, Chemicals Division, British Oxygen Ltd., 68–70. Rank Strand Electric Ltd., 70–72. Now Marketing Manager.

1355 **TEARE, Peter Donald,** b. 8 Sept. 42, 2nd s. of Prof. R. D. Teare, M.D., F.R.C.P. Sh, 56¹–60³; Levée. Brothers, 1019 & 1955.

1356 **TOZER, Robin Gerald,** b. 4 Sept. 42, s. of R. E. Tozer. Sh, 56¹–61²; Levée; XXII, 61; H. XI, 60, 61. A.C.A. Nevill Hovey Gardner & Co., Chartered Accountants, 62–71. Joined L. W. Lambourn & Co. Ltd., at Export House as Chief Accountant, 71. Played hockey for Surrey, 64–65 season. Hockey Association. Freeman of Merchant Taylors Company.

1357 **GOSLETT, David Nigel,** b. 13 July 42, elder s. of the late M. J. Goslett (OR St 27). St, 56¹–60³; Levée; Cap, 60; R. VIII, 60; Cadet Officer, 60. H.N.C. Business Studies. Dip.M., M.Inst.M. Brother, 1994.

1358 **JOHNSON-HILL, Kenelm Alan,** b. 16 Apr. 42, 2nd s. of K. C. Johnson-Hill, J.P. (OR T 19). St, 56¹–60². Stockbroker c/o Hong Kong & Shanghai Banking Corp., Hong Kong. Brothers, 940 & 1995.

1359 **LATIMER, Donald Courtenay,** b. 24 July 42, elder s. of G. D. Latimer

(OR St 28). St, 56¹–60². A.C.A., 65. Peat Marwick Mitchell & Co., 60–67. United Biscuits Ltd., (Asst. to Financial Director), 67–69. Burzl Pulp & Paper Ltd. (Group Chief Accountant) since 70.

1360 **NEWELL, Peter Monk,** b. 4 Dec. 42, younger s. of R. Newell. St, 56¹–60³; Levée; XV, 60; Tennis VI, 59, 60. Oxford Univ., M.A. Columbia Univ., New York, M.B.A. Barrister, Inner Temple, 65. Wolsey Hall, Oxford. Denbyware Canada Limited, Marketing Dir., 65–70. Gen. Man., 72–73. Brother, 717.

1361 **REID, Henry Derek Nevile,** b. 2 Sept. 42, s. of the late Lt.-Cdr. H. N. Reid, R.N. St, 56¹–60².

1362 **CARTWRIGHT, Peter Aubrey,** b. 21 June 42, younger s. of W. F. Cartwright, D.L., J.P. (OR Tu 20). Tu, 56¹–60². Man. Dir., Kemp Masts Ltd. *Royal Ocean Racing Club.* Brother, 1030.

1363 **CROWTHER, Jonathan,** b. 24 Sept. 42, s. of J. W. Crowther, M.B., Ch.B. Tu, 56¹–61¹; Scholar. Major Scholarship to Corpus Christi, Cambridge, M.A. Joined Oxford University Press, 64; worked in Madras and Calcutta branches of O.U.P., 65 and 66; Head of Import Dept., O.U.P., London, 67–72; currently Head of Branch Secretariat (Editorial) for O.U.P. London. Composer of AZED crossword in the "Observer" since Mar. 72.

1364 **TATTON-BROWN, Joe,** b. 8 Mar. 43, younger s. of W. E. Tatton-Brown. Tu, 56¹–60³; State Scholar; XV, 60. King's, Cambridge.

1365 **CARNEGIE, David Ronald Mackay,** b. 13 July 42, s. of R. M. Carnegie. W, 56¹–60³. St. Andrews Univ., B.Sc. Timber Merchant with Brownlee & Co. Ltd., Port Dundas, Glasgow.

1366 **DAGNALL, Hubert Alan Frederick,** b. 2 June 42, elder s. of H. J. A. Dagnall (OR C 30). W, 56¹–60².

ENTRANCES IN MAY 1956

1367 **ADDIS, Graham Humphrey,** b. 23 Dec. 42, 3rd s. of Sir W. Addis, K.B.E., C.M.G. (OR SH 16). SH, 56²–61¹. Magdalene, Cambridge. Brothers, 152 & 1663.

1368 **FRASER, John Howard Duncan,** b. 8 Aug. 42, s. of the late Wing-Cdr.

H. D. Fraser, O.B.E., R.A.F. SH, 56²-60³. Emmanuel, Cambridge, M.A., Dip. Arch.(Cantab)., R.I.B.A. Architect with Shankland Cox Partnership, London.

1369 JACKSON-POWNALL, Brian Assheton Hughes, b. 4 Dec. 42, elder s. of H. Jackson-Pownall. SH, 56²-60³; S. VIII, 58-60, Capt., 60. Brother, 2271.

1370 NASSIM, Michael Arnold, b. 10 Dec. 42, s. of J. R. Nassim, F.R.C.P. SH, 56²-61¹. Exhibition to Exeter, Oxford. St. George's Hospital Medical School, M.A., B.Sc., B.M., B.Ch., M.R.C.P. Investigating the flow conductivity of arterial walls at Guy's Hospital. *Bath Club.*

1371 TURCAN, William James, b. 4 Jan. 43, 2nd s. of H. H. Turcan, T.D. (OR SH 20). SH, 56²-60³; Scholar; XV, 60; Leaving Exhibition. Scholarship to Trinity, Oxford, B.A. Qualified C.A., 69. Dir., R. Hutchison & Co. Ltd., Kirkcaldy. *Vincent's, Oxford.* Brothers, 1102 & 2012.

1372 DAUNT, Michael Seton, b. 10 Mar. 42, elder s. of M. Daunt, O.B.E. T, 56²-58³.

1373 KING, Thomas William, b. 30 July 42, 2nd s. of F. W. King (OR B 20). B, 56²-61¹. Trinity, Cambridge, M.A. Teaching Classics, Ardingly College, Sussex.

1374 BLUNT, Andrew Nicholas, b. 14 Feb. 43, 3rd s. of A. G. Blunt, V.R.D. (OR C 23). C, 56²-58¹. Slade School of Fine Art. Diploma in Fine Art. Private Artist. *Friends of the Art Gallery of South Australia. The North Adelaide Society.* Brothers, 242 & 1123.

1375 DALRYMPLE, Robert Gordon, b. 1 Mar. 43, 3rd s. of I. M. Dalrymple, F.R.S.A. (OR C 17). C, 56²-60³. Trinity, Cambridge, B.A. Schoolmaster, 64-66. Financial Consultant in City, 67-73. Freelance Journalist. Financial Public Relations Man., British Leyland Motor Corporation since 73. Commissioned Author, "Education in England", 69 & "England *is* a Foreign Country", 70. Brothers, I. S. W. Dalrymple & 828.

1376 HACKMAN, John William, b. 27 July 42, s. of F. H. Hackman, LL.B. C, 56²-60³. Magdalene, Cambridge, B.A., A.C.I.S., A.I.B. Asst. Dir. of N. M. Rothschild & Sons Ltd. *Royal Lymington Yacht Club.*

1377 WHITE, Edwin Matthew, b. 9 Mar. 43, younger s. of Lt.-Col. P. F. White, O.B.E. (OR C 13). C, 56²-61¹; Levée; Head of House. Scholarship to Royal Marines. Capt., R.M. Liveryman, Worshipful Society of Apothecaries. Brother, 771.

1378 EVANS, John Alexander Llewellyn, b. 30 Nov. 42, elder s. of A. L. L. Evans, B.C.L. (OR K 20). K, 56²-61². Southampton Univ., B.Sc., Chemistry & Maths. Turner and Newall Ltd., as Management Trainee, 66. United Drapery Stores Ltd., Computer Division, 71. Currently Systems Consultant to a U.D.S. Company. British Computer Society. Brother, 1793.

1379 FRASER, John Robert, b. 28 July 42, s. of C. N. Fraser, LL.B. K, 56²-60².

1380 HACKETT, Nicholas George Grant, b. 4 Oct. 42, elder s. of D. C. Hackett. K, 56²-60². Diploma in Architecture (Leicester). Dip.Arch., A.R.I.B.A. Own private practice, Nicholas Hackett, Dip.Arch., A.R.I.B.A., Swithland, Leicester.

1381 FALK, William Edward, b. 14 Nov. 42, younger s. of Lt.-Col. C. J. Falk, M.C., T.D. (OR M 11). M, 56²-60². A.C.A. Audit Manager in firm of Chartered Accountants.

1382 GREENHALGH, Gerald Rodney, b. 20 Nov. 42, elder s. of G. Greenhalgh. M, 56²-61². Edinburgh, Univ. A.I.Q.S. John Laing & Son (Construction), 64-65. Arnold Sharrocks Ltd., (Surveying) since 65. Dir., 70. Dir. of Subsidiary Plastering Company, 72. British Chess Federation. Brother, 2060.

1383 HOWKINS, Ben Walter, b. 19 Aug. 42, elder s. of Col. W. A. Howkins, T.D. (OR T 23). M, 56²-60². Amherst Coll., Mass., U.S.A. Vintners Scholarship, 63. Wine Trade since 62, currently Sales Director, Croft & Co. (part of Grand Metropolitan Hotels). Member of Northamptonshire Yeomanry (Lt.), 63-68. *Oporto Cricket & Lawn Tennis Club, Portugal.* Brother, 1830.

1384 CROCKETT, Michael Robert, b. 23 Sept. 42, elder s. of J. R. Crockett (OR SF 29). SF, 56²-59³.

1385 KENNEDY, Peter Norman Bingham, b. 11 Oct. 42, eldest s. of B. B. Kennedy, T.D. (OR SF 33). SF, 56²-60²;

S. VIII, 59, 60. C.A.(Scotland). Stock-broking. Now Manager in Scotland for a Merchant Bank and Invoice Factoring Company in the Alex Lawrie Ltd. Group. Capt. in the Ayrshire Yeomanry Squadron of the Queen's Own Yeomanry, T.A. *Western Club, Cavalry Club*. Brothers, 2394 & 2692.

1386 **MASON, Harold Graham,** b. 19 Aug. 42, elder s. of J. L. Mason. SF, 56^2–60^2. King's College, London.

1387 **NAIRN, David Sherwood,** b. 19 Nov. 42, s. of S. J. G. Nairn, M.B., Ch.B., F.R.C.S. SF, 56^2–60^3; Levée; Sw. VIII, 57–60, Capt., 60. Downing, Cambridge. Middlesex Hospital, B.A., M.B., B.Chir., F.R.C.S. Surgeon, Mount Vernon Hospital, Northwood, Middlesex.

1388 **TULLOCH, Keith Farquhar,** b. 13 Aug. 42, 2nd s. of W. A. Tulloch, M.C., T.D. (OR SF 24). SF, 56^2–60^1. A.C.A. Stockbroker. *Cavalry Club, Western Club, Prestwick G.C.* Brothers, 1151, 2472 & 2473.

1389 **GRAHAM, Richard Humphrey Paxton,** b. 11 Nov. 42, s. of R. P. Graham, M.B., B.S., J.P. Sh, 56^2–61^1; Scholar; Major Classical Scholarship to Wadham, Oxford, B.A. External Degree in Philosophy (London). Diploma in Organization & Methods, 72. Inst. Administrative Management. Lecturer in Computing, Sunderland Polytechnic. *National Liberal Club*.

1390 **JACK, Raymond Evan,** b. 13 Nov. 42, elder s. of E. S. M. Jack (OR SH 23). Sh, 56^2–61^1; Levée; Head of House. Trinity, Cambridge, B.A. Barrister.

1391 **LAKE, John Jeffery,** b. 13 Oct. 42, s. of W. O. Lake. Sh, 56^2–61^2; Levée; Head of House; Head of School Music. Christ Church, Oxford, M.A. Working in family business, Lake Carpets Ltd. Currently Advertising Executive with the Nottingham Shopper-Free Distribution Paper. *National Liberal Club*.

1392 **MAY, Michael Osborne Pryce,** b. 17 Nov. 42, 2nd s. of D. O. May. Sh, 56^2–60^2. Building Engineer.

1393 **ROSSETTI, Charles William Madox,** b. 8 Aug. 42, younger s. of H. F. Rossetti. Sh, 56^2–60^2. Gonville and Caius, Cambridge, M.A. Solicitor in Private Practice.

1394 **WALKER, Richard Sebastian Maynard,** b. 11 Dec. 42, s. of R. F. Walker. Sh, 56^2–61^1. New College, Oxford, B.A. Honorary Exhibitioner. Lawrence Binyon Prize, 66. Engineering, 68–70. Publishing since 70 with Jonathan Cape & Chatto & Windus.

1395 **HELME, Anthony James Alexander,** b. 8 June 42, elder s. of A. Helme (OR C 28). St, 56^2–60^2. Chartered Accountant. 11 yrs. with City Head Office of Peat, Marwick, Mitchell & Co. Now Financial Dir. of Lane Fox & Co. Ltd., Quoted Property Company. Brother, 2162.

1396 **HERBERT, Richard Davis,** b. 19 Oct. 42, elder s. of G. B. Herbert, T.D., LL.B. St, 56^2–60^3; Cap, 60. Solicitor, Notary Public. Partner in Messrs. Stone & Co., Solicitors, Leicester. *Leicestershire Club*. Brother, 1956.

1397 **LEATHERS, David Frederick James,** b. 11 Dec. 42, younger s. of the Hon. L. J. Leathers. St, 56^2–60^3. A.C.A. Man. of Financial Consultants Dept., Messrs. Binder Hamlyn & Co. N. M. Rothschild & Sons Ltd., Investment Admin. since 72. *Lansdowne Club*.

1398 **AHMAD, Anees,** b. 1 Nov. 42, younger s. of N. Ahmad, M.B.E. Tu, 56^2–60^2. A.C.A. Budget Officer at the I.L.O.

1399 **LEWIS, David Gwynder,** b. 31 Aug. 42, elder s. of G. E. Lewis. Tu, 56^2–60^3; Levée; Head of House; XV, 59, 60; XI, 60. A.I.B. Hambros Bank Ltd. from 61. Seconded to Banca Privata Finanziaria, Milan, 67–68. Opened Hambros' Tokyo office, 73. 'C' Battery, H.A.C. (R.H.A.), 61–66. Battery Sergeant-Major. *Turf Club, R.A.C., H.A.C.* Brother, 1688.

1400 **ROBB, Andrew Mackenzie,** b. 2 Sept. 42, s. of W. M. Robb, M.B., Ch.B. F.R.C.S. Tu, 56^2–60^3; Sw. VIII, 58, 60. C.N.A.A. Degree in Business Administration. A.C.M.A. Unilever, Hoskyns Group Ltd. Now Financial Controller, P. & O. Bulk Shipping Division.

1401 **WHITE, Jeremy George Geoffrey Nethercote,** b. 8 Sept. 42, s. of the late Lt.-Col. G. C. White, C.M.G., O.B.E., Chief Constable of Kent. W, 56^2–60^2. R.M.A., Sandhurst, 60–62. Member, Institute of Marketing. Diploma in Marketing. Civil Servant Linguist (French). Regular Commission, H.M. Armed Forces. Coldstream Guards, 62–68. Retired substantive Captain. Lines Bros. Ltd., 68–70.

Personal Asst. to Jt. Man. Dir., Marketing Exec. in subsidiaries, Minimotels Ltd. & Leed Ltd. Measuring & Scientific Equipment Ltd., Marketing Exec., 69–72. Diversified Corporate Services Ltd., Security Agency, Sales Man., 72. Man. Dir., Anglian Textured Coatings Ltd., 73. Institute of Marketing. *Guards Club.*

ENTRANCES IN SEPTEMBER 1956

1402 HARROWES, David Hume Stewart, b. 6 Apr. 43, s. of W. McC. Harrowes, M.D., M.R.C.S., F.R.S., D.P.M. SH, 56^3–61^2. Christ Church, Oxford, M.A. Solicitor. Partner, Lloyd, Burch & Inskip, Bristol.

1403 HODDER-WILLIAMS, Richard, b. 18 Mar. 43, younger s. of Lt.-Col. P. Hodder-Williams, O.B.E., T.D. (OR SH 23). SH, 56^3–61^2; Scholar; Levée; Head of House; XI, 59, 60, 61, Capt.; Tom Hughes Prize. Corpus Christi, Oxford, M.A. Study and Serve Scholar, Min. of Overseas Development as Junior Fellow. University Coll. of Rhodesia and Nyasaland, 65–67. Lecturer in Politics, Bristol Univ. & Rep. on Standing Committee on University Studies of Africa. Contributing Editor, International Journal of Politics. Author of Public Opinion Polls, also British Politics & Articles on Rhodesian Politics. *Vincent's, M.C.C.* Brother, 803.

1404 HUTTON, Charles Edward Ilbert, b. 4 Mar. 43, younger s. of Sir N. K. Hutton, K.C.B. SH, 56^3–61^1. Keble, Oxford. Brother, 546.

1405 JEFFREY, John Stewart, b. 21 Nov. 42, s. of J. S. Jeffrey, M.D., F.R.C.S. SH, 56^3–60^3; Cap, 60. Trinity, Oxford, B.A. Sussex Univ., Certificate of Education, M.S.W. Asst. Teacher, St. Paul's School, N. Nigeria, 64–65. Haywards Heath Grammar School, 66–69. Probation Officer, Brighton since 71.

1406 LYDE, John William, b. 27 Nov. 42, elder s. of L. G. Lyde (OR K 18). SH, 56^3–59^3. Brother, 1855.

1407 RICHARDSON, John Layland, b. 3 Apr. 43, s. of J. H. Richardson. SH, 56^3–60^3. J. & P. Coats Ltd., 61 (in East Africa, 65–67), (in Malaysia & Singapore, 67–69), (in Thailand, 69–71). Presently General Sales Manager for J. & P. Coats (Pakistan) Ltd., Karachi. *Sind Club,* Karachi.

1408 SEARANCKE, John Edward Fermor, b. 7 Mar. 43, s. of A. E. F. Searancke. SH, 56^3–60^3. Hotel Proprietor. Ex 2nd Lt. (Sherwood Foresters). *R.A.C.*

1409 SMITH, Kenneth Frank Barbour, b. 12 May 43, younger s. of Lt.-Col. K. C. C. Smith, J.P. SH, 56^3–60^2.

1410 STURROCK, David Percival, b. 16 Mar. 43, s. of A. M. Sturrock, M.B.E. SH, 56^3–61^1. Edin. Univ., LL.B. Writer to the Signet (W.S.). Partner in law firm, Messrs. Turnbull, Simson & Sturrock, W.S., Jedburgh (as 4th generation Sturrock). Law Society of Scotland. Major, 2/52 Lowland Volunteers (T. & A.V.R.). *Caledonian Club, Edin., Lowland Brigade Officers' Club.*

1411 THOMPSON, Joseph Lefroy Courtenay, b. 4 Apr. 43, younger s. of J. M. Thompson. SH, 56^3–62^1. Trinity Coll., Dublin, B.B.S., B.A. Dir., Thompson-Reid Ltd., Automotive Engineers, Thompson-Reid (Tractors) Ltd., Agricultural Eng., and E. B. Smyth Ltd. (Pedigree Livestock Breeders). Royal Ulster Agricultural Society (Council Member). Belfast Junior Chamber of Commerce (Council Member). Brother, 765.

1412 BARBER, Andrew, b. 14 Aug. 43, younger s. of W. L. Barber. T, 56^3–60^2. Chartered Accountant. Partner in Barber & Co. Brother, 898.

1413 DEELEY, Roger Martyn, b. 1 Jan. 44, s. of Mrs. B. A. Newton. T, 56^3–61^3; School Leaving Exhibition. Magdalene, Cambridge.

1414 ELLIOTT, Ian Robert, b. 10 Mar. 43, s. of W. R. Elliott. T, 56^3–61^3; Levée; Head of School; Head of House; XV, 60, 61; XI, 60, 61; H. XI, 61. Queens', Cambridge, B.A. Exeter Univ., 66. Certificate of Education. Asst. Master, Sherborne School since 67.

1415 GOODWAY, David John, b. 25 Sept. 42, s. of L. T. H. Goodway. T, 56^3–61^1; Levée. Corpus Christi, Oxford, M.A. Birkbeck Coll., London. Lecturer in the Dept. of Adult Education & Extra-Mural Studies, Univ. of Leeds since 69.

1416 HARDWICK, William Austin, b. 19 Mar. 44, younger s. of J. V. Hardwick. T, 56^3–61^2. Brother, 962.

1417 HESKETH, Sean, b. 6 Sept. 42, s. of J. T. Hesketh. T, 56^3–60^3; R. VIII, 59.

Keble, Oxford, B.A. Management Consultant, Arthur Young Management Services.

1418 LEINSTER, Stephen George, b. 17 June 43, younger s. of R. S. Leinster. T, 56^3–59^3. Brother, 964.

1419 LISTER, Malcolm Keith, b. 26 Sept. 42, s. of J. L. Lister. T, 56^3–61^2.

1420 PAINE, Peter Liddell, b. 12 Apr. 43, younger s. of the Rev. E. L. Paine. T, 56^3–62^1; Levée; Head of House. London Bible Coll., King Alfred's Teacher Training Coll., Winchester. Qualified Teacher. Taught at Broadwater C. of E. Aided Primary School, Worthing, 67–70. Seconded to Besançon Univ. for a term in a French Univ., 69. Asst. Master at Sandroyd Prep. School, Wilts. since 70. Brother, 966.

1421 PATERSON, David John, b. 4 Nov. 42, s. of D. R. Paterson. T, 56^3–60^3; Senior Scholar, 59; State Scholarship, 60; Leaving Exhibition, 60; R. VIII, 59, 60; Holder of Bigside Bags, 60. Trinity Hall, Cambridge, M.A. Univ. of Pennsylvania, Philadelphia, U.S.A. Cert. in Industrial Management. Electronics Engineer with Measurex Ltd., California.

1422 SPINKS, John Ingham, b. 31 Jan. 43, elder s. of Capt. E. I. Spinks, R.N. (Retired). (OR T 18). T, 56^3–61^2; S. VIII, 60, 61, Capt., 61. Lancaster College of Technology, Hons. Degree. Mechanical Engineer, Rootes Motors Ltd., Coventry. Brother, 2505.

1423 WAIN, Christopher Paul, b. 15 Oct. 42, younger s. of C. A. Wain. T, 56^3–61^1; Levée; Head of House. Brasenose, Oxford, B.A. Chartered Patent Agent. A.R.I.C. Patent Agent, London. *National Club.* Brother, 394.

1424 ANDERSON, Peter George Lindsay, b. 12 Apr. 43, elder s. of P. G. Anderson (OR B 32). B, 56^3–61^2. Deceased. Brother, 1717.

1425 BAND, David, b. 14 Dec. 42, s. of D. Band, M.B., Ch.B., F.R.C.S. B, 56^3–61^1; R. VIII, 60, 61; Holder of Bigside Bags, 61. Leaving Exhibition to St. Edmund Hall, Oxford, B.A. Columbia Business School, New York. Morgan Guaranty Trust Company since 64. Now Vice-Pres. *Royal Highland Yacht Club.*

1426 GRAYBURN, John Richard, b. 7 Mar. 43, s. of the late J. H. Grayburn, V.C. B, 56^3–60^3. Trinity, Oxford.

1427 GREEN, Robert Tarrant Brunt, b. 22 Mar. 43, elder s. of J. W. Green, L.R.C.P., L.R.C.S. B, 56^3–60^2. South-West Essex Technical Coll. & School of Art. Chartered Accountant, 68. Previously Chief Accountant, Buck & Hickman Ltd., now Financial Controller, Sidal Aluminium Ltd. (subsidiary of Société Industrielle D'Aluminium, Belgium). *Monday Club.* Brother, 1668.

1428 STANGER, William John Nigel, b. 16 Jan. 43, s. of J. K. Stanger, F.R.C.S. B, 56^3–61^1; Levée. Oxford. Newcastle Univ. M.A.(Oxon.), B.A.(Arch. Studies), B.Arch. Architect.

1429 STEWART, Andrew Mervyn, b. 15 June 43, elder s. of H. St. C. Stewart, M.B.E. B, 56^3–61^2. Brother, 2440.

1430 WILLIAMSON, Robin Charles Noel, b. 19 Dec. 42, younger s. of the late J. C. F. Williamson, M.D., F.R.C.S. (OR B 18). B, 56^3–61^2; Scholar; Levée; Head of House; State Scholar, 60. Emmanuel, Cambridge, M.B., B.Chir. St. Bartholomew's Hospital Medical College, F.R.C.S. (Eng.). Surgical Registrar, Royal Berkshire Hospital, Reading.

1431 JEWSON, William Gilbert Laws, b. 28 Jan. 43, elder s. of C. B. Jewson, F.C.A., J.P. (OR C 23). C, 56^3–60^2. Univ. College of London, B.A. Brother, 1648.

1432 OLSBERG, Robert Nicholas, b. 3 Apr. 43, s. of H. Olsberg. C, 56^3–61^1.

1433 PEARL, Graham Murray, b. 11 May 43, s. of L. A. Pearl. C, 56^3–61^2. Birmingham Univ., B.Sc., Ph.D.

1434 RACKOWE, Adrian Stewart Basil Bulkyn, b. 15 Sept. 42, 3rd s. of S. S. A. B. Rackowe. C, 56^3–59^2. Attended City of London College. Institute of Transport Qualifications. Member of the Chartered Institute of Transport. With British Railways in various parts of the Western Region until 71. Now with National Carriers Ltd., as Transport Superintendent at Bristol. Brother, 555.

1435 REISS, David Willoughby, b. 16 June 43, s. of J. A. Reiss. C, 56^3–60^3; Scholar.

1436 **WOODWARD, Richard Anthony,** b. 23 June 43, elder s. of R. R. Woodward, T.D. C, 56^3–61^1. Brother, 2109.

1437 **BUCKLEY, Stephen George,** b. 3 May 43, s. of G. Buckley. K, 56^3–60^2.

1438 **CRESWELL, Colin Michael Edmund,** b. 5 Feb. 43, s. of Sir M. J. Creswell, K.C.M.G. (OR K 23). K, 56^3–60^3. New Coll., Oxford.

1439 **GREENLEAVES, John Everard Vivian,** b. 14 Feb. 43, s. of H. L. Greenleaves. K, 56^3–61^2. R.M.A., Sandhurst, 62–64. Army School of Education, Wilton Park, 68–70. Russian Interpretership. Lt., Queen's Royal Irish Hussars. Army Interpretership, German & Russian. Died Feb. 70.

1440 **LIGERTWOOD, Michael Alexander,** b. 25 Apr. 43, s. of K. A. Ligertwood. K, 56^3–60^2.

1441 **LUCAS, Sigurd Oliver,** b. 23 May 43, s. of the late F. L. Lucas, O.B.E. (OR K 10). K, 56^3–61^2. King's, Cambridge, B.A. In Hospital Administration.

1442 **MACLEOD, Colin William,** b. 27 June 43, younger s. of W. R. Macleod. K, 56^3–59^2.

1443 **MELLAND, Charles Glencairn Beith,** b. 10 June 43, s. of R. B. Melland (OR K 22). K, 56^3–60^1. Trinity College, Dublin. North British Trust Hotels Ltd., Edinburgh. *Edinburgh Sports Club.*

1444 **MUIRHEAD, Ian Peter Sutherland,** b. 8 Apr. 43, elder s. of W. C. Muirhead, O.B.E. K, 56^3–60^2. LL.B. (Sheffield). Solicitor. Executive Asst., Bass Charrington Vintners Ltd. The Law Society.

1445 **PERRY, Anthony Philip,** b. 25 Nov. 42, 2nd s. of J. P. Perry. K, 56^3–60^2.

1446 **THOMPSON, Rodney Howard,** b. 10 Apr. 43, 2nd s. of H. R. Thompson, F.R.C.S. (OR K 21). K, 56^3–61^2; Levée; Head of House; XXII, 60, 61; H. XI, 60, 61. Brothers, 1135 & 1740.

1447 **BOURNE, Samuel John,** b. 5 May 43, 3rd s. of J. Bourne (OR M 18). M, 56^3–60^2. Britannia R.N. College, Dartmouth. Lt., R.N. Joined Submarine Service, 65. Torpedo and Sonar Officer, H.M.S. *Revenge,* 69–71. 1st Lt., H.M.S. *Walrus,* 71–72. Liveryman, Worshipful Society of Apothecaries. *Royal Ocean Racing Club.* Brother, 255.

1448 **CHOLMELEY, Hugh Jerrard,** b. 21 Apr. 43, younger s. of Brig. L. N. Cholmeley, M.B.E. M, 56^3–61^3; Head of House; XV, 61. Property. Brother, 929.

1449 **ELLIS, Peter David Maitland,** b. 9 June 43, s. of D. Ellis, M.B., B.S. M, 56^3–61^2; Levée; Head of House; Cap, 60; XXII, 61; H. XI, 61. St. John's, Cambridge, Baines Exhibitioner, M.A., M.B., B.Chir. Guy's Hospital, London, F.R.C.S. (Eng.). Surgeon, E.N.T. Dept., Middlesex Hospital, London. Gold Medal, Guy's Hospital 66. *Denham G.C.*

1450 **HINTON, Jolyon Kirtland,** b. 13 Sept. 43, 3rd s. of W. K. Hinton, J.P. M, 56^3–61^3. Brother, 98.

1451 **HISCOX, Robert Ralph Scrymgeour,** b. 4 Jan. 43, s. of the late R. Hiscox, C.B.E. M, 56^3–61^1; Levée; Head of House. Corpus Christi, Cambridge, M.A., A.C.I.I. Underwriter at Lloyd's. Partner in Messrs. Roberts & Hiscox. *United Oxford & Cambridge University.*

1452 **HOPE, Michael Edmund,** b. 31 Jan. 43, younger s. of J. L. Hope, LL.B., T.D. (OR M 19). M, 56^3–61^1. T.C.D., B.A. St. Andrew's Univ., M.A. Worcester, Oxford, Cert. Ed. Master, Wycliffe College, Stonehouse, Glos. Brother, 995.

1453 **HORNE, Roger Cozens-Hardy,** b. 31 Jan. 43, elder s. of R. C.-H. Horne, J.P. M, 56^3–61^3. Brother, 1984.

1454 **SCOTT, Michael Colin Mackenzie,** b. 3 Dec. 42, elder s. of M. M. Scott. M, 56^3–60^3; Cap, 60. Cirencester Agricultural College. Brother, 1827.

1455 **SLEDGE, John Christopher,** b. 2 Feb. 43, s. of W. A. Sledge, Ph.D. M, 56^3–61^3; Scholar; Levée; XI, 61. Jesus, Cambridge. Transport, National Freight Corporation.

1456 **AUSTIN, Peter John,** b. 26 Feb. 43, elder s. of Col. J. Austin, O.B.E., D.L. SF, 56^3–61^2. Nottingham Univ., Electrical Engineering, B.Sc., A.M.I.E.E. Development Engineer, Marconi Avionics. Asst. Man., Marconi Middle East (S.A.R.L.) (Beirut).

1457 BRAZIER, Timothy John, b. 7 June 43, s. of the late Major J. B. Brazier, R.A. SF, 56³–61³.

1458 COVE-SMITH, John Rodney, b. 26 Jan. 43, s. of R. Cove-Smith, M.B., B.Ch., M.R.C.S., M.R.C.P., D.P.H. SF, 56³–61²; Scholar; Levée; Head of School; XV, 59, 60; H. XI, 60. Capt., 61. Exhibition to Gonville & Caius, Cambridge. Scholarship to St. Thomas's Hospital, London, M.A., M.B., B.Chir., M.R.C.P. Senior Registrar in General Medicine, City Hospital, Nottingham.

1459 JABRI, Ali Galeb, b. 18 Aug. 42, s. of H.E. M. Jabri. SF, 56³–60¹.

1460 LIVINGSTONE, Quentin Gavin, b. 5 June 43, younger s. of J. L. Livingstone, M.D., F.R.C.P. SF, 56³–61²; Levée; XV, 60; XI, 60, 61; H. XI, 60, 61. St. Thomas's Hospital Medical School, London, M.B., B.S., M.R.C.S., L.R.C.P., D.C.H., D.R.C.O.G. General Medical Practitioner, Ardgay, Wantage, Berks. B.M.A. *Seaford G.C.* Brother, 750.

1461 LLOYD, David Ellrington Burton, b. 17 Mar. 43, s. of G. J. Lloyd. SF, 56³–62¹; Levée; Head of House.

1462 MANNING, Geoffrey John Vernon, b. 16 Jan. 43, s. of J. V. Manning, M.B., Ch.B. SF, 56³–61². Trinity Hall, Cambridge, C.Eng., M.I.Mech.E. Works Director, Geo. L. Scott & Co. Ltd., Ellesmere Port.

1463 ROBERTS, Thomas John Blackburn, b. 12 Feb. 43, s. of T. B. Roberts. SF, 56³–61¹; XXII, 60; H. XI, 61. Liverpool Univ., College of Law, Guildford. Solicitor in Private Practice, Liverpool. Director various Development and Construction Companies. *Liverpool Racquet Club, Formby G.C.*

1464 SCORAH, Andrew Manock Neville, b. 30 Dec. 42, s. of N. Scorah, B.A., LL.B. SF, 56³–61²; Levée; XXII, 59, 60, 61; H. XI, 61. Emmanuel, Cambridge, M.A. Solicitor, Partner in Laces & Co., Solicitors, Liverpool. *Cambridge University Wanderers H.C.*

1465 TUCKETT, Andrew Charles Ivor, b. 16 May 43, younger s. of C. I. Tuckett, M.B.E., F.R.C.S. (OR SF 15). SF, 56³–61². College of Estate Management, London Univ., B.Sc., A.R.I.C.S. District Valuer's Office, Tunbridge Wells, 67–70. Messrs. Hillier Parker May & Rowden, London since 70. *B.Sc. (Estate Management) Club.*

1466 BARRATT, Mark Gilbert, b. 19 July 43, younger s. of Capt. G. A. Barratt, R.N. (Retired). Sh, 56³–61². Clare, Cambridge. Brother, 432.

1467 BUSBY, David Hugh Coysh, b. 12 Mar. 43, s. of H. D. C. Busby, T.D. (OR T 28). Sh 56³–61¹; Scholar. Levée. Magdalen, Oxford, M.A. Schoolmaster.

1468 EMBLING, John Richard, b. 30 Nov. 42 elder s. of J. H. Embling. Sh, 56³–61². University of Keele, B.A., Dip.Ed., A.M.I.P.M., Grad.I.T.D. Group Training Officer, United Dominions Trust Ltd.

1469 EVANS, The Hon. Broke Patrick Andvord, b. 1st Feb. 43, elder s. of The Rt. Hon. Lord Mountevans. Sh, 56³–61²; R. VIII, 61.

1470 FLEMING, Hugh, b. 5 May 43, younger s. of W. J. D. Fleming, M.B., B.Chir. Sh, 56³–61¹. Oriel, Oxford, B.A. In Travel with Global of London Ltd. *Lansdowne Club.* Brother, 1156.

1471 GEE, Peter Mackworth, b. 28 Mar. 43, younger s. of E. A. M. Gee. Sh, 56³–61². Christ's, Cambridge, M.A., A.C.A., A.T.I.I. Adviser, Liberian Government, 68–70. Audit Man., Arthur Young & Co., 70–72. Treasurer, Lex Hotels (U.S.) Inc. since 72. Brother, 866.

1472 LOCK, Brian Norman, b. 23 Apr. 43, s. of N. H. Lock. Sh, 56³–61². Magdalene, Cambridge, M.A. Wye College, Ashford, Kent, Farm Business Administration. Agricultural Seed Merchant & Farmer.

1473 LOURIE, John Adam, b. 9 Aug. 43, s. of the late E. M. Lourie, M.B., M.R.C.P., D.P.H. Sh, 56³–61²; Dewar Travelling Scholarship. Worcester, Oxford, M.A. Diploma in Human Biology, Oxford, 67. Scientific Coordinator, Int'l Biological Programme, 67–68. Member of Scientific Staff, Medical Research Council, 68–70. Ph.D. in Anthropology, London Univ., 71. University College Hospital Medical School, 70–73. Clinical Medical Student qualifying B.M., B.Ch.(Oxon.), 73. Treasurer, Anglo-Mongolian Society. Member, Society for the Study of Human Biology.

1474 **LOXTON-PEACOCK, Adam Anthony,** b. 26 Dec. 42, s. of G. Loxton-Peacock. Sh, 56³–60².

1475 **NELSON, Richard Campbell,** b. 11 Feb. 43, s. of C. L. Nelson. Sh, 56³–60³. London Univ., M.Sc. Chartered Accountant. Dir., Esperanza Trade & Transport Ltd.; Man. Dir., Hardy Amies (Holdings) Ltd.; Partner, Limebeer & Co., Chartered Accountants. *Bath Club, Royal Wimbledon G.C.*

1476 **PECK, Anthony John,** b. 3 Apr. 43, s. of J. Peck, J.P. Sh, 56³–60². Business Studies at Commercial Colleges. Accountant's Clerk & Asst. Co. Secretary, 60–64. Short Service Commission in Coldstream Guards, mainly in Aden & Germany, 64–67. Management Trainee in Lewis's of Manchester, 67–68. Middle Management appointments in Joseph Peck Ltd., Rotherham, 68–72. Chief Executive of Subsidiary T.V. Rental Company, 72. Commission in Royal Yeomanry. *Guards Club.*

1477 **PECK, John Forbes Steuart,** b. 28 Jan. 43, elder s. of D. R. Peck (OR B 28). Sh, 56³–61². Magdalene, Cambridge. Brother, 2476.

1478 **BERNERS-PRICE, Peter Devonald,** b. 27 Jan. 43, s. of A. M. Berners-Price. St, 56³–61²; Levée; Head of House; XV Capt., 61; XXII, 59; H. XI, 61, Junior Athletic Cup, 59; Senior Athletic Cup, 61; Cadet Officer C.C.F.; Tom Hughes Prize, 61. Hotel Training, Paris and Munich. Sales Man., Grosvenor House, London. Overseas Sales Man., Trust Houses Forte, London Division. Assoc. of Conference Executives, Hotel Sales Managers Assoc.

1479 **GLYNN, John Noel,** b. 15 Feb. 43, younger s. of N. T. Glynn, M.B., M.R.C.P. St, 56³–61².

1480 **HOGGARTH, Ian Frank,** b. 15 May 43, s. of F. E. Hoggarth. St, 56³–61¹; Levée. Trinity Hall, Cambridge, M.A., A.C.A. Financial Anaysis Man., Thomas Potterton Ltd., Warwick.

1481 **HOLLOWAY, Paul Anthony,** b. 24 Jan. 43, s. of A. J. Holloway. St, 56³–61². Southampton Univ., LL.B. Solicitor. The Worshipful Company of Solicitors.

1482 **KERSHAW, Timothy Ross,** b. 1 Nov. 42, elder s. of G. R. Kershaw, M.R.C.S., L.R.C.P., D.P.H. St, 56³–61²;

Paddison Art Prize, 61. Clare, Cambridge, M.A. G.E.C. Telecommunications Ltd., Technical Publicity Officer, 64–65. Plessey Automation Group, Publicity Officer, 65–66. Middle East Economic Digest, Regional Ed., then Man., 67–71. City & Industrial Publicity Services Ltd., Account Executive, 71. Member, Institute of Journalists. Liveryman, Worshipful Company of Framework Knitters. Brother, 2251.

1483 **POWNALL, George Henry,** b. 13 Mar. 43, s. of G. H. Pownall. St, 56³–61³. Exhibition in Modern Subject to Corpus Christi, Cambridge.

1484 **STEMBRIDGE, Christopher Peter,** b. 9 Jan. 43, younger s. of P. G. Stembridge. St, 56³–61³; Music Scholar; Levée. Organ Scholarship to Downing, Cambridge, F.R.C.O. Winner of the Turpin Prize.

1485 **BRINSDEN, Paul Hartwell,** b. 9 Jan. 43, 2nd s. of D. Brinsden. Tu, 56³–61². Reading Univ., B.Sc.(A). International marketing of chemicals in Shell International Chemical Co. Ltd., London. *Lensbury Club.* Brothers, 1060 & Mark Shelly, Tu, 70¹–.

1486 **BRYCE-SMITH, John Roderick,** b. 22 Dec. 42, s. of A. C. Bryce-Smith. Tu, 56³–58².

1487 **COWEN, Alastair Edward,** b. 12 Mar. 43, younger s. of G. A. Cowen (OR Tu 20). Tu, 56³–61²; Levée; Head of House. Steel Industry, Sales. *Northern Counties Club, Newcastle.* Brother, 1202.

1488 **DAVIES-JONES, Robert Peter,** b. 15 Feb. 43, s. of C. Davies-Jones, M.B., Ch.B. Tu, 56³–61². Birmingham Univ., B.Sc. Univ. of Colorado, Ph.D. Geophysical Fluid Dynamicist at National Severe Storms Laboratory, N.O.A.A., Oklahoma, U.S.A. Member, American Meteorological Society.

1489 **FORREST, James Frederick,** b. 25 July 43, younger s. of R. Forrest, M.B., Ch.B. Tu, 56³–61². Birmingham Univ., M.B., Ch.B. Surgical Registrar, United Birmingham Hospitals. Brother, 749.

1490 **GLEDHILL, Michael Charles Sinton,** b. 17 June 43, elder s. of W. C. Gledhill, M.B.E., M.B., F.R.C.S. Tu, 56³–60³; Scholar. King's, Cambridge, reading Medicine for 1 yr. Qualified Solicitor. Emigrated to Australia, 70. Now

Partner in Melbourne firm. Law Society, London & Australian Law Society. Brother, 2093.

1491 KEELING, Andrew Myles, b. 4 July 43, younger s. of R. G. M. Keeling, O.B.E., M.B. Tu, 56^3–61^2; H. XI, 61. Commissioned into Royal Marines, 61. Now Captain, R.M., serving as Instructor at R.M.A., Sandhurst. Served two tours in Far East, one in Middle East; also on the staff at R.N.C., Dartmouth. Brother, 1170.

1492 LAMBERTY, Byron George Harker, b. 13 Feb. 43, elder s. of G. B. Lamberty, L.R.C.P., L.R.C.S. Tu, 56^3–61^2; Levée. Cambridge Univ. St. Bartholomew's Hospital Medical College, M.A., M.B., B.Chir. House Officer, St. Bartholomew's Hospital, London. Lecturer Anatomy, St. Bart's Medical College, S.H.O. Plastic Surgery. Brother, 2134.

1493A WISNER, Frank George, jnr., b. 2 July 38, eldest s. of F. G. Wisner of Washington, D.C. Tu, 56^3–57^2.

1493B WOOD, David Ryan, b. 5 Jan. 43, elder s. of A. R. Wood. Tu, 56^3–61^2; XXII, 61; Tennis VI, 60. Brother, 1962.

1494 ARCHER, John Richard, b. 22 Mar. 43, 2nd s. of J. R. Archer, LL.B. W, 56^3–61^1; Scholar; Levée; Head of House; R. VIII, 61; State Scholarship, 59. Minor Scholarship to Emmanuel, Cambridge. Brothers, 757 & 2170.

1495 HINES, Roger Broughton, b. 16 Feb. 42, 2nd s. of G. C. Hines. W, 56^3–61^1. Trinity, Cambridge, B.A. Member of British Computer Society. In Computer Software & Bureau Services until 71, then into Computer Consultancy in W. Germany. *Manchester Canoe Club.*

1496 JACKSON, Andrew Kenneth Astbury, b. 3 Dec. 42, s. of K. L. T. Jackson, T.D. (OR C 27). W, 56^3–61^2; Fives IV, 61.

1497 LEEDHAM-GREEN, Kevin, b. 1 Jan. 43, s. of R. G. Leedham-Green (OR C 18). W, 56^3–60^2; Sw. VIII, 60. Cardiff College of Commerce. Bonn Chamber of Commerce Dipl. for Interpreting & Translation. H.N.C. Business Studies. Diploma of Institute of Marketing. Duport Iron and Steel Co., Export Sales Man.

1498 MAVITY, Harold Roger Wallace, b. 15 May 43, s. of H. F. L. Mavity. W, 56^3–61^1.

1499 PURSAILL, Thomas Julian Weale, b. 10 Jan. 43, younger s. of J. N. H. Pursaill. W, 56^3–57^2. Brother, 894.

1500 SIMMS, Nicholas Arthur Lewen, b. 2 Feb. 43, elder s. of G. O. Simms, D.D. W, 56^3–61^1. Trinity College, Dublin, B.A. Junior Statistician, Ministry of Finance, Botswana, 65–66. Irish Shell & B.P. Ltd., Dublin, 66–67. Irish Marketing Surveys, 67–69. Radio Telefis Eireann (Radio & Television Audience Research) since 69. Brother, 1691.

1501 VARNEY, Paul, b. 6 Nov. 42, s. of F. Varney. W, 56^3–61^1; Capt. of Fives. A.C.A. Chartered Accountant.

1502 WATTS, David, b. 6 July 43, s. of R. W. Watts, M.B., B.Ch. (OR W 26). W, 56^3–60^2. Died from accidental fall in Snowdonia on school expedition.

ENTRANCES IN JANUARY 1957

1503 ANDERSON, Andrew Charles, b. 18 May 43, 3rd s. of J. S. Anderson. SH, 57^1–61^3; Levée; Head of House; Cap, 61. Timber & Plywood Trade. Manager of branch of family business. Brother, 918.

1504 DURKE-BURDETT, Charles Edward Thomson, b. 22 July 43, s. of C. G. Burdett. SH, 57^1–61^2. Scholarship to Exeter, Oxford. (Name changed from Burdett). Stockbroker, Hoare & Co. of London. Died 12 Nov. 72.

1505 LUNN, Richard Michael Carter, b. 10 July 43, elder s. of C. D. Lunn. SH, 57^1–62^1; Levée; Head of House. Scholarship to Jesus, Oxford. Brother, 1815.

1506 SPENS, The Hon. William David Ralph, b. 23 Nov. 43, younger s. of The Rt. Hon. The Lord Spens (OR SH 27). SH, 57^1–61^2; Cap, 60; Sw. VIII, 60, Capt., 61. Corpus Christi, Cambridge, B.A. Barrister. *M.C.C.* Brother, 1248.

1507 WILMOTH, Charles John Maitland, b. 2 June 43, younger s. of V. J. Wilmoth. B, 57^1–61^3. Publisher. *Island Sailing Club.*

1508 KIEFT, Andrew Thomas, b. 7 July 43, elder s. of B. T. Kieft, M.B., B.Chir., D.C.R.O.G. C, 57^1–60^2. Articled to Deloitte & Co. A.C.A. Chief Accountant & Company Secretary, Thomas Christy & Co. Ltd. since 69. *M.C.C.*

1509 LEE WARNER, Martin Paul, b. 22 Aug. 43, elder grandson of the late E. H. Lee Warner (OR C oo). C, 57^1–61^2; H. XI, 61. Capt., Royal Green Jackets (T.A.). Dir., P. Murray-Jones Ltd. & P. Murray-Jones International Ltd. (International Money Brokers). *Junior Carlton Club, Hong Kong Club.* Brother, 1790.

1510 TAYLOR, Michael Robert, b. 8 Sept. 43, s. of K. B. Taylor. C, 57^1–61^2; XI, 61.

1511 CLIFF, Peter Antony Champain, b. 13 June 43, s. of A. D. Cliff (OR M 27). M, 57^1–61^3; Levée; Cadet Officer. LL.B., Southampton. George Wimpey & Co., 66–69. Outward Bound Instructor since 70. *Ski Club of Gt. Britain.*

1512 PAYNE, Neil Lewin, b. 5 June 43, s. of R. L. Payne (OR M 28). M, 57^1–61^3; XV, 60, 61. Articled Clerk, B. Davis & Co., 62–66. A.C.A., M.A.C.P.A. Cooper Brothers & Co., London, 66–70. Partner in Cooper Brothers & Co., Kuala Lumpur since 70. *Richmond R.F.C., Selangor Club, Kuala Lumpur.*

1513 BLAKE, Sir Francis Michael, Bt. b. 11 July 43, s. of the late Sir F. E. C. Blake, Bt. SF, 57^1–61^2; XI, 61; Fives IV, 61. St. Andrew Trust Ltd., Edinburgh. *M.C.C.*

1514 CADBURY, Peter Hugh George, b. 8 June 43, 3rd s. of J. C. Cadbury. SF, 57^1–62^1. Solicitor. Morgan Grenfell & Co. Ltd. Asst. Director/Corporate, Finance Dept.

1515 FRANKLIN, John Andrew, b. 21 Nov. 43 s. of B. Franklin. SF, 57^1–61^3; Levée; Head of House; XV, 61. Pembroke, Cambridge, M.A. Solicitor with Slaughter & May, 68–72. Merchant Banking with Morgan Grenfell & Co. Ltd. from 72. *Bath Club, H.A.C.*

1516 MIDGLEY, Andrew Michael, b. 27 July 43, younger s. of A. R. Midgley. SF, 57^1–61^2; R. VIII, 61; Holder of Bigside Bags. Leather Factor. *M.C.C.*

1517 LYONS, Stuart Randolph, b. 24 Oct. 43, 3rd s. of B. Lyons. Sh, 57^1–61^3; Scholar; State Scholarship, 61. Major Scholarship in Classics to King's, Cambridge, M.A. Man. Dir., John Collier Tailoring Ltd. and associated companies. Member, Yorkshire & Humberside Economic Planning Council since 71. Member, Leeds City Council, 70–73. Prospec-tive Conservative Parliamentary Candidate, Halifax, 72. Brothers, 936 & 1346.

1518 CROWE, Philip Gordon, b. 27 July 43, s. of G. G. Crowe, M.B., Ch.B., F.R.C.S. St, 57^1–61^3.

1519 SLINGSBY, Charles Anthony, b. 7 June 43, s. of C. H. Slingsby. St, 57^1–61^3; Levée. Minor Exhibition to University College, Oxford, M.A. Solicitor. Partner in Payne Hicks Beach & Co. *United Oxford & Cambridge University Club, H.A.C.*

1520 BELOFF, Jeremy Benjamin, b. 2 July 43, younger s. of M. Beloff, B.Litt. Tu, 57^1–61^3. St. Catherine's, Oxford.

1521 ALBAN DAVIES, Ifor John David, b. 29 July 43, elder s. of J. Alban Davies. W, 57^1–61^2. Brother, 2168.

1522 BALDWIN, William Norris, b. 20 July 43, younger s. of Major C. L. Baldwin, M.C. (OR W 11). W, 57^1–61^2. Bio. Chem. Farmer. *Naval & Military Club.* Brother, 730.

ENTRANCES IN MAY 1957

1523 GRYLLS, Richard Gerveys, b. 19 Sept. 43, s. of S. H. Grylls, C.B.E. (OR SH 23). SH, 57^2–61^3. Edinburgh Univ., Mus.Bac. Massachusetts Institute of Technology, B.Arch. Teacher/Educator.

1524 HARDEN, Alastair Geoffrey, b. 8 July 43, elder s. of C. G. Harden (OR SH 18). SH, 57^2–61^3. Univ. of St. Andrews, B.Sc. 3 yrs. in "Cigarette Development" with Gallaher Ltd. Now working in B.B.C. Gramophone Library. Brother, 1968.

1525 GREGORY, Colin Clive, b. 18 Sept. 43, younger s. of R. H. Gregory. C, 57^2–59^2. Brother, 829.

1526 HALL, Benjamin Robert Hadley, b. 20 Sept. 43, 2nd s. of G. S. Hall, M.D., F.R.C.P. C, 57^2–62^1; Levée; Head of House; Head of School; XV, 60, 61; H. XI, 62; Parry Exhibition. St. Edmund's Hall, Oxford. Brothers, 1728 & 1975.

1527 CASSELS, Niel Andrew Kennedy, b. 19 Apr. 43, youngest s. of A. K. Cassels (OR K 20). K, 57^2–60^1. In Advertising. Brothers, 31, 347 & 773.

1528 COOPMAN, Peter David, b. 14 Sept. 43, s. of G. E. Coopman (OR K 23). K, 57^2–61^2; R. VIII, 61; Second in Crick, 61; Junior Rackets Cup, 59. Gonville & Caius, Cambridge, M.A. Solicitor. Law Society.

1529 HILLS, Timothy James, b. 18 Sept. 43, elder s. of Brig. J. Hills, D.S.O. (OR K 16). K, 57^2–62^1; R. VIII, 61, 62; Holder of Bigside Bags. Lincoln's Inn & Council of Legal Education. Barrister, Lincoln's Inn. *H.A.C.* Brother, 2050.

1530 MORRIS, Charles Benedict, b. 15 Dec. 43, s. of A. H. Morris (OR K 21). K, 57^2–61^2; Tennis VI, 61. R.A.C., Cirencester. A.R.I.C.S. Chartered Surveyor in General Practice, 66–72. Self-employed Architectural Designer since 72.

1531 SAMUEL, Christopher Scott, b. 4 Oct. 43, elder s. of A. C. I. Samuel, C.M.G., C.V.O. (OR M 30). K, 57^2–61^2. R.N. Reserved Cadetship. Dartmouth, 62–65. Long Communications Course, 71–72. Royal Navy in Command H.M.S. *Wotton.* Brother, Adrian Charles, K, 72^3–.

1532 WAINWRIGHT, Reginald Anthony, b. 13 Nov. 43, younger s. of D. Wainwright, M.B., M.Ch.Orth., F.R.C.S. K, 57^2–61^3; R. VIII, 61. Army. Brother, 990.

1533A EDMISTON, James Stuart Moray, b. 23 Oct. 43, elder s. of J. H. F. Edmiston. M, 57^2–61^3; XV, 61; Sw. VIII, 60, 61. Production Engineering.

1533B VALLINGS, Robert Ross, b. 18 Nov. 43, younger s. of Lt.-Cdr. R. A. Vallings, D.Sc., R.N.R. Sh, 57^2–61^3; Levée; Head of House; Capt. of Fives, 61; Dewar Travelling Scholarship. Solicitor. Partner, Radcliffes & Co. of Westminster. Lt., R.N.R. *Army & Navy, Richmond F.C.*

1534 BANCROFT, Gordon Nicholas, b. 20 Sept. 43, younger s. of G. Bancroft. SF, 57^2–62^1; Levée. English Speaking Union Scholarship to America for 1 yr. 1 yr. at Lawrenceville School, New Jersey, 3 yrs. at Stanford Univ., California, B.A. and 1 yr. as Graduate, Hertford, Oxford, Dip.Econ. 4 yrs. at Slater Walker Investments, Investment Analyst. Member of Society of Investment Analysts.

1535 COWPER, Christopher Roland, b. 22 Sept. 43, s. of R. D. Cowper. SF, 57^2–61^2. A.C.A. Residing in Australia.

1536 FRAYMOUTH, Patrick Rupert Neil, b. 24 Sept. 43, s. of Major D. R. Fraymouth. St, 57^2–60^2. Faraday House Engineering College, Holborn, W.C.1. Man., Rotraco Thailand Ltd. (Subsidiary of Inchcape Group). *The British Club, Bangkok, The Royal Bangkok Sports Club.*

1537 GARVIN, Michael J. Moore, b. 12 Sept. 43, s. of S. Garvin, M.B.E. St, 57^2–61^3. A.C.A. Man., Price Waterhouse & Co., 62–71. Group Finance Controller and Co. Secretary, Barclay Security Ltd. since 71. *Travellers' Club, Hurlingham Club.*

1538 CHALLEN, Stephen Henry, b. 29 Nov. 43, 2nd s. of H. D. Challen (OR Tu 24). Tu, 57^2–61^2. Chartered Accountant, 67.

1539 HAWKESWORTH, Thomas Simon Ashwell, b. 15 Nov. 43, elder s. of C. P. E. Hawkesworth (OR Tu 24). Tu, 57^2–61^3; Levée; Head of House. Evers Exhibition to Queen's, Oxford, B.A. Barrister. Brother, 2482.

1540 HEARN, David Neill Barclay, b. 19 Jan. 44, younger s. of Col. J. N. W. Hearn (OR Tu 27). Tu, 57^2–62^2. Middlesex Hospital. Farming. Brother, 1090.

1541 SELWYN, Christopher Thomas, b. 25 Jan. 44, s. of the late C. A. Selwyn. Tu, 57^2–62^2. Corpus Christi, Cambridge, B.Sc. Working for Ph.D. in Social Anthropology.

1542 ALLISON, Shaun Michael, b. 12 Jan. 44, younger s. of Lt.-Cdr. J. L. W. M. Allison, R.N. (Retired). W, 57^2–61^3. Member, London Stock Exchange. Stockbroker. *Royal Southern Yacht Club.* Brother, 1173.

1543 FORREST, Thomas George, b. 1 Dec. 43, s. of Cdr. J. W. Forrest, O.B.E., R.N. (Retired). W, 57^2–61^2.

1544 FREEMAN, Donald John, b. 15 Nov. 43, s. of J. O. Freeman (OR W 24). W, 57^2–61^3; Rackets Pair, 61; Tennis VI, 60, Capt., 61; Head of House. Royal Agricultural College, Cirencester. Farmer.

1545 GREGSON, Michael Julian Guy, b. 28 June 43, s. of Brig. J. H. Gregson, C.B.E., A.D.C. (OR W 17). W, 57^2–61^2. Passed Staff College Entrance Examination, 72. Capt., Royal Marines. R.M. Liaison Officer & Qualified Helicopter Instructor at Army Aviation Centre, Middle Wallop.

WALTER HAMILTON, D.Litt
Elected Headmaster in 1957

ENTRANCES IN SEPTEMBER 1957

1546 ADDIS, David, b. 10 Mar. 44, s. of the late R. G. Addis, D.S.C. (OR SH 29). SH, 57³–61². National Diploma in Agriculture. Diploma in Agricultural Extension. Work in context of Agricultural Extension overseas.

1547 BRUNYATE, Peter Hilliard, b. 16 Apr. 44, s. of the late J. W. Brunyate. SH, 57³–62¹. Trinity, Cambridge. St. Thomas's Hospital, London, M.A., M.B., B.Chir., D.Obst.R.C.O.G. Senior House Officer, Paediatrics, Royal Devon and Exeter Hospital.

1548 CLARKE, Charles Richard Astley, b. 12 Feb. 44, 3rd s. of C. A. Clarke, C.B.E., F.R.S. SH, 57³–61³. Birkenhead Technical College. Gonville & Caius, Cambridge. Guy's Hospital, London, M.A., M.B., B.Ch., M.R.C.P. (U.K.). Physician, N.H.S. *Alpine Club, Himalayan Club.* Brother, 656.

1549 LAWSON DICK, Nigel John, b. 27 Nov. 43, younger s. of the late I. A. Lawson Dick, F.R.C.S. SH, 57³–62¹. Edinburgh Univ., M.A. Sun Life of Canada Assurance Co., 65–66. John Lewis Partnership, Retail Distribution since 67. *R.O.R.C., Island Sailing Club.* Brother, 594.

1550 HANCOCK, Robert Peter Daubney, b. 21 Apr. 44, elder s. of F. W. Hancock (OR SH 23). SH, 57³–62²; Levée; Head of House. Guy's Hospital, L.R.C.P., M.R.C.S. Surgeon, British Military Hospital, Iserlohn, B.F.P.O. 24. Brother, 2008.

1551 HOLMES, Timothy John Douglas, b. 22 Jan. 44, s. of Major D. G. Holmes. SH, 57³–62²; XV, 61; XI, 62. R.M.A., Sandhurst. Capt., 1st The Queen's Dragoon Guards. Qualified Army Helicopter Pilot. Service in N. Ireland, 65–66. Aden, 66–67; as Army Pilot in B.A.O.R. with United Nations in Cyprus. Second-in-Command of Cavalry Regiment Helicopter Squadron in N. Ireland, 71–72. Now with the "Observer". Minor Counties Cricket for Dorset. Cricket & Hockey for the Army. *Cavalry Club.*

1552 JOCKELSON, Bruce Lionel Marsden, b. 28 May 44, elder s. of Major J. J. Jockelson, M.C. SH, 57³–62²; XI, 61, 62. Brother, 2299.

1553 KARNEY, Kevin Wigham, b. 12 May 44, 3rd s. of Rev. G. H. P. Karney (OR SH 23). SH, 57³–62². Trinity, Cambridge, M.A. V.S.O. as Science Teacher in Malaysia, 66–68. Société Prospection Electrique Schlumberger as Petroleum Engineer, 68–72. Shell International Petroleum Co., as Petroleum Engineer since 73. Brother, 1244.

1554 BACON, Trevor David, b. 8 Feb. 44, s. of B. D. Bacon. T, 57³–61¹; Cap, 60; Sw. VIII, 59, 60. Lloyds Bank Ltd., Rugby.

1555 COLES, Christopher John, b. 22 Feb. 44, s. of W. V. Coles. T, 57³–62². Warwick Univ., Ph.D. Research Biochemist, California, U.S.A.

1556 COOK, Paul Jeremy, b. 9 Sept. 43, elder s. of L. Cook. T, 57³–58¹.

1557 FORSTER, Peter David, b. 7 Apr. 44, younger s. of E. W. Forster. T, 57³–62³; Levée; Head of House; XV, 61, 62; H. XI, 62. University College, London, B.Sc. Columbia University Graduate School of Business, M.B.A. Kidder, Peabody & Co. Inc., Investment Bankers, New York. *Columbia University Club, N.Y.*

1558 GILBERT, John Duncan, b. 9 Apr. 44, younger s. of the late R. C. Gilbert. T, 57³–62²; Levée; Head of House; Cap, 61; H. XI, 62; State Scholarship, 61; Baines Exhibition. Trinity, Cambridge, M.A. Certificate of Competent Knowledge in Russian. Hockey Blue, 65. Information Dept., Unilever Research Laboratory, Bedford, 65–66 and in the Netherlands since 66. Head of this Dept. since 72. Represented E. Netherlands at Hockey and Indoor Hockey. *Hawks Club.* Brother, 1256.

1559 JONES, Christopher Henry, b. 28 Nov. 43, elder s. of H. Jones. T, 57³–61³; State Scholarship, 61. Jesus, Cambridge, M.A., Cert. Ed. Schoolmaster, Oundle School.

1560 LARMOUR, James Martin, b. 16 Nov. 43, s. of J. Larmour (A). T, 57³–62³. St. John's, Cambridge. Died 11 Apr. 71.

1561 MURRAY, Peter Ian, b. 30 May 43, s. of L. Murray. T, 57³–61².

1562 PHILLIMORE, Gilbert Arthur, b. 30 Dec. 43, s. of A. Phillimore. T, 57³–62¹. St. Salvator's College, St. Andrews University. Died 1970.

1563 RIGG, Alan, b. 23 Dec. 43, 4th s. of J. Rigg. T, 57^3–62^1.

1564 ROSS, Ian Kenneth Peter, b. 21 Feb. 44, s. of H. L. Ross, M.B. T, 57^3–61^3; Scholar; XV, 61. Industrial Scholarship to A.E.I. Ltd. St. John's, Cambridge.

1565 SPROSTON, John Peter, b. 21 Jan. 44, s. of J. G. H. Sproston. T, 57^3–62^2. Levée; Head of School Music, 62. Exhibition to Trinity, Cambridge. Lecturer, Dept. of Pure Mathematics, Hull Univ.

1566 WEST, Philip Anthony, b. 28 Oct. 43, s. of H. E. West. T, 57^3–62^2. Univ. of Birmingham, B.D.S., L.D.S.R.C.S. (Eng.). Commissioned R.A.F., 66. Engaged on 5-yr. Short Service Commission as Dental Surgeon, R.A.F. Present rank, F/Lt. *R.A.F. Club.*

1567 BELGRAVE, Robert Richard Dacre, b. 4 Jan. 44, s. of R. J. D. Belgrave. B, 57^3–61^2; S. VIII, 60, 61. R.M.A., Sandhurst.

1568 HAWKINS, Hilary Malcolm, b. 8 Mar. 44, elder s. of A. C. Hawkins (OR B 22). B, 57^3–62^1. Royal Academy of Music, B.Mus., L.R.A.M. Diploma of the Mozarteum, Salzburg. At present teaching music at Cranleigh School, Surrey.

1569 LEISK, Alexander Thomas, b. 24 Mar. 44, younger s. of J. Leisk, O.B.E. B, 57^3–62^1. Hatch, Mansfield & Co. Ltd., London. Wine Trade. *R.A.C.* Brother, 824.

1570 MAHMOOD, Ali Raza, b. 25 Feb. 44, elder s. of the late M. Mahmood. B, 57^3–61^3. Brother, 1871.

1571 SHAW, The Rev. Graham, b. 21 Feb. 44, s. of C. F. Shaw. B, 57^3–62^2; Scholar; Levée; Head of House; Stovin Exhibition. Scholarship to Worcester, Oxford, M.A. Cuddesdon College, Princeton Theological Seminary, U.S.A., M.Th. Rector of Winford, Somerset.

1572 TETT, Elyot Seymour, b. 12 Feb. 44, elder s. of G. S. Tett. B, 57^3–62^2. Millfield School, 62–63. F.C.I.I. Presently employed by Price Forbes Schlencker in Holland, having previously been with Price Forbes (now Sedgwick Collins Price Forbes) as Manager of Ndola office in Zambia.

1573 WALKER, Allan, b. 18 Feb. 44, s. of Dr. A. Walker. B, 57^3–62^2. Died Jan. 68.

1574 YELLIG, William Franklin, b. 12 Nov. 42, s. of H. F. Yellig. B, 57^3–60^3. St. John's, Oxford.

1575 DEHLAVI, Saidulla Khan, b. 18 May 41, elder s. of H.E. S. K. Dehlavi of Pakistan. C, 57^3–59^2. Worcester, Oxford. Brother, 1726.

1576 KENYON, Hugh Matthew, b. 18 May 44, s. of H. Kenyon. C, 57^3–62^2; Levée; Head of House. Sheffield Univ., B.Eng. James Waller & Co. Ltd.

1577 LEE, Peter Geoffrey, b. 19 July 44, 2nd s. of R. H. G. Lee. C, 57^3–62^2. Peterhouse, Cambridge. St. Thomas's Hospital, M.B., B.Chir. Brothers, 1273 & 2309.

1578 OASTLER, Michael David, b. 3 June 44, younger s. of E. G. Oastler, T.D., M.B., F.R.C.P., F.R.C.P.S. (OR C 17). C, 57^3–62^3. F.C.I.I. Chartered Loss Adjuster. R.S.P.B. Brother, 831.

1579 OWEN-THOMAS, Geoffrey John, b. 29 Jan. 44, s. of T. Thomas. C, 57^3–61^3. Aberystwyth Univ. Law. Solicitors' Articled Clerk.

1580 SMITH, Peter Jeffrey, b. 24 Apr. 44, elder s. of E. H. Smith. C 57^3–62^3; Levée; Head of House. Basil Johnson Cup 62. Jesus Cambridge, M.A. 3 yrs. as Marketing Trainee with G.D. Searle & Co. Ltd. Now Senior Product Manager with J. G. Franklin & Sons (a Division of G. D. Searle & Co. Ltd.), Manufacturers of Hospital Equipment. Hon. Secretary (and founder), Hertfordshire Chamber Orchestra.

1581 TAYLOR, William Hinde, b. 2 June 44, s. of E. E. T. Taylor. C, 57^3–61^2; XV, 60; Tennis VI, 61.

1582 BEAUMONT, Stephen Bryce, b. 27 May 44, s. of A. B. Beaumont. K, 57^3–60^3. College of Estate Management. A.R.I.C.S. European Man., Reamhurst Properties.

1583 CALDERWOOD, David Kells O'Donel, b. 25 Mar. 44, s. of Dr. W. D. Calderwood. K, 57^3–62^2; H. XI, 62. St. Andrews Univ., M.B., Ch.B., D.A. Principal in General Practice, B'Ham. Previously Registrar in Anaesthetics, Dundee

Teaching Group. Surg.-Lt., Tay Division, R.N.R.

1584 CLOUGH, Anthony Hugh Butler, b. 7 Apr. 44, elder s. of F. H. B. Clough (OR K 30). K, 57³–62². Announcer & Broadcaster, Australian Broadcasting Commission, Perth, W.A. *M.C.C.* Brother, 2119.

1585 COOPER, Christopher Simon, b. 16 Apr. 44, s. of the late C. F. Cooper. K, 57³–63². Jesus, Cambridge, M.A. Westfield College, London, Ph.D. Research Associate, Westfield College, 70–71. Research Physicist in High Energy (Elementary Particle) Physics. Presently at Univ. of Durham as Research Asst. Past Vice-Pres. of *University of London Mountaineering Club.*

1586 DRIVER, Arthur John Roberts, b. 2 Mar. 44, s. of A. J. Driver. K, 57³–62³. Sidney Sussex, Cambridge.

1587 HAMPTON, George Arthur, b. 7 Feb. 44, s. of P. G. Hampton, M.C., T.D. (OR K 29). K, 57³–62²; Levée; Head of House; Cadet Officer, 62. R.M.C., Sandhurst.

1588 HANKEY, Christopher Ceri Alers, b. 25 Mar. 44, eldest s. of the Hon. H. A. A. Hankey. C.M.G., C.V.O. (OR K 28). K, 57³–62¹; Levée; Head of House. Trinity, Cambridge, M.A. Asst. Architect. Royal Institute British Architects. Brothers, 1887 & 2819.

1589 HOWARTH, Alan Thomas, b. 11 June 44, eldest s. of T. E. B. Howarth, M.C. (OR K 28). K, 57³–62¹; Queen's Medal, 61. Major Scholarship to King's, Cambridge. Asst. to Field-Marshal Montgomery of Alamein in writing "A History of Warfare", 65–67. Editor at George Rainbird Ltd., 67. Asst. Master at Westminster School since 68.

1590 IRWIN, Robert William, b. 7 Apr. 44, s. of W. Irwin. K, 57³–61³. Died 1973.

1591 MILLER, Douglas John, b. 16 Dec. 43, s. of J. M. Miller. K, 57³–59³.

1592 STUBLEY, James Christopher Stewart, b. 2 Apr. 44, elder s. of J. R. S. Stubley. K, 57³–62¹. St. Catherine's, Cambridge. H.M. Diplomatic Service, Third Secretary, British Embassy, Tokyo, 65–69. Stockbroker at Merrill Lynch, Pierce, Fenner & Smith, S.A. Tokyo Office since 69. *Tokyo Club.* Brother, 2883.

1593 AITKEN, Roger Antony Hay, b. 11 June 44, s. of A. P. H. Aitken. M, 57³–62³; Levée; Head of House; Head of School. B.A.(Oxon.), M.Sc. Mgt., M.I.T., 72. A.C.M.A. Personal Asst. to Sir Anthony Burney, O.B.E. (OR W 23). *Royal Thames Yacht Club.*

1594A APPLEBY, Michael Ian, b. 3 Apr. 44, s. of Dr. I. B. Appleby (OR M 31). M, 57³–62²; XI, 60, 61, 62. Guy's Hospital. London Univ., M.B., B.S., L.R.C.P., M.R.C.S., D.R.C.O.G. Medical Practice at present in Durban, S. Africa. Various Hospital Appointments as S.H.O., 68–72.

1594B EATOCK-TAYLOR, William Rodney, b. 10 Jan. 61, younger s. of W. Eatock-Taylor. Sh, 57³–61³; Scholar. Minor Scholarship in Mathematics to King's, Cambridge, M.A. Stanford Univ., California, U.S.A., Ph.D. Ove Arup & Partners, Consulting Engineers, 68–70. Lecturer, University College, London, 70.

1594C KAY, Martin Robert, b. 30 Aug. 44, elder s. of G. N. Kay. M, 57³–62³; Dewar Scholarship, 62. Jesus, Cambridge, M.A., G.M.I.Mech.E. 9 yrs. (including 3 at Cambridge) with B.P. Now with High Duty Alloys Ltd., Slough. Jesus Coll., Cambridge Society.

1594D LANDALE, William Stenard, b. 25 Mar. 44, s. of S. E. A. Landale, O.B.E. M, 57³–62³. Edinburgh Univ., B.Sc. Asst. Divisional Forester, Vancouver Island, B.C. S. Calif. Film Institute Graduate. Started Film Company in Scotland. Future in Forestry & Estate Management. British Film Institute. Royal Scottish Forestry Society.

1595A WADIA, Nusli Neville, b. 15 Feb. 44, s. of N. N. Wadia of Bombay. M, 57³–61². Yale University.

1595B WILLIAMS, Vaughan Martyn Floyer, b. 23 Mar. 44, younger s. of the late A. F. Williams (OR M 09). M, 57³–62³; Levée; XXII, 62. Exeter Univ., B.A. Raw Materials Agency. *M.C.C., Travellers'.*

1596 BRYSON, Charles Roger Harrison, b. 11 Feb. 44, s. of C. C. Bryson, M.D., B.Chir. SF, 57³–62³; Levée.

1597 BUCHANAN, Roger Brade, b. 17 Mar. 44, elder s. of W. W. Buchanan. SF, 57³–61³. Middlesex Hospital Medical School, M.B., B.S.(Lond.), M.R.C.P.

(U.K.), D.M.R.T. At present Senior Registrar, Radiotherapy Dept., Middlesex Hospital, London. Chelsea Clinical Society.

1598 CLARK, Timothy Richmond Rowland (now known as T. R. Rowland Clark), b. 17 Feb. 44, s. of R. C. Rowland Clark (OR SF 22). SF, 57^3–62^2; XXII, 62. London College of Printing. Printer. *H.A.C.*

1599 EVERS, John Alexander, b. 7 Nov. 44, 3rd s. of C. R. Evers (OR SF 21). SF, 57^3–63^2; Scholar; Levée; Head of House; Sproat Leaving Exhibition. Scholarship to Trinity, Oxford, B.A., B.M., B.Ch.(Oxon.). St. Thomas's Hospital, L.R.C.P., M.R.C.S. Medicine: House Surgeon at St. Thomas's Hospital, now House Physician at St. Luke's Hospital, Guildford, Surrey. *M.C.C., Band of Brothers.* Brothers, 697, 837 & 2226.

1600 GOODBODY, Michael Hardress, b. 14 Apr. 44, s. of G. M. Goodbody (OR SF 19). SF, 57^3–62^2; Levée; Head of House; H. XI, 62. 3 yrs. 5th Royal Inniskilling Dragoon Guards. Stud Farmer. Company Director. *Cavalry Club.*

1601 HANNAY, Anthony Hewitt Scott, b. 2 May 44, s. of T. S. Hannay (OR SF 28). SF, 57^3–62^2. LL.B., Liverpool. Solicitor, Notary Public. Partner, Laces & Co., Solicitors & Notaries, Liverpool.

1602 McMULLEN, Alan Patrick, b. 1 Apr. 44, elder s. of L. McMullen (OR SF 19). SF, 57^3–61^3; Scholar; Levée; School Exhibition, 61; Scholar Trinity, Cambridge, B.A. De la Rue & Co. Ltd. & Hardley Walker (Europe) Ltd. as Management Consultant, now Commercial Division of a Shipowning Company (Common Brothers Ltd.). Brother, 2067.

1603 PAYNE, Christopher Meyrick, b. 11 Mar. 44, eldest s. of M. F. Payne. SF, 57^3–61^3; Sw. VIII, 61. Amos Tuck School, Dartmouth College, Hanover, U.S.A. M.B.A., A.C.A. Certified Public Accountant (U.S.A.). Financial Consultant, McKinsey & Company, New York City, U.S.A. *H.A.C.* Brothers, 2068 & 2538.

1604 PRESCOTT, John James, b. 9 Feb. 44, s. of G. H. Prescott. SF, 57^3–61^3. Winner of Helmsman Sailing Trophy, 61.

1605 AKED, Arthur Niel Gordon, b. 23 Jan. 44, s. of A. Aked. Sh, 57^3–61^2.

A.I.B. Investment Officer, Barclays Bank Trust Co. Ltd., Kendal.

1606 ALLISON, Joseph Philip Sloan, b. 6 Feb. 44, s. of J. W. S. Allison, D.S.C. (OR C 33). Sh, 57^3–63^1; Levée; Head of House; Head of School; Parry Leaving Exhibitioner. Churchill, Cambridge, M.A. Shipping Executive, Jardine Matheson & Co. Ltd., Hong Kong & Taiwan, 67–70. Asst. Master, Belhaven Hill School, Dunbar, E. Lothian, 70–73. *Royal Northern Yacht Club.*

1607 CATER, John Greville, b. 2 Feb. 44, s. of D. J. Cater. Sh, 57^3–62^2. Executive Director, Cater Bros. (Provs.) Ltd. *R.A.C., Bogey Golfing Society.*

1608 COWIN, Maurice John, b. 18 June 44, s. of Dr. P. J. Cowin. Sh, 57^3–62^1; Levée; XV, 61; H. XI, 62 (Capt.). 10 yrs. service in the Royal Navy, 62–73. Served in H.M.S. *Berwick,* H.M.S. *Eagle,* H.M.S. *Zulu*; and 2 yrs. service in Singapore. *R.A.C., Hurlingham.*

1609 LEWIS, Richard Samuel, b. 2 Dec. 43, elder s. of Dr. B. Lewis. Sh, 57^3–62^1.

1610 McGLASHAN, Kenneth Michael John, b. 28 Nov. 43, s. of K. McGlashan, M.R.C.S., L.R.C.P. (OR Sh 30). Sh, 57^3–62^2; Levée; Cadet Officer. M.A.(Edin.). Accountancy Profession. *Royal Scottish Pipers' Society.*

1611 MACKINTOSH, Ian Duncan Macpherson, b. 26 Mar. 44, 3rd s. of J. A. Mackintosh. Sh, 57^3–62^2; Levée; Head of House; Cap, 61; XI, 62. St. Catherine's, Oxford, B.A. Leicester Univ. School of Education, Dip. Ed. Teacher. Head of History Dept., Beaufort School, Gloucester. *Butterflies C.C.* Brother, 1157.

1612 MARKS, David Poole, b. 21 June 43, s. of J. M. Marks. Sh, 57^3–62^2; Sw. IX, 60, 61, Capt., 62.

1613 MONTAGU, Nicholas Lionel John, b. 12 Mar. 44, s. of J. E. Montagu. Sh, 57^3–62^1; Scholar; Levée; Jex-Blake Leaving Exhibition. Scholar of New College, Oxford, M.A. Lecturer in Philosophy, University of Reading since 69 (Asst. Lecturer, 66–69).

1614 ROWLEY, John Robert, b. 26 Nov. 43, younger s. of L. J. Rowley. Sh, 57^3–61^3. University of Surrey, B.Sc., M.I.C.E., C.Eng. Employed as Bridge Engineer by

W. S. Atkins & Partners of Epsom. The Concrete Society. Brother, 752.

1615 BALL, John Stewart (now Bruce-Ball, J. S.), b. 12 Mar. 44, younger s. of E. Bruce Ball, C.B.E. St, 57^3–62^2. Southampton University, B.A. Computer Programmer.

1616 CAMERON, Allan John Ewen, b. 5 Apr. 44, s. of I. L. Cameron. St, 57^3–62^3; Levée; Head of House. St. Andrews Univ., M.A. Univ. Coll. of N. Wales, Bangor, Dip. Ed. English Language Teacher, National College, Choueifat, Lebanon.

1617 CHOPRA, Romesh, b. 21 July 43, elder s. of I. S. Chopra of India. St, 57^3–58^2. St. Stephen's College, Delhi.

1618 HILTON-JONES, Gavin Bryan, b. 4 Dec. 43, eldest s. of the late B. Hilton-Jones, M.C. (OR St 32). St, 57^3–62^3. Freiburg University, Bristol University, B.A. Export Executive for Wiggins Teape Ltd., Papermakers, London since 67.

1619 HUXLEY, Charles Grant, b. 10 Feb. 44, s. of the late G. Huxley, C.M.G., M.C. (OR St 08). St, 57^3–61^3; Scholar; XI, 61. Oriel, Oxford, B.A. Ogilvy & Mather (Advertising), New York & London, 65–71. Whitbread & Co. (Brewers) since 72. *Oriental Club.*

1620 LIVINGSTON, Charles David, b. 29 Mar. 44, eldest s. of C. G. S. Livingston (OR St 34). St, 57^3–62^1; Levée; Head of House; R. VIII, 62. Pembroke, Cambridge, M.A. Sailing Blue, 67. Senior Sales Consultant, Burroughs Machines Ltd., 67–70. Now Man. Dir., Anglesey Boat Co. Ltd., Beaumaris. *Oxford & Cambridge Sailing Society, Royal Anglesey Yacht Club.*

1621 MACKAY, Ian Robert, b. 13 Apr. 44, s. of R. H. Mackay. St, 57^3–62^2; Sw. VIII, 62. Chartered Accountant.

1622A PERRIN, Michael, b. 5 May 44, s. of J. Perrin, M.D., M.R.C.P. (OR St 31). St, 57^3–62^3. Flying Scholarship. Private Pilot's Licence. Gonville & Caius, Cambridge.

1622B SEYMOUR, Paul Antony Colin, b. 12 Mar. 44, elder s. of D. R. G. Seymour. St, 57^3–61^3; Scholar; State Scholarship. Exhibition in Mathematics-with-Physics to Trinity, Cambridge, B.A., F.I.A. Actuarial Manager, Target Life

Assurance Co. Ltd., Aylesbury, Bucks. *The Debtors, Aylesbury Squash Club.*

1622C SOSNOW, Norman Martyn, b. 22 Feb. 44, s. of E. C. Sosnow. St, 57^3–61^3. Minor Scholarship in History to Christ's, Cambridge. Killed in air crash in S. Africa, 13 March 67.

1623 BROWN, Stewart Martin, b. 23 Mar. 44, s. of A. J. S. Brown. Tu, 57^3–62^2; Levée; Head of House. Diploma in Commercial Administration with Engineering at the Polytechnic, Regent Street. Now Overseas Controller, Marine & Mechanical Division, Stone Platt Industries Ltd.

1624 CAMPBELL, Peter Gordon Vere, b. 28 Dec. 43, s. of B. A. Campbell. Tu, 57^3–62^2. A.C.A. with Peat, Marwick Mitchell & Co., Cardigan, N. Wales.

1625 CLARK, Thomas Aldam, b. 28 May 44, 3rd s. of J. A. Clark, J.P. Tu, 57^3–62^1.

1626 DOULTON, Peter Donald, b. 10 June 44, 3rd s. of A. J. F. Doulton, O.B.E., T.D. Tu, 57^3–62^2; R. VIII, 62; Winner of Crick, 62. Brothers, 1332, 1635 & 2429.

1627 PROCOPÉ, Carl Fredrik Hjalmar, b. 3 July 44, younger s. of the late H. J. F. Procopé. Tu, 57^3–61^3. Nottingham University. Solicitor. Brother, 1033.

1628 ROBERTS, Michael John, b. 24 June 44, s. of H. R. Roberts. Tu, 57^3–61^3; Scholar. Major Scholarship in Classics to Queen's, Oxford, B.A. Merchant Banking, Lazard Brothers & Co. Ltd.

1629 SELKIRK, Stuart Joseph Angus, b. 16 Nov. 43, 3rd s. of W. L. Selkirk. Tu, 57^3–61^3; XV, 61. Surveyor. Brothers, 591 & 943.

1630 STEEL, Kenneth James, b. 17 Nov. 43, younger s. of Sir J. Steel, C.B.E., J.P. Tu, 57^3–62^2; Levée; Cap, 61. Selwyn, Cambridge, M.A. Farmer. Brother, 728.

1631 BARNETT, Colin Thorold, b. 12 May 44, younger s. of G. W. T. Barnett. W, 57^3–62^3. Jesus, Cambridge; Royal School of Mines, London; Colorado School of Mines, U.S.A. M.A., M.Sc., D.I.C., Ph.D. Exploration Geophysicist with Newmont Exploration Ltd., Danbury, Connecticut, U.S.A. Institution of Mining & Metallurgy. Society of Exploration Geophysicists. Brother, 887.

1632 CARTWRIGHT, John Patrick William, b. 13 June 44. W, 57^3–62^1.

1633 CHASE, Simon George, b. 19 Apr. 44, younger s. of F. J. A. Chase (A). W, 57^3–62^2. Advertising, Doyle Dane Bernbach Ltd. Brother, 1330.

1634 DAVIES, David John Alban, b. 24 Oct. 43, s. of D. H. Davies. W, 57^3–61^3.

1635 DOULTON, Angus Farre, b. 10 June 44, 2nd s. of A. J. F. Doulton, O.B.E., T.D. W, 57^3–63^1; Levée; Fives IV, 62, Capt., 63. St. Edmund Hall, Oxford, B.A. Wm. Collins Sons & Co. Ltd., 66–70. Evans Brothers (Books) Ltd. since 70. Executive Editor, U.K. Education from 73. Brothers, 1332, 1626 & 2429.

1636 GUEST, Melville Richard John, b. 18 Nov. 43, s. of the late F/Lt. E. M. C. Guest, D.F.C. W, 57^3–62^2; Levée; Head of House; XV, 60, Capt., 61; XI, 60, 61, Capt., 62; H. XI, 62; Rackets Pair, Capt., 60–62. Exhibition to Magdalen, Oxford, B.A. Sproat Exhibition. President, *Vincent's Club*, 65/66. Cricket Blue, 64–66. Rackets Blue, 65, 66. Member, H.M. Diplomatic Service since 66. *M.C.C., Travellers', Tennis & Rackets Assoc.*

1637 MEGAW, Robert Chapman, b. 30 Mar. 44, s. of Sir John Megaw. W, 57^3–61^3. A.C.A. Audit Manager, Price Waterhouse & Co., Frankfurt, A.M. *Richmond Football Club, Sport Club* 1880, *Frankfurt.*

1638 MORLEY, Nigel John, b. 4 Apr. 44, elder s. of J. G. Morley. W, 57^3–62^2; Levée; R. VIII, 62; Holder of Bigside Bags, 62; Leaving Exhibition. St. Edmund Hall, Oxford, B.A. V.S.O., Senegal, 62–63. Joined H.M. Diplomatic Service, 66. Third Secretary, Saigon, 67–69. Second Secretary, Vienna, 70–73. *M.C.C.* Brother, 2485.

ENTRANCES IN JANUARY 1958

1639 SEAMAN, Robert John Hugh, b. 19 June 44, s. of C. M. E. Seaman (A). SH, 58^1–63^2.

1640 WILSON, Charles Hugh Cobbe, b. 15 June 44, younger s. of Rev. E. R. Wilson. SH, 58^1–62^2. Brother, 58.

1641 ERWIN, Christopher Grahame, b. 13 June 44, s. of G. S. Erwin, M.D. B, 58^1–63^1. St. Edmund Hall, Oxford, M.A.

Member of Stock Exchange. Research Partner, Wise, Speke & Co., Newcastle upon Tyne.

1642 NICHOLLS, Rodney Paul Chester, b. 11 June 44, elder s. of J. C. Nicholls. B, 58^1–62^3; Scholar; Levée; Head of House. Exhibitioner of Peterhouse, Cambridge, M.A. Leeds Town Planning School, Diploma Course (not completed). Member of Sindacato Nazionale di Mercanti D'Arte Moderna, Italy. Director, "Galleria D'Arte Sant Ambrogio", Milan. Author of "Gauguin", Tudor Publishing Co., New York, 67. "Fattori", Martello, Milan, 68. *Milan Squash Club.*

1643 SMITH, Timothy Gervase Cloudesley, b. 30 June 44, younger s. of A. C. Smith, F.R.C.S. B, 58^1–62^3.

1644 WIGLEY, Peter John Gardiner, b. 7 July 44, s. of J. G. Wigley, F.R.C.S., L.R.C.P. (OR B 16). B, 58^1–62^3; Levée; XV, 62. Trinity, Cambridge, B.A. Birmingham Art College, A.M.I.C.E. Civil Engineer with British Railways, at present personal assistant to Executive Director, Systems & Operations.

1645 CRAWFORD, William James, b. 7 Sept. 44, 2nd s. of Lt.-Cdr. W. H. Crawford, R.N. (Retired). C, 58^1–62^2. Edinburgh University, B.Sc.(Agric.). In Motor Trade. General Manager, "Lothian Sports Cars"; Company Secretary, "Cadzow Cars Ltd.". Scottish Motor Trade Assoc. *Scottish Motor Racing Club.*

1646 GOVER, William John Sudmersen, b. 7 Oct. 44, s. of J. C. H. Gover. C, 58^1–62^2. Emmanuel, Cambridge, M.A. Sheffield Polytechnic, Diploma in Management Studies. M.I.C.E. Corporate (Associate) Member, British Institute of Management. Technical Sales, Redpath Dorman Long Ltd., Structural and Civil Engineers.

1647 HATCH, Henry Peter, b. 1 Mar. 41, s. of G. F. Hatch. C, 58^1–59^2. Christ's, Cambridge.

1648 JEWSON, Richard Wilson, b. 5 Aug. 44, younger s. of C. B. Jewson, F.S.A., J.P. (OR C 23). C, 58^1–62^2; Scholar; Levée. Pembroke, Cambridge, M.A., A.M.B.I.M. Director, Jewson & Sons Ltd. *Norfolk Club.* Brother, 1431.

1649 WOLFF, Michael Paul David, b. 25 Sept. 44, elder s. of E. F. W. Wolff. K, 58^1–62^3; State Scholar; Levée; Head of House. Exhibition in Modern Languages to Trinity, Cambridge. Brother, 2122.

1650 **FEARNLEY, Frederick Thomas Kneale,** b. 5 May 44, elder s. of F. J. Fearnley. M, 58^1–63^1. Worcester, Oxford. Managing Director, Omega Data Processing Services Ltd. of Manchester, Computer Consultants.

1651 **TANNETT, William Morton,** b. 3 July 44, eldest s. of O. D. Tannett. M, 58^1–62^2. A.C.A. with Peat, Marwick Mitchell & Co., London. Brothers, 2678 and Benjamin, M, 70^3–.

1652 **DICK, Robert Graham Staveley,** b. 20 July 44, s. of T. B. S. Dick, M.D., F.R.C.P. SF, 58^1–61^2. Medical Laboratory Technician.

1653 **HERIOT, John Michael,** b. 11 Sept. 44, eldest s. of A. J. Heriot, M.S., F.R.C.S. SF, 58^1–62^2. King's College, London, LL.B. Asst. Solicitor with Messrs. Baileys Shaw & Gillett, London.

1654 **BAYMAN, Jeremy Gray,** b. 2 Aug. 44, younger s. of E. G. G. Bayman. Sh, 58^1–62^3; Levée; XV, 62, H. XI, 62. C.S.M. in C.C.F., 62. Company Director. Brother, 1154.

1655 **SCIENCE, Adrian Lewis,** b. 5 Oct. 44, s. of P. Science, M.B., Ch.B., M.D. St, 58^1–62. Area Manager, Precision Data Co., Canada.

1656 **VAN DEN BERGH, Jack Malcolm Bruce,** b. 23 Sept. 44, elder s. of J. Van Den Bergh. St, 58^1–62^3; Tennis VI, 61, Capt., 62. Degree Mech. Eng., B.Sc., D.M.S. Engineer. Brother, 2087.

1657 **BERRILL, William Trevor,** b. 9 July 44, s. of T. H. Berrill, F.R.C.S. Tu, 58^1–62^3, XXII, 62. Middlesex Hospital Medical School, London University, M.B., B.S. M.R.C.P. Medical Registrar on Wessex Regional Renal Unit, St. Mary's Hospital, Portsmouth.

1658 **DRYSDALE, Peter Nicholson,** b. 26 Aug. 44, elder s. of A. M. Drysdale, LL.B., T.D. (OR Tu 29). Tu, 58^1–62^2. Royal Agricultural College, Cirencester. Insurance Broker, James M. Macalaster & Alison Ltd., Glasgow. Brother, 2420.

1659 **GEORGE, David John,** b. 7 June 44, s. of C. H. George, M.R.C.S., L.R.C.P. Tu, 58^1–62^2.

1660 **GILBERT, Peter Hamlyn,** b. 20 May 44, younger s. of B. H. Gilbert. W, 58^1–62^3. Pembroke, Cambridge. Insurance Broker and Member of Lloyd's. Brother, 652.

1661 **GREANY, The Rev. Richard Andrew Hugh,** b. 8 Aug. 44, 3rd s. of H. W. Greany, C.B.E. (OR W 14). W, 58^1–62^3; Scholar; Evers Exhibition; Fives IV, Capt., 62. Exhibition in Classics to Queen's, Oxford, B.A. College of the Resurrection, Mirfield, 67–69. Curate of St. Oswald's, Hartlepool, 69–72. Curate of All Saints, Clifton with St. Mary's, Tyndalls Park, Diocese of Bristol since 72. Brother, 146.

1662 **STIRRUP, Jeremy Newsome,** b. 8 June 44, younger s. of T. C. Stirrup, M.C. W, 58^1–62^2; Sw. IX, 60. Brother, 509.

ENTRANCES IN MAY 1958

1663 **ADDIS, Robert Cameron,** b. 23 Oct. 44, 4th s. of H. E. Sir W. Addis, K.B.E., C.M.G. (OR SH 16). SH, 58^2–62^3; Cap, 62. Sir John Cass College & College of Distributive Trades, both part-time. Retail Jeweller's Diploma (Distinction). Jeweller. *Tonbridge R.F.C.* Brothers, R. T. Addis and 152 & 1367.

1664 **BOWEN, Christopher Richard Croasdaile,** b. 7 Oct. 44, s. of the late C. J. C. Bowen (OR SH 27). SH, 58^2–62^3; Dewar Travelling Scholarship. Short Service Commission, 4th Royal Tank Regt. Computer Marketing, I.B.M. *Army & Navy.*

1665 **BUENO de MESQUITA, Nicholas David,** b. 26 Oct. 44, elder s. of D. M. Bueno de Mesquita, Ph.D. SH, 58^2–63^1; Levée; Head of House. Corpus Christi, Oxford, B.A. University of Essex. Research Executive, Public Attitude Survey, 67–70. Research Executive, Makrotest Ltd. since 70. Brother, 2626.

1666 **GRILLO, Richard James,** b. 10 Aug. 44, 2nd s. of B. F. Grillo. SH, 58^2–62^3; Cap, 62. B.Sc., College of Estate Management, London University. A.R.I.C.S. Messrs. Debenham & Nightingale Page, Kingston upon Thames. Brother, 1852.

1667 **HOLDEN, Peter Edward,** b. 25 Sept. 44, s. of A. Holden. SH, 58^2–62^3; XV, 62. Middlesex Hospital Medical

School, M.B., B.S., M.R.C.P. Medicine. At present at St. Richard's Hospital, Chichester.

1668 GREEN, Peter Warwick Brunt, b. 17 Sept. 44, younger s. of J. W. Green, L.R.C.P., M.R.C.S. B, 58^2–62^2. Middlesex Hospital, M.B., B.S. Surgical Unit, St. Mary's Hospital, London. Brother, 1427.

1669 PURSSELL, Roger William, b. 22 Dec. 44, younger s. of F. J. Purssell. C, 58^2–62^3. Brother, 161.

1670 BENDER, Michael Philip, b. 2nd Dec. 44, s. of H. L. Bender. K, 58^2–60^1.

1671 FEHR, Basil James, b. 25 Oct. 44, younger s. of B. H. F. Fehr (OR K 26). K, 58^2–62^3. Royal Academy of Music, Vienna Academy for Music. Bachelor of Music (London), A.R.C.M. Asst. Music Master at Frensham Heights till 72. Institute of Education, studying for Dip. Ed., London University. Brother, 1278.

1672 SMITH, George Norman (now known as Phipson, George Norman), b. 14 Aug. 44, younger s. of N. H. W. Smith. K, 58^2–62^3. University of Bristol, B.Sc., Cert.Ed. Head of Department at Woodberry Down Comprehensive School, London. *Ski Club of Gt. Britain.* Brother, 1078.

1673 BERKELEY, David James, b. 7 Aug. 44, elder s. of A. W. G. Berkeley (OR M 34). M, 58^2–62^2; Tennis VI, 61, 62. Chartered Accountant with E. D. & F. Man, Commodity Merchants. Brother, 2150.

1674 SLOTOVER, Robert John Elliot, b. 5 Oct. 44, elder s. of M. L. Slotover, F.R.C.S. M, 58^2–62^3. East Anglia University.

1675 SUTTON, Peter Braham, b. 5 Sept. 44, younger s. of H. B. Sutton, M.D. SF, 58^2–62^2. Associate Member of the Institute of Chartered Shipbrokers. Estate Agent. *Ashridge G.C., The Whaddon Chase, False Bay Rugby Club, Cape Town.*

1676 VOSPER, Nicholas Charles, b. 14 July, 44, elder s. of J. L. Vosper. SF, 58^2–62^3. Clare, Cambridge, B.A. Institute of Education, London, P.G.C.E. Asst. Lecturer in Liberal Studies (P/T Student Counsellor), Harrow College of F.E. Brother, Robert James, SF, 69^2–.

1677 WESTON, Jonathan Peter, b. 25 Feb. 45, 3rd s. of W. G. Weston, C.M.G. SF, 58^2–62^3. Brothers, 360 & 1303.

1678 BAKER, John Hugh, b. 28 Aug. 44, s. of R. W. Baker. Sh, 58^2–62^2. Cap, 61. Chartered Accountant. Articled, 63–67. Commerce, 68–70. World Travel, 70–72. Restaurateur since 73.

1679 CANDLER, Nicholas John Pycock, b. 5 Sept. 44, elder s. of H. J. P. Candler, T.D. Sh, 58^2–62^2. Newport College of Science & Technology. Solicitor. Partner in Messrs. Gabb & Co. Officer in T. & A.V.R. 35 (SM) Signal Regt. *Cavalry Club.* Brother, 1910.

1680 DODSON, Christopher John, b. 24 Dec. 44, younger s. of J. H. Dodson. Sh, 58^2–62^3. Exhibition in Classics. Trinity Hall, Cambridge, M.A., LL.B. Asst. Solicitor, Bevan Hancock & Co., Bristol, 70–72. Asst. Solicitor, Addleshaw Sons & Latham, Manchester from 73.

1681 HAGENBACH, Keith Macdonald, b. 24 Oct. 44, s. of T. M. Hagenbach. Sh, 58^2–63^1; Levée. Branch Manager. Lever Brothers & Associates, London.

1682 KENNEDY, Robert Keith Milroy, b 14 Sept 44, younger s. of R. K. I. Kennedy, M.B., B.Chir., M.R.C.S., L.R.C.P. Sh, 58^2–62^3; Senior Scholarship, 61; Levée. Scholarship in Classics to Clare, Cambridge. Lansil Ltd., Lancaster. Brother, 1685.

1683 LEWIS, Richard Nicholas Baynggs, b. 10 Sept. 44, s. of Lt.-Col. R. G. Lewis, T.D. Sh, 58^2–62^3.

1684 MACKAY, Reay, b. 21 Sept. 44, s. of R. Mackay. Sh, 58^2–62^3.

1685 KENNEDY, Michael Kirk Inches, b. 14 Sept. 44, elder s. of R. K. I. Kennedy, M.B., B.Chir., M.R.C.S., L.R.C.P. St, 58^2–62^3; Scholar; Levée. Scholarship in Classics. Trinity Hall, Cambridge, B.A. Practising Barrister. *Pegasus.* Brother, 1682.

1686 VINEY, Mark Nigel Merriam, b. 12 Sept. 44, elder s. of L. W. M. Viney (OR K 32). St, 58^2–62^2; Tennis VI, 61. A.C.A. Merchant Banking. Brother, 2479.

1687 DAVIES, Christopher Mark, b. 24 Aug. 44, elder s. of R. S. Davies. Tu, 58^2–62^3. R.A.C., Cirencester. N.D.A. Farming. Brother, 1924.

1688 LEWIS, William Timothy Gwynder, b. 27 Oct. 44, younger s. of G. E. Lewis. Tu, 58^2–62^3; XV, 61, 62; XXII, 62. Banking Diploma Examination, Part I. Banker, Lloyds Bank Ltd.

1689 MATHESON, Robert Maitland, b. 5 Jan. 45, elder s. of N. S. Matheson. Tu, 58^2–63^1; Cap, 62. Oriel, Oxford. Brother, 1998.

1690 PENNOCK, David Roderick Michael, b. 27 Dec. 44, s. of R. W. Pennock. W, 58^2–63^2; Levée; Head of House; Cap, 61; Fives IV, 63. Merton, Oxford. Cranfield School of Management, Bedford, M.B.A. Shell International Chemical Co., 67–70. Merchant Banker, Singer & Friedlander Ltd. since 71. *United Universities Club.*

1691 SIMMS, Christopher Michael, b. 15 Nov. 44, younger s. of G. O. Simms, D.D. W, 58^2–. Trinity College, Dublin, B.A., Ph.D. Psychologist, Educational Research Centre, Dublin. Brother, 1500.

ENTRANCES IN SEPTEMBER 1958

1692 BEVAN, William Anthony, b. 3 Feb. 45, younger s. of T. R. A. Bevan. SH, 58^3–63^2. Brother, 919.

1693 BROWN, Simon John, b. 14 Apr. 45, 2nd s. of L. W. Brown, O.B.E. SH, 58^3–63^3; Levée; Head of House; S. VIII, 63. F/Sgt. R.A.F., C.C.F., 63. Peterhouse, Cambridge, M.A. Univ. Coll. of Wales, Bangor, Dip.Ed. Pilot, B.E.A. *Alpine Club.* Brother, 1065.

1694 DENISON-CROSS, Jonathan Cherney, b. 12 Sept. 45, s. of E. R. Denison-Cross. SH, 58^3–63^2.

1695 FLEMMING, William Haden, b. 30 Nov. 45, younger s. of C. W. Flemming, C.B.E., M.D., M.Ch., F.R.C.S. (OR SH 15). SH, 58^3–63^3. Trinity, Oxford. Brother, 800.

1696 FRASER-CAMPBELL, James Ronald, b. 1 Dec. 44, elder s. of E. J. Fraser-Campbell, T.D. (OR SH 32). SH, 58^3–63^2; XV, 62; XXII, 62. Asst. Accountant, Wm. Teacher & Sons Ltd., Scotch Whisky Distillers. *West of Scotland R.F.C.* Brother, William Patrick, SH, 67^3–71^3.

1697 LEBURN, Hugh Gilmour, b. 3 July 45, elder s. of W. G. Leburn, T.D., M.P. SH, 58^3–63^3. M.A.(Edin.). Post

Grad. Certificate of Primary Education, Leicester. Teacher at Chisenhale Primary School, London, 69–72. N.U.T. Brother, 2431.

1698 MARR, David Courtenay, b. 19 Jan. 45, s. of D. P. Marr. SH, 58^3–63^2; Scholar; Levée; Head of House; Head of School Music, 63. Member of the National Youth Orchestra, 62; C.C.F.; R.A.F. Scholarship, 62. Scholarship Maths & Physics to Trinity, Cambridge, M.A., Ph.D. Prize Research Fellow, Trinity, Cambridge. Senior Research Fellow, King's College, 68–72. Staff Scientist at Medical Research Council Laboratory of Molecular Biology, Cambridge since 72. British Biophysical Society (Committee Member).

1699 MAXWELL, Terence David, b. 17 Mar. 45, younger s. of Col. A. T. Maxwell, T.D. (OR SH 18). SH, 58^3–63^2; Cap, 61. McGill University, Montreal. Banker. *Hurlingham.* Brother, 605.

1700 ORLEBAR, Christopher John Dugmore, b. 4 Feb. 45, s. of Col. J. H. R. Orlebar. O.B.E. SH, 58^3–63^2; S. VIII, 60, 61, 62, Capt., 63. Southampton University. College of Air Training, Hamble, 67–69. B.O.A.C., 69, Airline Pilot; currently 2nd Pilot on VC10s. Flight Navigator, Asst. Flying Instructor, Technical Committee of the Guild of Air Pilots & Air Navigators. Currently reading for an external LL.B. at London University. Involved in recruiting for B.O.A.C. *Royal Commonwealth Society, Guild of Air Pilots and Air Navigators.*

1701 RIPMAN, Giles Michael Armstrong, b. 26 Feb. 45, eldest s. of H. A. Ripman, F.R.C.S., F.R.C.O.G. (OR SH 31). SH, 58^3–62^2; S. VIII, 61, 62. Royal Agricultural College, Cirencester. Shipping Manager (Australian) with J. A. Peden Ltd., International Bloodstock Shippers, Windsor. Brothers, 2735, 2949 & James Jervis Hugo, SH, 72^3–.

1702 WALSH, William Nicolas Francis, b. 6 Apr. 45, s. of Rev. T. L. Walsh. SH, 58^3–63^2; Levée. Trinity, Oxford, M.A. Asst. Master, Windsor Grammar School, 67–69. Asst. Manager, Oxford Playhouse, The University Theatre since 69. Commissioned Royal Armoured Corps (T. & A.V.R.), 66. Reservist, 13/18th Royal Hussars since 68.

1703 ANSCOMBE, Hugh Allen, b. 30 May 45, s. of L. D. Anscombe. T, 58^3–

63³; Levée; Head of House; Leaving Exhibition. Emmanuel, Cambridge, B.A. Negotiating Officer, British Steel Corporation. Personnel Officer, Systems Analyst, I.C.I.

1704 ARMS, William Yeo, b. 11 Apr. 45, s. of H. S. Arms, D.Phil. T, 58³–63²; Levée; Head of School; Head of House; Leaving Exhibition, 62; State Scholarship. Scholar of Balliol, Oxford. Lecturer, School of Applied Science, Sussex Univ.

1705 BEEBY, Michael James, b. 7 Dec. 44, s. of E. V. Beeby. T, 58³–62³; Cap, 62. Charing Cross Hospital.

1706 BOOTH, Stephen Nicholas, b. 26 Dec. 44, elder s. of H. Booth. T, 58³–63². Birmingham University, M.B., Ch.B., M.R.C.P. Medicine, Research Fellow in Dept. of Experimental Pathology, University of Birmingham. Brother, 2345.

1707 COULTAS, Stephen John, b. 2 Aug. 45, younger s. of G. Coultas. T, 58³–63³; Sproat Leaving Exhibition. Demyship at Magdalen, Oxford, B.A., M.I. Struct.E. Ove Arup & Partners, Consulting Structural Engineers, 67–71. Studying Architecture at University College, London.

1708 DARBY, Michael Douglas, b. 2 Sept. 44, s. of A. D. Darby. T, 58³–63¹.

1709 GRAY, Nigel Paul, b. 27 Apr. 45, s. of P. H. Gray, T.D. (OR T 25). T, 58³–63²; XI, 62, 63; Rackets Pair, 62, Capt., 63. Royal Veterinary College, London, Bachelor of Veterinary Medicine, M.R.C.V.S. Formerly private practice in Ontario, Canada. Now in Gloucester.

1710 JONES, Philip Ioan Ellis, b. 20 Jan. 45, s. of D. J. Jones, M.B., B.Ch. T, 58³–63². Minor Foundationer; Cap, 62. London Hospital Medical School, M.B., B.S.(London), L.R.C.P., M.R.C.S., D.Obst.R.C.O.G., D.A.

1711 MACKENZIE, Peter Thomas, b. 21 Dec. 44, younger s. of T. H. Mackenzie. T, 58³–62³.

1712 MORGAN, David Orrin, b. 29 Apr. 45, elder s. of D. V. Morgan. T, 58³–62³.

1713 ROLAND, Andrew Osborne, b. 23 Apr. elder s. of P. E. Roland, M.B., B.S., F.R.C.S. T, 58³–62³. Scholarship in History to Merton, Oxford, B.A. Diploma

in Personnel Management, Aston University. A.M.I.P.M. Deputy Personnel Officer at Hammersmith Hospital. *Civil Service Riding Club.*

1714 RUSSELL, Ian Archibald, b. 4 Apr. 45, elder s. of A. J. Russell. T, 58³–62³. St. Thomas's Hospital. Brother, 2191.

1715 STANWORTH, Robin Howard, b. 9 Apr. 45, s. of J. E. Stanworth, D.Sc. T, 58³–63¹; Benn Entrance Scholarship; Senior Scholarship, 61; Levée. L.S.E.

1716 WIGGINS, William John, b. 5 Jan. 45, s. of H. J. Wiggins (OR T 19). T, 58³–63. Guy's Hospital (Univ. of London), M.B., B.S., D.Obst.R.C.O.G., M.R.C.S., L.R.C.P., D.Ch. Paediatrician to Canadian Forces Europe at Lahr, W. Germany.

1717 ANDERSON, Robert John Bancroft, b. 14 Apr. 45, younger s. of P. G. Anderson (OR B 32). B, 58³–63²; H. XI, 63. C.A.(Scotland). Accountant with Allied Chemical Canada Ltd., Montreal. Brother, 1424.

1718 BARSTOW, Christopher John, b. 20 Dec. 44, 2nd s. of Capt. G. B. Barstow, R.N. (retd.) B, 58³–62³. Brothers, 1341 & 2358.

1719 CLAYTON, Richard Stephen, b. 18 Dec. 44, s. of S. G. Clayton, M.D., M.S., F.R.C.S., F.R.C.O.G. B, 58³–63²; Levée; Head of House. King's College, London, B.Sc. Army Officer. Captain, Royal Horse Artillery.

1720 GOLDING, Stephen Robert, b. 21 Mar. 45, younger s. of L. A. Golding. B, 58³–62³.

1721 HAYLEY, James Brian, b. 24 Aug. 45, s. of P. W. Hayley, F.C.A. B, 58³–62¹.

1722 HODGKINSON, George Howard, b. 4 Mar. 45, s. of F. H. Hodgkinson. B, 58³–62³. Voluntary Service overseas (Punjab, India, teaching Maths), 63. St. John's, Oxford, B.A. Solicitor, 70. Asst. Solicitor, Coward Chance, London, 70–72. Legal Adviser with B.P. Tanker Co. Ltd. since 72. *Little Ship Club, Island Cruising Club, Salcombe.*

1723 HORSBURGH, Michael Robert, b. 18 Apr. 45, 2nd s. of I. H. Horsburgh (OR SH 28). B, 58³–63². C.S.M., C.C.F., 63. R.M.A., Sandhurst. Passed Stock Exchange Membership Exam. Stockbroker with Hoare & Co., Govett Ltd. *Lansdowne Club.*

1724 HOWARTH, Jeremy John Alan, b. 8 July 45, s. of J. M. E. Howarth. B, 58^3–63^3; Levée; Head of House. Peterhouse, Cambridge. A.C.A., Dip. INSEAD. Peat, Marwick Mitchell & Co., 67–71. Rowntree-Mackintosh, European Division, since 72. *R.A.C., M.C.C.*

1725 LEONARD, James Vivian, b. 12 Dec. 44, elder s. of the Rt. Rev. G. D. Leonard, Bishop of Truro. B, 58^3–63^1; Levée; Head of House; Baines Leaving Exhibition. Exhibition to Pembroke, Cambridge. St. Thomas's Hospital Medical School, M.B., B.Chir., M.R.C.P. Various Hospital Appointments. Registrar at the Hospital for Sick Children, London. Brother, 2031.

1726 DEHLAVI, Jarnil Ahmed Khan, b. 18 Aug. 44, younger s. of H.E. S. K. Dehlavi of Pakistan. C, 58^3–62^2. Brasenose, Oxford. Brother, 1575.

1727 DRUMMOND, Robert Malcolm, b. 6 June 45, s. of G. M. D. Drummond. C, 58^3–63^1; Peter Mayo Award, 63. Queen's College, St. Andrews Univ.

1728 HALL, David Francis, b. 7 Apr. 45, 3rd s. of G. S. Hall, M.D., F.R.C.P. C, 58^3–63^2. Solicitor. Practised as Solicitor in private practice. Joined Legal Service of European Commission in Brussels and, as International Civil Servant, participated in negotiations for accession of the U.K. to the European Communities. Now advising in London on legal aspects of European Communities, at present with Linklater & Paines. Brothers, 1526 & 1975.

1729 HARVEY, Andrew Shearer, b. 17 Jan. 45, younger s. of J. L. Harvey. C, 58^3–63^2; Levée; XI, 62, 63; H. XI, 62, Capt., 63; Golf Team, 60–63, Capt., 62–63. Member of the Institute of Chartered Shipbrokers. Shipbroker, Houlder Brothers & Co. Ltd., London. *Worplesdon G.C.* Brother, 678.

1730 LEWIS, Antony Peter, b. 18 Feb. 45, s. of A. A. G. Lewis, M.D., F.R.C.P. C, 58^3–63^1; Levée. Trinity Hall, Cambridge. St. Thomas's Hospital Medical School, M.B., B.Chir., D.C.H. General Practitioner. Association for Child Psychology & Psychiatry.

1731 McVITIE, David Robison Craig, b. 19 Mar. 45, s. of G. E. McVitie,

M.B., Ch.B. C, 58^3–63^2. Edinburgh Univ., M.B., B.S. Maryfield Hospital, Dundee.

1732 MARR, Alastair Stuart Munro, b. 14 Sept. 45, s. of the late D. M. Marr, M.B.E. C, 58^3–63^3; Levée; Head of House; XV, 62, 63; XXII, 62 & 63; Rackets Pair, Capt., 63; Tennis, 1st Pair in Youll Cup, 62, 2nd Pair 63. A.C.A. Banker.

1733 MEHTA, Rozal Jal, b. 12 Feb. 45, elder s. of J. H. Mehta. C, 58^3–62^3.

1734 STOREY, Christopher Thomas, b. 13 Feb. 45, s. of L. H. Storey. C, 58^3–62^2. Chartered Accountant, A. E. Smith Coggins (Holdings) Ltd., Liverpool.

1735 BENTON, Timothy John, b. 21 June 45, s. of K. C. Benton. K, 58^3–63^1; Sw. IX, 61, 62. Exhibition to Clare, Cambridge.

1736 GODLEY, The Hon. Christopher John, b. 1 Jan. 45, s. of J. R. Godley, D.Sc., 3rd Baron Kilbracken. K, 58^3–63^2. Reading University, B.Sc.(Agr.). Agriculturalist, I.C.I. Agricultural Division.

1737 HANKEY, Robin Noel Alers, b. 16 Dec. 44, s. of Lt.-Cdr. O. C. A. Hankey R.N.V.S.R. (OR K 26). K, 58^3–63^1; Scholar; Levée; Head of House. Exhibition, 62 and Scholarship, 63 in Classics to Balliol, Oxford, B.A. St. Andrews Univ., M.Litt. School Teacher, Civil Servant and now University Lecturer.

1738 POLLARD, John Patrick, b. 9 Feb. 45, elder s. of S. C. Pollard. K, 58^3–63^1. Gonville & Caius, Cambridge, M.A. St. Thomas's Hospital Medical School, M.B., B.Chir. Surgeon. Surgical Registrar, Wolverhampton Group of Hospitals. Brother, 2214.

1739 STIRLING, Geoffrey Warren, b. 27 Nov. 44, s. of G. A. C. Stirling (OR K 24). K, 58^3–62^2. A.C.A. Stockbroker. With Storey Bros. & Pim, Chartered Accountants of Dublin, 62–68. Goodbody & Webb, Stockbrokers of Dublin since 68. *University Club, Dublin.*

1740 THOMPSON, Andrew Arnold, b. 23 Feb. 45, youngest s. of H. R. Thompson, M.B., B.Ch., F.R.C.S. (OR K 21). K, 58^3–62^2; Tennis VI, 61. Section Manager in Carpets Dept., John Lewis & Co. Ltd., London. Brothers, 1135 & 1446.

1741 **ABRAHAMIAN, Shahen Vahan,**
b. 11 Sept. 45, younger s. of V. M.
Abrahamian. M, 58³–63¹; Leaving Exhibition. History Scholarship to Peterhouse,
Cambridge. Brother, 1136.

1742 **ADAMS, John Sherard,** b. 3
Jan. 45, elder s. of C. E. M. Adams. M,
58³–62².

1743 **BRAY, Richard Winston Atter-
ton,** b. 10 Apr. 45, s. of W. Bray. M, 58³–
63²; Scholar; Levée; Head of House; XI,
61, 62, Capt., 63; Rackets Pair, 63.
Scholarship to Corpus Christi, Oxford,
B.A. Barrister, 70. *M.C.C.*

1744 **BURTON, Peter Harman,** b. 24
Feb. 45, s. of H. Burton, B.M., F.R.C.S.E.,
M.R.C.O.G. M, 58³–62².

1745 **MARCUSE, Hugh Douglas,** b. 19
Mar. 45, s. of the late W. D. Marcuse.
M, 58³–63¹; Levée; Head of House; XV,
62. Scholarship in Classics to Pembroke,
Oxford, M.A., Cert.Ed. Asst. Master,
Stowe School since 68.

1746 **MOUSLEY, David John,** b. 20
Feb. 45, elder s. of J. A. Mousley. M,
58³–63². Bristol University, B.Sc. Engineering. Logging oil wells in Algeria.

1747 **ROBERTS, Peter William Den-
by,** b. 1 Aug. 45, younger s. of the late
W. D. Roberts (OR M 23). M, 58³–63².
Royal Agricultural College, Cirencester.
A.R.I.C.S. Partner in firm of Land Agents,
Messrs. Davis & Bowring, Kirkby Lons-
dale. Brother, 782.

1748 **RUMBELLOW, James William,**
b. 14 Jan. 45, s. of J. F. Rumbellow,
O.B.E. M, 58³–62³; Scholar. St. John's,
Cambridge, M.A. Standard and Chartered
Bank. *Junior Carlton.*

1749 **CHISWELL-JONES, Jonathan,** b.
17 Nov. 44, younger s. of H. Chiswell-
Jones, O.B.E. SF, 58³–63³; Levée;
Rackets Pair, 63; Capt. Trinity, Oxford,
B.A. Head of English Dept., Ashfold
School, 68–72. Student at West Surrey
College of Art. Plans to be a Studio
Potter.

1750 **HASE, James Richard,** b. 26 Feb.
45, s. of Group Capt. R. W. Hase, R.A.F.
SF, 58³–62³.

1751 **JENKINS, David James Richmond,** b. 13 July 45, elder s. of C. R.
Jenkins, F.F.A.R.C.S., D.A. SF, 58³–64¹;

Scholar; Levée; Head of House; Jex-
Blake Exhibition. Classical Scholarship to
Trinity, Cambridge. Schoolmaster, Brad-
field College. Brother, 2228.

1752 **JOSEPH, Michael Antony,** b. 4
Nov. 44, elder s. of H. Joseph. SF, 58³–
62³. Licence es Sciences Economiques at
the University of Neuchâtel, Switzerland.
General Manager of a subsidiary of an
English Company, located in Belgium,
offering services to computer users.

1753 **McMULLEN, David Shaun,** b. 27
Apr. 45, younger s. of Lt.-Col. R. P.
McMullen, D.S.O., M.B.E., T.D., J.P.
(OR SF 27). SF, 58³–63³; Levée; Head of
School; Head of House. Clare, Cambridge.
Chartered Accountant. Merchant Banker.
Brother, 1300.

1754 **PEARSON, Nigel Hetley Allan,**
b. 1 Jan. 45, elder s. of M. Pearson, M.C.
(OR SF 29). SF, 58³–63²; Levée; XV, 62;
S. VIII, 60–63. Fitzwilliam, Cambridge,
A.C.A., I.C.L. Brothers, 2129 & 2744.

1755 **RINTOUL, Peter,** b. 10 Sept. 45,
s. of A. Rintoul. SF, 58³–. Chartered
Accountant. Investment Manager. Associate Director, Gartmore Investment Ltd.
Western Club, Glasgow, Prestwick G.C.

1756 **SAMPSON, Alastair Hugh,** b. 25
Sept. 44, s. of H. Sampson. SF, 58³–62²;
Music Scholar. Music Scholarship to
Corpus Christi, Oxford.

1757 **SCORAH, John Baddeley,** b. 10
Apr. 45, s. of F. C. Scorah, LL.B. SF,
58³–62³.

1758 **BRUCE, Jonathan James Gavin,**
b. 10 Feb. 45, s. of the late J. A. G. Bruce
(A). Sh, 58³–63²; Levée; Head of House.
Exhibition to Pembroke, Cambridge.
School Leaving Exhibition.

1759 **CLEMENT-JONES,   Nicholas
Trevor,** b. 12 Mar. 45, elder s. of M. L.
Clement-Jones (OR Sh 31). Sh, 58³–62³.
University of Newcastle upon Tyne,
B.Sc.

1760 **DIXON, John Michael Fraser,** b.
12 July 45, elder s. of J. E. Dixon. Sh,
58³–62². McGill University, Canada.
Personnel Officer, Lowndes Lambert Ltd.
of London. Brother, 2131.

1761 **DURIE, Alistair John Lindsay,** b.
25 Nov. 44, s. of A. C. Durie. Sh, 58³–63¹.
Christ Church, Oxford, B.A., A.C.A.

Chartered Accountant (Manager) with Binder, Hamlyn & Co., London. *Junior Carlton.*

1762 HARRIS, Milton Henry, b. 4 Apr. 45, youngest s. of M. W. A. Harris. Sh, 58³–63². Shuttleworth Agric. College, Cert.Ag. Self-employed Pig Farmer. Brothers, 117 & 567.

1763 NOBLE, William Francis, b. 14 Mar. 45, 2nd s. of Col. Sir A. Noble, K.B.E., D.S.O., T.D., D.L. Sh, 58³–62³. Diploma of Institute of Health Service Administrators. Hospital Management, Central Middlesex Hospital, London.

1764 ZUCKERMAN, Paul Sebastian, b. 22 June 45, s. of Lord Zuckerman, O.M., K.C.B., F.R.S., M.D., D.Sc. Sh, 58³–. Trinity, Cambridge, B.A. Postgraduate Diploma in Agricultural Studies. University of Reading, 71–73, for Ph.D. Agricultural Economist employed by the International Institute of Tropical Agriculture, Nigeria. *Brooks's.*

1765 ALBAN-DAVIES, John Lewis, b. 10 Aug. 45, 2nd s. of J. S. Alban-Davies. St, 58³–63²; Cadet Pair, 60. Aberystwyth. Brother, 1779.

1766 BOYES, Nicholas John Bailey, b. 22 June 45, eldest s. of E. S. Boyes (OR St 29). St, 58³–63³; Levée; Head of House. Brothers, 2408 & 2855.

1767 DENBY, Charles Frederick, b. 4 Mar. 45, elder s. of C. H. Denby. St, 58³–62³. College of Estate Management, London University, B.Sc., A.R.I.C.S. Director of Permanent Land Ltd., a property investment and development company. *R.A.C.* Brother, 2248.

1768 LING, Simon James, b. 24 Jan. 45, eldest s. of P. H. L. Ling, T.D. St, 58³–63². Queens', Cambridge, M.A., A.C.A. With Turquands Barton Mayhew of London. W. B. Peat Medal for 1st place in the Final Part II exam. of the Institute of Chartered Accountants, 70.

1769 MORISON, John Lowson, b. 6 May 45, s. of J. M. Morison (OR W 17). St, 58³–62³; Cap, 61; XV, 62. East of Scotland College of Agriculture, Edinburgh. Diploma in Agriculture. Farmer.

1770 PIKE, Terence Oliver, b. 16 Nov. 44, s. of O. N. Pike. St, 58³–63²; Levée; Head of House; Tennis VI, 63. Clare, Cambridge, B.A. Contract Sales Engineer, Chicago Bridge Ltd.

1771 STEWART, John Berkeley, b. 7 May 45, younger s. of R. D. Stewart. St, 58³–63². Cap, 62. St. Andrews University. Chartered Accountant with Cooper Bros., London (temporarily at Arusha, Tanzania). *Bath Club.*

1772 TRACY, Charles Peter Gervais, b. 23 Oct. 45, younger s. of Rear-Admiral H. G. H. Tracy, D.S.C., R.N. St, 58³–63²; Scholar. State Scholarship, 61. Trinity, Cambridge, B.A. Hambros Bank Ltd., 67–72. Drayton Corporation Ltd. since 72. Investment Manager. Brother, 1226.

1773 WEBB, George Richard, b. 2 Sept. 44, elder s. of the late Wing-Cdr. G. F. H. Webb, D.F.C. (OR St 28). St, 58³–62³. Queen's Univ., Belfast, B.Sc. Slough Tech., Postgraduate Business Studies. M.I.Q.A. Sales Manager, W. J. Baker & Sons of Birmingham, manufacturers of stainless steel for hotel trade and reproduction silverware. Member of Birmingham Chamber of Commerce.

1774 WILLANS, William Jolyon, b. 17 Apr. 45, s. of J. L. Willans, T.D. (A). St, 58³–63². Lt. Regular Army.

1775 BENNETT, Simon Piers, b. 1 Feb. 45, s. of P. R. Bennett. Tu, 58³–62³; Scholar. King's, Cambridge, M.A. President of Chetwynd Society. Senior English Master & Master i/c Rugby, Trent College. Housemaster, Hanbury Junior. Head of Drama, Malvern College from Jan. 74. *United Oxford & Cambridge Club, Somerset Stragglers & Notts R.F.C.*

1776 DAVIDSON, Anthony William, b. 5 May 45, s. of Lt.-Col. G. H. Davidson. Tu, 58³–63²; Levée; Head of House. St. Bartholomew's Hospital Medical College, M.B., B.S. Doctor. Junior Registrar, Charing Cross Hospital.

1777 HARDING, David Bruce, b. 24 Dec. 44, s. of H. A. Harding, C.M.G. (OR Tu 30). Tu, 58³–63²; Sailing VI, 63. Imperial College, London, B.Sc., A.C.G.I. Joined I.C.I., Plastics Division, Welwyn Garden City, 67 as trainee engineer. Transferred to Dumfries factory, 68 as Development Engineer. *Solway Yacht Club*; Capt., *City & Guilds College Hockey Club*, 62.

1778 MACDONALD, Ian Nigel, b. 23 May 45, s. of G. S. Macdonald. Tu, 58³–63². British Institute in Paris (3-month course). University of Essex, B.A. Initially Concorde Programme Officer with British

Aircraft Corporation (Commercial Aircraft Division). Now awaiting industrial rehabilitation following serious motor car accident. *R.A.C., B.A.R.C.*

1779 ALBAN-DAVIES, James David, b. 10 Aug. 45, eldest s. of J. S. Alban-Davies. W, 58³–63²; Cap, 62; Cadet Officer, 63. Brother, 1765.

1780 COLE, Barry Martin, b. 24 Oct. 44, youngest s. of T. Cole. W, 58³–61²; Sw. IX, 61. Brothers, 916 & 1331.

1781 INGLIS, Robert John Murray, b. 6 Feb. 45, younger s. of Brig. W. M. Inglis, C.B.E. (OR W 28). W, 58³–63²; Levée; Head of House; XV, 62; XXII, 62; Senior Athletics Cup, 62. Brother, 1334.

1782 KENNY, Charles Michael, b. 10 Jan. 45, s. of T. E. Kenny. W, 58³–63². Chartered Accountant.

1783 NEAME, Stuart Fraser Beale, b. 14 Jan. 45, 2nd s. of L. B. Neame. W, 58³–62³; Scholar. Pembroke, Cambridge, M.A. Senior Systems Engineer and Salesman with I.B.M. (U.K.) Ltd., 66–72. Company Secretary, Shepherd Neame Ltd. (Brewers) since 72. Brothers, 550 & 1933.

1784 PEARSON, Christopher Michael, b. 19 Jan. 45, s. of R. S. B. Pearson, D.M., F.R.C.P. W, 58³–63²; R. VIII, 61–63; Holder of Bigside Bags, 61, 62.

1785 RICHARDSON, Michael Jeremy, b. 14 July 45, s. of P. A. Richardson (OR W 31). W, 58³–63²; R. VIII, 62. R.A.F. College, Cranwell. Churchill, Cambridge. R.A.F. Wings, 66. Airline Transport Pilot's Licence, 72. Company Pilot. *Ski Club of Great Britain.*

1786 WILLIAMS, Peter Martin, b. 29 Oct. 44, s. of Rev. J. C. Williams. W, 58³–63¹; Scholar; Levée; Stovin Leaving Exhibition. Open Scholarship in Mathematics to King's, Cambridge.

ENTRANCES IN JANUARY 1959

1787 de PAULA, Julian Frederic Jervis, b. 14 Sept. 45, s. of H. F. M. de Paula, T.D. (OR B 27). B, 59¹–63³; Cap, 63. A.C.A. Senior Accountant, Shampur Chemical Co. Ltd., Abadan, Iran, 69–71. Clarks Ltd. (Shoemakers), Administration Manager, Plymouth Factory, 71–72. *United Service & Royal Aero Club.*

1788 HAWKSLEY, Thomas Joseph, b. 5 Aug. 45, younger s. of Dr. J. C. Hawksley. B, 59¹–63³. St. John's, Cambridge, M.A. National Standard Co. Ltd., Kidderminster since 67.

1789 WALLER, Gary Peter Antony, b. 24 June 45, s. of J. Waller. B, 59¹–63³; R. VIII, 62. University of Lancaster, B.A. Governor, George Green's School, Poplar, 69–70. Governor, Isaac Newton School, Kensington since 71. Asst. Editor, "Planned Savings" Magazine, 68–70. Executive with F. J. Lyons Public Relations Ltd. since 72. Chairman of the Conservative Research Group PEST, 68–70. Member of the Bow Group. Vice-Chrmn. of the Nat. Assoc. of Conservative Graduates, 70–73. Chairman, Newham South Conservative Assoc. since 71.

1790 LEE WARNER, David Hugh, b. 11 Oct. 45, younger grandson of the late E. H. Lee Warner (OR C 00). C, 59¹–63². Graduate of International Accountants Society, Chicago. N.C.R. International. Manager, EDP Sales & Support, N.C.R. Do Brasil. *Junior Carlton Club.* Brother, 1509.

1791 ROBERTSON, Christopher John Guy, b. 28 Aug. 45, s. of C. H. W. Robertson (OR C 23). C, 59¹–63³. London University, Postgraduate Certificate in Education, Academic Diploma in Education. Presently studying for M.Phil. in Education. Birmingham Univ., B.Sc. Teacher/Lecturer. *M.C.C.*

1792 CLEMINSON, Robin Beauclerk, b. 23 June 45, 2nd s. of J. A. S. Cleminson (OR K 28). K, 59¹–62².

1793 EVANS, Michael James Llewellyn, b. 1 Sept. 45, younger s. of A. L. L. Evans, B.C.L. (OR K 20). K, 59¹–63³. Died 9 Apr. 1970. Brother, 1378.

1794 CAMPBELL, Robert George, b. 3 Aug. 45, younger s. of W. H. D. Campbell, F.C.A. M, 59¹–63³; Levée; Head of House; Cap, 62; R. VIII, 62, 63; Winner of Mile, ½ Mile & Steeplechase, 62. A.C.A. Partner in a firm of Agricultural Contracting Specialists. Brother, 1052.

1795 DOVE, Anthony Charles, b. 22 July 45, s. of I. M. Dove, M.B., Ch.B. M, 59¹–63²; Scholar; Levée; State Scholarship, 62. St. John's, Cambridge. Solicitor.

1796 **LUPTON, Stephen Martineau,** b. 23 July 45, s. of C. M. Lupton. M, 59^1–62^2; Fives IV, 62. Three years in Accountancy (Messrs. Peat, Marwick, Mitchell). At present banking with Midland Bank Ltd., 2 yrs. Wetherby, 4 yrs. York, now at Scunthorpe. Institute of Bankers. Junior Chamber of Commerce.

1797 **MACINNES, Ian Malcolm,** b. 23 July 45, 3rd s. of K. L. MacInnes, C.B.E., J.P., D.L. (OR M 19). M, 59^1–63^3; XV, 63. Trinity, Cambridge. Brothers, 263 & 745.

1798 **COLE, Peter Max,** b. 5 Aug. 45, s. of R. A. Cole. SF, 59^1–63^3; Levée. Open Exhibition in Modern Languages to Lincoln, Oxford.

1799 **STRAUSS, James Martin,** b. 18 Sept. 45, s. of the Rt. Hon. Lord Conesford, Q.C. (OR SF 06). SF, 59^1–64^1. Cap 63, H. XI, 64. Christ Church, Oxford, M.A. King's College, London, Dip. Ed. Schoolmaster since 68.

1800 **BADENOCH, Ian James Forster,** b. 24 July 45, elder s. of J. Badenoch, D.M. M.R.C.P. (OR Sh 33). Sh, 59^1–63^3; Levée. Demyship in Classics to Magdalen, Oxford, B.A. Barrister, Lincoln's Inn. Brother, 2935.

1801 **de FREITAS, Graham Anthony,** b. 20 July 45, eldest s. of Rt. Hon. Sir G. de Freitas, K.C.M.G., M.P. Sh, 59^1–; Scholar. Clare, Cambridge, B.A. Michigan State Univ., M.Sc.(Agric. Econ.). At present at University of Utah. After Cambridge, spent two years in Africa working for the United Nations Development Programme. Brother, 2545.

1802 **FOX, Andrew Staley,** b. 25 June 45, youngest s. of H. S. Fox. Sh, 59^1–63^1. A.C.A. Asst. to Group Accountant of a Motor Vehicle Distributor. *Royal Mid-Surrey G.C.* Brother, 704.

1803 **FORSYTH, Michael John Alexander,** b. 15 May 45, s. of C. J. Forsyth. St, 59^1–63^2. Farmer.

1804 **PETTERSON, John Walter,** b. 5 June 45, s. of S. W. Petterson. St, 59^1–63^2. Sheffield University, B.Eng., M.I.C.E. Civil Engineer, Freeman Fox & Partners. *R.C.Y.C.*

1805 **FISHER, Steven Anthony,** b. 20 July 45, s. of W. Fisher. Tu, 59^1–63^3.

1806 **INGLEBY, James Richard,** b. 20 Mar. 45, 2nd s. of J. A. Ingleby, J.P. Tu, 59^1–63^2; Levée; XV, 61, 62, Capt., 62. Royal Agricultural College, Cirencester, XV, 64, 65, 66, Capt., 65. A.R.I.C.S. Committee of Scottish Landowners Federation (Regional), N. of Scotland Grassland Society and The Sussex Cattle Society. Partner with J. J. & T. Ingleby farming 800 acres. *Royal Findhorn Yacht Club.* Brothers, 1228 & 1960.

1807 **McCALL, John Stewart,** b. 4 Sept. 45, s. of J. D. McCall. Tu, 59^1–63^3; Levée; Head of House; XV, 61, 62, Capt., 63; XXII, 62, 63; H. XI, 62, 63; Junior Athletics Champion, 61. Churchill, Cambridge. Bar, Middle. Temple. City, Mining Finance. Consolidated Gold Fields Ltd. *Harlequins, Caledonian Club.*

1808 **MILLER, Nicholas John,** b. 12 Jan. 46, younger s. of C. C. Miller. Tu, 59^1–62^3. Brother, 1324.

1809 **WESSEL, Andrew Stephen,** b. 14 July 45, youngest s. of W. P. Wessel. Tu, 59^1–63^2. Imperial College, London, B.Sc. (Eng.). Harpsichord Maker.

1810 **GRAHAM, Richard Anthony,** b. 28 Aug. 45, eldest s. of H. Graham. W, 59^1–63^3. Pembroke, Oxford. Brother, 2727.

1811 **WALKER, Nicholas Ewen,** b. 22 July 45, younger s. of D. D. Walker (OR K 19). W, 59^1–63^3; Levée; Head of House; R. VIII, 62. Pembroke, Cambridge.

ENTRANCES IN MAY 1959

1812 **BAKER, David Ascroft Clutton,** b. 10 Oct. 45, s. of Lt.-Cdr. J. C. Baker, D.S.C., R.N. (Retired). SH, 59^2–64^1. Travel Operator, Swans Tours.

1813 **BLACKBURN, Simon John,** b. 13 Nov. 45, s. of H. Blackburn. SH, 59^2–64^1; Levée; Head of House. C.S.M., 64. Worcester, Oxford.

1814 **CHESTERTON, Michael Sidney,** b. 7 Oct. 45, elder s. of Sir O. S. Chesterton, M.C. (OR SH 26). SH, 59^2–64^2. Irish Guards, 64–69. Short Service Commission. Insurance Broker with Fenchurch Group of Brokers Ltd. *Hurlingham.*

1815 **LUNN, Denis Christopher Carter,** b. 21 Sept. 45, younger s. of C. D. Lunn. SH, 59^2–63^3. École de Commerce, Neuchâtel. A.C.A., 70. Group Accountant

& Company Secretary of Michael Birch Group Ltd. of Tunbridge Wells since 70. Worshipful Company of Gold & Silver Wyre Drawers. Brother, 1505.

1816 LEATHERS, The Hon. Jeremy Baxter, b. 11 Apr. 46, younger s. of the Viscount Leathers. B, 59^2–64^1; Levée; Head of House. Trinity College, Dublin, B.B.S. Ocean Steam Ship Co. Ltd. Brother, 1189.

1817 WILLIAMSON, Andrew George, b. 18 Dec. 45, s. of G. I. Williamson. B, 59^2–63^3. Pembroke, Oxford, B.A. Studying for D.Phil. 73. Director of Antiquities, Sultanate of Oman, Arabia.

1818 HAWKINS, Thomas Reeve, b. 31 Jan. 46, younger s. of J. H. Hawkins. C, 59^2–64^1; Levée; Head of House; XV, 63. Wye College, B.Sc. Farming. *Farmers' Club.*

1819 MORRISON, John Cochrane, b. 2 Nov. 45, elder s. of A. Morrison, L.D.S. C, 59^2–63^2. St. Bartholomew's Hospital Medical School. M.B., B.S. General Practitioner, Health Centre, Worcester. Brother, 2373.

1820 TAGGART, Redmond David Hind, b. 28 Sept. 45, s. of R. T. Taggart, V.R.D. (OR C 17). C, 59^2–63^2. Strathclyde University, B.Sc. Civil Engineer, working with Murray & Roberts (Roads and Earthworks). Elansfontein, nr. Johannesburg, S.A. (working for Corporate Membership of the I.C.E.).

1821 BAYLISS, Christopher Richard Butler, b. Oct. 45, s. of R. I. S. Bayliss (OR K 30). K, 59^2–63^3; Levée; Head of House; Sw. IX, 62, 63. Clare, Cambridge, M.A., M.B., B.Chir. Middlesex Hospital Medical School, L.R.C.P., M.R.C.S., D.Obst.R.C.O.G. Doctor of Medicine.

1822 CHARLES, William Peter Barry, b. 12 Oct. 45, s. of B. Charles, D.Sc. K, 59^2–63^2.

1823 EDGE, John Greer, b. 12 Aug. 45, s. of P. N. G. Edge, D.S.C. K, 59^2–63^3.

1824 HANLEY, Jeremy James, b. 17 Nov. 45, younger s. of late J. H. Hanley. K, 59^2–63^2. A.C.A. Chartered Accountant. Tutor in Jersey, C.I.

1825 HALFORD, Stephen Edgar, b. 22 Sept. 45, s. of W. R. Halford. M, 59^2–63^3.

1826 PAUL, James Robert, b. 25 Sept. 45, s. of Major R. G. Paul, T.D. (OR M 26). M, 59^2–63^3; XI, 63. Clare, Cambridge, B.A. Manchester Business School (Diploma in Business Administration). Marley Buildings Ltd., Guildford since 68.

1827 SCOTT, James Patrick, b. 18 Aug. 45, younger s. of M. M. Scott. M, 59^2–63^2. Trinity College, Dublin. Brother, 1454.

1828 EARDLEY, Jonathan Wilmot, b. 12 July 45, s. of E. D. Eardley. SF, 59^2–63^2; XXII, 63. Computer Management and Traffic Consultancy with GEC-Elliott Traffic Automation Ltd. Ex-Merchant Navy Officer.

1829 HARPER GOW, Maxwell Eric, b. 1 Aug. 45, elder s. of L. M. Harper Gow, M.B.E. (OR SF 32). SF, 59^2–63^2. C.A. Brother, Leonard Paul, SF, 69^2–.

1830 HOWKINS, John Anthony, b. 3 Aug. 45, younger s. of Col. W. A. Howkins, T.D. (OR T 23). SF, 59^2–63^3. Keele University Architectural Association. B.A., A.A.(Diploma). Journalist, currently T.V. Editor, "Time Out"; Books Editor, "Time Out"; Director, "Time Out" Ltd. Brother, 1383.

1831 EASTWOOD, Gordon Dinsdale, b. 1 Nov. 45, s. of J. V. Eastwood, F.C.A. Sh, 59^2–64^2.

1832 KENNEDY, Ian Glen, b. 31 Aug. 45, s. of A. M. Kennedy. Sh, 59^2–63^3; Cap, 63. Classical Scholar of Magdalene, Cambridge, B.A. Courtauld Institute of Art, London University, M.A. Worked in Prints & Drawings Dept. of Christie, Manson & Woods, London, 68–70. Visited the main art centres in Europe, 70–72. Published articles in various art journals. *Eaton G.C.*

1833 PARKINSON, Kenneth John, b. 1 Sept. 45, elder s. of the late E. Parkinson. Sh, 59^2–61^2; Fives IV, 61.

1834 PARRY, David John Hugh, b. 19 Aug. 45, elder s. of the late A. W. Parry, J.P. Sh, 59^2–63^2. Agriculture N.C.A. Agricultural Contractor. Brother, 2244.

1835 SNELL, Christopher John, b. 18 Sept. 45, younger s. of W. Snell. Sh, 59^2–63^2. Brother, 1018.

1836 WREFORD-BROWN, Christopher Louis, b. 10 Aug. 45, elder s. of

L. C. Wreford-Brown (OR SF 33). Sh, 59²–63²; Cap, 62. Britannia Royal Naval College, Dartmouth. Lt., R.N. Navigating Officer, H.M.S. *Repulse*. Brother, 2588.

1837 LANKESTER, Andrew Morgan, b. 6 Oct. 45, s. of H. A. Lankester. St, 59²–63³. Trinity Hall, Cambridge, M.A. Systems Engineer, I.B.M. U.K. Ltd.

1838 LAWTHER, Ian Charles Mask-rey, b. 10 Oct. 45, s. of T. H. B. Lawther. St, 59²–64². C.S.M., C.C.F., 64. Insurance Broker.

1839 PLUMB, John Martin, b. 10 Aug. 45, s. of C. C. Plumb. St, 59²–64²; Levée; Head of House. Westminster Medical School, M.B., B.S. Doctor.

1840 RUNAGALL, Ronald Beverley, b. 14 Oct. 45, s. of W. F. Runagall. St, 59²–64². École Hôtelière, Lausanne, Switzerland.

1841 WALTON, David Anthony, b. 28 Jan. 46, s. of A. J. Walton, M.B., F.R.C.S. (OR Tu 27). Tu, 59²–63³; Cap, 63. London Hospital Medical School. A.C.A. Chartered Accountants, Audit Group Manager. *Woodford R.F.C.*

1842 WHITEHOUSE, Simon Andrew, b. 30 Nov. 45, younger s. of H. A. Whitehouse, M.R.C.S., L.R.C.P. Tu, 59²–63³. Medical College of St. Bartholomew's Hospital, M.B., B.S., M.R.C.S., L.R.C.P. General Practice.

1843 WILDBLOOD,   Christopher Michael Garside, b. 9 Oct. 45, s. of R. G. Wildblood. Tu, 59²–64¹; Levée; Head of School; Head of House; R. VIII, 63; Holder of Bigside Bags, 63–64; Baines Leaving Exhibition. Corpus Christi, Cambridge, M.A. Edward S. Prior Prize, 67. Brancusi Travel Fellowship, 68. Diploma in Architecture, 70. Registered Architect, 71. Joined Colin St. John Wilson, M.A., F.R.I.B.A., 70.

1844 HEYMAN, Timothy Robert, b. 9 Feb. 46, s. of H. W. Heyman. W, 59²–63³; Scholar; Levée; XV, 63. Classical Scholarship to Balliol, Oxford, B.A. Massachusetts Institute of Technology, M.S. International Adviser, N.M. Rothschild & Sons Ltd. Harkness Fellow, 68–70.

ENTRANCES IN SEPTEMBER 1959

1845 BAILEY, Roger Charles, b. 12 Aug. 46, younger s. of D. Bailey. SH, 59³–

R.S.W.W.—13

64³. Exhibition to Queens', Cambridge, B.A. Wiggins Teape Ltd.

1846 BRADBY, Edward Hugh, b. 6 Nov. 45, 2nd s. of E. L. Bradby (OR SH 20). SH, 59³–64¹; Levée. Classical Scholarship to New College, Oxford, B.A. Volunteer working for Operation Mobilisation, doing Christian Evangelistic work in India. Brothers, 1236 & 2625.

1847 CORBETT, Patrick Hugh Spens, b. 12 Aug. 46, eldest s. of Capt. H. A. Corbett, D.S.O., D.S.C., R.N. SH, 59³–64³; Scholar; XXII, 64. Corpus Christi, Cambridge.

1848 CRAIG, Adam James, b. 28 Jan. 46, s. of the late F. B. Craig (OR SH 16). SH, 59³–64².

1849 DEAN, Paul, b. 29 May 46, s. of R. W. Dean. SH, 59³–64²; Scholar; Levée; Head of House; XI, 63, 64, Capt., 64. Scholarship to Trinity, Cambridge, B.A., M.A., D.Phil. Oxford, 73. Research Scientist, Department of Experimental Psychology, Oxford.

1850 GARDHAM, Martin Phelps, b. 8 Apr. 46, s. of Brig. H. P. Gardham, C.B.E. SH, 59³–63²; Senior Scholarship, 62; School Leaving Exhibition. Scholarship to Wadham, Oxford, B.A. Post graduate student at Oxford, studying for B.Litt. in English Literation, 71.

1851 GREEN, Michael James, b. 26 Feb. 46, younger s. of Major J. M. S. Green, M.B.E., T.D. (OR SH 20). SH, 59³–64¹. University College, Oxford. Laming Fellow, Queen's, Oxford, 72–73. Lloyds and Bolsa International Bank Ltd. (London, Brazil, Japan). Brother, 604.

1852 GRILLO, Harry Bernard Noel, b. 28 Dec. 45, younger s. of G. F. Grillo. SH, 59³–63³. Trinity, Cambridge, M.A., Dip. Arch. Registered Architect, Asst. Architect for Central Bank of India, Ahmedabad, India. British Museum New Extension, London. Sultan's Armed Forces H.Q., Muscat. Griston Prison, Norfolk. Now working on housing. Cambridge Union. Brother, 1666.

1853 GUEDALLA, Martin Lionel, b. 23 Apr. 46, younger s. of F. B. Guedalla (OR SH 18). SH, 59³–64²; Cap, 63.

1854 HARGREAVES-ALLEN, Peter Meredith, b. 30 Mar. 46, s. of Brig. K. Hargreaves, C.B.E., T.D., D.L., Lord

Lieutenant. SH, 59^3–64^3. Open Exhibition to University College, Oxford, B.A. London School of Economics. Merchant Bank Executive with Slater Walker Ltd., London. Worshipful Company of Cloth Workers. *Queen's Club*.

1855 **LYDE, Richard Lionel,** b. 8 Oct. 45, younger s. of L. G. Lyde (OR K 18). SH, 59^3–62^2. Brother, 1406.

1856 **THOMAS, Anthony,** b. 16 Mar. 46, elder s. of B. A. Thomas. SH, 59^3–63^3; XV, 63. Solicitor. Birmingham Law Society. *Solihull R.U.F.C.* Brother, 2183.

1857 **APPLEYARD, Michael,** b. 28 Feb. 46, younger s. of A. N. Appleyard. Tu, 59^3–64^1. Churchill, Cambridge.

1858 **CAPRON, David Cooper,** b. 8 Oct. 45, s. of F. J. Capron. T, 59^3–64^2. Barclays Bank Ltd., 64–66. Thomas Howell Selfe & Co., Chartered Loss Adjusters, 67–71. Resident at Salisbury & Wells Theological College since 71. Reading for the Certificate of Theology (Southampton University). To be made Deacon in June 74 and ordained Priest in June 75 (C. of E.).

1859 **CARTWRIGHT, Lester Dennis,** b. 16 Feb. 46, s. of F. Cartwright. T, 59^3–63^3. Jesus, Cambridge.

1860 **EDMUNDSON, Henry Norfolk,** b. 2 Mar. 46, younger s. of D. Edmundson. T, 59^3–64^1; Levée; Head of House; Head of School Music. A.E.I. Scholarship, Pembroke, Cambridge, B.A. College Scholarship. Bristol Univ., completing M.Sc. in pure mathematics. Employed by Schlumberger Ltd., Oilfield Exploration Consultants. *Alpine Club*. Brother, 1253.

1861 **HEWITT, Thomas Anthony George,** b. 19 Jan. 46, s. of J. Hewitt. T, 59^3–64^1; Chess VI, 62–64. University of St. Andrews, B.Sc. Taught in Malta & England. Now training for Catholic Priesthood in Ireland, at Milltown Institute, Dublin.

1862 **HOLMAN, Derek John,** b. 6 May, 46, younger s. of D. L. Holman. T, 59^3–64^1. Liverpool University, B.Sc. Computer Programming, International Computers Ltd.

1863 **KYLE, Robert John Blacker,** b. 25 June 46, s. of J. B. Kyle, L.D.S. T, 59^3–63^2; S. VIII, 60–62.

1864 **MASON, Peter John,** b. 28 June 46, younger s. of C. A. Mason. T, 59^3–64^3; Levée; Head of House. Jesus, Cambridge.

1865 **WADKIN, James William,** b. 18 Mar. 47, s. of W. Wadkin. T, 59^3–64^3. Queens', Cambridge, M.A. Mechanical Engineer.

1866 **WHITEHEAD, Ian Roger,** b. 17 Oct. 45, s. of E. A. Whitehead. T, 59^3–64^3. Gonville & Caius, Cambridge, M.A., Cert.Ed. Asst. Biologist, Malvern College, Worcs., 69–72. Now Head of Biology Dept., Annie Holgate Technical Grammar School, Hucknall, Notts.

1867 **de BOURSAC, Guy,** b. 21 Jan. 46, elder s. of V. de Boursac (OR W 28). B, 59^3–63^3; Scholar; R. VIII, 62–63. Open Scholarship in Mod. Languages to Christ Church, Oxford, B.A. Diploma in Management Studies (Distinction), Diploma in Marketing. 5 yrs. with British European Airways. *Achilles Club*. Brothers, 2361 & 2914.

1868 **FAIRCLOUGH, Paul John,** b. 27 May 46, eldest s. of Col. J. Fairclough, O.B.E. (OR B 29). B, 59^3–64^2. St. Bartholomew's Hospital Medical College, M.B., B.S., D.Obst.R.C.O.G. General Medical Practitioner, nr. Salisbury, Wilts. Brothers, 2110 & 3204.

1869 **FREEMAN, Clyde John,** b. 1 Jan. 46, 2nd s. of E. H. R. Freeman (OR B 17). B, 59^3–63^2; Sw. IX, 62, 63. Guildford College of Law. Solicitor. Partner in Freeman Daly & Jacks, Darlington. Brother, 2805.

1870 **KEMP, Timothy John Reginald,** b. 26 Feb. 46, s. of J. A. Kemp. B, 59^3–63^2.

1871 **MAHMOOD, Zulfiquar-A-Ali Haqubool,** b. 7 Jan. 46, youngest s. of the late M. Mahmood. B, 59^3–63^3. Brother, 1570.

1872 **NIMMO, Walter Gilbert Mearns,** b. 10 June 46, 3rd s. of J. A. D. Nimmo (OR B 20). B, 59^3–64^2; Cap, 42. Emmanuel, Cambridge, M.A. C.A. With Messrs. Thomson McLintock & Co., Edinburgh, 72. Now Budget Control Accountant, Abbott Laboratories Ltd., Queenborough, Kent. *Edinburgh Sports Club*. Brothers, 1116, 1268 & 2364.

1873 **SALMON, Jonathan Greville Isodore,** b. 31 July, 46, s. of S. I. Salmon. B, 59^3–64^1. Sorbonne, Paris.

1874 **SMITH, Nicholas Ronald Rathbone,** b. 13 May 46, eldest s. of R. H. Smith, LL.B. B, 59^3–63^3. Notary Public, partner in the firm of De Pinna, Scorer & John Venn. Liveryman of the Scriveners Company. Member of the Institute of Linguists.

1875 **WIGLEY, David Christopher Gardiner,** b. 20 May 46, s. of E. S. G. Wigley (OR B 27). B, 59^3–64^2. Durham University, B.A. Systems Analyst for Hospitals Dept., Cape Province, South Africa.

1876 **WOODALL, Richard Corbet,** b. 18 Sept. 45, s. of J. D. C. Woodall, T.D. (OR K 26). B, 59^3–63^3.

1877 **BOURNE, Richard Alfred,** b. 7 May 46, younger s. of H. R. Bourne (OR C 19). C, 59^3–63^3. Pembroke, Cambridge. Brother, 243.

1878 **DEAN, John Antony Farquhar,** b. 21 May 46, s. of M. J. Dean. C, 59^3–64^2; XXII, 64. Trinity, Cambridge, B.A. Massachusetts Institute of Technology, S.M. Schick Razor Co., Milford, Connecticut, U.S.A. *Royal Wimbledon G.C.*

1879 **HADMAN, Robert John,** b. 21 May 46, younger s. of the late G. Hadman. C, 59^3–64^3; Cap, 64. St. John's, Oxford.

1880 **PUGSLEY, Ian Lutley,** b. 21 June 46, s. of R. L. Pugsley. C, 59^3–64^2. Solicitor. Partner, Messrs. Hole Pugsley, Tiverton, Devon.

1881 **REISNER, Colin,** b. 22 Aug. 46, younger s. of A. Reisner. C, 59^3–64^2; Levée; Head of House. Trinity, Cambridge (Senior Exhibition). St. Bartholomew's Hospital, M.A., M.B., B.Chir. Medicine, Senior House Physician.

1882 **SMITH, Michael John Gordon,** b. 31 Aug. 46, s. of J. M. A. Smith. C, 59^3–64^2; Scholar; Jex-Blake Exhibition. Scholarship to King's, Cambridge, B.A. Civil Service Dept. of Education & Science. *Caledonian.*

1883 **STAUNTON, Hugh Christopher Thorpe,** b. 19 Sept. 46, eldest s. of H. N. T. Staunton. C, 59^3–64^3. Articles with Stone & Co., Solicitors, Leicester, 66–71. Solicitor, 71. Asst. Solicitor with Frere Cholmeley & Co., Paris, 72–73 and London since 73. Brothers, Nigel Howard, W, 67^3–72^2 & Robin Mark, W, 70^3–.

1884 **SUTHERLAND, Ian Alexander,** b. 20 Dec. 45, s. of the late P. C. Sutherland. C, 59^3–64^2; Levée; XV, 63. C.S.M. in C.C.F., 64. Parry Leaving Exhibition. Bristol University, B.Sc., Ph.D. Research Fellow, George C. Marshall Space Flight Centre, N.A.S.A. M.I.Mech.E.

1885 **WAREHAM, Frederick Giles,** b. 26 Apr. 46, elder s. of F. C. Wareham. K, 59^3–64^3; XV, 63, 64; H. XI, 64; Athletic Colours, 64. Southampton University, LL.B. City of Westminster Assurance Co. Ltd.

1886 **ALLAN, Anthony Gordon Bruce,** b. 30 June 46, s. of W. B. Allan, M.B., B.S. K, 59^3–64^1; Senior Scholarship, 62; Leaving Exhibition. Scholarship to Corpus Christi, Oxford, B.A. Post-Graduate in Journalism, University of Indiana, U.S.A. Station Asst., B.B.C. Radio Durham. Asst. Editor, "Honey" Magazine. Staff Writer, "Réalités" Magazine, Paris.

1887 **HANKEY, Maurice Peregrine Alers,** b. 30 Aug. 45, 2nd s. of the Hon. H. A. A. Hankey, C.M.G., C.V.O. (OR K 28). K, 59^3–63^2; Scholar, Levée; Head of House. Classical Scholarship to New College, Oxford. Brothers, 1588 & 2819.

1888 **HEAGERTY, Richard James,** b. 29 Apr. 46, younger s. of W. B. Heagerty. K, 59^3–63^3; Scholar; Leaving Exhibition. King's, Cambridge. Brother, 1279.

1889 **LOMAX, Robert Anthony,** b. 29 Apr. 46, elder s. of H. R. Lomax, M.R.C.S., L.R.C.P. K, 59^3–64^2. Guy's Hospital Medical School, M.B., B.S., M.R.C.S., L.R.C.P. Medical Publisher, Blackwell Scientific Publications, Oxford. Brother, Ian Graham, K, 67^3–.

1890 **McNAIR, Nigel John Edward,** b. 8 Oct. 45, s. of Brig. J. K. McNair, C.B.E. (OR K 07). K, 59^3–63^2.

1891 **MORRIS, Paul Masterman,** b. 20 June 46, younger s. of E. M. Morris. K, 59^3–63^3. Trinity Hall, Cambridge.

1892 **MORROW, James Hunter,** b. 29 May 46, s. of I. T. Morrow. K, 59^3–63^2. Cambridge College of Arts & Technology. Journalist. Financial Journalist, "Exchange Telegraph" since 72. National Union of Journalists.

1893 **SERGEANT, Jonathan James Holroyd,** b. 25 Nov. 45, younger s. of

J. H. Sergeant, M.C. K, 59^3–63^2; Capt. of Fencing. Brighton College of Art. Courtauld Institute, London University. Free University of Berlin. B.A. Lecturer, College of Further Education.

1894   CAIRNS, David Nigel Hooper, b. 17 Dec. 45, s. of A. C. H. Cairns. M, 59^3–64^1; Levée; Head of House. St. John's, Oxford, B.A. Associate of the Institute of Physics. Research Scientist, Central Electricity Research Laboratories.

1895   DOW, Kenneth, b. 15 Feb. 46, s. of J. D. Dow, M.C., M.D., F.F.R. M, 59^3–64^3. Exeter Univ., B.A. Bar, Lincoln's Inn. Barrister.

1896   DYDE, Nicholas Hewitt, b. 25 Dec. 45, younger s. of J. H. Dyde, O.B.E. M, 59^3–63^2; XI, 62; H. XI, 63. Agricultural College, Cirencester. Brother, 257.

1897   GADNEY, John, b. 26 Dec. 45, 2nd s. of B. C. Gadney. M, 59^3–64^2. St. Catharine's, Cambridge, M.A. Whatton School, University of Pennsylvania, U.S.A., M.B.A. Financial Management. *East India & Sports Club, Kandahar Ski Club.*

1898   HURST, Henry Robert, b. 1 Aug. 46, s. of Lt.-Col. T. R. Hurst. M, 59^3–63^3.

1899   JESSEL, Daniel Philip, b. 13 May 46, s. of P. A. Jessel. M, 59^3–64^2. Balliol, Oxford.

1900   BLACKSTONE, Timothy Vaughan, b. 21 May 46, younger s. of G. V. Blackstone, C.B.E., G.M. SF, 59^3–64^3. Pembroke, Oxford.

1901   BLAIR, Alan Hatchard, b. 26 Mar. 46, 3rd s. of Sir A. C. Blair, K.C.V.O., LL.B., T.D. SF, 59^3–63^3. University of St. Andrews, M.A. University of Edinburgh, LL.B. W.S. Solicitor with Dundas & Wilson, C.S., Davidson & Syme, W.S. Brothers, 932, 1146 & 2224.

1902   BROMLEY, Charles Roderick Keith, b. 5 Jan. 46, elder s. of F. K. Bromley (OR SF 25). SF, 59^3–60^3.

1903   CAVAGHAN, Dennis Edgar, b. 22 Dec. 45, 3rd s. of H. D. Cavaghan. SF, 59^3–63^2; XI, 62. 1-yr. short course at Cirencester Royal College of Agriculture. Now reading for Bachelor of Theology at St. John's College, Nottingham, leading to ordination into Church of England. Student. Brother, 854.

1904   HUNTING, Richard Hugh, b. 30 July 46, elder s. of C. P. M. Hunting, T.D. (OR SF 24). SF, 59^3–64^3; Levée; Head of House. Sheffield University, B.Eng. Manchester Business School, M.B.A. Headquarters Planning Manager, Hunting Group of Companies. *Travellers' Club.* Brother, 2393.

1905   MACLACHLAN, Alan Michael Moncrieffe, b. 28 Feb. 46, s. of W. P. G. Maclachlan. SF, 59^3–64^2; Levée; Head of School; Head of House; XV, 63, Capt., 64. University of Edinburgh, LL.B. Due to qualify as Solicitor in 73. Solicitor's Articled Clerk.

1906   PREST, Richard Jullion, b. 2 May 46, s. of E. C. Prest, D.F.C. (OR SF 34). SF, 59^3–63^3. Bristol University, B.Sc., C.Eng. Associate Member of the Institute of Marine Engineers. 5-yr. Short Service Commission in R.N., Lt. Service in H.M.S. *Eagle,* 68–70. H.M.S. *London,* 70–72. Now with National & Grindlays Bank Ltd., London, E.C.3. *Army & Navy Club, Royal Naval Sailing Association.*

1907   TEMPLE, Tom Guy Eccles, b. 30 Apr. 46, s. of J. M. Temple, J.P., M.P. SF, 59^3–64^2; Tennis VI, 62–64, Capt., 63; Rackets Pair, 64. College of William & Mary, Williamsburg, Virginia, B.A. Ecôle de Neûchatel, Switzerland. Insurance. Lloyd's Broker. Robt. Bradford Hobbs Savill Ltd. *Bath Club.*

1908   WRIGHT, David Harold, b. 6 Feb. 46, elder s. of T. Wright, M.D., B.Ch., D.C.H. SF, 59^3–63^3. St. Thomas's Hospital Medical School, M.B., B.S. Late prosector in Anatomy, St. Thomas's Hospital Medical School. At present Senior House Officer in Surgery, Crawley Hospital. Late Sherwood Rangers Yeomanry (T.A.). *Cavalry Club.* Brother, 2156.

1909   BOON, Christopher John, b. 19 Apr. 46, elder s. of J. T. Boon. Sh, 59^3–64^2. York Univ.

1910   CANDLER, Anthony Hugh Barton, youngest s. of H. J. P. Candler, T.D. Sh, 59^3–64^1. Clare, Cambridge, B.A. Partner in firm of Solicitors. *Abergavenny Hockey Club* (Hon. Sec.). Brother, 1679.

1911   EDWARDS, Anthony William Charlton, b. 13 Mar. 46, youngest s. of W. C. Edwards. Sh, 59^3–63^2; XXII, 62, 63. Solicitor. Partner in Farrer & Co., London. *I. Zingari C.C., Fly Fishers Club.* Brothers, 500 & 788.

1912 **FLETCHER, Simon,** b. 1 Aug. 46, elder s. of J. R. Fletcher, M.R.C.S., L.R.C.P. Sh, 59³–64².

1913 **HAMILTON, Donald Rankin Douglas,** b. 15 June 46, s. of His Honour, Judge A. McN. Hamilton. Sh, 59³–64¹; Scholar. Warner Exhibition to Balliol, Oxford, B.A. Bar, Gray's Inn, 69. Atkin Scholar, 70. Barrister. *National Liberal Club.*

1914 **MERTON, Bryan Edward,** b. 20 Jan. 46, younger son of D. D. Merton. Sh, 59³–64¹; Levée; Head of House. University of York, B.A. University of Bristol, Dip.Ed. Teaching in Secondary School, 68–71. Community Worker since 71. Brother, 1158.

1915 **AXON, John Temperley,** b. 5 July 46, elder s. of P. E. Axon, O.B.E., Ph.D. St. 59³–64³; Levée; Head of House. Sheffield University. A.C.A. Chartered Accountant. *Reform.*

1916 **HAYES, Guy de Vere Wingfield,** b. 21 Mar. 46, s. of Air-Cdr. G. W. Hayes, O.B.E. St, 59³–63³; S. VIII, 61, 62, Capt., 63. C.S.M. in C.C.F. R.M.A., Sandhurst. Commissioned, 65. Regular Army Officer. Capt. in Royal Green Jackets.

1917 **LAMOND, Alexander William,** b. 25 Feb. 46, s. of A. W. Lamond. St, 59³–64².

1918 **LESLIE, Michael Francis Bruce,** b. 25 Mar. 46, elder s. of B. S. Leslie (OR St 34). St, 59³–64²; Cap, 63; H. XI, 64. Royal Agricultural College, Cirencester. A.R.I.C.S. Area Manager, James Jones & Sons, Larbert, Scottish Home Timber Merchants. *R. & A. G.C., H.C.E.G.* Brother, 2253.

1919 **MARTIN, Simon Charles Ross,** b. 20 June 46, s. of M. H. A. Martin (OR St 24). St, 59³–64³. Oriel, Oxford.

1920 **PRIEST, David Michael,** b. 3 Oct. 46, s. of W. M. Priest, M.D., M.R.C.P. St, 59³–64³; Scholar. University of Toronto, Honors B.A. (not yet completed). Student.

1921 **VERNÈDE, Charles Arthur,** b. 29 May 46, s. of J. R. Vernède. St, 59³–64¹. Chartered Accountant. *M.C.C., H.A.C.*

1922 **ANDERSON, Stuart Hunt,** b. 23 Apr. 46, 3rd s. of Brig. W. F. Anderson, C.B.E., M.C. (OR Tu 19). Tu, 59³–64²; Scholar. Dundee Univ. Brothers, 912 & 1167.

1923 **CRABBIE, Christopher Donald,** b. 17 Jan. 46, elder s. of W. G. Crabbie. Tu, 59³–64². Liverpool Univ.

1924 **DAVIES, Paul Louis,** b. 29 Mar. 46, younger s. of R. S. Davies. Tu, 59³–64¹. Downing, Cambridge. Restaurateur, Ristorante Rosemary, Costa Smeralda, Sardinia, Italy. Brother, 1687.

1925A **DEFORD, Thomas McAdams,** b. 16 July 42, 2nd s. of B. F. Deford, Jnr. Tu, 59³–60². Yale University, B.A. 2nd Secretary (Political Officer), American Embassy, Jiddah, Saudi Arabia.

1925B **DRAYTON, Robin Michael,** b. 8 July 46, elder s. of G. L. Drayton. Tu, 59³–64². A.C.A. Self-employed Farmer/Accountant. N.F.U. Country Landowners Assoc. Fellow of Nat. Inst. of Agric. Botany.

1926 **SPILLANE, John Alban,** b. 8 June 46, s. of J. D. Spillane, M.D., F.R.C.P. Tu, 59³–64²; Levée; Head of House; Sw. IX, 62, 63, Capt., 64; Head of School Music. Middlesex Hospital Medical School, M.B., B.S. Late House Officer, Middlesex Hospital. Rotating Medical Registrar, University Hospital of Wales, Cardiff. O.R.G.S.

1927 **BERESFORD, Christopher Charles Howard,** b. 9 July 46, s. of the late R. M. Beresford. W, 59³–63³; Scholar. Leaving Exhibition to Trinity, Cambridge, M.A., A.C.A. Peat, Marwick Mitchell & Co., Chartered Accountants. *Ski Club of Great Britain.*

1928 **COULSON, Nevil Andrew Eltringham,** b. 19 Jan. 46, elder s. of Sir J. E. Coulson, K.C.M.G. (OR W 23). W, 59³–64¹; Levée; Head of House. Pembroke, Cambridge, B.A. Collège d'Europe, Bruges, Belgium, Diploma in Advanced European Studies. J. Henry Schroder Wagg & Co. Ltd., London, 68–71. J. Henry Schroder Banking Co., New York, 71–72. European Institute of Business Administration (INSEAD), Business School, 72–73.

1929 **GABBEY, Hugh Christopher Gelston,** b. 10 June 46, s. of H. M. Gabbey. W, 59³–64²; Fives IV, 63.

1930 **GREGSON, Marcus John,** b. 20 June 46, s. of Maj.-Gen. G. P. Gregson, C.B., C.B.E., D.S.O., M.C. W, 59³–63³. Magdalene, Cambridge, M.A. Solicitor. Vickers da Costa & Co., Stockbrokers, London.

1931 **HALL, Brian Arthur,** b. 25 Dec. 45, younger s. of the late Col. J. V. Hall (OR W 15). W, 59³–64²; Levée; Head of House; Cadet Officer, 64. Commodore Sailing, 64. Articled to Peat, Marwick, Mitchell & Co., Chartered Accountants. A.C.A. Brother, 1036.

1932 **MILLINGTON, John Gilbert,** b. 12 Dec. 45, s. of G. L. Millington. W, 59³–63².

1933 **NEAME, Roderick Laurence Beale,** b. 22 May 46, 3rd s. of L. B. Neame. W, 59³–64¹; Levée; Junior Athletic Cup, 62; Open Athletic Cup, 63; Winner 440 yds. in record time 52·2 secs. in 63. St. John's, Cambridge, M.A. St. Thomas's Hospital Medical School, Dept. of Physiology, Wellcome Research Scholar, Ph.D. Appointed Visiting Lecturer in Pharmacology to the Polytechnic of the South Bank, London, 69. Lecturer in Physiology, St. Bartholomew's Hospital, 70. Appointed Medical Research Council Investigator, 72. Recently resigned lectureship at Bart's to become a student of Anatomy leading to clinical studies and medical degree in 76. Author or co-author of ten papers in scientific journals. Brothers, 550 & 1783.

1934 **NIGHTINGALE, Peter Ray,** b. 31 Mar. 46, eldest s. of E. H. Nightingale, C.M.G. (OR W 18). W, 59³–63³; School Leaving Exhibition. Emmanuel, Cambridge, B.A. Unilever. Brothers, 2573 & Richard Mervyn, W, 68¹–72².

1935 **SOLLEY, Anthony Peter,** b. 25 Aug. 46, s. of R. Solley, M.B., B.Chir., F.R.C.S. W, 59³–63³. St. Bartholomew's Hospital, M.B., B.S., M.R.C.S., L.R.C.P., D.A., D.Obst.R.C.O.G. Anaesthetist.

ENTRANCES IN JANUARY 1960

1936 **GRIBBON, Antony St. George,** b. 5 Sept. 46, elder s. of Maj.-Gen. N. St. G. Gribbon (OR SH 30). SH, 60¹–64³. St. Edmund Hall, Oxford. Third Secretary, Foreign & Commonwealth Office, 67–71. McGraw-Hill Book Company, 71–72. Marketing Executive, Training Division, Sir Isaac Pitman & Sons Ltd. since 72. Brother, 2733.

1937 **HUNG, Timothy William,** b. 31 Aug. 46, 2nd s. of the late W. C. Hung, J.P. SH, 60¹–63². Chelsea College of Automobile Engineering, Diploma in Automobile Engineering. Associate Member of Institute of Motor Industries. Design & Development Engineer for Firestone Tyre & Rubber Co., International Racing Division. *Royal Automobile Club & Country Club.* Brother, 953.

1938 **EVELEIGH, Simon Brian,** b. 22 Aug. 46, elder s. of M. Eveleigh, M.C. (OR B 27). B 60¹–63³.

1939 **HAYWARD, James Roderick Hansell,** b. 28 July 46, s. of R. J. Hayward, C.B.E. B, 60¹–64². L'Institut D'Etudes Français, Tours. Chartered Accountant. Executive with Corporate Finance Dept., Old Broad Street Securities Ltd., London. *R.A.C.*

1940 **OLDHAM, Christopher Russell,** b. 18 Sept. 46, s. of the late H. R. Oldham. B, 60¹–64³. 10th Royal Hussars (P.W.O.), 65–70. Diploma Advances Accounting (Metropolitan D.M.S.), 73. In family business, Guthrie & Co. (U.K.) Ltd., Management Executive. *Cavalry Club.*

1941 **EVERS, Ralph Owen,** b. 7 Aug. 46, elder s. of R. H. K. Evers (OR C 30). C, 60¹–65¹; Tennis VI, 63, 64; H. XI, 65. Oriel, Oxford, M.A. Solicitor. Law Society. Brother, 2114.

1942 **PASSMORE, Colin,** b. 13 Sept. 46, younger s. of D. Passmore, D.F.C. (OR C 32). C, 60¹–64¹. The London School of Printing. Diploma in Graphic Arts. Printing Director of Alabaster Passmore and Sons Ltd., Printers. *Walton Heath G.C.*

1943 **POULTON, Robin Edward Iremonger,** b. 23 July 46, eldest s. of E. M. Poulton, D.M., M.R.C.P., D.P.H. (OR C 27). C, 60¹–64³. St. Andrews Univ. Brother, 2921.

1944 **RICHARDSON, William Wigham,** b. 7 Sept. 46, s. of M. F. W. Richardson (OR C 19). C, 60¹–64³; Levée. Magdalene, Cambridge, M.A. The Medical Coll. of St. Bartholomew's Hospital. Medical Student.

1945 **WRIGHT, William Hugh,** b. 23 Aug. 46, 2nd s. of C. G. Wright, L.D.S., R.C.S.Eng. C, 60¹–63³. R.M.A., Sandhurst. Army Officer, Capt. in the 9/12th Royal Lancers (Prince of Wales's). Second in Command of an Armoured Car Sabre Squadron in Northern Ireland. Captain. *Cavalry Club.* Brothers, 772 & 2982.

1946 **HIGSON, Richard Harry,** b. 22 Aug. 46, s. of J. H. Higson, D.S.C. K, 60¹–65². Bolton Institute of Technology, Diploma in Civil Engineering. A.M.I.C.E. Graduate Engineer with Lancashire County Council, Surveyor's Dept. Lt. (S.C.C.) R.N.R. in the Sea Cadet Corps.

1947 **MOORE, Richard Daniel St. Aubyn,** b. 4 July 46, s. of M. St. A. Moore. K, 60¹–61³.

1948 **KELLY, Antony Christopher Scott,** b. 6 July, 46, elder s. of G. S. Kelly, F.R.I.B.A. M, 60¹–64². Caen Univ., France. Brother, 2605.

1949 **LINE, Timothy Robert Maxim,** b. 30 Sept. 46, s. of G. M. Line. M, 60¹–64²; Rackets, 2nd Pair, 64. Chartered Accountant. Professional Practice, Chartered Accountant in Paris.

1950 **VANHEGAN, John Andrew David,** b. 12 Aug. 46, younger s. of J. Vanhegan. M, 60¹–64³; R. VIII, 64; Athletics Team, 64; Head of House. St. Bartholomew's Medical School, L.R.C.P., M.R.C.S., M.B., B.S. House Surgeon at St. Bartholomew's Hospital, 71–72. Senior House Officer, Royal National Orthopaedic Hospital. Orthopaedic Surgery. B.M.A. Brother, 1144.

1951 **HAMBLIN, Peter Raymond,** b. 22 June 46, s. of Air Cmdre. R. K. Hamblin, C.B.E. (OR SF 20). SF, 60¹–64².

1952 **DAVIES, Henri Lloyd,** b. 12 Dec. 46, s. of H. L. G. Davies, M.B., B.S. Sh, 60¹–65²; Levée; Head of House. H.N.D. Business Studies. Postgrad. Diploma Industrial Admin. Bath University. Chief Executive, Harri Llwyd ap Dafydd Cyf Ltd.

1953 **FRASER, Colin Stuart,** b. 12 Aug. 46, s. of J. G. Fraser. Sh, 60¹–63²; S. VIII, 61, 62, 63. Chelsea College, London University, B.Sc. Stock Control, Douglas Fraser & Sons Ltd., Friockheim. *Naval & Military.*

1954 **SOMERS, Robert Preston,** b. 26 May 46, younger s. of Col. T. V. Somers, O.B.E. (OR B 22). Sh, 60¹–64²; Levée; S. VIII, 62, 63, Capt., 64. R.M.A., Sandhurst. Commissioned Rifle Brigade 66. Served U.K. and B.A.O.R. Left Army

and joined Bowater Paper Corporation Sales.

1955 **TEARE, Jonathan James,** b. 13 Dec. 46, youngest s. of Prof. R. D. Teare, M.D., F.R.C.P. Sh, 60¹–64³; Levée; Head of School; Head of House; S. VIII, 62, 63, 64; Cadet Officer, 64. Brothers, 1019 & 1355.

1956 **HERBERT, Martin Geoffrey Greenham,** b. 9 Dec. 46, younger s. of G. B. Herbert, T.D., LL.B. St, 60¹–64³; Senior Scholar, 63; XV, 64. Balliol, Oxford. Brother, 1396.

1957 **REID, Alan David Bedford,** b. 28 June 46, s. of D. G. Reid (OR St 25). St, 60¹–64¹; Capt. of Fencing, 63, 64. Magdalen, Oxford, B.A. Cranfield Institute of Technology (M.B.A.). Export Marketing, Hand Tools, Sheffield. *Sheffield Club.*

1958 **SHORT, Christopher Clifford,** b. 18 June 46, younger s. of R. W. Short. St, 60¹–62². Short's (Lifts) Ltd., Director, 68. Man. Dir., 71. Chrmn., 73. *Yorkshire C.C.C., Shipley G.C.* Brother, 910.

1959 **HOLMES, David Salway Wilesmith,** b. 6 July 46, s. of the late A. R. Holmes. Tu, 60¹–64². Trinity College, Dublin, B.A.

1960 **INGLEBY, Thomas Campbell,** b. 8 July 46, 3rd s. of J. A. Ingleby, J.P. Tu, 60¹–64²; XV, 64. Brothers, 1228 & 1806.

1961 **NORTON, Richard George Henry,** b. 22 Aug. 46, s. of Maj.-Gen. C. H. Norton, C.B., C.B.E., D.S.O. (OR Tu 12). Tu, 60¹–64². A.C.A. Moved to Canada. Member of Institute of C.A., Canada. Employed in Managerial capacity by Thorne Gunn & Co., Toronto.

1962 **WOOD, Richard Charles,** b. 1st Sept. 46, younger s. of A. R. Wood. Tu, 60¹–64¹. Brother, 1493B.

1963 **FIELDING, John Kenneth Spencer,** b. 30 Oct. 46, elder s. of A. K. L. Fielding. W, 60¹–64². Tours Univ., France. Brother, 3038.

1964 **KITCHING, John Richard Howard,** b. 30 July 46, s. of E. H. Kitching, M.D., M.R.C.P. W, 60¹–64³; Levée; Head of House; Head of School Music, 64. Gonville & Caius, Cambridge.

1965 **CHARNAUD, Arthur Benjamin,** b. 6 Nov. 46, younger s. of the late J. G. R. Charnaud (OR W 14). SH, 60²–64³. Bristol Univ.

1966 **COOK, Christopher Patrick Eason,** b. 29 Dec. 46, elder s. of F. P. Cook (OR K 33). SH, 60²–65¹; Levée; Head of House; XV. Trinity Hall, Cambridge, B.A., B.B.C. Television Production (Documentaries). Radio Arts Programmes. Brother, Frank Edward, SH, 67²–71³.

1967 **DAY, Johnathan Rory,** b. 23 Nov. 46, younger s. of M. D. Day. SH, 60²–64³; Cap, 64. Clare, Cambridge.

1968 **HARDEN, Richard Charles,** b. 13 Sept. 46, younger s. of C. G. Harden (OR SH 18). SH, 60²–64²; S. VIII, 64. B.Sc. (Eng.). (London External taken at R.N. Engineering College.) R.N. "Wings". Lt., R.N. 845 Naval Air Commando Sqdn. Brother, 1524.

1969 **KENT-LEMON, David George,** b. 12 Oct. 46, younger s. of the late Lt.-Col. E. N. Kent-Lemon, M.B.E., T.D. (OR SH 10). SH, 60²–64³. Brother, 1970.

1970 **KENT-LEMON, Nigel William,** b. 12 Oct. 46, elder s. of the late Lt.-Col. E. N. Kent-Lemon, M.B.E., T.D. (OR SH 10). SH 60²–65². Levée; Head of House. Brother, 1969.

1971 **WHEATCROFT, Richard Frederick John,** b. 19 Dec. 46, elder s. of Lt.-Col. A. J. Wheatcroft (OR SH 33). SH, 60²–65¹. Pembroke, Oxford. Brother, Robert Anthony Hopton, SH, 70¹–.

1972 **MURRAY, James Anthony Stoddard,** b. 26 Oct. 46, elder s. of D. Murray, LL.B. (OR SH 23). B, 60²–64³. Sidney Sussex, Cambridge, B.A. (Classical Exhibitioner). Edinburgh Univ., LL.B. Enrolled Solicitor (Scotland). Presently with Maclay Murray & Spens, Solicitors, Glasgow. *Royal Northern Yacht Club.*

1973 **RITCHIE, Edmund,** b. 23 Dec. 46, younger s. of T. H. W. Ritchie, M.B., B.Ch. B, 60²–64³. Agricultural College, Cirencester. Brother, 1118.

1974 **COULSON, Nicholas John,** b. 2 Jan. 47, s. of J. H. A. Coulson. C, 60²–64³.

1975 **HALL, Stephen John,** b. 17 Sept. 46, youngest s. of G. S. Hall, M.D., F.R.C.P. C, 60²–65²; Levée; Head of House; Cap, 64; H. XI, 63, 64, Capt., 65;

Athletics Colours. Partner in firm of Solicitors. *Brighton Festival Chorus.* Brothers, 1526, 1728.

1976 **MITFORD, Thomas Theodore Bruce,** b. 21 Nov. 46, 3rd s. of T. B. Mitford, F.S.A., T.D. C, 60²–65²; Scholar. Corpus Christi, Oxford. Brothers, 681 & Rupert Edward Bruce, C, 68³–.

1977 **STROSS, Richard Brian,** b. 24 Sept. 46, s. of L. S. Stross. C, 60²–64³; XV, 64; S. VIII, 63, 64, Capt., 64.

1978 **ATTENBOROUGH, Charles Anthony,** b. 21 Apr. 47, elder s. of A. R. Attenborough (OR K 26). K, 60²–64²; H. XI, 64. Trinity, Oxford, M.A. Solicitor. Brother, 2296.

1979 **CRANSTON, Robert Ian,** b. 9 Sept. 46, elder s. of R. S. Cranston (OR K 29). K, 60²–64³; Levée; Head of House; XI, 63, 64; H. XI, 64. Fitzwilliam, Cambridge. A.C.A. Accountant. Brother, 2377.

1980 **CRASTER, Edmund John,** b. 23 Dec. 46, s. of O. E. Craster. K, 60²–65²; Sailing VI, 65. Newcastle upon Tyne Univ., B.A. Hallgarten Scholar, 72. Vintners Scholar, 73. Lt. 3rd Bn. The Royal Green Jackets, 69–70. Distribution Executive, Grants of St. James's Ltd., Wine Merchants.

1981 **FORGE, John Carey,** b. 26 Nov. 46, s. of C. C. J. Forge. K, 60²–64³. Exhibition to University Coll., Oxford. Cornel Univ., B.A.Chem. McGill Univ., Dip. Ed. M.A.(London). Qualified Teacher (Quebec Province, Canada). Doing Ph.D.(Phil.) at University College, London. Founder member, *Cornel Yumac Society.*

1982 **ROWLAND, Bruce,** b. 13 Nov. 46, s. of H. A. K. Rowland, D.M., M.R.C.P. K, 60²–66². Edinburgh Univ.

1983 **URLING CLARK, John Antony,** b. 26 Nov. 46, s. of A. U. Clark (OR K 27). K, 60²–64².

1984 **HORNE, Martin Charles Silvester,** b. 9 Aug. 46, younger s. of R. C.-H. Horne. M, 60²–64². Brother, 1453.

1985 **MACLEHOSE, Jeremy Spencer James,** b. 21 Oct. 46, younger s. of N. D. Maclehose, D.S.O., T.D. (OR W 28). M, 60²–64²; Levée; Head of House; Cap, 63; XI, 63–64; Fives IV, 62–64, Capt., 63, 64. Brother, 1140.

1986 **CLUTTON-BROCK, Timothy Hugh,** b. 13 Aug. 46, s. of H. A. Clutton-

Brock (OR SF 18). SF, 60²–64²; Levée. Magdalene, Cambridge, B.A., Ph.D. Royal Society Leverhulme Scholarship. S.R.C. Studentship, N.E.R.C. Fellowship to study behaviour and ecology of red deer. Ethologist, currently holding N.E.R.C. Research Fellowship in animal behaviour, research group, Zoology Dept., Oxford. British Ecological Society.

1987 **MANSON-BAHR, Philip Gordon Patrick,** b. 8 Nov. 46, s. of P. E. C. Manson-Bahr, M.D., F.R.C.P. (OR SF 24). SF, 60²–64²; Cap, 63; R. VIII, 63, 64. St. Thomas's Hospital Medical School, L.R.C.P., M.R.C.S. Medical Practitioner.

1988 **PYBUS, Anthony Mark,** b. 25 June 46, elder s. of M. A. Pybus (OR SH 28). SF, 60²–64². Newcastle Univ.

1989 **TALUKDAR, Partha,** b. 4 Sept. 46, elder s. of P. N. Talukdar. SF, 60²–64³.

1990 **CHOPRA, Ian,** b. 6 Oct. 46, s. of S. N. Chopra, M.R.C.S. Sh, 60²–64³. Trinity College, Dublin, M.A. Bristol Univ., Ph.D. Post-Doctoral Research Asst. in Bacteriology, Bristol University.

1991 **LEDWARD, Timothy John Davenport,** b. 10 July 46, s. of the late R. T. D. Ledward (OR C 29). Sh, 60²–63².

1992 **MORTON, William Stuart,** b. 28 Oct. 46, 3rd s. of K. V. F. Morton, C.I.E., O.B.E. Sh, 60²–64³. Queen's, Oxford. Solicitor. Brothers, 1015, 1307 & 2772.

1993 **CAWKWELL, Simon Allerton,** b. 11 Oct. 46, elder s. of G. L. Cawkwell. St, 60²–64³. A.C.A. Management Accountant & Director of a Stationery Wholesale Company, a Foundry & Engineering Company and a Car Hire Company. *Mbuyu Country Club, Ndola Flying Club* (in Zambia).

1994 **GOSLETT, Nicholas Stephen,** b. 19 Nov. 46, younger s. of the late M. J. Goslett (OR St 23). St, 60²–64³; XV, 64. Trinity College, Dublin. Brother, 1357.

1995 **JOHNSON-HILL, Nigel Maurice,** b. 8 Dec. 46, 3rd s. of K. C. Johnson-Hill, J.P. (OR T 19). St, 60²–65². Foreign Banking. Presently Hong Kong & Shanghai Banking Corp., Hong Kong. *Royal Hong Kong Jockey Club.* Brothers, 940 & 1358.

1996 **SYMINGTON, Robin Nicholas,** b. 15 Oct. 46, 2nd s. of the late S. P.

Symington, M.C., T.D., J.P. (OR St 23). St, 60²–64². Brothers, 878 & 2254.

1997 **CARSLAKE, Hugh Bampfield,** b. 15 Nov. 46, 2nd s. of J. Carslake (OR Tu 21). Tu, 60²–65¹; Levée; Head of House; S. VIII, 64, Capt., 65. Trinity College, Dublin, B.A., LL.B. Taking Solicitor's finals, Feb. 73. Brothers, 1169 and Richard Charles, Tu, 69²–.

1998 **MATHESON, David Torquil,** b. 21 Nov. 46, younger s. of N. S. Matheson. Tu, 60²–64³; R. VIII, 64; Athletics Team, 64. Edinburgh Univ. Chartered Accountant with Messrs. Arthur Young McClelland Moores & Co., London. Brother, 1689.

1999 **WATERS, Howard Brocas,** b. 13 Oct. 46, s. of H. R. B. Waters (OR Tu 20). Tu, 60²–65¹.

2000 **HAWKINS, Michael John,** b. 1 Oct. 46, s. of C. F. Hawkins, M.D., F.R.C.P. W, 60²–64³; Cap, 64; Capt. of Fives, 64. Guy's Hospital Medical School (London Univ.), M.R.C.S., L.R.C.P., M.B., B.S., D.Obst.R.C.O.G. Shortly entering career of general practice.

2001 **SPENCER, Anthony John Crosland,** b. 24 Sept. 46, s. of J. C. Spencer (OR W 09). W, 60²–64². Apprentice, J. Stone & Co. Ltd., Deptford. Woolwich Polytechnic. Accountant, Security Express Ltd.

2002 **WHEELWRIGHT, Thomas Michael,** b. 19 Nov. 46, younger s. of J. M. H. Wheelwright (OR W18). W, 60²–64³. Bristol Univ. Royal Agricultural Coll., Cirencester. Brother, 1093.

2003 **WOOD, John Garrard Chatterton,** b. 20 Aug. 46, elder s. of R. C. Wood. W, 60²–64². University of Tours, France. Honours Graduate of the École Hôtelière de la S.S.H. Lausanne in Hotel & Business Administration. Training in various Swiss Hotels & Restaurants. Asst. Project Manager, Mellieha Bay Hotel, Malta. Duty Manager, Cumberland Hotel, London. Asst. Managing Director, Tower Hotels Ltd. (Salaminia Tower & Esperia Tower Hotels, Famagusta), Cyprus. Brother, 2335.

ENTRANCES IN SEPTEMBER 1960

2004 **ABBOTT, David Stuart,** b. 4 Feb. 47, youngest s. of S. E. Abbott, O.B.E. (OR SH 24). SH, 60³–64³; Scholar. Churchill, Cambridge. Affiliate Member, British Computer Society. Computer Programmer, Systems Analyst since 67. Brothers, 654 & 945.

2005 BEATTIE, Timothy Charles Halden, b. 12 Mar. 47, 4th s. of Capt. S. H. Beattie, V.C., R.N. (OR SH 22). SH, 60³–64³. Brother, 176.

2006 FORRESTER, Julian Andrew Arthur Robert, b. 13 Dec. 46, younger s. of Major B. T. C. Forrester (OR SH 24). SH, 60³–64³; Cap, 64. McGill Univ., Montreal, B.A. Victoria Univ., B.C., Canada, M.A. Theatre Manager, Clarence Brown Theatre, Knoxville, Tennessee, U.S.A. *Royal Northern Yacht Club.* Brother, 950.

2007 GOYDER, Henry Peter Giles, b. 4 Feb. 47, 3rd s. of G. A. Goyder. SH, 60³–65¹; Scholar. Trinity, Cambridge, B.A. Planning Asst. with West Suffolk County Council since 69. On secondment to Nottingham Univ., 71, on M.A. Course in Environmental Planning. Brothers, 735 & 2945.

2008 HANCOCK, Christopher John, b. 29 Apr. 47, younger s. of F. W. Hancock (OR SH 23). SH, 60³–64³. A.C.A., Turquands Barton Mayhew, Paris. Brother, 1550.

2009 LESLIE, Richard David, b. 24 May 47, eldest s. of K. A. S. Leslie (OR SH 28). SH, 60³–65³; Head of House; Cap. Dewar Travelling Scholarship. University Coll., Durham Univ., B.A., A.C.I.S. Stockbroker. *Lansdowne Club.* Brothers, 2339 & 2785.

2010 NICOL, Randall Lewis, b. 22 May 47, eldest s. of Lt.-Col. J. W. Nicol, D.S.O., D.L. SH, 60³–65²; Levée. Magdalene, Cambridge, B.A. Commissioned in Regular Army, 66. Capt. in Scots Guards, 72. Freeman of the Grocers Company. *Kandahar Ski Club.* Brothers, 2437 & 2947.

2011 THOMSON, Nicholson Aidan Langdon, b. 18 Feb. 47, s. of A. H. Thomson. SH, 60³–65¹. Churchill, Cambridge.

2012 TURCAN, Robert Cheyne, b. 28 May 47, 3rd s. of H. H. Turcan, T.D. (OR SH 20). SH, 60³–64³. Trinity, Oxford. Brothers, 1102 & 1371.

2013 WOODHEAD, Conrad Martin, b. 28 June 47, elder s. of C. Woodhead, L.D.S. SH, 60³–65². Univ. of St. Andrews, B.D.S. Appointed Junior House Surgeon at Dundee Dental Hospital, 71. Senior House Surgeon at Newcastle Dental Hospital since 72. Brother, 2577.

2014 WRIGHT, Roger Hugh Peter, b. 30 June 47, elder s. of R. P. Wright, D.F.C. (A). SH, 60³–65²; Leaving Exhibition. Exhibition in Classics to Corpus Christi, Oxford, B.A. Wolfson, Oxford, D.Phil. Lecturer in Spanish at Liverpool Univ. Brother, 2953.

2015 BAKER, Christopher Henry, b. 23 Mar. 47, elder s. of Major H. Baker. T, 60³–65³; Levée. Bristol Univ.

2016 BOLTER, Christopher Paul, b. 11 Feb. 47, s. of P. Bolter. T, 60³–65²; R. VIII, 63–65; Holder of Bigside Bags, 65; Athletics Colours, 64, 65. Bristol Univ.

2017 BURTON, Anthony Levesley, b. 26 June 47, s. of D. A. E. Burton. T, 60³–65¹. Scholarship to St. John's, Cambridge.

2018 DRISCOLL, Michael John, b. 22 Feb. 47, s. of J. Driscoll. Exhibition to St. John's, Cambridge.

2019 HAMPTON, Michael George, b. 21 Oct. 46, s. of H. Hampton. T, 60³–65²; R. VIII, 63, 64, 65; Capt. of Athletics, 64, 65. London Hospital Medical Coll. At present studying for Associateship of Institute of Bankers. Clerk with Lloyds Bank Ltd. *Blackheath Harriers.*

2020 INGRAM, Philip Richard Pugh, b. 29 Nov. 46, younger s. of A. W. K. Ingram. T, 60³–65². Univ. of East Anglia, B.Sc. Systems Programming, I.C.I. Mond Div. Brother, 607.

2021 MARSHALL, Ian, b. 25 Feb. 47, s. of D. Marshall. T, 60³–65³; Levée; Head of House. C.S.M., 65. Magdalene, Cambridge. Solicitor's Articled Clerk.

2022 RICHARDS, Francis Alan, b. 31 Jan. 47, s. of F. Richards, M.M. T, 60³–64³. Bristol Univ.

2023 SPARKES, Keith William, b. 13 Aug. 47, s. of W. F. Sparkes. T, 60³–65². Bristol Univ., B.Sc. Inspector of Taxes (Inland Revenue). *G.E.C./A.E.I. (Rugby) Hockey Club.*

2024 STAVELEY, David Arthur, b. 6 Oct. 46, elder s. of H. A. Staveley (A). T, 60³–64². Art. Clerk, Peat, Marwick Mitchell, 64–66. Underwriter, Royal Exchange Assur. Group, 66–68. Systems Analyst & Salesman, International Computers Ltd., 68–72. Computer Salesman, Singer Business Machines since 72. *Bedford and County G.C.* Brother, 2355.

2025 WAINE, Stephen Philip, b. 9 June 47, elder s. of T. E. Waine, M.R.C.S., L.R.C.P., F.F.A. T, 60³–65²; Levée; Head of School; Head of House; XXII, 64. Southampton Univ., LL.B. Bar, Lincoln's Inn, 69.

2026 WILLIAMSON, Alan, b. 7 Feb. 47, s. of H. Williamson. T, 60³–65¹; Levée. Exeter Univ., LL.B. Solicitor with Stanley, Wasbrough & Co., Bristol.

2027 WILSON, Rohan Cameron Stuart, b. 24 Mar. 47, s. of E. H. Wilson. T, 60³–65²; Music Scholar; Head of School Music, 65; Leader of School Orchestra, 62–65. Trinity, Cambridge, B.A. At present Programme Manager, Clarkson Holidays Ltd. *British Schools Exploring Society.*

2028 GLASGOW, Malcolm Mervyn Stanley, b. 8 May 47, elder s. of J. E. Glasgow, M.B., B.Ch., D.M.R.E. B, 60³–64³. Westminster Hospital Medical School, M.B., B.S. Medicine. Studying for F.R.C.S. at present. Casualty Officer to London Hospital. Brother, 2578.

2029 GREENWOOD, John Gerald, b. 12 Dec. 46, elder s. of G. M. Greenwood (OR B 21). B, 60³–65²; Levée; Head of House. Edinburgh Univ., B.A. Japanese Govt. Scholar studying Monetary Economics at Graduate School of Economics, Univ. of Tokyo. V.S.O. in Nigeria, 69–70.

2030 JAMES, John Anthony, b. 10 Dec. 46, elder s. of J. A. C. James, M.R.C.S., L.R.C.P., M.A. B, 60³–65²; R. VIII, 63–65. Bristol Univ., M.B., Ch.B. Medical Research, studying for M.D. in Dental Medicine.

2031 LEONARD, Mark Meredith, b. 10 Feb. 47, younger s. of Rt. Revd. G. D. Leonard, Bishop of Truro B, 60³–64³. Pembroke, Cambridge, M.A. Teaching. Brother, 1725.

2032 SHEARER, Richard Hamish Robin, b. 24 May 47, elder s. of J. F. Shearer, O.B.E. (OR B 26). B, 60³–65³. Magdalene, Cambridge. Brother, 2304.

2033 SOUTHWARD, Ian Douglas, b. 30 June 47, 4th s. of R. Southward, M.B., F.R.C.P. B, 60³–65³; Sw. IX, 65. A.C.A. Chartered Accountant. Brothers, 484 & 1121.

2034 WHITELOCK, Hugh Radclyffe, b. 19 Mar. 47, elder s. of M. E. Whitelock (OR B 32). B, 60³–65².

2035 YOUNG, Sir Stephen Stewart Templeton, Bt., b. 24 May 47, s. of the late Sir A. S. T. Young, Bt. (OR B 31). B, 60³–64³; Levée; Head of House. Trinity, Oxford, B.A. Edinburgh Univ., LL.B. V.S.O. in Sudan, 68–69. Scots Law. Baronet.

2036 ALLEN, Nicholas James, b. 11 July 47, 3rd s. of G. C. Allen, C.B.E. (OR C 22). C, 60³–64³. Sussex Univ. (European Studies). Opera singing in Vienna, 67–69. Tour Manager for English Theatre Company of Vienna. Performer on Austrian T.V. & Radio. Asst. Director for stage and film in Austria.

2037 BRACEGIRDLE, James, b. 13 Mar. 47, s. of J. Bracegirdle. C, 60³–64³. Lincoln, Oxford.

2038 COLE, Michael Richard, b. 22 Feb. 47, 2nd s. of Col. J. R. Cole. C, 60³–64³. Brothers, 1074, 2305 & 2515.

2039 COLPOYS, Peter John, b. 13 Feb. 47, s. of W. V. Colpoys. C, 60³–64³. Geologist in Nairobi.

2040 DICK, Robert Learmonth, b. 4 June 47, elder s. of A. L. Dick, M.B., Ch.B., D.O.M.S. C, 60³–65³. Accountant's Articled Clerk. Knox Cropper Gedge & Co., of London. Brother, 2368.

2041 EVANS, John Christopher, b. 31 Jan. 47, s. of H. N. Evans. C, 60³–63³. Edinburgh Univ., M.A. Tutor.

2042A FRITH, Robin Michael Patrick, b. 17 Mar. 47, s. of M. R. Frith (OR C 31). C, 60³–64³. Pembroke, Cambridge.

2042B KERR-MUIR, Malcolm Gallaway, b. 31 Jan. 47, younger s. of R. J. Kerr-Muir, O.B.E., T.D. C, 60³–65²; Levée; Cap, 64; XI, 65; H. XI, 65. St. Thomas's Hospital Medical School, M.B., B.S., L.R.C.P., M.R.C.S. Medicine. *M.C.C.*

2043 MARRIAGE, Jeremy Peter, b. 3 May 47, s. of P. Marriage, LL.B. (OR C 28). C, 60³–65²; S. VIII, 64. Solicitor, 72. Asst. Solicitor with Linklaters & Paines, London.

2044 MATTISON, Nicholas Ellis Duncan, b. 5 May 47, s. of L. H. Mattison, M.R.C.S., L.R.C.P., D.P.H. C, 60³–65². Royal Free Hospital, London, M.R.C.S., L.R.C.P., M.B., B.S. Paediatric Officer, Harari Hospital, Salisbury, Rhodesia.

2045 NORMANTON, Simon Christopher, b. 20 Dec. 46, younger s. of T. Normanton, T.D. C, 60³–65². Queens', Cambridge.

2046 SEDDON, Peter, b. 1 May 47, s. of A. F. Seddon. C, 60³–64³. Rugby College Eng. Technology, B.Sc., A.M.I.E.E. Systems Design Engineer, G.E.C. Elliott Electrical Projects Ltd. of Rugby.

2047 STOCKBRIDGE, Alastair Ian Alexander, b. 14 Apr. 47 (name changed to Garrow in 71), youngest s. of W. Stockbridge. C, 60³–65¹. Magdalene, Cambridge. With Bowater Corporation Ltd. *Manchester Tennis & Racquets Club.*

2048 BECKETT, Patrick Robert Antony, b. 16 July 47, s. of the late R. A. Beckett (OR K 26). K, 60³–65³; Levée. Reading Univ.

2049 FROOME, Clive Todd, b. 3 June 47, s. of R. W. Froome. K, 60³–65³; Levée; XI, 65; H. XI, 65. Oriel, Oxford.

2050 HILLS, Robert John Kerr, b. 9 Mar. 47, younger s. of Brig. J. Hills, D.S.O. (OR K 16). K, 60³–65². Brother, 1529.

2051 IRWIN, Brian Christopher, b. 22 Nov. 46, younger s. of Maj.-Gen. B. St. G. Irwin (OR K 31). K, 60³–65². St. Thomas's Hospital Medical School, B.Sc., M.B., B.S. Medical Practitioner. Royal Navy Short Service Commission as Surg.-Lt. from 72. Worshipful Society of Apothecaries. Brother, 1132.

2052 KNIGHT, Graham Richard Harday, b. 22 May 47, s. of R. H. Knight. K, 60³–65³. Birmingham Univ., B.Sc. Electrical Engineer employed in Research Div., Marconi Co. Ltd.

2053 MATHESON, Philip Greville, b. 29 Nov. 46, elder s. of H. G. Matheson (OR K 24). K, 60³–64³; Scholar; Wadding-

ton Leaving Exhibition. Scholarship to New College, Oxford, B.A., A.C.A. Accountancy. Brother, 2824.

2054 RIGBY, Anthony John, b. 3 Oct. 46, eldest s. of Sir H. J. M. Rigby, Bt., E.R.D. (OR K 28). K, 60³–65³. Manchester Coll. of Commerce Accountancy. V.S.O. in India, 66–68. Sales Director of Canned Surprise & Two-Minute-T-Shirt (Personalised Gifts). Offshoot & subsidiary of Park Green Textiles Ltd. of Macclesfield, Cheshire. Brothers, 2215, 2380 & 2825.

2055 SWANSTON, Michael Timothy, b. 6 June 47, eldest s. of M. Swanston (OR K 35). K, 60³–64³. Pembroke, Cambridge. Brothers, 2381, 2672 & David Mungo, K, 67³–71².

2056 VAIZEY, John Russell, b. 19 May 47, s. of the late J. M. Vaizey, M.D., M.R.C.P. (OR K 22). K, 60³–64³. Clare, Cambridge.

2057 WILLIAMS, Edward Aston, b. 20 Oct. 47, s. of H. A. Williams, D.F.M. K, 60³–65¹. Senior Scholar, 64. Scholarship to Trinity, Cambridge, B.A. Princeton Univ., M.A., Ph.D. Research Associate, Dept. Astrogeophysics, Univ. of Colorado, Boulder, U.S.A. American Physical Society.

2058 WOODHEAD, Nicholas Jesse, b. 16 Jan. 47, younger s. of J. A. Woodhead, M.Sc., M.B., Ch.B. K, 60³–62². Stand Grammar School for Boys, Whitefield. Manchester Univ. Medical School, M.B., Ch.B. General Medical Practitioner in the practice of Drs. Woodhead, Law & Garland. Committee Member, *Manchester Film Institute Society.* Brother, 991.

2059 BOLTON, David Charles, b. 31 Jan. 47, elder s. of P. J. Bolton (OR M 28). M, 60³–64³; Leaving Exhibition. Trinity, Cambridge. Brother, 2385.

2060 GREENHALGH, Jeremy Peter Sharrocks, b. 25 Apr. 47, younger s. of G. Greenhalgh. M, 60³–65². Brother, 1382.

2061 LAW, David Nigel Duncan, b. 5 Feb. 47, s. of Major D. D. Law, R.A. M, 60³–65². Accountant, Thornton Baker & Co. of Leeds.

2062 TOWNE, Edward David, b. 18 Mar. 47, eldest s. of C. E. A. Towne. M, 60³–65³; Levée; Head of School; Head of House. E. Anglia Univ., B.A. V.S.O. in Zambia, 66. English Language Asst., École Normale, France, 68–69. Asst. French Master, Portsmouth Grammar School, 71–72. Reading for Camb. Univ., Post Graduate Cert. in Education, 72–73. Teaching practice at Solihull School, Warwick, 73. Brothers, 2388 & 2930.

2063 **WAGLÉ, Nikhil Nityanand,** b. 13 Feb. 47, s. of N. M. Waglé. M, 60³–63².

2064 **WHITSON, Gordon Michael Alexander Pitt,** b. 6 Jan. 47, elder s. of H. A. Whitson (OR M 30). M, 60³–65².

2065 **WOOD, Roger David,** b. 12 Mar. 47, s. of R. H. Wood (OR M 21). M, 60³–65². Alliance Française, Paris. Lanchester Polytechnic, Coventry, B.A. (Acting) General Manager of Janet Jones (Manchester) Ltd., a subsidiary company of the William Timpson Group. *Prestbury Squash Rackets Club.*

2066 **ELLIS, Trevor Stanley,** b. 21 Jan. 47, s. of J. S. Ellis. SF, 60³–63².

2067 **McMULLEN, Colin Peter,** b. 22 Feb. 47, younger s. of L. McMullen (OR SF 19). SF, 60³–65¹; Head of House. Trinity, Cambridge. Various jobs connected with computers in Toronto. *Royal St. George Yacht Club.* Brother, 1602.

2068 **PAYNE, David Antony,** b. 17 Jan. 47, 2nd s. of M. F. Payne. SF, 60³–64². University of Granada, Spain. Advertising. Now with Masins, Wynne-Williams Ltd. of London. *Royal Cruising Club.* Brothers, 1603 & 2538.

2069 **STROTHER-SMITH, Peter Charles,** b. 22 Jan. 47, s. of N. C. Strother-Smith (OR SF 31). SF, 60³– 64².

2070 **SYKES, Charles Jeremy,** b. 9 Oct. 46, younger s. of the late C. M. Sykes (OR SF 21). SF, 60³–64².

2071 **TRENTHAM, Andrew Bruce,** b. 21 Dec. 46, youngest s. of Capt. D. P. Trentham, R.N. SF, 60³–64³; Levée; XV, 63, Capt., 64; XI, 62–64; H. XI, 62–63, Capt., 64. B.R.N.C. Dartmouth. Lt. R.N. Commanding Officer A510. Capt., R.N. Hockey, 69–72. Olympic Games, Mexico (Hockey), 68. *I.Z., M.C.C., United Service Club.* Brother, 279.

2072 **WILD, Maxwell Patrick,** b. 7 Feb. 47, elder s. of P. D. Wild (OR SF 32). SF, 60³–65². Accountant. Studying for

Part V. Institute of Chartered Accountants of Scotland. Brother, 2542.

2073 **ADAMSON, Christopher Campbell,** b. 2 Feb. 47, elder s. of W. O. C. Adamson (OR Sh 36). Sh, 60³–64³. York Univ. Brother, 3009.

2074 **BOYES, John,** b. 1 May 47, s. of J. Boyes. Sh, 60³–65². C.A. Company Secretary & Accountant. *British Interplanetary Society.*

2075 **FOX, Christopher Alan,** b. 5 July 47, s. of A. G. Fox. Sh, 60³–65³. Jesus, Cambridge, B.A. Bristol Univ., Cert. Ed. Teacher of English, King Edward's Five Ways School, Birmingham. Asst. Leader, Kingswinford Crusaders.

2076 **JAMES, Colin Dudley,** b. 10 June 47, s. of K. L. James, M.S., F.R.C.S. Sh, 60³–65².

2077 **SMITH, Christopher Henry David,** b. 24 Dec. 46, s. of E. H. D. Smith. Sh, 60³–65².

2078 **ZIMMERN, Ronald Leslie,** b. 15 Feb. 47, s. of F. Zimmern, J.P. Sh, 60³–65¹; Levée; Head of House. Trinity, Cambridge. Middlesex Hospital Medical School, M.A., M.B., B.Chir. At present House Physician, Dept. of Neurology, Middlesex Hospital, London.

2079 **DICKSON, Martin Maitland,** b. 19 June 47, elder s. of Capt. S. W. S. Dickson. St, 60³–65¹; Scholar. Clare, Cambridge. Brother, 2555.

2080 **FOX, Simon John Collins,** b. 30 Dec. 46, s. of Dr. K. M. Fox. St, 60³–65²; Athletics Colours. St. Andrews Univ.

2081 **HERBERT, William Anthony,** b. 27 July 47, s. of W. D. B. Herbert (OR St 29). St, 60³–65²; Levée; Head of House. Magdalene, Cambridge, B.A. Reading Univ., M.Sc. Agricultural Adviser, North of Scotland College of Agriculture, 69–71. Consulting Officer, Milk Marketing Board since 71.

2082 **JAMES, Charles Knyvett,** b. 18 May 47, s. of C. T. A. James, M.R.C.S., L.R.C.P. St, 60³–64². St. Bartholomew's Hospital Medical School.

2083 **LEVERSEDGE, Francis John Spencer,** b. 19 May 47, s. of L. F. Leversedge, C.M.G. St, 60³–65². Coats Patons Ltd., Glasgow. Manager of Company's

branch in Nigeria. *Lagos Yacht Club,*
Lagos Cricket Club.

2084 **PITT, Christopher Robert Lovel,**
b. 4 Feb. 47, eldest s. of Lt.-Cdr. R. J.
Pitt, M.B.E., R.N. (OR St 35). St, 60³–64³;
XV, 63, 64. Nottingham Univ., B.Sc.,
G.I.Mech.E. Currently employed by a
large engineering company in Leicester.
Brothers, 2558 & 2859.

2085 **SCOTT, Tom,** b. 2 May 47, s. of
A. Scott (OR St 18). St, 60³–64³. Exhibi-
tion in History to Clare, Cambridge,
Ph.D. Research Fellow of Clare since 72 in
Medieval German History.

2086 **THOMSON, William Gordon,** b.
6 Dec. 46, s. of The Hon. Lord Migdale,
D.L., Q.C. St, 60³–65². Edinburgh Univ.

2087 **VAN DEN BERGH, Richard**
John Andrew, b. 30 July 47, younger s.
of J. Van Den Bergh. St, 60³–65¹; Levée;
Head of House; XV, 64, Capt., 65; Tennis
VI, 63–65. Pembroke, Cambridge, B.A.,
A.C.A. Environmental Economist, Con-
sultant on Environmental Affairs (with
Atkins Research & Development). *Lans-*
downe Club. Brother, 1656.

2088 **WHARTON, David Franklin,** b.
19 Sept. 47, s. of T. R. B. Wharton (OR
St 32). St, 60³–64³; Scholar. Scholarship to
Trinity, Cambridge, M.A. Fellow of the
Institute of Actuaries, 72. Provident
Mutual Life Assurance Assoc., London
since 68. *Frinton G.C., Society of Genealo-*
gists.

2089 **WILLS, Arthur Alexander Noel,**
b. 24 Dec. 46, s. of J. G. Wills (OR St 29).
St, 60³–65.

2090 **BONNER, Stephen Dunraven,** b.
11 Feb. 47, s. of G. D. Bonner, M.B.,
Ch.B. Tu, 60³–65²; Levée; Head of
House; XI, 64, 65. Magdalene, Cambridge,
B.A. Solicitor with Clifford-Turner & Co.,
London. *M.C.C., Royal West Norfolk*
G.C.

2091 **BROOME, John Richard,** b. 17
May 47, younger s. of R. N. Broome,
O.B.E., M.C. (OR Tu 23). Tu, 60³–64³;
Senior Scholarship, 63; Leaving Exhibition
(Maths.), 64. Trinity Hall, Cambridge.
Brother, 1319.

2092 **COOPER, Peter Thomas,** b. 1
Feb. 47, younger s. of H. T. Cooper. Tu,
60³–64². A.R.I.C.S. Self-employed Chartered Surveyor & Chartered Auctioneer &
Estate Agent. *Coventry G.C.* Brother, 450.

2093 **GLEDHILL, Anthony James**
Sinton, b. 22 May 47, younger s. of W. C.
Gledhill, M.B.E., M.B., F.R.C.S. Tu,
60³–64². Took up articles in Accountancy,
resigned, then moved to Advertising, into
Sales and now Personal Assistant to Sales
Director of Joseph Cheaney & Sons,
Desborough, Northants, Shoemakers.
Brother, 1490.

2094 **LEWIS-CROSBY, Robert Antony**
Cornwall, b. 8 April 47, s. of R. C.
Lewis-Crosby, M.C. (OR Tu 28). Tu, 60³–
65². Trinity College, Dublin, B.A. Sales
Administrator, Girling Ltd. Now with
Ibbs & Tillett (Concert Agents), Promo-
tion Dept.

2095 **THOMPSON, Nicholas Vernon,**
b. 5 Dec. 46, s. of V. C. Thompson,
F.R.C.S. Tu, 60³–65². Univ. of Edinburgh,
B.Arch. Architect, Maurice Pickering
Associates, London, W.1.

2096 **BOTTOMLEY, James Francis**
Kelvin, b. 30 Mar. 47, s. of the late J. K.
Bottomley (OR W 28). W, 60³–65²; Levée;
Head of House. Peterhouse, Cambridge.

2097 **DEWS, Robert John,** b. 30 May 47,
s. of J. Dews. W, 60³–65². Solicitor.
Partner in firm of Leicester Solicitors.

2098 **HALDANE, Richard Wilkie,** b. 6
May 47, s. of T. G. N. Haldane. W, 60³–
65². Imperial Coll., London Univ., B.Sc.
Parsons Peebles Ltd., Edinburgh. *New*
Club, Edin., R.A.C.

2099 **LAMBLEY, Richard John Gor-**
don, b. 6 May 47, eldest s. of D. G.
Lambley, M.B., F.R.C.S. W, 60³–65²;
Scholar. Lincoln, Oxford. Asst. Producer,
B.B.C.

2100 **RENNIE, Charles Tatham Ogil-**
vy, b. 9 Mar. 47, s. of J. O. Rennie,
C.M.G., W, 60³–63².

2101 **RICHARDS, William Roderick,**
b. 8 Jan. 47, s. of W. E. Richards. W,
60³–65¹; Scholar; Levée; Head of School;
Head of House; H. XI, 64. Exhibition to
Merton, Oxford, B.A. Chase Manhattan
Bank, N.A., London, New York, Hong
Kong, Jakarta.

2102 **RUNECKLES, Peter,** b. 28 Feb.
47, s. of R. L. Runeckles, L.D.S. W, 60³–
65². Univ. College Hospital Dental School.

2103 **SVASTI, Mom Rajwongs Jisnu-**
son, b. 25 Sept. 47, s. of Prince A. Svasti

of Thailand. W, 60^3–65^1; Levée. Trinity, Cambridge, M.A., Ph.D. Lecturer, Faculty of Sciences, Dept. of Biochem., Mahidol Univ., Bangkok, Thailand. *Royal Bangkok Sports Club.*

2104 **THORN, Nigel Alexander,** b. 7 Feb. 47, s. of S. A. Thorn (OR St 10). W, 60^3–64^3; Cap, 64. St. Catherine's, Oxford, B.A., A.C.A. Audit Supervisor, Cooper & Lybrand, 73.

ENTRANCES IN JANUARY 1961

2105 **DAVIDSON, Christopher Robert,** b. 19 June 47, s. of R. F. Davidson. SH, 61^1–62^2.

2106 **FORDE, Nicholas John Francis,** b. 30 Aug. 47, elder s. of N. H. B. Forde. SH, 61^1–65^2.

2107 **HILTON, James Richard Woodin,** b. 26 Apr. 47, younger s. of Lt.-Col. P. Hilton, M.C. SH, 61^1–62^1. Royal Agricultural Coll., Cirencester. Died suddenly in his sleep, 28 Nov. 69.

2108 **SULAIMAN, Mohamad Zubayr Careem,** b. 28 June 47, younger s. of Dr. A. C. M. Sulaiman. SH, 61^1–65^3. St. Andrews Univ.

2109 **WOODWARD, John Michael,** b. 26 May 47, younger s. of R. R. Woodward, T.D. SH, 61^1–64^2. Brother, 1436.

2110 **FAIRCLOUGH, David Edwin,** b. 4 July 47, 2nd s. of Col. J. Fairclough, O.B.E. (OR B 29). B, 61^1–64^3. Bath Technical Coll., Univ. Coll. Hospital. Brothers, 1868 and Clive Anthony, B, 68^1–72^1.

2111 **LEARMOUNT, David Wright,** b. 3 May 47, eldest s. of Capt. D. K. L. Learmount, D.S.C., R.N. (OR B 33). B, 61^1–65^2; Athletics Colours. B.R.N.C., Dartmouth, 65–66. In publishing, 66–70. Commission in R.A.F., 70. Awarded R.A.F. Flying Badge, 71. Present rank in R.A.F., Flying Officer. No. 70 Squadron, R.A.F. Akrotiri, Cyprus (Hercules Aircraft). *R.A.F. Club.* Brother, 2807.

2112 **RUSHDIE, Ahmed Salman,** b. 19 June 47, s. of A. A. Rushdie. B, 61^1–65^1; Queen's Medal, 64; Leaving Exhibition in History, 64. Exhibition to King's, Cambridge.

2113 **SCRIMSHAW, James Gilbert,** b. 2 July 47, s. of A. G. Scrimshaw, F.C.A. B, 61^1–65^1. Jesus, Cambridge, M.A. Indiana Univ., U.S.A., M.B.A. Chief Production Engineer, British Ropes Ltd., Peterlee, Co. Durham. *South Shields Sailing Club*

2114 **EVERS, Stephen Andrew,** b. 28 Sept. 47, younger s. of R. H. K. Evers (OR C 30). C, 61^1–64^3. Brother, 1941

2115 **HEYS, David Walter,** b. 6 June 47, s. of W. Heys. C, 61^1–65^2; Fives IV, 64, Capt., 65. Royal Agricultural College, Cirencester. College Certificate. Farming.

2116 **HINKS, Jonathan Linney,** b. 29 June 47, eldest s. of J. A. Hinks, O.B.E., J.P. C, 61^1–65^3. New College, Oxford, B.A. Civil Engineer. Brothers, 2308 & 2740.

2117 **LEA, Michael Simcox,** b. 20 Apr. 47, s. of Rev. A. B. Lea (OR C 20). C, 61^1–65^2; XV. Guildhall School of Music & Drama. B.B.C. Training Orchestra, 68–70. City of Birmingham Symphony Orchestra, 70–72. B.B.C. Concert Orchestra since 72.

2118 **BOARDMAN, Julian Walter,** b. 26 Apr. 47, s. of Lt.-Col. J. Boardman, M.B.E. K, 61^1–65^3; XV, 64, 65. Brasenose, Oxford.

2119 **CLOUGH, Roger Howard Butler,** b. 30 June 47, 2nd s. of F. H. B. Clough (OR K 30). K, 61^1–65^2. Brother, 1584.

2120 **KING, Nicholas Kersteman,** b. 11 Apr. 47, 3rd s. of E. P. King. K, 61^1–64^3. Royal Agricultural Coll. Sales, Agricultural Division, I.C.I.

2121 **PALMER, Robert Chambley Callander,** b. 14 July 47, s. of Major E. M. Palmer. K, 61^1–64^2. Welbeck Coll., R.M.A., Sandhurst. Army Officer, Royal Signals, Lt. Student at R.M.C.S., Shrivenham, working for B.Sc. in Communications.

2122 **WOLFF, Anthony Stephen Richard,** b. 29 Sept. 47, younger s. of E. F. W. Wolff. K, 61^1–65^2. Brother, 1649.

2123 **GROVE-WHITE, Charles Dermot,** b. 11 July 47, younger s. of R. J. Grove-White, M.D., F.R.C.P. (OR M 29). M, 61^1–64^3; Sw. IX, 63, 64. Trinity College, Dublin, B.A., M.B., B.Ch., B.A.O. Doctor.

2124 HUDSON, Nicholas Charles Lawrence, b. 19 Aug. 47, s. of the late L. E. Hudson. M, 61^1–65^3. St. Catharine's, Cambridge.

2125 MACINNES, Miles, b. 24 Mar. 47, s. of G. MacInnes. M, 61^1–65^2. R.N. Reserved Cadetship, 64. Trainee Estate Agent, Earl of Lonsdale's Estates, Lowther, Penrith.

2126 WASS, John Andrew Hall, b. 14 Aug. 47, 3rd s. of S. H. Wass, M.S., F.R.C.S. M, 61^1–65^3; Levée; Head of School Music, 65. Guy's Hospital, M.R.C.S., L.R.C.P., M.B., B.S. Registrar in Renal Medicine, King's Coll. Hospital.

2127 FARGUS, David Nigel Alexander, b. 31 July 47, s. of Col. B. A. Fargus, O.B.E. (OR SF 31). SF, 61^1–65^1. Edinburgh Univ., LL.B. Asst. Manager in British Shipping Company's Far Eastern Branch Offices.

2128 McILWRAITH, William Anthony, b. 15 June 47, eldest s. of W. G. McIlwraith (OR SF 29). SF, 61^1–65^2; Levée; Head of House; XI, 64–65. Tech. College, Kingston upon Thames. Driver/ Courier, Encounter Overland (Transcontinental Safaris by truck). *R.A.C.*

2129 PEARSON, Henry Gervis, b. 2 Aug. 47, 2nd s. of M. Pearson, M.C. (OR SF 29). SF, 61^1–65^2; XV, 64; XXII, 64, 65; H. XI, 64, 65. Mansfield College, Oxford, B.A. Student at St. John's College, Bramcote, Notts., 2-yr. course, training to be ordained minister of the Church of England. *Vincent's Club, Oxford.* Brothers, 1754 & 2744.

2130 WILLIAMS, Toby Robert Nicholas, b. 15 Sept. 47, s. of N. J. D. Williams (OR SF 38). SF, 61^1–64^3.

2131 DIXON, Neil Henry Fraser, b. 6 Mar. 47, younger s. of J. E. Dixon. Sh, 61^1–63^3. Grimes' Tutorial College, Manchester. Employed at present as Timber Importer in East End of London. *Vintage Sports Car Club.* Brother, 1760.

2132 TAYLOR, Michael, b. 2 June 47, eldest s. of A. Taylor. Sh, 61^1–65^2. Brother, 2851.

2133 WATTS, Michael John Colin, b. 17 July 47, elder s. of C. E. Watts, T.D. St, 61^1–65^3. St. Catharine's, Cambridge, B.A., A.C.A. Chartered Accountant. Brother, 3027.

2134 LAMBERTY, Mark Julian Harker, b. 17 Aug. 47, younger s. of G. B. Lamberty, L.R.C.P., M.R.C.S. Tu, 61^1–65^2. Keble, Oxford, B.A., B.C.L. Barrister-at-Law. Northern Circuit. Brother, 1492.

2135 WALKER, Peter John, b. 10 Aug. 47, s. of W. B. S. Walker (OR Tu 29). Tu, 61^1–64^2. Died 23 Sept. 64.

2136 WILLIAMSON, Hugh Godfrey Maturin, b. 15 July 47, s. of T. B. Williamson, C.M.G. Tu, 61^1–65^3; Levée; Head of House. Trinity, Cambridge. Double first in Theology. St. John's, Cambridge, Part III. Old Testament Theology. Research at St. John's for Ph.D.

ENTRANCES IN MAY 1961

2137 BURN, David Richard Beveridge, b. 6 Oct. 47, s. of Lt.-Col. R. S. Burn (OR SH 21). SH, 61^2–. Newcastle Univ., B.Sc., G.I.Mech.E. Contracts Engineer, Reyrolle Parsons Africa Ltd., Ndola, Zambia. *E.S.U.*

2138 GOLLIN, Richard Lionel Alfred, b. 15 Aug. 47, younger s. of G. J. Gollin. SH, 61^2–65^3. Brother, 1240.

2139 McDOWALL, James Ian, b. 9 Dec. 47, s. of J. McDowall. SH, 61^2–65^2. Fitzwilliam, Cambridge, B.A. Grenoble Univ. (1 yr.). College of Law, Guildford. Articled Clerk to Solicitor. *M.C.C.*

2140 CARNEGIE, Stuart Francis, b. 6 July 47, elder s. of D. M. Carnegie, M.B., B.S., F.F.A.R.C.S., D.A. (OR B 31). B, 61^2–65^3. Articled Clerk with Peat Marwick Mitchell & Co., 66–70, and now with same firm. A.C.A., 72. *Royal Lymington Yacht Club, Royal Yachting Assoc.*

2141 COLLINGRIDGE, Hugh John, b. 1 Oct. 47, s. of H. G. Collingridge. B, 61^2–65^2. Career in Horse Racing. Asst. Trainer to G. B. Barling, Newmarket.

2142 DIXON, Matthew, b. 27 Feb. 48, younger s. of J. F. Dixon. C, 61^2–65^2; Cap, 65; Athletics Team, 65. Univ. of Southampton, B.Sc. Athletics & Hockey colours. Clare, Cambridge, Ph.D. 400m. title vs. Oxford (May 72); Full Blue. Awarded Thirkhill Travel Grant, 72. Director, Cambridge Univ. Hispanic Society Play, 71. *Hawks Club.* Brother, 1270.

2143 **MITCHELL, Iain Maurice,** b. 3 Jan. 48, youngest s. of M. N. Mitchell. C, 61^2–65^3; Levée; Head of House; XXII, 65. Clare, Cambridge, M.A. College of Law. Solicitor's Articled Clerk. *Junior Carlton Club, Royal St. Georges G.C., Sandwich.*

2144 **BOOTH, Martin Richard Kendall,** b. 13 Nov. 47, s. of G. K. Booth (OR K 29). K, 61^2–65^3; Tennis VI, 64, 65. City Life Inspector, Sun Alliance & London Insurance Group, Manchester. Manchester Life & Pensions Society.

2145 **BOURNE, Edward Leeson Stafford,** b. 18 Oct. 47, s. of S. Bourne (OR M 14). K, 61^2–65^3; Sw. IX, 64. Corpus Christi, Cambridge, B.A. Career with Bourne & Hollingsworth Ltd., London. Now Director. *Pitt Club.*

2146 **HANKEY, The Hon. Alexander Maurice Alers,** b. 18 Aug. 47, younger s. of The Rt. Hon. Lord Hankey, K.C.M.G., K.C.V.O. (OR K 19). K, 61^2–65^1; XXII; Rackets Pair; Senior Scholarship, 64. Scholar of Trinity, Cambridge, B.A. M.I.T. Cambridge, Mass., Ph.D. Physicist and teacher in Transcendental Meditation. Stanford Linear Accelerator Centre, California since 72.

2147 **PICKFORD, James Alfred Compton,** b. 29 Aug. 47, younger s. of R. E. Pickford, T.D., LL.B. K, 61^2–66^2; Levée. Commodore of Sailing. Sheffield Polytechnic, A.M.I.C.E. Civil Engineer with Cementation Construction. *Itchenor Sailing Club.* Brother, 1217.

2148 **RICHARDS, James William Bruce,** b. 30 July 47, eldest s. of N. A. Richards, M.D., M.R.C.O.G. K, 61^2–65^1; Scholar; Tennis VI, 62–64. Scholarship to Wadham, Oxford, B.A. Foreign & Commonwealth Officer. Learning Mandarin in Hong Kong. Brothers, 2923 & Nicholas Peter, K, 67^3–71^2.

2149 **WEBB, William Grierson,** b. 16 Oct. 47, younger s. of H. J. H. Webb. K, 61^2–65^3. Member of National Youth Orchestra of G.B., 65. Merton, Oxford, B.A. Studied Conducting at the Mozarteum in Salzburg, 70–73. Asst. Conductor at the Trier Opera House, Rheinland-Pfalz, W. Germany from Aug. 73.

2150 **BERKELEY, Rodney Guy,** b. 1 Sept. 47, younger s. of A. W. G. Berkeley (OR M 34). M, 61^2–65^2; Tennis VI, 64, 65. Freiburg Univ. A.C.A. and C.A.

(Jamaica). Audit Manager, Pannell, Fitzpatrick & Co., Kingston, Jamaica. Brother, 1673.

2151 **CULLEN, Christopher William,** b. 4 Oct. 47, eldest s. of P. Cullen, D.S.C. (OR M 34). M, 61^2–66^1. Exeter Univ. Brother, 2446.

2152 **HOPE, Alexander Robertson Boyle,** b. 22 June 47, 3rd s. of Lt.-Col. A. H. C. Hope, O.B.E., T.D., B.L. (OR M 11). M, 61^2–65^2. Durham Univ. (St. John's Coll.), B.A. Aberdeen College of Education, Certificate in Secondary Education. Asst. Master at New Park School, St. Andrews, Fife from Sept. 70. Brother, 744.

2153 **SAWERS, Ian James,** b. 2 Dec. 47, elder s. of Maj.-Gen. J. M. Sawers, M.B.E. (OR M 34). M, 61^2–65^2; Sw. IX, 63–65. Army Officer. Brother, Nigel Charles, M, 68^2–71^2.

2154 **BARCLAY, Robert Lyford,** b. 23 Oct. 47, elder s. of J. F. Barclay, T.D. SF, 61^2–65^3. St. Andrews Univ., M.A. Stock Exchange exams 74. Hedderwick Borthwick & Co., of London. *E.S.U.*

2155 **LUSTY, Peter Alan,** b. 13 Aug. 47, elder s. of A. C. Lusty (OR SF 24). SF, 61^2–65^3. Chartered Accountant until 74. Now joined father in business on finance and management side, also running chain of specialised bakeries. Own firm of Chartered Accountants operated privately. Member of Worshipful Company of Loriners, N.A.M.B. member. Brother, 2843.

2156 **WRIGHT, Trevor,** b. 24 Aug. 47, younger s. of T. Wright, M.D., B.Ch. SF, 61^2–65^2. Brother, 1908.

2157 **CUTLER, Roden David,** b. 1 Oct. 47, eldest s. of Sir A. R. Cutler, V.C., K.C.M.G., K.C.V.O., C.B.E. Sh, 61^2–65^3; Cap, 65; Sw. XI, 63, 64, Capt., 65. Sydney Univ., B.Com. Brother, 2321.

2158 **DRAYCOTT, Philip Anthony,** b. 16 Sept. 47, elder s. of D. P. Draycott. Sh, 61^2–66^1; Levée; Head of House; Head of School. Clare, Cambridge. Filmmaker. British Film Institute.

2159 **LLOYD, David Richard,** b. 4 Oct. 47, elder s. of D. F. Lloyd. Sh, 61^2–65^3. Aberystwyth.

2160 **RITCHIE, Robin James,** b. 20 Jan. 48, elder s. of P. Ritchie (OR C 31). Sh, 61²–65². Asst. Branch Manager, Gillette France, Annecy. Brother, 2694.

2161 **ELLIS, Roland Alexander,** b. 12 Jan. 48, s. of Col. W. D. Ellis, O.B.E., T.D., A.D.C., D.L. St, 61²–65³. Mons Officer Cadet School. Short Service Commission, 15/19th The King's Royal Hussars. Sheep Farming Contractor. *M.C.C.*, *Bath Club.*

2162 **HELME, Charles Thomas Alexander,** b. 17 Nov. 47, younger s. of A. Helme (OR C 28). St, 61²–66²; Levée; Head of House; Cap, 64. Bristol Univ., B.Sc. International Computers Ltd. (System/Sales) since 70. *Lansdowne Club, London.* Brother, 1395.

2163 **LATIMER, Colin Gordon Courtenay,** b. 23 Sept. 47, s. of Sir C. R. Latimer, C.B.E. (OR St 25). St, 61²–66²; Levée; XXII, 66. Kingston Polytechnic, Kingston upon Thames, LL.B. Departmental Manager, Marks & Spencer Ltd., 70–72. Administration Asst., Open University since 72.

2164 **SURTEES, William James Conyers,** b. 29 June 47, 3rd s. of C. A. Surtees (OR St 21). St, 61²–65³; XV, 64, Capt., 65. Rackets Pair, 64, Capt., 65; Tennis VI, 62–65, Capt., 64 & 65; Levée; Head of House. Balliol, Oxford. Advertising in Chicago. Brothers, 446 & 447.

2165 **COCKERTON, Michael Richard,** b. 13 Aug. 47, s. of R. W. P. Cockerton (OR Tu 18). Tu, 61²–65³; Levée; Cap, 65. Imperial Coll., London, B.Sc. Graduate Apprenticeship with Davy & United Engineering Co. Presently with Goodwin Cockerton & Colhoun, Solicitors, Bakewell.

2166 **HINGSTON, Peter Alan,** b. 2 Oct. 47, elder s. of R. C. Hingston. Tu, 61²–65³.

2167 **WARNER, Nigel George,** b. 14 Dec. 47, 2nd s. of Sir Edward R. Warner, K.C.M.G., O.B.E. Tu, 61²–65³; R. VIII; Athletics Team, 65. Clare, Cambridge, B.A., A.C.A. Peat, Marwick, Mitchell & Co. Brother, 2483.

2168 **ALBAN-DAVIES, Huw Jenkin,** b. 22 Feb. 48, younger s. of J. Alban-Davies. W, 61²–65³. Exeter, Oxford. Brother, 1521.

2169 **ALDERSON SMITH, Peter Francis,** b. 16 Oct. 47, s. of B. M. Alderson Smith, W, 61²–65¹.

2170 **ARCHER, Edward Peter,** b. 20 Jan. 48, 3rd s. of J. R. Archer, J.P., LL.B. W, 61²–65³. Liverpool Univ. Brothers, 757 & 1494.

2171 **COBB, Stephen Stogdon,** b. 18 Oct. 47, youngest s. of M. H. Cobb. W, 61²–65³; Tennis VI, 65. R.M.A., Sandhurst. Magdalene, Cambridge. 2nd Lt. Commission, 69. Lt., 71. Army Officer in 17/21 Lancers serving in Wolfenbuttel, W. Germany. *Cavalry Club, Scientific Exploration Society.*

2172 **DOBBS, George Denis Kildare,** b. 4 Sept. 47, s. of Major W. B. D. Dobbs. W, 61²–65³; Levée; Head of House. Trinity College, Dublin, B.A., T.C.D. General Manager of W. Weddel & Co. Ltd., Zürich, Switzerland.

2173 **DOXFORD, Richard Andrew,** b. 11 Sept. 47, s. of T. B. Doxford, J.P. (OR W 20). W, 61²–63³.

2174 **THOMAS, Roger John Laugharne,** b. 22 Oct. 47, s. of R. E. L. Thomas. W, 61²–65³; Levée; Senior Scholarship, 64. Leaving Exhibition, 65. Trinity Hall, Cambridge, B.A. Univ. of Chicago Law School (J.D., 70). Commonwealth Fellow. Bar, Gray's Inn, 69.

ENTRANCES IN SEPTEMBER 1961

2175 **BAND, Stephen Henry,** b. 14 Mar. 48, s. of T. H. Band, T.D., LL.B. SH, 61³–65³; XV, 64, 65; H. XI, 64. Univ. of Sussex, M.A. Postgraduate student working for a D.Phil. in Modern French Literature.

2176 **DAVID, Jonathan Miles,** b. 10 June 48, elder s. of W. M. David (OR SH 29). SH, 61³–64³; Scholar. Exeter Univ. Brother, 2435.

2177 **HAMILTON - WILKES, John Keene Christopher,** b. 11 Jan. 48, s. of J. L. Hamilton-Wilkes. SH, 61³–66².

2178 **MAITLAND, David Graham,** b. 8 July 48, eldest s. of A. Maitland (OR SH 27). SH, 61³–66²; Scholar. Trinity, Cambridge. Wm. Brandt's Sons & Co. Ltd. Brothers, 2946 & Robert Forbes, SH, 68³–.

2179 **NEWTON, John Owen,** b. 30 Jan. 48, s. of K. O. Newton. SH, 61³–65³; Scholar; XI, 64, 65; H. XI, 65. Clare, Cambridge, B.A. Capt. of Real Tennis Team. Fine Art Expert, Sotheby & Co. *M.C.C., Royal Tennis Court.*

2180 **OSBOURNE, Kerry,** b. 14 Nov. 47, s. of K. Osbourne. SH, 61³–66¹. Bristol Univ., Law Society College, LL.B. Birmingham Law Society Bronze Medal, 70. Asst. Solicitor in private practice. *Lichfield City Orchestral Society.*

2181 **POOLE, Adrian Douglas Bruce,** b. 2 Sept. 48, s. of the late L. N. B. Poole. SH, 61³–66²; Scholar; Levée; Head of House; XV, 65; XI, 64, 65, Capt., 66. Classical Scholarship to Trinity, Cambridge, B.A. Senior Scholarship and Research Scholarship at Trinity, 70. Research Student for Ph.D., English, Cambridge Univ.

2182 **SCOTT, John George Stewart,** b. 25 Dec. 47, s. of Professor G. I. Scott, F.R.C.P.E., F.R.C.S.Ed., F.R.S.E., C.B.E. SH, 61³–66². University of Stirling, B.A. Morgan Grenfell & Co. Ltd. *R.A.C., Royal Philatelic Society.*

2183 **THOMAS, Patrick Anthony,** b. 30 Oct. 48, younger s. of B. A. Thomas. SH, 61³–66³; Scholar; Leaving Exhibition; Dewar Travelling Scholarship. Open Scholarship to Lincoln, Oxford. Brother, 1856.

2184 **BATT, Philip John,** b. 18 July 48, eldest s. of P. A. Batt (OR T 33). T, 61³–66³. Exhibition to Emmanuel, Cambridge, B.A. Valuer, District Valuer's Office (Inland Revenue), Brixton, London.

2185 **BLOOM, Geoffrey Michael,** b. 19 Nov. 47, elder s. of L. H. Bloom, B.E.M. T, 61³–66²; Levée; Head of House; XI, 65, 66. Bristol Univ., B.Sc. Commercial Pilot's Licence with Instrument Rating & Performance "A", 70. Commercial Airline Pilot with B.E.A. since 71.

2186 **BRUCE, George James,** b. 23 Aug. 47, s. of G. A. Bruce. T, 61³–66². Newcastle Univ.

2187 **FOOTTIT, George Thomas Welch,** b. 29 May 48, younger s. of E. H. Foottit. T, 61³–66³; Levée; Head of House. Exhibition to St. John's, Cambridge, B.A. Postgraduate Student at present with Univ. of Ghana. Brother, 1254.

2188 **HARRIS, Philip Andrew,** b. 29 Jan. 48, younger s. of L. Harris. T, 61³–66². Durham Univ., B.Sc. Birmingham Univ., Cert.Ed. Schoolmaster. Second in Physics Dept., King Edward's School, Birmingham.

2189 **KEY, Roger Vincent,** b. 29 Dec. 47, elder s. of M. Key. T, 61³–66²; R. VIII, 66; Athletics Colours, 66. Univ. of Warwick, B.A. Louvaine Univ. (Belgium), Grande Distinction N/Sc. Balliol, Oxford. Associate Member, Institute of Linguists (German), 69. Economist. World Bank of Development & Construction, Washington, D.C. Brother, 2792.

2190 **PROUT, David John,** b. 13 Nov. 47, s. of D. C. Prout, B.Sc. T, 61³–65³. Reading Univ., B.A., L.S.I.A. Publicity Manager, Graphic Systems Ltd., London.

2191 **RUSSELL, Robert John Caird Gus,** b. 25 Apr. 48, younger s. of A. J. Russell, B.Sc. T, 61³–65³. Imperial College, London. Brother, 1714.

2192 **SIMPSON, Peter James,** b. 8 Oct. 47, 2nd s. of the late Rev. J. R. Simpson (OR B & T 17). T, 61³–66²; Levée; Holder of Bigside Bags; Athletics Colours. Liverpool Univ., B.A., C.Q.S.W. Probation Officer. *Liverpool Potholing Club.* Brother, 2503.

2193 **WILLIAMSON, Jonathan,** b. 18 Aug. 48, s. of A. Williamson. T, 61³–66³. St. Edmund Hall, Oxford.

2194 **ADAMS, William Richard Christopher,** b. 24 Dec. 47, elder s. of W. A. Adams, J.P. (OR B 23). B, 61³–66¹. Exeter Univ., B.A., A.C.A. Chartered Accountant. Brother, Michael Edward, B, 68¹–.

2195 **ETCHES, Nicholas Peter,** b. 22 June 48, elder s. of Col. W. W. Etches, M.C. (OR B 35). B, 61³–66²; Levée; Head of House; S. VIII, 64, Capt., 65. Chartered Accountant with Peat Marwick Mitchell & Co. *North London Rifle Club.* Brother, John Philip, B, 69²–.

2196 **GRIFFITHS, Nigel Ernest Frederick,** b. 9 June 48, s. of E. E. Griffiths. B, 61³–65³; Scholar; Levée; Head of House. Scholar of Jesus, Cambridge. Rex-Moir Prize for highest 1st Cl. Hons. in Mech. Sc. Tr. & Distinction in Man. Studies. C.Eng. M.I.Mech.E., M.I.E.E. Partner, Ernest Griffiths & Son, Consulting Engineers, in Mechanical & Electrical

Systems in Buildings. *Royal Liverpool G.C.*

2197 HARDCASTLE, Corin Geoffrey Kenyon, b. 9 Jan. 48, twin (elder) s. of H. K. Hardcastle, T.D. B, 61^3–65^3; Cap, 64. Reading Univ.

2198 MORRISON, David Peter, b. 14 Feb. 48, s. of P. Morrison. B, 61^3–65^3. Downing, Cambridge.

2199 REED-HERBERT, Peter Anthony Fry, b. 7 Mar. 48, eldest s. of R. Herbert, T.D. B, 61^3–66^2. Exeter Univ., B.Sc. College of Law, Guildford. Solicitor. Brother, 2973.

2200 TALLON, John Mark, b. 19 Mar. 48, younger s. of C. R. Tallon (OR T 23). B, 61^3–65^3; Levée; XI, 65. Worcester, Oxford. Accountant. Brother, 1071.

2201 WHEATLEY, Philip Andrew, b. 25 Mar. 48, 3rd s. of Sir G. A. Wheatley, C.B.E., B.C.L. (OR B 22). B, 61^3–66^2. Southampton University, LL.B. Assistant Solicitor to Berkshire County Council. *Ski Club of Great Britain.* Brothers, 768 & 1072.

2202 BROWN, Alan James, b. 9 June 48, s. of Dr. H. J. Brown. C, 61^3–66^2; Levée; XV, 63–65; Athletics Colours, 65–66.

2203 BROWN, David Farrer (name changed to Farrer-Brown), b. 2 May 48, s. of J. Brown, M.D., F.F.R., D.M.R.D. C, 61^3–65^3. Exhibition to Jesus, Cambridge. St. Thomas's Hospital, London, B.A., M.B., B.Chir. Medical Profession.

2204 DEMAN, Michael Timothy Dent, b. 4 June 48, elder s. of E. P. Deman, M.C. C, 61^3–66^1. Kent University. Brother, Peter Humphrey, C, 71^3–.

2205 DOEL, Christopher John, b. 29 Mar. 48, s. of W. H. Doel. C, 61^3–65^3. St. Catherine's, Oxford.

2206 HILLS, Nicholas Hyde, b. 9 Dec. 47, s. of W. H. Hills, M.B.E., T.D. C, 61^3–66^2; Levée; Head of House; XV, 65; XI, 65. Pembroke, Cambridge, B.A. Solicitor's Articled Clerk with Trower, Still & Keeling, Lincolns Inn. *M.C.C., Royal St. George's G.C.*

2207 JACKSON, Rowan Anthony Frederick Paul, b. 20 Mar. 48, elder s. of Lt.-Col. A. F. J. G. Jackson, E.R.D. C,

61^3–66^2. Birmingham University Medical School. Royal Marines since 69. Lt. *M.C.C.* Brother, 2663.

2208 JONES, Robin David Russell, b. 5 Mar. 48, s. of J. L. R. Jones, J.P. C, 61^3–66^1; Cap, 65; Leaving Exhibition. Scholar of Peterhouse, Cambridge, M.A. St. Thomas's Hospital, M.B., B.Chir. Medical Practitioner.

2209 BLASKEY, John David, b. 28 Mar. 48, elder s. of M. Blaskey. K, 61^3–66^2. Scottish Regional Retail Supervisor with Leyland Paints & Wallpaper Co. Ltd. Nat. Chrmn., Younger Jewish Nat. Fund. Brother, 2668.

2210 de CHASSIRON, Charles Richard Lucien, b. 27 Apr. 48, s. of Brigadier H. E. C. de Chassiron, C.B.E. K, 61^3–65^3; Scholar. Jesus, Cambridge, B.A. Harvard University, Boston, U.S.A., M.P.A. Member of H.M. Diplomatic Service, at present Third Secretary, British Embassy, Stockholm, Sweden.

2211 GEBOLYS, Julian Christopher, b. 20 Mar. 48, s. of J. Gebolys, A.F.C. K, 61^3–66^3; Levée; Cap, 66; H. XI, 66. Trinity Hall, Cambridge, B.A. Barrister. *Manchester Tennis & Racquets Club, St. James' Club.*

2212 HOLDSWORTH, David John Melrose, b. 9 Apr. 48, s. of J. R. N. Holdsworth, LL.B. K, 61^3–66^3.

2213 KELLETT, John Charles, b. 10 Mar. 48, 3rd s. of late C. N. Kellett. K, 61^3–66^3; XV, 65. Fitzwilliam, Cambridge.

2214 POLLARD, Christopher Vincent, b. 22 Aug. 48, younger s. of S. C. Pollard. K, 61^3–66^3. Civil Engineering degree at Bristol University. Articled Clerk to Chartered Accountant. *Sidmouth G.C., Bristol Arts Centre.* Brother, 1738.

2215 RIGBY, Hugh Macbeth, b. 18 Apr. 47, 2nd s. of Sir H. J. M. Rigby, Bt., E.R.D. (OR K 28). K, 61^3–66^2; Levée; Cap, 66; H. XI, 66; Capt. of Athletics, 66. Art Student, Manchester Polytechnic. Brothers, 2054, 2380 & 2825.

2216 CARR, Stephen James, b. 25 June 48, 3rd s. of S. D. Carr. M, 61^3–66^2. Southampton University. Brothers, 846 & 1286.

2217 COLLINS, Philip Geoffrey Hugh, b. 19 Jan. 48, s. of Sir G. A.

Collins, LL.B. (OR M 02). M, 61³–66³; Levée; Head of House. Exeter University.

2218 FAIRBANK, Jeremy Charles Thomas, b. 14 May 48, elder s. of T. J. Fairbank, F.R.C.S. (OR M 26). M, 61³–65³. Trinity, Cambridge. St. Thomas's Hospital Medical School, M.B., B.Chir. House Surgeon, Lambeth Hospital. House Physician, Southampton General Hospital, from Feb. 73.

2219 HIBBIT, Michael Oliver Douglas, b. 12 Mar. 48, s. of D. C. Hibbit, B.Sc., Ph.D. M, 61³–66². Trinity College, Ontario.

2220 KENRICK, Philip Michael, b. 9 Oct. 48, 3rd s. of W. E. Kenrick (OR M 22). M, 61³–66²; Scholar. Balliol, Oxford, B.A. Presently studying for Diploma in Classical Archaeology. *British Astronomical Assoc.* Brother, 996.

2221 PITT, William Hewitt Armine, b. 1 Jan. 48, s. of late S. H. Pitt, M.C. (OR M 05). M, 61³–66²; Fencing IV, 63–65. Southampton University, LL.B. Civil Servant (Foreign Office). *Soton Univ. Boat Club.*

2222 SLOTOVER, Richard Emil Simmon, b. 24 Feb. 48, younger s. of M. L. Slotover, F.R.C.S. M, 61³–66². The College of Law. Barrister at Law. Trainee Executive, Hardy & Co. Furnishers Ltd. Brother, 1674.

2223 BEDDINGTON, Norman Roger, b. 17 Mar. 48, s. of R. E. L. Beddington. SF, 61³–66². Bristol University, B.A. Kingston Polytechnic, Diploma in Town Planning. Town Planning Assistant, London Borough of Ealing, 72. *British Film Institute, Covent Garden Community Assoc.*

2224 BLAIR, David Howie, b. 10 Apr. 48, youngest s. of A. C. Blair, C.V.O., T.D., W.S. SF, 61³–65³; Levée; Head of House. Aberdeen University, LL.B. Merchant Banking. Brothers, 932, 1146 & 1901.

2225 BRUN, Edward Henrik Constantin, b. 24 Feb. 48, 3rd s. of H. C. Brun. SF, 61³–66². Dundee University. Brothers, 853 & 1147.

2226 EVERS, Hugh Simon, b. 15 May 48, 4th s. of C. R. Evers (OR SF 21). SF, 61³–66³; Levée; Head of House; Head of School Music. Edinburgh University, 67–68. V.S.O. Teacher in Lesotho, 69–70.

Christ Church College, Canterbury, 70–72, Cert.Ed. Teacher i/c Biology, Rugger & English, Betteshanger School (I.A.P.S. Co-ed), Nr. Deal, Kent, since 72. Brothers, 697, 837 & 1599.

2227 GOW, David William Mearns, b. 15 Dec. 47, s. of the late H. M. Gow (OR SF 22). SF, 61³–65²; XV, 64; Capt. of School Fencing, 63–64. Newspaper Executive, Times Newspaper Ltd., London. *Army & Navy Club.*

2228 JENKINS, Roger Nicholas Richmond, b. 31 Mar. 48, younger s. of C. R. Jenkins, F.F.A.R.C.S., D.A. SF, 61³–66²; Scholar; Levée; Head of House; Head of School; XI, 65–66; XV, 65, Capt., 66; H. XI, 66, Capt. Open Scholar in Classics to Trinity, Cambridge, B.A. Capt. in the Royal Green Jackets. *Hawks Club.* Brother, 1751.

2229 KING, Patrick Anthony, b. 25 Feb. 48, s. of D. C. King. SF, 61³–66². Sir George Williams University, Montreal, B.Com. Internal Auditor, Burns Foods Ltd., Calgary, Alberta, Canada. American Marketing Assoc.

2230 LUTYENS, Richard David, b. 1 July 48, elder s. of J. L. Lutyens (OR SF 31). SF, 61³–66²; H. XI. St. Edmund Hall, Oxford. Brother, 2449.

2231 MACFARLANE, Alistair Tom Robert, b. 12 Mar. 48, s. of T. A. Macfarlane. SF, 61³–66¹; Levée; XV, 65. Exeter University. Articled to Harwood, Banner & Co., Chartered Accountants, Liverpool.

2232 OAKLEY, George David Gastineau, b. 26 Apr. 48, s. of Dr. D. E. Oakley. SF, 61³–65³. Internal Scholar of King's, Cambridge, B.A. Westminster Medical School, taking final M.B., B.Chir., 73. Medical Student.

2233 SIMPSON, Walter Robert, b. 14 Jan. 48, elder s. of G. R. Simpson, D.S.O., T.D. (OR SF 30). SF, 61³–66¹; S. VIII. Brother, 2540.

2234 VARLEY, James Gilbert, b. 7 May 48, s. of the late E. F. Varley (OR SF 26). SF, 61³–65².

2235 VAUDREY, Jonathan Clough, b. 11 May 48, 3rd s. of J. R. Vaudrey, M.B.E. (OR SF 29). SF, 61³–66²; Levée; Sw. IX, 64–66; Cadet Officer, C.C.F., 66. University of Bristol, B.Vet.Sc. Member of The Royal College of Veterinary Surgeons. General Practice. British Veterinary Assoc. Brother, 1302.

2236 ALCOCK, Michael Reginald, b. 11 Feb. 48, s. of R. J. Alcock, M.B.,B.Chir. (OR Sh 31). Sh, 61³–65³; Scholar. University of Bristol, B.A. Export Sales, Oxford University Press, 70–72. Deputy Managing Editor, Tom Stacey Ltd., London from 72.

2237 BATES, Marcus Frank Vincent, b. 23 Mar. 48, elder s. of J. A. V. Bates, M.B., B.Chir. (OR Sh 32). Sh, 61³–65². St. Catharine's, Cambridge for two years. Suffered serious motor accident and lost memory. Intend to return to University when fit again. Brother, 2486.

2238 BICKERSTETH, Michael Cameron, b. 5 July 48, eldest s. of E. J. Bickersteth. Sh, 61³–66². Dundee University. Brother, 2696.

2239 BRUCE, William Alexander, b. 15 July 48, s. of I. D. Bruce. Sh, 61³–66²; Levée; Head of House; Sw. IX, 66. City of London College, business studies. A.C.A. Chartered Accountant.

2240 DOYLE, Richard, b. 10 Jan. 48, 2nd s. of the late W. P. Doyle, T.D. (OR B 18). Sh, 61³–63³. Lincoln, Oxford.

2241 FRAZER, John Anthony, b. 22 May 48, elder s. of J. W. Frazer, V.R.D. Sh, 61³–66³; Levée; Head of House. Trinity College, Dublin. Brother, 2747.

2242 MILLER, Gerald James, b. 23 Aug. 48, s. of I. G. Miller (OR Sh 30). Sh, 61³–66²; Athletics Colours, 66. University of Newcastle, B.A., Dip.Ed. At present in Ceylon.

2243 MOYERS, William Peter Richard, b. 4 June 48, s. of H. W. Moyers (OR Sh 30). Sh, 61³–66². Diploma in Social Studies. Trainee Social Worker.

2244 PARRY, Richard Alan, b. 29 May 48, younger s. of the late A. W. Parry, J.P. Sh, 61³–66²; Sw. IX, 64–66. Brother, 1834.

2245 YOUNG, Jonathan Peter Andrew, b. 8 Mar. 48, s. of D. A. Young. Sh, 61³–66². University of Exeter, B.A. Articled Clerk, Deloitte & Co., Chartered Accountants.

2246 BARKLA, Charles Harvard, b. 17 Nov. 47, s. of P. C. Barkla, F.R.C.S., F.R.C.O.G. St, 61³–66³. Cap, 66.

2247 BOVEY, Philip Henry, b. 11 July 48, eldest s. of N. H. Bovey, O.B.E., D.S.C. St, 61³–66³; Queen Victoria Memorial Prize, 66; Leaving Exhibition, 66. Peterhouse, Cambridge, Entrance Scholar, 67–69; Senior Scholar, 69–70; B.A., 70. At present studying also for LL.B.(Cantab). Diplomatic Service, 70–71. Solicitor's Articled Clerk since 71. Brothers, 2854 & William Evan Norman, M, 69³–.

2248 DENBY, Peter Jonathan, b. 25 Jan. 48, 2nd s. of C. H. Denby. St, 61³–66². Brother, 1767.

2249 FARMAN, Ian Glencairn Crisp, b. 27 Oct. 47, s. of S. C. Farman, M.B., B.S. St, 61³–65³. Southampton University, LL.B. College of Law. Legal & Taxation Specialist in the field of Occupational Pension Schemes, with Metropolitan Pensions Ltd., Chichester. Royal Air Force Reserves at the *Naval Club.*

2250 FORSTER-COOPER, Clive John, b. 21 Apr. 48, s. of J. Forster-Cooper, T.D. (OR St 27). St, 61³–66².

2251 KERSHAW, David Ross, b. 25 Mar. 48, younger s. of G. R. Kershaw, M.R.C.S., L.R.C.P., D.P.H. St, 61³–66². Reinsurance Correspondent with Willis, Faber & Dumas Ltd. Brother, 1482.

2252 LAING, John Stuart, b. 22 July 48, elder s. of G. D. Laing, M.B., B.Chir. (OR St 30). St, 61³–66¹; Scholar; Levée; Head of School Music; Capt. of Squash. Scholar of Corpus Christi, Cambridge, B.A. H.M. Diplomatic Service. Studied Arabic at Middle East Centre for Arab Studies, 71–72. 3rd Secretary, British Embassy, Jedda from Feb. 73. Brothers, Richard George, St, 67³–71³ & Andrew Marcus, K, 68³–.

2253 LESLIE, Malcolm Christopher Stewart, b. 8 Apr. 48, younger s. of B. S. Leslie (OR St 33). St, 61³–66². St. Andrews University, M.A. Banking, presently with a U.S. Bank. *M.C.C.; R. & A.* Brother, 1918.

2254 SYMINGTON, Nigel Howard, b. 9 Aug. 48, 3rd s. of the late S. P. Symington, M.C., T.D. (OR St 23). St, 61³–65². Clare, Cambridge, B.A. Currently reading for Masters Degree in Business Admin. (M.B.A.) at Cornell University. Voluntary Service Overseas, 69–70, teaching Physics in Guyana. Productivity Services Engineer with Richard Costain Ltd., 70–72. Brothers, 878 & 1996.

2255 **COMPSTON, David Alastair Standish,** b. 23 Jan. 48, elder s. of N. D. Compston, M.D., F.R.C.P. Tu, 61³–65²; XXII, 64–65. Middlesex Hospital Medical School, M.B., B.S., M.R.C.P. At Dept. of Medicine, Royal Postgraduate Medical School, Hammersmith Hospital. Brother, Robin James Dean, Tu, 68³–.

2256 **GRIME, Peter Anthony,** b. 16 Feb. 48, s. of D. H. Grime. Tu, 61³–66²; Levée; Sailing VI, 66. Southampton University.

2257 **HARTLEY, William Thomas,** 2 June 48, s. of J. E. Hartley. Tu, 61³–66³; Levée; Head of House; XV, 64–66; XI, 66. Director of Farming Co. in Yorks./ Lincs.

2258 **JACKSON-SMYTH, Richard Meredith,** b. 28 Nov. 47, s. of Lt.-Col. M. G. Jackson-Smyth, R.A.M.C. Tu, 61³–66²; Sw. IX, 63–65, Capt., 66. Birmingham University, B.Sc. Diploma in Management Studies. Completed indentured apprenticeship with Rolls-Royce Ltd., Bristol Engine Div., Coventry. Presently employed in the Industrial Engineering Dept., Rolls-Royce, Ansty, Nr. Coventry.

2259 **KNOWLES, James Burbank, jnr.,** b. 27 Dec. 43, elder s. of J. B. Knowles of Conn., U.S.A. Tu, 61³–62². Yale University.

2260 **NEWMAN, Michael Sebastian Hugh,** b. 6 Jan. 48, eldest s. of J. H. Newman. Tu, 61³–65². Six months as Filing Clerk. Six years as Journalist. At present Milkman and Property Tycoon. *Wellingborough Chess Club.*

2261 **OLIVER, Simon Kingston Howard,** b. 14 Nov. 47, s. of W. B. Oliver, D.F.C. Tu, 61³–66²; Levée; Head of House; Sw. IX, 64–65; Athletics Colours, 65. The University of British Columbia, B.C., Canada, B.A. Teacher, St. George's School, Vancouver. V.S.O. in Botswana, 66–67.

2262 **ALLEN, Ronald Hugh Taylor,** b. 20 Mar. 48, 2nd s. of the Rev. Canon R. E. T. Allen, M.C. (OR W 10). W, 61³–66¹. Trained in Personnel Management. Personnel Dept., Joseph Lucas Ltd., B'ham., 67–70. Took an expedition to Bombay. Wrote history of Indian branch of G.K.N. Writer & Partner in Sailing School/Outdoor Activities Development in West Highlands. Brother, 2724.

2263 **COMMON, John Dermot Ainslie,** b. 12 July 48, s. of S. A. Common. W, 61³–65³.

2264 **CULLINGWORTH, Michael Jonathan,** b. 5 Nov. 47, s. of J. J. Cullingworth, J.P. W, 61³–66²; Sw. IX, 66. St. Clare's Hall, Oxford, B.A. Studying Fine Art at Goldsmith's College, S.E.14.

2265 **GARVEY, William Francis Bonaventure,** b. 27 June 48, elder s. of T. W. Garvey, C.M.G. W, 61³–66¹. University College, Oxford. Brother, 2779.

2266 **GRAY, Anthony John Gordon,** b. 3 May 48, s. of S. T. G. Gray, M.B., Ch.B., D.P.H. W, 61³–65³. Peterhouse, Cambridge, B.A., M.B., B.Chir. St. Bartholomew's Hospital, Medical College. Medicine. House Officer, Norfolk & Norwich Hospital, Norwich.

2267 **HASTINGS, John Christopher,** b. 4 May 48, s. of W. M. Hastings. W, 61³–65². Williams College, Mass., U.S.A., B.A. Yale School of Drama, Conn., U.S.A. Actor. Long Wharf Theatre, New Haven, Conn., U.S.A., 70–72. Edinburgh Festival, 71. Broadway, 72–73 ("Butley", starring Alan Bates). Television, 72–73 (C.B.S. T.V.).

2268 **NEWBOLD, John,** b. 19 June 48, s. of J. C. Newbold, M.B., B.Ch., F.R.C.S., F.R.C.O.G. W, 61³–66³. Liverpool University, LL.B. Solicitor's Articled Clerk.

2269 **SMITH, Mark Peter Victor,** b. 5 Feb. 48, s. of Lt.-Cdr. V. C. S. Smith, R.N. W, 61³–66¹; Levée; Head of House. Durham University, B.Sc. Postgraduate Cert. in Education. Research Asst. at Durham University Business School.

ENTRANCES IN JANUARY 1962

2270 **GILCHRIST, Christopher Graham,** b. 29 Sept. 48, elder s. of Sir A. G. Gilchrist, K.C.M.G. SH, 62¹–66³. Trinity, Cambridge. Brother, 2584.

2271 **JACKSON-POWNALL, Charles Ian Hughes,** b. 26 Aug. 48, 2nd s. of H. Jackson-Pownall. SH, 62¹–66². Brother, 1369.

2272 **LUMSDEN, James Malcolm Campbell,** b. 3 Aug. 48, eldest s. of J. A. Lumsden, LL.B., M.B.E. (OR SH 28). SH, 62¹–66². Royal Agricultural College, Cirencester. A.R.I.C.S. Assistant in firm of Chartered Surveyors & Land Agents. Also Farming. Brothers, 2632 & 2907.

2273 **MELVILLE, Temple Douglas Mitchell,** b. 3 Sept. 48, s. of G. B. T. Melville. SH, 62^1–66^2. L.S.E.

2274 **BAYLY, Peter John,** b. 10 Aug. 48, s. of L. P. Bayly. B, 62^1–66^3. Mid-Herts. College of Further Education.

2275 **BRUCE, Anthony James Lewis,** b. 25 June 48, younger s. of R. R. F. Bruce. D.F.C., B.Mus. (OR B 29). B, 62^1–66^2; H. XI, 66. University of Wales, Institute of Science & Technology, Cardiff, B.Sc. Laboratory Assistant, C.E.G.B., Anglesey. Brother, 1342.

2276 **BRYANT, Henry Harcourt,** b. 2 July 48, s. of J. M. Bryant. B, 62^1–65^2.

2277 **FETHERSTON-DILKE, Michael Charles,** b. 30 Dec. 48, s. of Capt. F. C. B. Fetherston-Dilke, R.N. B, 62^1–66^2. Bristol University.

2278 **FRANKS, David Arthur,** b. 9 July 48, s. of A. T. Franks, C.M.G. (OR B 34). B, 62^1–66^2. B.A., Business Studies. The British Oxygen Co. Ltd., London. *Sunningdale G.C.*

2279 **CLIFT, Hugh Williams Paul,** b. 2 Aug. 48, elder s. of F. P. Clift. C, 62^1–66^2. High Wycombe College of Technology & Art. Postgraduate Diploma in Export Marketing. S.E. Asia Area Man., Sanitas Group of Cos. Brother, 2660.

2280 **BRAITHWAITE, Jeremy Hunter,** b. 18 Aug. 48, elder s. of Lt.-Col. T. C. Braithwaite, O.B.E., T.D. (OR K 26). K, 62^1–65^1.

2281 **IRWIN, Keith Henry Adamson,** b. 19 Aug. 48, s. of H. F. G. Irwin, M.B., B.Ch., B.A.O. K, 62^1–66^3. Emmanuel, Cambridge.

2282 **DOBELL, Anthony Russell,** b. 15 Sept. 48, s. of T. R. Dobell, M.B.E., T.D. M, 62^1–66^2. Chartered Accountant.

2283 **DUNKERLEY, Eric Peter,** b. 19 Sept. 48, elder s. of late E. W. Dunkerley. (OR M 19). M, 62^1–65^2.

2284 **WILSON, Malcolm MacArthur,** b. 12 Mar. 48, younger s. of T. I. Wilson. M, 62^1–66^3. Exhibition to St. Peter's, Oxford.

2285 **FRASER, Simon Beaufort,** b. 8 Aug. 48, s. of D. B. Fraser, M.B., B.S. SF, 62^1–67^2; Levée; S. VIII, 65–66, Capt., 67. Army officer in the 1st Bn. Coldstream Gds. G.S.M. (Northern Ireland). Stick of Honour on passing out of Mons, O.C.S.

2286 **WALTERS, John Latimer,** b. 15 Sept. 48, s. of J. P. Walters. SF, 62^1–66^3; Balliol, Oxford, B.A. *Naval & Military Club.*

2287 **HUCKLE, Alan Edden,** b. 15 June 48, s. of A. A. Huckle. Sh, 62^1–64^1. Warwick University.

2288 **MICHAEL, Nicholas David,** b. 25 July 48, s. of V. D. Michael. Sh, 62^1–66^2. Neuchâtel, Switzerland.

2289 **SMALLPAGE, Quentin Nigel,** b. 26 July 48, s. of F. N. Smallpage. Sh, 62^1–66^2. Leeds University.

2290 **WRIGHT, John Nicholas Budd,** b. 1 Aug. 48, elder s. of R. B. Wright, M.B., B.Chir., F.F.A.R.C.S. (OR Sh 30). Sh, 62^1–66^2; Levée; H. XI, 66, XI, 64–66. St. Thomas's Hospital, M.B., B.S. Houseman, St. Thomas's Hospital since Jan. 73. Orthopaedics. Medicine. Brother, Michael James Robert, Sh, 69^3–.

2291 **COLVER, Allan Froggatt,** b. 15 July 48, elder s. of late T. Colver, V.R.D., M.D. St, 62^1–67^1; Levée; Head of House; XV, 66; Tennis VI, 66; Fives IV, 65–67. Magdalene, Cambridge, B.A. St. Bartholomew's Hospital. Medical Student. Brother, 2554.

2292 **WALKER, David Frank,** b. 13 May 48, eldest s. of H. G. Walker, LL.B. Tu, 62^1–66^2. Brothers, 2566 & 2941.

2293 **BURROWS, James Lee,** b. 22 June 48, 3rd s. of J. D. Burrows. W, 62^1–66^3; Levée; Cap, 66; XI, 66; H. XI, 65–66. Royal Agricultural College, M.R.A.C. N.D.A. Farmer. *Leicester Hockey Club, Leicestershire Gents C.C.*

2294 **CONNELL, Simon Richard de Belair,** b. 13 Aug. 48, 3rd s. of Capt. R. H. Connell, D.S.C., R.N. W, 62^1–66^2; Athletic Colours, 66. Trinity College, Dublin, B.A. English Assistant in Lycée, St. Louis, Paris, 71–72. At present working in Austin Reed, with intention of moving to Personnel Management in the near future.

2295 **HOMFRAY-DAVIES, Michael David,** b. 7 July 48, s. of B. R. A. Homfray-Davies. W, 62¹–66².

ENTRANCES IN MAY 1962

2296 **ATTENBOROUGH, Jonathan James,** b. 26 Nov. 48, younger s. of A. R. Attenborough (OR K 26). SH, 62²–66³; XV, 65, Capt., 66; H. XI, 65, Capt., 66; XXII, 66. Went to Australia. Brother, 1978.

2297 **BRIGGS, Roger Selwyn James,** b. 29 Oct. 48, s. of late J. R. Briggs, V.R.D., F.R.C.S. SH, 62²–66². King's College, London & King's College Hospital Medical School. M.B., B.S., L.R.C.P., M.R.C.S. House Physician to Professional Medical Unit, King's College Hospital. Awarded Sir William Simpson Prize in Tropical Medicine, 70.

2298 **HANSON-LAWSON, Michael John,** b. 10 Oct. 48, s. of J. G. Hanson-Lawson (OR SH 28). SH, 62²–66².

2299 **JOCKELSON, David Andrew Wainwright,** b. 30 Nov. 48, younger s. of Major J. J. Jockelson, M.C. SH, 62²–66². Warwick University. Brother, 1552.

2300 **ODGERS, Robin Charles Blake,** b. 17 Dec. 48, s. of P. R. Odgers, C.B., M.B.E., T.D. (OR Tu 29). SH, 62²–67¹; Levée; Head of House. New College, Oxford, B.A. Guy's Hospital, London. Medical Student. *Vincent's Club, Oxford.*

2301 **RUSSELL, Malcolm Alexander,** b. 5 Oct. 48, eldest s. of M. McC. Russell, M.B., B.S. SH, 62²–66². Exeter University. Brother, 2462.

2302 **WILSON, Richard Alwyn,** b. 23 Nov. 48, s. of C. J. Wilson, T.D. (OR SF 18). SH, 62²–66³; XV, 66; H. XI, 65–66; Tennis VI, 66. Vancouver City Tech. University of British Columbia.

2303 **MACGREGOR, Thomas David,** b. 23 Nov. 48, s. of T. R. Macgregor (OR B 29). B, 62²–66³; Levée; Cap, 65. St. Andrew's University. Stockbroking, Wood Mackenzie & Co. *R. & A. G.C., H.C.E.G.*

2304 **SHEARER, Anthony Patrick,** b. 24 Oct. 48, younger s. of J. F. Shearer, O.B.E. (OR B 26). B, 62²–66²; Cap, 65. Brother, 2032.

2305 **COLE, Peter Gerald,** b. 24 Sept. 48, 3rd s. of Col. J. R. Cole. C, 62²–66³; Cap, 65; XXII, 66. Jesus, Cambridge. Brothers, 1074, 2038 & 2515.

2306 **DAVIES, Thomas Stephen Graham,** b. 31 Sept. 48, s. of B. G. Davies, L.D.S. C, 62²–66³; Levée; Head of House; Sw. IX. Jesus, Oxford.

2307 **DALBY, Patrick Claude John,** b. 6 Nov. 48, younger s. of Col. C. Dalby, C.B.E. (OR C 16). C, 62²–66³; S. VIII, 65–66. Served with 2nd Bn. The Royal Green Jackets (The King's Royal Rifle Corps), 67–70. *Muthaiga Club, Nairobi.*

2308 **HINKS, Francis George,** b. 24 Dec. 48, 2nd s. of J. A. Hinks, O.B.E. M.A., B.Sc., J.P. C, 62²–66². Pembroke, Cambridge, Land Economy. M.R.I.C.S. Chartered Surveyor employed by Gerald Eve & Co. *Farmer's Club.* Brothers, 2116 & 2740.

2309 **LEE, Robert Nicholas,** b. 10 Dec. 48, youngest s. of R. H. G. Lee. C, 62²–67². British Rail (London Midland Region). Brothers, 1273 & 1577.

2310 **GIRDLER, Peter Thomas Michael Hilsdon,** b. 21 Nov. 48, s. of late Col. A. H. Girdler, O.B.E. K, 62²–66³; XV, 65–66; Athletics Colours. Southampton University.

2311 **HASLAM, Humphrey Edward McConnell,** b. 19 Nov. 48, 3rd s. of E. C. Haslam, J.P. K, 62²–66². Newcastle University.

2312 **WARD, Richard Peter Clifford,** b. 6 July 48, s. of R. C. Ward. K, 62²–66³. The New University of Ulster, Coleraine. Studied English. Accountancy (not yet qualified).

2313 **GOODHART, Robert Anthony Gordon,** b. 15 Dec. 48, s. of Sir J. G. Goodhart, Bt., M.B., B.Chir. (OR M 30). M, 62²–67²; Levée; Head of House; Cap, 66; XI, 66, Capt., 67. Tom Hughes Prize, Guy's Hospital Medical School. London University, M.B., B.S., M.R.C.S., L.R.C.P. Medicine. Junior Medical. Registrar, Vocational Training Scheme in General Practice, Guy's Hospital, London. I. Zingari.

2314 **ORTMANS, Richard Maxwell,** b. 20 Nov. 48, eldest s. of D. H. Ortmans (OR M 36). M, 62²–65³. Brother, 2607.

2315 **WASS, William Blaikie Shafto,** b. 11 Feb. 49, 4th s. of S. H. Wass, M.S., F.R.C.S. M, 62^2-67^2; Sw. IX, 67. London University, LL.B. Solicitor's Articled Clerk. Brothers, 557 & 2126.

2316 **HAY, Alexander Douglas,** b. 2 Aug. 48, elder s. of Lt.-Col. G. H. Hay, D.S.O., D.L. SF, 62^2-66^3. Edinburgh University, B.Sc. Apprentice Chartered Accountant. Brother, 2537.

2317 **RAYMOND, Crispin Piers,** b. 25 Sept. 48, eldest s. of P. Raymond (OR SF 34). SF, 62^2-66^3. Bristol University, B.Sc. Reserve Bank of Australia, Sydney & Melbourne. Brothers, 2693 & Giles Anthony, SF, 67^3-71^3.

2318 **SWAYNE, Anthony William John,** b. 22 Sept. 48, s. of W. G. F. Swayne. SF, 62^2-66^2. Bristol University, B.Sc. A.M.I.E.E. Articled Clerk, Accountancy, 71, passed intermediate.

2319 **ADAM, Christopher James,** b. 13 Dec. 48, elder s. of M. C. Adam (OR Sh 34). Sh, 62^2-66^3; S. VIII, 64–65; Athletics Team, 65. The Architectural Assoc., London. Technician, Nuffield Laboratory of Ophthalmology, Oxford. Brother, Nicholas John, Sh, 70^2-72^2.

2320 **CAREY-HUGHES, Richard John,** b. 18 Dec. 48, s. of J. C. Hughes, M.B., B.Ch. Sh, 62^2-66^3.

2321 **CUTLER, Anthony Morris,** b. 5 Dec. 48, 2nd s. of Sir A. R. Cutler, V.C., K.C.M.G., K.C.V.O., C.B.E. Sh, 62^2-65^3; Athleics Team, 64; Sw. IX, 64. Sydney University, Australia, B.Sc. Brother, 2157.

2322 **GOATLY, Jonathan Howard,** b. 8 Sept. 48, elder s. of J. Goatly (OR Sh 31). Sh, 62^2-67^1; Levée; Head of House; Cap, 66; Athletics Team, 66. The City of London Polytechnic, School of Business. Studying for Finals B.A.(Hons.) Degree in Business Studies. Employed by De Zoete, Bevan & Co., Stockbrokers, London. Brothers, 2487 & 3012.

2323 **TAYLOR, Nigel Philip Seth,** b. 1 Oct. 48, s. of Lt.-Col. P. S. Taylor, M.C. (OR Sh 30). Sh, 62^2-66^3. Chartered Accountant.

2324 **CUNDELL, Peter David,** b. 20 Dec. 48, 2nd s. of K. S. Cundell. St, 62^2-67^2; Levée; XI, 67; Capt. of Rackets, 66–67. Assistant Racehorse Trainer to father. *Butterflies C.C.*

2325 **DAWE, Simon Frank Ramsay,** b. 6 Nov. 48, s. of Lt.-Col. A. R. Dawe, O.B.E. St, 62^2-66^2; Fives IV, 65–66. H.N.D. Business Studies. A.I.L., German. Tufted Carpets Manager, Monsante Textiles Ltd., Bradford.

2326 **RUSSELL, Benjamin Peter,** b. 14 Sept. 48, s. of late B. H. A. Russell (OR St 26). St, 62^2-65^3. O.N.D. & H.N.D. in Textiles at Leicester Polytechnic, 66–70. Started doing Human Sciences course at Hertford, Oxford, Oct. 72.

2327 **AUSTER, Vivian John Whorwood,** b. 11 Nov. 48, s. of P. W. Auster Tu, 62^2-66^3. St. Andrew's University, M.A. Foreign & Commonwealth Office since 71. *East India, Sports & Public Schools Club, M.C.C.*

2328 **BLANDY, Nicholas John,** b. 10 Sept. 48, s. of P. M. Blandy, M.B.E. (OR Tu 28). Tu, 62^2-66^2. College of Law. Articled Clerk to Solicitor.

2329 **LLOYD, Michael William Aubrey,** b. 8 Sept. 48, s. of D. A. Lloyd (OR Tu 36). S. VIII, 65. Southampton University.

2330 **VAN SCHELLE, Charles Jean Francois,** b. 5 Aug. 48, 2nd s. of C. J. Van Schelle. Tu, 62^2-66^2.

2331 **WARREN, Andrew James,** b. 9 Sept. 48, s. of J. F. Warren (OR SH 26). Tu, 62^2-66^2. University of Exeter, B.A. Public Relations Consultant, Burson, Marsteller Ltd. *Aldeburgh G.C.*

2332 **COLLIE, Anthony Mark Robert,** b. 11 Oct. 48, elder s. of H. D. Collie. W, 62^2-66^3. Trinity College, Dublin, B.B.S. Articled Clerk, Price, Waterhouse & Co., Chartered Accountants.

2333 **GORDON, Raymond Francis,** b. 24 Nov. 48, s. of Lt.-Col. W. H. L. Gordon, C.B.E., M.C. (OR St 28). W, 62^2-65^1; Junior Rackets Pair, 64. College of Estate Management. Presently employed by Jones, Lang, Wootten, Surveyors. R.I.C.S. *Lansdowne Club.*

2334 **KAY, Martin Randle,** b. 13 Oct. 48, s. of late H. N. R. Kay (OR W 33). W, 62^2-66^3; Levée; Head of House; XV, 66. Southampton University, LL.B. Solicitor's Articled Clerk, qualifying in 73. Herbert Smith & Co., London. *The Strolling Players.*

2335 **WOOD, David Anthony Chatterton,** b. 12 Nov. 48, 2nd s. of R. C. Wood, W, 62²–66³; XV, 66; Athletics Team, 66. Brother, 2003.

ENTRANCES IN SEPTEMBER 1962

2336 **CHAPMAN, Timothy James,** b. 21 May 49, s. of A. Chapman. SH, 62³–66². Solicitor with Messrs. Elliott & Buckley, Manchester. *St. James's Club, Manchester.*

2337 **DEAN, James Patrick,** b. 30 Jan. 49, elder s. of Sir P. H. Dean, G.C.M.G. (OR SH 22). SH, 62³–67²; Cap, 66. Diploma in Management Studies, Hatfield Polytechnic. Commissioning Certificate, June 68. Direct Short Service Commission in the 1st Bn. The Royal Green Jackets, 68–71. Lt. At present with Bowater Containers Ltd. Div. of the Bowater Corp. Ltd., Sales, since 72. *Brooks's.* Brother, 2630.

2338 **JONES, Robert David,** b. 5 Sept. 49, elder s. of J. D. T. Jones, M.B. M.S., F.R.C.S. SH, 62³–67³; Senior Scholar, 66; Levée; Head of House; XV, 65–67; R. VIII, 65–67; Holder of Bigside Bags, 66–67; Athletics Team; Capt. of Golf, 67. University College, Oxford, Mynors Scholar, B.A. Reading for the Bar. *Vincent's Club, Oxford.* Brother, 2806.

2339 **LESLIE, Malcolm Archibald,** b. 23 Apr. 49, 2nd s. of K. A. S. Leslie, LL.B., W.S. (OR SH 28). SH, 62³–67²; Levée; Head of House. Magdalene, Cambridge, B.A. Merchant Banker with J. Henry Schroder, Wagg & Co. Ltd., London. Brothers, 2009 & 2785.

2340 **MILLS, George Edward,** b. 22 Sept. 46, younger s. of H. R. Mills, O.B.E. SH, 62³–65¹. Bristol University.

2341 **MURRAY, Iain Gordon Peter,** b. 14 Nov. 48, s. of M. G. Murray. SH, 62³–67¹; Levée; Exhibition to Queen's, Oxford. Numismatist with Spink & Son Ltd., London.

2342 **NEWLING, Peter John,** b. 30 May 49, 2nd s. of late A. J. Newling, C.B., C.B.E., M.V.O., T.D. SH, 62³–66³.

2343 **NUSSEIBEH, Jaki Anwar,** b. 29 Apr. 46, eldest s. of H.E. A. Z. Nusseibeh (Governor of Jerusalem). SH, 62³–64². Queen's, Cambridge. Brother, 2786.

2344 **THORNTON, Jeremy Finchett,** b. 23 Mar. 49, s. of G. F. Thornton, T.D. SH, 62³–66³. Bideford School of Art. Hornsey College of Art. Diploma in Art & Design. Free-lance Artist in Mexico & Part-time Lecturer at Mexico University.

2345 **BOOTH, Simon Jonathan,** b. 18 Oct. 48, younger s. of H. Booth. T, 62³–67². University of London, LL.B. Articled Clerk to Sarginson & Co., Solicitors, Coventry. Master of Moots, Warwickshire Law Students Society. Brother, 1706.

2346 **CLAYTON, Anthony Styles,** b. 4 Feb. 49, s. of P. S. Clayton. T, 62³–67³; Levée; Head of House. Sussex University, B.Sc., M.A. Long-term planning studies for British Steel Corp., London since 73.

2347 **CRAXTON, Robert Stephen,** b. 14 May 49, eldest s. of R. T. Craxton. T, 62³–66³. Trinity, Cambridge. Research at Imperial College, London. Theoretical Physics. Brothers, 2788 & Julian Robert, T, 70³–.

2348 **CRESSWELL, Pearson John,** b. 49, s. of J. L. S. Cresswell, M.R.C.S., L.R.C.P. T, 62³–65³.

2349 **HARRATT, Peter John,** b. 20 May 49, elder s. of J. J. Harratt. T, 62³–67³. St. Catherine's, Oxford.

2350 **HARRIS, Richard Michael,** b. 30 Dec. 48, s. of H. C. Harris. T, 62³–67². Merton, Oxford.

2351 **MILWARD, Stephen Henry,** b. 29 Nov. 48, s. of V. E. Milward. T, 62³–67². Manchester University, B.Sc. Trainee Civil Engineer with Costain Civil Engineering Ltd.

2352 **MORGAN, John Hutchinson,** b. 5 Mar. 49, elder s. of R. J. Morgan. T, 62³–67². B.R.N.C., Dartmouth. Lt., Royal Navy. H.M.S. *Gurkha. Naval & Military Club.* Brother, 2644.

2353 **SHAW, Michael Maurice,** b. 7 Mar. 49, elder s. of M. E. Shaw. T, 62³–67¹. Athletics Team. Guy's Hospital Medical School, M.B., B.S., L.R.C.P., M.R.C.S. House Physician, St. Mary's Hospital, Newport, I.O.W. Brother, 2502.

2354 **STANBROOK, Peter Herbert,** b. 20 Feb. 49, elder s. of E. W. Stanbrook, T, 62³–67²; Levée; Head of House. Nottingham University.

2355 STAVELEY, Peter, Herbert, b. 21 June 49, younger s. of H. A. Staveley (A), T, 62^3–67^2. Higher National Certificate, Business Studies. Diploma in Marketing, Institute of Marketing. Retail Sales Executive, Shell-Mex & B.P. Ltd., in the Southampton Area. Brother, 2024.

2356 TOSSWILL, Timothy Maurice Stephen, b. 28 Apr. 49, s. of T. D. Tosswill, T.D. (OR B 28). T, 62^3–65^3. Holborn College of Law.

2357 UNDERWOOD, Malcolm Parnell, b. 8 June 49, s. of D. Underwood. T, 62^3–67^2. B.Sc. Engineering Geology, Portsmouth. Assistant Quarry Man., A.P.C. Ltd., Northfleet, Kent.

2358 BARSTOW, Charles William, b. 19 Jan. 49, 3rd s. of Capt. G. B. Barstow, R.N. (rtd.). B, 62^3–66^2. Brothers, 1341 & 1718.

2359 BOOTH, Peter Maurice, b. 9 Jan. 49, eldest s. of M. Booth, D.F.C. B, 62^3–66^2; S. VIII, 66. Leeds University, B.Sc. Army Officer in the Coldstream Guards. Scientific Exploration Society.

2360 DARLINGTON, Gavin Leslie Brook, b. 27 June 49, s. of A. B. Darlington. B, 62^3–67^3; Levée; Head of School; XV, 67; R. VIII, 66. Downing, Cambridge, B.A. Solicitor's Articled Clerk.

2361 de BOURSAC, Nicholas, b. 5 Apr. 49, 2nd s. of V. de Boursac. (OR W 28). B, 62^3–67^3; Levée; R. VIII, 66–67; Athletics Team, 66–67. Manchester University, B.Sc. Management Trainee, Chase Manhattan Bank, Geneva, Switzerland. Brothers, 1867 & 2914.

2362 de JONGE, Gerald Ashley, b. 3 Dec. 48, s. of W. G. de Jonge, F.C.A. B, 62^3–67^1. Corpus Christi, Oxford, B.A. Articled Clerk, Coopers & Lybrand, Chartered Accountants. *Walton Rowing Club.*

2363 EGERTON BROWNE, Nicholas, b. 12 Apr. 49, s. of C. Egerton Browne. B, 62^3–67^3; R. VIII, 67. University of Edinburgh, B.Sc. Articled Clerk, Chartered Accountancy. *The Flyfishers Club.*

2364 NIMMO, Hugh Gordon, b. 9 Feb. 49, 4th s. of J. A. D. Nimmo (OR B 20). B, 62^3–66^3; Senior Scholarship, 65. Emmanuel, Cambridge, Exhibitioner, 67–69. Senior Scholar, 69–70, B.A. Research Student studying for a Ph.D. in Bio-chemistry at Cambridge Univ. Captain of Emmanuel College Squash Rackets Club, 69–70. Brothers, 1116, 1268 & 1872.

2365 ROBERTS, Jocelyn Guerin Law b. 21 Jan. 49, 4th s. of A. C. Roberts. B, 62^3–66^2. One-year pre-diploma course at Coventry College of Art. Three years diploma course at Central School of Art & Design. Three years postgraduate studies at the Royal College of Art. Completing final year of studies at the Royal College of Art. Dip.A.D.Cert. C.S.A.D, working to M. des R.C.A. Brothers, 673 & 1119.

2366 TIPPETTS, Michael Berriman, b. 19 May 49, s. of R. B. Tippetts (OR B 26). B, 62^3–67^2.

2367 ARMSTRONG, David Stanley, b. 30 Mar. 49, elder s. of H. J. Armstrong. C, 62^3–66^3. Christ Church, Oxford. Computer Consultant. *Naval & Military Club.*

2368 DICK, Gordon Cameron, b. 25 Jan. 49, younger s. of A. L. Dick, M.B., Ch.B., D.O.M.S. C, 62^3–67^2. Brother, 2040.

2369 EVANS, Peter William George, b. 7 Apr. 49, s. of A. J. Evans, M.B., B.Ch. C, 62^3–66^3; Scholar; XV, 66; XI, 66; H. XI, 65–66. Pembroke, Cambridge, B.A. St. Thomas's Hospital, London. Student. Welsh Hockey International, 70. *Hawks & Travellers Hockey Club.*

2370 FERGUSON, Clive Wigham, b. 21 Mar. 49, younger s. of D. J. Ferguson. C, 62^3–67^2; XI, 67; H. XI, 67. Ship Broker employed by P. Wigham Richardson & Co. Ltd. Member of the Baltic Exchange.

2371 HAWKINS, Richard Livingston, b. 15 May 49, s. of R. Hawkins. C, 62^3–67^3; Levée; Winner of Queen's Medal, 67; H. XI, 67. Pembroke, Oxford. St. Thomas's Hospital.

2372 McCOSH, Edward Andrew Hasell, b. 4 Feb. 49, eldest s. of B. K. McCosh. C, 62^3–67^2. Brother, 2977.

2373 MORRISON, Alexander Allan, b. 29 May 49, younger s. of A. Morrison, L.D.S. C, 62^3–67^2. Leeds University. Brother, 1819.

2374 RASHLEIGH - BELCHER, Ormonde Philip Paul, b. 28 Apr. 49, elder s. of J. Rashleigh-Belcher, M.S., F.R.C.S. C, 62^3–67^2.

2375 **CAVE - BROWNE - CAVE, Myles Alfred,** b. 26 Aug. 49, s. of B. W. Cave-Browne-Cave, O.B.E. K, 62³–67³.

2376 **CRAIG, John Jenkinson,** b. 8 Jan. 49, s. of L. J. P. J. Craig. K, 62³–67². U.C.N.W., Bangor, B.Sc. F.C.O., London. *Public Schools Club.*

2377 **CRANSTON, James Neil Percival,** b. 16 June 49, younger s. of R. S. Cranston (OR K 29). K, 62³–67³; Levée; XV, 67; H. XI, 67; XI, 67. Fitzwilliam, Cambridge. Articled Accountant. *Hawks Club, United Oxford & Cambridge Universities Club.* Brother, 1979.

2378 **LLOYD, Jonathan David Henry,** b. 6 Apr. 49, s. of Lt.-Col. H. L. Lloyd, O.B.E., M.C. K, 62³–67².

2379 **MIDDLETON, Colin Tyson,** b. 4 May 49, s. of Lt.-Cdr. H. T. Middleton, R.N., O.B.E. K, 62³–67². City of London College, Chartered Accountant Course, abandoned after 2½ years. Bede College, Durham University & Pennsylvania State University, Teacher Training Course. Training to be a Teacher. *Huntercombe Golf Club.*

2380 **RIGBY, James Erskine,** b. 26 May 49, 3rd. s. of Lt.-Col. Sir H. J. M. Rigby, Bt., E.R.D. (OR K 28). K, 62³–67². Harper Adams Agricultural College, Newport, Salop. National Diplomas Poultry Husbandry & College Dip. in Agric. Marketing & Business Admin. Trooper in "C" Squadron (Cheshire) Queen's Own Yeomanry. *Alderley Edge Cricket, Hockey & Squash Clubs, A.E.C.C.* Brothers, 2054, 2215 & 2825.

2381 **SWANSTON, Andrew Douglas,** b. 19 Jan. 49, 2nd s. of M. Swanston (OR K 35). K, 62³–66¹; Cap, 65; H. XI, 65–66; Athletics Team, 65; Golf Team, 63–66. Pembroke, Cambridge. Brothers, 2055, 2672 & David Mungo, K, 67²–71².

2382 **TWALLIN, Richard Charles Roe,** b. 29 Oct. 48, s. of T. R. Twallin (OR K 25). K, 62³–67²; Levée; Head of House. Emmanuel, Cambridge. With International Computers Ltd., London.

2383 **YOUELL, Nicholas Knights,** b. 6 Dec. 48, s. of A. E. Youell. K, 62³–67²; Tennis VI, 65–67; Capt., 66–67. Fitzwilliam, Cambridge, B.A., LL.B. Studying for Part II Law Society Examinations. To commence Articled Clerkship, 73. *Hawks.*

2384 **BOIS, John Andrew,** b. 6 Jan. 49, 3rd s. of C. H. Bois (OR M 20). M, 62³–67¹; H. XI, 67. Coventry, Cardiff and Birmingham Colleges of Art. Artist.

2385 **BOLTON, Alan James,** b. 1 May 49, younger s. of P. J. Bolton (OR M 28). M, 62³–67². University College of North Wales, Bangor, B.Sc. Currently employed as Research Wood Scientist at University of Aberdeen, Dept. of Forestry. Brother, 2059.

2386 **COLLENETTE, James David Sebastian,** b. 5 Oct. 49, 2nd s. of D. B. Collenette, M.C. M, 62³–67². Scholar. Trinity, Oxford, B.A. Patents publishing firm in London. Shortly to work as analytical chemist at Fisons Agrochemicals, Cambridge.

2387 **PARRY, Anthony,** b. 18 Jan. 49, s. of Prof. C. Parry, LL.D. M, 62³–66³; S. VIII, 66. Queen's, Cambridge, B.A. Licence spéciale en Droit Européen, Institute of European Studies, Brussels University. Bar, (Middle Temple), 71. Assistant Legal Adviser, H.M. Diplomatic Service. Publication: "An Introduction to E.E.C. Law" (with S. P. Hardy). *United Universities Club.*

2388 **TOWNE, Christopher Charles Withers,** b. 11 July 49, 2nd s. of C. E. A. Towne. M, 62³–67²; Levée. Brothers, 2062 & 2930.

2389 **FORSYTH, Charles Martin,** b. 22 Apr. 49, s. of P. A. Forsyth, M.R.C.S., L.R.C.P. (OR SF 22). SF 62³–67²; Levée; Head of House; XV, 66; XI, 66–67; H. XI, 66–67; Capt.; Tennis IX, 64–66. Two years at London Hospital Medical School & Mons O.C.S. Army officer, 2nd Lt., 15th/19th The King's Royal Hussars.

2390 **GARFORTH - BLES, Robert Michael,** b. 20 Mar. 49, elder s. of M. W. Garforth-Bles (OR SF 27). SF, 62³–67²; Athletics Team, 65–67. Colours, 67. Chartered Accountant, 72. Brother, 2688.

2391 **HAWORTH, Charles David,** b.16 June 49, s. of C. W. Haworth (OR SF 18). SF, 62³–67²; XXII, 67. Jesus, Cambridge, B.A. Grad. I.M. Technical Assistant with British United Shoe Machinery Co. Ltd., Leicester. *Cryptics C.C.*

2392 **HINGLEY, Christopher James Howard,** b. 29 Dec. 48, elder s. of A. C. M. Hingley, C.V.O. (OR SF 21). SF, 62³–67¹; Senior Scholar, 65. Open Scholarship to

Trinity, Oxford, B.A. Schoolmaster in Rhodesia, 71–72. Teacher Training at Oxford, 72–73.

2393 HUNTING, Gordon Robert, b. 31 Mar. 49, younger s. of C. P. M. Hunting (OR SF 24). SF, 62³–67³. Bristol University, B.Sc. Articled Clerk to Chartered Accountant (Peat, Marwick Mitchell), commencing Jan. 73. *Royal Ashdown G.C.* Brother, 1904.

2394 KENNEDY, James Stephen Bingham, b. 8 June 49, 2nd s. of B. B. Kennedy (OR SF 33). SF, 62³–67²; Athletics Team, 67. University of Edinburgh, B.Sc. Lt. in Queen's Own Yeomanry (T. & A.V.R.). Tobacco buyer for British American Tobacco Co. Ltd. Brothers, 1385 & 2692.

2395 KINROSS, Robin David, s. of J. B. Kinross, O.B.E., F.F.A.R.C.S. SF, 62³–67².

2396 TIERNAY, Peter John Benedict, b. 21 Mar. 49, s. of J. F. Tiernay. SF, 62³–67²; Levée. A.C.A., 72. Practising Chartered Accountant.

2397 TURNER, The Hon. Philip Noel Nigel, b. 8 May 49, 4th s. of Rt. Hon. Lord Netherthorpe, LL.B., B.Sc. SF, 62³–66²; XI, 65–66. Worcester, Oxford. International Banking, The Northern Trust Bank of Chicago. *Racquet Club of Chicago, M.C.C.* Brothers, 497 & 1152.

2398 BANTING, Quentin Charles Lindsay, b. 3 Apr. 49, elder s. of J. L. Banting (OR Sh 35). Sh, 62³–67²; Sailing, VI. Naval Officer, S/Lt., Royal Navy. G.S.M., Northern Ireland, 72. Brother, 2845.

2399 BELL, Donald Richard, b. 20 May 49, elder s. of F. O. Bell, O.B.E. Sh, 62³–67³; Levée; Head of House; XV, 65–67. A.C.A. With Peat, Marwick, Mitchell & Co. Brother, 2888.

2400 BURKE, David Claude, b. 31 Mar. 45, s. of C. H. Burke, of Quebec, Canada. Sh, 62³–63². McGill University, Montreal.

2401 CONEYS, Marcus Compton De Vere, b. 19 Nov. 48, youngest s. of T. G. De V. Coneys, L.R.C.P. Sh, 62³–67².

2402 DAMERELL, William Patrick Stirling, b. 1 June 49, s. of D. V. Damerell. Sh, 62³–66³.

2403 KNOTT, Herbert Espenett, b. 11 Mar. 49, s. of late R. B. Knott, O.B.E., M.C. Sh, 62³–67³; S. VIII, 66–67. University College, Oxford.

2404 LUARD, Roger David Eckford, b. 21 Nov. 48, 3rd s. of J. C. E. Luard. Sh, 62³–67². Brother, 868.

2405 McNICOL, Andrew Boyd, b. 17 Dec. 48, elder s. of K. M. McNicol, M.B., B.Ch. (OR Sh 37). Sh, 62³–67². Brother, Angus Martin, Sh. 68³–.

2406 PIERCE, David John, b. 21 Aug. 49, s. of P. V. Pierce. Sh, 62³–66³; Scholar. Sussex University, B.A. Solicitor's Articled Clerk.

2407 STEPHEN, Frederick Murray Alexander, b. 18 Apr. 49, s. of J. F. Stephen, V.R.D. (OR Sh 37). Sh, 62³–66³. Glasgow University, M.A. Economic Assistant, Barclays Bank International, Group Economic Intelligence Unit. *Royal Northern Yacht Club, Inter-Varsities Club.*

2408 BOYES, Jeremy Charles Bailey, b. 18 Dec. 48, 2nd s. of E. S. Boyes (OR St 29). St, 62³–67²; Levée; Head of School; Head of House; Cap, 66. College of Estate Management, B.Sc. A.R.I.C.S. Chartered Surveyor/Land Agent, working for Strutt & Parker at Lewes. Brothers, 1766 & 2855.

2409 CLEAVER, Michael John, b. 20 Apr. 49, s. of E. E. Cleaver (OR St 26). St, 62³–68¹; Levée; Head of House; Head of School; XXII, 67; Fives IV, 64–68; Capt., 67–68. Choral Scholar to Durham University, B.A. Bristol University, Cert. Ed. Assistant Master, Sherborne School, Dorset.

2410 DICKINSON, Timothy Stamper, b. 27 Mar. 49, s. of R. F. Dickinson, J.P. (OR St 30). St, 62³–67². Diploma in Bookings, Reservations & Ticketing. European, Trans-Asia & Africa Driver/Courier/ Expedition Leader.

2411 HOBSON, Nigel Lockhart, b. 18 Dec. 48, elder s. of B. H. Hobson (OR St 28). St, 62³–67¹. Vienna University. Royal Holloway College, London. Assistant Tours Executive, United Touring Co., Nairobi.

2412 JONES-DAVIES, Henry Ellis, b. 30 Mar. 49, s. of late T. E. Jones-Davies, M.D., F.R.C.P., D.L., J.P. St, 62³–67².

2413 LYNDON - SKEGGS, Andrew Neville, b. 10 Jan. 49, elder s. of P. Lyndon-Skeggs, B.M., B.Ch. (OR St 35). St, 62³–66³. Magdalene, Cambridge. A.R.I.C.S. Savills, 70–72. Trafalgar House Developments Ltd. since 72. Master of the Cambridge University Drag Hunt, 68–70. *Travellers, Pitt Club.*

2414 WILMOT, Brian Sacheverel, b. 25 Mar. 49, elder s. of Major M. S. Wilmot (OR St 28). St, 62³–67³. Royal School of Church Music, Associate Trinity College of Music, London. Forestry Conservation Society. Brother, 2617.

2415 ABBISS, John Charles, b. 17 Dec. 48, elder s. of C. A. Abbiss. Tu, 62³–67²; Levée; Head of House; Athletics Colours, 67. Nottingham University.

2416 ASTBURY, Nicholas John, b. 21 Feb. 49, s. of J. S. Astbury, B.M., B.Ch. (OR Tu 27). Tu, 62³–67¹. Guy's Hospital Medical School. L.R.C.P., M.R.C.S., M.B., B.S. Doctor, lately House Surgeon, at Orpington Hospital, Kent.

2417 BROADBENT, Jonathan Miles, b. 25 Jan. 49, s. of R. Broadbent. Tu, 62³–67². Bristol University. Bath University. Still studying.

2418 DAWSON, Francis Andrew Oliver Duff, b. 29 Nov. 48, s. of F. L. McC. Dawson, Ph.D. Tu, 62³–67¹. Keble, Oxford, B.A., Cert. Ed. With United Society for Propagation of the Gospel. Employed in the Anglican Archdiocese of Tanzania as Youth Officer, & part-time teacher in St. Mark's Theological College, Dar-es-Salaam, 72–74. Candidate for Orders in the C. of E.

2419 DOHERTY, Derek Carrington, b. 5 Feb. 49, s. of H. C. Doherty (OR Tu 31). Tu, 62³–67²; Scholarship to R.N.C. Dartmouth, 67. Then R.M.C.S. Shrivenham (3-year App. Science Degree Course). B.Sc. (C.N.A.A.). Lt., R.N. *Public Schools Club.*

2420 DRYSDALE, John Alexander Reid, b. 17 July 49, younger s. of A. M. Drysdale, LL.B., T.D. (OR Tu 29). Tu, 62³–67²; Scholar; Levée. Exhibition to Corpus Christi, Oxford, B.A. Law Student at Edinburgh University (LL.B.(Ord.) course) since 72. *Vincent's Club, Oxford, Elie Golf House Club.* Brother, 1658.

2421 ERSKINE, Keith Francis, b. 16 Feb. 49, younger s. of J. F. Erskine, M.B.,

B.Ch., D.P.H. (OR Tu 28). Tu, 62³–67². Leeds University.

2422 HANDY, Frank Philip, b. 29 Apr. 44, 2nd s. of F. L. Handy of U.S.A. Tu, 62³–63². Princeton University, A.B.(Econ.). Harvard University, M.B.A. Presently, Pres. of Personal Resources Management Group, a division of Donaldson, Lufkin & Jenretle Securities Corp., New York City.

2423 McCOSH, William Gow, b. 21 July 49, eldest s. of A. R. McCosh. Tu, 62³–67³; Levée; Head of House; XV, 67; XXII, 67; Cadet Officer. Sidney Sussex, Cambridge, B.A. Chartered Surveyor. *Pitt Club.* Brothers, 2719, Colin Andrew Tu, 69³– & Roger James, Tu, 72³–.

2424 THOMAS, David Richard Hugh, b. 8 Mar. 49, s. of D. L. Thomas. Tu, 62³–67³. Merton, Oxford, B.A., Pres. of O.U.D.S., 70–71. Stage & Film Actor—Hamlet in "Hamlet", Fortune Theatre, 71. Films include "If", 68 & "Oh Lucky Man", 72. Also writer for the "Theatre & Composer".

2425 TONGE, William Morris, b. 23 Jan. 49, eldest s. of late G. M. M. Tonge, J.P. (OR Tu 32). Tu, 62³–63³. Died in Jan. 64 during the holidays after a short illness. Brother, 2723 & 3032.

2426 BRADBURY, Philip John, b. 7 May 49, s. of P. R. K. Bradbury. M.B., Ch.B. W, 62³–66³. Keele University, B.A. Chandler.

2427 BRANSON, Anthony Nigel, b. 8 Aug. 49, s. of J. F. H. Branson (OR SH 30). W, 62³–67³; Levée; Head of House. Trinity, Cambridge.

2428 CALVERT, Paul Thornton, b. 17 Mar. 49, s. of J. T. Calvert. W, 62³–67¹; Levée; Head of House; Senior Scholar, 65; Rackets Pair, 66. Trinity, Cambridge. Guy's Hospital, London. Medical Student. *Hawks Club.*

2429 DOULTON, Roger Stewart, b. 28 Mar. 49, youngest s. of A. J. F. Doulton, O.B.E. W, 62³–67³; R. VIII, 67. Brothers, 1332, 1626 & 1635.

2430 HARE, John Edmund, b. 26 July 49, s. of R. M. Hare (OR K 32). W, 62³–67¹; Scholar; Music Scholar. Nettleship Scholar to Balliol, Oxford, B.A. Graduate College, Princeton University, U.S.A. since 72.

2431 **LEBURN, Eden Gilmour,** b. 28 Sept. 48, younger s. of W. G. Leburn, T.D., M.P. W, 62^3–67^2; XV, 66; XI, 66–67. Dir. of Textile Accessories firm, Fife. Brother, 1697.

2432 **MACKESSACK-LEITCH, Nigel Keir,** b. 8 Dec. 48, s. of K. Mackessack-Leitch, M.B., Ch.B., F.R.C.S. W, 62^3–66^1; S. VIII, 65. Insurance.

2433 **ROSS, Shane Peter Nathaniel,** b. 11 July 49, elder s. of J. N. Ross, LL.B. W, 62^3–66^3. Trinity College, Dublin.

2434 **SCOTT, Robin Howard Avison,** b. 6 Nov. 48, s. of Lt.-Cdr. D. C. R. Scott, R.N. (rtd.). W, 62^3–66^3; Scholar; Waddington Exhibition. Corpus Christi, Oxford, B.A. Farm Labourer.

ENTRANCES IN JANUARY 1963

2435 **DAVID, Sandeman Mark,** b. 16 July 49, younger of W. M. David (OR SH 29). SH, 63^1–65^2. Brother, 2176.

2436 **HOLLAND, Roderick Alfred,** b. 17 Aug. 49, s. of A. C. W. Holland, D.F.C. SH, 63^1–67^3. LL.B.(Lon.). Articled Clerk to Messrs. Stevens & Bolton of Camberley, Surrey, Solicitors.

2437 **NICOL, Andrew Harry,** b. 31 July 49, 2nd s. of Lt.-Col. J. W. Nicol, D.S.O., D.L. SH, 63^1–68^1; Levée; Head of House. Aberdeen University, B.Sc. Assistant Land Agent with Strutt & Parker, Chelmsford. Royal Scottish Forestry Society. Subaltern in the 51st Highland Volunteers (T. & A.V.R.). Brothers, 2010 & 2947.

2438 **COLBY, James,** b. 10 June 49, s. of R. Colby (OR B 23). B, 63^1–67^2.

2439 **DIX, Charles Peter Carlton,** b. 15 Aug. 49, eldest s. of P. C. Dix (OR B 31). B, 63^1–67^3. R.M.A., Sandhurst. Southampton University, LL.B. Joined Parachute Regt., Sept., 68. Lt., serving in Belfast. Brothers, 2803B, William Tage Edward Carlton, B, 68^3– & Robert George Carlton, B, 70^3–.

2440 **STEWART, Michael Henley,** b. 6 June 49, younger s. of H. St. C. Stewart, M.B.E. B, 63^1–67^3; Sailing VI, 66–67. Southampton University. Brother, 1429.

2441 **TODD, David Cargill,** b. 16 July 49, elder s. of D. C. Todd, T.D. (OR C 22). C, 63^1–67^2. Brother, 2666.

2442 **WARD, Charles Patrick,** b. 9 July 49, 2nd s. of Major R. P. Ward, M.C. C, 63^1–67^3.

2443 **WILSON, Christopher Denis Langton,** b. 8 Aug. 49, s. of A. D. Wilson. C, 63^1–67^3; Levée; Head of House; XV, 65–66; Capt., 67; XI, 67. Royal School of Mines. London University. Mining Engineer, Vaal Reefs Exploration & Mining Co. Ltd.

2444 **WOOLLAN, Geoffrey,** b. 5 July 49, elder s. of Rev. J. E. M. Woollan (OR C 30). C, 63^1–67^2; 2-year Diploma Course, Social Administration at L.S.E. Youth Leader & Resident Warden at The Rugby Clubs. Brother, 2765.

2445 **SKINNER, Robin Charles Owen,** b. 20 Sept. 49, youngest s. of M. O. Skinner (OR K 32). K, 63^1–68^3; Levée; Head of School; Head of House; XV, 66–67, Capt., 68; Tennis VI, 66–68; Fives IV, 67–68. Fitzwilliam, Cambridge. Cambridge XV, 70–71; Fives Half-Blue, 72. Law Society College of Law, Guildford. Clerk with Linklaters & Paines, Solicitors. _Hawks Club._ Brother, 1284.

2446 **CULLEN, Charles Patrick,** b. 8 Aug. 49, 2nd s. of P. Cullen, D.S.C. (OR M 34). M, 63^1–67^2. Brother, 2151.

2447 **EASTMAN, Richard Kipke,** b. 12 Aug. 49, younger s. of Col. C. E. C. Eastman. M, 63^1–67^3. Sheffield University, B.Sc. Employed by Arthur Andersen & Co., Chartered Accountants, in process of serving articles.

2448 **LEVITEN, Eliot Stephen,** b. 22 Aug. 49, s. of Dr. S. Leviten. M, 63^1–67^1. Sussex University.

2449 **LUTYENS, Charles Patrick,** b. 23 Nov. 49, younger s. of J. L. Lutyens (OR SF 31). SF, 63^1–67^3; Athletics Team, 67. St. Catharine's Cambridge, B.A. Administrative Officer, Government of British Solomon Islands Protectorate. Brother, 2230.

2450 **ACKNER, Christopher Brian,** b. 11 June 49, s. of B. G. C. Ackner, M.D., F.R.C.P., D.P.M. (OR Sh 32). Sh, 63^1–67^2.

2451 **GORDON BROWN, Mark Edmund,** b. 16 July 49, eldest s. of T. P. Gordon Brown (OR Sh 31). Sh, 63^1–67^3. Brothers, 2771 & Nicholas Charles, Sh, 69^3–.

2452 **HAMILTON, John Nicholas,** b. 15 July 49, s. of D. P. Hamilton. Sh, 63^1–67^3. Trinity, Cambridge, B.A. Now at Ridley Hall, Cambridge for ordination to the ministry of the Church of England in 75.

2453 **MURTON, Richard Benjamin Walter,** b. 23 May 49, s. of J. R. C. Murton. Sh, 63^1–67^3; Levée.

2454 **BROOK, David Thomas,** b. 20 June 49, 2nd s. of L. E. G. Brook. St, 63^1–66^2. Assistant Advertising Man., London. Brother, 3023.

2455 **CLAYTON, Roger Andrew,** b. 28 Aug. 49, s. of H. T. Clayton. St, 63^1–67^2.

2456A **O'BRIEN, Richard Anthony,** b 27 May 49, s. of W. J. O'Brien. St, 63^1–66^3. Rensselaer, N.Y., U.S.A., B.Sc. Currently studying for Master of Science Degree in Electrical Engineering. Member, Institute of Navigation (U.S.A.). Brother, William H. St, 68^1–70^3.

2456B **SOTHMANN, Günther,** b. 6 Apr. 47, youngest s. of H. A. L. G. Sothmann of Germany. W, 63^1–63^1. Exchange Scholarship for one term from Staatl Landschullheim Marquartstein.

2457 **CARTWRIGHT - TAYLOR, Ian Randall,** b. 5 Aug. 49, younger s. of Col. H. C. G. Cartwright-Taylor (OR Tu 28). Tu, 63^1–67^3; Levée. Nottingham University.

2458 **VENTERS, John,** b. 13 July 49, 2nd s. of P. Venters. Tu, 63^1–67^3; Sw. IX, 65–67.

2459A **GOURLAY, Wilfrid George Normand,** b. 2 Sept. 49, elder s. of D. W. Gourlay. W, 63^1–67^3. Royal Agricultural College, Cirencester. Diploma in Rural Estate Management. Assistant Land Agent, Strutt & Parker, Cheshire. R.I.C.S.

2459B **BÖCKLER, Ernst,** b. 4 Mar. 45, s. of E. Böckler. W, 63^1–63^1. Exchange Scholarship for one term from Staatl Landschullheim Marquartstein. Marquartstein School leaving exam (Abitur), 65. Munich University, studies in Civil Engineering & Architecture since 66.

ENTRANCES IN MAY 1963

2460 **BOCKRIS, Victor Francis,** b. 23 July 49, s. of J. O'M. Bockris, B.Sc., Ph.D., D.Sc. SH, 63^2–64^3.

2461 **HEPWORTH, Charles Gordon,** b. 3 Dec. 49, 2nd s. of A. D. Hepworth, T.D., M.A., LL.B. (OR SH 29). SH, 63^2–68^2. College of Estate Management, Reading University, B.Sc. Chartered Surveyor (Probationer). *Wilmslow G.C.*

2462 **RUSSELL, Andrew Victor Manson,** b. 7 Dec. 49, 2nd s. of M. McC. Russell, M.B., B.S. SH, 63^2–65^2. Brother, 2301.

2463 **HENDRY, John Edmund Gordon,** b. 28 Sept. 49, 2nd s. of A. G. Hendry, T.D. (OR B 21). B, 63^2–68^1; XV, 67; XXII, 66; H. XI, 67, Capt., 68. Edinburgh University, LL.B. Law Apprentice. Brother, David Robert Charles, B, 69^2–.

2464 **GARROD, Christopher Philip,** b. 19 Oct. 49, s. of N. J. Garrod. K, 63^2–67^3.

2465 **HAY, Peter Andrew,** b. 10 Oct. 49, elder s. of I. H. Hay. K, 63^2–68^3; Scholar; R. VIII, 68; Holder of Bigside Bags, 68. St. Andrew's University.

2466 **PLUMPTRE, John Nicholas,** b. 20 Aug. 49, elder s. of J. H. Plumptre (OR K 23). K, 63^2–68^1; R. VIII, 67–68; Squash, 66–68; Badminton, 64–68. College of Estate Management, Reading University, B.Sc. Chartered Surveyor. Brother, Paul Huntingdon, K, 68^3–.

2467 **STRACHAN, Hew Francis Anthony,** b. 1 Sept. 49, elder s. of M. F. Strachan, M.B.E. (OR K 33). K, 63^2–67^3; Levée. Corpus Christi, Cambridge, B.A. Museum Assistant, National Army Museum, 68. Shipping Trainee with Wm. Thomson & Co. Edinburgh (Ben Line Steamers Ltd.), 72. A research student in nineteenth-century British Military History at Corpus Christi, Cambridge since Oct. 72. *Hawks (Cambridge)*. Publication, "British Military Uniforms 1768–1796". Brother, 2827.

2468 **BOLTON, Peter Graham Hickman,** b. 28 Sept. 49, elder s. of P. R. Bolton. M, 63^2–67^2. Kitson College of Engineering, Leeds.

2469 **SCHICK, Philip Michael,** b. 12 Nov. 49, s. of K. F. Schick. M, 63^2–68^2; Levée; Head of House. Aberdeen University, B.Sc. Robert Gordon's Institute of Technology, D.M.S. Management Trainee with Prestcold (Northern) Ltd., Manchester. Student Membership, I.E.E. & B.I.M.

2470 AKENHEAD, Robert, b. 15 Sept. 49, younger s. of E. Akenhead, T.D. (OR SF 27). SF, 63²–67³; Levée; Head of House; H. XI, 67. Exeter University, LL.B. Council of Legal Education. Barrister, Inner Temple.

2471 McLAREN, John Muirhead, b. 11 Oct. 49, s. of Prof. H. C. McLaren. M.D., F.R.C.S., F.R.C.O.G. SF, 63²–68¹; Levée; Head of House; R. VIII, 67.

2472 TULLOCH, Angus John, b. 29 Sept. 49, 3rd s. of W. A. Tulloch, M.C., T.D. (OR SF 24). SF, 63²–67³. Clare, Cambridge, B.A. Lt. in T. & A.V.R. 154th Regt., Royal Corps of Transport. C.A. Apprentice with Whinney, Murray & Co., Glasgow. *Prestwick G.C., Western Club (Glasgow).* Brothers, 1151, 1388 & 2473.

2473 TULLOCH, Mungo Farquhar, b. 29 Sept. 49, 4th s. of W. A. Tulloch, M.C., T.D. (OR SF 24). SF, 63²–67²; Cap, 66. Diploma in Land Economy. Lt. in T. & A.V.R. (Queen's Own Yeomanry—Ayrshire Squadron). Surveyor with Metropolitan Estates Ltd. *Prestwick G.C., Western Club (Glasgow).* Brothers, 1151, 1388 & 2472.

2474 EDEN, Morton Roger, b. 12 Nov. 49, elder s. of the Hon. R. Q. E. Eden (OR Sh 36). Sh, 63²–68². Durham University, B.Sc. Assistant Engineer, Nottingham City Corp. since 71.

2475 FLEW, Jonathan Peter, b. 9 Jan. 50, 2nd s. of the late J. D. S. Flew, M.D., F.R.C.O.G. Sh, 63²–67³. St. Thomas's Hospital Medical School. Medicine. Royal Yachting Assoc. *London Corinthian Sailing Club.* Brother, 924.

2476 PECK, Christopher Wallace, b. 25 July 49, younger s. of D. R. Peck (OR B 28). Sh, 63²–67³; Levée. East Anglia University, B.A. Student for B.A. in Theology at London Bible College. Taught in Kenya for 1½ years after leaving Rugby. Brother, 1477.

2477 CORRY, David Herbert Cyril, b. 18 Sept. 49, elder s. of J. S. Corry (OR St 26). St, 63²–68².

2478 PALING, Michael Francis, b. 12 Nov. 49, younger s. of Lt.-Cdr. S. C. Paling, R.N.R. St, 63²–68¹; Levée; Cap, 66; Sw. IX, 66–67; Capt., 67. Died 20 Jan. 71.

2479 VINEY, Paul Spencer Laurence, b. 4 Sept. 49, younger s. of L. W. M. Viney (OR K 32). St, 63²–68²; Athletics Team, 68. Antiques Auctioneer with Phillips Auctioneers, London. *Ashridge G.C.* Brother, 1686.

2480 COULDREY, Peter Odlum, b. 31 Oct. 49, s. of R. W. Couldrey, M.B.E. Tu, 63²–67². North Staffordshire Polytechnic, B.Sc. Systems Analyst. Member of Kent Archaeological Society.

2481 GOSSET, Brian David, b. 26 Sept. 49, younger s. of late I. H. Gosset, B.M., F.R.C.P. (OR T 21). Tu, 63²–67³. Southampton University.

2482 HAWKESWORTH, Walter Gareth, b. 29 Dec. 49, younger s. of C. P. E. Hawkesworth (OR Tu 24). Tu, 63²–67³. Brother, 1539.

2483 WARNER, Alan Tristram Nicholas, b. 18 Oct. 49, 3rd s. of Sir E. R. Warner, K.C.M.G., O.B.E. Tu, 63²–68¹; Levée; Head of House; Cap, 67; R. VIII, 66–68; Holder of Bigside Bags, 68; Winner of the Crick, 67–68; Athletics Team, 65–67; Victor Ludorum, 67. St. Andrew's University, M.A. Overseas Containers Ltd., London. Brother, 2167.

2484 BUNTING, Timothy John, b. 22 Oct. 49, elder s. of G. W. W. Bunting, LL.B. (OR W 22). W, 63²–66². Farm Manager. Brother, 2899.

2485 MORLEY, Robin Francis James, b. 20 Nov. 49, younger s. of J. G. Morley. W, 63²–68²; Capt., Badminton. Under Officer, R.A.F. C.C.F. J. Sainsbury Ltd., Assistant Man. (Supermarkets). Founder & Secretary of the *Pterodactyls C.C.*

ENTRANCES IN SEPTEMBER 1963

2486 BATES, Alan Bartholomew, b. 12 Feb. 50, younger s. of J. A. V. Bates, M.B., B.Chir. (OR Sh 32). SH, 63³–65². Brother, 2237.

2487 GOATLY, Robert Duval, b. 10 Apr. 50, 2nd s. of J. Goatly (OR Sh 31). SH, 63³–68². Brothers, 2322 & 3012.

2488 HOWARD, Nicholas Fraser, b. 11 July 50, s. of J. J. Howard (OR SH, 36). SH, 63³–68². Scholar. Hotel & Catering Administration, Hendon College. Graduate member of the Hotel & Catering &

Institutional Management Assoc. With Grand Metropolitan Hotels. *St. George's Hill G.C.*

2489 ILLINGWORTH, Robin Nigel, b. 1 Oct. 50, s. of Prof. R. S. Illingworth, M.D., F.R.C.P., D.P.H., D.C.H. SH, 63^3–68^2. Scholar; Levée; Head of House; Leaving Exhibition; Open Scholarship to Clare, Cambridge, B.A. Balliol, Oxford since 71. Medical student at Radcliffe Infirmary, Oxford. Brathay Exploration Group.

2490 KAMATH, Vasant, b. 15 Dec. 46, s. of Capt. V. A. Kamath, Indian Navy. SH, 63^3–65^2. University College, London.

2491 LEE, Robert Andrew, b. 16 Aug. 50, s. of H. Lee. SH, 63^3–68^3; Scholar.

2492 PHAYRE, Robert Dermot Spinks, b. 3 Nov. 49, s. of Col. R. D. H. Phayre (OR SH 29). SH, 63^3–67^3. Trent Polytechnic (Nottingham), B.A. Commissioned as 2nd Lt. (Light Infantry), 71; promoted to Lt. with seniority from July 71. In 1st Bn. The Light Infantry; served in Ulster July–Nov., 72.

2493 POULTON, Hugh Ronald, b. 2 Apr. 50, s. of R. W. Poulton (OR SH 30). SH, 63^3–68^2. Westfield College, Regent St. Polytechnic, Plymouth Polytechnic. Running a guitar group.

2494 SPENS, David Patrick, b. 2 May 50, s. of Lt.-Col. H. S. Spens, M.B.E., M.C., T.D. (OR SH 30). SH, 63^3–68^3. University of Kent, B.A. College of Law, London, 72–73. Reading for Bar Finals. Member of Hon. Soc. of Inner Temple.

2495 AINSWORTH, Anthony Francis Curtin, b. 12 Aug. 50, s. of F. G. Ainsworth. T, 63^3–68^2; S. VIII. Birmingham University.

2496 BARTHOLOMEW, Paul William, b. 21 Nov. 49, s. of A. H. Bartholomew. T, 63^3–67^3. Nottingham University, Faculty of Agriculture, Sutton Bonington, B.Sc. Research Student, Queen's University, Belfast since 72. Scientific Officer, Northern Ireland Ministry of Agriculture. Agricultural Research Institute of N. Ireland, Hillsborough, Co. Down.

2497 FARRINGTON, David John, b. 7 May 50, s. of J. Farrington, M.B., Ch.B. SH, 63^3–68^3; Levée; Head of House. Brasenose, Oxford.

2498 HOCKEY, Michael Stanley, b. 25 Dec. 49, s. of W. S. Hockey. T, 63^3–67^3. R. VIII. St. Georges Hospital Medical School, M.B., B.S. House Surgeon, St. Georges, Hospital, London.

2499 HOUNSELL, Edwin Alexander Baillie, b. 23 Apr. 50, elder s. of A. E. Hounsell. T, 63^3–66^2. Welbeck College.

2500 KELLETT, John Keith, b. 23 Sept. 49, s. of K. G. Kellett, F.R.I.B.A. T, 63^3–68^1. St. Bartholomew's Hospital.

2501 PELL, Richard Montague, b. 26 July 50, s. of M. N. Pell. T, 63^3–68^2.

2502 SHAW, Peter Edmund, b. 7 Aug. 50, younger s. of M. E. Shaw. T, 63^3–68^2; Athletics Team, 67. Brother, 2353.

2503 SIMPSON, Richard Hugh, b. 24 Sept. 49, 3rd s. of the late Rev. J. R. Simpson (OR B 17). T, 63^3–68^2; Levée; Head of House; R. VIII, 66, 68. Undergraduate at University of Kent, Canterbury. Brother, 2192.

2504 SLEIGHT, Peter James, b. 8 May 50, s. of A. Sleight. T, 63^3–68^1; Levée; Head of House. St. Bartholomew's Hospital.

2505 SPINKS, Patrick Nugent, b. 7 Mar. 50, younger s. of Inst. Capt. E. I. Spinks, R.N. (rtd.). (OR T 18). T, 63^3–68^2. Brother, 1422.

2506 WILLIAMS, Christopher Neil, b. 6 Sept. 49, s. of I. Williams, B.Sc. T, 63^3–67^3; S. VIII, 65–67, Capt., 67. Southampton University.

2507 ADY, Peter John, b. 31 Dec. 49, s. of J. E. Ady. B, 63^3–67^2; Music Scholar. Guildhall School of Music & Drama.

2508 CAMPBELL, David Gratton, b. 12 Feb. 50, s. of D. D. Campbell, M.C. B, 63^3–68^2.

2509 EDDISON, John Michael, b. 2 Mar. 50, s. of J. A. Eddison (OR B 34). B, 63^3–68^1; R. VIII, 67, 68; Winner of Crick, 67; Athletics Colours, 67. Trinity, Cambridge, M.A. V.S.O. in Lae, Papua New Guinea; teaching at Lae Technical College on Engineering Certificate Course.

2510 ENTWISLE, Timothy Kevan, b. 15 June 50, s. of P. K. Entwisle (OR B 31). B, 63^3–68^2; Levée; Head of House; Athletics Team, 68. Chartered Accountant. *Ilkley G.C.*

2511 **HILL, John James Stephen,** b. 26 Oct. 49, elder s. of R. Hill. B, 63³–68³; Levée; Head of House; Cap, 68; XXII, 67, 68. University of Sussex. Student.

2512 **OUTCALT, John Stuart Kearns,** b. 26 Feb. 50, eldest s. of late D. B. Outcalt. B, 63³–67³. Brothers, 2659 & David Lionel, B, 67¹–70².

2513 **WATTS, Charles Henry,** b. 7 Feb. 50, s. of Rev. G. R. Watts. B, 63³–67³. Brasenose, Oxford.

2514 **WRIGHT, Andrew Michael,** b. 13 Feb. 50, younger s. of J. A. Wright (OR B 25). B, 63³–68²; Manchester Polytechnic, B.A. Solicitor's Articled Clerk with Messrs. Fox, Brooks, Marshall & Co. of Manchester.

2515 **COLE, Christopher Francis,** b. 6 Feb. 50, 4th s. of Col. J. R. Cole. C, 63³–67²; XI, 67. Brothers, 1074, 2038 & 2305.

2516 **MONYPENNY, Ian James,** b. 11 Apr. 50, s. of E. R. Monypenny, M.B., F.R.C.S., F.F.R. C, 63³–68¹; Levée; Head of House; Cap, 67. Exhibition to Pembroke, Cambridge.

2517 **RUBIN, Peter Alan John,** b. 15 Sept. 49, younger s. of M. E. Rubin. C, 63³–67².

2518 **THORLEY, Simon Joe,** b. 22 May 50, s. of G. B. Thorley, T.D. C, 63³–67³; Sailing VI, 66; Commodore, 67. Keble, Oxford, B.A. Barrister at Law, Inner Temple. *Naval & Military Club.*

2519 **DINGWALL, Christopher Hubert,** b. 21 May 50, elder s. of J. H. Dingwall. K, 63³–68². Grenoble University (France), Cert. d'Etudes Françaises. University College, London, B.Sc. Field Assistant (Teaching) at Kindrogan Field Centre, Perthshire, teaching Geography/Ecology. Royal Geographical Society.

2520 **HUTCHINS, Anthony Guy Rollo,** b. 5 Dec. 49, elder s. of H. R. Hutchins. K, 63³–67³. Brother, Robin Charles Neville, K, 67³–72³.

2521 **McCRACKEN, Robert Henry Joy,** b. 15 Mar. 50, elder s. of D. McCracken, M.B., B.Ch., M.R.C.P. K, 63³–67³; Fencing, 67, Capt. Worcester, Oxford. Brother, James Justin, K, 68³–72³.

2522 **MAY, Michael Walter,** b. 19 Nov. 49, s. of W. A. H. May, M.C. K, 63³–67³.

2523 **MONRO, Andrew Hugh,** b. 2 Mar. 50, s. of A. K. Monro, M.D., F.R.C.S. K, 63³–68³; Levée; XV, 66–68. Pembroke, Cambridge, B.A. Metal Box Co. *Hawks, Blackheath R.F.C.*

2524 **SEBESTYEN Henry Martin,** b. 5 May 50, s. of P. M. Sebestyen. K, 63³–67³.

2525 **WETHERILL, Martin Harry,** b. 20 Oct. 49, elder s. of P. H. Wetherill (OR K 33). K, 63³–68²; Levée; XI, 67, Capt., 68. Charing Cross Medical School. Brother, 2926.

2526 **ARTHUR, Michael Anthony,** b. 28 Aug. 50, s. of J. R. Arthur. M, 63³–68²; Scholar; Levée; Head of School. Scholar of Balliol, Oxford. Dewar Travelling Scholarship.

2527 **COWIE, Thomas Andrew,** b. 17 Feb. 50, s. of T. Cowie. M, 63³–68³; Levée; Head of House; XV, 67–68; Fives IV, 66–67, Capt., 68. Dewar Scholarship. Tom Hughes Prize. Magdalene, Cambridge. Reading for Part II of the Land Economy Tripos. Fives Blue, 70–72, Capt.; Squash Blue, 71–72, Capt. *Hawks.*

2528 **HUTCHINGS, Ian Michael,** b. 6 May 50, s. of D. G. Hutchings, M.B., Ch.B. M, 63³–67²; Scholar; Lees Knowles Exhibition. Trinity, Cambridge, B.A. Physics Research for Ph.D. at Cavendish Lab., Cambridge University. *M.C.C.*

2529 **LLOYD-DAVIES, Edward Roderick Vaughan,** b. 26 May 50, s. of O. V. Lloyd-Davies, M.S., F.R.C.S. M, 63³–67³. St. Bartholomew's Hospital Medical College, M.B., B.S., M.R.C.S., L.R.C.P.

2530 **PAUL, Thomas Stephen,** b. 9 Feb. 50, eldest s. of T. N. Paul (OR M 23). M, 63³–68².

2531 **RUSSENBERGER, Paul Jonathan,** b. 25 Apr. 50, s. of the Rev. A. Russenberger. M, 63³–68³. At present on full-time B.Sc. course in Mechanical Engineering at University College, London. Railway Engineering; employed at present with British Rail as an Engineering Scholar. Member of the Locomotive Club of Great Britain.

2532 **SCOTT, Colin John Patrick,** b. 27 Apr. 50, s. of W. P. Scott, T.D. M, 63³–

68³. Whisky Management, The Glenlivet Distillers Ltd. *New Club, Edinburgh.*

2533 WYE, Roderic Francis, b. 13 Sept. 50, s. of F. T. E. Wye (OR M 38). M, 63³–68. Corpus Christi, Cambridge, B.A. Now at University of London.

2534 BAIN, David Graham Shenton, b. 13 Nov. 49, 3rd s. of A. T. S. Bain. SF, 63³–67³; Scholar. Bristol University, B.Sc. Articled Clerk for Chartered Accountancy, with Cooper Bros. & Co. Brother, 852.

2535 DEWAR, Nicholas Alan Richard, b. 5 Apr. 50, elder s. of R. A. R. Dewar. SF, 63³–68²; Levée; Head of House. Trinity, Cambridge, B.A. Banking. J. Henry Schroder, Wagg & Co. Ltd. *Leander Club.*

2536 DICKSON, David Seton Pollok-Morris, b. 29 Jan. 50, elder s. of Col. S. G. Dickson, D.L., J.P. (OR Tu 23). SF, 63³–68². R.M.A., Sandhurst. Commissioned, Dec. 70. Promoted Lt., June 72. Platoon Commander, 1st Bn. The Royal Scots (The Royal Regt.), Tidworth. *United Services & Aero Club.*

2537 HAY, Philip Antony, b. 13 Sept. 50, younger s. of Lt.-Col. G. H. Hay, D.S.O. SF 63³–68³. St. Andrew's University, 69–73. Brother, 2316.

2538 PAYNE, Peter Michael, b. 31 Mar. 50, 3rd s. of M. F. Payne. SF, 63³–67². A.C.A., 72. Now with Peat, Marwick, Mitchell & Co., London. *Royal Cruising Club, Thurlestone G.C.* Brothers, 1603 & 2068.

2539 RUSSELL-SMITH, Charles Rupert, b. 26 Mar. 50, 3rd s. of R. S. Russell-Smith, M.R.C.S., L.R.C.P. (OR SF 29). SF, 63³–68². St. Bartholomew's Hospital.

2540 SIMPSON, Alan Gordon, b. 15 Feb. 50, younger s. of G. R. Simpson, D.S.O., T.D. (OR SF 30). SF, 63³–68³; Levée; Head of House. Magdalen, Oxford. Consultant Engineer with Brian Colquhoun & Partners, London. Brother, 2233.

2541 TAYLOR, Christopher Paul, b. 22 May 50, s. of N. Taylor. SF, 63³–68²; XI, 68; H. XI, 68. St. Thomas's Hospital Medical School, London. Medical Student.

2542 WILD, Simon Peter, b. 15 Feb. 50, younger s. of P. D. Wild (OR SF 32). SF, 63³–68². Brother, 2072.

2543 BEZANT, Terence John, b. 27 July 50, elder s. of F. H. Bezant. Sh, 63³–68¹; Scholar. Brasenose, Oxford.

2544 BROSTOFF, David Mark, b. 2 Aug. 50, s. of S. Brostoff. Sh, 63³–67³. Harrogate College of Art, Diploma in Graphic Design. Polytechnic of Central London, B.A. in Photographic Arts. Independent Film-Maker/Photographer. Member of British Film Institute. Member of I.C.A. *The East India, Sports & Public Schools Club.*

2545 de FREITAS, Patrick Somers, b. 21 Mar. 50, youngest s. of the Rt. Hon. Sir G. de Freitas, K.C.M.G., M.P. Sh, 63³–68²; Levée; Head of House. Carlton College, Minnesota, U.S.A., B.A. Brother, 1801.

2546 FORRESTER-PATON, Graham Shaw, b. 6 Dec. 49, s. of A. P. Forrester-Paton. Sh, 63³–68². Durham University, B.A. Leeds University, postgraduate Cert. Ed. Currently Student Teacher with a view to a career in Education.

2547 KAGAN, Michael George, b. 24 Aug. 50, elder s. of J. Kagan. Sh, 63³–67³. Imperial College, London, M.Sc. Owner of garage. Brother, 2943A.

2548 LATHAM, Anthony Piers, b. 23 Apr. 50, s. of Sir J. Latham, C.B.E. Sh, 63³–68².

2549 LOCKWOOD, Richard Adrian, b. 14 Feb. 50, s. of R. H. M. Lockwood. Sh, 63³–68².

2550 MASON, Jeremy Seabrook Farrer, b. 16 Mar. 50, s. of G. F. Mason. Sh, 63³–68¹; Levée; Head of House. Open Exhibition to Trinity Hall, Cambridge.

2551 OLLIFF-LEE, Michael John, b. 31 Oct. 49, s. of J. D. St. C. Olliff-Lee. Sh, 63³–67³; XXII, 67. Bullion Dealer. At present employed with Ralli, Merrill Lynch (International) Ltd. Commissioned Acting S/Lt., R.N.R., May 72. *Mid-Sussex Hockey Club.*

2552 SPARLING, George Arthur James, b. 13 July 49, s. of G. F. Sparling. Sh, 63³–67². Trinity, Cambridge.

2553 BROWN, Geoffrey Rupert Stuart, b. 15 Dec. 49, s. of J. M. Brown, M.C., T.D., M.B., B.Chir., D.Obst.R.C.O.G. (OR St 31). St, 63³–68¹. Senior Scholar. Balliol, Oxford.

2554 **COLVER, Graham Borland,** b. 3 Mar. 50, younger s. of the late T. Colver, V.R.D., M.D. St, 63^3–67^3. Trinity, Oxford, B.A. Capt., Rugby Fives, 69–71. St. Thomas's Hospital, studying medicine. *Vincent's.* Brother, 2291.

2555 **DICKSON, Ian William,** b. 14 Mar. 50, younger s. of Capt. S. W. S. Dickson. St, 63^3–67^3. N.S.W. University. Brother, 2079.

2556 **HACKETT, Adam Jonathan Patrick,** b. 9 Mar. 50, s. of C. T. Hackett, T.D. St, 63^3–68^2; Levée; Sw. IX, 68. Junior Sales Executive, The Metal Box Co. Ltd., Plastics Group. *The Bath Club, St. Georges Hill G.C.*

2557 **HOBSON, Jonathan Londesborough,** b. 12 Apr. 50, 3rd s. of J. W. Hobson (OR St 22). St, 63^3–68^3. XXII, 68. Brothers, 573 & 939.

2558 **PITT, Edward Brindley,** b. 19 Apr. 50, 2nd s. of Lt.-Cdr. R. J. Pitt. M.B.E., R.N. (OR St 35). St, 63^3–68^3. University College, Oxford. Solicitor's Clerk. Brothers, 2084 & 2859.

2559 **PITT, Nicholas Brindley,** b. 17 Apr. 50, eldest s. of S. W. Pitt (OR St & W 37). St, 63^3–68^2; Senior Under-Officer, C.C.F., 68. Athletics Colours, 68. Queen Mary College, London University, B.Sc., M.I.C.E. Civil Engineering.

2560 **PLATTS, Alexander George,** b. 19 May 50, s. of A. W. Platts (OR St 22). St, 63^3–67^2.

2561 **RIDLEY-THOMPSON, Timothy Percy,** b. 16 May 50, s. of Lt.-Col. A. P. Ridley-Thompson, T.D. St, 63^3–67^2.

2562 **FIRTH, Richard Guthrie,** b. 23 Aug. 50, s. of B. G. Firth (OR Tu 27). Tu, 63^3–68^2; Scholar. Nottingham University, B.A. Full-time Voluntary Worker.

2563 **JOHNSON, Dwight Alan,** b. 26 Dec. 45, s. of O. F. Johnson. Tu, 63^3–64^2. Exchange student from Toomis School, Windsor, Conn., U.S.A. Princeton University, A.B. Yale Law School, J.D. (to be completed 74). To work in a law firm in Washington, D.C.

2564 **KENDALL, Gilbert John,** b. 31 May 50, elder s. of A. C. Kendall, M.B., Ch.B., F.R.C.P. Tu, 63^3–67^3; Scholar. New College, Oxford, B.A. Articled Clerk studying for Solicitor's qualifying exam. Brother, 2864.

2565 **POWER, Timothy Michael Trevor,** b. 9 Feb. 50, elder s. of Major E. W. A. Power (OR Tu 37). Tu, 63^3–67^2. Boatbuilding Industry, Aquafibre International, 68–72. Commissioned as 2nd Lt. into Royal Anglian Regt. from Mons O.C.S., Aug. 72. Currently serving in B.A.O.R. *Royal Norfolk & Suffolk Yacht Club.*

2566 **WALKER, Grenville James,** b. 23 Feb. 50, 2nd s. of H. G. Walker, LL.B. Tu, 63^3–68^2. Brothers, 2292 & 2941.

2567 **CAMPBELL, Andrew Malcolm,** b. 3 June 50, s. of the late A. M. G. Campbell, D.M., F.R.C.P. W, 63^3–68^3. St. John's, Oxford, B.A. Solicitor's Articled Clerk.

2568 **FAULKNER, George,** b. 22 Jan. 50, s. of T. Faulkner, F.R.C.S. (OR T 27). W, 63^3–68^2. H.N.D. in Agriculture. Studying Diploma in Management Studies, Seale-Hayne Agricultural College, Newton Abbot, Devon.

2569 **FEILDEN, Richard John Robert,** b. 29 Mar 50, s. of G. B. R. Feilden, F.R.S. W, 63^3–67^3; Scholar; Cap, 67, King's, Cambridge.

2570 **GREANY, Michael John,** b. 30 Jan. 50, s. of W. H. Greany, M.C., D.M., B.Ch. W, 63^3–68^2. Articled to Solicitor in private practice. *The Button Club, The Poole Harbour Yacht Club.*

2571 **MACINNES, Duncan,** b. 10 Apr. 50, younger s. of R. MacInnes. W, 63^3–69^1; Levée; Head of House. Trinity Hall, Cambridge, B.A. One year with I.V.S.—Food Aid Programme, Maseru, Lesotho, till Sept. 73.

2572 **MARQUIS, Edward John Alexander,** b. 13 Aug. 50, s. of R. M. Marquis, M.B.E., M.B., Ch.B., F.R.C.P. W, 63^3–68^3; Levée; Head of House; Cap, 68; XI, 68. London University, School of Slavonic & East European Studies, B.A. London College of Printing, course in Book Production Management.

2573 **NIGHTINGALE, Charles Edward,** b. 7 Dec. 49, 2nd s. of E. H. Nightingale. C.M.G. (OR W 18). W, 63^3–68^2; S. VIII, 68, Capt. Reading University, B.Sc. Brothers, 1934 & Richard Mervyn, W, 68^1–72^2.

2574 **WOODS, William Gustave Arnold,** b. 30 May 50, s. of A. W. W. B.

Woods, B.M., M.R.C.P. W, 63³–68¹; Scholar; Levée; Head of House; XXII, 67. Exeter, Oxford and The London Hospital. *Vincent's.*

ENTRANCES IN JANUARY 1964

2575 **COHEN, Richard Hugh Rodel,** b. 15 Sept. 50, s. of Sir A. B. Cohen, K.C.M.G., K.C.V.O., O.B.E., LL.D. SH, 64¹–68³; Levée; Head of House; Dewar Scholarship. Balliol, Oxford.

2576 **MILLER, Harry Dawson,** b. 27 Aug. 50, elder s. of J. D. Miller (OR SH 33). SH, 64¹–67².

2577 **WOODHEAD, Christopher John,** b. 9 Sept. 50, younger s. of C. Woodhead, L.D.S. SH, 64¹–68². College of Art, Sunderland. Brother, 2013.

2578 **GLASGOW, Julian Raymond,** b. 20 June 50, younger s. of J. E. Glasgow, B.Sc., M.B., D.M.R.E. B, 64¹–68². Trainee with Knight, Frank & Rutley (Estate Agents). Brother, 2028.

2579A **CHOUDHURY, Nauman Rasheed,** b. 22 Aug. 50, s. of H. R. Choudhury of Pakistan. C 64¹–68². King's College, London.

2579B **WRIGHT, Nigel Charles Comstive,** b. 8 May 50, eldest s. of C. H. Wright, F.R.S.A. (OR C 18). C, 64¹–68³; Levée; Head of House; Cap., 67, 68; H. XI, 68; Athletics Team, 68. Articled Clerk with Mann Judd, Chartered Accountants. *Harlequins F.C.* Brothers, 2834 & Christopher Philip Comstive, C, 67³–.

2580 **FENTON, Charles John Vincent,** b. 25 May 50, s. of B. V. Fenton, B.Sc. K, 64¹–68³; University College Hospital Medical School, Medical Student in 3rd year. Enlisted in Royal Navy, Mar. 72, as Medical Cadet, Surgeon S/Lt. *Public Schools Club.* Royal Overseas League.

2581A **CRUICKSHANK, Richarn Ian Sarell,** b. 17 June 50, s. of I. J. O. Cruickshank. M, 64¹–68²; XXII, 67. London University, reading for LL.B. *M.C.C.*

2581B **SCHLEIMER, Jochen,** b. 20 Dec. 47, s. of G. Schleimer. M, 64¹–64¹. Exchange student from Marquartstein Bavarian State Boarding School. Munich University, M.D.

2582 **SIDGWICK, David Benson Twining,** b. 19 May 50, elder s. of T. B.

Sidgwick, T.D. M, 64¹–68². Articled Clerk with firm of Chartered Accountants.

2583 **SIDGWICK, John Benson,** b. 17 June 50, 2nd s. of R. B. Sidgwick (OR M 32). M, 64¹–67³; XV, 67; Sw. IX, 67. Cornwall Technical College. Brother, 2999.

2584 **GILCHRIST, Jeremy Graham,** b. 8 Nov. 50, younger s. of Sir A. G. Gilchrist, K.C.M.G. SF, 64¹–68². Brother, 2270.

2585A **BICKERSTETH, Richard John,** b. 28 May 50, elder s. of P. M. G. Bickersteth (OR Sh 38). Sh, 64¹–68²; Athletics Team, 64–66 & 68. At present Head Stockman on a farm in Kent, as the middle year of a 3-year O.N.D. course at Hadlow Agricultural College. Brother, 3010.

2585B **BUZZARD, David Farquhar,** b. 16 Sept. 50, s. of E. M. Buzzard, B.M., B.Ch., F.R.C.P. Sh, 64¹–68³; Levée; Head of House; H. XI, 67, 68. Magdalen, Oxford, M.A. 1st B.M. but due to chronic ill health gave up and now doing part-time Picture Framing. *Founder of Brazil Nuts Hockey Club.*

2586 **LAUBER, Charles Ronald John,** b. 24 Nov. 50, s. of H. C. J. Lauber, M.D. Sh, 64¹–68²; Scholar; Levée. Scholarship to King's, Cambridge, B.A. Management Trainee, Lever Bros. Ltd.

2587 **NAYDLER, Nicholas Murray,** b. 4 July 50, elder s. of M. Naydler. Sh, 64¹–68². Dundee University. Student.

2588 **WREFORD - BROWN, Charles Carless,** b. 6 June 50, younger s. of L. C. Wreford-Brown (OR SF 33). Sh, 64¹–66². South Devon Technical College. Chartered Surveyor/Estate Agent. Brother, 1836.

2589A **SPRINGER, Frank Mathias,** b. 19 Aug. 45, s. of Dr. K. Springer of Germany. St, 64¹–64¹.

2589B **VICKERS, Jolyon Martin Hedley,** b. 12 July 50, elder s. of M. Vickers, A.M.I.E.E. (OR St & K 38). St, 64¹–68². 2 years' Hotel Management Course, Savoy Hotel, London. Student, Queen Mary's Hospital for Sick Children, working for R.S.C.N.; S.R.N. in 75. Rep. for Royal College of Nursing.

2590 **DODSWORTH, Simon Leonard,** b. 27 Aug. 50, elder s. of B. L. C. Dodsworth, M.C. (OR Tu 34). Tu, 64¹–68². Brother, 2939.

2591 FALCONER, Iain Rhoderick Scott, b. 2 June 50, s. of Cdr. R. S. Falconer, R.N. Tu, 64^1–68^2.

2592 KENTISH, William Edmund Cranstoun, b. 16 Aug. 50, s. of J. W. Kentish (OR Tu 23). Tu, 64^1–68^2. Westminster Tech. Cambridge Tech. Studio/ Electronic/Technician, Electronic Music Studios, Putney.

2593 NORCOTT, Jonathan Philip, b. 8 Aug. 50, s. of R. Norcott. Tu, 64^1–68^3; Levée; Head of House; XV, 67, 68; Sw. IX, 66–68, Capt., 68; Athletics Team, 66–68.

2594 KUIPERS, Matthew Melles, b. 17 Sept. 50, s. of J. M. Kuipers. W, 64^1–68^2. Advertisement Sales, I.P.C. Magazines Ltd., London.

2595 LEACH, Derek John, b. 1 May 50, s. of E. R. Leach (OR W 19). W, 64^1–68^2.

ENTRANCES IN MAY 1964

2596 JACOBSON, Robin Richard, b. 19 Nov. 50, s. of B. M. Jacobson, M.R.C.P. D.M.R. SH, 64^2–68^3. Magdalene, Cambridge, B.A. Middlesex Hospital Medical School, London, since 72. Medical Student. Cambridge University Psychological Society.

2597 BEHRENS, Andrew James, b. 18 Sept. 50, s. of D. J. Behrens (OR B 30). B, 64^2–68^2. Kelham Theological College, 69–70. King's College, London, A.K.C. course since 70. Training for the Priesthood by 75.

2598 BROWNE, Stephen John Storey, b. 14 Oct. 50, s. of D. F. E. Browne. C, 64^2–68^1.

2599 ARTHUR, Gordon Drake, b. 7 Feb. 51, elder s. of A. J. V. Arthur, M.B.E. (OR K 29). K, 64^2–69^2; Levée; Head of House; Sw. IX, 68, 69. Magdalene, Cambridge, B.A. Brother, 2983.

2600 AUSTIN, Giles Neville John, b. 6 Sept. 50, youngest s. of F. B. Austin. K, 64^2–68^2. Brother, 835.

2601 DAVIS, Julian Mark, b. 9 Oct. 50, s. of G. M. Davis, LL.B. K, 64^2–68^3. Southampton University.

2602 SHELLIM, Arthur Michael, b. 14 Nov. 50, 4th s. of M. F. Shellim. K, 64^2–69^2.

2603 YOUNG, Gavin Sheridan, b. 5 Oct. 50, s. of H. K. L. Young, M.B., Ch.B. K, 64^2–68^2.

2604 FRANKAU, Timothy George, b. 18 Dec. 50, younger s. of Col. J. H. Frankau, R.E. (rtd.), M.C. (OR M 32). M, 64^2–68^2; R. VIII. King's College, London for 18 months, preclinical to 2nd M.B. & B.S. St. George's Hospital Medical School (University of London), 3 years.

2605 KELLY, Philip Adair Scott, b. 7 Sept. 50, younger s. of G. S. Kelly, T.D., F.R.I.B.A. M, 64^2–68^2. Brother, 1948.

2606 MOSS, David, b. 11 Dec. 50, s. of W. Moss. M, 64^2–68^3.

2607 ORTMANS, Jeremy Charles, younger s. of D. H. Ortmans (OR M36). M. 64^2–66^2. Brother, 2314.

2608 BOOTH, Clive William, b. 11 Oct. 50, s. of W. H. Booth. SF, 64^2–68^3; XV, 67, 68. Southampton University, LL.B.

2609 DALZELL-PAYNE, Gillies Monoux MacArthur, b. 18 Oct. 50, youngest s. of Major G. L. Dalzell-Payne. SF, 64^2–69^1. St. Edmund Hall, Oxford, B.A. Half-Blue in Archery. Articled Clerk to Solicitor. *Naval & Military Club.*

2610 KENNEDY, William Robin, b. 24 Aug. 50, s. of the late W. M. C. Kennedy, C.B.E. SF, 64^2–68^2; R. VIII, 67; H. XI, 68; Capt of Athletics, 68. Warwick University, Hons. Degree in Engineering Science. Industrial Engineer with Leyland Motor Corp. (Australia). *East India, Sports & Public Schools Club; Northern Suburbs Rugby Club (Sydney).*

2611 RABB, Leigh Michael, b. 21 Nov. 50, elder s. of S. Rabb, C.A. Sh, 64^2–68^2. Guy's Hospital. Medical Student. Brother, Nicholas Charles Rupert, Sh, 68^2–72^2.

2612 SCHRYVER, Hugh Jocelyn Peter, b. 26 Sept. 50, 3rd s. of P. J. Schryver. Sh, 64^2–68^2.

2613 de BOINVILLE, Nicolas Vivian Chastel, b. 25 Jan. 51, s. of G. N. P. C. de Boinville, M.C., T.D. St, 64^2–69^2.

2614 HOBSON, Bruce Denison, b. 21 Sept. 50, younger s. of B. H. Hobson (OR St 28). St, 64^2–69^1. Brother, 2411.

2615 **LESLIE, Jonathan Charles Alexander,** b. 13 Dec. 50, s. of J. A. K. Leslie. St, 64^2–69^2; Levée; Head of House. Trinity, Oxford. Blue for Lawn Tennis & Squash Rackets.

2616 **MACDONALD-HALL, Caspar,** b. 4 Dec. 50, younger s. of R. MacDonald-Hall. St, 64^2–69^3; XV, Capt., 69; Levée. Management Trainee course with F. W. Cook Mechanical Services Ltd. Com. Dir. of the "C" Group of Cos. Member of the Worshipful Co. of Pattenmakers.

2617 **WILMOT, Robin Woollett,** b. 26 Oct. 50, younger s. of Major M. S. Wilmot (OR St 28). St, 64^2–68^2. Walbrook College, Westminster, Sept. 72. Student. *H.A.C.* Brother, 2414.

2618 **COPE, Richard,** b. 26 Nov. 50, younger s. of J. W. Cope, M.B., B.Chir., F.R.C.S. Tu, 64^2–68^2. Brother, 1061.

2619 **SWANNELL, Robert William Ashburnham,** b. 18 Nov. 50, s. of Major D. W. A. Swannell, M.B.E. (OR Tu 32). Tu, 64^2–68^3. Grenoble University, France. Articled Clerk with Peat, Marwick, Mitchell & Co., Chartered Accountants. Final results in July 73. Joined Lincoln's Inn to read for the Bar in Sept. *United Service Club.*

2620 **HASSAN, Victor,** b. 7 Oct. 50, s. of C. Hassan (OR W 37). W, 64^2–69^2. Articled to Solicitor.

2621 **MILLER, Stephen Raymond,** b. 6 Sept. 50, s. of M. Miller. W, 64^2–68^2; Cap, XI, 68; Capt. of Rackets Pair, 67. Kilburn Polytechnic, London. Student.

2622 **RIDGWICK, Adrian John,** b. 16 Oct. 50, s. of J. H. Ridgwick, M.R.C.S., L.R.C.P., D.R.C.O.G. W, 64^2–69^2; Levée; Head of House; Capt. of Fives, 69. The Charles Clifford Dental Hospital, University of Sheffield. University Squash V, Capt. Dental Student. *Rugby Fives Club.*

2623 **WILLIAMS, Robert Gerrard,** b. 14 Dec. 50, s. of L. H. Williams. W, 64^2–69^2; Athletics Team; F/Sgt., R.A.F. (C.C.F.). London University, reading Physics, Chemistry & Space Science. Sound Technician for Pink Floyd (Musical Group).

R.S.W.W.—14*

ENTRANCES IN SEPTEMBER 1964

2624 **BAXTER, Christopher John,** b. 15 Mar. 51, elder s. of M. R. Baxter. SH, 64^3–69^2. Brother, 2918.

2625 **BRADBY, James Christopher,** b. 6 June 51, 3rd s. of E. L. Bradby (OR SH 20). SH, 64^3–69^1; Scholar; Levée; Exhibition to New College, Oxford. Undergraduate. Brothers, 1236 & 1846.

2626 **BUENO de MESQUITA, Stephen Jonathan,** b. 14 Sept. 51, younger s. of D. M. Bueno de Mesquita, Ph.D. SH 64^3–69^3; Levée; Head of House. Christ Church, Oxford. Undergraduate. Brother, 1665.

2627 **BULLOCK, Osmund Haddan Watson,** b. 25 July 51, s. of R. H. W. Bullock (OR SH 34). SH, 64^3–68^3. Webber-Douglas Academy of Dramatic Art, London. Student Actor. Cert. of Institute of British Fight Directors. Have acted with Hammersmith Municipal Opera & B.B.C. T.V.

2628 **CAHAN, Charles Ellis Flint,** b. 25 Mar. 51, elder s. of late J. F. Cahan. SH, 64^3–67^2.

2629 **CUNNINGHAM, David Jonathan,** b. 26 July 51, elder s. of Rev. J. Cunningham (OR SH 36). SH, 64^3–69^2. H.N.D., Business Studies. Under Articles for Chartered Accountancy.

2630 **DEAN, Peter Henry,** b. 5 Jan. 51, younger s. of Sir P. H. Dean, G.C.M.G. (OR SH 22). SH, 64^3–69^1; Levée; Head of House; XV, 69. Trinity, Cambridge, Part I Classical Tripos, 72, currently reading for Part II Law Tripos for 74. Student. Lincoln's Inn, London. Brother, 2337.

2631 **GHANDI, Phiroze Rustom,** b. 16 Jan. 51, s. of Cmdre. R. K. Ghandhi. Indian Navy. SH, 64^3–68^3. New College, Oxford, B.A. At present doing LL.M. degree at King's College, London.

2632 **LUMSDEN, Ian George,** b. 19 Mar. 51, 2nd s. of J. A. Lumsden, M.B.E., T.D. (OR SH 28). SH, 64^3–68^3. Corpus Christi, Cambridge, B.A. At present at Edinburgh University, taking LL.B. Brothers, 2272 & 2907.

2633 **SECCOMBE, Philip Stanley,** b. 21 July 51, elder s. of H. L. Seccombe. SH 64^3–69^2; R. VIII, 69; Athletics Team, 69. Royal Agricultural College, Cirencester.

2634 STUBBS, Roger Gordon, b. 1 Apr. 51, elder s. of K. G. Stubbs, F.C.A. SH, 64³–69². Brother, Christopher Birchall, SH, 68¹–.

2635 TROUNSON, Richard Noy, b. 16 May 51, elder s. of Dr. E. N. Trounson. SH, 64³–69³. Modern History Exhibition to Christ Church, Oxford. Brother, William Noy, Tu, 67³–72².

2636 VARLEY, James Sagar, b. 4 Mar. 51, elder s. of J. A. Varley, LL.B. SH, 64³–68³. Sussex University, B.Sc. Manchester University, M.Sc. Brother, John Peter Dyson, SH, 72³–.

2637 GERAGHTY, Paul Alban Christopher Vincent, b. 25 Dec. 50, 2nd s. of P. J. Geraghty. T, 64³–69¹; Dewar Travel Scholarship; Walker Leaving Exhibition. Selwyn, Cambridge, B.A.

2638 GODDARD, Ian Lester, b. 24 May 51, younger s. of E. Goddard. T, 64³–69³.

2639 HUNTINGFORD, John Rodney, b. 8 Jan. 51, elder s. of R. H. Huntingford. T, 64³–69¹; Levée; Head of House. Pembroke, Oxford, B.A. Articled Clerk with Peat, Marwick, Mitchell & Co., London. Brother, 2958.

2640 JONES, Graham Colin, b. 4 Mar. 51, s. of D. R. Jones. T, 64³–68³; Leaving Exhibition. University College, London. St. George's Hospital Medical School, B.Sc. Medical Student (Clinical).

2641 LINDOP, Clifford Bromley, b. 2 Jan. 51, s. of C. B. Lindop, A.F.C. T, 64³–69². Warwick University.

2642 MARTINDALE, Richard Geoffrey, b. 8 Sept. 50, s. of G. P. Martindale. T, 64³–69²; Levée; Head of House. Southampton University, LL.B. British Railways (London Midland Region).

2643 MILLER, Christopher James Richard, b. 10 Nov. 50, eldest s. of Col. J. A. Miller. T, 64³–69².

2644 MORGAN, Brian William Ernest, b. 8 Jan. 51, younger s. of R. J. Morgan. T, 64³–68². B.R.N.C., Dartmouth. Qualified as Midshipman but left Navy in Oct. 70. Emigrated to Australia, Feb. 71. Brother, 2352.

2645 NOCON, Andrew, b. 25 July 51, s. of W. Nocon. T, 64³–69²; Scholarship

to Balliol, Oxford. Undergraduate till July 73.

2646 PARSONS-CHANDLER, John Anthony, b. 10 Oct. 51, s. of J. C. G. V. Parsons-Chandler. T, 64³–68³; Scholar. Southampton University, LL.B. Solicitor's Articled Clerk with Coward Chance & Co. of London.

2647 ROLAND, Martin Oliver, b. 7 Aug. 51, younger s. of P. E. Roland, M.B., B.S., F.R.C.S. T, 64³–68³. Merton, Oxford. Brother, 1713.

2648 SLATER, Anthony Ian, b. 28 July 51, s. of I. G. Slater (OR T 28). T, 64³–69¹. University College, London, B.Sc. Associate Member, Institute of Physics. Student of Illuminating Engineering Society. Research Assistant (Environmental Physics), Polytechnic of the South Bank.

2649 WIGG, Christopher Graham, b. 14 Mar. 51, elder s. of R. E. Wigg, B.Sc. T, 64³–68³. Imperial College, London. Graduate Trainee at British United Shoe Machinery Co. Ltd. Engineering. Brother, 2964.

2650 BOOTH, William Thomas, b. 2 Feb. 51, s. of T. N. Booth, F.C.A. B, 64³–68²; Sailing VI. Articled Clerk, Accountancy. *S.C.Y.C.*

2651 DAVIES, James William, b. 10 Jan. 51, younger s. of Rear-Admiral A. Davies, C.B., C.V.O. B, 64³–68³. Trinity Hall, Cambridge. Agricultural Officer (Research) in Min. Ag. & Nat. Resources, Kano State, Kano, Nigeria, from Sept. 73. Brother, 1210.

2652 DODD, Andrew Hervey Crosley, b. 3 Mar. 51, elder s. of R. C. C. Dodd, M.C., T.D. B, 64³–69². Exeter University.

2653 DUNCAN, John David, b. 23 June 51, elder s. of Col. A. A. Duncan, O.B.E. (OR B 28). B, 64³–69³; Levée; Head of House. Exeter University. Brother, 2967.

2654 EVELYN-JONES, Colin Frank, b. 25 Apr. 51, s. of L. Evelyn-Jones, M.B.E. (OR B 21). B, 64³–69²; Levée; Head of House. Tex Abrasives Ltd. *Royal Thames Yacht Club.*

2655 FASSBENDER, Richard Julian, b. 15 Dec. 50, s. of H. Fassbender. B, 64³–

69². University of Wales, B.Sc. Since Aug. 72, Marketing Assistant with Hobson, Bates & Partners. Advertising Agency.

2656 HOBBISS, John Holland, b. 15 Feb. 51, s. of M. A. H. Hobbiss, F.R.I.B.A. T.D. B, 64³–69². Bristol University Medical School. Student.

2657 JAKOBI, Julian Alexander Robert, b. 23 Apr. 51, youngest s. of Dr. J. Jakobi. B, 64³–69¹; Levée; Head of House; Rackets Pair, 69; Tennis VI, 68. Worcester Oxford, B.A. Chartered Accountant with Thomson McLintock & Co., London. *Queen's Club, Vincent's Club.*

2658 JOHNSON, Paul Frederick Parry, b. 16 Dec. 50, s. of Major K. I. E. Johnson. B, 64³–69². Edinburgh University.

2659 OUTCALT, Peter Paul, b. 8 June 51, 2nd s. of late D. B. Outcalt. B, 64³–69². Killed in automobile accident at Narbonne, France, in July 71. Brothers, 2512 & David Lionel, B, 67¹–70².

2660 CLIFT, Francis Charles, b. 23 Sept. 51, younger s. of F. P. Clift. C, 64³–68³; Scholar. Emmanuel, Cambridge, undergraduate studying Economics. Brother, 2279.

2661 DUNLOP, Michael William Beckett, b. 4 May 51, 2nd s. of W. B. Dunlop. (OR C 29). C, 64³–69²; Levée; Head of House; H. XI, 68, 69; Tennis VI, 69; Head of School. Edinburgh University reading Law.

2662 HASHEM, Ameed Ihsan, b. 3 Nov. 47, s. of H.E. I. Hashem, K. St. J., M.B.E. of Jerusalem. C, 64³–66³. University of Illinois.

2663 JACKSON, Mark Lucien, b. 22 Jan. 51, younger s. of Lt.-Col. A. F. J. G. Jackson, E.R.D. C, 64³–69²; Cap, 68; XI, 69. R.M.A., Sandhurst. Commissioned 2nd Lt., 1st Bn. Worcestershire & Sherwood Foresters Regt. Lt., 73. Served U.K., N. Ireland & Berlin. Now Commdg. 13 Army Youth Team in Nottingham. G.S.M., N. Ireland. Brother, 2207.

2664 KNOWLES, Gregory James, b. 31 July 51, elder s. of B. W. Knowles. C, 64³–69²; Athletics Team, 67. Queen's, Cambridge, 70–73.

2665 PAINE, Martin Roger, b. 12 Mar. 51, younger s. of C. R. Paine. C,

64³–69²; XV, 68; Basket Ball, VIII. University of Sussex, studying for B.Sc. in Biology & Cultural & Community Studies. *Seaview Yacht Club.*

2666 TODD, John Farquhar, b. 10 July 51, younger s. of D. C. Todd, T.D. (OR C 22). C, 64³–69². Guildhall School of Music & Drama. A.G.S.M. Musician. Brother, 2441.

2667 BALLANTYNE, Anthony Alexander, b. 30 May 51, s. of A. H. Ballantyne, C.V.O., C.B.E. (OR K 24). K, 64³–64³. Goethe Gymnasium & Music Hochschule, Frankfurt-am-M. Passed Arbitur. Studying Modern Languages & Music in France. Diplôme Universitaire d'Etudes Littéraires, at Nice University. Now studying music at the École Normale in Paris.

2668 BLASKEY, Roger Waldo, b. 28 Apr. 51, younger s. of M. Blaskey. K, 64³–68³. Manchester University, College of Science & Technology. Brother, 2209.

2669 BULL, Nigel Cecil, b. 13 Jan. 51, s. of R. C. Bull (OR K 35). K, 64³–69¹. Exhibition to Trinity Hall, Cambridge.

2670 DEL MAR, Jonathan René, b. 7 Jan. 51, elder s. of N. R. Del Mar. K, 64³–68³. Christ Church, Oxford, B.A. Brother, 2985.

2671 LEE, Roger Gordon, b. 23 Feb. 51, elder s. of G. L. Lee. K, 64³–69³; Levée; Head of House. Southampton University. Student. Brother, 2987.

2672 SWANSTON, James Murray, b. 15 Mar. 51, 3rd s. of M. Swanston (OR K 35). K, 64³–69². Brothers, 2055, 2381 & David Mungo, K, 67³–71².

2673 BRACEWELL, Christopher Charles, b. 4 Dec. 50, elder s. of G. A. Bracewell, M.B., B.Chir. (OR M 36). M, 64³–69².

2674 KINMONT, Patrick William John, b. 21 Jan. 51, s. of P. D. C. Kinmont, M.B.E., T.D., M.D., F.R.C.P. M, 64³–69²; Levée; Head of House; XXII, 67–69. Trinity College, Dublin. Student.

2675 MACKENZIE, Christopher Iain, b. 10 Dec. 50, s. of I. C. K. Mackenzie, T.D., M.D., F.R.C.P. (OR M 27). M, 64³–69³; Tennis VI, 4 years; Capt. of Fives. Medical student, 3rd year, at Guy's Hospital.

2676 **MASTERS, John Bertram,** b. 12 May 51, younger s. of M. B. E. Masters. M, 64³–69². Nottingham College of Art.

2677 **MURRAY, Angus Duncan James,** b. 5 Feb. 51, s. of J. A. Murray, T.D., F.C.A. M, 64³–69³. Christ Church, Oxford. Student. Life-saving Bronze Medal. Gliding Licence.

2678 **TANNETT, Jack Owen,** b. 11 June 51, 2nd s. of O. D. Tannett. M, 64³–69²; Levée; XV, 68. Portsmouth Polytechnic. Trainee Mechanical Engineer with George Wimpey (M. E. & C.) Ltd. Brothers, 1651 & Benjamin, M, 70³–.

2679 **WALKER, Robert Charles,** b. 2 Apr. 51, elder s. of T. C. Walker, F.C.A. (OR M 36). M, 64³–68³; Scholar. Entrance Exhibition to Clare, Cambridge, B.A. With Hawker-Siddeley Aviation, Kingston-upon-Thames, Aug. 72–Mar. 73. Since Apr. 73, with Marks & Clerk in London, training to become Chartered Patent Agent. Brother, 2832.

2680 **WILSON, Andrew Norman,** b. 27 Oct. 50, younger s. of N. Wilson. M, 64³–68³; Senior Scholarship, 67; Queen's Medal, 68. New College, Oxford, B.A. Chancellor's English Essay Prize.

2681 **YOUNG, Gavin Leslie,** b. 23 Apr. 51, elder s. of I. S. Young, M.B., Ch.B., F.R.C.S. (OR M 33). M, 64³–68³. Scholarship to Magdalen, Oxford. B.A. Clinical student, University College Hospital, London. Brother, John Strang Walker, M, 68³–.

2682 **ZIMMERMAN, Michael John,** b. 17 Aug. 51, 2nd s. of P. R. Zimmerman. (OR M 35). M, 64³–68³; XXII, 68. Undergraduate, Yale University, U.S.A.

2683 **AUSTIN, Jonathan Charles Hope,** b. 15 June 51, s. of C. H. Austin. SF, 64³–69²; Levée; Head of House; XV, 69, Capt.; H. XI, 69; XI, 67–68, Capt. 69. Management Trainee, Union International Co. *The Button Club.*

2684 **BAYLY, Richard Dion,** b. 25 Feb. 51, elder s. of E. H. Bayly (OR SF 26). SF, 64³–69³; Levée; Head of House; Commodore of Sailing. University of Bristol. Undergraduate. Brother, Jeremy John, SF, 68³–.

2685 **BURTON, Jeremy John,** b. 18 May 51, 2nd s. of A. J. Burton, F.R.C.S. SF, 64³–68². Brothers, 3002 & Mark Timothy, SF, 68³–.

2686 **DUNLOP, Thomas,** b. 22 Apr. 51, s. of Sir T. Dunlop, Bt. SF, 64³–69². Glasgow University, reading Accountancy.

2687 **DUVAL, Roderick Charles,** b. 11 Dec. 50, elder s. of H. R. Duval, M.D., C.M., F.R.C.S., F.R.C.O.G. SF, 64³–69²; Golf Team, 68–69. College of Law, Guildford. Solicitor's Articled Clerk, finals in Feb. 74. *The Norfolk Club, Eaton (Norwich)* G.C. Brother, Nicolas Kenneth, SF, 72²–.

2688 **GARFORTH - BLES, Hugh Charles,** b. 12 Jan. 51, younger s. of M. W. Garforth-Bles (OR SF 27). SF, 64³–69²; Levée. Exeter University. Brother, 2390.

2689 **HABERSHON, John Joseph,** b. 21 Mar. 51, s. of M. E. Habershon, O.B.E. SF, 64³–69². Sheffield University. Student.

2690 **HOROWITZ, Lionel Philip,** b. 3 Apr. 51, elder s. of M. Horowitz. SF, 64³–68³. Scholar. I.C.I. Investment Research Dept. Career uncertain. *Public Schools Club.*

2691 **IRWIN, Gordon Harley Fenwick,** b. 27 Mar. 51, elder s. of K. G. F. Irwin, C.P.M. (OR SF 39). SF, 64³–69²; Commodore Sailing. Final year at Oriel, Oxford, reading Politics & Economics. Undergraduate.

2692 **KENNEDY, John Anthony Bingham,** b. 2 Apr. 51, youngest s. of B. B. Kennedy, T.D. (OR SF 33). SF, 64³–68³. Royal Agricultural College, Cirencester on 3-year Land Agents Course, M.R.A.C. Land Agent with Michael Barne & Partners, Ayr. Brothers, 1385 & 2394.

2693 **RAYMOND, Jeremy Michael,** b. 21 Mar. 51, 2nd s. of P. Raymond (OR SF 34). SF, 64³–68³. Christ's, Cambridge. Brothers, 2317 & Giles Anthony, SF, 67³–71³.

2694 **RITCHIE, Ian Peter,** b. 30 Oct. 50, younger s. of P. Ritchie, T.D. (OR C 31). SF 64³–68². Royal Naval Cadetship, 67. S/Lt., Royal Navy. Brother, 2160.

2695 **SELLAR, Robert John,** b. 8 Dec. 50, s. of R. M. Sellar. SF, 64³–69²; Levée. St. Thomas's Hospital Medical School. Degree in Psychology and completing medical training.

2696 **BICKERSTETH, Anthony Charles**, b. 9 Feb. 51, 2nd s. of E. J. Bickersteth. Sh, 64³–68³; XV, 68; XI, 68. Social Worker. Brother, 2238.

2697 **HALLIFAX, Peter James**, b. 20 Feb. 51, younger s. of Cdr. J. C. Hallifax, R.N. (OR B 37). Sh, 64³–69³. Student at University of Surrey, reading for B.Mus. Musician's Union.

2698 **HASSALL, Harold Richard**, b. 16 July 51, s. of H. Hassall, M.B., Ch.B., F.R.C.S. Sh, 64³–69². Leeds University, studying for B.A.(Hons.) in Philosophy/Psychology. Expect to complete course in 74.

2699 **LOAKE, Jonathan David**, b. 21 Mar. 51, eldest s. of J. E. Loake. Sh, 64³–69³; Levée; Head of House; Capt. of Swimming; Capt. of Basketball; Jex-Blake Prize for English Literature; Leaving Exhibition for English Literature to Trinity, Oxford. Undergraduate. Brothers, 3031 & Andrew Ernest, Sh, 71³–.

2700 **PAIN, David Trevor**, b. 13 Mar. 51, elder s. of T. G. Pain (OR Sh 32). Sh, 64³–69²; Capt. of Shooting, 69. Royal Agricultural College, Cirencester. M.R.A.C., N.D.A. Agricultural Sciences. Brother, James Andrew, Sh, 67²–.

2701 **SCOTT, John Adrian Douglas**, b. 4 Aug. 51, s. of the late Wing-Cdr. J. H. Scott. R.A.F. Sh, 64³–69³.

2702 **STONEMAN, Richard John**, b. 20 Jan. 51, s. of K. J. T. Stoneman. Sh, 64³–68³; Scholar. Scholarship to New College, Oxford, B.A.

2703 **WALLACE-HADRILL, Andrew Frederic**, b. 29 July 51, elder s. of J. M. Wallace-Hadrill. Sh, 64³–69¹; Scholar; Levée; Head of School; Head of House. Corpus Christi, Oxford. Hertford & Le Paravincini Scholarships. B.A. Remaining at Oxford as Graduate.

2704 **BINNEY, Peter Lockhart**, b. 27 May 51, elder s. of H. L. Binney (OR St 34). St, 64³–69². Manchester University, B.A. Electronic Test Engineer. Brother, Timothy Hugh, St, 67³–71³.

2705 **CLIFFORD SMITH, Michael Miles**, b. 11 July 51, s. of M. R. Clifford Smith. St, 64³–69². Thames Polytechnic. Student (Business Studies) with British Radio Corp., Newhaven.

2706 **GRAY, Thomas Anthony Gordon**, b. 14 Dec. 50, eldest s. of K. G. Gray, M.B.E. St, 64³–69¹. Brother, 2936B.

2707 **KITOVITZ, Paul Alexander**, b. 25 Apr. 51, s. of N. Kitovitz. St, 64³–69¹.

2708 **McKENZIE JOHNSTON, Robert Alexander**, b. 25 Mar. 51, s. of H. B. McKenzie Johnston (OR St 35). St, 64³–68³. Trinity Hall, Cambridge. 2nd Lt. 17th/21st Lancers (Regular Commission). *Cavalry Club.*

2709 **MARX, Nicholas Paul**, b. 15 May 51, s. of R. I. Marx (OR St 36). St, 64³–68³.

2710 **SALISBURY, Ian Meredith**, b. 15 Apr. 51, s. of G. C. Salisbury, F.C.A. St, 64³–69³; Levée. St. Catherine's, Oxford, B.A. From Oct. 73, Leaf Buying Dept., British American Tobacco Co.

2711 **SISSONS, David Chamberlain**, b. 17 May 51, younger s. of R. C. Sissons (OR St 19). St, 64³–69³. Pembroke, Cambridge, to June 73.

2712 **SPENS, John Hope**, b. 23 May 51, younger s. of C. H. Spens, C.B. St, 64³–69². St. John's College & Collingwood College, Durham University. Undergraduate. *Royal Solent Yacht Club.*

2713 **SPOTTISWOODE, David Martin**, b. 21 Feb. 51, elder s. of H. D. Spottiswoode, F.C.A. (OR St 34). St, 64³–69². Youth Service in Kenya, 69–70. City of Birmingham Polytechnic Accountancy course. Chartered Accountant under articles with Thomson McLintock & Co., London. *Ski Club of Great Britain.*

2714 **COWPER, Michael Jeremy**, b. 26 Apr. 51, s. of M. R. Cowper, LL.B. (OR Tu 30). Tu, 64³–68².

2715 **CURZON, Frederick Richard Penn**, b. 29 Jan. 51, s. of C. G. W. P. Curzon. Tu, 64³–69¹; Scholar; Levée; Head of House; Classical Leaving Exhibition. Scholarship to Christ Church, Oxford, B.A.

2716 **DALGLEISH, John Gordon**, b. 13 July 51, s. of P. G. Dalgleish, M.D., M.R.C.P. Tu, 64³–68³.

2717 **HARDING, Roland Arthur**, b. 28 June 51, elder s. of G. R. Harding, T.D. (OR Tu 29). Tu, 64³–68²; XI, 67–68. B.R.N.C., Dartmouth. Royal Naval

Engineering College, Manadon. Royal Navy. Lt. Brother, Robert John Bruce, Tu, 67^3–72^2.

2718 HOWE, Richard Turner, b. 17 Apr. 46, younger s. of W. Howe. Tu, 64^3–65^2; R. VIII, 65; Athletics Colours, 65. Harvard, B.A., M.B.A. Legislative Analyst, State Government (Massachusetts).

2719 McCOSH, Peter Reid, b. 14 June 51, 2nd s. of A. R. McCosh. Tu, 64^3–68^3; Cap, 67. Emmanuel, Cambridge, B.A. Indentured to Graham, Smart & Annan, Chartered Accountants, in Edinburgh. Brothers, 2423 & Colin Andrew, Tu, 69^3–.

2720 REES, Richard Michael, b. 5 Feb. 51, s. of R. R. Rees, M.C. Tu, 64^3–69^2.

2721 SETHIA, Babulal, elder s. of B. Sethia. Tu, 64^3–68^3; Levée; Head of School Music, 68; Capt. of Fencing. St. Thomas's Hospital Medical School, B.Sc. Medical Student reading for M.B. B.S.

2722 SYNGE, Arthur Hugh Millington, b. 4 Aug. 51, elder s. of P. M. Synge (OR Tu 24). Tu, 64^3–68^2. Edinburgh University. Wye College, University of London, Horticulture.

2723 TONGE, George Charles, b. 31 Jan. 51, 2nd s. of late G. M. M. Tonge, J.P. (OR Tu 32). Tu, 64^3–68^2. Killed in motor accident, Dec. 1971. Brothers, 2425 & 3032.

2724 ALLEN, Robert Geoffrey Briere, b. 13 Feb. 51, 3rd s. of the Rev. Canon R. E. T. Allen, M.C. (OR W 10). W, 64^3–68^3; XV, 68. University College, Oxford, B.A. Student, Middle Temple. *Vincent's, Oxford.* Brother, 2262.

2725 BESLY, Edward Michael, b. 11 Aug. 51, elder s. of D. M. Besly, B.Sc. (OR W 29). W, 64^3–69^2; Scholar. Scholarship to Exeter, Oxford. Studying Chemistry in 3rd year. Brother, Bernard Maurice, W, 68^3–.

2726 BRYANT, Edward de Courcy, b. 8 May 51, elder s. of E. J. Bryant. W, 64^3–69^3; Tennis VI; Runner-up, Renny Cup at Queen's; Winner, Thomas Bowl Tennis with J. C. A. Leslie; Runner-up, P. S. Youll Cup. 18 months with Vestey Organization to West Indies, up the Amazon, Peru, Colombia, Brazil, Argentine, Uruguay, Antarctica, Chile, Bolivia, Paraguay & Portugal. Magdalene, Cam-

bridge. Rackets Blue, Capt., 71–72. L.T.A. Junior Wimbledon Competitor for 2 years. Reading for the Bar. Middle Temple. *M.C.C., Pitt Club & Hawks.* Brother, David de Courcy, W, 68^2–72^2.

2727 GRAHAM, David Lionel, b. 19 Feb. 51, youngest s. of H. Graham. W, 64^3–69^1. Merchant Banking. Dir. of Investment Corp. Brother, 1810.

2728 SCHELL, Peter Robson, b. 7 May 46, eldest s. of H. R. Schell of Ontario, Canada. W, 64^3–65^2.

2729 STANSFIELD, James Hampson, b. 29 May 51, younger s. of His Honour Judge J. W. Stansfield, LL.B. W, 64^3–69^3. Fitzwilliam, Cambridge. Undergraduate. Brother, 1040.

2730 WALFORD, Timothy David, b. 29 Jan. 51, elder s. of D. de G. Walford, T.D. (OR M 31). W, 64^3–69^2; Cap. H. XI; Athletics Team. Royal Agricultural College, Cirencester. H.N.D. in Agriculture. At present pursuing practical studies towards farm management. Farm Management Association.

2731 WARNER, Richard Thomas Weston, b. 6 Mar. 51, elder s. of P. A. W. Warner. W, 64^3–69^3; Levée; Head of House; Cap, 69. Christ Church, Oxford, reading Classics. Half-Blue, Fives, 70–71. Student. *Harlequins R.F.C.*

2732 WILLIAMS, Quentin, b. 1 Nov. 51, s. of V. W. Williams. W, 64^3–66^2.

ENTRANCES IN JANUARY 1965

2733 GRIBBON, Angus John St. George, b. 25 Dec. 51, younger s. of Major-General N. St. G. Gribbon, O.B.E. (OR SH 30). SH, 65^1–69^3; Levée; Head of House. New College, Oxford, studying Politics & Economics. Undergraduate. Brother, 1936.

2734 KARNCHANACHARI, Phornsake, b. 11 Apr. 51, s. of S. Karnchanachari of Bangkok, Thailand. SH, 65^1–69^2. Wharton School of Finance & Commerce, University of Pennsylvania, U.S.A.

2735 RIPMAN, Jeremy Guy Christian, b. 20 July 51, 2nd s. of H. A. Ripman, F.R.C.S., F.R.C.O.G. (OR SH 31). SH, 65^1–69^2. King Alfred's College, Winchester. Student from 71. Brothers, 1701 & James Jervis Hugo, SH, 72^3–.

2736 **WATSON, David Mark,** b. 5 May 51, s. of A. R. Watson. B, 65¹–69³; Dewar Travelling Scholarship. Downing, Cambridge. Undergraduate.

2737 **BANCROFT, John Britten,** b. 10 Sept. 51, elder s. of D. B. Bancroft. C, 65¹–69³; R. VIII, 69; Athletics Team, 69. College of Estate Management, Reading University. Student. Brother, Patrick Arthur, C, 70³–.

2738 **HALLAWELL, Philip Charles,** b. 31 July 51, younger s. of D. V. Hallawell. C, 65¹–68². Haverford College, Philadelphia, U.S.A. Fine Arts Major, 68–70, left before completing B.A. degree. Plastic Artist. Work in Gouache pen & ink, graphics & tempera paint. Preparing for exhibitions in France, England & Brazil.

2739 **HEAD, Henry John,** b. 22 Apr. 48, 3rd s. of R. G. Head, B.Sc. (OR T 23). C, 65¹–66²; Imperial College (Royal School of Mines), London, B.Sc., A.R.S.M. Mine Engineer with C.S.I.R.O. at Cobar, N.S.W., Australia.

2740 **HINKS, Edward Christopher,** b. 14 June 51, 3rd s. of J. A. Hinks, O.B.E., M.A., B.Sc., J.P. C, 65¹–68². Hollins College, Manchester. With Scottish & Newcastle Breweries Ltd. Brothers, 2116 & 2308.

2741 **LEIGH-BRAMWELL, Brian Herbert,** b. 28 July 51, s. of P. Leigh-Bramwell. C, 65¹–68³. Bolton Institute of Technology and Bolton School. Christ Church, Oxford, taking Hons. degree in Chemistry until June 74. Awarded Roger Prentice Exhibition, June 72. *Christ Church Boat Club, Oxford.*

2742A **RICHARDS, Michael Whitmore,** b. 18 May 51, s. of C. I. W. Richards (OR C 23). C, 65¹–69². Full-time Photography Diploma course at West Surrey College of Art & Design. Freelance Photographer. *Butterflies C.C.*

2742B **SCHULTZ, Willi.** C, 65¹–65¹.

2743 **SIDEBOTTOM, Nigel Geoffrey Nowell,** b. 20 Aug. 51, s. of D. N. Sidebottom (OR M 29). M, 65¹–69². Sheffield University, 70–73, reading Economics. Student. Capt., *University of Sheffield Sailing Club.*

2744 **PEARSON, Simon Mark,** b. 30 May 51, youngest s. of M. Pearson (OR SF 29). SF, 65¹–70¹; Levée; Head of

House; Head of School; XV; XXII. University of Geneva. Auslands—und Dolmetscherinstitut Germersheim. Trainee in a wine firm. Brothers, 1754 & 2129.

2745 **BLAKE, David Russell,** b. 3 Oct. 51, s. of L. R. Blake, B.Sc., Ph.D. Sh, 65¹–69². Sheffield University Medical School, M.B., Ch.B.

2746 **DIXON, David John,** b. 25 May 51, s. of late J. A. Dixon. Sh, 65¹–69¹. Army Language Training. Accountant. A.C.C.A.

2747 **FRAZER, Andrew David,** b. 24 July 51, younger s. of Cdr. J. W. Frazer, R.N. (rtd.), V.R.D., J.P. Sh, 65¹–69³. Bristol University, taking S.P. Hon. Degree in Greek. Undergraduate. *Mountain Club of Kenya, Austrian Alpine Club.* Brother, 2241.

2748 **BENTLEY, John,** b. 23 Aug. 51, younger s. of J. Bentley. Tu, 65¹–69³; Athletics Team, 69. Magdalene, Cambridge, in 3rd year. *Royal Anglesey Yacht Club.*

2749A **ENGHOFER, Erich,** b. 15 Feb. 49. St, 65¹–65¹. Exchange Student of West Germany.

2749B **MACDONALD, James Malcolm Canmore,** b. 5 July 51, 2nd s. of J. A. MacDonald (OR Tu 36). Tu, 65¹–69². St. Andrew's University.

2750 **QUINLAN, Michael Henry,** b. 6 Oct. 51, s. of Rev. D. W. A. Quinlan. W, 65¹–70²; Levée; Head of House; Cadet Officer, C.C.F. Queen's, Cambridge. Engineering Tripos, 71–74.

2751 **WINSKELL, Andrew Dane,** b. 24 June 51, s. of R. D. H. Winskell, T.D. (OR W 33). W, 65¹–69². Art Student.

ENTRANCES IN MAY 1965

2752 **ARNOTT, Christopher Melville,** b. 19 Oct. 51, s. of Sir M. Arnott, T.D., M.D., F.R.C.P. SH, 65²–69³. Magdalene, Cambridge. Undergraduate.

2753 **DIBSDALL, David Dean,** b. 11 Oct. 51, s. of Col. D. Dibsdall, O.B.E. SH, 65²–69³.

2754 **KENNEDY, Simon Ralph,** b. 15 Jan. 52, s. of Dr. A. R. Kennedy, M.B.E. SH, 65²–70²; Levée; Sw. VI, 66. Dundee

University, reading Chemistry, 71. *Dundee University Rugby Club.*

2755 MASSINGHAM, Adam Hugh le M., b. 4 Jan. 51, only s. of Mrs. R. Massingham, SH, 65^2–66^2.

2756 SIMPKISS, Richard Jonathan, b. 21 Oct. 51, s. of Dr. M. J. Simpkiss. SH, 65^2–70^2; Levée; Head of House; Holder of Bigside Bags, 69; Capt. of Athletics, 69. Magdalene, Cambridge. Undergraduate.

2757 WILLIAMS, Nigel Jestyn, b. 1 Oct. 51, s. of H. J. Williams, M.B., B.Chir. SH, 65^2–69^3; Sw. IX, 67–69.

2758 SWINDELLS, David Martin, b. 18 Dec. 51, younger s. of P. C. Swindells (OR B 35). B, 65^2–70^2; Levée; Head of House. Newcastle-upon-Tyne, Polytechnic, studying for B.A. Law (Hons.).

2759 DUNCAN, William Gordon, b. 23 Nov. 51, elder s. of A. T. E. Duncan. C, 65^2–69^2; Cap, 68. Royal Agricultural College, Cirencester. Pig Farmer. Brother, Michael Graham, C, 73^1–.

2760 HUNTER, Mark Summers, b. 2 Nov. 51, s. of G. L. Hunter. C, 65^2–69^2. Cirencester Agricultural College.

2761 MARTIN, Christopher D'Arcy, b. 2 Oct. 51, eldest s. of D. D'A. Martin. C, 65^2–69^3. Pembroke, Oxford, reading Engineering Science.

2762 PASCALL, Philip Antony Richard, b. 20 Nov. 51, s. of R. J. Pascall. C, 65^2–69^2. Southampton University, B.Sc. Eng. *Sub-Aqua Club.*

2763 PENNISTON, Simon Rupert Thomas, b. 8 Jan. 52, s. of P. Penniston. C, 65^2–70^3; Head of House; Levée; H. XI, 70; XV, 68–69, Capt., 70; XXII, 70. Guildford College of Law, 71–72. Articled Clerk to Solicitor in Leeds. *Headingley Rugby Club, Harlequins Rugby Club.*

2764 THOMSON, George Edward, b. 11 Oct. 51, elder s. of Dr. G. W. R. Thomson, J.P. C, 65^2–69^2. Derby Technical College. St. Thomas's Hospital. Medical Student. Brother, Charles Mowat, C, 70^2–72^2.

2765 WOOLLAN, Edward Bruce, b. 15 Oct. 51, younger s. of Rev. J. E. M. Woollan (OR C 30). C, 65^2–69^3; Cap, 69. Brother, 2444.

2766 PLAZZOTTA, Richard Luciano, b. 27 Dec. 51, eldest s. of E. M. Plazzotta. K, 65^2–69^2.

2767 SCRUBY, Philip Robinett, b. 8 Nov. 51, elder s. of A. J. Scruby, T.D. K, 65^2–70^2; Squash Team, 69–70; Golf Team, 70. Nottingham College of Further Education, studying for A levels for 1 year. Employed at Kennings Ltd., Peterborough. Studying Motor Trade Practice & Management. *Peterborough & Northants Squash Club.* Brother, James Anthony, K, 69^3–.

2768 HARLAND, John Michael, b. 1 Jan. 52, elder s. of S. W. Harland, M.A., LL.B. M, 65^2–70^1; Levée; Head of House; XV, 68–69; XI, 68, Capt., 69; Fives IV, 68–69, Capt., 70. Gonville & Caius, Cambridge, B.A. Half-Blue for Fives. *Hawk's Club, Butterflies.* Brother, 2995.

2769 BUCHANAN, Andrew John Scouler, b. 1 Dec. 51, elder s. of J. H. S. Buchanan. M.B., B.Chir. (OR Sh 36). Sh, 65^2–70^2; Levée; Head of House. St. Andrew's University. Brother, Charles Robert Scouler, Sh, 71^2–.

2770 DIZER, Peter Malcolm, b. 6 Aug. 51, eldest s. of late J. M. Dizer (OR Sh 33). Sh 65^2–69^1.

2771 GORDON BROWN, David Hugh, b. 31 Jan. 52, 2nd s. of T. P. Gordon Brown (OR Sh 31). Sh, 65^2–69^2.

2772 MORTON, James Freeland, b. 28 Nov. 51, 4th s. of K. V. F. Morton. Sh, 65^2–69^3; Scholar. School of Oriental & African Studies, London. Studying for Arabic Degree, 3rd year (of four). Brothers, 1015, 1307 & 1992.

2773 HAWORTH, Christopher, b. 6 Nov. 51, eldest s. of P. Haworth. St, 65^2–70^3; Levée; XV, 69–70; Head of School Music, 70. 2nd year at Reading University, reading B.Sc. in Estate Management. *Reading University R.F.C.* Brother, Mark, St, 70^2–.

2774 NUNN, Christopher John, b. 15 Sept. 51, 2nd s. of K. E. Nunn. St, 65^2–69^1.

2775 SYMINGTON, Noel Ian, b. 21 Oct. 51, s. of late N. H. Symington (OR St 27). St, 65^2–70^2. Athletics Team, 69. East Anglia University.

2776 HAMILTON, Timothy David, b. 8 Oct. 51, younger s. of H. A. Hamilton. Tu, 65²–70²; Levée. XV, 69; XI, 70; Athletics Team, 69–70. Royal Agricultural College, Cirencester. Student. *M.C.C.*

2777 HEARN, Nigel John Stewart, b. 11 Nov. 51, s. of Lt.-Col. R. F. Hearn (OR Tu 35). Tu, 65²–69²; Levée; Head of House.

2778 JONES, Christopher Kenneth Richard Thursfield, b. 10 Sept. 51, s. of A. G. I. Jones, Q.C. Tu, 65²–70²; Levée; Head of School. Bristol University.

2779 GARVEY, John Christopher, b. 11 Nov. 51, younger s. of T. W. Garvey, C.M.G. W, 65²–70². Brother, 2265.

ENTRANCES IN SEPTEMBER 1965

2780 CARTER, Harold Hugh John, b. 6 Feb. 52, s. of H. Carter. SH, 65³–70¹; Senior Scholarship, 68; Queen's Medal, 69. Gonville & Caius, Cambridge, B.A. Founder/Dir., Youth Action, Halifax, 71. Community Service Volunteers Committee, 71, Vice-Chrmn., 72. Sec. Cambridge Union Society, 73. *R.A.C.*

2781 CHANDRIS, Michael Demetri, b. 6 Dec. 51, younger s. of D. J. Chandris. SH, 65³–69³.

2782 EDMEADES, William James, b. 14 Feb. 52, eldest s. of Col. A. W. Edmeades, M.B.E. (OR SH 23). SH, 65³–70². Outward Bound Course. Diploma of the Newmarket School of Stud Management. Assistant Trainer in Racing Stable. Brothers, Michael David, **SH, 67²–** & Evelyn Hugh, SH, 69³–.

2783 HANCOCK, Peter Geoffrey, b. 20 Dec. 51, s. of G. A. J. Hancock. SH, 65³–68³. Queen's, Oxford, B.A. Leeds University, Research Student in Logic.

2784 HOPE, Robert Darsie, b. 22 June 52, s. of R. A. Hope. SH, 65³–70³. Exeter University, B.A.

2785 LESLIE, Simon Alexander, b. 20 Jan. 52, 3rd s. of K. A. S. Leslie (OR SH 28). SH, 65³–70³; Levée. University of Kent at Canterbury. Now in Law Degree. *H.C.E.G.* Brothers, 2009 & 2339.

2786 NUSSEIBEH, Sari Anwar, b. 12 Feb. 49, 2nd s. of H.E. A. Z. Nusseibeh,

Governor of Jerusalem. SH, 65³–66². Brother, 2343.

2787 SHERIDAN, Richard Cecil Ercaut, b. 16 July 52, elder s. of C. M. Sheridan, C.M.G. SH, 65³–70³. Brother, Michael John Ercaut, SH, 69³–72³.

2788 CRAXTON, Adrian Harold Robert, b. 3 Nov. 51, 2nd s. of R. T. Craxton. T, 65³–69³. Brothers, 2347 & Julian Robert, T, 70³–.

2789 CRUICKSHANKS, Gordon Iaan, b. 13 Nov. 51, s. of T. Cruickshanks. T, 65³–69³. Glasgow University, taking course in Business Management.

2790 EDWARDS, Rodney George, b. 1 Apr. 52, s. of A. G. Edwards. T, 65³–69³; Exhibitioner of Clare, Cambridge, reading Electrical Sciences Tripos (Part II) (first two years Natural Sciences Tripos). Student Engineer, Procurement Executive. M.O.D.

2791 FOXCROFT, Richard Edward, b. 1 May 52, s. of G. E. Foxcroft (A). T, 65³–70². University of Leeds. At present still a student of Fine Art.

2792 KEY, William, b. 21 Mar. 52, younger s. of M. Kay. T, 65³–70². University of Dundee, 70. Biology Dept. Hockey XI. Student. Brother, 2189.

2793 KILNER, John Stephen, b. 4 Feb. 52, s. of S. R. Kilner. T, 65³–69³. Gonville & Caius, Cambridge. Undergraduate studying Law.

2794 MACARTHUR, John Tennant, b. 16 Jan. 52, s. of D. MacArthur. T, 65³–69².

2795 NEALE, Andrew James, b. 12 Apr. 52, eldest s. of A. J. Neale. T, 65³–69³; Exhibitioner of Gonville & Caius, Cambridge. Studying Engineering (passed Part I). Undergraduate Trainee with Tube Investments Ltd.

2796 PICKERILL, Clive Edwin, b. 4 Sept. 51, elder s. of E. F. Pickerill. T, 65³–70²; Levée; Head of House; XI. Student at Westhill College of Education, Birmingham. Teacher. *Rugby G.C.* Brother, Roy Anthony, T, 70³–.

2797 PROWSE, Ian John, b. 21 Dec. 51, elder s. of D. W. Prowse. T, 65³–69³. Undergraduate, Magdalene, Cambridge, reading Engineering (final year). Brother, Graham David Windsor, T, 68³–72³.

2798 RABY, Nigel John Francis, b. 18 Feb. 52, elder s. of K. F. Raby. T, 65³–70². Brother, Angus William, T, 71³–.

2799 SOUTHERN, Paul Kenneth, b. 5 Sept. 51, s. of Rev. K. F. Southern. T, 65³–69³; Exhibition to Corpus Christi, Cambridge. At present Part II Natural Science Tripos. C.I.C.U.

2800 WILSON, David Edwin, b. 22 Feb. 52, s. of E. C. H. Wilson. T, 65³–69³; Mynors Exhibition to University College, Oxford, reading Modern Languages.

2801 BRONNERT, Nicholas Henry, b. 18 Dec. 51, elder s. of D. H. Bronnert. B, 65³–69². XV, 68. North Cheshire Central College of Further Education. St. Mary's Hospital Medical School, Clinical Medical Student. *St. Mary's Hospital R.F.C.* Brother, Adam Henry, B, 70¹–.

2802 CALEY, Richard Michael, b. 29 Dec. 51, elder s. of J. P. Caley, M.B., Ch.B. B, 65³–70². XXII, 70; H. XI, 70. City Univ. London, B.Sc. Nottinghamshire County V22, Hockey. Brother, Timothy Edward, B, 68¹–72².

2803A COCKBURN, Simon Nicholas, b. 13 Apr. 52, younger s. of D. Cockburn. B, 65³–71². Levée. Cadet Officer. Inns of Court School of Law—Bar Exams. Bar Student. Hon. Soc. of Inner Temple.

2803B DIX, John David Carlton, b. 19 May 52, 2nd s. of P. C. Dix (OR B 31). B, 65³–69³. Churchill, Cambridge, 70–73. Engineering. 2nd Lt. 39 Engineer Regt. (A), R.E. Commissioned, 70. Brothers, 2439, William Tage Edward Carlton, B, 68³– & Robert George Carlton, B, 70³–.

2804 FOOTERMAN, David Simon, b. 16 Feb. 52, eldest s. of M. Footerman, M.R.C.S., L.R.C.P. B, 65³–69³. Scholar. London Univ.

2805 FREEMAN, Timothy Hugh, b. 29 July 52, 4th s. of E. H. R. Freeman (OR B 17). B, 65³–70³. Levée; Head of House; XV, 70; Fencing III. Guildford College of Law. Articled Clerk with Freeman Daly & Jacks, Solicitors, of Darlington. Teesside Law Students' Society. *Darlington Rugby Club.* Brother, 1869.

2806 JONES, Richard Edward, b. 22 Apr. 52, younger s. of J. D. T. Jones, M.B., B.S., M.S., F.R.C.S. B, 65³–69².

2807 LEARMOUNT, Robin Thomas, b. 31 Mar. 52, 3rd s. of Capt. D. K. L. Learmount, D.S.C., R.N. (OR B 33). B 65³–70³. Awaiting place at University. Student. Brother, 2111.

2808 MUSCOTT, Nicolas Bruce, b. 14 Jan. 52, elder s. of B. B. Muscott. B, 65³–69². H. XI. Royal Agricultural College, Cirencester. Estate Management.

2809 PRINGLE, Alan Keith, b. 20 Jan. 52, elder s. of J. Pringle. B, 65³–70². XV, 69. Athletics Team, 68–70. Rice Univ., Houston, Texas. Undergraduate. Univ. Football Varsity, 70, 71, 72. *Young Houstonian Club.* Brother, Duncan Robert, B, 67³–70².

2810 BARBER, Ian Henry, b. 18 May 52, s. of A. H. Barber. C, 65³–70². Badminton, 69, 70.

2811 BOYLES, Paul Christopher Garvin, b. 7 Mar. 52, elder s. of C. J. Boyles. C, 65³–69². Brother, Nigel Stanley John, C, 67²–71².

2812 BROOKS, Richard Sam, b. 30 June 52, s. of S. Brooks. C, 65³–69³. Keble, Oxford.

2813 DERRY-EVANS, Robert Stephen, b. 2 Mar. 52, elder s. of N. S. Derry-Evans. C, 65³–70¹. Scholar. Christ Church, Oxford. Undergraduate. Brother, Jonathan Edward, C, 71¹–.

2814 HELME, Timothy Michael, b. 18 June 52, s. of Wing-Cdr. J. M. Helme, D.F.C., A.F.C. (OR C 33). C, 65³–69³. Trinity, Cambridge. Medical Sciences Tripos, 70–73. Medical Student, Middlesex Hosital, since 73.

2815 POOLE, Nicholas Wallis, b. 10 Apr. 52, 3rd s. of G. A. Poole. C, 65³–70³. Levée. Senior Scholarship, Merton, Oxford.

2816 BROWN, Fredric Scott, b. 29 May 48, eldest s. of N. Brown, Ph.D., of U.S.A. K, 65³–66³. York Univ.

2817 EVANS, Nigel Lagouge, b. 1 Sept. 52, eldest s. of A. L. Evans. K, 65³–70¹. XV, 69; XXII, 69; H. XI, 70. Cape Town Univ., S. Africa, 71. Brasenose, Oxford since 72. Brothers, Mark Hally, K, 72¹– & Stuart Anthony, K, 72¹–.

2818 GOULD, Michael Ross, b. 17 Mar. 52, elder s. of G. W. Gould, O.B.E.,

M.C., K.M.N. (OR K 38). K, 65^3–70^2. XI, 70. Shell Mex-B.P., Strand, London. *Butterflies C.C.*

2819 HANKEY, Peter John Alers, b. 2 Aug. 51, youngest s. of Hon. H. A. A. Hankey, C.M.G., C.V.O. (OR K 28). K, 65^3–69^3. Scholar. Musical Scholar of Queen's, Oxford. Brothers, 1588 & 1887.

2820 HARDY, Peter Howard Rex, b. 21 May 52, elder s. of R. W. H. Hardy. K, 65^3–70^2. Commodore of Sailing. Birmingham Univ. Brother, Neil William Henry, K, 69^1–.

2821 LAMBALLE, Adrian Kedward, b. 8 July 52, s. of A. K. Lamballe, M.B., B.S. K, 65^3–70^3. Charing Cross Hospital Medical School. Medical Student.

2822 LOTINGA, David Anthony, b. 26 May 52, s. of J. K. Lotinga, M.B., B.S. K, 65^3–70^2. Taking Degree in Social Administration at New University of Ulster.

2823 MAISEY, Joshua Charles, b. 2 Feb. 52, elder s. of J. C. Maisey. K, 65^3–70^3. Levée; Head of House; Cap, 70. Pembroke, Cambridge. Undergraduate. *Kilstanton Club.* Brother, Simon Cecil, K, 68^2–.

2824 MATHESON, Bruce Ewing, b. 25 Oct. 51, younger s. of H. G. Matheson (OR K, 24). K, 65^3–69^2. Management Trainee, Shell Mex-B.P. Ltd. Brother, 2053.

2825 RIGBY, Stephen Leacock, b. 11 Apr. 52, 4th s. of Sir Hugh J. M. Rigby, Bt., E.R.D. (OR K, 28). K, 65^3–69^3. XV, 68, 69; XI, 68, 69; H. XI, 69. In 3rd yr. for B.A. (Classics) Cape Town Univ. Brothers, 2054, 2215 & 2380.

2826 ROSS, Andrew Hill, b. 6 Apr. 52, younger s. of J. H. Ross. K, 65^3–69^3.

2827 STRACHAN, Gavin Michael Jasper, b. 24 June 52, younger s. of M. F. Strachan, M.B.E. (OR K 33). K, 65^3–71^1. Levée; Head of School; Head of House; XV, 69; Capt. of Fencing, 69–71. Corpus Christi, Cambridge. Studying Old Norse Language & Celtic History. *Pitt Club.* Brother, 2467.

2828 URQUHART, David Andrew, b. 14 Apr. 52, s. of H. M. Urquhart, F.R.C.S. (OR C 31). K, 65^3–70^3. Levée; Head of School; Head of House; XV, 69,

70. With Shell Mex-B.P., London. *Kilstanton Club.*

2829A BHANDARE, Ajoy R., b. 5 Aug. 49, s. of R. V. Bhandare. M, 65^3–67^1. Imperial College, London, B.Sc., A.C.G.I. M.Sc. (O.R.M.S.), D.I.C. With Glaxo Laboratories (India) Ltd., Bombay. *The Willingdon Club, Bombay.* O.R. Society of India.

2829B BLABER, Giles Michael, b. 7 Mar. 52, s. of M. P. W. Blaber (OR M 20). M, 65^3–70^3. Durham Univ.

2830 CHAPMAN, Peter, b. 26 May 52, eldest s. of A. C. Chapman. M, 65^3–70^2. Dundee Univ. Medical School. Student. Brothers, David, M, 68^3– & Michael M., 70^2–.

2831 CLARK, Henry James, b. 31 May 52, s. of D. G. Clark, M.C. (OR M 32). M, 65^3–70^2. XI, 69, 70; Capt., 70; Second Rackets Pair, 70. Royal Agricultural College, Cirencester.

2832 WALKER, Philip Malzard, b. 16 July 52, younger s. of T. C. Walker, F.C.A. (OR M 36). M, 65^3–69^3. Scholar of Clare, Cambridge, B.A. V.S.O. in Malawi, 73–74. Research in Nuclear Physics at National Univ. of Australia, Canberra, towards Ph.D. Brother, 2679.

2833 WILLIAMS, Julian Outfin, b. 6 May 52, s. of F. O. Williams. M, 65^3–67^2.

2834 WRIGHT, Richard James Comstive, b. 26 Feb. 52, 2nd s. of C. H. Wright, F.R.S.A. (OR C 18). M, 65^3–69^3. Levée; Head of House; XV; H. XI. College of Estate Management, Reading Univ. Student. Brothers, 2579 & Christopher Philip Comstive, C, 67^3–.

2835 WYAND, Roger Nicholas Lewes, b. 31 Oct. 47, younger s. of Major J. B. Wyand, C.B. M, 65^3–66^3. Levée. Downing, Cambridge, B.A. Half-Blue Ice Hockey. Barrister.

2836 BLACK, William Allan, b. 1 Oct. 51, 3rd s. of W. A. Black of Mexico. SF, 65^3–66^2.

2837 FARQUHARSON, David Ian Malcolm, b. 11 Mar. 52, s. of I. M. D. N. Farquharson, M.B., Ch.B., F.R.C.S., SF, 65^3–70^1. Middlesex Hospital Medical School. Medical Student.

2838 **GOODMAN, Paul Sabel,** b. 6 May 52, eldest s. of C. J. Goodman. SF, 65³–70³. Capt. of Fives. Dewar Travelling Scholarship to teach in Swaziland. Reading Law at Queen's, Cambridge. *Royal Corinthian Y.C.* Brothers, 3006 & Andrew Michael, SF, 68³–.

2839 **HENDERSON, Peter John William,** b. 1 Apr. 52, s. of J. Henderson, D.F.C. (OR SF 33). SF, 65³–70². Cap, 69. Bristol Univ., studying Economics with Statistics, 70–73. Intending Chartered Accountancy training with Touche Ross after University. Capt., *University Canoe Club.*

2840 **JAVANAUD, Roland,** b. 21 Apr. 52, s. of P. G. Javanaud. SF, 65³–68³. Worcester, Oxford.

2841 **LEATHER, Peter Harvey,** b. 5 June 52, s. of W. H. Leather. SF, 65³–70³. Levée; Head of House; Cap, 69. Cadet Officer. Exeter Univ.

2842 **LUCKING, Stephen Charles,** b. 22 Jan. 52, s. of P. C. Lucking. SF, 65³–69³. Exhibitioner of Pembroke, Cambridge. Undergraduate. Cambridge Union Society.

2843 **LUSTY, Andrew William Kevin,** b. 30 Nov. 51, younger s. of A. C. Lusty (OR SF 24). SF, 65³–70¹. Levée; Cap, 69; Squash V. Social Sciences at Bristol Univ. 3rd-yr. student. *Churchillians Squash Racket Touring Club* (Founder & Secretary). Brother, 2155.

2844 **PILLMAN, Joseph Charles,** b. 7 July 52, elder s. of J. R. Pillman, T.D. (OR SF 28). SF, 65³–69³. Neuchâtel, Diplôme Eurocentres. Exhibitioner of Clare, Cambridge, B.A. Brother, Rowland Henry Meirion, SF, 67¹–70³.

2845 **BANTING, David Percy,** b. 8 Nov. 51, 2nd s. of J. L. Banting (OR Sh 35). Sh, 65³–69³. Scholar; XI; 68, 69; H. XI, 68, 69; Squash V, 69. Peter Walker Exhibitioner. Exhibition to Magdalene, Cambridge. Undergraduate in 3rd yr. of Classics Hons. Degree. *Hawks Club.* Brother, 2398.

2846 **FORD, Nigel Peter,** b. 24 Jan. 52, s. of J. P. Ford. Sh, 65³–70². Hockey XI, 69, 70; Athletics Team, 69. Training in Chartered Accountancy with firm in the City. *Royal Wimbledon G.C., East India, Sports & Public Schools Club.*

2847 **MACARTHUR, Duncan MacLeod,** b. 5 Apr. 52, s. of A. M. Macarthur, M.B., B.S., F.R.C.S. Sh, 65³–70³. Cap, Sw. IX; Capt. of Squash Rackets; Capt. of Chess. Bristol Univ., B.A. *Bridge Society Squash Club.* English University Squash v. Eire, Scotland.

2848 **MACDONALD, John Andrew Charles,** b. 28 June 52, s. of J. N. Macdonald, B.M., B.Ch. Sh, 65³–69².

2849 **MILLER, Geoffrey Robin Mitchell,** b. 28 Feb. 52, s. of I. M. Miller (OR Sh 37). Sh, 65³–70³. Squash Rackets V. Liverpool University. Student.

2850 **PAWSON, Nicholas Charles Thoresby,** b. 7 Mar. 52, s. of K. V. F. Pawson (OR Sh 37). Sh, 65³–70². Levée; S. VIII, 68; Capt., 69, 70. Exhibition to Trinity Hall, Cambridge. Scholarship in Maths, 72. Capt., Cambridge Univ. Rifle Assoc., 72, 73. Undergraduate.

2851 **TAYLOR, Stephen,** b. 7 Apr. 52, 2nd s. of A. Taylor, F.R.S.S. Sh, 65³–66². Brother, 2132.

2852 **VAKEEL, Fali Hormusjee,** b. 6 May 52, s. of H. F. Vakeel. Sh, 65³–70¹.

2853 **ATKINSON, Antony,** b. 28 Nov. 51, elder s. of R. Atkinson. St, 65³–69¹.

2854 **BOVEY, Andrew John,** b. 5 July 52, 2nd s. of N. H. Bovey, O.B.E., D.S.C., V.R.D. St, 65³–66³. Brother, 2247.

2855 **BOYES, Simon David Bailey,** b. 1 May 52, 3rd s. of E. S. Boyes (OR St 29). St, 65³–69³. Scholar: Trinity, Oxford. Brothers, 1766 & 2408.

2856 **CLARKE, Brian Martin,** b. 27 Aug. 50, s. of L. D. Clarke. St, 65³–68³. Leeds. Univ.

2857 **CLARKE, Stephen Patrick,** b. 22 Jan. 52, eldest s. of R. C. G. Clarke (OR St 21). St, 65³–69². Exeter Univ. In 2nd yr. reading for LL.B.

2858 **PENNELL, Follett Mark Montague,** b. 26 May 52, s. of M. M. Pennell. St, 65³–69¹.

2859 **PITT, Andrew Michael,** b. 19 July 52, youngest s. of Lt.-Cdr. R. J. Pitt, M.B.E. (OR St 35). St, 65³–70³. Levée; Head of House; XV, 69, 70; XXII, 69, 70. Clare, Cambridge, 71³–, reading Maths & Economics. *Butterflies C.C.* Brothers, 2084 & 2558.

2860 **POWELL, John Mark Heywood,** b. 18 July 52, s. of J. H. Powell, M.C. St, 65³–70². Scholar; Levée; XV, 70; XXII, 70; H. XI, 70 (Capt.). London Univ.

2861 **STRACHAN, Charles Antony,** b. 8 Feb. 50, s. of the late M. Strachan, M.R.C.S., L.R.C.P. St, 65³–68³. Levée; Head of House. Exhibition Christ's, Cambridge, B.A. Articled Clerk, Peat Marwick, Mitchell & Co., Chartered Accountants.

2862 **BLINCOW, Derek Paul,** b. 21 Jan. 52, s. of S. A. Blincow. Tu, 65³–69³. Levée; R. VIII; Holder of Bigside Bags, 69; Athletics Team, 69. King's, Cambridge.

2863 **HAMADA, Geoffrey Mark,** b. 30 July 47, eldest s. of R. M. Hamada of U.S.A. Tu, 65³–66². California Univ.

2864 **KENDALL, Charles Henry,** b. 11 May 52, younger s. of A. C. Kendall, M.B., Ch.B. Tu, 65³–69³. Scholar; Rackets Team. Birmingham Medical School. Student. Brother, 2564.

2865 **NICHOLAS, Richard Charles,** b. 15 May 52, s. of C. P. Nicholas, V.R.D., Ch.M., F.R.C.S. Tu, 65³–70². Levée; Head of House; Cap, XI, 69, 70. Guy's Hospital Medical School.

2866 **SAMUEL, William Meredith,** b. 20th Feb. 52, s. of E. Samuel, M.D., F.R.C.S., F.R.C.P.E., F.F.R. Tu, 65³–69³. Hatfield Coll., Durham. Final Year Student.

2867 **THOMSON, James Caldwell,** b. 27 Apr. 52, s. of R. S. Thomson. Tu, 65³–69³. H.N.D. in Business Studies and studying for Institute of Marketing Diploma. Present employment G. K. N. Sankey of Wolverhampton. *East India, Sports & Public Schools Club.*

2868 **WILLIAMSON, Patrick Malet,** b. 7 Mar. 52, s. of R. P. Williamson. Tu, 65³–69³. XXII, 69. Correspondence Course with College of Estate Management. Chartered Surveyor Finals, March 73. Surveyor with Walker Watton & Hanson, Chartered Surveyors, Auctioneers & Estate Agents, Nottingham. *Notts. G.C.*

2869 **BAKER, Anthony David,** b. 27 May 22, s. of G. H. Baker, D.S.C. W, 65³–69¹.

2870A **GROVES, Raymond Michael,** b. 3 Feb. 52, s. of E. M. Groves. W, 65³–69². Athletics Team, 69. Stock Jobber, Authorised Clerk, R. A. Blackwell, Stock Exchange.

2870B **GUTTERIDGE, Charles Norman,** b. 15 Mar. 52, 2nd s. of F. Gutteridge (OR W 34). W, 65³–69³. Cambridge. Univ. Medical Student.

2871 **RUSSELL, Charles Harvie,** b. 12 Nov. 51, s. of Major-Gen. G. N. Russell, C.B., C.B.E. (OR W 13). W, 65³–69³. Scholar; Cap, 69; Exhibition to Exeter, Oxford.

2872 **SMART, Robert Bruce,** b. 20 Oct. 49, s. of W. R. Smart. W, 65³–68².

2873 **VAUGHAN, Clive Jonathan,** b. 8 May 52, s. of S. J. P. Vaughan, M.A., M.B., B.Ch. W, 65³–69³. Durham Univ. but left 74. Teaching appointment at Belmont, Mill Hill Prep. School with view to obtaining external qualifications. National Youth Theatre, 70–72.

ENTRANCES IN JANUARY 1966

2874 **BURTON, Hamish Russell,** b. 18 July 52, elder s. of F. S. Burton. SH, 66¹–70³. Articled Clerk to Accountants, Everett, Pinto & Co., of London. Brother, Russell Templeton, SH, 69³–.

2875A **EARP, Jonathan Harkness,** b. 16 June 52, 2nd s. of A. J. Earp, M.Litt. SH, 66¹–66². Brother, 2882.

2875B **LLOYD, Michael Ernest Penry,** b. 7 Nov. 49, s. of J. P. F. Lloyd. SH, 66¹–66¹. Staatliches Landschulmein Marquartstein, 59–68, with one term as exchange student. Kingston Coll. of Further Education, 68–69. Magdalene, Cambridge, B.A. Heriot-Watt Univ., Edinburgh, M.Sc. Since 1st Oct. 73 with ICL/Dataskil Ltd.

2876A **KILPATRICK, David Davies,** b. 28 Sept. 52, youngest s. of T. S. Kilpatrick. B, 66¹–68².

2876B **SCHRECKENBERGER, Stephan,** b. 19 May 49, exchange student from Germany. B, 66¹–66¹.

2877 **CAMPBELL, David Graham,** b. 9 Sept. 52, s. of D. Campbell, M.R.C.V.S. C, 66¹–70³. Bath Univ.

2878 **FRANCIS, Adam Charles Edward,** b. 23 June 52, s. of Major K. B. Francis, R.E. C, 66¹–69³.

2879 **HAYLES, Nicholas Paul,** b. 21 Sept. 52, younger s. of G. V. Hayles. C, 66¹–69². Manchester Univ.

2880 **JETHA, Iqbal Noorali,** b. 11 Aug. 52, elder s. of N. M. Jetha. C, 66¹–70². Scholar of Haverford Coll., Pennsylvania.

2881 **COOPER, Nicholas Robert Leslie,** b. 24 Aug. 52, elder s. of L. C. S. Cooper (OR K 39). K, 66¹–70². Brother, Barnaby William Andrew, K, 68¹–.

2882 **EARP, Stephen Bruce Tobias,** b. 1 Oct. 50, eldest s. of A. J. Earp, M.Litt. K, 66¹–68². Trinity College, Univ. of Toronto, Canada. Brother, 2875A.

2883 **STUBLEY, Thomas Stephen Angus,** b. 13 Aug. 52, younger s. of J. R. S. Stubley. K, 66¹–70². Hendon Coll. of Technology, B.A. E. Anglia Univ., Norwich (Development Economics). Student. Brother, 1592.

2884 **DEAKIN, Donald Irving Ireland,** b. 17 May 52, s. of P. W. I. Deakin (OR M 17). M, 66¹–70². Involved in Environmental Health. Killed Apr. 73 in motor accident.

2885A **GREEN, Christopher Nigel,** b. 7 Aug. 52, younger s. of the late J. Green. M, 66¹–70³.

2885B **SCHMIDLE, Lothar,** b. 29 Dec. 48. Exchange student from Germany. M, 66¹–66¹.

2886 **McLINTOCK, Duncan Charles Alastair,** b. 31 May 52, s. of A. G. McLintock (OR SF 31). SF, 66¹–69³.

2887 **SHAILER, Michael John Anthony,** b. 21 Nov. 52, elder s. of T. F. C. Shailer. SF, 66¹–70¹. At present in 2nd yr. at Cambridge Univ. reading Physics. Brother, Nicholas Charles Thomas, SF, 69³–.

2888 **BELL, Robert David,** b. 11 Nov. 52, younger s. of F. O. Bell, O.B.E. Sh, 66¹–70¹. At Christ's, Cambridge, reading History. Union Society. Brother, 2399.

2889 **MARSDEN, Michael Laurence,** b. 10 May 52, elder s. of W. M. Marsden. Sh, 66¹–70¹. Brother, Guy Norman, SH, 70³–.

2890 **TOD, Ian Alexander Arthur,** b. 5 June 52, s. of G. J. R. Tod, C.B.E. Sh, 66¹–70³. Levée; Head of House. Newcastle-upon-Tyne Univ. Medical School Student. *Swiss Alpine Club.*

2891 **ELLIOTT, Thomas Richard,** b. 10 July 52, s. of R. D. Elliott. St, 66¹–70².

2892 **JAMIESON, Michael Douglas,** b. 15 July 52, elder s. of K. D. Jamieson, C.M.G. (OR St 34) St, 66¹–70².

2893 **KENNEDY, Colin Riddiford,** b. 16 July 52, s. of the late A. M. Kennedy. St, 66¹–70². Fives & Squash IV. Open Scholarship to Univ. Coll., Oxford. Studying Medicine after completing B.A. Course in Psychology & Physiology. V.S.O. Teaching in Ghana, 70–71. Royal Overseas League.

2894 **ROSSDALE, James Haines,** b. 11 Oct. 52, s. of I. T. H. Rossdale. St, 66¹–70³. Ealing Tech. Coll. Language Teacher at Knoll Prep. School. Photographer. *M.C.C., Arts Theatre Club.*

2895 **GRAHAM, Oliver Lindsay Mark,** b. 6 Oct. 52, s. of G. E. Graham. Tu, 66¹–70². Levée; Head of House. City of London Polytechnic. Studying for B.A. (Hon.) Business Studies.

2896 **RODGERS, Nigel Christopher Norval,** b. 19 Sept. 52, s. of A. M. N. Rodgers. Tu, 66¹–67².

2897 **SPITTLE, Thomas Edward Trevor,** b. 30 July 52, s. of L. T. Spittle (OR Tu 30). Tu, 66¹–69³.

2898 **BLACKBURN, Robert Wesley,** b. 27 Aug. 52, s. of G. R. Blackburn, V.R.D. W, 66¹–70³. Leeds Univ.

2899 **BUNTING, Edward Arthur,** b. 11 Dec. 52, younger s. of G. W. W. Bunting, LL.B. (OR W 22). W, 66¹–. Worked for one year as musician, then for two terms at Leeds Univ. studying Econ. Polit. & Sociology. Returned to music, now studying for L.R.A.M. and working as professional musician. Brother, 2484.

2900 **EMIN, Ulfet Ilker,** b. 2 July 52, s. of U. Emin of Cyprus. W, 66¹–69².

2901 **GREENWELL, Thomas William,** b. 3 Sept. 52, elder s. of T. A. Greenwell. W, 66¹–69³. Brother, David Robert, W, 70²–.

ENTRANCES IN MAY 1966

2902 **ALLEN, Simon Richard Burton,** b. 5 Nov. 52, elder s. of Lt.-Col. W. R. B. Allen. SH, 66²–70². R.M.A., Sandhurst. Commissioned, 72. 2nd Lt. Royal Scots Dragoon Guards.

2903 **BEAMAN, Hugh William Guise,** b. 11 Nov. 52, 3rd s. of M. A. C. Beaman, M.C., J.P. (OR SH 34). SH, 66²–70³. At present undergoing an A.R.C.M. (Singing, Drama & Opera) at Royal Coll. of Music.

2904 **BRAGG, Nigel Lawrence,** b. 26 Aug. 52, eldest s. of S. L. Bragg (OR SH 37). SH, 66²–70³. At present at Trinity, Cambridge, reading for National Sciences Tripos. Brother, Andrew Christopher, SH, 71¹–.

2905 **JONES, Nicholas Reginald Maurice,** b. 21 Dec. 52, s. of C. M. Jones (OR SH 32). SH, 66²–70³. Cap, 70; XXII, 69. Morehead Scholar: 2nd-yr. student at North Carolina Univ., U.S.A.

2906 **KENNEDY, David Valder Wynn,** b. 14 Sept. 52, s. of the late J. W. Kennedy (OR SH 33). SH, 66²–69³.

2907 **LUMSDEN, Michael Robert,** b. 22 Dec. 52, 3rd s. of J. A. Lumsden, M.B.E. (OR SH 28). SH, 66²–71². Warwick Univ., Coventry, entered Oct. 72. Student. Brothers, 2272 & 2632.

2908 **McWILLIAM, Graeme Peadair Campbell,** b. 20 Aug. 52, elder s. of I. C. McWilliam. SH, 66²–71². Brother, Jeremy Neil Campbell, SH, 69³–.

2909 **OGLETHORPE, Charles Stuart,** b. 31 Dec. 52, eldest s. of J. K. Oglethorpe, M.C., T.D., F.C.A. (OR SH 35). SH, 66²–70². Articled Clerk to Harmood Banner & Co. (Chartered Accountants). Brother, Miles Kenneth, SH, 71¹–.

2910 **SMYTHIES, Adrian Greville,** b. 3 Mar. 53, elder s. of J. R. Smythies, M.D., F.R.C.S., D.P.M. (OR SH 36). SH, 66²–71². Levée; Head of School; Head of House. St. Mary's Hospital, London Univ. Brother, Christopher John Evelyn, SH, 70³–.

2911 **THOMAS, Evan David,** b. 19 Jan. 53, s. of the late E. L. Thomas (OR SH 18). SH, 66²–70².

2912 **TORRIE, Robin Michael,** b. 12 Oct. 52, elder s. of Rev. A. R. R. Torrie.

SH, 66²–70³. Brother, Alan Hamish Brandon, SH, 71³–.

2913 **CORLETT, Colin Ernest,** b. 3 Nov. 52, 3rd s. of D. R. Corlett. B, 66²–71². College of Estate Management, 71³–. Student.

2914 **de BOURSAC, Charles Mark Sergei,** b. 29 Dec. 52, 3rd s. of V. de Boursac (OR W 28). B, 66²–71³. Levée; Head of House; Cap, 70; Athletics Team, 69; Capt., 70, 71. First yr. at North Carolina Univ. Brothers, 1867 & 2361.

2915 **MACDONALD, Kenneth John Stewart,** b. 10 Nov. 52, elder s. of J. S. Macdonald, M.B., Ch.B. B, 66²–70³. Student at Edinburgh Univ. Medical School. Brother, Murdo James Stewart, B, 68³–.

2916 **NICKOLS, Clive Fraser,** b. 12 Nov. 52, s. of I. Nickols. B, 66²–70². Agricultural Contractor.

2917 **SIMON, Graham Bennett,** b. 3 Oct. 52, elder s. of R. H. Simon. B, 66²–70³. Athletics Team, 68–70. Manchester Univ. Brother, Nigel Timothy, B, 69³–71².

2918 **BAXTER, Julian Simon,** b. 7 Oct. 52, younger s. of M. R. Baxter, C, 66²–71². XV, 69; 70; H. XI, 70; Rackets Pair, 71. Brother, 2624.

2919 **CROWE, Andrew George,** b. 7 Nov. 52, s. of late A. H. Crowe (OR C 24). C, 66²–71². Park Lane College of Further Education, Leeds. Student. *Headingley R.U.F.C., B.A.R.C.*

2920 **MELLIAR-SMITH, John Alistair Nicholas,** b. 24 Nov. 52, s. of D. J. Melliar-Smith. C, 66²–70³. School of Slavonic & East European Studies, London Univ. Student.

2921 **POULTON, Nigel Rupert Aethelwood,** b. 28 Nov. 52, 2nd s. of E. M. Poulton, D.M., M.R.C.P., D.P.H. (OR C 27). C, 66²–71². Brother, 1943.

2922 **CLARENCE - SMITH, Thomas Alton,** b. 2 Oct. 52, eldest s. of K. Clarence-Smith (OR K 35). K, 66²–70³. Commodore of Sailing, 70. Southampton Univ., reading Mechanical Engineering (B.Sc. Hons.), 2nd yr. Brother, Peter Kenneth, K, 68¹–71³.

2923 **RICHARDS, Andrew John,** b. 26 Oct. 52, 2nd s. of N. A. Richards, M.D.,

F.R.C.O.G. K, 66²–70². Brothers, 2148 &
Nicholas Peter, K, 67³–71².

2924 ROBINSON, David Nigel, b. 17
Sept. 52, twin s. of N. B. Robinson. K,
66²–71². Liverpool Univ. Brother, 2925.

2925 ROBINSON, Richard Bernard,
b. 17 Sept. 52, twin s. of N. B. Robinson,
K, 66²–70¹. Dewar Scholarship. Newcastle Univ., studying Medicine. Newcastle Univ. Exploration Society. Brother,
2924.

2926 WETHERILL, Timothy Henry,
b. 15 July 52, younger s. of P. H. Wetherill
(OR K 33). K, 66²–70³. Capt. of Rackets;
Tennis VI. Articled Clerk to Chartered
Accountant (passed Inter.). *Queen's Club,
All England Lawn Tennis Club, East India
Sports Club.* Brother, 2525.

2927 GILBERT, Richard John, b. 27
Sept. 52, elder s. of D. D. Gilbert. M,
66²–70².

2928 MacINNES, Robert John, b. 26
Nov. 52, s. of R. I. MacInnes, M.R.C.S.,
L.R.C.P. (OR M 35). M, 66²–71². Medical
Student at Corpus Christi, Oxford, since
Michaelmas 71.

2929 TAPP, Simon Charles Edward,
b. 9 Oct. 52, eldest s. of N. C. Tapp, Q.C.
M, 66²–70³. Univ. Coll., Durham, reading
Geography. Brother, Jonathan Charles,
M, 69³–.

2930 TOWNE, Anthony Annable, b. 7
Nov. 52, youngest s. of C. E. A. Towne,
M, 66²–70². Brothers, 2062 & 2388.

2931 WHEATLEY, Simon Jeremy, b.
3 Nov. 52, s. of J. R. W. Wheatley. M,
66²–70². Music & Record Producer and
Entertainer. Musicians' Union.

2932 AUSTEN, John Stuart, b. 3 Dec.
52, elder s. of S. Austen. SF, 66²–70². At
present at Wye Coll. Brother, Charles
Evershed, SF, 67³–71².

**2933 HANDS, Christopher Andrew
Henry,** b. 5 Nov. 52, s. of Dr. A. H.
Hands. SF, 66²–71². Levée; Head of
House; H. XI, 71. St. Bartholomew's
Hospital Medical Coll. Medical Student.
Hightown Hockey Club, Ormskirk G.C.

2934 SIMPSON, Robert Russell, b. 25
Dec. 52, s. of P. W. Simpson (OR SF 35).
SF, 66²–71¹. Levée; Head of House; R.
VIII, 69–71; Holder of Bigside Bags, 70,

71. Mynors Exhibition to University Coll.,
Oxford. Reading Physics.

**2935 BADENOCH, Andrew John
Fraser,** b. 2 July 52, younger s. of J.
Badenoch, D.M., F.R.C.P. (OR Sh 33).
Sh, 66²–70². Brother, 1800.

**2936A DAVIES, Richard Oliver Hen-
ry,** b. 15 Sept. 52, s. of O. J. H. Davies (OR
St 32). St, 66²–71². Levée; Cap, 69;
H. XI, 70, 71. Royal Agricultural College.
Cirencester.

2936B GRAY, Colin Robert Gordon,
b. 2 Oct. 52, 2nd s. of K. G. Gray, M.B.E.
St, 66²–70³. Brother, 2706.

**2937 GRIMWOOD - TAYLOR,   Paul
William Sancroft,** b. 9 Aug. 52, elder s.
of Col. J. R. S. Grimwood-Taylor, T.D.,
D.L., LL.B. (OR St 30). St, 66²–70². Kent
Univ. 3 yrs., B.A. Hons. Course in Law
from 71. Brother, James Lawrence, St,
70²–.

2938 WILSON, Ian Gordon, b. 14 Nov.
52, s. of the late G. C. E. Wilson (OR
St 40). St 66²–71². Athletics Team, 71.
Bristol Univ., reading Physics (2nd yr.).
Graduating July 74.

2939 DODSWORTH, Roger Charles,
b. 3 Dec. 52, 2nd s. of B. L. C. Dodsworth, M.C. (OR Tu 34). Tu, 66²–70³.
London Univ. Brother, 2590.

2940 PARRY, Arthur Guy, b. 8 Sept.
52, younger s. of G. N. Parry (OR Tu 30).
Tu, 66²–70². Queen's, Univ. of Belfast,
studying Economic History & Politics.
Brother, James Geoffrey, Tu, 68²–73².

2941 WALKER, Clive Gendall, b 17.
Jan. 53, youngest s. of H. G. Walker, LL.B.
Tu, 66²–70². Brothers, 2292 & 2566.

2942 BLAAUW, Jan Elliott, b. 21 Oct.
52, s. of A. J. Blaauw. W, 66²–70². Sw.
IX, 68–70. Southampton Univ., reading
Economics.

2943A KAGAN, Daniel, b. 25 Feb. 53,
younger s. of J. Kagan, W, 66²–71¹.
Levée; Head of House. E. Anglia Univ.,
reading Economics, Brother, 2547.

**2943B PARIBATRA, M. R. Sukhumb-
hand,** b. 22 Sept. 52, from Bangkok,
Thailand. W, 66²–70³. Scholar; Levée;
Head of House. Pembroke, Oxford.

ENTRANCES IN SEPTEMBER 1966

2944 BATTY, Charles James Keith, b. 8 Mar. 53, s. of J. K. Batty. SH, 66^3–70^3. Scholar. Postmastership to Merton, Oxford, 71. Studying Maths.

2945 GOYDER, Edward Mark, b. 11 June 53, 5th s. of G. A. Goyder. SH, 66^3–70^1. Trinity, Cambridge, studying for Part I: Economics, Part II: Social & Political Sciences. Community Service Volunteer with the Community Council of Shropshire, 71, and with Hewell Grange Borstal, 72. Resident, Camb. Union Society, Michaelmas Term, 73. Brothers, 735 & 2007.

2946 MAITLAND, James Tyler, b. 22 May 53, 2nd s. of A. Maitland (OR SH 27). SH, 66^3–71^3. Head of House. 1st yr., Trinity, Cambridge, reading Engineering. Half-Blue Boxing. Brothers, 2178 & Robert Forbes, SH, 68^3–.

2947 NICOL, Malcolm James, b. 2 Apr. 53, 3rd s. of Col. J. W. Nicol, D.S.O., D.L., J.P. SH, 66^3–71^2. Levée; Head of House; XV, 69. Student, Hatfield Coll., Durham. Brothers, 2010 & 2437.

2948 PAINE, Jonathan, b. 3 Oct. 52, s. of C. F. Paine. SH, 66^3–70^2. Scholar. Exhibition to Merton, Oxford. Undergraduate.

2949 RIPMAN, Jonathan Wynne, b. 13 June 53, 3rd s. of H. A. Ripman, F.R.C.S., F.R.C.O.G. (OR SH 31). SH, 66^3–71^2. H. XI, 70, 71; XI, 71. St. Catharine's, Cambridge, Oct. 72. Undergraduate. Brothers, 1701, 2735 & James Jervis Hugo, SH, 72^3–.

2950 SERIES, Robert William, b. 13 May 53, eldest s. of G. W. Series, D.Phil., F.R.S., SH, 66^3–70^3. Exhibition to St. Edmund Hall, Oxford. Brothers, Julian John, SH, 69^3– & Hugh George, SH, 72^3–.

2951 SOUTHWELL, Julian Philip, b. 6 Mar. 53, elder s. of K. S. Southwell. SH, 66^3–71^2. S. VIII, 69. Jewellery Salesman for Aspreys. *West Surrey Squash Club.*

2952 WILCOX, John Nicholas, b. 19 Mar. 53, s. of Lt.-Col. M. Wilcox, R.A.O.C. (OR SH 30). SH, 66^3–70^2. Kingston Coll. of Art since 70. 2nd-yr. Graphic Design Diploma A.D. Course. Career in Graphic Design/Films.

2953 WRIGHT, Michael Bruce, b. 17 May 53, younger s. of R. P. Wright, D.F.C. (A). SH, 66^3–70^3. Oxford. Brother, 2014.

2954 BARTH, Julian Howard, b. 11 May 53, eldest s. of B. Barth, M.D. T, 66^3–71^2. Minor Foundation Scholar; H. XI, 70–71. Scholarship to St. Bartholomew's Hospital, London Univ. Student. Brothers, Stephen Benedict John, T, 68^3– & Philip Nigel, T, 69^3.

2955 FRANKTON, James Richard, b. 30 Mar. 53, younger s. of P. T. Frankton. T, 66^3–71^2. Levée; Head of House; XXII, 71. Sheffield Univ., reading Law. O.R.G.S.

2956 HILLYARD, Anthony John, b. 29 May 53, s. of M. G. Hillyard. T, 66^3–70^3. Exhibition to St. John's, Cambridge. Undergraduate.

2957 HOSSACK, Ian Milne, b. 25 Aug. 53, s. of P. G. M. Hossack, A.R.I.B.A. T, 66^3–71^2.

2958 HUNTINGFORD, Geoffrey, b. 30 May 53, younger s. of R. H. Huntingford. T, 66^3–71^1. Levée. Dept. of Town & Country Planning. Heriot-Watt Univ., Edinburgh. Edinburgh Coll. of Art. Heraldry Society (Environmental Design Group, Edin.). Brother, 2639.

2959 MILLER, Michael Bernard, b. 24 May 53, s. of the Rev. I. N. Miller. T, 66^3–71^1.

2960 REIDY, David Sean, b. 28 Oct. 52, younger s. of C. A. Reidy. T, 66^3–69^3.

2961 SAVAGE, Andrew Martin, b. 2 Nov. 52, younger s. of W. B. Savage. T, 66^3–70^3. Kent Univ.

2962 SOUTER, Nicholas James, b. 19 Dec. 52, younger s. of J. Souter. T, 66^3–70^3.

2963 SPEED, Jonathan Richard Bentinck, b. 27 July 53, eldest s. of R. F. B. Speed. T, 66^3–70^3. Gonville & Caius, Cambridge.

2964 WIGG, Howard Raymond, b. 27 Dec. 52, younger s. of R. E. Wigg. T, 66^3–70^3. Minor Foundationer. Sydney Sussex, Cambridge. Reading for B.A. Degree Engineering. Presently with the British Petroleum Co. Ltd. Brother, 2649.

2965 BALLANTINE, Richard James, b. 17 Mar. 53, s. of J. Ballantine, M.B., B.Ch. B, 66³–70². King's College, London for M.B., B.S. in 3rd yr. Westminster Hospital Medical School. Medical Student. London Library.

2966 CLEVERLY, Robert William, b. 6 Mar. 53, elder s. of W. G. Cleverly, M.B., B.S. (OR B 40). B, 66³–70³. St. Catherine's, Oxford, studying Geology. Undergraduate. *M.C.C.*, Oxford Univ. Geological Society. Brother, William Bernard, B, 69³–.

2967 DUNCAN, Peter Anthony, b. 27 May 53, younger s. of Col. A. A. Duncan, O.B.E. (OR B 28). B, 66³–70². Guildford Tech. Coll., 70–71. Exeter Univ., 72–. Brother, 2653.

2968 HALE, Timothy Thomas Marshall, b. 11 Jan. 53, s. of W. T. Hale. B, 66³–71². Univ. of Wales, Institute of Science & Technology, 71–72, doing Electronics, then Course transfer to Sheffield Polytechnic. Now doing H.N.D. Business Studies.

2969 HALL, Stephen Gawain Durham, b. 19 Dec. 52, elder s. of J. D. Hall, M.R.C.S., L.R.C.P., M.F.C.M., D.P.H. B, 66³–67². Alleynes School, Stevenage. Army, R.E.M.E. Northern Ireland Medal.

2970 MAIER, Thomas Nicholas Ivo, b. 7 Nov. 72, elder s. of A. J. Maier (OR C 36). B, 66³–67¹.

2971 MILLER of Glenlee, Stephen William Macdonald, b. 20 June 53, s. of Sir Macdonald Miller of Glenlee, Bt. B, 66³–71². Athletics Colours, 70–71. St. Bartholomew's Hospital Medical College. Medical Student.

2972 MORFEE, David Richard Edward, b. 15 Jan. 53, s. of R. Morfee. B, 66³–68³.

2973 REED-HERBERT, William Nicholas Fry, b. 7 Dec. 52, younger s. of R. Herbert, T.D. B, 66³–70². Student. *Leicestershire Club*. Brother, 2199.

2974 COOKSON, Peter Richard Hatton, b. 18 Apr. 53, s. of R. W. Cookson. C, 66³–71².

2975 JOHNS, Duncan Edward, b. 4 Mar. 53, s. of S. H. Johns. C, 66³–71³. Imperial Coll., London. Student. Member of British Film Institute.

2976 JOHNSON, Henry Nicholas, b. 1 June 53, s. of C. F. Johnson, T.D. (OR C 31). C, 66³–70³. Scholar. Emmanuel, Cambridge. Undergraduate.

2977 McCOSH, Arthur Bryce Hasell, b. 21 Feb. 53, 2nd s. of B. K. McCosh. C, 66³–70². Royal Agricultural College, Cirencester. Brother, 2372.

2978 PALFREYMAN, Philip Richard Arthur, b. 28 July 53, elder s. of R. A. Palfreyman, B.Sc., F.C.A. C, 66³–70². Trent Polytechnic. Articled Clerk with Pannell, Fitzpatrick Co. (Chartered Accountants), Nottingham. *Belper Hockey Club* (Hon. Team Secretary). Brother, Robert Adrian, C, 72³–.

2979 STABLES, Christopher Ian Fraser, b. 2 May 53, s. of J. Stables. C, 66³–70². Just completed A Level Exams in the sixth form of the Nelson Thomlinson School, Wigton, Cumberland. *Wigton Fell-Walking Club*.

2980 STIRLING, Alistair John, b. 23 Nov. 53, elder s. of T. B. Stirling, M.B., Ch.B. C, 66³–72². Levée; Head of House; Cap, 71; H. XI, 72. Birmingham Univ. Medical School. Medical Student. *Little Aston G.C.* Birmingham Medical Society. *Four Oaks Squash Club*. Brother, Iain Boyd, C, 69¹–.

2981 WATTAM-BELL, John Richard Buchan, b. 6 June 53, s. of R. F. Wattam-Bell. C, 66³–70³. Magdalen, Oxford.

2982 WRIGHT, Donald Charles, b. 3 Feb. 53, youngest s. of C. G. Wright, L.D.S., R.C.S., Eng. C, 66³–70¹. Banking. *Leamington Spa & County G.C.* Brothers, 772 & 1945.

2983 ARTHUR, Charles Vincent, b. 13 Jan. 53, younger s. of A. J. V. Arthur, M.B.E. (OR K 29). K, 66³–71¹. Sw. IX, 69, 70; Capt., 71. Undergraduate. Studying Classics at Magdalene, Cambridge. *Pitt Club*. Brother, 2599.

2984 ASHWORTH, Richard Peter, b. 4 Sept. 52, younger s. of R. C. Ashworth. K, 66³–69³. Scholar. Jex-Blake Prize & Rupert Brook Prize, 69. Sussex Univ.

2985 DEL MAR, Robin Howard, b. 16 Jan. 53, younger s. of N. R. Del Mar. K, 66³–70³. Royal Coll. of Music. A.R.C.M. Student. Brother, 2670.

2986 GILBERT, Stephen Donald, b. 4 Mar. 53, s. of A. D. Gilbert. K, 66³–69³.

2987 **LEE, Jeremy Stuart,** b. 4 Apr. 53, younger s. of G. L. Lee. K, 66³–70³. Exhibitioner. Open Scholarship to Corpus Christi, Cambridge. Presently in 2nd yr., reading Psychology & Chemistry. Brother, 2671.

2988 **PHILLIPS, David John,** b. 4 May 53, elder s. of Sir R. Phillips, M.C., Q.C., (OR K 29). K, 66³–71³. Law Student at Balliol, Oxford, 72³–. *1896 Club, Oxford.* Brother, Richard Anthony Rupert, K, 68³–.

2989 **SWAINSON, William John Gallienne,** b. 28 Mar. 53, s. of R. G. Swainson. K, 66³–71³. Levée; Head of House. Leeds Univ. Undergraduate studying English.

2990 **VEALE, Philip Ralph,** b. 7 Nov. 51, younger s. of A. J. R. Veale. K, 66³–68³. ONC. Mech. Engineering. Working for Associateship of Chartered Institute of Insurers. Insurance Broker for Leslie & Godwin (Contractors' Dept.). R.N.R.

2991 **WALKER, Ronald James Wilson,** b. 2 Nov. 52, s. of R. J. Walker, M.B., B.Ch. K, 66³–70³. St. John's, Cambridge. Undergraduate.

2992 **WALLACE, David Adair,** b. 3 June 53, s. of B.A. Wallace, T.D. (OR K 27). K, 66³–71³. XXII. Manchester Univ. Undergraduate.

2993 **BELLAMY, John,** b. 11 Apr. 53, elder s. of Dr. R. C. T. Bellamy. M, 66³–70³. Univ. Coll. London, studying Law. Suffered brain damage Dec. 71. Now roadman for Farnborough, Hants., Urban District Council (studying rudiments of Psychology). Brother, Richard Edward, B, 68³–.

2994 **GRIFFIN, Harry Patrick Hindle,** b. 27 Mar. 53, s. of G. P. E. Griffin. M, 66³–70².

2995 **HARLAND, David Martin,** b. 23 Aug. 53, 2nd s. of S. W. Harland, LL.B. M, 66³–70³. Balliol, Oxford. Fives Half-Blue, 72. Brother, 2768.

2996 **HYMAN, Michael Rayner,** b. 27 Mar. 53, s. of E. Hyman, M.D., Ch.B. M, 66³–71². Manchester Univ. Student, 2nd yr. B.A.(Econ.)Hons. Football League Referee, Grade III (qualified 72).

2997 **LITTLER, Philip John,** b. 12 Jan. 53, s. of F. M. J. Littler. M, 66³–68¹.

Filton Technical Coll., Bristol. A Levels Economics/British Constitution. Storeman, Severnside Foods Ltd., Patchway, Bristol.

2998 **PAUL, Stephen Harvey,** b. 5 Apr. 53, s. of R. A. Paul. M, 66³–69².

2999 **SIDGWICK, Antony Benson,** b. 6 Jan. 53, 3rd s. of R. B. Sidgwick (OR M 32). M, 66³–70². Brother, 2583.

3000 **SKETCHLEY, Mark William Bennett,** b. 1 Jan. 53, s. of F. H. Sketchley. M, 66³–70³. Sailing VI. Downing, Cambridge, in 2nd yr.

3001 **BULLARD, Arthur Reader,** b. 9 Apr. 53, elder s. of the late C. M. Bullard. SF, 66³–70³. Lincoln, Oxford. Brother, Clive Heyworth, SF, 70¹–.

3002 **BURTON, Nicholas Anthony,** b. 7 May 53, 3rd s. of A. J. Burton, F.R.G.S. SF, 66³–70³. Exhibition in Classics to St. John's, Cambridge. In 2nd yr. of Classics. Degree course. Brothers, 2685 & Mark Timothy, SF, 68³–.

3003 **CHAPMAN, Nigel Cedric Benjamin,** b. 16 Aug. 53, elder s. of C. D. Chapman, Q.C. SF, 66³–71². Bristol Univ.

3004 **DUNNETT, Alan David Michael,** b. 7 July 53, elder s. of J. J. Dunnett, LL.B., M.P. SF, 66³–70³. Trinity, Oxford. Brother, Charles Richard Ian, SF, 69¹–71³.

3005 **GILLINGHAM, Allan Timothy,** b. 14 Jan. 49, s. of A. G. Gillingham, Ph.D. of Mass., U.S.A. SF, 66³–67².

3006 **GOODMAN, Martin David,** b. 1 Aug. 53, 2nd s. of C. J. Goodman. SF, 66³–70³. Scholar. Dewar Travelling Scholarship. Exhibition to Trinity, Oxford, B.A. Humanities at Jerusalem. Undergraduate. *Royal Corinthean Yacht Club.* Member of English Team International Junior Regatta, 70 & 72. Brothers, 2838 & Andrew Michael, SF, 68³–.

3007 **HEWITT, Simon Guy Brett,** b. 7 May 53, eldest s. of P. D. Hewitt, LL.B. (OR SF 40). SF, 66³–71². Levée; XI, 71. Joined Shell-Mex as Business Trainee, 71. Sponsored by Shell-Mex to do Short Service Commission in Army, 72. Brother, James Neil Terry, SF, 72²–.

3008 WILLIAMS, Mark Paul Mynors, b. 8 June 53, s. of J. M. Williams (OR SF 40). SF, 66³–71². XI, 71. Cambridge Tutors, Croydon. Started in Stockbrokers Office, Apr. 73. *Penryn R.F.C.*

3009 ADAMSON, Evan John Alistair, b. 13 Jan. 53, younger s. of W. O. C. Adamson (OR Sh 36). Sh, 66³–70³. Sussex Univ. Student. Brother, 2073.

3010 BICKERSTETH, Robin Ralph, b. 4 June 53, younger s. of P. M. G. Bickersteth (OR Sh 38). Sh, 66³–71². Brother, 2585A.

3011 FRIEND, Richard Henry, b. 18 Jan. 53, elder s. of J. H. Friend, M.D., F.R.C.P. Sh, 66³–70³. Senior Exhibition, 69; Sw. IX, 70. Entrance & Senior Scholarship, Trinity, Cambridge. Undergraduate. Brother, Peter John, Sh, 67³–71².

3012 GOATLY, Peter James, b. 29 Apr. 53, 3rd s. of J. Goatly (OR Sh 31). Sh, 66³–71³. Levée; Head of House. Christ Church, Oxford. Undergraduate. Brothers, 2322 & 2487.

3013 LOAKE, Simon Philip, b. 19 Apr. 53, 2nd s. of J. E. Loake. Sh, 66³–71². Levée; Head of House; Sw. IX, 68–71 (Capt.). Brothers, 2699 & Andrew Ernest, Sh, 71³–.

3014 MAITLAND, Sir Richard John, Bt., b. 24 Nov. 52, elder s. of the late Major Sir A. Maitland, Bt. (OR Sh 33). Sh, 66³–70². Dundee Coll. of Commerce. Exeter Univ. Student. Brother, Robert Ramsay, Sh, 69³–.

3015 MARS-JONES, Timothy David, b. 9 Feb. 53, eldest s. of the Hon. Sir W. L. Mars-Jones, M.B.E. Sh, 66³–71¹. Levée; Head of House. Trinity, Cambridge. Undergraduate.

3016 PILLANS, Charles Henry, b. 14 Feb. 53, younger s. of the late R. N. A. Pillans. Sh, 66³–70². Brother, 1017.

3017 RIVINGTON, Michael Adrian Thurston, b. 5 June 53, elder s. of C. T. Rivington. Sh, 66³–71¹. In printing industry with David Greenaway & Sons Ltd. (City Printers). The Stationers Company.

3018 SAGE, Jonathan Malcolm, b. 2 Sept. 53, s. of J. L. Sage, M.C. Sh, 66³–71³. Scholar. Magdalene, Cambridge.

3019 SHARLAND, Nicholas David, b. 26 Mar. 53, eldest s. of D. J. Sharland (OR Sh 36). Sh, 66³–70². Trinity, Cambridge.

3020 WADDILOVE, Andrew Ernest James, b. 27 May 53, s. of D. E. Waddilove, M.B.E., LL.B. (OR Sh 31). Sh, 66³–71². Magdalene, Cambridge.

3021 AHAMED, Liaquat, b. 14 Nov. 52, s. of T. Ahamed. St, 66³–70².

3022 BAIN, David Ian, b. 3 Feb. 53, s. of D. W. Bain. St, 66³–71². Levée; H. XI, 71. Mid-Essex Technical College & School of Art. Reading for LL.B. Degree (Ext. London Univ.). Student.

3023 BROOK, Michael Robin, b. 7 June 53, youngest s. of L. E. G. Brook. St, 66³–71². Cap. Brother, 2454.

3024 TAYLOR, Peter George Grimwood, b. 5 Apr. 53, elder s. of C. B. G. Taylor (OR St 38). St, 66³–70³. Bristol Univ.

3025 NADARAJAH, Kumaraj Chittranjan, b. 12 June 53, s. of K. C. Nadarajah of Ceylon. St, 66³–71². Levée; Head of House; XI, 71.

3026 REES-JONES, Richard Gareth, b. 2 May 53, s. of A. Rees-Jones, B.Sc., Ph.D. St, 66³–70³. Pembroke, Oxford since Oct. 71. Student.

3027 WATTS, Timothy Eatough, b. 21 Feb. 53, younger s. of C. E. Watts, M.A., T.D. St, 66³–71³. Levée; Head of House. At present taking London LL.B. at Polytechnic of Central London. Brother, 2133.

3028 BOWKER, Timothy John, b. 28 Aug. 53, s. of Rev. A. E. Bowker. Tu, 66³–71³. Levée; Head of School; Head of House; Cap, 71; Athletics Team, 71. Reading Medical Sciences at Trinity, Cambridge. Cambridge Union Society.

3029A COWAN, Anthony Evelyn Comrie, b. 28 Mar. 53, elder s. of Brig. J. A. C. Cowan, M.B.E. (OR Tu 37). Tu, 66³–70³. Trinity, Oxford, 71³–. Literae Humaniores Exhibition, 72³–, Scholarship, 73²; First in Mods. Student. Brother, Adrian Malcolm Comrie, Tu, 68³–72³.

3029B PELGRIFT, Robert Young, Jnr., b. 15 Mar. 48, s. of R. Y. Pelgrift of U.S.A. Tu, 66³–67². Princeton Univ.

3030 **SHENKMAN, Ivan Alexander,** b. 24 Jan. 53, younger s. of A. I. Shenkman. Tu, 66³–71².

3031 **SILBERMAN, Peter Henry,** b. 19 Sept. 53, s. of L. Silberman. Tu, 66³–70³. Exhibition to Magdalen, Oxford. Undergraduate studying Modern Languages for B.A. Honours School.

3032 **TONGE, Martin Richard,** b. 27 Jan. 53, 3rd s. of the late G. M. M. Tonge (OR Tu 32). Tu, 66³–70³. Valparaiso Univ., Indiana, U.S.A. Rose Bruford College of Speech & Drama, Sidcup, Kent. Actor. Brothers, 2425 & 2723.

3033 **WALKER, Alexander Gordon,** b. 27 Mar. 53, elder son of G. G. Walker. M.B., B.Ch. (OR Tu 37). Tu, 66³–71², Levée; H. XI, 71. Commodore of Sailing, 71. St. Andrews Univ. Brothers, Ian Randel, Tu, 67³–72² & Michael Lawrence, Tu, 69³–.

3034 **WILKINSON, John Nicholas,** b. 24 Aug. 53, younger s. of P. Wilkinson. Tu, 66³–70³. Scholar; R. VIII, 70. Athletics Team, 70. Exhibition to Emmanuel, Cambridge. Undergraduate.

3035 **ADAMS, Jonathan,** b. 11 July 53, elder s. of J. H. Adams. W, 66³–71². Mid-Essex Technical College & School of Art. Law Student. *Leek Rugby Club/Archery Club.* Brother, Timothy, W, 72¹–.

3036 **BARRETT, Neil Andrew,** b. 5 Jan. 53, s. of E. C. Barrett. W, 66³–69².

3037 **CLARKE, Charles Giles,** b. 29 May 53, eldest s. of C. N. Clarke. W, 66³–71². Levée. Oriel, Oxford. Brother, John Henry, W, 72³–.

3038 **FIELDING, Marcus Miles,** b. 4 Mar. 53, younger s. of A. K. L. Fielding. W, 66³–71². R. VIII, 71. Brother, 1963.

3039 **HOWE, Samuel Armstrong,** b. 15 July 48, elder s. of A. Howe, Jnr., O.B.E., D.Lit. (OR C 38). W, 66³–67². Middlebury Coll., U.S.A., B.A. Teaching English and History at Kingswood—Oxford School in West Hertford, Conn., U.S.A.

3040A **ISMAIL, Ali Hyder,** b. 20 Jan. 53, s. of M. C. Ismail, W, 66³–71². Keele University Undergraduate. Committee Member of *Keele Univ. Judo Club.*

3040B **OGLE, Christopher John Slingsby,** b. 24 Feb. 53, s. of the late D. S. Ogle. W, 66³–71².

3041 **SILVERSTON, Keith Bertram,** b. 23 Jan. 53, s. of J. V. Silverston. W, 66³–71². R. VIII, 70; Athletics Team, 70. Leeds Univ.

3042 **STONE, Anthony Lawrence,** b. 12 July 53, s. of F. L. Stone, LL.M. W, 66³–71².

INDEX TO THE LIST OF ENTRIES (PART II)

(The reference is in all cases to the number in the text)

Collenette, J. D. S. 2386
Collie, A. M. R. 2332
Collingridge, H. J. 2141
Collins, K. W. 335
Collins, P. G. H. 2217
Colpoys, P. J. 2039
Colston, C. C. 647
Coltman, A. L. S. 714
Colver, A. F. 2291
Colver, G. B. 2554
Colville, The Hon. A. R.
    863
Colville, The Hon. C. A.
    280
Colville, P. R. 748
Common, J. D. A. 2263
Compston, D. A. S. 2255
Compton, A. S. 1212
Coneys, M. C. D. 2401
Connell, M. J. 827
Connell, S. R. de B. 2294
Conway, H. R. G. 1047
Conway, M. J. 1208
Cook, C. P. E. 1966
Cook, D. M. 889
Cook, H. M. 731
Cook, P. J. 1556
Cookson, P. R. H. 2974
Cooper, A. F. 778
Cooper, C. S. 1585
Cooper, J. A. 1238
Cooper, N. R. L. 2881
Cooper, P. E. 218
Cooper, P. T. 2092
Cooper, R. W. G. 450
Coopman, P. D. 1528
Coote, J. 460
Coote, N. H. N. 292
Cope, P. J. 1061
Cope, R. 2618
Corbett, P. H. S. 1847
Corbould-Warren, A. 603
Corbould-Warren, R. 2
Corlett, C. E. 2913
Corry, D. H. C. 2477
Corry, M. 566
Corry, R. 938
Couldrey, P. O. 2480
Coulson, N. A. E. 1928
Coulson, N. J. 1974
Coultas, S. J. 1707
Coulton, P. T. 353
Courts, G. E. 662
Cove-Smith, J. R. 1458
Cowan, A. E. C. 3029A
Cowan, G. W. B. 1209
Cowen, A. E. 1487
Cowen, D. A. 1202
Cowgill, C. R. 344
Cowie, T. A. 2527
Cowin, M. J. 1608
Cowlin, J. B. 336
Cowper, C. R. 1535
Cowper, M. J. 2714
Cox, P. G. 454
Cox, R. H. 16
Crabbie, C. D. 1923
Craig, A. J. 1848
Craig, C. J. 1263
Craig, J. J. 2376
Cramb, E. C. 514

Cranston, J. N. P. 2377
Cranston, R. I. 1979
Craster, E. J. 1980
Crawford, G. F. 502
Crawford, G. M. W. B.
    1295
Crawford, W. J. 1645
Crawhall, J. M. 723
Crawley, J. M. 38
Crawley, T. H. R. 433
Crawley, W. F. 1084
Crawshaw, T. S. B. 944
Craxton, A. H. R. 2788
Craxton, R. S. 2347
Creswell, C. M. E. 1438
Cresswell, G. D. 1252
Cresswell, P. J. 2348
Crichton-Miller, H. A. 934
Crockett, M. R. 1384
Croft, M. B. 506
Crofts, J. F. 686
Crofts, R. B. 1129
Crofts, R. F. 761
Crowe, A. G. 2919
Crowe, P. G. 1518
Crowther, J. 1363
Cruickshank, R. I. S. 2581A
Cruickshank, M. M. 13
Cruickshanks, G. I. 2789
Cullen, C. P. 2446
Cullen, C. W. 2151
Cullingworth, M. J. 2264
Cundell, P. D. 2324
Cunliffe, J. J. 164
Cunningham, D. J. 2629
Currie, G. A. A. 434
Currie, G. E. 86
Curzon, F. R. P. 2715
Cuthbertson, J. L. 1277
Cutler, A. M. 2321
Cutler, R. D. 2157

Dagnall, H. A. F. 1366
Dalby, P. C. J. 2307
Dalgleish, J. G. 2716
Dalgleish, R. N. 668
Dalrymple, D. H. M. 828
Dalrymple, R. G. 1375
Dalzell-Payne, G. M. M.
    2609
Damerell, W. P. S. 2402
Daniel, O. R. 356
Darby, M. D. 1708
Darlington, G. L. B. 2360
Dauncey, H. R. 370
Daunt, M. S. 1372
Davenport, J. D. 1269
Davenport, M. T. 1085
Davenport, P. L. 305
David, J. M. 2176
David, S. M. 2435
Davidson, A. W. 1776
Davidson, B. S. 948
Davidson, C. R. 2105
Davidson, J. G. W. 87
Davidson, W. S. W. 251
Davies, C. M. 1687
Davies, D. A. 17
Davies, D. J. A. 1634
Davies, Henri L. 1952
Davies, Hugh L. 1310

Davies, J. J. W. 935
Davies, J. W. 2651
Davies, M. C. A. 1210
Davies, P. L. 1924
Davies, P. H. C. 1311
Davies, R. O. H. 2936A
Davies, R. J. 1336
Davies, T. S. G. 2306
Davies-Jones, R. P. 1488
Davis, A. 228
Davis, J. M. 2601
Dawe, S. F. R. 2325
Dawson, A. C. 1339
Dawson, F. A. O. D. 2418
Dawson, R. G. 286
Dawson, W. B. 627
Day, Jeremy R. 593
Day, Johnathan R. 1967
Day, J. T. 244
Deakin, D. I. I. 2884
Dean, J. A. F. 1878
Dean, J. P. 2337
Dean, J. T. 202
Dean, P. 1849
Dean, P. H. 798
Dean, P. H. 2630
Deane, L. D. 298
Deane, T. H. W. (see
    Walker, T. H.) 1274
de Boinville, N. V. C. 2613
de Boursac, C. M. S. 2914
de Boursac, G. 1867
de Boursac, N. 2361
de Chassiron, C. R. L. 2210
Deeley, R. M. 1413
Deford, T. McA. 1925A
de Freitas, G. A. 1801
de Freitas, P. S. 2545
Dehlavi, J. A. K. 1726
Dehlavi, S. K. 1575
de Jonge, G. A. 2362
Delacave, J. T. L. 143
Del Mar, J. R. 2670
Del Mar, R. H. 2985
Deman, M. T. D. 2204
Denby, C. F. 1767
Denby, P. J. 2248
Denholm, P. 1178
Denison-Cross, J. C. 1694
Denis-Smith, D. 203
Denny, W. 1320
de Paula, J. F. J. 1787
de Penning, R. G. 799
Dereham, D. J. 1264
Dereham, O. G. 767
Dereham, S. W. B. 531
Derry-Evans, R. S. 2813
de Salis, H. J. A. F. 299
Dewar, N. A. R. 2535
Dews, R. J. 2097
Dezelski, D. E. 157
Dibsdall, D. D. 2753
Dick, G. C. 2368
Dick, R. G. S. 1652
Dick, R. L. 2040
Dickinson, T. S. 2410
Dickson, D. S. P-M. 2536
Dickson, I. W. 2555
Dickson, M. M. 2079
Dimmick, A. M. 811
Dingwall, C. H. 2519

Dix, C. P. C. 2439
Dix, J. D. C. 2803B
Dixon, D. 1270
Dixon, D. J. 2746
Dixon, J. M. F. 1760
Dixon, Matthew 2142
Dixon, Michael 22
Dixon, N. H. F. 2131
Dixon, T. G. 71
Dizer, P. M. 2770
Dobbs, G. D. K. 2172
Dobell, A. R. 2282
Dodd, A. H. C. 2652
Dodds, P. G. R. 1312
Dodson, C. J. 1680
Dodsworth, R. C. 2939
Dodsworth, S. L. 2590
Doel, C. J. 2205
Doherty, C. G. 165
Doherty, D. C. 2419
Donald, C. D. 96
Doodson, M. G. 1155
Doulton, A. F. 1635
Doulton, J. H. F. 1332
Doulton, P. D. 1626
Doulton, R. S. 2429
Dove, A. C. 1795
Dow, K. 1895
Dow, P. A. 532
Dowling, P. J. O. 1350
Doxford, R. A. 2173
Doyle, R. 2240
Drake, N. J. 52
Draper, D. W. 464
Draycott, P. A. 2158
Drayton, R. M. 1925B
Driscoll, M. J. 2018
Driver, A. J. R. 1586
Drummond, D. S. 584
Drummond, R. M. 1727
Drury, M. D. 694
Drury, N. G. D. 1348
Drysdale, J. A. R. 2420
Drysdale, J. D. 418
Drysdale, P. N. 1658
Dumbell, M. R. 927
Dummett, T. I. P. 1063
Duncan, J. D. 2653
Duncan, P. A. 2967
Duncan, W. G. 2759
Dunkerley, E. P. 2283
Dunlop, C. V. C. 405
Dunlop, M. W. B. 2661
Dunlop, T. 2686
Dunnett, A. D. M. 3004
Durie, A. J. L. 1761
Durke-Burdett, C. E. T. 1504
Duthy-James, C. D. 412
Duval, R. C. 2687
Dyde, J. A. 257
Dyde, N. H. 1896
Dyer, M. G. G. 1271
Dykes, J. B. 503

Eager, M. A. 123
Eardley, J. W. 1828
Earp, J. H. 2875A
Earp, S. B. T. 2882
Eastman, R. K. 2447
Easton, R. J. 882

Eastwood, G. D. 1831
Eatock-Taylor, W. R. 1594B
Eaves, E. W. 144
Eddison, D. W. 258
Eddison, J. M. 2509
Eddowes, H. 406
Eden, M. R. 2474
Edge, J. G. 1823
Edmeades, W. J. 2782
Edmiston, J. S. M. 1533A
Edmundson, H. N. 1860
Edmundson, J. W. 1253
Edwards, A. W. C. 1911
Edwards, C. H. C. 500
Edwards, C. M. 648
Edwards, H. G. O. 788
Edwards, J. H. 480
Edwards, R. G. 2790
Egerton Browne, N. 2363
Eley, P. D. R. 836
Elliot, A. C. 560
Elliot, G. A. 1296
Elliot, I. C. 1297
Elliott, I. R. 1414
Elliott, R. P. 1023
Elliott, T. R. 2891
Ellis, B. A. 663
Ellis, P. D. M. 1449
Ellis, R. A. 2161
Ellis, T. S. 2066
Ellis-Jones, P. G. A. 1239
Embling, J. R. 1468
Emin, U. I. 2900
Enghofer, E. 2749A
Entwisle, T. K. 2510
Erskine, K. F. 2421
Erwin, C. G. 1641
Esslemont, R. J. 1229
Esslemont, W. A. 758
Etches, N. P. 2195
Evans, The Hon. B. P. A., 1469
Evans, E. J. J. 472
Evans, J. A. L. 1378
Evans, J. C. 2041
Evans, M. G. C. 739
Evans, M. J. L. 1793
Evans, N. L. 2817
Evans, P. D. 61
Evans, P. W. G. 2369
Evans, R. W. 389
Evans, S. T. E. 920
Eveleigh, S. B. 1938
Evelyn-Jones, C. F. 2654
Evers, C. C. 837
Evers, D. B. 697
Evers, F. M. 676
Evers, H. S. 2226
Evers, J. A. 1599
Evers, M. R. 1333
Evers, R. O. 1941
Evers, R. P. G. 361
Evers, S. A. 2114
Ewing, J. F. 145
Eyre, D. A. G. 677
Eyre, J. A. G. 78
Eyre, J. G. R. 855

Fagan, B. M. 477
Fagan, D. P. 657

Fairbairn, D. H. L. 872
Fairbank, J. C. T. 2218
Fairclough, D. E. 2110
Fairclough, D. J. 972
Fairclough, P. J. 1868
Falconer, I. R. S. 2591
Falk, S. J. 1321
Falk, W. E. 1381
Fanshawe, H. G. 245
Fargus, D. N. A. 2127
Farman, I. G. C. 2249
Farmer, P. S. 348
Farquharson, D. I. M. 2837
Farrer-Brown D. (see Brown, D. F.)
Farrington, D. J. 2497
Farris, C. A. 838
Farris, D. J. M. 864
Farris, R. E. 9
Fassbender, R. J. 2655
Faulkner, A. M. T. 890
Faulkner, C. S. 982
Faulkner, G. 2568
Faure, P. C. H. 1082
Fawcett, J. P. 515
Fawcett, T. 177
Fearnley, F. T. K. 1650
Feather, M. G. 79
Fehr, B. J. 1671
Fehr, R. J. F. 1278
Feilden, R. J. R. 2569
Fenton, C. J. V. 2580
Fenwick, C. M. 537
Fenwick, P. T. 160
Ferguson, C. W. 2370
Fergusson, D. A. 1012
Fergusson, D. S. B. 949
Fergusson, I. L. C. 1305
Fergusson, M. L. 188
Fetherston-Dilke, M. C. 2277
Field, R. J. J. 80
Fielding, J. K. S. 1963
Fielding, M. M. 3038
Figgis, A. St. J. H. 1075
Finburgh, S. P. 219
Finn, A. R. C. 896
Firth, R. G. 2562
Fisher, S. A. 1805
Fleming, A. S. 902
Fleming, H. 1470
Fleming, L. D. 703
Fleming, S. 1156
Flemming, J. S. 1095
Flemming, J. H. 800
Flemming, N. C. 483
Flemming, W. H. 1695
Fletcher, C. M. 104
Fletcher, G. T. F. 572
Fletcher, S. 1912
Flew, J. P. 2475
Flew, T. J. 924
Florey, C. du Vé 189
Folkes, P. 440
Folland, D. D. 1287
Folland, M. H. D. 847
Fontes, A. R. 53
Fontes, S. S. 801
Footerman, D. S. 2804
Foottit, G. T. W. 2187

Foottit, R. E. 1254
Forbes-Robertson, K. H. 35
Ford, N. P. 2846
Forde, N. J. F. 2106
Forge, J. C. 1981
Forrest, I. R. 903
Forrest, J. F. 1489
Forrest, Robert J. 749
Forrest, Robin J. 1288
Forrest, T. G. 1543
Forrester, G. C. F. 950
Forrester, J. A. A. R. 2006
Forrester, M. A. H. 1035
Forrester-Paton, G. S. 2546
Forster, B. C. 259
Forster, J. N. A. 762
Forster, P. D. 1557
Forster-Cooper, C. J. 2250
Forsyth, C. M. 2389
Forsyth, M. J. A. 1803
Foster, E. W. 740
Fowle, W. M. T. 1024
Fox, A. S. 1802
Fox, C. A. 2075
Fox, H. McL. 812
Fox, J. I. S. 704
Fox, J. McL. 62
Fox, S. J. C. 2080
Foxcroft, R. E. 2791
Francis, A. C. E. 2878
Francis, D. H. 628
Francis, F., jnr. 15
Francis, P. 451
Frankau, T. G. 2604
Franklin, D. H. 481
Franklin, D. P. (see Belwood D. P.)
Franklin, J. A. 1515
Franks, D. A. 2278
Frankton, J. R. 2955
Fraser, C. S. 1953
Fraser, J. H. D. 1368
Fraser, J. R. 1379
Fraser, S. B. 2285
Fraser-Campbell, J. R. 1696
Fraser-Mackenzie, C. L. A. 629
Fraymouth, P. R. N. 1536
Frazer, A. D. 2747
Frazer, J. A. 2241
Freeman, C. J. 1869
Freeman, D. J. 1544
Freeman, T. H. 2805
French, N. J. 899
French, T. J. 865
Friend, R. H. 3011
Frith, R. M. P. 2042A
Froomberg, D. L. 81
Froomberg, R. H. 538
Froome, C. T. 2049
Fry, C. S. C. 1003
Furber, R. M. 1105

Gabbey, H. C. G. 1929
Gaddum, A. H. 839
Gadney, J. 1897
Galloway, M. M. 426
Gamble, P. C. D. 1076
Gardham, M. P. 1850
Garforth-Bles, G. W. 1220

Garforth-Bles, H. C. 2688
Garforth-Bles, R. M. 2390
Garratt, F. P. 544
Garrett, D. R. 357
Garrod, C. P. 2464
Garrow, A. I. A. (see Stockbridge, A. I. A.)
Garton, R. A. 1113
Garvey, J. C. 2779
Garvey, W. F. B. 2265
Garvin, M. J. M. 1537
Gebbels, D. E. 465
Gebolys, J. C. 2211
Geddes, E. M. R. 632
Gee, P. M. 1471
Gee, R. M. 866
Gemmill, R. W. J. 1179
George, D. J. 1659
Geraghty, P. A. C. V. 2637
German, P. D. 873
Gessler, H. 220
Ghandhi, P. R. 2631
Gibb, R. J. A. 874
Gibson, P. J. M. 1255
Gilbert, B. C. 1256
Gilbert, J. D. 1558
Gilbert, J. S. 652
Gilbert, P. H. 1660
Gilbert, R. J. 2927
Gilbert, S. D. 2986
Gilchrist, A. O. 204
Gilchrist, C. G. 2270
Gilchrist, J. G. 2584
Giles, G. F. A. 229
Gillingham, A. T. 3005
Gingold, N. J. D. 1298
Girdler, P. T. M. H. 2310
Given, J. A. 252
Glasgow, J. R. 2578
Glasgow, M. M. S. 2028
Gledhill, A. J. S. 2093
Gledhill, M. C. S. 1490
Gluckstein, J. M. H. 378
Glynn, J. N. 1479
Goatly, J. H. 2322
Goatly, P. J. 3012
Goatly, R. D. 2487
Goddard, I. L. 2638
Godfrey, I. T. G. 324
Godley, The Hon. C. J. 1736
Golding, S. R. 1720
Gollin, D. E. F. 1240
Gollin, R. L. A. 2138
Goodbody, K. W. 328
Goodbody, M. H. 1600
Goodhart, R. A. G. 2313
Goodman, M. D. 3006
Goodman, P. S. 2838
Goodway, D. J. 1415
Goodwin, R. B. 124
Gordon, A. S. 97
Gordon, R. F. 2333
Gordon Brown, D. H. 2771
Gordon Brown, M. E. 2451
Gorman, M. E. W. 633
Goslett, D. N. 1357
Goslett, N. S. 1994
Gosset, B. D. 2481
Gould, M. R. 2818
Gourlay, W. G. N. 2459A

Gover, W. J. S. 1646
Gow, D. W. M. 2227
Goyder, D. G. 735
Goyder, E. M. 2945
Goyder, H. P. G. 2007
Graham, D. L. 2727
Graham, J. T. 1257
Graham, O. L. M. 2895
Graham, R. A. 1810
Graham, R. H. P. 1389
Grant, D. E. 1004
Grant, R. W. 698
Gray, A. J. G. 2266
Gray, C. J. 813
Gray, C. R. G. 2936B
Gray, D. F. 390
Gray, N. P. 1709
Gray, R. A. 300
Gray, T. A. G. 2706
Grayburn, J. R. 1426
Greany, J. M. 146
Greany, M. J. 2570
Greany, R. A. H. 1661
Green, A. E. M. 604
Green, C. N. 2885A
Green, M. J. 1851
Green, P. W. B. 1668
Green, R. T. B. 1427
Greenfield, R. H. 24
Greenhalgh, G. R. 1382
Greenhalgh, J. P. S. 2060
Greenleaves, J. E. V. 1439
Greenway, I. P. 1068
Greenwell, T. W. 2901
Greenwood, J. G. 2029
Gregg, R. N. 732
Gregory, A. P. 308
Gregory, C. C. 1525
Gregory, R. B. 829
Gregson, M. J. 1930
Gregson, M. J. G. 1545
Gribbon, A. J. St. G. 2733
Gribbon, A. St. G. 1936
Grierson, J. A. C. 1013
Griffin, H. P. H. 2994
Griffiths, N. E. F. 2196
Grillo, H. B. N. 1852
Grillo, R. J. 1666
Grime, P. A. 2256
Grimwood-Taylor, P. W. S. 2937
Grove-White, C. D. 2123
Grove-White, I. G. 906
Groves, R. M. 2870A
Grundy, G. W. 687
Grylls, R. G. 1523
Guedalla, M. L. 1853
Guest, M. R. J. 1636
Guinness, G. N. 802
Guinness, J. R. S. 333
Guinness, L. F. 1044
Gutteridge, C. N. 2870B

Habershon, J. J. 2689
Hackett, A. J. P. 2556
Hackett, N. G. G. 1380
Hackman, J. W. 1376
Hadman, R. J. 1879
Hagenbach, K. M. 1681
Haldane, R. W. 2098
Hale, T. T. M. 2968

Rowland Clark, T. R. (see
  Clark, T. R. R.)
Rowley, C. O. B. 777
Rowley, J. R. 1614
Rowley, M. J. 752
Rubin, P. A. J. 2517
Ruff, C. R. 1260
Rumbellow, J. W. 1748
Runagall, R. B. 1840
Rundell, G. F. W. 1062
Runeckles, P. 2102
Rushdie, A. S. 2112
Russell, A. C. 214
Russell, A. V. M. 2462
Russell, B. P. 2326
Russell, C. H. 2871
Russell, I. A. 1714
Russell, M. A. 2301
Russell, N. C. 215
Russell, R. J. C. G. 2191
Russell, W. M. 82
Russell-Smith, C. R. 2539
Russenberger, P. J. 2531
Rutherford, D. C. 384

Sage, J. M. 3018
Salisbury, I. M. 2710
Sallitt, T. W. B. 139
Salmon, J. G. I. 1873
Sampson, A. H. 1756
Samuel, C. S. 1531
Samuel, W. M. 2866
Samuelson, M. 190
Sargant, J. E. 322
Saunders, P. W. W. 700
Savage, A. M. 2961
Savage, M. B. R. 459
Saville-Sneath, R. C. 743
Sawers, I. J. 2153
Saxton, C. B. 1045
Schell, P. R. 2728
Schick, P. M. 2469
Schleimer, J. 2581B
Schmidle, L. 2885B
Schreckenberger, S. 2876B
Schryver, H. J. P. 2612
Schultz, W. 2742B
Science, A. L. 1655
Scorah, A. M. N. 1464
Scorah, J. B. 1757
Scott, C. J. P. 2532
Scott, D. T. 710
Scott, J. A. D. 2701
Scott, J. G. S. 2182
Scott, J. P. 1827
Scott, M. C. M. 1454
Scott, R. H. A. 2434
Scott, T. 2085
Scott, W. 968
Scott Graham, P. J. 493
Scrimshaw, J. G. 2113
Scruby, P. R. 2767
Seaman, R. J. H. 1639
Sear, L. R. 309
Searancke, J. E. F. 1408
Sebestyen, H. M. 2524
Seccombe, P. S. 2633
Seddon, J. A. 414
Seddon, P. 2046
Seeley, L. C. R. 614
Selkirk, A. R. L. 591

Selkirk, F. D. L. 943
Selkirk, S. J. A. 1629
Sellar, R. J. 2695
Sellors, P. J. H. 131
Sells, C. C. L. 849
Selwyn, C. T. 1541
Sergeant, J. J. H. 1893
Series, R. W. 2950
Sethia, B. 2721
Seymour, P. A. C. 1622B
Seymour, R. K. 1247
Shackel, G. G. 859
Shailer, M. J. A. 2887
Sharland, N. D. 3019
Sharp, A. T. 474
Sharp, S. C. R. 403
Shaw, C. W. 445
Shaw, E. N. 109
Shaw, G. 1571
Shaw, G. D. C. 268
Shaw, G. D. G. 535
Shaw, J. G. 755
Shaw, M. M. 2353
Shaw, M. W. 1008
Shaw, N. M. 1100
Shaw, P. E. 2502
Shaw, R. C. A. 783
Shaw, T. R. 355
Shawcross, F. W. 552
Shearer, A. P. 2304
Shearer, R. H. R. 2032
Shellim, A. M. 2602
Shenkman, I. A. 3030
Sheridan, R. C. E. 2787
Sherrard, A. C. 623
Shilladay, T. J. 1120
Short, A. D. 910
Short, C. C. 1958
Short, R. A. M. 1039
Sidebottom, N. G. N. 2743
Sidgwick, A. B. 2999
Sidgwick, D. B. T. 2582
Sidgwick, J. B. 2583
Silberman, P. H. 3031
Silverston, K. B. 3041
Simms, C. M. 1691
Simms, N. A. L. 1500
Simon, G. B. 2917
Simonds, R. D. 1283
Simpkiss, R. J. 2756
Simpson, A. G. 2540
Simpson, A. M. H. 349
Simpson, M. J. R. 1301
Simpson, P. J. 2192
Simpson, R. H. 2503
Simpson, R. R. 2934
Simpson, W. R. 2233
Sinclair, M. F. 784
Sissons, D. C. 2711
Skailes, J. A. D. 646
Skeggs, A. N. L. (see
  Lyndon-Skeggs, A. N.)
Sketchley, M. W. B. 3000
Skinner, D. M. B. 1284
Skinner, J. J. B. 488
Skinner, R. C. O. 2445
Skinner, R. P. B. 1193
Slade, S. J. 46
Slater, A. H. 711
Slater, A. I. 2648
Slatter, A. G. M. 275

Sledge, J. C. 1455
Sleight, P. J. 2504
Slingsby, C. A. 1519
Slotover, R. E. S. 2222
Slotover, R. J. E. 1674
Smallpage, Q. N. 2289
Smart, R. B. 2872
Smellie, J. D. C. 1150
Smith, C. H. D. 2077
Smith, G. N. 1672
Smith, H. J. 23
Smith, J. A. 168
Smith, J. N. 1078
Smith, J. R. B. 806
Smith, K. F. B. 1409
Smith, M. J. G. 1882
Smith, M. P. V. 2269
Smith, N. G. 833
Smith, N. R. R. 1874
Smith, P. J. 1580
Smith, R. S. 10
Smith, T. G. C. 1643
Smith, W. D. N. 625
Smythies, A. G. 2910
Snell, C. J. 1835
Snell, P. D. 1018
Snowdon, J. A. 1009
Solley, A. P. 1935
Somers, R. P. 1954
Sosnow, N. M. 1622C
Sothmann, G. 2456B
Souter, N. J. 2962
Southern, P. K. 2799
Southward, D. C. 484
Southward, I. D. 2033
Southward, N. R. 1121
Southwell, J. P. 2951
Sparkes, K. W. 2023
Sparling, G. A. J. 2552
Speed, J. A. 102
Speed, J. R. B. 2963
Spence, R. E. 364
Spence, R. W. R. 345
Spencer, A. J. C. 2001
Spens, D. P. 2494
Spens, J. A. 21
Spens, J. H. 2712
Spens, P. M. R. 1248
Spens, W. D. R. 1506
Spillane, J. A. 1926
Spinks, J. I. 1422
Spinks, P. N. 2505
Spittle, T. E. T. 2897
Sporborg, C. H. 877
Spottiswoode, D. M. 2713
Springer, F. M. 2589A
Sproston, J. P. 1565
Spurrier, N. J. M. 834
Spurrier, S. H. W. 1126
Stabler, R. J. 610
Stables, C. I. F. 2979
Stallworthy, J. H. 288
Stanbrook, P. H. 2354
Stanford, A. T. J. 232
Stanford, J. K. E. 479
Stanger, W. J. N. 1428
Stansfield, J. H. 2729
Stansfield, W. H. 1040
Stanworth, R. H. 1715
Staunton, H. C. T. 1883
Staveley, D. A. 2024

PART III

PART III

Date of appointment	Name	By whom appointed	Date of vacating office
1961	Sir Edmund G. COMPTON, G.C.B., K.B.E. (Chrmn., 1969–71)	Governing Body	1971
1963	Sir Alan H. WILSON, F.R.S., D.Sc.	Governing Body	
1964	Sir Edward R. LEWIS, F.S.A.	Governing Body	
1966	Prof. Sir Robert BIRLEY, K.C.M.G., LL.D., F.S.A.	Oxford University	
1966	B. W. M. YOUNG	Governing Body	
1967	Sir Derek HILTON, M.B.E. (Dep. Chrmn., 1971–)	Lord Chancellor	
1968	Prof. A. G. GUEST	London University	
1968	Ald. C. M. T. SMITH-RYLAND, J.P., The Lord-Lieutenant of the County of Warwick	Ex-officio	
1968	H. A. STAVELEY	Headmaster & Masters	1970
1970	A. J. HUNT	Headmaster & Masters	
1972	D. E. C. STEEL, D.S.O., M.C.	Governing Body	
1972	Sir Oliver CHESTERTON, M.C., F.R.I.C.S.	Governing Body	
1973	C. A. McLINTOCK	Governing Body	
1974	T. E. B. HOWARTH, M.C.	Cambridge University	

CLERKS

1895	C. F. HARRIS, Solicitor, Rugby		1949
1949	P. D. BENNETT, M.A., Solicitor, Rugby		1967
1967	P. A. SNOW, M.A., F.R.A.I., J.P.		

BURSARS

1927	J. C. DUNKIN		1954
1954	P. A. SNOW		

ASSISTANT BURSARS

1964	Cdr. J. H. MELVIN		1968
1968	Lt.-Col. D. E. M. INGRAM		

MEDICAL OFFICERS

1931	R. E. SMITH		1950
1950	J. P. SPARKS		

HEADMASTERS OF RUGBY SCHOOL

1931   LYON, Percy Hugh Beverley. Scholar of Rugby School, 07–12. Exhibitioner of Oriel College, Oxford. 6th Bn. Durham Light Infantry. Capt. M.C., 17. Wounded. Prisoner, 18. Newdigate Prize Poem, 19. 1st Class Lit. Hum., 21. Asst. Master at Cheltenham College, 21. Rector of the Edinburgh Academy, 26. Headmaster of Rugby School, 31–48. Director, Public Schools Appointment Bureau from 50–61. Address: Springhill, Amberley, Nr. Stroud, Glos.

1948   FFORDE, Sir Arthur (Frederic Brownlow). Scholar of Rugby School, 14–19. Trinity College, Oxon., 19–22. B.A. (Lit. Hum. Cl. III), 22 (M.A., 38).

Solicitor, 25. Partner, Linklaters & Paines, 28–48. Council, Law Society, 37–48. Under Secretary, Ministry of Supply, 43–44, and of H.M. Treasury, 44–45. Kt., 46. Headmaster, Rugby School, 48–57. Member of Committee of H. M. C. and Chrmn. of Religious Advisory Committee of National Association of Boys Clubs 49–57. Nominated member of Church Assembly and Central Board of Finance of Church of England, 57 (Vice-Chrmn. of C.B.F., 57–60, Chrmn., 60–65. Standing Committee of Ch. Assembly, 60–65). Chrmn. of B.B.C., 57–64. G.B.E., 64. Director, Equity & Law Life Assurance Society, 43–48 and 57–70. Westminster Bank (and National Westminster Bank), 57–70. Hon.LL.D., University of Wales. Publications: Occasional Verses and Addresses only. Address: Wall's End, Wonersh, Surrey.

1957   HAMILTON, Walter. St. Dunstan's College. Trinity College, Cambridge (Scholar). Classical Tr., Pt. I, Cl. I, 27; Pt. II, Cl. I, 29. Craven University Scholarship, 27. Chancellor's Classical Medal, 28. B.A., 29. M.A., 33. Hon.D.Litt (Durham), 58. F.R.S.L. Fellow (31–35 and 46–50) and Tutor (47–50), Trinity College, Cambridge. Assistant Master, Eton College, 33–46 (Master in College, 37–46). University Lecturer in Classics, Cambridge, 47–50. Headmaster, Westminster School, 50–57. Headmaster, Rugby School, 57–66. Master, Magdalene College, Cambridge, 67–. Chrmn., Headmasters' Conference, 55–56, 65–66. Chrmn., Governing Body, Shrewsbury School, 68–. Chrmn. Governing Bodies' Association, 69–. Fellow of Eton College, 72–. Publications: "A new translation of Plato's Symposium" (Penguin), 51; "Plato's Gorgias" (Penguin), 60; "Plato's Phaedrus and 7th and 8th Letters" (Penguin), 73. Articles in "Classical Quarterly", "Classical Review", etc. Address: The Master's Lodge, Magdalene College, Cambridge.

ASSISTANT MASTERS IN 1947

Details in Vol. IV

Appointed	Name	Left	Died
1916	Miss A. M. F. Dukes	1949	
1917	A. R. Tatham	1952	
1920	H. P. Sparling	1954	
	F. C. Slater	1954	

Details in 1911–46 Register

1922	R. Broxton	—	1962
	R. M. Carey	1957	
	K. A. Stubbs	—	1949
1924	G. A. Keay	1954	
	W. N. Hughes	1965	
1925	C. L. Salmons	1960	1968
	J. Farrant		
	E. H. L. Jennings	1962	
1926	R. C. Watt	1951	
1927	E. V. Reynolds	1949	
1928	R. H. Walker	1959	
	J. R. A. Smith	1962	
	E. J. Harris	1968	
1929	R. B. Talbot Kelly	1966	1971
1930	D. J. Watkins-Pitchford	1947	
	O. R. C. Prior	1963	
1931	M. W. de la P. Beresford	1969	
	W. W. Inge	1969	

Appointed	Name	Left	Died
1932	P. Falk	1972	
1933	R. W. Stott	1963	1963
	J. B. Channon	1967	
1934	W. G. R. Loughery	1969	
1935	J. B. E. Garstang	1952	
	H. R. F. Bosman	1947	1963
1936	J. Larmour	1969	
	O. R. Fulljames	1955	
	F. J. A. Chase		
1937	H. T. J. Gebbels	1965	1968
	J. L. Willans		
	A. N. W. Saunders	1965	
1938	K. Stagg	—	1957
1939	D. Bulmer	1970	
1940	A. W. V. Mace	1962	
	G. H. Dazeley		
	R. P. Wright		
	C. E. Rogers	1963	1963
	M. G. Dolden	1953	
1942	J. A. M. MacDonogh	1971	
1943	J. P. B. Clark	1951	
1944	E. P. Courtnell	—	1956
	C. H. Potter	1950	
	J. B. Hope-Simpson	1969	
	A. Constant	1948	
	L. E. Godfrey Jones	1959	
1945	A. F. Hunt	1970	
	H. A. Staveley	1958	
	Miss E. A. Bennett	1964	
1946	P. G. Mason	1949	
	A. W. E. Winlaw	1954	
	P. Lewis		
	F. H. Murray	1969	
	M. S. Tillett	1968	
	C. P. Mortimer		

ASSISTANT MASTERS

Assistant Masters to Mr. P. H. B. Lyon appointed from 1947

1947[1]　TOSSWILL, Timothy Dymond. Left 70[2]. Rugby School, 28–32. Exhibitioner to Exeter College, Oxford. Pass Mods., 32. 2nd Class Hons. English, B.A., 38. M.A., 39. Senior English Master, Royal Masonic (Senior) School, 35–39. Pte., The Devonshire Regiment, Sept. 39. Adjutant, 12th Devons, 42. Staff Capt., H.Q. 2nd Army, 44. Despatches, 44. Transferred to R.A.E.C. in rank of Major, Sept. 45. Visiting Lecturer, University of California at Berkeley, 65–66. Associate Professor, Whitman College, Washington, U.S.A., 70–73. Published five Text Books & B.B.C. Broadcaster. Address: c/o Dept. of English, Whitman College, Walla Walla, Washington, U.S.A.

1947[3]　BARRACLOUGH, Fabio Geoffrey. Appointed Art Master, Sept. 47. Educated Madrid and Cardinal Vaughan School, 34–40. Graduated San Fernando Royal Academy of Fine Art, 40–43. Diploma de Pintura y Bellas Artes, John Cass & Slade, 46–47. R.N.V.R., 43–46. Nat. Dip. in Design (Sculpture), 46. Fellow, Royal Society of British Sculptors, 65. Publications: "Light as Medium in Sculpture", 50; "Short History of Art", 57; "Sculpture & Environment", 73. Editor, Sculpture Review, 65. Address: Upper Stowe Studio, Stowe-IX-Churches, Northampton.

1948³ McCRUM, Michael William. Left 50². Sherborne School. Corpus Christi College, Cambridge (Scholar), 46–48. Tr. Pt. I, Cl. I; Pt. II, Cl. I. Fellow and Tutor, Corpus Christi College, Cambridge, 50. Headmaster, Tonbridge School, 62–70. Headmaster, Eton College, 70. Publications (with A. G. Woodhead): "Select Documents of the Principates of the Flavian Emperors, A.D. 68–96". Address: Eton College, Windsor, Berks.

1949¹ BAISS, John Llewelyn Reynolds. Marlborough College. Sidney Sussex College, Cambridge, 35–38. Hist. Tr. Pt. I; Geog. Tr. Pt. I, Cl. II, Div. 1. Junior Tutor, Bonar Law College, 39. Military service, R.E.(Svy.), 40–46. Despatches, 45. Major. Merchant Taylor's School, 46–48. Lt.-Col. C.C.F., 58–62. T.D. Housemaster, Michell House, 63.

1949³ SILVER, Colin Hubert. Malvern College, 39–43. Oriel College, Oxford (Scholar), 47–49. Classical Hons. Mods. Cl. II; Lit. Hum. Cl. II. M.A. Housemaster, Tudor House, 64.

1949³ SPURGIN, John Alistair Wingrove. Left 59¹. Rugby School (Hon. Scholar). Trinity College, Cambridge (Scholar), 42–48. Mod. and Med. Lang. Tr. Pt. I, Cl. I; English Tr. Pt. I, Cl. II. B.A. Address: 5, Millington Road, Cambridge.

1949³ GRAVES, John Douglas. Oswestry High School. R.C.M., London, 38–39. R.C.M., Manchester, 48–49. B.Mus. (London), 40. F.R.C.O., 49 (Harding Prize). Publications: Five Instrumental Compositions and seven Anthems, etc. Address: 12a, Hillmorton Road, Rugby.

1950³ ASHCROFT, David. Left 59¹. Rugby School. Gonville and Caius College, Cambridge (Scholar). Classical Tr. Pt. I, Cl. I. Rossall School, 46–50. Headmaster, Cheltenham College, 59. Address: Cheltenham College, Cheltenham, Glos.

1950³ BOYES, James Ashley. Left 55¹. Rugby School. Clare College, Cambridge (Scholar), 43, 46–48. Hist. Tr. Cl. I. B.A., 48. Fellow, Yale University, 48–50. M.A., Yale, 50. Headmaster, Kendal Grammar School, 55–60. Director of Studies, R.A.F. College, Cranwell, 60–65. Headmaster, City of London School, 65. Address: City of London School, London, E.C.4.

1950³ PEIRSON, John. Marlborough College. Peterhouse, Cambridge (Exhibitioner), 47–50. Hon. Degree (B.A.) Nat. Sci. Tr. Cl. II, 50. Housemaster, Whitelaw House, 65.

1950³ MILLER, Ian Gerald. Rugby School. Caius College, Cambridge, 35–38. Econ. Tr. Pts. I and II, Cl. II, 1 and Cl. II, 2; French Tr. A. I. Cl. II. Dip.Ed. Assistant, College Classique, Lausanne, 47–48. Lancaster Royal G.S., 48–50. Address: 7, Horton Crescent, Rugby.

1951³ HARE, Peter Macduff Christian. Canford School. Worcester College, Oxford (Scholar), 39–40 & 45–47. War Degree, 40. Hist. Cl. II. M.A., 48. Temp. Lecturer, Modern Studies, R.M.A., Sandhurst, 48. Geelong C. of E. G. S., Australia, 49–50. King's School, Worcester, 51. Housemaster, Stanley House, 64.

1951³ BUCKNEY, Thomas Austin. Radley College. Corpus Christi College, Cambridge (Scholar), 48–51. Classical Tr. Pts. I and II, Cl. II, Div. 1 and Cl. I. Housemaster, School Field, 64. Publications: "Scipio Africanus".

1952¹ LUPTON, Arthur Ralph Ransome. Left 65². Rugby School. Trinity College, Cambridge. Mech. Tr., Cl. II, 44. De Havilland Engine Co., 44–46. English Electric Co., 46–52. Address: 26, Connaught Avenue, Loughton, Essex.

1952³ CAMPBELL, Iain Parry. Left 57². Canford School. Trinity College, Oxford. Hist. Cl. III. Oxford XI. King's School, Worcester, 52.

1953³ CASTLE, David Langstaff. Ottershaw College & Univ. of London School of Slavonic and East European Studies, Cl. I. B.A. Postgraduate studentship, Treasury, 50–53. Died 23 September 67.

1953³ ROBINS, Michael Frank. Left 70¹. Clifton College. King's College, Cambridge (Scholar), 45–48. Wrangler, Maths. Tr. Pt. II and Hons. with distinction. Maths. Tr. Pt. III. M.A. Senior Mathematics Master, Sedbergh

School, 48–53 and at Rugby, 59–70. Fellow of the Institute of Mathematics and its Applications (F.I.M.A.), 67. Headmaster, Liverpool College, 70. Address: Beechlands, Liverpool College, Mossley Hill, Liverpool L18 8BE.

1953[3]   DEWES, John Gordon. Left 58[2]. Aldenham School. St. John's College, Cambridge. Geog. Tr. Pt. I, Cl. II. Law Tr. Pt. II, Cl. II, Div. 1, 49. Cambridge XI. England XI (cricket) in Australia. B.A., 49. M.A., 53. Tonbridge School, 50–53. Barker College, N.S.W., 58–63. Dulwich College, 63. Address: 90, Burbage Road, London, S.E.21.

1953[3]   STEPHENSON, Graham Gordon. Left 56[2]. Bradfield College. Trinity College, Oxford (Scholar). Mod. Hist. Cl. II. M.A. and B.Litt., 53. Sherborne School, 56.

1953[3]   HALL, John Ruthven. Left 59[3]. Sidcot School. Peterhouse, Cambridge (Exhibitioner), 49–52. Nat. Sc. Tr. Pt. I, Cl. 2, Div. 1. B.A. (Hons.). King's College School, Wimbledon, 53. Rugby, 53[3]–59[3]. King's College, Budo, Kampala, Uganda, 59–64. University College, Makerere, Kampala, 64–66. University of Newcastle-upon-Tyne, 66–. Publications: "Journal of the Uganda Science Teachers' Association", "Senior Tropical Biology". Address: 8, Keyes Gardens, Jesmond, Newcastle-upon-Tyne, 2.

1954[1]   GARDNER, Patrick Michael. Wellington College. Peterhouse, Cambridge, 34–37. Mod. Lang. Pt. I, Cl. II, Div. 2 and Econ. Tr. Pt. II, Cl. III, 39–46. 17/21 Lancers (Major, M.B.E.), 47–51. T.O.I. Allied Commission for Austria (F.O. temp.). Cranbrook School, 51–52. Dover College, 52–53. Address: 44, Hillmorton Road, Rugby.

1954[3]   VIVIAN, Thomas Keith. Left 62[2]. Truro School. St. John's College, Cambridge, 45–49. Moral Sc. Tr. Pt. II, Cl. II, Div. 1. M.A., 52. Cert. Education, 49. Cambridge XV, 48–49. Rugger for Harlequins (Capt., 55–57) also Cornwall, Sussex & Warwickshire (Capt., 56–57). Christ's Hospital, 49–54. Headmaster, Lucton School, 62. Address: Lucton School, Leominster, Herefordshire.

1955[2]   CREESE, Nigel Arthur Holloway. Left 63[2]. Blundell's School, 40–45. Brasenose College, Oxford, 48–52. Hon. Mods. Cl. IV and Lit. Hum. Cl. III. Oxford XV, 51. Bromsgrove School, 52–55. Headmaster, Christ's College, Canterbury, New Zealand, 63–70. Headmaster, Melbourne C. of E. Grammar School, 70–. Address: Melbourne Church of England Grammar School, Melbourne, Australia.

1955[3]   MAGILL, Waller Brian Brendan. Left 62[2]. Campbell College, Belfast. Trinity College, Dublin (Scholar). Mental and Moral Science Cl. I. B.A., 42; B.D. Curate-Assistant, Knock, Belfast, 44–47, and Holywood, 47–50. Vice-Principal, The Queen's College, Birmingham, and Lecturer at Birmingham University, 50–55. Head of Religious Studies Department, Nottingham College of Education, 62–. Address: 16, Parkcroft Road, West Bridgford, Nottingham.

1955[3]   HELE, James Warwick. Left 73[2]. Sedbergh School. Hertford College, Oxford, 44–45. Trinity Hall, Cambridge (Scholar), 48–51. Hist. Tr. Pts. I and II, Cl. II, Div. 1 and Cl. I. B.A., 51. Oxford XV, 44. M.A., 55. Master, King's College School, Wimbledon, 51–55. Housemaster, Kilbracken, 65. Second Master, 70. Appointed High Master of St. Paul's School, 73[3]. Address: High Master's House, St. Paul's School, Lonsdale Road, Barnes, London, S.W.13.

1956[3]   COATES, James Michael Campbell. Left 67[2]. Marlborough College. Clare College, Cambridge, 50–54. Hist. Tr. Pts. I and II, Cl. II, Div. 1 and Cl. II, Div. 1. B.A. Dip.Ed., 54. Sedbergh School, 56. Headmaster, Bramcote School, 67–69. Headmaster, Monkton Combe Junior School, 69–. Address: Monkton Combe Junior School, Combe Down, Bath.

1956[3]   BURTON-BROWN, Michael. Left 58[2]. Charterhouse. Pembroke College, Oxford (Scholar). Hon. Mods. Cl. II; Lit. Cl. III. M.A. Lyceum Alpinum, Zuoz, Switzerland, 54–56. T.D. Headmaster of Edgeborough Preparatory School, Frensham, Surrey. Address: Edgeborough, Frensham, Surrey.

1956³   INGLIS, John. Cranleigh School. Magdalene College, Cambridge, 52–56. Cambridge Univ. Eton Fives, 53–56 (Capt., 55). Cranleigh Junior School, 51–52. Chavakali Sec. School, Maragoli, Kenya, 67–68. Housemaster, Cotton House, 69.

1956²   MORLEY, Leslie. Royal Military School of Music, 36–42. A.R.C.M., 41. Bandmaster, The King's Own Regiment, 41–56. Address: 139, Hillmorton Road, Rugby.

1957¹   CHAMPNISS, Alfred Bertram. Left 65¹. Harrow School (Entrance Scholar). Oriel College, Oxford (Organ Scholar), Hons. Juris Prudence, 54. Royal College of Music, M.A., F.R.C.O., A.R.C.M. Harrow School, 56. Director of Music, Sedbergh School, 65. Address: Guldrey Lodge, Sedbergh, Yorkshire.

Assistant Masters to Dr. Hamilton

1957³   SWINFEN, Thomas Christopher. Left 66¹. Fettes College, St. John's College, Cambridge (Scholar), 51–54. Nat. Sci. Tr. Pt. I and Cl. II, Div. 1 and Pt. II, Cl. I. M.A., 58. B.Sc. Lond., 54. London Postgraduate Certificate in Education, F.R.I.C., 71. Senior Science Master, Uppingham School, 66–. Address: Tudor House, 8 High Street, West Uppingham.

1957³   HORSLEY, Francis John. Left 59². Malvern College. Queen's College, Cambridge (Exhibitioner). Math. Tr. Pts. I & II, Cl. I & II. Bristol Grammar School, 60–63. Tiffin School, 63 (Head of Mathematics Department and Senior House Master). Address: Greenways, 62, Harriotts Lane, Ashtead, Surrey.

1957³   SCHLICH, Robin Anthony. Left 69³. Bradfield College. St. John's College, Oxford (Exhibitioner), 53–56. Mod. Lang. Cl. II. Assistant (Ministry of Education), Einbeck, Germany, 56–57. Trent College, 70. Address: Wright House, Trent College, Long Eaton, Nottingham NG10 4AD.

1957³   PITT, John David. Left 66³. Huddersfield College. Plymouth College, 51–53. Trinity College, Cambridge (Scholar), 53–57. Maths. Tr. Cl. I. Senior Mathematics Master at The Thomas Bennett School, Crawley, 67–72. Deputy Headmaster, Cirencester School, 72–. Address: "Blakedean", Gosditch, Ashton Keynes, Swindon, Wilts.

1958²   BRIDGEMAN, Laurence Julian. Left 61³. De Aston School, Lincs. Loughborough College Dip. Loughborough College, Cl. I, 55. Churcher's College, Petersfield, 55–58.

1958³   FOXCROFT, Geoffrey Edward. Birkenhead Institute. Trinity College, Cambridge (Senior Scholar), 42–44 & 48–50. Nat. Sci. Tr. Pts. I & II, Cl. II & I. B.A., 45. M.A., 49. Moseley Grammar School, Birmingham, 46–48. William Hulme's Grammar School, Manchester, 50–52. Westminster School, 52–58. Publications: "Lasers", by G. Wright & G. E. Foxcroft, "The Electronics Kit" and "The Lasers Accessories Kit". Address: 39, Hillmorton Road, Rugby.

1958³   TYSON, John Baird. Rugby. Commissioned Argyll & Sutherland Highlanders; served with Seaforth Highlanders, 48–49. M.C. (Malaya), 50. Magdalen College, Oxford, 49–52. Geog. Hons. B.A., 52. M.A., 58. Outward Bound Mountain School, Eskdale, 53–54. Rugby, 55. Christ's Hospital, 56–58. Leader of scientific expeditions to Nepal, Himalaya, 61, 64, 69. Ness Award of Royal Geographical Society. Goldsmiths' Travelling Scholarship, 64. Council Member of Royal Geographical Society, 65–67. Committee, Mount Everest Foundation since 63. Executive member of British Council Nepal School project, 66–68. Housemaster, Sheriff House, 69. Publications: various articles in "Geographical Journal", and "Geographical Magazine", "Alpine Journal", etc. Travel films made for B.B.C. Television.

1958³   HELLIWELL, Geoffrey Maurice. Giggleswick. Corpus Christi College, Oxford, 49–53. Eng. Hons. Cl. II. B.A., 52. Dip. Ed. M.A., 57. Abingdon School, 53–58. Housemaster, Bradley House, 69.

1958[3]   TOOMER, John Winsor. Left 63[2]. Oakham School. Keble College, Oxford, 52–56. Chemistry Cl. II. Warwick School, 58. Eton College, 63[3]–. Address: Eton College, Windsor, Berks.

1958[3]   EATON, James Leonard. Left 62[2]. King Edward School, Birmingham. Wadham College, Oxford. Hon. Mods. Cl. II; Lit. Hum. Cl. II. B.A., 56.

1958[3]   MOORE, Richard Julian. Left 71[1]. Harrow. Christ Church, Oxford, 54–58. Mods. Cl. II; Lit. Hum. Cl. II. Running his own Picture Gallery. Address: Tauranga, Restronguet Point, Feock, Nr. Truro, Cornwall.

1958[3]   ELVINS, Brian Sedgley. Wrekin College. Birmingham University. Chemistry Cl. IIb. Address: 12, Hillmorton Road, Rugby.

1959[3]   MARSHALL, John Campbell. Rugby. Brasenose College, Oxford, 49–53. Oxford XI, 53. Hist. Cl. II. Dragon School, Oxford, 53–56 and 57–59. Radley College, 56–57. Tutor in Cotton House, 59–69. Housemaster, School House, 69–. Rugger for Scotland v. France, New Zealand, England, Ireland & Wales in 54. Captain, O.U. Greyhounds R.F.C., 52. Toured Japan with O.U.R.F.C. in 52. Manager Wagtails C.C. Tour to Canada, 66.

1959[3]   SHAVE, Michael John Ramage. Left 64[2]. Hymer's College, Hull. Manchester Grammar School. Wadham College, Oxford (Scholar). Maths. Mods. Cl. I. Final Honour School of Maths. Cl. I. Dip. Ed., 57. B.A. Westminster School, 57. St. Edward's School, Oxford, 57–59.

1959[3]   BOYS, Geoffrey Robert Hodson. Left 63[2]. Tonbridge School. Trinity Hall, Cambridge (Exhibitioner). Maths. Tr. 1, Pts. II & III, Cl. II. B.A., 57. Eton College, 57–59. Westminster School, 63–72. Head of Maths Dept., 64–72. Editor of Schools Council Mathematics Curriculum Project at University of Nottingham, 73–. Publications: "Problems in Applied Mathematics", 1972. Address: Cliff House, Hermitage Walk, The Park, Nottingham NG7 1DR.

1959[3]   BARLOW, Ian Mitford Mohun. Clifton College. Corpus Christi College, Cambridge (Scholar), 56–59. Classical Tr. Pts. I & II, Cl. I & Cl. II 1. B.A. Address: 1, Springhill, Barby Road, Rugby.

1960[1]   MARSHALL, John. Left 62[2]. Haversham Grammar School, Westmorland & Magdalene College, Cambridge. Nat. Sc. Tr. Pt. I, Cl. II.; Geog. Tr. Pt. II, Cl. II. Whitgift Middle School, 52–54. The Edinburgh Academy, 55–59.

1960[3]   TURNER, Nigel Jeremy Bunting. Left 62[2]. Tonbridge School. Corpus Christi College, Cambridge (Exhibitioner). Lang. Tr. Pts. I & II, Cl. II 1 & Cl. II 2. Bolton School, 59–60.

1960[3]   YOUNGMAN, Donald Alexander Hay. Merchant Taylor's School. Jesus College, Oxford (Exhibitioner). B.A., 46. B.Mus, 55. A.R.C.M., 39. A.R.C.O. 49. M.A., 47. Oundle School, 47–52. Director of Music, Monkton Combe School, 52–60. Appointed Director of Music, Rugby School, 60. Address: The Stables, Dunchurch Road, Rugby.

1961[3]   BOWER, David Ian. Left 63[2]. Bradford Grammar School. Oriel College, Oxford (Scholar). Hon. Mods., Maths. Cl. II; Final Hons. Physics Cl. II.

1961[3]   BAYLISS, John Edward. Left 62[2]. Emmanuel School. St. Edmund Hall, Oxford. Mod. Langs. Cl. II. Assistant d'Anglais, Lycée Janson de Sailly, Paris, 58–59. Address: 49, Melrose Road, London, S.W.18.

1962[1]   HALL, Martin James. Left 64[2]. Westminster School. Christ Church, Oxford (Exhibitioner). Hon. Mods. Cl. II; Lit. Hum. Cl. II.

1962[2]   NEWMAN, Donald Charles. Left 65[1]. Lancaster Royal Grammar School. K.E.S., Nuneaton, 48–50. St. Paul's College, Cheltenham, 54. Dip. Physical Education, 55. Sibford School, 55–57. Leominster Grammar School, 57–59. Ross C.P. School, 59–62.

1962[2]   MORRISON, Leonard Haslett. Left 69[2]. Rugby. Corpus Christi College, Cambridge. Econ. Tri. Cl. II, Div. 1; Law Tr. Cl. II, Div. 1. Bar Exam. Finals, Cl. I, 49. B.A., 38. M.A., 49. Chaplain & Housemaster, Cheltenham College, 51–62. Chaplain, Charterhouse, 69–. Address: Sutton Cottage, Charterhouse, Godalming, Surrey.

1962³ BLACKSHAW, John Bantock. Left 67². Sherborne School. Lincoln College, Oxford, 57–60. Hon. Sch. of Mod. Lang. Cl. II. M.A. Hockey Blue, 59, 60. Master at Malvern College, 67–. Address: Flat 1, Radnor Lodge, College Road, Malvern, Worcs.

1962³ TRENTHAM, David George. Left 67². Rugby. Worcester College, Oxford, 55–58. Mod. Hist. Cl. II. Oxford Blue, Squash Rackets, 56; Lawn Tennis, 58. Uppingham School, 58–62. Monkton Combe School, 69¹ (Second Master, 71³–). Address: Monkton Combe School, Combe Down, Bath.

1962³ GORDON JONES, Christopher Roy. Left 69³. Rossall School. Jesus College, Cambridge (Scholar). Classics Pts. I & II, Cl. I & II, Div. 1. Marlborough College, 61–62. Industry—Courtaulds Ltd. Address: "The Beeches", Mapperley Rise, Nottingham NGE 5GE.

1962³ McMENEMEY, James Desmond Scott. Westminster School. Christ Church, Oxford (Scholar). Final Hon. Sch. Physics Cl. III, 60. B.A., 60. Sebright School, 60–62. M.A., 64. Address: 12, Hillmorton Road, Rugby.

1962³ EMMS, Peter Fawcett. Derby School. Magdalen College, Oxford (Scholar), 56–59. M.A., 63. Abingdon School, 59–62. Groton School Massachusetts, 66–67. Head of Modern Languages Dept., 69–71. Housemaster, Town House, 71.

1962³ MORLEY, Stephen. Left 66². Kingswood School. Merton College, Oxford. B.A., 61. Address: 44, St. Mary's Road, Bingham, Notts. NG13 8DW.

1962³ GRANT, Alastair Ruari. Left 69². Trinity College, Glenalmond. Christ's College, Cambridge, 59–62. Nat. Sc. Tr. Pt. 1, Cl. II, Div. 2. Dundee Technical College, 57–59. Higher Nat. Dip. in Elec. Sherborne School, 69²–. Address: 1, Ridgeway, Sherborne, Dorset.

1963³ SKIPPER, David John. Left 69². Watford Grammar School. Brasenose College, Oxford. Nat. Sci. (Chemistry). Cl. II. M.A., 50–53. Oxford XV, 52. R.A.F. S.S.C. (Educ.), 53–55. Radley College, 56–63. Headmaster, Ellesmere College, 69³. Address: Ellesmere College, Ellesmere, Shropshire.

1963³ EVANS, John Alfred Eaton. Bristol Grammar School. Worcester College, Oxford. Mods. Cl. III; Lit. Hum. Cl. III. Blundell's School, 58–63. Housemaster, Kilbracken House, 73³.

1963³ GRAINGE, Gerald. Left 66². Worcester Royal Grammar School. Grange School, Bradford. Erith Grammar School. Christ's College, Cambridge (Minor Scholar). B.A., 56. M.A., 60. R.A.F. (Education), 56–59. Apsley Grammar School, 60–63. Deputy Divisional Education Officer Dacorum Division of Hertfordshire, 66–69. Assistant Education Officer, London Borough of Croydon, 69–. Address: 197, Shaftesbury Court, Regency Walk, Orchard Way, Shirley, Croydon CRO 7UW.

1963³ HEAD, Henry Charles. Gordonstoun School. King's College, Cambridge (Exhibitioner), 59–62. Mech. Sci. Tr. Pt. I, Cl. II, Div. 1, Bryanston School, 62–63. Publications: "New General Mathematics", Vols. I–IV (Part Author). Address: 16B, Horton Crescent, Rugby.

1963³ PRICE, John Thomas. Left 67². Maidstone Grammar School. Downing College, Cambridge, 59–63. Nat. Sci. Tr. Pts. I and II, Cl. II, Div. 2 and Cl. III. Certificate of Education. Athletics Blue, 59–63. C.U.A.C. Secretary, 62–63. Member of the Institute of Biology. Bishop Wordsworth School, Salisbury, 67–. Publications: "The Origin & Evolution of Life", E.U.P. 71. Address: Head of Biology Department, Bishop Wordsworth School, Salisbury, Wilts.

1963³ HOSEN, Roger Wills. Left 66². Falmouth Grammar School. Dip. Loughborough College. Northampton G.S., 56–58. England XV, 63/67. Warwick School, 59–63. Cornwall Cricket Club (Captain). Cheltenham College, 66–. Address: Highworth, College Road, Cheltenham, Glos.

1964¹ ALLEN, John Patrick. Pocklington School. Gresham's School. Sidney Sussex College, Cambridge (Exhibitioner), 60–64. Nat. Sci. Tr. Pt. I, Cl. II, Div. 1, 62. Chem. Pt. II, Cl. II, Div. 1, 63. Dip. Ed., 64. A.R.I.C., 66. Publications: Nuffield Advanced Science, Chemistry. Co-ordinator of the development team for the Teachers' Guide for the Metallurgy—a Special Study, 70. Address: 2, Springhill, Barby Road, Rugby.

1964[3]   IRWIN, John M. Left 68[2]. Trinity College School, Ontario. Trinity College, Toronto. Scholar. B.A., 49. Selhurst Grammar School, Croydon, 61–64. Marlborough College. Address: 8, Hyde Lane, Marlborough, Wilts.

1964[3]   FRIEND-SMITH, Jeremy Nicol. Eastbourne College. Jesus College, Oxford. Maths Mods. Cl. II & Cl. III. B.A., 57. M.A., 61. Worksop College, 60–64. Address: 12, Hillmorton Road, Rugby.

1964[3]   EVEREST, Alan Samuel. Left 72[2]. Christ's Hospital. Brasenose College, Oxford. Physics Cl. II. B.A. Uppingham School, 61–64. S.E.A.M.E.O., Regional Centre for Education in Science & Mathematics, Penang, Malaysia, 71–. Publications (with Professor R. J. Taylor): "The Stars: their Structure and Evolution", "The Origin of the Chemical Elements". Address: Cifn Cottage, Llanveynoe, Hereford.

1964[3]   MACLENNAN, William Ian Keith. Westminster School. Corpus Christi College, Oxford, 59–63. Hon. Mods. Cl. I; Lit. Hum. Cl. II. V.S.O., Sainik School, Satara, India, 63–64. Address: 11, Horton Crescent, Rugby.

1964[3]   HERFORD, John Brooke. Trinity College, Glenalmond. Royal Scottish Academy of Music. L.R.A.M. (Piano Performer's & Teacher's), 63. D.R.S.A.M., 63. Address: 11, Horton Crescent, Rugby.

1965[3]   SMITH, John Richard. Felsted School. Trinity College, Cambridge. Mod. & Med. Lang. Tr. Pts. I & II, Cl. II, Div. 2 & Cl. II, Div. 1. B.A., 58. M.A., 63. Exchange Assistant, Innsbruck, Austria, 58–59. Newcastle High School, 59–60. Dulwich College, 60–65. Address: 14, Hillmorton Road, Rugby.

1965[3]   GATWARD, David Raban. Caterham School, Royal College of Music. Royal School of Church Music. A.R.C.M., 54. L.R.A.M., 56. L.T.C.L., 58. Articled at Canterbury Cathedral, 57–58. Organist, Christchurch, Purley, 58–60. F.R.C.O., 62. Summerfields School, 60–65. Address: 38, Hillmorton Road, Rugby.

1965[3]   BLAND, Hamilton Edward. Left 67[3]. Hayward School, Bolton. Loughborough Training College. D.L.C. (Hons.), 62–65. British Swimming Coach. Olympic Games, Mexico, 68; Munich, 72; European Championships, Barcelona, 72. Winston Churchill Fellow, 69. Publications: "Swimming to Win", "Water Polo" (Know the Game). Educational Production. Address: 207, Green Lane, Bolton, Lancs.

1966[1]   COURTNELL, Raymond Ernest. Left 69[3]. Lawrence Sheriff School. Trinity College of Music, London. Royal Military School of Music, 24. Bandmaster, 4/7 Royal Dragoon Guards, 26. Stowe School, 63–65. Uppingham School, 69. Leader, Brathay Exploration Group, 66–. Address: Uppingham School, Uppingham, Rutland.

1966[3]   PARKER, Ronald Henry George. Raynes Park Grammar School. St. John's College, Cambridge. 44–47 & 50–51. Churcher's College, Petersfield, 51. Selhurst Grammar School, Croydon, 52–66 (Senior Science Master, 64–66). Address: 1, Rokeby House, Barby Road, Rugby.

1966[3]   TOVEY, Michael Duncan. Sherborne School. Guildford School of Art, 48/52. Regional College of Art, Manchester, 52/53. Nat. Dip. in Design, 52. Art Teacher's Cert. and Dip. (Manchester), 53. Portora Royal School, 55–66. Address: Temple Library House, 1, Barby Road, Rugby.

1966[3]   MORGAN, Eric. Blundell's School. Exeter College, Oxford. Scholar. Chem. Cl. II, 58. D.Phil.Chem., 60. Fettes College, 60–66. Address: 78, Dunchurch Road, Rugby.

1966[3]   HOGG, David Campbell. Left 70[2]. Giggleswick School. Selwyn College, Cambridge. Cl. II, 59–62. London Cert. Ed., 63. English High School, Istanbul, 63–66. Address: c/o Mr. and Mrs. L. Hogg, Spencer Brook, Chelford Road, Prestbury, Cheshire SK10 4AW.

1966[3]   ANTHONY, John George Henry. Left 73[1]. Plymouth College. St. John's College, Cambridge, 59–62, 63–66. Scholar. Maths Tr. Pt. II (Wrangler),

61. Maths. Tr. III, 62, Distinction. B.A., 62. M.A., 66. Assistant Lecturer, Liverpool University, 62–63. S.R.C. Research Grant, Cambridge, 63–66. Visiting Teacher of Mathematics, Groton School, Mass., U.S.A., 70–71. Head of Mathematics Dept., Glasgow Academy, 73–. Address: Glasgow Academy.

1966[3] WATKINSON, John Taylor. Left 71[2]. Bristol Grammar School. Worcester College, Oxford. Cl. III. Amateur Fives Champion. Repton, 64–66. Labour Candidate for Leamington and Warwick, General Election, 69. Address: c/o I. G. Miller, 7, Horton Crescent, Rugby.

1966[3] DREWETT, Francis. Windsor Grammar School. Dip. Loughborough College. Upper II. Trinity School, Croydon, 61–66. Founder Member, Public Schools Physical Education Conference Committee. Founder Sec., Rugby Sports Advisory Council. Address: 10, Moultrie Road, Rugby.

1950 SPARKS, John Peel (Medical Officer). Rugby School. Durham Univ. College of Medicine. M.B. B.S., 38. M.D., 40. M.R.C.P.(Lond.), 48. House Surgeon, House Physician, etc., Royal Victoria Infirmary, Newcastle-upon-Tyne, 38–41. R.N.V.R., 41–45. Senior Medical Registrar, British Postgraduate Medical School, London, 46–47. Assistant Registrar, The National Hospital for Nervous Diseases, Queen Square, London, 48–50. Chrmn., Medical Officers of Schools' Association. Address: 3, Horton Crescent, Rugby.

1952 SNOW, Philip Albert. Second Bursar. Bursar, 54 Clerk to Governing Body, 67. Newton's Sch., Leicester. Christ's Coll., Camb. (Senior Open Exhibitioner), 34–37. M.A., 40. H.M. Colonial Administrative Service, Fiji and W. Pacific, 37. Magistrate, Provincial Commissioner and Asst. Colonial Secretary, Fiji, 38–52. Founder, Fiji Cricket Association, 46. F.R.A.I., 52. Chrmn., Pub. Schs. Bursars' Assn., Gt. Britain and Commonwealth, 61–64. J.P., 67. Publications: Author of several publications relating to Fiji and the South Seas. Address: Horton House, 6, Hillmorton Road, Rugby.

1964 COLE, Cdr. John Henry Melvin. Appointed Assistant Bursar, 64. Left 68. Mountjoy, Dublin, 25–31. R.N. College, Greenwich, for Staff Course, 53. Royal Navy, 32–64. Domestic Bursar, Hall of Residence, Hull University, 68.

1968 INGRAM, Lt.-Col. David Eric Major. Appointed Assistant Bursar, 68. Shrewsbury High School. L.R.I.B.A. Army (Royal Engineers), 39–68. O.B.E. Address: 2, Southfield, 8, Horton Crescent, Rugby.

SCHOOL HOUSES

With Housemasters from 1947 and locations

SH=	School House
	Head Master
1968	Assistant Housemaster: J. C. Marshall
T=	Town House: 1, Hillmorton Road until 1971
	14, Horton Crescent from 1971
1930	H. P. Sparling
1950	W. W. Inge
1958	R. P. Wright
1971	P. F. Emms
B=	Bradley House: 5, Barby Road
1945	J. R. A. Smith
1959	G. H. Dazeley
1969	G. M. Helliwell
C=	Cotton House: 10, Hillmorton Road
1945	R. W. Stott
1956	D. Bulmer
1969	J. Inglis

K=   Kilbracken: 11, Barby Road
1943   E. H. L. Jennings
1958   W. W. Inge
1965   J. W. Hele
1973   J. A. E. Evans

M=   Michell House: 3, Hillmorton Road
1936   G. A. Keay
1951   O. R. C. Prior
1963   J. Ll. R. Baiss

SF=   School Field: 2, Barby Road
1944   R. C. Watt
1951   J. L. Willans
1964   T. A. Buckney

Sh=   Sheriff House: 7, Barby Road
1945   R. H. Walker
1956   A. J. Hunt
1970   J. B. Tyson

St=   Stanley House: 3, Barby Road
1944   E. V. Reynolds
1949   F. J. A. Chase
1964   P. M. C. Hare

Tu=   Tudor House: 4, Horton Crescent
1941   R. Broxton
1949   P. Falk
1964   C. H. Silver

W=   Whitelaw House: 4, Hillmorton Road
1936   W. N. Hughes
1951   W. G. R. Loughery
1965   J. Peirson

Presidents of the Old Rugbian Society since 1946

1946   H. H. Hardy, C.B.E.
1947   C. D. Webb
1948   Colonel F. C. Temple, C.I.E., C.B.E.
1949   General Sir George Gifford, G.C.B., D.S.O.
1950   P. J. W. Straus
1951   Colonel F. W. Watson, C.B., M.C., T.D.
1952   Colonel A. H. Maude, C.M.G., D.S.O., T.D., D.L.
1953/4   Colonel J. Attenborough, C.M.G.
1955/6   T. P. W. Norris
1957/8   W. F. S. Hawkins, C.B.
1959   Lieut.-General Sir Henry Pownall, K.C.B., K.B.E., D.S.O., M.C.
1960/1   Sir Denis Truscott, G.B.E., T.D., J.P.
1962/3   Air Marshal Sir John Baldwin, K.B.E., C.B., D.S.O., D.L.
1964/5   Dr. J. M. Brown, M.C., T.D., M.B.
1966/7   P. H. B. Lyon, M.C.
1968/9   D. E. C. Steel, D.S.O., M.C.
1970/1   F. D. Physick
1972/3   The Right Hon. Lord Geddes, K.B.E., D.L.
1974   Sir Frank Roberts, G.C.M.G. G.C.V.O.